NOTES

The following change occurred in the membership of the 89th Congress after the election of November 3, 1964:

Name	Died	Resigned	Successor	Sworn in
Albert Watson, 2d S.C.		Feb. 1, 1965		

The following changes occurred in the membership of the 88th Congress after the election of November 6, 1962:

Name	Died	Resigned	Successor	Sworn in
SENATORS				
Dennis Chavez, N. Mex.	Nov. 18, 1962		Edwin L. Mechem [1]	Jan. 9, 1963
			Joseph M. Montoya [2]	
Robert S. Kerr, Okla.	Jan. 1, 1963		J. Howard Edmondson [1]	Jan. 9, 1963
			Fred R. Harris [2]	
Estes Kefauver, Tenn.	Aug. 10, 1963		Herbert S. Walters [1]	Aug. 27, 1963
			Ross Bass [2]	
Clair Engle, Calif.	July 30, 1964		Pierre Salinger [1]	Aug. 5, 1964
Hubert H. Humphrey, Minn.		Dec. 29, 1964	Walter F. Mondale [1]	
Pierre Salinger, Calif.		Dec. 31, 1964	George Murphy [1]	
REPRESENTATIVES				
Clem Miller, 1st Calif.	Oct. 7, 1962		Don Clausen [3]	Jan. 28, 1963
Clyde Doyle, 23d Calif.	Mar. 14, 1963		Del Clawson	June 20, 1963
Francis E. Walter, 15th Pa.	May 31, 1963		Fred B. Rooney	Aug. 6, 1963
Hjalmar C. Nygaard, 1st N. Dak.	July 18, 1963		Mark Andrews	Oct. 30, 1963
Leon H. Gavin, 23d Pa.	Sept. 15, 1963		Albert W. Johnson	Nov. 27, 1963
Homer Thornberry, 10th Tex.		Dec. 20, 1963	J. J. (Jake) Pickle	Dec. 24, 1963
William J. Green, Jr., 5th Pa.	Dec. 21, 1963		William J. Green	May 12, 1964
John F. Shelley, 5th Calif.		Jan. 7, 1964	Phillip Burton	Feb. 24, 1964
Howard H. Baker, 2d Tenn.	Jan. 7, 1964		Irene B. Baker	Mar. 19, 1964
Thomas J. O'Brien, 6th Ill.	Apr. 14, 1964			
Robert W. Hemphill, 5th S.C.		May 1, 1964	Tom S. Gettys	
Clarence Cannon, 9th Mo.	May 12, 1964		William L. Hungate	
John B. Bennett, 12th Mich.	Aug. 9, 1964			
Walter Norblad, 1st Oreg.	Sept. 20, 1964		Wendell Wyatt	
Ross Bass, 6th Tenn.		Nov. 3, 1964		
Joseph M. Montoya, At L., N. Mex.		Nov. 3, 1964		
Edward R. Finnegan, 9th Ill.		Dec. 6, 1964		

[1] Appointed by Governor to fill vacancy until successor is elected.
[2] Elected Nov. 3, 1964.
[3] Elected Jan. 22, 1963.

JANUARY

Sun	M	Tu	W	Th	F	Sat
					1	2
3	4	5	6	7	8	9
10	11	12	13	14	15	16
17	18	19	20	21	22	23
24	25	26	27	28	29	30
31						

JULY

Sun	M	Tu	W	Th	F	Sat
				1	2	3
4	5	6	7	8	9	10
11	12	13	14	15	16	17
18	19	20	21	22	23	24
25	26	27	28	29	30	31

FEBRUARY

Sun	M	Tu	W	Th	F	Sat
	1	2	3	4	5	6
7	8	9	10	11	12	13
14	15	16	17	18	19	20
21	22	23	24	25	26	27
28						

AUGUST

Sun	M	Tu	W	Th	F	Sat
1	2	3	4	5	6	7
8	9	10	11	12	13	14
15	16	17	18	19	20	21
22	23	24	25	26	27	28
29	30	31				

MARCH

Sun	M	Tu	W	Th	F	Sat
	1	2	3	4	5	6
7	8	9	10	11	12	13
14	15	16	17	18	19	20
21	22	23	24	25	26	27
28	29	30	31			

SEPTEMBER

Sun	M	Tu	W	Th	F	Sat
			1	2	3	4
5	6	7	8	9	10	11
12	13	14	15	16	17	18
19	20	21	22	23	24	25
26	27	28	29	30		

APRIL

Sun	M	Tu	W	Th	F	Sat
				1	2	3
4	5	6	7	8	9	10
11	12	13	14	15	16	17
18	19	20	21	22	23	24
25	26	27	28	29	30	

OCTOBER

Sun	M	Tu	W	Th	F	Sat
					1	2
3	4	5	6	7	8	9
10	11	12	13	14	15	16
17	18	19	20	21	22	23
24	25	26	27	28	29	30
31						

MAY

Sun	M	Tu	W	Th	F	Sat
						1
2	3	4	5	6	7	8
9	10	11	12	13	14	15
16	17	18	19	20	21	22
23	24	25	26	27	28	29
30	31					

NOVEMBER

Sun	M	Tu	W	Th	F	Sat
	1	2	3	4	5	6
7	8	9	10	11	12	13
14	15	16	17	18	19	20
21	22	23	24	25	26	27
28	29	30				

JUNE

Sun	M	Tu	W	Th	F	Sat
		1	2	3	4	5
6	7	8	9	10	11	12
13	14	15	16	17	18	19
20	21	22	23	24	25	26
27	28	29	30			

DECEMBER

Sun	M	Tu	W	Th	F	Sat
			1	2	3	4
5	6	7	8	9	10	11
12	13	14	15	16	17	18
19	20	21	22	23	24	25
26	27	28	29	30	31	

CONTENTS

(For List of Individuals, see Index on p. 913)

Contents

Contents

Contents

Contents

Contents

Contents

Contents

Contents

Contents XXVII

XXVII

BIOGRAPHICAL

BIOGRAPHICAL*

THE VICE PRESIDENT

HUBERT H. HUMPHREY, Democrat-Farmer-Labor, of Waverly, Minn.; born in Wallace, S. Dak., May 27, 1911; educated in South Dakota schools; graduated with degree from Denver College of Pharmacy; University of Minnesota with A.B. degree (Phi Beta Kappa); University of Louisiana with M.A. degree; National University Law School, Washington, D.C., honorary LL.D. degree; honorary LL.D. degree from Brandeis University; honorary Doctor of Pharmacy degree from Rhode Island College of Pharmacy and Allied Sciences; Doctor Humane Letters (honorary), Hebrew Union College; State Director War Production, Training, 1942; assistant director War Manpower Commission, 1943; professor in political science, Macalester College, 1943 and 1944; married Muriel Buck; four children; elected mayor of Minneapolis in 1945 and 1947; member of First Congregational Church of Minnesota; elected to the United States Senate on November 2, 1948, for the term commencing January 3, 1949; reelected in 1954 and again in 1960 for term ending January 3, 1967; Senate Majority Whip, 1961–64; served until his resignation December 29, 1964, having been elected Vice President November 3, 1964, for term beginning January 20, 1965.

ALABAMA

(Population (1960), 3,266,740)

SENATORS

LISTER HILL, Democrat, of Montgomery, Ala., where he was born December 29, 1894; was graduated from Starke University School, Montgomery, Ala., in 1911; from University of Alabama at Tuscaloosa, Ala., in 1914; from the law school of the University of Alabama in 1915; and from the law school of Columbia University, New York City, in 1916; took a special course at the law school, University of Michigan, at Ann Arbor, Mich., in the summer of 1914; honorary LL.D. degree, University of Alabama, 1939, Alabama Polytechnic Institute, 1939; National University, 1941; Woman's Medical College of Pennsylvania, 1956; Columbia University, 1960; Washington University (St. Louis), 1961; University of Pennsylvania, 1965; honorary Sc. D. degree, Hahnemann Medical College, 1958; New York Medical College, 1961; honorary fellow, American College of Hospital Administrators, 1954; honorary member of American Dental Association, 1958; and honorary fellow, International College of Surgeons, 1959; honorary fellow, American Psychiatric Association, 1960; honorary fellow, American College of Dentists, 1961; was admitted to the bar of Alabama in 1915 and commenced the practice of law at Montgomery, Ala., in October 1916; president of the Montgomery Board of Education, 1917–22; served in the Army with the Seventeenth and Seventy-first United States Infantry Regiments during First World War, 1917–19; member of Phi Beta Kappa; married Henrietta Fontaine McCormick, of Eufaula, Ala.; children, Mrs. Charles Hubbard and Luther Lister; elected to the 68th Congress to fill the vacancy caused by the death of John R. Tyson; renominated and reelected without opposition to the 69th, 70th, 71st, 72d, 73d, 74th, and 75th Congresses, and served from August 14, 1923, until his resignation on January 11, 1938; appointed to the United States Senate on January 10, 1938, and elected on April 26, 1938, to fill the vacancy in the term ending January 3, 1939; reelected on November 8, 1938, for the term ending January 3, 1945; reelected on November 7, 1944, for the term ending January 3, 1951; reelected on November 7, 1950, for the term ending January 3, 1957; reelected on November 6, 1956, for the term ending January 3, 1963; reelected November 6, 1962, for the term ending January 3, 1969.

---

*Biographies are based on information furnished or authorized by the respective Senators and Representatives.

3

JOHN J. SPARKMAN, Democrat, of Huntsville, Ala., was born near Hartselle, Morgan County, Ala., December 20, 1899; attended rural elementary schools, Morgan County High School at Hartselle, and the University of Alabama, at Tuscaloosa, where he received the degrees of A.B. in 1921, LL.B. in 1923, and A.M. in 1924; LL.D. University of Alabama 1958 (honorary); LL.D. Auburn University, 1960 (honorary); Phi Beta Kappa and Pi Kappa Alpha fraternities; a Mason, Woodmen of the World; Kiwanian; member American Legion; is a lawyer by profession; was admitted to the bar in 1923 and commenced practice in Huntsville, being a member of the firm of Taylor, Richardson & Sparkman, of Huntsville, until he retired upon election to Congress in order to give full time to his congressional duties; served in Army during World War I; is a colonel in the Organized Reserves; married to Miss Ivo Hall, of Albertville, Ala., on June 2, 1923, and they have one daughter—Julia Ann (Mrs. Tazewell T. Shepard, Jr.); he, his wife, and daughter are members of the Methodist Church; elected to the 75th Congress on November 3, 1936; reelected to the 76th, 77th, 78th, 79th, and 80th Congresses; served as member of Military Affairs Committee and as majority whip; on November 5, 1946, was also elected to the United States Senate to fill out the unexpired term of the late Senator John H. Bankhead; following the election resigned from the House of Representatives and entered upon his duties in the Senate; reelected in 1948, 1954, and again in 1960 for the term ending January 3, 1967; was Democratic candidate for Vice President in 1952.

REPRESENTATIVES

FIRST DISTRICT.—COUNTIES: Choctaw, Clarke, Mobile, Monroe, Washington, and Wilcox (6 counties). Population (1960), 414,392.

JACK EDWARDS, Republican, of Mobile, Ala.; born in Birmingham, Ala., September 20, 1928; attended the public schools of Homewood, Ala., and the U.S. Naval School (academy and college preparatory) 1947–48; served in U.S. Marine Corps July 1946 to July 1948 (corporal) and from September 1950 to September 1951 (sergeant); graduated from the University of Alabama, B.S. 1952 and LL.B. 1954; was admitted to the bar and practiced law in Mobile since 1954; taught business law in 1954; member of American Bar Association, Mobile Bar Association, and Mobile Junior Bar Association; legal adviser, Emergency Port Operations, Port of Mobile; elder, Spring Hill Presbyterian Church and Sunday-school teacher; married the former Jolane Vander Sys of Mobile January 30, 1954; two children, Susan Lane and Richard Arnold; member of board of directors of America's Junior Miss Pageant and of Transportation Advisory Committee to Mobile City Planning Commission; one of the organizers of Freedom Over Communism (FOCUS) in Mobile and active in other anti-communism projects; division chairman of United Fund; selected as one of Outstanding Young Men of America by U.S. Junior Chamber of Commerce, 1964; elected to the 89th Congress November 3, 1964.

SECOND DISTRICT.—COUNTIES: Baldwin, Butler, Conecuh, Covington, Crenshaw, Escambia, Lowndes, Montgomery, and Pike (9 counties). Population (1960), 386,075.

WILLIAM LOUIS DICKINSON, Republican, of Montgomery, Ala.; born in Opelika, Ala., June 5, 1925; graduated from University of Alabama Law School June 5, 1950; 3 years in Navy; veteran World War II and captain in USAF Reserve; married the former Mary Patterson Stanfield; four children, Chris, Mike, Tara, and Bill, Jr.; member, First Methodist Church of Montgomery, Kiwanis, Elks, Alabama Bar Association, Masons, SAE Social Fraternity, and Alabama Alumni Association; Opelika city judge, 2 years; judge, Lee County Court of Common Pleas and Lee County Juvenile Court, 4 years; circuit judge, Fifth Judicial Circuit of Alabama, 4 years; assistant vice president, Southern Railway System, 1½ years; served as vice president and president of Opelika Junior Chamber of Commerce, national director for Alabama Junior Chamber of Commerce; commander of Alabama Jaycee's Rebel Corps, Opelika's "Man of the Year" 1960, one of Alabama's "Four Outstanding Young Men" 1961; president, vice president, and member of the board of Alabama Mental Health Association and of Lee County Mental Health Clinic; member, Opelika Board of Education 6 years and president of board 1 year; member board of directors Lee County Rehabilitation Center; member of Governor's Industrial Development Committee of 100; elected to the 89th Congress November 3, 1964.

THIRD DISTRICT.—COUNTIES: Barbour, Bullock, Chambers, Coffee, Dale, Geneva, Henry, Houston, Lee, Macon, Russell, and Tallapoosa (12 counties). Population (1960), 383,782.

GEORGE WILLIAM ANDREWS, Democrat, of Union Springs, Ala.; born in Clayton, Ala., December 12, 1906; attended the academic department of the University of Alabama and was graduated with LL. B. degree in 1928; is a lawyer by profession; served as circuit solicitor for the third judicial circuit of the State of Alabama (Barbour, Bullock, Russell, and Dale Counties) from 1931 to 1943; at time of election to Congress was serving as lieutenant (junior grade), United States Naval Reserve, at Pearl Harbor, and had been in the United States Naval Reserve 14 months; was released from active duty by the Navy Department to serve in Congress; married Elizabeth Bullock, of Geneva, Ala., November 25, 1936; one daughter, Jane Andrews Hinds, one son, George W., 3d; fraternities, Sigma Nu, Omicron Delta Kappa, and Phi Delta Phi (legal); elected to the 78th Congress on March 14, 1944, to fill the vacancy caused by the death of Henry B. Steagall, serving on Committee on Expenditures in Executive Departments, Roads Committee, and Committee on World War Veterans' Legislation; reelected to the 79th and 80th Congresses, serving on Appropriations Committee and Independent Offices; reelected to the 81st, 82d, 83d, 84th, 85th, 86th, 87th, 88th, and 89th Congress.

FOURTH DISTRICT.—COUNTIES: Autauga, Calhoun, Clay, Cleburne, Coosa, Dallas, Elmore, Randolph St. Clair, and Talladega (10 counties). Population (1960), 346,205.

GLENN ANDREWS, Republican, of Anniston, Ala.; born in Anniston January 9, 1909; attended Birmingham public schools; graduated, Phillips High School, Mercersburg Academy, Princeton University, and the IBM Sales School; associated with the National City Bank of New York 3 years, International Business Machines 3 years, Eastman Kodak subsidiary as district manager 10 years, and in advertising 18 years; member of Rotary Club, YMCA, and the Episcopal Church; wife, Ethel Jackson Andrews; three children, Mrs. George Kilby, Arthur Glenn Andrews, Jr., and Frank Scott Andrews; hobbies: bird dogs, horses, golf, and farming; delegate to 4th District Convention 1952; Calhoun County chairman 1954; 4th District chairman 1960; State committeeman 1960; regional coordinator 1963; served on State nominating and constitutional committees 1962; served on platform committee 1964; candidate house of representatives 1956; candidate secretary of state 1958; elected to the 89th Congress November 3, 1964.

FIFTH DISTRICT.—COUNTIES: Bibb, Chilton, Greene, Hale, precincts 33 and 53 of Jefferson, Marengo, Perry, Pickens, Shelby, Sumter, and Tuscaloosa. Population (1960), 433,327.

ARMISTEAD INGE SELDEN, JR., Democrat, of Greensboro, Ala.; born in Greensboro, Ala., February 20, 1921; was graduated from Greensboro High School in 1938; University of the South (Sewanee, Tenn.), A. B. degree, in 1942; entered United States Navy in August 1942 and was discharged with rank of lieutenant in March 1946; spent 31 months aboard ship, primarily in North Atlantic; graduated from University of Alabama, LL. B. degree in 1948; lawyer by profession; practiced at Greensboro, Ala.; member of Alabama and American bar associations; elected to Alabama House of Representatives in 1950; member Episcopal Church, Phi Delta Phi legal fraternity, Blue Key and ODK leadership fraternities, SAE social fraternity, American Legion, V. F. W., Rotary International; married Mary Jane Wright of Talladega, Ala., August 1948; children, Martee Graham Selden, Armistead I. Selden 3d, Jack Wright Selden, Edith Cobbs Selden, and Thomas Lawson Selden; elected to the 83d Congress, November 4, 1952; reelected to the 84th, 85th, 86th, 87th, 88th, and 89th Congresses; member Committee on Foreign Affairs and chairman of Inter-American Affairs Subcommittee.

SIXTH DISTRICT.—JEFFERSON COUNTY, except precincts 33 and 53. Population (1960), 502,282.

JOHN HALL BUCHANAN, JR., Republican, of Birmingham, Ala.; born in Paris, Tenn., March 19, 1928; served in the U.S. Navy during World War II; graduated from Howard College in 1949 with majors in economics and history and did graduate work in economics at the University of Virginia; also graduated from Southern Theological Seminary in Louisville; served as pastor of churches in Tennessee, Virginia, and Alabama 1953–62; resigned his church in 1962 to be a Republican candidate for Congress; since 1962 served as a supply pastor in the Birmingham area; director of finance for the Alabama Republican Party and chairman of the Jefferson County Republican Committee; married the former Elizabeth Moore of Birmingham, Ala.; two children; elected to the 89th Congress November 3, 1964.

SEVENTH DISTRICT.—COUNTIES: Blount, Cherokee, Cullman, De Kalb, Etowah, Fayette, Franklin, Lamar, Marion, Marshall, Walker, and Winston (12 counties). Population (1960), 417,052.

JAMES DOUGLAS MARTIN, Republican, of Gadsden, Ala.; born in Tarrant, Ala., near Birmingham, September 1, 1918; educated in the public schools of Jefferson County and the Birmingham School of Law; engaged in the petroleum industry in 1937; enlisted in the U.S. Army in July 1941, attended Officers Training School at Fort Sill, Okla., was commissioned and commanded a battery of artillery in Europe; served as an Intelligence officer in the Army of Occupation and was discharged as a major in March 1946; returned to the oil industry and now is president of the Martin Oil Co. in Gadsden, Ala.; married the former Patricia Huddleston; two children, James Douglas, Jr., and a daughter, Annette; member of the First Methodist Church of Gadsden and teaches a men's bible class; served two terms as president of the Gadsden-Etowah Chamber of Commerce, was Gadsden's Man of the Year, past president of American Oil Jobbers and of Associated Industries of Alabama; past chairman of the board of Associated Industries; candidate in 1962 for the U.S. Senate; elected to the 89th Congress November 3, 1964, by 609 majority.

EIGHTH DISTRICT.—COUNTIES: Colbert, Jackson, Lauderdale, Lawrence, Limestone, Madison, and Morgan (7 counties). Population (1960), 383,625.

ROBERT E. JONES, Democrat, of Scottsboro, Ala.; born June 12, 1912; graduate University of Alabama; lawyer by profession; married Miss Christine Francis; one son; member of Methodist Church, American Legion, Veterans of Foreign Wars; in 1940 elected judge of Jackson County Court and served until entered Navy in 1943; elected to 80th and succeeding Congresses.

ALASKA

(Population (1960), 226,167)

SENATORS

E. L. BARTLETT, Democrat, of Juneau, Alaska; born, Seattle, Wash., April 20, 1904; resident of Alaska since 1905; married former Vide Gaustad of Fairbanks, Alaska; two daughters, Mrs. Burke Riley of Juneau, Alaska, and Sue Bartlett of Baltimore, Md.; elected as Delegate to Congress from Alaska in 1944; reelected in 1946, 1948, 1950, 1952, 1954, and 1956; elected to Senate November 25, 1958, for the term ending January 3, 1961; reelected November 8, 1960, for the term ending January 3, 1967.

ERNEST GRUENING, Democrat, of Juneau, Alaska; born in New York City, February 6, 1887; son of Emil and Phebe Gruening; graduated from Hotchkiss School in 1903; Harvard College, 1907; and Harvard Medical School, 1912; left medicine; entered journalism and continued as newspaperman for some years; appointed the adviser to the U. S. delegation to the 7th Inter-American Conference, Montevideo, in 1933 where the "good neighbor" policy for Latin America was established; appointed director of the Division of Territories and Island Possessions of the Department of Interior, 1934, serving in that capacity until 1939; was appointed administrator of the Puerto Rico Reconstruction Administration, serving 1935–37; member of Alaska International Highway Commission, 1938–42; appointed Governor of Alaska, 1939; twice reappointed, serving until 1953; delivered keynote address to the Alaska Constitutional Convention, 1955; elected U. S. Senator under Alaska-Tennessee plan, 1956; reelected, 1958 and 1962; married Dorothy Elizabeth Smith of Norwood, Mass., November 19, 1914; three sons, Ernest, Jr. (deceased), Peter Brown (deceased), and Huntington Sanders Gruening, resident of Juneau, Alaska, and three grandsons.

REPRESENTATIVE

AT LARGE.—Population (1960), 226,167.

RALPH J. RIVERS, Democrat, of Fairbanks, Alaska; born in Seattle, Wash., May 23, 1903, son of Julian Guy and Louisa (Lavoy) Rivers; LL. B., University of Washington, 1929; wife, Martha Marie Rivers; children, Julian Ralph Rivers and Joyce Carol Rivers Mansfield; gold miner, Flat, Alaska, 1921–23; admitted to Washington bar, 1930; admitted to Alaska bar, 1931; private law practice, Fairbanks, Alaska, 1931–33; U. S. district attorney, 4th Judicial Division, District of Alaska, 1933–44, resigned; elected to office of attorney general of Alaska for 4-year term, 1945–49; returned to private law practice at Fairbanks upon expiration of term; chairman, Employment Security Commission of Alaska, 1950–52; mayor of Fairbanks, 1952–54; president, League of Alaskan Cities, 1954; member, Alaska Territorial Senate, 1955; 2d Vice President, Alaska Constitutional Convention at College, Alaska, 1955–56; U. S. Representative-elect under Alaska-Tennessee Plan, Washington, D.C., working for passage of Alaska Statehood Bill, 1957–58; member of Sigma Chi Fraternity, Phi Alpha Delta Law Fraternity, Elks, Pioneers of Alaska, Sons of American Revolution, Society of Mayflower Descendants; elected to the 86th Congress November 25, 1958; reelected to the 87th, 88th, and 89th Congresses.

ARIZONA

(Population (1960), 1,302,161)

SENATORS

CARL HAYDEN, Democrat, of Phoenix, Ariz.; born Hayden's Ferry (now Tempe), Ariz., October 2, 1877; educated in public schools of Tempe, Normal School of Arizona, and Stanford University; delegate to the Democratic National Convention in 1904; elected treasurer of Maricopa County in 1904 and sheriff in 1906 and again in 1908; married Nan Downing, February 14, 1908 (died June 25, 1961); upon the admission of Arizona as a State into the Union was elected to the 62d Congress; reelected to seven succeeding Congresses and served from February 19, 1912, to March 3, 1927; elected to the U.S. Senate in 1926 for term beginning March 4, 1927; reelected in 1932, 1938, 1944, 1950, 1956, and 1962.

PAUL JONES FANNIN, Republican, of Phoenix, Ariz.; born January 29, 1907, in Ashland, Ky., son of Thomas N. and Rhoda Catherine Fannin; moved to Phoenix, Ariz., in October, 1907; educated in public schools, Phoenix, Ariz.; attended University of Arizona and Stanford University (B.A. degree, Stanford 1930); married Elma Addington, May 6, 1934; four children: Tom, Bill, Bob, and Linda; five grandchildren; former partner in Fannin Bros., liquefied petroleum gas and agricultural chemicals distributions business; elected Governor of Arizona 1958, reelected 1960, 1962; member: Methodist Church, National Council of Boy Scouts of America, Elks, Moose, Rotary, Kappa Sigma Fraternity; past president of Maricopa County Better Business Bureau; past chairman of Industrial Development Committee of the Phoenix Chamber of Commerce; served while Governor of Arizona as: chairman Western Governors' Conference, chairman Committee on Roads and Highway Safety of the National Governors' Conference, Executive Committee of the Council of State Governments, member of the National Civil Defense Advisory Council; elected United States Senator November 3, 1964, for the term beginning January 3, 1965.

REPRESENTATIVES

FIRST DISTRICT.—MARICOPA COUNTY. Population (1960), 663,510.

JOHN J. RHODES, Republican, of Mesa, Ariz.; born in Council Grove, Kans., on September 18, 1916, son of J. J. Rhodes and Gladys Thomas Rhodes; educated in the public schools of Council Grove, Kans.; B.S. degree, Kansas State College, 1938; LL.B. degree, Harvard Law School, 1941; member of Kansas, Arizona, and D.C. bars; served 4 years and 9 months in Air Force, World War II; married Mary Elizabeth Harvey, May 24, 1942; four children: John J. Rhodes 3d, born September 8, 1943; Thomas H. Rhodes, born December 4, 1946; Elizabeth Campbell Rhodes, born September 10, 1953, and James Scott Rhodes, born May 21, 1957; former vice chairman Arizona Board of Public Welfare; member: F. & A.M., Scottish Rite 33°, B.P.O.E., L.O.M., Rotary, Mesa Junior Chamber of Commerce, Mesa Chamber of Commerce (past president), Mesa Post, American Legion (past senior vice commander), Beta Theta Pi, Blue Key, Scabbard and Blade, and Sons of the American Revolution; elected to the 83d Congress November 4, 1952; reelected to 84th, 85th, 86th, 87th, 88th, and 89th Congresses; former member: Committee on Education and Labor and Committee on Interior and Insular Affairs, 83d through 85th Congresses; member of Committee on Appropriations, 86th Congress to present.

SECOND DISTRICT.—COUNTIES: Cochise, Pima, Pinal, Santa Cruz, and Yuma (5 counties). Population (1960), 440,415.

MORRIS K. UDALL, Democrat, of Tucson, Ariz.; born in St. Johns, Ariz., June 15, 1922, son of Arizona Supreme Court Chief Justice Levi S. Udall and Louise Lee Udall; attended public schools of St. Johns, Ariz.; member LDS (Mormon) Church; married Patricia Emery of Denver, 1949; children—Mark, Randy, Judy, Anne, Brad, and Kathy; enlisted U.S. Army 1942; discharged 1946; captain U.S. Air Force with service Pacific Theater; LL. B. University of Arizona 1949 (president student body 1947–48, co-captain basketball team); played professional basketball with Denver Nuggets 1948–49; county attorney, Pima

County (Tucson) 1952–54; partner, law firm Udall & Udall 1949–61; vice president Arizona State Bar Association 1961; author "Arizona Law of Evidence," West Publishing Co., 1960, and various articles on legal subjects; cofounder and director of the Bank of Tucson and Catalina Savings and Loan Association; president, Tucson YMCA 1960; trustee of Arizona-Sonora Desert Museum; elected to 87th Congress May 2, 1961, to vacancy created by resignation of his brother, Stewart L. Udall; reelected to 88th and 89th Congresses.

THIRD DISTRICT.—COUNTIES: Apache, Coconino, Gila, Graham, Greenlee, Mohave, Navajo, and Yavapai (8 counties). Population (1960), 198,236.

GEORGE FREDERICK SENNER, JR., Democrat; born in Miami, Ariz., November 24, 1921; graduated from Miami High School, studied prelaw at Arizona State University, and graduated from the University of Arizona Law School in 1952; served in the United States Marine Corps May 1942–October 1945; served in the South Pacific; admitted to the Arizona State Bar in October 1952, and engaged in private practice with the law firm of Senner and Senner until December 31, 1954; appointed assistant town attorney for the town of Miami, 1952–54; elected Gila County attorney in 1954 and reelected in 1956; member of the Arizona Corporation Commission, August 1957 to January 1963, serving as chairman from 1958; Arizona Department Commander of the Veterans of Foreign Wars, 1956–57; married to the former Willodene Waldon of Phoenix and has two sons, George 3d and Gregg; member of Elks, Lions, Masons, Shriners, V.F.W., American Legion, American Bar Association, State Bar of Arizona, Gila County Bar Association, Shepherd Valley Lutheran Church of Phoenix; elected to the 88th Congress; reelected to the 89th Congress.

ARKANSAS

(Population (1960), 1,786,272)

SENATORS

JOHN L. McCLELLAN, Democrat, of Camden, Ark.; born at Sheridan, Grant County, Ark., February 25, 1896; first lieutenant of A. S. S. C. during the First World War; lawyer; prosecuting attorney of the seventh judicial district of Arkansas, 1926–30; member of 74th and 75th Congresses from the Sixth Congressional District of Arkansas; elected United States Senator November 3, 1942, for the term beginning January 3, 1943; reelected in 1948, 1954, and again in 1960 for the term ending January 3, 1967.

J. W. FULBRIGHT, Democrat, of Fayetteville, Ark.; son of Jay and Roberta Waugh Fulbright; University of Arkansas, B.A.; Rhodes Scholar, Oxford University B.A., M.A.; George Washington University LL.B.; attorney, United States Department of Justice; instructor in law, George Washington University; president, University of Arkansas; elected to the 78th Congress on November 3, 1942; elected to the United States Senate November 7, 1944, for the term ending January 3, 1951; reelected November 7, 1950, for the term ending January 3, 1957; reelected November 6, 1956, for the term ending January 3, 1963; reelected November 6, 1962, for the term ending January 3, 1969.

REPRESENTATIVES

FIRST DISTRICT.—COUNTIES: Clay, Craighead, Crittenden, Cross, Greene, Lee, Mississippi, Phillips, Poinsett, and St. Francis (10 counties). Population (1960), 360,183.

EZEKIEL CANDLER GATHINGS, Democrat, of West Memphis, Crittenden County, Ark.; born in Prairie, Monroe County, Miss., November 10, 1903; attended Earle (Ark.) High School and University of Alabama; was graduated from the University of Arkansas with LL. B. degree in 1929; married Miss Tolise Kirkpatrick on April 6, 1939, and they have two children, one daughter, Tolise Kirkpatrick Gathings, and one son, Joseph Royston Gathings 2d; lawyer; member of the State senate, 1935–39; member of the Baptist Church; Mason and Shriner, Order of the Eastern Star, Rotary Club, and Pi Kappa Alpha, Phi Alpha Delta, and Blue Key fraternities; elected to the 76th and succeeding Congresses.

SECOND DISTRICT.—COUNTIES: Arkansas, Cleburne, Conway, Faulkner, Fulton, Independence, Izard, Jackson, Lawrence, Lonoko, Monroe, Perry, Prairie, Pulaski, Randolph, Sharp, Stone, White, and Woodruff (19 counties). Population (1960), 517,860.

WILBUR D. MILLS, Democrat, of Kensett, Ark., was born there May 24, 1909; attended Hendrix College and Harvard Law School; married Miss Clarine Billingsley, of Kensett, May 27, 1934, and they have two daughters—Martha Sue and Rebecca Ann; lawyer; admitted to practice law before Supreme Court of Arkansas in November 1933, the Supreme Court of the United States in 1939; served as county and probate judge of White County, Ark., 1934 to 1938, inclusive; Methodist; thirty-third degree Mason; elected to 76th and succeeding Congresses.

THIRD DISTRICT.—COUNTIES: Baxter, Benton, Boone, Carroll, Crawford, Franklin. Johnson, Logan, Madison, Marion, Newton, Pope, Scott, Searcy, Sebastian, Van Buren, Washington and Yell (18 counties). Population (1960), 332,844.

JAMES WILLIAM TRIMBLE, Democrat, of Berryville. Ark.; born near Osage, Carroll County, Ark., February 3, 1894; was graduated from the University of Arkansas in 1917; lawyer; prosecuting attorney; circuit judge; married Miss Ruth Maples, of Berryville, Ark., on February 14, 1922; two children (twins), a daughter, Martha Carol (deceased), and James Kerry, Reserve major in United States Army; Mason, Methodist, Legionnaire; elected to the 79th Congress November 7, 1944; reelected to each succeeding Congress.

FOURTH DISTRICT.—Counties: Ashley, Bradley, Calhoun, Chicot, Clark, Cleveland, Columbia, Dallas, Desha, Drew, Garland, Grant, Hempstead, Hot Spring, Howard, Jefferson, Lafayette, Lincoln, Little River, Miller, Montgomery, Nevada, Ouachita, Pike, Polk, Saline, Sevier, and Union (28 counties).   Population (1960), 575,385.

 OREN HARRIS, Democrat, of El Dorado, Ark., was born December 20, 1903, in Hempstead County, Ark., son of Homer and Bettie Lee Harris; educated in public schools of Hempstead County and Prescott High School, Nevada County, Ark., Henderson College, Arkadelphia, Clark County, Ark., with A. B. degree, and LL. B. degree from Cumberland University Law School, Lebanon, Tenn.; engaged in the practice of law since 1930; admitted to practice in the United States Supreme Court; deputy prosecuting attorney of Union County, 1933–36; elected prosecuting attorney of the thirteenth judicial circuit in 1936; reelected in 1938; member of the Baptist Church, a Mason (thirty-second degree and Shriner), Knights of Pythias, S. A. E. fraternity, and Lions International Civic Club (district governor, 1939–40); married to Miss Ruth Ross, of Clark County, Ark., May 9, 1934; two children, Carolyn Marie and James Edward; elected to 77th Congress November 5, 1940; reelected to 78th, 79th, 80th, 81st, 82d, 83d, 84th, 85th, 86th, 87th, 88th, and 89th Congresses; chairman of the Committee on Interstate and Foreign Commerce 85th to 89th Congresses, inclusive.

CALIFORNIA

(Population (1960), 15,717,204)

SENATORS

THOMAS H. KUCHEL, Republican, of Anaheim, Calif.; born in Anaheim, Calif., on August 15, 1910; son of the late Henry Kuchel, who owned, edited, and published the Anaheim Gazette for 48 years and whose parents were among the pioneers who founded the city in 1859; the Senator's mother continues to reside there; attended local public schools and graduated from the University of Southern California with an LL.B. degree; admitted to the State bar in 1935, practiced law until appointed State controller; elected to the State assembly from Orange County in 1936, served two terms; elected to State senate in 1940, served two terms; volunteered for active duty in the United States Naval Reserve while State senator in 1942 and served until released in 1945; appointed State controller by Gov. Earl Warren on February 11, 1946; elected to that office in November of that year, reelected in 1950; appointed United States Senator by Gov. Earl Warren on December 22, 1952; took oath of office January 2, 1953; elected United States Senator 1954; reelected in 1956 and 1962; has four times been elected Senate Assistant Republican Leader; married and has one daughter, Karen; member Episcopal Church; Mason; BPOE; Anaheim Post No. 72, American Legion; Native Sons of the Golden West.

GEORGE LLOYD MURPHY, Republican, of Beverly Hills, Calif.; born in New Haven, Conn., July 4, 1902, son of Mike Murphy who trained the first two American Olympic track teams; educated at Peddie Institute, the Pauling School, and studied engineering at Yale University; married the former Julie Johnson in 1926; two children, Dennis and Melissa (Mrs. Robert W. Ellis III); appeared in four Broadway shows and 45 motion pictures; recognized by the Army, Navy, Marine Corps, Air Force, and Coast Guard for activities in entertainment during World War II; received awards and honors from U.S. Department of State, American Red Cross, Friendly Sons of St. Patrick, USO, Boy Scouts, Cancer Prevention Society, University of Southern California, and received the first national award by the National Conference of Christians and Jews; lifetime union member; elected twice as president of the AFL–CIO affiliated Screen Actors Guild and served on the board of directors for 15 years; chairman of the Republican State Central Committee of California in 1953 and 1954; delegate to four Republican National Conventions and was in charge of programs in 1956 and 1960; elected to the United States Senate November 3, 1964, for a full term, commencing January 3, 1965; subsequently appointed December 31, 1964.

REPRESENTATIVES

FIRST DISTRICT.—COUNTIES: Del Norte, Humboldt, Marin, Mendocino, Napa, and Sonoma (6 counties). Population (1960), 533,807.

DON H. CLAUSEN, Republican, of Crescent City, Calif.; born in Ferndale, Calif., April 27, 1923; married Ollie Piper; two daughters, Beverly and Dawn Marie; graduated from elementary and high school in Ferndale; attended San Jose State College; V5 Program, U.S. Navy; California Polytechnic; Weber College, Ogden, Utah; St. Mary's College, California; business: insurance, Clausen Associates, Crescent City; Air Ambulance Service, Clausen Flying Service, Crescent City; military service: U.S. Navy, carrier pilot, Asiatic-Pacific, World War II; member of Del Norte County Chamber of Commerce; past member board of supervisors, Del Norte County; past president, Supervisors' Unit, Redwood Empire Association; County Supervisors Association of California; elected to the 88th Congress January 22, 1963, to fill vacancy caused by the death of Clem Miller; reelected to the 89th Congress.

SECOND DISTRICT.—COUNTIES: Alpine, Amador, Butte, Calaveras, El Dorado, Inyo, Lassen, Mariposa, Modoc, Mono, Nevada, Placer, Plumas, Shasta, Sierra, Siskiyou, Tehama, Trinity, and Tuolumne (19 counties). Population (1960), 406,506.

HAROLD T. (BIZZ) JOHNSON, Democrat, of Roseville, Calif.; born in Yolo County; attended Roseville schools and University of Nevada; supervisor of Pacific Fruit Express Co.; district chairman, Brotherhood of Railway Clerks;

married to Albra I. Manuel, has one son and one daughter; served as school trustee, city councilman, and for 7 years as mayor of Roseville; president, American River Development League; member: Lambda Chi Alpha, Eagles, Moose, Brotherhood of Railway Clerks, Elks; elected to State senate in 1948; reelected without opposition in 1952 and 1956; elected to 86th Congress on November 4, 1958; reelected to the 87th, 88th, and 89th Congresses.

THIRD DISTRICT.—SACRAMENTO COUNTY. Population (1960), 502,778.

JOHN EMERSON MOSS, Democrat, of Sacramento, Calif.; born in Carbon County, Utah; attended Sacramento public schools and Sacramento College; businessman and real estate broker; served in the United States Navy during World War II; elected member California State Assembly for ninth district November 2, 1948; reelected November 7, 1950; assistant Democratic floor leader of the assembly 1949–52 sessions; married Jean Kueny September 15, 1935; two daughters, Jennifer Afton and Allison Effie; elected to the 83d Congress November 4, 1952; reelected to 84th Congress November 2, 1954; reelected to the 85th Congress November 6, 1956; reelected to the 86th Congress November 4, 1958, after being nominated by both Democratic and Republican parties; reelected to the 87th Congress without opposition; reelected to the 88th and 89th Congresses.

FOURTH DISTRICT.—COUNTIES: Colusa, Glenn, Lake, Solano, Sutter, Yolo, and Yuba (7 counties). Population (1960), 310,669.

ROBERT LOUIS LEGGETT, Democrat, of Vallejo, Calif.; born in Richmond, Calif., on July 26, 1926; veteran, enlisted man of the U.S. Navy Air Corps; B.A., University of California, political science, 1947; LL.B., University of California Boalt Hall School of Jurisprudence, 1950; married the former Barbara Burnett of San Francisco; three children—Diana, 13; Jeanne, 11; and Rob, 6; practiced law in Northern California 12 years; senior partner, firm of Leggett & Gianola; elected member California State Assembly November 5, 1960; member 20–30 International, Kiwanis, Elks, Redmen, Sons of Italy, and American Legion No. 104; elected to the 88th Congress November 6, 1962; reelected to the 89th Congress.

FIFTH DISTRICT.—COUNTY OF SAN FRANCISCO: Assembly districts 18 and 20. Population (1960), 301,872.

PHILLIP BURTON, Democrat, of San Francisco, Calif.; born in Cincinnati, Ohio, June 1, 1926; graduate George Washington High School, San Francisco, 1944; currently serving as president of George Washington High Alumni Association; graduated in 1947 from University of Southern California; A.B. degree in political science; president, Campus Chapter of Blue Key; received LL.B. degree in 1952 from Golden Gate Law School; attorney at law, admitted to practice before U.S. Supreme Court in 1956; veteran of World War II and the Korean conflict; married to the former Sala Galant; one daughter, Joy; elected in 1956 to California State Assembly as youngest member; the only Democrat to defeat incumbent Republican in that year in California; served as chairman of Assembly Committee on Social Welfare for 5 years, until election to Congress; former national officer of Young Democrats; a founder of the California Democratic Council; youngest delegate to represent the United States at the Atlantic Treaty Association Conference in France in 1959; elected to the 88th Congress February 18, 1964, in a special election; elected as secretary-treasurer of the 88th Congress Democratic Club by fellow freshman members; unopposed for reelection to the 89th Congress; member of the Interior and Insular Affairs Committee.

SIXTH DISTRICT.—COUNTY OF SAN FRANCISCO: Assembly districts 19, 21, and 23. Population (1960), 438,444.

WILLIAM S. MAILLIARD, Republican, of San Francisco, Calif.; born June 10, 1917, in Belvedere, Calif.; Yale University, B. A., 1939; with American Trust Co. of San Francisco 1940–41, and 1946; assistant to director, California Academy of Sciences, 1951–52; military service: assistant naval attaché, Embassy, London, 1939–40; Bureau of Naval Personnel 1941–42; Naval War College 1942; Seventh Amphibious Force, aide and flag lieutenant to Vice Adm. D. E. Barbey, 1943–46; captain, USNR; awarded Silver Star, Legion of Merit, Bronze Star; assistant to director California Youth Authority 1947; Republican nominee for Congress 1948; secretary to Gov. Earl Warren 1949–51; Protestant; married Millicent Fox, July 10, 1957; elected to the 83d Congress November 4, 1952, and subsequent Congresses; 1963, U.S. Delegate to 18th Session of the United Nations General Assembly.

SEVENTH DISTRICT.—COUNTY OF ALAMEDA: Assembly districts 16 and 17. Population (1960), 333,530.

JEFFERY COHELAN, Democrat, of Berkeley, Calif.; born in San Francisco, Calif., June 24, 1914; A. B. degree (Econ.), University of California; Graduate School of Economics, University of California; Fulbright research scholar, United Kingdom, Leeds and Oxford Universities, 1953–54; elected secretary-treasurer Milk Drivers and Dairy Employees Local 302, Alameda and Contra Costa Counties, 1942; consultant, University of California Institute of Industrial Relations; member of Berkeley Welfare Commission, 1949–53; elected to Berkeley City Council, May 1955; council representative on planning and recreation commissions; member of San Francisco Council on Foreign Relations; Commonwealth Club of California; Loyal Order of Moose, Oakland Lodge 324; Fraternal Order of Eagles, California Aerie; married Evelyn Elizabeth Ellis February 10, 1939; two daughters—Pamela Joy, now a Peace Corps volunteer in the Philippines, and Catherine Anna, 16—and two sons—Terrence Daniel (married to Sondra Wilson Cohelan September 1964), University of Maryland, and Timothy Douglas, University of Arizona; elected to the 86th Congress November 4, 1958; former member Armed Services and District of Columbia Committees; member Appropriations Committee; reelected to the 87th, 88th, and 89th Congresses.

EIGHTH DISTRICT.—COUNTY OF ALAMEDA: Assembly districts 14 and 15. Population (1960), 373,286.

GEORGE P. MILLER, Democrat, of Alameda, Calif.; born in San Francisco, Calif., January 15, 1891; was graduated from St. Mary's College with the degree of B.S. in C.E.; during the 1962 Centennial Year was presented with an honorary doctor of science degree from St. Mary's College; veteran of World War I, serving as lieutenant, Field Artillery, and was graduated from the School of Fire for Field Artillery at Fort Sill, Okla.; executive secretary to the California Division of Fish and Game, 1941–44; served two terms in the California State Assembly, 52d and 53d sessions, 1937 and 1939; married Esther Perkins and they have one daughter, Mrs. Donald B. (Ann) Muir; two grandsons, Christopher and Peter, and one granddaughter, Katherine Ann; elected to the 79th Congress on November 7, 1944; reelected to the 80th, 81st, 82d, 83d, 84th, 85th, 86th, 87th, 88th, and 89th Congresses; chairman of the committee on Science and Astronautics Committee, a permanent committee of the House of Representatives; appointed in the 88th Congress to the Special Select Committee on Government Research; special advisor to the U.S. Ambassador to the United Nations of the Peaceful Uses of Outer Space; and a member of the National Historical Publications Commission.

NINTH DISTRICT.—COUNTY OF ALAMEDA: Assembly district 13. COUNTY OF SANTA CLARA: Assembly district 25. Population (1960), 383,498.

DON EDWARDS, Democrat, of San Jose, Calif.; district offices: 40 North First Street, San Jose, and 1065 A Street, Hayward; born in San Jose, Calif.; married; wife, Clyda Edwards; five sons—Leonard Perry Edwards II, Thomas Charles Edwards, Samuel Dyer Edwards, Bruce Haven Edwards, and William Don Edwards; attended public schools in San Jose and graduated Stanford University; Stanford Law School, 1936–38; admitted State Bar of California; special agent, Federal Bureau of Investigation, 1940–41; U.S. Navy, 1942–45, Naval Intelligence and gunnery officer; occupation, president, Valley Title Company, San Jose, Calif.; elected to the 88th Congress November 6, 1962; reelected to the 89th Congress.

TENTH DISTRICT.—COUNTY OF SANTA CLARA: Assembly districts 22 and 24. Population (1960), 460,210.

CHARLES S. GUBSER, Republican, of Gilroy, Calif.; born February 1, 1916, in Gilroy, Calif.; graduate of Gilroy Union High School, San Jose State Junior College, and University of California (A. B. 1937); 2 years' graduate work at University of California; taught in California secondary schools; now a farmer; married to former Joan Brimberry; one daughter, Mrs. Raymond Camino; one grandson, Kenneth Allan Camino; elected as assemblyman to California State Legislature in 1950; elected to the 83d Congress November 4, 1952; reelected to the 84th, 85th, 86th, 87th, 88th, and 89th Congresses.

ELEVENTH DISTRICT.—SAN MATEO COUNTY. Population (1960), 444,387.

J. ARTHUR YOUNGER, Republican, of San Mateo, Calif.; born in Albany, Oreg., April 11, 1893; married Norma W. Younger; graduated from the University of Washington in 1915, and served as graduate manager of athletics until 1917; was called into service with the Washington National Guard CAC during First World War, and went overseas with the Forty-eighth Artillery CAC; discharged as a captain in June 1919; life member and past commander of Seattle Post, American Legion; served as vice president, director and manager of the mortgage loan department, Seattle Title Trust Co., 1920–30; president Seattle Mortgage Loan Co., 1930–34; served as regional appraiser of the HOLC, assistant appraiser-adviser Home Loan Bank Board, and Chief of the Savings and Loan Division, Federal Home Loan Bank Board, Washington, D. C., 1934–37; executive vice president Citizens Federal Savings & Loan Association, San Francisco, since 1937; moved to San Mateo in December 1937; member: Rotary Club, Congregational Church, Delta Upsilon Fraternity, Islam Temple, A. A. O. N. M. S., Newcomen Society, Commonwealth Club of California, Menlo Country Club, and Congressional Country Club; elected to the 83d Congress November 4, 1952; reelected to the 84th, 85th, 86th, 87th, 88th, and 89th Congresses.

TWELFTH DISTRICT.—COUNTIES: Monterey, San Benito, San Luis Obispo, and Santa Cruz (4 counties). Population (1960), 379,010.

BURT L. TALCOTT, Republican, of Salinas, Calif.; born in Billings, Mont., February 22, 1920; graduated Stanford University, Calif., B.A., political science, 1942, LL.B. 1948; Sigma Chi and Phi Delta Phi fraternities; attorney, of counsel Pioda, Leach, Stave, Bryan & Ames and Burt L. Talcott, Salinas, Calif.; former journeyman carpenter, union member; U.S. Air Corps, 1942–45, B–24 pilot, German prisoner of war 14 months, honorably discharged as first lieutenant, winner Air Medal and Purple Heart with clusters, major, USAF Reserve; married the former Lee G. Taylor of Great Falls, Mont.; one son, Ronald, cadet USAF Academy, Class '66; formerly: trustee, Methodist Church; Commissioner of Athletics, Coast Counties Athletic League, 1954–58; Monterey County supervisor, 1954–62; Outstanding Young Man of Salinas, 1955; past director of: Salinas Chamber of Commerce, Salinas JayCees, Junior Achievement, Inc., American Red Cross, American Field Service, Community Chest, Council for Retarded Children, Little League Baseball, California Roadside Council, and Stanford Alumni Association; honorary life member PTA; member, Commonwealth Club of California, American Legion, and Monterey and California bar associations; elected to the 88th Congress November 6, 1962; reelected to the 89th Congress; member, Committee on Banking and Currency.

THIRTEENTH DISTRICT.—COUNTIES: Santa Barbara and Ventura (2 counties). Population (1960), 368,100.

CHARLES M. TEAGUE, Republican, of Ojai, Calif.; born in Santa Paula, Calif., September 18, 1909; educated in the public schools of Santa Paula; graduated from Stanford University in 1931 and from Stanford Law School in 1934; lawyer; married to the former Marjorie Cowden; three children—Norma Teague Potter (Mrs. J. B. Potter, Jr., North Hollywood, Calif.), Alan Teague (married to the former Elizabeth Lee McKee of Ventura, Calif.), and Judith Teague (Mrs. Robert Kenyon, Terra Linda, Calif.); elected to the 84th Congress November 2, 1954; reelected to the 85th, 86th, 87th, 88th, and 89th Congresses.

FOURTEENTH DISTRICT.—CONTRA COSTA COUNTY. Population (1960), 409,030.

JOHN F. BALDWIN, Republican, of Martinez, Calif.; born June 28, 1915, in Oakland, Calif.; graduate of University of California (1935) and University of California Boalt Hall School of Jurisprudence (1949); assistant manager, South-Western Publishing Co., San Francisco (1936–41); enlisted in the Army as a private in April 1941, and served for 5½ years in the armed service, being discharged as a lieutenant colonel in October 1946; served as director of training, Army Finance School (1943–44), Chief of Foreign Fiscal Affairs Branch, Office of Fiscal Director, War Department (1945), and Executive Officer, Office of Fiscal Director, Mediterranean Theater (1946); was decorated by Italian Government for work in the devaluation of the lire currency in 1946; president of his law class all three years in law school (1946–49); practiced law in Martinez from

1949 to 1954; past director of Contra Costa County Park and Recreation Council; life member of Sierra Club; past director of Contra Costa Public Health Association; past director of Martinez Kiwanis Club; past president of East Contra Costa University of California Alumni Club; married Mary Isaacs, December 20, 1944; three daughters—Georgia, 18 years; Doris, 12 years; and Sylvia, 10 years; elected to the 84th Congress November 2, 1954; reelected to 85th, 86th, 87th, 88th, and 89th Congresses.

FIFTEENTH DISTRICT.—COUNTIES: San Joaquin and Stanislaus (2 counties). Population (1960), 407,283.

JOHN J. McFALL, Democrat, of Manteca, Calif.; born February 20, 1918, in Buffalo, N.Y.; married to former Evelyn Anklam; three children: Joseph, 14; Alicia, 11; and Sarah, 8; attended the public schools of Manteca; graduated from Modesto Junior College in 1936, from University of California in 1938, A. B. (political science), and from University of California (Boalt Hall) LL. B. 1941; admitted to California bar in 1941; during World War II served as a staff sergeant in the Security Intelligence Corps 1942–46; engaged in the practice of law in Manteca, Calif., since 1946; mayor of Manteca, 1948–50; Assemblyman, California Legislature, 1951–56; member of: I.O.O.F., Masons, Scottish Rite and Shrine, Eagles, Lions Club, Grange, American Legion, California Bar Association; elected to 85th Congress November 6, 1956; reelected to 86th, 87th, 88th, and 89th Congresses.

SIXTEENTH DISTRICT.—COUNTIES: Fresno, Madera, and Merced (3 counties). Population (1960), 496,859.

B. F. SISK, Democrat, of Fresno, Calif.; born Montague, Tex., December 14, 1910, the son of Arthur Lee and Lavina (Thomas) Sisk; graduated from Meadow, Tex., high school; attended Abilene Christian College, Abilene, Tex.; moved to San Joaquin Valley of California in 1937; married April 20, 1931, to Reta Mitchell; daughters, Mrs. J. Martin Temple and Mrs. John H. Pittenger; home address: 3860 Balch Avenue, Fresno, Calif.; elected to 84th Congress November 2, 1954; reelected to the 85th, 86th, 87th, 88th, and 89th Congresses.

SEVENTEENTH DISTRICT.—COUNTY OF LOS ANGELES: Assembly districts 67 and 68. Population (1960), 376,115.

CECIL R. KING, Democrat, of Los Angeles, Calif.; born in Youngstown, Fort Niagara, N. Y., January 13, 1898; educated in the public schools of Los Angeles; businessman; married; one child; veteran of the First World War; member of the California State Legislature, 1932–42; elected to the 77th Congress at a special election held on August 25, 1942; reelected to the 78th and each succeeding Congress through the 89th; member, House Ways and Means Committee, Joint Committee on Internal Revenue Taxation, Joint Committee on Reduction of Nonessential Federal Expenditures, appointed one of the two House of Representative Members of the United States Common Market Negotiating Team; congressional adviser to the United Nations Conference for Trade and Development, and is chairman of the California Congressional Delegation.

EIGHTEENTH DISTRICT.—COUNTIES: Kern, Kings, and Tulare (3 counties). Population (1960), 510,341.

HARLAN HAGEN, Democrat, of Hanford, Calif.; born in Lawton, N. Dak., October 8, 1914; resident of California since 1929; A.B. degree in economics, University of California, and LL. B. in law, University of California School of Jurisprudence; member of California Legislature 1949–52; senior partner, law firm of Hagen & McInturff, Hanford, Calif.; World War II veteran with principal service in Army Counter-Intelligence Corps; holds reserve commission as lieutenant colonel in Army Intelligence; married to the former Martha Ritz; elected to the 83d Congress November 4, 1952; reelected to 84th Congress November 2, 1954; reelected to the 85th Congress, November 6, 1956; reelected to 86th Congress, by winning both Democratic and Republican nominations in primary election June 3, 1958; reelected to the 87th, 88th, and 89th Congresses.

NINETEENTH DISTRICT.—COUNTY OF LOS ANGELES: Assembly districts 51 and 66. Population (1960), 377,991.

CHET HOLIFIELD, Democrat, of Montebello, Calif.; born in Mayfield, Ky., December 3, 1903, son of Ercie V. and Bessie Lee (Brady) Holifield; educated in the public schools of Arkansas; resided in Montebello, Calif., since 1920; engaged in manufacturing and selling of men's apparel for over 38 years; member of the Christian Church; delegate to the Democratic National Conventions in 1940, 1944, 1948, 1952, 1956, 1960, and 1964; married Miss Vernice Caneer; four daughters—Lois Anita (Mrs. William Mulholland), Betty Lee (Mrs. Robert H. Feldmann), Willa Mae (Mrs. Donald Lee Douglas), and Jo Ann (Mrs. Donald Williams); fourteen grandchildren; elected to the 78th Congress in November 1942 as the first representative from the newly reapportioned Nineteenth Congressional District of California; reelected to the 79th, 80th, 81st, 82d, 83d, 84th, 85th, 86th, 87th, 88th, and 89th Congresses; member of President's Special Evaluation Commission on Atomic Bomb Tests at Bikini Atoll; Chairman, Joint Committee on Atomic Energy; member of the Committee on Government Operations; member of the Commission on Organization of the Executive Branch of the Government (new Hoover Commission); congressional adviser on the United States Delegation to the International Conference on the Peaceful Uses of Atomic Energy, Geneva, Switzerland, 1955; representative of Joint Committee on Atomic Energy at first organizational meeting of the International Atomic Energy Agency at Vienna, Austria, October 1957; congressional adviser to U.S. Delegation to the Third General Conference of the International Atomic Energy Agency at Vienna, Austria, in 1959; congressional adviser to the American Delegation at the Conference on the Discontinuance of Nuclear Weapons Tests at Geneva, Switzerland, in 1959 and 1961; congressional adviser to U.S. Delegation to the Seventh General Conference of the International Atomic Energy Agency at Vienna, Austria, in 1963.

TWENTIETH DISTRICT.—COUNTY OF LOS ANGELES: Assembly districts 43 and 47. Population (1960), 388,171.

H. ALLEN SMITH, Republican, of Glendale, Calif.; born in Dixon, Ill., October 8, 1909; moved to California in 1924; attended Hollywood High School and University of California, Los Angeles; obtained A. B. degree in 1930 and LL. B. degree in 1933 from the University of Southern California; admitted to the practice of law in 1934 and practiced until December 1935 and then became a special agent of the Federal Bureau of Investigation; served as special agent until the latter part of 1942, at which time became manager of plant protection at Lockheed Aircraft Corp.; returned to law practice in 1944; married Elizabeth McKay in 1934 and has two sons—Stephen Allen Smith and Lauren McKay Smith; member of Masons, Al Malaikah Shrine, Los Angeles County Peace Officers Association, California State Peace Officers Association, Society of Former Special Agents of FBI, Alpha Tau Omega, Alpha Kappa Psi; elected to California State Assembly, 43d district, in 1948; reelected three times and fourth term expired December 31, 1956; elected to the 85th Congress on November 6, 1956; reelected to the 86th, 87th, 88th, and 89th Congresses; member of Rules Committee and Small Business Committee.

TWENTY-FIRST DISTRICT.—COUNTY OF LOS ANGELES: Assembly districts 53 and 55. Population (1960), 364,865.

AUGUSTUS F. HAWKINS, Democrat, of Los Angeles, Calif.; born in Shreveport, La., August 31, 1907; at age 11 came to California; attended local schools, including Jefferson High in district now representing; graduated from U.C.L.A. with A.B. in economics, and from Institute of Government, U.S.C.; married, no children; active in juvenile delinquency prevention work, Los Angeles County; first legislation as a member of the assembly gave legal recognition to the Coordinating Council movement to help youth; engaged in real estate business; Mason, and active in civic, church, and social clubs throughout the State; elected to assembly, 1934; reelected every 2 years thereafter; served as chairman, committees on Public Utilities, Unemployment, and Labor and Capital; and special subcommittees on Housing, Rapid Transit, and Sales Taxes; in 1953, elected to Rules Committee and reelected 1955, 1957, 1959, and 1961; in 1959 appointed chairman of Assembly Rules Committee and elected chairman of the Joint Committee on Legislative Organization; elected to the 88th Congress November 6, 1962; reelected to the 89th Congress.

TWENTY-SECOND DISTRICT.—COUNTY OF LOS ANGELES: Assembly districts 41 and 64. Population (1960), 393,907.

JAMES C. CORMAN, Democrat, of Van Nuys, Calif.; born October 20, 1920, in Galena, Kans.; moved to California in 1933; graduate of University of California, Los Angeles, 1942 and University of Southern California Law School, 1948; during World War II served in the U.S. Marine Corps, 3d Marine Division, at Bougainville, Guam, and Iwo Jima, 1942–46, and subsequent service 1950–52; married the former Virginia Little in Atlanta, Ga., in 1946; two children Mary Anne and James C., Jr.; admitted to the California bar in 1949 and engaged in private law practice until 1957; member of city council, Los Angeles, 1957–60; member of the Methodist Church, Lions International, American Legion, Elks, the Los Angeles and San Fernando Valley bar associations, Los Angeles Community Relations Conference, the American Christian Association for Israel; elected to the 87th Congress November 8, 1960; reelected to the 88th and 89th Congresses.

TWENTY-THIRD DISTRICT.—COUNTY OF LOS ANGELES: Assembly districts 38 and 52. Population (1960), 408,099.

DELWIN (DEL) MORGAN CLAWSON, Republican, of Compton, Calif.; born in Thatcher, Ariz., January 11, 1914; educated in Pima and Safford, Ariz., public schools; attended Gila College, Thatcher, Ariz.; married the former Marjorie Anderson of Salt Lake City, Utah, in 1934; two sons, Larry and James; employed as salesman and bookkeeper, 1934–41; United States Employment Service and Federal Public Housing Authority, 1941–47; manager, Mutual Housing Association of Compton, 1947–63; member: Church of Jesus Christ of Latter Day Saints, Kiwanis International, Executives Dinner Club, Compton Chamber of Commerce; "Citizen of Year" award, 1960; chairman, Midland District, Boy Scouts of America (1960), Community Chest and Red Cross city chairman; member Park and Recreation Commission, Compton, 1950–53; member, City Council of Compton 1953–57; mayor of Compton, 1957–63; director of Los Angeles County Sanitation Districts 1, 2, 8, 1957–63; elected to the 88th Congress in special election on June 11, 1963; reelected to the 89th Congress.

TWENTY-FOURTH DISTRICT.—COUNTY OF LOS ANGELES: Assembly districts 49 and 54. Population (1960), 399,322.

GLENARD P. LIPSCOMB, Republican, of Los Angeles, Calif.; born in Jackson, Mich., August 19, 1915; came to California with his parents in 1920; attended Los Angeles city schools, University of Southern California, and Woodbury College; married Virginia Sognalian September 4, 1936; two daughters, Diane Marie (Mrs. Louis Grasso) and Joyce Elaine (Mrs. Robert Murrell); public accountant; served in the Finance Corps, United States Army World War II; member Kiwanis International, Elks, Masons, American Legion, Atwater Park Baptist Church, Society of California Accountants, and National Society of Public Accountants; former senior partner in the Los Angeles public accountancy firm of Lipscomb, Hahn & Brown; elected to California Legislature in 1947 and reelected in 1948, 1950, and 1952; elected to the 83d Congress at special election held November 10, 1953; reelected to the 84th, 85th, 86th, 87th, 88th, and 89th Congresses.

TWENTY-FIFTH DISTRICT.—COUNTY OF LOS ANGELES: Assembly districts 50 and 58. Population (1960), 372,357.

RONALD BROOKS CAMERON, Democrat, of Whittier, Calif.; born in Kansas City, Mo., August 16, 1927; educated in public schools in Kansas, Missouri, and Ohio; attended Western Reserve Academy, Hudson, Ohio; enlisted in U.S. Marine Corps in 1945; attended Western Reserve University, Cleveland, and University of California, Los Angeles; admitted to practice as certified public accountant in 1954; member of California Society of Certified Public Accountants and American Institute of CPAs; wife, Constance, and children, Victoria Brooks and Richard Malcolm, are native Californians; served the Democratic Party in many capacities including club president, council president, delegation chairman of Los Angeles County Central Committee, cochairman 25th District State Central Committee, and delegate to 1960 and 1964 National Conventions; elected to California Legislature in 1958, reelected in 1960; vice chairman committees on Finance and Insurance and Public Health; chairman of Subcommittee of Medical Insurance; member of committees on Military and Veterans Affairs, Governmental Efficiency and Economy, and Public Utilities and Corporations; elected to the 88th Congress November 6, 1962; reelected to the 89th Congress.

TWENTY-SIXTH DISTRICT.—COUNTY OF LOS ANGELES: Assembly districts 59 and 61. Population (1960), 388,421.

JAMES ROOSEVELT, Democrat, of Los Angeles, Calif.; born in New York City, December 23, 1907; son of Franklin D. Roosevelt and Anna Eleanor Roosevelt; married to Irene Owens Roosevelt; graduated, Groton School in 1926; Harvard Class of 1930; secretary to the President of the United States, 1937–38; former chairman, California Democratic State Central Committee; former California Democratic National Committeeman; active service, United States Marine Corps, 1940 through 1945; brigadier general (ret.), United States Marine Corps Reserve; decorated, Navy Cross and Silver Star; member, American Legion, Veterans of Foreign Wars, and President of the Eleanor Roosevelt Cancer Foundation; member, Board of Directors of the American Cancer Society; Episcopalian; elected to the 84th Congress November 2, 1954; reelected to the 85th, 86th, 87th, 88th, and 89th Congresses.

TWENTY-SEVENTH DISTRICT.—COUNTY OF LOS ANGELES: Assembly districts 42 and 62 (including central portion of the San Fernando Valley and western half of the Antelope Valley). Population (1960), 360,558.

ED REINECKE, Republican, of Tujunga, Calif.; born January 7, 1924, Medford, Oreg.; resident of Los Angeles County area 39 years; attended El Rodeo G.S., Beverly Hills, Calif., Beverly Hills H.S., and California Institute of Technology (1946–50), B.S. mechanical engineering; participated in varsity water polo and diving; World War II Navy veteran; member: Emmanuel Lutheran Church, North Hollywood, Calif., Sunland-Tujunga American Legion Post 250; North Hollywood VFW Post 10040; board of directors, Sun Valley Chamber of Commerce; national board of directors, American Society of Sanitary Engineering; Water Committee, California State Chamber of Commerce; Technical Standards Committee, Western Plumbing Officials Association; Republican Associates; California Republican State Central Committee; president: Febco, Inc. (mfr. lawn irrigation equipment), Sun Valley, Calif. (1954–64); Los Feliz Kiwanis Club (1963); chairman: Kiwanis Division 2 Committee, Public and Business Affairs (1964); professional mechanical engineer, Calif. M10979; inventor; author, numerous articles for trade publications; former assistant congressional district precinct chairman, 27th District, Calif.; nominated in California primary June 2, 1964; elected: 89th Congress, November 3, 1964; whip, California Republican Delegation, January 6, 1965; appointed: Interior and Insular Affairs Committee; subcommittees on Mines and Mining, Irrigation and Reclamation, and National Parks and Recreation.

TWENTY-EIGHTH DISTRICT.—COUNTY OF LOS ANGELES: Assembly districts 46, 57, and 60. Population (1960), 588,933.

ALPHONZO BELL, Republican, of Los Angeles, Calif.; born in Los Angeles, September 19, 1914, the son of Alphonzo and Minnewa Bell; graduated from Occidental College with a B.A. degree in political science; veteran of Army Air Corps, World War II, presently a lieutenant colonel in the Air Force Reserve; chairman of the board of directors of Bell Petroleum Co. prior to election to Congress; chairman of the Republican State Central Committee and member of the Republican National Committee 1956–58; chairman of the Republican Central Committee of Los Angeles County 1958–60; wife, Sally; sons, Stephen, Matthew, Robert, and Anthony Edward; daughter, Fonza; first elected from the 16th District to 87th Congress, November 1960; reelected to 88th and 89th Congresses from reapportioned 28th District (most heavily populated in California); sole California Republican on the House Science and Astronautics and on the House Education and Labor Committees.

TWENTY-NINTH DISTRICT.—COUNTY OF LOS ANGELES: Assembly districts 45 and 48. Population (1960), 396,813.

GEORGE E. BROWN, JR., Democrat, of Monterey Park, Calif.; born in Holtville, Calif., March 6, 1920; married to Rowena Somerindyke; five children; graduated from University of California at Los Angeles, B.A. in industrial physics; employed by city of Los Angeles, 12 years, personnel and engineering; management consultant; veteran of U.S. Army, World War II; mayor and city councilman, Monterey Park, 1954–58; State assemblyman, 45th District, Calif., 1959–62; elected to the 88th Congress November 6, 1962; reelected to 89th Congress.

THIRTIETH DISTRICT.—COUNTY OF LOS ANGELES: Assembly districts 40 and 56. Population (1960), 391,541.

EDWARD R. ROYBAL, Democrat, of Los Angeles, Calif.; born in Albuquerque, N. Mex., February 10, 1916; moved to Los Angeles in 1922 and attended the public schools; graduated from Roosevelt High School in 1934 and then joined the Civilian Conservation Corps until April 1, 1935; trained in business administration at the University of California at Los Angeles, and at Southwestern University in Los Angeles, Calif.; served in the U.S. Army from 1944 to 1945; married the former Lucille Beserra of Los Angeles, September 27, 1940; three children—Lucille, Lillian, and Edward R., Jr.; social worker and public health educator with the California Tuberculosis Association and a director of health education for the Los Angeles County Tuberculosis and Health Association 1942–49; member of the Los Angeles City Council 1949–62 and served as president pro tempore from July 1961; president of Eastland Savings & Loan Association; member of the Catholic Church, Knights of Columbus, and American Legion; elected to the 88th Congress November 6, 1962; reelected to the 89th Congress.

THIRTY-FIRST DISTRICT.—COUNTY OF LOS ANGELES: Assembly districts 63 and 65. Population (1960), 396,220.

CHARLES H. WILSON, Democrat, of Los Angeles, Calif.; born in Magna, Utah, February 15, 1917; resident of Los Angeles, Calif., since 1922; attended public schools in Los Angeles and Inglewood; employed by Security First National Bank for 7 years; served in the U.S. Army from June 1942 until December 1945 with 2 years' service in the European Theater of Operations; after discharge from the Army established the Charles H. Wilson Insurance Agency; in 1954 was elected to the California Legislature from the 66th Assembly District and was serving his fourth consecutive term when elected to Congress; served as chairman of the Committee on Revenue and Taxation; member of the American Legion, Angeles Mesa Masonic Lodge, Al Malaikah Shrine, Elks, and Kiwanis; married Betty Gibbel and they have four sons—Steve, Don, Kenneth, and Billy; elected to the 88th Congress November 6, 1962, and appointed to committees on Banking and Currency and Post Office and Civil Service; reelected to the 89th Congress.

THIRTY-SECOND DISTRICT.—COUNTY OF LOS ANGELES: Assembly districts 39 and 44. Population (1960), 435,458.

CRAIG HOSMER, Republican, of Long Beach, Calif.; born in Brea, Calif., May 6, 1915, son of Chester C. and Mary Jane Hosmer; educated in public schools of California, University of California, A. B., 1937, University of Michigan Law School, University of Southern California Law School, LL. B., 1940; attorney; active naval service from 1940 to 1946 in all war theaters; attorney for Atomic Energy Commission and special assistant United States district attorney at Los Alamos, N. Mex., during 1948; married Marian Swanson of Minneapolis in 1946, two children: Susan Jane and Craig Larkin; member, Phi Kappa Psi fraternity, Phi Alpha Delta law fraternity; captain, USNR; elected to the 83d Congress; reelected to the 84th, 85th, 86th, 87th, 88th, and 89th Congresses; member of Joint Committee on Atomic Energy and Interior and Insular Affairs Committee.

THIRTY-THIRD DISTRICT.—SAN BERNARDINO COUNTY. Population (1960), 503,591.

KENNETH WARREN DYAL, Democrat, of San Bernardino, Calif.; born in Bisbee, Ariz., July 9, 1910; educated in public schools; married to Miss Gladys Fulkerson January 10, 1934; four children; served as lieutenant commander in U.S. Naval Reserve World War II; postmaster San Bernardino 1947–54; vice president Pioneer Title Insurance & Trust Co. and Title Insurance and Trust; past president of National Orange Show; member of Advisory Board of Feather River Project Association; member of Kiwanis, American Legion, and Latter Day Saints (Mormon Church); active for over 30 years in civic, governmental, and Democratic Party activities; elected to the 89th Congress November 3, 1964.

THIRTY-FOURTH DISTRICT.—COUNTY OF ORANGE: Assembly districts 69 and 70. Population (1960), 447,421.

RICHARD T. HANNA, Democrat, of Huntington Beach, Calif.; born in Kemmerer, Wyo., June 9, 1914; moved to Long Beach, Calif., with family in 1923; attended Compton public schools, Pasadena Junior College, A.A.; University of

California at Los Angeles, B.A.; and U.C.L.A. Law School, LL.B.; during World War II served in the Navy Air Corps 1942–45; married the former Doris Muriel Jenks April 1, 1945; three children—Pamela, Alexander, and Kimberly; member of Lions, Veterans of Foreign Wars, American Legion, Elks, Lambda Chi Alpha and Phi Delta Phi fraternities; member State assembly 1957–62; attorney at law; admitted to U.S. Supreme Court June 1963; member of law firm of Launer, Chaffee & Hanna, of Fullerton, Calif.; elected to the 88th Congress November 6, 1962; reelected to the 89th Congress.

THIRTY-FIFTH DISTRICT.—COUNTY OF ORANGE: Assembly district 71. COUNTY OF SAN DIEGO: Assembly district 80. Population (1960), 473,511.

JAMES B. UTT, Republican, of Santa Ana, Calif.; born in Tustin, Orange County, Calif., March 11, 1899; graduate of Orange County schools and University of Southern California Law School; engaged in citrus and agriculture most of lifetime; practicing attorney in Santa Ana; served 4 years as assemblyman from Orange County and 16 years as inheritance tax appraiser in the State controller's office; chairman of Legislative and Taxation Committee of Associated Chambers of Commerce; married to Charlena Dripps of Santa Ana, Calif.; one son; one grandson and two granddaughters; member of Tustin Presbyterian Church; elected to 83d Congress; reelected to 84th, 85th, 86th, 87th, 88th, and 89th Congresses.

THIRTY-SIXTH DISTRICT.—COUNTY OF SAN DIEGO: Assembly districts 76 and 78. Population (1960), 420,015.

BOB (ROBERT C.) WILSON, Republican, of San Diego, Calif.; born in Calexico, Calif., April 5, 1916, son of George Wellington and Olive Blanche Wilson; attended California public schools, San Diego State College, and Otis Art Institute, Los Angeles; married Laura Jean Bryant October 24, 1936; three children: Mrs. James E. Wilson, Mrs. Michael W. Chapple, and Bryant, 15; during World War II operated Conship Commissary and served as private in U.S.A.; now major, U.S.M.C.R.; elected "Young Man of the Year 1950"; past president of 20–30 Club and San Diego Junior Chamber of Commerce (1951); researched and originated several projects to bring recognition to John J. Montgomery, "the forgotten man of aviation"; director of San Diego USO Advisory Council and Boys' Club; member of Chula Vista Rotary Club, First Baptist Church, American Legion Post 434, B.P.O.E. No. 168, Aztec Alumni Association, San Diego Advertising and Sales Club, Republican Associates, and other civic organizations; distinguished as designer of award winning floats for San Diego City and County in Tournament of Roses; vice president of The Tolle Company, San Diego advertising and public relations consultants; elected chairman of Republican National Congressional Campaign Committee 1962–65; elected to 83d, 84th, 85th, 86th, 87th, 88th, and 89th Congresses.

THIRTY-SEVENTH DISTRICT.—COUNTY OF SAN DIEGO: Assembly districts 77 and 79. Population (1960), 395,989.

LIONEL VAN DEERLIN, Democrat, of San Diego, Calif.; born July 25, 1914, in Los Angeles, Calif., to Lionel Van Deerlin, Sr., and the former Gladys Mary Young; married Mary Jo Smith on October 8, 1940; six children—Lionel James, Lawson John, Victoria, Elizabeth, Mary Susan, and Jeffrey; graduate University of Southern California, 1937, with B.A. in journalism; Army veteran of World War II with overseas service in the Mediterranean Theater; newspaperman; radio and television news editor and analyst; Episcopalian; elected to the 88th Congress; reelected to the 89th Congress; member of Committee on Interstate and Foreign Commerce.

THIRTY-EIGHTH DISTRICT.—COUNTIES: Imperial and Riverside (2 counties). Population (1960), 378,296.

JOHN VARICK TUNNEY, Democrat, of Riverside, Calif.; born in New York City, N.Y., June 26, 1934; lived in Stamford, Conn., for 6 years and then on a small farm in Amenia, N.Y., until age 13, when the family returned to Stamford, Conn.; graduated from Westminster High School, Simsbury, Conn., in 1952, Yale University B.A. in 1956; attended the Academy of International Law at The Hague, Netherlands, in 1957; graduated from the University of Virginia,

LL.B. in 1959, and won the Appellate Court Competition; married the former Mieke Sprangers of Nijemgen, Netherlands; two sons, Edward Eugene and Mark Andrews; was admitted to the bar in Virginia and New York in 1959 and practiced law in New York City until April 1960 when he joined the U.S. Air Force as a judge advocate and assigned to March Air Force Base, serving until discharged as a captain in April 1963; taught business law, University of California, in 1961 and 1962; resumed the practice of law in Riverside, Calif.; special adviser, President's Committee on Juvenile Delinquency and Youth Crime; member Lions Club and Junior Chamber of Commerce of Riverside; former adviser to Riverside area ALSAC leukemia drive; elected to the 89th Congress November 3, 1964.

COLORADO

(Population (1960), 1,753,947)

SENATORS

GORDON LLEWELLYN ALLOTT, Republican, of Lamar, Colo.; born in Pueblo, Colo., January 2, 1907; graduated from the University of Colorado, B.A. 1927 and LL.B. 1929; honorary degree LL.D., Colorado College 1964; lawyer; county attorney of Prowers County in 1934 and 1940–46; district attorney 1946–48; Lieutenant Governor, two terms, 1950–54; member of Legislative Council; member State Board Bar Examiners, 1949–50; president, Lamar Rotary Club, 1937; secretary, Southeast Colorado Livestock Association, 1933–35; director and attorney, First Federal Savings & Loan Association; commissioned in U.S. Army Air Force, served 1942–46, South Pacific Theater with 339th Fighter Squadron; member, American Legion and Veterans of Foreign Wars; first chairman, Young Republican League of Colorado, 1935–38; chairman, Young Republican National Federation, 1941–46; Executive Committee, Young Republican National Federation, 1946–49; married to the former Welda O. Hall, May 15, 1934; two children: Roger H., and Gordon L., Jr.; Episcopalian; Mason; United States Congressional Representative to the 17th General Assembly of the United Nations 1962; elected to the United States Senate November 2, 1954, for the term commencing January 3, 1955; reelected in 1960 for the term ending January 3, 1967.

PETER H. DOMINICK, Republican, of Englewood, Colo.; born July 7, 1915, in Stamford, Conn., son of Gayer G. and Eleanor Hoyt Dominick; graduated from St. Mark's School in 1933, Yale University in 1937, and Yale Law School, LL.B., in 1940; married the former Nancy Parks in 1940; four children, Peter, Jr., Michael, Lynne, and Sandy; during World War II served in the Army Air Corps as an aviation cadet and through the ranks to captain from January 1942 to December 1945; awarded Air Medal and Cluster and Distinguished Flying Cross; engaged in legal practice in New York, N.Y., 1940–42 and moved to Englewood, Colo., in 1945; partner of law firm of Holland & Hart, 500 Equitable Building, Denver 2, Colo., 1946 to January 1, 1961, and resigned to enter Congress; attorney for Cherry Hills Village 1946–56 and trustee 1956–58; member of State House of Representatives 1957–61; active in community and civic affairs; former director and officer of several business corporations and the Denver Art Museum; elected to the 87th Congress November 8, 1960; elected to the United States Senate November 6, 1962, for the term ending January 3, 1969.

REPRESENTATIVES

FIRST DISTRICT.—CITY AND COUNTY OF DENVER. Population (1960), 493,887.

BYRON GILES ROGERS, Democrat, of Denver, Colo.; born August 1, 1900, in Hunt County, Tex., son of Peter and Minnie M. (Gentry) Rogers; graduated public schools, Checotah, Okla., 1919; served in United States Army 1918; attended University of Oklahoma 1919–22, Universities of Colorado and Denver 1923–25, LL. B. degree; practiced law, Las Animas, Colo., 1925–33; city attorney of Las Animas and county attorney of Bent County, Colo.; member of Colorado General Assembly 1931–35 (speaker 1933); Department of Agriculture and N. R. A., Washington, D. C., 1933–34; assistant United States attorney, District of Colorado, 1934–36; appointed attorney general of Colorado, July 3, 1936; elected attorney general 1936–38; State chairman Democratic State Central Committee of Colorado 1941–42; public member War Labor Board 1942–45; county chairman, Denver Democratic Central Committee, 1945–50; married; two children, Mrs. Hollis Martin and Byron, Jr.; member of: First Baptist Church of Denver, Phi Alpha Delta, the Denver, Colorado, and American Bar Associations, Lions International, Mystic Shrine, B. P. O. E., American Legion, I. O. O. F., Disabled American Veterans (life member); elected to the 82d Congress November 7, 1950; reelected to the 83d, 84th, 85th, 86th, 87th, 88th, and 89th Congresses.

SECOND DISTRICT.—COUNTIES: Adams, Arapahoe, Boulder, Clear Creek, Gilpin, and Jefferson (6 counties). Population (1960), 438,974.

ROY HARRISON McVICKER, Democrat, of Wheat Ridge, Colo.; born in Edgewater, Jefferson County, Colo., February 20, 1924, son of Reverend and Mrs. Roy H. McVicker; educated South Denver High School, Denver University, Columbia College, and Columbia Law School (LL.B. 1950); served in the U.S. Navy in the Southwest Pacific during World War II; lay preacher in Methodist Church since 18 years of age; assistant professor in psychology at Colorado State College 1946–47; worked under President Truman in establishment of the Admiral Nimitz Commission on Internal Security and Civil Rights 1950–51; lawyer in Wheat Ridge 1953 to present; wife, Harriett Runge McVicker; three children, Bill, Theresa, and Lisa; member of the State senate 1956–64; elected to the 89th Congress November 3, 1964.

THIRD DISTRICT.—COUNTIES: Baca, Bent, Cheyenne, Costilla, Crowley, Custer, Douglas, Elbert, El Paso, Fremont, Huerfano, Kiowa, Kit Carson, Las Animas, Lincoln, Otero, Prowers, Pueblo, Teller, Washington, and Yuma (21 counties). Population (1960), 415,187.

FRANK EDWARD EVANS, Democrat, of Pueblo, Colo., born September 6, 1923; lived and attended elementary and secondary schools in Colorado Springs; entered Pomona College, Claremont, Calif., in 1941; education interrupted in 1943 by service in U.S. Navy as a patrol pilot; returned to Colorado to complete education; received B.A. and law degrees from University of Denver; passed bar examinations and returned to Pueblo to begin law practice in 1950; active in civic and community projects; past president of Kiwanis and Junior Achievement, board member of YMCA, Family Service Society, and State Historical Society of Colorado; formerly active in Single Fund; past board member of Pueblo Industrial Development Corp.; former chairman of a Pueblo Community Welfare Council committee; former member of board of trustees of First Presbyterian Church of Pueblo; married the former Eleanor Trefz of Pueblo; children—Peter (11), Frances (9), Susan (5), and Charles (3); elected to public office first in 1960 as State representative; during first term (1961–62) was selected as the outstanding freshman representative by the Denver press; during second term (1963–64) was chosen Democratic floor whip; elected to the 89th Congress November 3, 1964.

FOURTH DISTRICT.—COUNTIES: Alamosa, Archuleta, Chaffee, Conejos, Delta, Dolores, Eagle, Garfield, Grand, Gunnison, Hinsdale, Jackson, Lake, La Plata, Larimer, Logan, Mesa, Mineral, Moffat, Montezuma, Montrose, Morgan, Ouray, Park, Phillips, Pitkin, Rio Blanco, Rio Grande, Routt, Saguache, San Juan, San Miguel, Sedgwick, Summit, and Weld (35 counties). Population (1960), 405,899.

WAYNE NORVIEL ASPINALL, Democrat, of Palisade, Colo.; born in Middleburg, Ohio, April 3, 1896, the oldest child of Mack Aspinall and Jessie Edna Norviel Aspinall, who moved to Colorado in 1904 and settled in Palisade, engaging in the peach-orchard industry; educated in the Mt. Lincoln public schools of Palisade, Colo.; graduated from the University of Denver, A.B. degree in 1919, and from the Denver Law School, LL.B. degree in 1925; recipient of honorary degree of doctor of laws from the University of Alaska in 1962; admitted to the Colorado Bar in 1925; taught school in 1919, 1921, and 1925–33; also engaged in the practice of law and the peach-orchard industry; president of the school board, 1920–22; member of board of trustees, town of Palisade, 1926–34; member of the Colorado House of Representatives, 1931–38, serving as Democratic Whip in 1931 and 1933 and as Speaker in 1937 and 1938; member of the Colorado Senate 1939–48, serving as Democratic Whip in 1939, Majority Floor Leader in 1941, and as Minority Floor Leader, 1943–45–47; during World War I served in the air service of the Signal Corps as a corporal and staff sergeant and was discharged as a flying cadet soon after the armistice; during World War II was commissioned a captain in Military Government in 1943, serving overseas as a legal expert with the American and English forces, participating in the Normandy drive as an American officer with the English Second Army; during college years was a member of social fraternity of Beta Theta Pi, the legal fraternity of Phi Delta Phi, and the honorary biological fraternity of Phi Sigma; is a member of Blue Lodge of the Masonic Fraternity, Scottish Rite, thirty-third degree, Knights Templar, A.A.O.N.M.S., I.O.O.F., American Legion, Forty and Eight, Veterans of Foreign Wars, B.P.O.E., Lions International, the Farmers Educational and Cooperative Union of America, and the Mesa County and Colorado Bar Associations; member of the Methodist Church; elected chairman of the State Democratic Central Committee of Colorado, chairman of the Democratic Congressional Central Committee of the Fourth Congressional District of Colorado, and chairman of the Mesa County Democratic Central Committee; married Julia Edith Kuns of Lincoln, Nebr., January 27, 1920; four children— Wayne Norviel II, Owen Stewart, Richard Daniel, and Ruth JoAnne Flora; elected to the 81st Congress November 2, 1948; reelected to the 82d, 83d, 84th, 85th, 86th, 87th, 88th, and 89th Congresses.

CONNECTICUT

(Population (1960), 2,535,234)

SENATORS

THOMAS J. DODD, Democrat, of West Hartford, Conn.; born in Norwich, Conn., May 15, 1907; graduated St. Anselm's Preparatory School, 1926; Providence College, Ph. B., 1930; Yale University Law School, LL.B., 1933; executive trial counsel for the United States at Nurnberg, Germany, 1945 and 1946; elected to 83d and 84th Congresses; married Grace Murphy, of Westerly, R.I.; six children—Thomas J., Jr.; Carolyn, Jeremy, Martha, Christopher, and Nicholas; elected to the United States Senate November 4, 1958; reelected to the U.S. Senate November 3, 1964, 89th Congress.

ABRAHAM A. RIBICOFF, Democrat, of Hartford, Conn.; born in New Britain, Conn., April 9, 1910; attended public schools of New Britain, Conn., New York University and University of Chicago Law School, LL.B. 1933; holds honorary degrees from 20 colleges and universities; married to the former Ruth Siegel; two children—Peter and Jane; lawyer; member of the Connecticut General Assembly 1938–42; municipal judge, Hartford, 1941–43 and 1945–47; elected to Congress 1948; reelected 1950; elected Governor of Connecticut, 1954; reelected, 1958; Secretary, Department of Health, Education, and Welfare, 1961–62; elected to the United States Senate November 6, 1962, for the term ending January 3, 1969.

REPRESENTATIVES

FIRST DISTRICT.—HARTFORD COUNTY: Towns of Bloomfield, East Hartford, East Windsor, Glastonbury, Hartford, Manchester, Marlborough, Newington, Rocky Hill, South Windsor, West Hartford, Wethersfield, and Windsor. Population (1960), 422,766.

EMILIO QUINCY DADDARIO, Democrat, of Hartford, Conn.; born in Newton Center, Mass., September 24, 1918; graduated from Tilton (N.H.) Academy in 1934; attended Newton (Mass.) Country Day School for 1 year; graduated Wesleyan University in Middletown, Conn., B.A. degree, 1939; attended Boston University Law School 1939–41; transferred to University of Connecticut, received law degree, 1942; member of Connecticut and Massachusetts bars; enlisted in Army in February 1943; assigned to Mediterranean Theater; awarded U.S. Legion of Merit and Italian Medaglia d'Argento medals; resumed practice of law in Middletown in 1945; member of the National Guard; mayor of Middletown, Conn., 1946–48; judge of Middletown Municipal Court, 1948–50; reactivated with the 43d Division at the outbreak of the Korean conflict; served as major with the Far East Liaison Group in Korea and Japan; resumed practice of law in Hartford in 1952; member board of trustees, Wesleyan University; married the former Berenice Carbo of Middletown, Conn., in 1940; three sons; elected to the 86th Congress, November 1958; reelected in 1960, 1962, and 1964; member of the House Committee on Science and Astronautics; chairman of the Special Subcommittee on Patents and Scientific Inventions; chairman of the Subcommittee on Science, Research and Development; member of the Manned Space Flight Subcommittee.

SECOND DISTRICT.—COUNTIES: Middlesex, New London, Tolland, and Windham (4 counties). Population (1960), 411,919.

WILLIAM LEON ST. ONGE, Democrat, of 88 Mechanics Street, Putnam, Conn.; born in Putnam, Conn., October 9, 1914; Tufts College, B.A. 1941; University of Connecticut School of Law, LL.B. 1948; enlisted in U.S. Army, served in North Africa and Europe, discharged September 1945; attorney at law; member of Connecticut and Windham County bar associations; judge of probate, State representative, mayor of city of Putnam, judge of city court of Putnam; prosecutor of city court of Putnam; board of education, chairman and executive director of redevelopment agency of city of Putnam, corporation counsel; married to Dorothy R. Hughes of Bridgeport, Conn., September 1945; five children—William H., Mary, Suzanne, Constance, and Anne; elected to the 88th Congress November 6, 1962; reelected to the 89th Congress; member of the House Judiciary Committee; member of the Board of Visitors to the U.S. Coast Guard Academy.

THIRD DISTRICT.—NEW HAVEN COUNTY: Towns of Branford, East Haven, Guilford, Hamden, Madison, Milford, New Haven, North Branford, North Haven, Orange, West Haven, and Woodbridge. FAIRFIELD COUNTY: Town of Stratford. Population (1960), 409,693.

ROBERT N. GIAIMO, Democrat, of North Haven, Conn.; born in New Haven, Conn., October 15, 1919, son of Rose Giaimo and the late Rosario Giaimo, of North Haven, Conn.; attorney, firm of Sachs, Sachs, Giaimo & Sachs; educated in North Haven public schools; graduated Hillhouse High School, New Haven, Conn., 1937; Fordham College, A. B., 1941; University of Connecticut, LL. B., 1943; served in the United States Army, 1943–46; captain, Judge Advocate General Corps, United States Army Reserve; chairman, Personnel Appeals Board, State of Connecticut, 1955–58; third selectman, town of North Haven, 1955–57; member, Board of Education, 1949–55; member, Board of Finance, 1952–55; New Haven County and Connecticut State Bar Associations; married to Marion F. Schuenemann and they have one daughter, Barbara Lee; elected to the 86th Congress on November 4, 1958; reelected to the 87th, 88th, and 89th Congresses.

FOURTH DISTRICT.—FAIRFIELD COUNTY: Towns of Bridgeport, Darien, Fairfield, Greenwich, New Canaan, Norwalk, Stamford, Weston, Westport, and Wilton. Population (1960), 482,135.

DONALD J. IRWIN, Democrat, of Norwalk, Conn.; born September 7, 1926, of American parents in Argentina; B.A., Yale University, 1951; LL.B., Yale Law School, 1954; member of law firm, Relihan & Irwin, with offices in Norwalk and Bridgeport; married to former Mary Stapleton of Norwalk; four children, Patrick, Marion, Lucile, and Stephen; former member of Norwalk Board of Education; served with Joint Brazil-U.S. Military Commission in Rio de Janeiro; elected to 86th Congress; appointed general counsel of U.S. Information Agency in 1961 by Edward R. Murrow; appointed treasurer of the State of Connecticut by Governor John N. Dempsey; elected to 89th Congress November 3, 1964.

FIFTH DISTRICT.—NEW HAVEN COUNTY: Towns of Ansonia, Beacon Falls, Bethany, Cheshire, Derby, Meriden, Naugatuck, Oxford, Prospect, Seymour, Wallingford, Waterbury, and Wolcott. FAIRFIELD COUNTY: Towns of Bethel, Danbury, Easton, Monroe, Newton, Redding, Ridgefield, Shelton, and Trumbull. Population (1960), 404,520.

JOHN STEPHEN MONAGAN, Democrat, of 103 Buckingham Street, Waterbury, Conn., 06710; born in Waterbury, Conn., December 23, 1911; Dartmouth College, A. B. 1933; Harvard Law School, LL. B. 1937; attorney at law; law office at 193 Grand Street, Waterbury, Conn., 06702; mayor, Waterbury, Conn., 1943–48; married Rosemary Brady, Bayonne, N. J., May 23, 1949; children: Charles A., Michael, Parthenia, Laura, and Susan; elected to 86th Congress November 4, 1958; reelected to 87th, 88th, and 89th Congresses; member Committee on Foreign Affairs and Committee on Government Operations; as member of Committee on Foreign Affairs, recipient of 1963 Award of Assembly of Captive Nations, and 1964 congressional observer at Disarmament Conference in Geneva.

SIXTH DISTRICT.—FAIRFIELD COUNTY: Towns of Brookfield, New Fairfield, and Sherman. HARTFORD COUNTY: Towns of Avon, Berlin, Bristol, Burlington, Canton, East Granby, Enfield, Farmington, Granby, Hartland, New Britain, Plainville, Simsbury, Southington, Suffield, and Windsor Locks. LITCHFIELD COUNTY: Towns of Barkhamsted, Bethlehem, Bridgewater, Canaan, Colebrook, Cornwall, Goshen, Harwinton, Kent, Litchfield, Morris, New Hartford, New Milford, Norfolk, North Canaan, Plymouth, Roxbury, Salisbury, Sharon, Thomaston, Torrington, Warren, Washington, Watertown, Winchester, and Woodbury. NEW HAVEN COUNTY: Towns of Middlebury and Southbury. Population (1960), 404,201.

BERNARD F. GRABOWSKI, Democrat, of Bristol, Conn.; born in New Haven, Conn., June 11, 1923; attended St. Stanislaus Parochial School, Bristol High School, and graduated from the University of Connecticut in 1949 and from the University of Connecticut Law School in 1952; served 3 years in the Infantry, U.S Army; member of the law firm of Hanrahan & Grabowski; admitted to practice before the U.S. Supreme Court; councilman, city of Bristol, 1953–55; judge, city court of Bristol, 1955–60; Coordinator of Redevelopment, city of Bristol, 1957–59; Catholic; married; two children; member of the Disabled American Veterans, Civitan, Elks, Bristol Polish American Citizens Club, Polish Legion of American Veterans, and Knights of Columbus; elected to the 88th Congress November 6, 1962; reelected to the 89th Congress.

DELAWARE

(Population (1960), 446,292)

SENATORS

JOHN J. WILLIAMS, Republican, of Millsboro, Sussex County, Del.; born on a farm near Frankford, Del., in Sussex County, May 17, 1904; attended Frankford High School; moved to Millsboro, Del., in 1922, and entered grain business; member of Methodist Church; Mason; Shriner; Rotarian; married to Elsie E. Steele, of Millsboro, Del., May 4, 1924; one child, Blanche W. Baker; three grandchildren, Janet Rae McCarty, Lora W. Baker, and Holly A. Baker; elected to the United States Senate on November 5, 1946; reelected November 4, 1952; reelected November 4, 1958; reelected November 3, 1964.

JAMES CALEB BOGGS, Republican, of Wilmington, Del.; born on a farm in Kent County, Del., May 15, 1909; educated in the public schools of Delaware; A.B. degree, University of Delaware; LL.B. degree, Georgetown University, Washington, D.C.; honorary LL.D. degree, Delaware State College; married Elizabeth Muir; two children, James Caleb Boggs, Jr., born October 31, 1934, and Marilu Boggs, born June 29, 1946; Methodist; member of the bar of the State of Delaware and the United States Supreme Court; former judge of the Family Court of New Castle County, Delaware; elected as U.S. Representative at Large from Delaware to the 80th, 81st, and 82d Congresses; elected Governor of the State of Delaware for two 4-year terms, November 1952 and reelected November 1956; elected chairman of the National Governors Conference 1959; elected president of the Council of State Governments 1960; enlisted as private in Delaware National Guard, June 1926; colonel USAR, ret.; brigadier general, ret., Delaware National Guard; five campaigns in the European Theater of Operations during World War II; Legion of Merit, Bronze Star with cluster, French Croix de Guerre with Palm; elected to the United States Senate November 8, 1960, for the term ending January 3, 1967.

REPRESENTATIVE

AT LARGE.—Population (1960), 446,292.

HARRIS B. McDOWELL, Jr., Democrat, of Middletown, Del.; born on family farm, near Middletown, February 10, 1906; educated in Middletown public school, Wilmington High School, Beacon Business College. Engaged in farming, insurance and real estate; married Florence R. Neary and has three children—Kendall, Joan, and Harris 3d; appointed to the State Board of Agriculture 1937–40; elected to the State house of representatives in 1940; elected to State senate 1942–46; chairman of Democratic State Committee 1946–54; secretary of state of the State of Delaware 1949–53; member of the New Castle County Zoning Commission 1953–54; elected to the 84th Congress November 2, 1954; elected to 86th Congress November 4, 1958; reelected to 87th, 88th, and 89th Congresses; member Foreign Affairs and Veterans' Affairs Committees.

FLORIDA

(Population (1960), 4,951,560)

SENATORS

SPESSARD LINDSEY HOLLAND, Democrat, of Bartow, Fla.; born at Bartow, Fla., July 10, 1892; son of Benjamin Franklin and Fannie V. (Spessard) Holland; married Mary Agnes Groover, of Lakeland, Fla., February 8, 1919; four children—S. L., Jr., Mary Groover, William B., and Ivanhoe; graduated, Bartow public schools; Ph. B. (magna cum laude), Emory College, 1912; LL. B., University of Florida, 1916; honorary LL. D., Rollins College, Florida Southern College, Emory University, Florida State University; D. C. L., University of Florida; HH. D., University of Tampa; taught in public schools, Warrenton, Ga., 1912–14; practiced law in Bartow, Fla., since 1916; prosecuting attorney, Polk County, Fla., 1919–20; county judge, Polk County, Fla., two terms, 1921–29; member, Florida State Senate, two terms, 1932–40; Governor of Florida, 1941–45; served with Coast Artillery Corps in all grades through captain, United States Army, World War I; served as aerial observer Twenty-fourth Squadron, Army Air Corps, in France; awarded Distinguished Service Cross, 1918; Methodist; member of American Legion, Veterans of Foreign Wars; a Kiwanian, Mason, Shriner, Elk; member of Phi Beta Kappa, Phi Kappa Phi, Alpha Tau Omega, Phi Delta Phi; trustee, Emory University, Atlanta, and Florida Southern College, Lakeland; member, Florida State and American Bar Associations; member, Executive Council University of Florida Alumni Association since 1924 (president, 1931); Democratic nominee to United States Senate from Florida, May 7, 1946; appointed September 25, 1946, by Governor Caldwell to succeed the late Charles O. Andrews in the United States Senate for the term ending January 3, 1947; elected November 5, 1946, for full term ending January 3, 1953; reelected November 4, 1952, for term ending January 3, 1959; reelected November 4, 1958, for term ending January 3, 1965; reelected November 3, 1964, for term ending January 3, 1971.

GEORGE ARMISTEAD SMATHERS, Democrat, of Miami, Fla.; born in Atlantic City, N. J., November 14, 1913; son of Frank Smathers and Lura Jones Smathers; moved to Miami in 1919 and educated in public schools of Dade County, Fla.; received A. B. degree, University of Florida, and LL. B. degree, College of Law, University of Florida; admitted to Florida bar in 1938; married Rosemary Townley in 1939 and has two sons, John and Bruce; appointed assistant United States district attorney in 1940; resigned in 1942 to enter Marine Corps; discharged from the Marine Corps in October 1945; colonel, USMC Reserve; appointed special assistant to the Attorney General upon discharge from service; resigned in January 1946, to enter campaign for Congress; elected to the 80th Congress on November 5, 1946; reelected to the 81st Congress on November 2, 1948; elected to the United States Senate November 7, 1950; reelected in 1956 and 1962.

REPRESENTATIVES

FIRST DISTRICT.—COUNTIES: Bay, Escambia, Gulf, Holmes, Okaloosa, Santa Rosa, Walton, and Washington (8 counties). Population (1960), 379,288.

ROBERT L. F. SIKES, Democrat, of Crestview, Okaloosa County, Fla.; born at Isabella, Worth County, Ga., June 3, 1906, son of Ben F. and Clara Ford Sikes; farm reared; received bachelor's degree, University of Georgia, 1927; master's, University of Florida, 1929; married Inez Tyner of Laurel Hill, Fla.; two children, Mrs. Edward F. Wicke, Oldsmar, Fla., and Robert K., Martin-Marietta Co., Orlando, Fla.; newspaper publisher; chairman county planning committee, 1934; chairman, county Democratic executive committee, 1934; elected to Florida State Legislature in 1936 and 1938; assistant to Treasurer Democratic National Committee during 1936–1940–1944 national elections; member of Phi Kappa Phi, Alpha Zeta, Sigma Delta Chi, Phi Sigma, Alpha Gamma Rho, Blue Key, 32° Mason, K.R.C.C.; K.C.C.H.; Grotto, Knights Templar, Shrine, Knights of Pythias, Moose, B.P.O.E., V.F.W., American Legion, 40 and 8, Military Order of World War; major general, U.S.A.R.; president, Florida Press Association, 1937; lieutenant governor, Kiwanis, 1940; recipient, Distinguished Service Award, Reserve

Officers Association of the United States; vice president, National Rivers and Harbors Congress 1959, 1960, 1961 and 1962; recipient of Governor's Conservation Award, State of Florida, 1960; recipient Guatemalan Order of Merit, 1961; Young Democratic Clubs' Florida Award, 1961; Distinguished Service Award, Florida Council of 100, 1962; delegate to Pan American Roads Conference, Caracas, Venezuela, 1954; delegate to Interparliamentary Conference, Warsaw, Poland, 1959; honorary member, Rotary, Lions, Civitan, Retired Officers Association, and National Association of Supervisors; Methodist; elected to the 77th Congress on November 5, 1940, and reelected to succeeding Congresses; chairman Florida delegation to Democratic National Conventions in 1956 and 1960; honorary member American Federation of Government Employees; United Federation of Postal Clerks; recipient of National Affairs League's Leadership Award, 1951; American Legion Distinguished Service Award, 1962; Navy Times Good Neighbor Award, 1962; 1963 Achievement Award from Children's Asthma Research Institute; Reserve Officers Association Hall of Fame, 1964; Florida National Guard Outstanding Service Award, 1963; Board of Directors of Florida Historical Society; Vice President National Rivers and Harbors Congress, 1959–65; Director, National Rifle Association; honorary member National Association of Master Mechanics and Foremen; American Gun Dealers' Leadership Award, 1959.

SECOND DISTRICT.—DUVAL COUNTY. Population (1960), 455,411.

CHARLES E. BENNETT, Democrat, of Jacksonville, Fla.; born December 2, 1910; educated in Florida schools, from first grade in grammar school through college; graduated University of Florida in 1934 (B. A. and Juris Doctor degrees; was president of student body and editor of school paper); received honorary degree of Doctor of Humanities from University of Tampa in 1950; practiced law in Jacksonville since 1934; president of Jacksonville Junior Chamber of Commerce in 1939; served as member of Florida House of Representatives in 1941; enlisted March 13, 1942, and served 58 months in Infantry in World War II, including guerrilla combat in the Philippines; awarded Silver Star, Bronze Star, and Combat Infantry Badge; discharged as captain January 13, 1947; elected to Infantry Hall of Fame, Fort Benning Officer Candidate School, in 1958; affiliated with Disabled American Veterans, American Legion, Veterans of Foreign Wars, Masons, Lions, and Sons of the American Revolution; member board of trustees of Lynchburg (Christian Church) College; awarded certificate by Freedoms Foundation "for outstanding achievement in bringing about a better understanding of the American way of life during 1951" and a similar award for 1956; awarded Good Government Award for 1952 by Jacksonville and United States Junior Chambers of Commerce; has missed no roll call votes since June 4, 1951, to date; elder in the Riverside Avenue Christian Church; married to Jean Fay Bennett; four children: Bruce, Charles, James, and Lucinda; elected to the 81st Congress on November 2, 1948; reelected to the 82d, 83d, 84th, 85th, 86th, 87th, 88th, and 89th Congresses.

THIRD DISTRICT.—DADE COUNTY: Northern part, including the northern parts of Miami and Miami Beach. Population (1960), 507,426.

CLAUDE DENSON PEPPER, Democrat, of Miami, Fla.; born on a farm near Dudleyville, Chambers County, Ala., September 8, 1900, son of J. W. and Lena C. (Talbot) Pepper; attended the public schools, Camp Hill, Ala.; taught in public schools, Dothan, Ala., 1917–18; served in Students' Army Training Corps, University of Alabama October 7–December 12, 1918; A.B. University of Alabama 1921; LL.B. Harvard Law School 1924; instructor in law University of Arkansas 1924–25; engaged in the general practice of law at Perry, Fla., 1925–30 and at Tallahassee, Fla., 1930, until elected to the United States Senate in 1936; married Mildred Irene Webster of St. Petersburg, Fla., December 29, 1936; member house of representatives, Florida Legislature, Taylor County 1929–30; member Florida State Democratic Executive Committee 1928–29; the Florida State Board of Public Welfare 1931–32; the Florida State Board of Law Examiners 1933–34; the executive council, Florida State Bar Association 1934; elected United States Senator from Florida November 4, 1936; reelected 1938 and 1944, term expiring January 3, 1951; unsuccessful candidate for renomination for the Senate 1950 and for nomination 1958; elected United States Representative from Florida's Third Congressional District November 6, 1962, to the 88th Congress; reelected to the 89th Congress November 3, 1964; member, House Committee on Banking and Currency; subcommittees Domestic Finance, International Trade, International Finance, 88th Congress; member, Rules Committee, House of Representatives, 89th Congress; chairman, Florida Delegation, Democratic National Convention 1940–44; alternate delegate 1948, 1952, 1956, 1960, and 1964; delegate to the Interparliamentary Union from the United States Senate at The Hague 1938, Dublin 1950; delivered Marfleet Lectures, University of Toronto, 1942; member Senate Foreign Relations Committee 1937–47, 1949–50; chairman Subcommittee on Middle East; member of subcommittee on Latin America; also member Senate committees on Military Affairs, Patents, Commerce, Labor and Public Welfare; Select Committee on Small Business; chairman Senate Inter-Oceanic Canal; chairman, Senate subcommittee on Wartime Health and Education, 1943–46; honorary degrees: (LL.D.) McMaster University (Canada) 1941; University of Toronto (Canada) 1942; University of Alabama 1942; Rollins College (Florida) 1944; American Legion, 40 and 8, Baptist, Mason, Shriner, Elk, Moose, Kiwanian; member Phi Beta Kappa, Kappa Alpha, Omicron Delta Kappa, Sigma Upsilon, Phi Alpha Delta; author of various articles in law reviews, magazines and newspapers; member, Tallahassee, Dade County, Miami Beach, Coral Gables, the Florida Bar and American Bar Association, 1934; Lieutenant Governor, Western Division of Florida Kiwanis International; the Inter-American, the International Bar Associations and the Association of the Bar of the City of New York; former member board of directors, Chamber of Commerce of the Americas; clubs: Jefferson Island, Washington; Harvard, Washington, Miami; Coral Gables Country Club, Coral Gables, Fla.; Miami Shores Country Club, Miami Shores, Florida; officer and director Washington Federal Savings & Loan Association, Miami Beach; officer and director Cape Kennedy Federal Savings & Loan Association, Cocoa; by profession an attorney with offices: Miami Beach, Cocoa, and Tallahassee, Fla.

FOURTH DISTRICT.—MONROE COUNTY. DADE COUNTY: Southern part, including the southern parts of Miami and Miami Beach. Population (1960), 475,542.

DANTE B. FASCELL, Democrat, of Miami, Fla.; born in Bridgehampton, L. I., N. Y., March 9, 1917; moved to Miami, Fla., in 1925; graduated from Ponce de Leon High School, Coral Gables, Fla., in 1933; received LL. B. degree from the University of Miami in 1938; member of Epsilon Beta Chapter Kappa Sigma Fraternity; at university was president of local fraternity; tapped as a member of Iron Arrow Society, highest honorary fraternity for men; active in the practice of law since 1938, now a member of the law firm of Turner, Hendrick, Fascell & Guilford; president of the Miami Junior Chamber of Commerce, 1947–48; president of Dade County Young Democratic Club, 1947–48; president of Italian-American Club, 1947–48; legal attaché to the State legislative delegation from Dade County, 1947–50; elected State representative in 1950 and selected in the 1951 session as one of the ten outstanding legislators and one of the outstanding freshmen; reelected in 1952 without opposition and selected as one of the outstanding members of the 1953 session; selected in 1951 by the Florida Junior Chamber of Commerce as one of the five outstanding men in the State of Florida; inducted into the Federal service with the Florida National Guard on January 6, 1941, commissioned second lieutenant May 23, 1942, served in the African, Sicilian, and Italian campaigns, separated from the Armed Forces as a captain January 20, 1946; affiliated with the Miami Junior Chamber of Commerce, Lions, Coral Gables Bar Association, Dade County Bar Association, Florida Bar Association, American Bar Association, Federal Bar Association, American Legion, Military Order of the World Wars (Miami chapter); married to former Jeanne-Marie Pelot of Arcadia, Fla.; two daughters, Sandra Jeanne and Toni; son, Dante Jon; elected to the 84th Congress November 2, 1954; reelected to the 85th, 86th, 87th, 88th, and 89th Congresses.

FIFTH DISTRICT.—COUNTIES: Citrus, Hernando, Lake, Marion, Osceola, Pasco, Seminole, Sumter, and Volusia (9 counties). Population (1960), 377,421.

A. SYDNEY HERLONG, JR., Democrat, of Leesburg, Lake County, Fla.; born February 14, 1909, in Manistee, Ala., son of Albert Sydney and Cora Knight Herlong; moved to Florida in 1912; educated in public schools of Sumter and Lake Counties; graduated from Leesburg High School in 1925, and from the law college of the University of Florida in 1930; married December 26, 1930, to Mary Alice Youmans of Fairfax, S. C., and has four daughters, Mary Alice (Mrs. A. G. Pattillo, Jr.), Margaret (Mrs. James H. Mayfield), Dorothy (Mrs.

Charles H. Hay), and Sydney; engaged in the practice of law in Leesburg from 1930 to 1937; elected county judge in 1936, reelected in 1940 and 1944; past president of Florida State Baseball League; past lieutenant governor of Kiwanis International; past president Florida County Judges Association; past president University of Florida Alumni Association; member of Methodist Church; Kiwanis; F. & A.M. (thirty-third degree); Shriner; Elks; Pi Kappa Phi; Phi Delta Phi; Florida Blue Key Honor Fraternity; Omicron Delta Kappa; elected to the 81st Congress on November 2, 1948; reelected to all succeeding Congresses.

SIXTH DISTRICT.—COUNTIES: Broward, Collier, Glades, Hendry, Lee, Martin, and Palm Beach (7 counties). Population (1960), 660,345.

PAUL G. ROGERS, Democrat, of West Palm Beach, Fla.; born in Ocilla, Ga., June 4, 1921; son of the late Dwight L. Rogers, first Congressman of the Sixth Congressional District of Florida, and Florence Roberts Rogers; married December 15, 1962, to Rebecca Bell Mozley of Andalusia, Ala.; one daughter, Rebecca Laing; at age of 4, family moved to Fort Lauderdale, Fla.; attended Fort Lauderdale public schools; attended University of Florida; president of the university's honor society, Florida Blue Key; national debate champion of Tau Kappa Alpha Debate Fraternity; A. B. degree from University of Florida in 1942; following graduation served 4 years in the Field Artillery of the U. S. Army; battalion commander, European Theater, earning two battle stars and Bronze Star Medal; separated from service with rank of major; studied law at George Washington University and received LL. B. degree University of Florida in 1948; moved from Broward County to West Palm Beach, Fla., in 1948; joined law firm of Burns, Middleton, Rogers, and Farrell; selected as Outstanding Man-of-the-Year in 1953 by West Palm Beach Junior Chamber of Commerce; recipient in 1956 of Distinguished Service Award given to five outstanding young men by Florida Junior Chamber of Commerce; steward of Methodist Church; member of Kiwanis Club; Phi Delta Theta fraternity; Phi Delta Phi; admitted to practice of law in State and Federal courts, and United States Supreme Court; elected to 84th Congress, special election, January 11, 1955; reelected to the 85th, 86th, 87th, 88th, and 89th Congresses.

SEVENTH DISTRICT.—COUNTIES: Charlotte, De Soto, Hardee, Highlands, Manatee, Okeechobee, Polk, and Sarasota (8 counties). Population (1960), 405,611.

JAMES ANDREW HALEY, Democrat, of Sarasota, Sarasota County, Fla.; born in Jacksonville, Ala., January 4, 1899; son of Andrew Jackson and Mary Lee (Stevenson) Haley; student at University of Alabama 1919–20; married Aubrey B. Ringling; accountant, Sarasota, Fla., 1925–33; general manager John Ringling estate 1933–43; first vice president Ringling Circus 1943–45; president and director Ringling Brothers Barnum & Bailey Circus, Sarasota, Fla. 1946–48; president Halcoe Printing Co., Inc.; United States Army, First World War; elected to the Florida House of Representatives in 1948 and 1950; chairman, Democratic Executive Committee of Sarasota County 1925–52; delegate to the 1952 and 1960 National Democratic Conventions; member of the American Legion, 40 and 8, Veterans of Foreign Wars, Sons of the American Revolution, Methodist Church, Masons and Elk Clubs; elected to the 83d Congress November 4, 1952, as the Representative of the newly created Seventh District; reelected to the 84th, 85th, 86th, 87th, 88th, and 89th Congresses.

EIGHTH DISTRICT.—COUNTIES: Alachua, Baker, Bradford, Clay, Columbia, Dixie, Flagler, Gilchrist, Levy, Nassau, Putnam, St. Johns, and Union (13 counties). Population (1960), 241,250.

DONALD RAY (BILLY) MATTHEWS, Democrat, of Gainesville, Alachua County, Fla.; born October 3, 1907, in Micanopy, Fla., son of D. H. and Flora A. Matthews; educated in public schools of Hawthorne, Fla.; higher education was received at the University of Florida; holds A. B. and M. A. degrees; school teacher at Leesburg and Orlando, Fla., and high-school principal at Newberry, Fla.; member, Florida State Legislature, 1935; member of the administrative staff of the University of Florida for 16 years, serving first as director of the Florida Union, the student activity center, and later as director alumni affairs; served 4 years in World War II, and was discharged as captain, Infantry; assistant State 4-H agent for Florida (10 summers); past district governor of Lions International; past chairman of the Florida Council for the Blind; past president Gainesville Kiwanis Club; past chairman, Alachua County Chapter of the

National Foundation for Infantile Paralysis; member Kiwanis, American Legion, Knights of Pythias, Alpha Phi Epsilon, Pi Gamma Mu, Tau Kappa Alpha, Florida Blue Key, Scabbard and Blade, Sigma Phi Epsilon, and Gainesville Chamber of Commerce; elder, First Presbyterian Church, Gainesville; B. P. O. E., Moose, past president of the National Association of College Unions (composed of directors of student activity centers at colleges and universities in the United States and Canada); married Sara Lewis of Orlando, Fla., in 1941; three children: Carolyn, Ann, and Donald Ray, Jr.; elected to the 83d Congress November 4, 1952; reelected to the 84th, 85th, 86th, 87th, 88th, and 89th Congresses; member Committee on Appropriations.

NINTH DISTRICT.—Counties: Calhoun, Franklin, Gadsden, Hamilton, Jackson, Jefferson, Lafayette, Leon, Liberty, Madison, Suwannee, Taylor, and Wakulla (13 counties). Population (1960), 237,235.

DON FUQUA, Democrat, of Altha, Fla.; born in Jacksonville, Fla., August 20, 1933, son of J. D. and Lucille Langford Fuqua; attended secondary schools in Calhoun County; graduated from Altha High School in 1951; attended University of Florida 1951–53; during the Korean War served in the U.S. Army Medical Corps from August 1953 to June 1955 and was discharged with the rank of sergeant; resumed studies at University of Florida and graduated with a degree in agricultural economics in 1957; engaged with his father in operating a 600-acre dairy and general farm; married the former Doris Akidakis of Beulah, N. Dak.; two children—Laura and John Eric; elected to the Florida House of Representatives in 1958; reelected in 1960; selected in a poll by press, radio, and TV as one of the most valuable members in the 1961 session of the legislature; member of Presbyterian Church, American Legion, Elks, Jaycees, W.O.W., Florida Sheriffs Boys Ranch Board of Trustees, Masons, and many local, county, and State organizations; named by Florida Jaycees as one of Five Outstanding Young Men in State for 1963; elected to the 88th Congress November 6, 1962; reelected to the 89th Congress; serves as member of Science and Astronautics Committee.

TENTH DISTRICT.—Hillsborough County. Population (1960), 397,788.

SAM M. GIBBONS, Democrat, of Tampa, Fla.; born in Tampa, January 20, 1920, son of Gunby Gibbons and Jessie Kirk Cralle Gibbons; educated in public schools of Tampa; received LL. B. degree from the University of Florida; named to the University's Hall of Fame and to its honor society Florida Blue Key; member of Alpha Tau Omega Fraternity; practiced law in Tampa since 1947 as a member of the firm of Gibbons, Gibbons, Tucker & Cofer; member of the American Bar Association, the Florida Bar, and former director of the Tampa and Hillsborough County Bar Association; married to the former Martha Hanley; they have three sons—Clifford, born 1950; Mark, born 1952; and Timothy, born 1958; elected to the Florida House of Representatives in 1952 and served for 6 years; elected to the Florida Senate in 1958 and served for 4 years; named one of the top ten members of each body; named Tampa's Outstanding Young Man of the Year in 1954; received Chamber of Commerce president's award; deacon First Presbyterian Church of Tampa; first president of and member of University of South Florida Foundation; served in U.S. Army 5 years during World War II with 501st Parachute Infantry, 101st Airborne Division; awarded Bronze Star; was in initial assault force landing before D-Day in Europe; took part in other major combat actions, including operations at Bastogne; released from active duty as major; elected to the 88th Congress November 6, 1962; reelected to the 89th Congress; member of Education and Labor and House Administration Committees.

ELEVENTH DISTRICT.—Counties: Brevard, Indian River, Orange, and St. Lucie (4 counties). Population (1960), 439,578.

EDWARD JOHN GURNEY, Republican, of Winter Park, Fla.; born January 12, 1914, in Portland, Maine; attended public schools of Skowhegan and Waterville, Maine; Colby College, B.S. 1935; Harvard Law School, LL.B., 1938; Duke Law School, LL.M. 1948; member law firm of Gurney & Skolfield; member Florida and New York bars; served in U.S. Army 1941–46, European Theater, attained rank of lieutenant colonel, holds Silver Star and Purple Heart decorations; city commissioner in Winter Park 1952–58; elected mayor of Winter Park January 1961; married to Natalie Ahlborn Gurney; three children; elected to the 88th Congress November 6, 1962; reelected to the 89th Congress.

TWELFTH DISTRICT.—Pinellas County.   Population (1960), 374,665.

WILLIAM C. (BILL) CRAMER, Republican, of St. Petersburg, Fla.; representing the Twelfth District, Pinellas County; born in Denver, Colo., August 4, 1922, son of Walter B. and Doreen Emma Walters Cramer; moved to St. Petersburg in 1925; attended public schools in St. Petersburg and attended St. Petersburg High School; was a three-time winner of the outstanding student award and president of the student government; attended St. Petersburg Junior College and was class president; graduated University of North Carolina, 1946, Phi Beta Kappa; graduated Harvard Law School, 1948; honorary Dr. Jurisprudence, Tampa University 1957; enlisted in Naval Reserve in 1943 and served on active duty, being discharged as lieutenant (j.g.) in 1946; was cited for the invasion of Southern France; in 1950 directed the successful campaign in Pinellas County that saw, for the first time in Florida history, a majority of county offices going to the Republican Party; leading the GOP ticket, served in the Florida State Legislature (1950–52) and was first minority leader of that body; in 1952 was Republican nominee for the United States House of Representatives and was defeated only by a narrow margin; county attorney for Pinellas County (1953–54); regional director (1951–53) and vice chairman (1953–55) of the Young Republican National Federation; as chairman Florida College of Electors cast the ballot for President Eisenhower in 1952; delegate to Republican convention 1952–60, vice chairman of Florida delegation to Republican convention 1956–60; married Alice Janet Jones of Mobile, Ala., and Pensacola, Fla., the daughter of Clifton V. and Myrtle Jones; three sons—William C., Jr., Mark C., and Allyn Walters; member of V.F.W., American Legion, Amvets, Elks, Moose, Ahepa, Army and Navy Club, Masons, Shrine, Eastern Star, Chamber of Commerce; and the American, Massachusetts, Florida, and St. Petersburg Bar Associations; Methodist Church and Sigma Chi (Alpha Tau chapter) Fraternity; nominated in Republican primary of 1954 and elected as the first Republican from Florida since 1875 (reconstruction days) to the 84th Congress November 2, 1954; reelected to the 85th, 86th, 87th, 88th, and 89th Congresses; serves on Public Works and Judiciary Committees of the House; vice chairman Republican Congressional Campaign Committee, vice chairman Republican Conference, Assistant Whip, member of Policy Committee; ranking Republican on Public Works Committee, Roads Subcommittee, and Federal Aid Highway Investigating Committee; elected Republican National Committeeman from Florida (1964–68).

GEORGIA

(Population (1960), 3,943,116)

SENATORS

RICHARD BREVARD RUSSELL, Democrat, of Winder, Ga.

HERMAN EUGENE TALMADGE, Democrat, of Lovejoy, Ga.; born Telfair County, near McRae, Ga., August 9, 1913, son of Eugene and Mattie Thurmond Talmadge; graduated from the University of Georgia in 1936 with LL. B. degree; joined his father in the practice of law in Atlanta; married Elizabeth Shingler of Ashburn, Ga., in December 1941; have two sons—Herman Eugene Talmadge, Jr., and Robert Shingler Talmadge; served in United States Navy, World War II and was discharged in November 1945; upon the death of his father, Gov.-elect Eugene Talmadge, was elected to the Governorship by the State Legislature in 1947; served 67 days, then vacated the office due to a decision of the State Supreme Court; elected in the September 1948 primary to fill the unexpired term; reelected in 1950 for a full term and served until January 10, 1955; owns and operates 2 farms; member of the Baptist Church; clubs—Shriner; Mason; Junior Order of American Mechanics; American Legion; 40 and 8; Veterans of Foreign Wars; Farm Bureau Federation; Georgia, Atlanta, and American Bar Associations; Sons of the American Revolution; Elks; Navy League; fraternities—Sigma Nu; Omicron Delta Kappa; president of the Alumni Society of the University of Georgia 1955–56; elected to the United States Senate for the term commencing January 3, 1957, and reelected to a second term ending January 3, 1969.

REPRESENTATIVES

FIRST DISTRICT.—COUNTIES: Bryan, Bulloch, Burke, Candler, Chatham, Effingham, Emanuel, Evans, Jenkins, Johnson, Laurens, Liberty, Long, McIntosh, Montgomery, Screven, Tattnall, Toombs, Treutlen, and Wheeler (20 counties). Population (1960), 420,354.

G. ELLIOTT HAGAN, Democrat, of Sylvania, Ga.; born May 24, 1916, in Sylvania, Screven County, Ga.; educated in the Screven County public schools, University of Georgia, Emory University, and John Marshall Law School; served five terms in the State house of representatives and one term in the State senate; during World War II resigned from the house of representatives and enlisted in the U.S. Army, serving 2 years in the Signal Corps; formerly engaged in life insurance-estate planning and farming; secretary-treasurer and deputy director, State Board of Workmen's Compensation, 1946; served two terms as State member of National Council of State Governments; district director, Office of Price Stabilization, in 1951 and 1952, and deputy regional director, Atlanta Regional Office, in 1953; life member, Million Dollar Round Table, NALU; member of Rotary, American Legion, Farm Bureau, York Rite and Scottish Rite, Alee Temple of the Shrine, Chamber of Commerce, B.P.O.E., Association of the United States Army, Georgia Livestock Association, National Rivers and Harbors Congress, Peace Officers Association of Georgia, University of Georgia Alumni Society, United States Capitol Historical Society, Loyal Order of Moose, Gridiron Secret Society, board of trustees of Tift College, former member of Boy Scouts of America Coastal Empire Council, board of directors of the Grace Home, and board of managers of the Georgia Press Association; former weekly newspaper editor; Baptist; vice president, Georgia Baptist Convention, 1963; married the former Frances Bryant; three children, G. Elliott, Jr., Charles Franklin, and Frances Bryant; elected to the 87th Congress November 8, 1960; reelected to the 88th and 89th Congresses.

SECOND DISTRICT.—COUNTIES: Baker, Brooks, Calhoun, Clay, Colquitt, Crisp, Decatur, Dougherty, Early, Grady, Miller, Mitchell, Quitman, Randolph, Seminole, Terrell, Thomas, Tift, Turner, and Worth (20 counties). Population (1960), 358,133.

MASTON EMMETT O'NEAL, JR., Democrat, of Bainbridge, Ga.; born in Bainbridge, Decatur County, Ga., July 19, 1907; attended the public schools and

Marion Military Institute; graduated from Davidson College, A.B. degree, in 1927; attended Lamar School of Law, Emory University; principal, Shellman High School 1927–28; admitted to practice law in Albany circuit January 16, 1930; married the former Charlotte Tyson June 4, 1934; two children, Susan Charlotte (Mrs. Jerry Montgomery Bowden) and Maston Emmett, 3d; Presbyterian; during World War II served as a lieutenant USNR Amphibs, Pacific Theater, 1944–46; solicitor general, Albany Judicial Circuit, January 1, 1941, to May 1, 1964; member of American Legion, VFW, Georgia Historical Society, Florida Historical Society, Pi Kappa Alpha, Scottish Rite Masons, Georgia Bar Association, and American Bar Association; first president of Solicitors General Association of Georgia; former director National Association of County and Prosecuting Attorneys; elected to the 89th Congress November 3, 1964.

THIRD DISTRICT.—COUNTIES: Chattahoochee, Crawford, Dooly, Harris, Houston, Lee, Macon, Marion, Muscogee, Peach, Pulaski, Schley, Stewart, Sumter, Talbot, Taylor, Twiggs, Webster, and Wilkinson (19 counties). Population (1960), 340,110.

HOWARD H. (BO) CALLAWAY, Republican, of Pine Mountain, Ga.; born in La Grange, Troup County, Ga., April 2, 1927; attended the public schools of La Grange, Ga., 1932–37 and of Hamilton, Ga., 1937–39; Episcopal High School, Alexandria, Va., 1939–44; Georgia Institute of Technology, Atlanta, Ga., 1944–45; U.S. Military Academy, West Point, N.Y., 1945–49 (B.S. in Military Engineering); married the former Elizabeth Walton of Hamilton, Ga., June 11, 1949; five children, Elizabeth, Howard, Edward, Virginia, and Ralph; commissioned second lieutenant, U.S. Army (Infantry), June 1949; Infantry platoon leader, 1949–50; instructor in tactics, Infantry School, Ft. Benning, Ga., 1951–52; president, Callaway Gardens and of Ida Cason Callaway Foundation; director, Georgia Power Co., Trust Co. of Georgia, Young Presidents Organization, Inc., and Y.M.C.A. of Georgia; vice president Georgia State Chamber of Commerce; trustee, Freedoms Foundation at Valley Forge and National Recreation Association; member, National 4-H Service Committee, Inc., Georgia State 4-H Advisory Committee, and St. Mark's Episcopal Church of La Grange, Ga. (vestryman); elected to the 89th Congress November 3, 1964.

FOURTH DISTRICT.—COUNTIES: DeKalb and Rockdale, and that part of Fulton County consisting of precincts 1–B, 1–D, 1–E, 1–G, 1–H, 4–C, 4–F, 4–H, 4–I, 4–J, 5–E, 5–I, 6–A, 6–B, 6–C, 6–D, 6–E, 6–F, 6–H, 6–I, and 8–B. Population (1960), 424,917.

JAMES ARMSTRONG MACKAY, Democrat, of Atlanta, Ga.; born in Fairfield, Ala., June 25, 1919; son of Rev. Edward George Mackay (deceased) and Mrs. Beulah Mason Mackay; Methodist; educated in public schools of Alabama and Atlanta; graduated Emory University (A.B.), attended Duke University, and graduated Emory University School of Law (LL.B.) 1947; served 52 months in U.S. Coast Guard Reserve, awarded Bronze Star Medal for meritorious service in combat in the Mediterranean; married to the former Mary Caroline Lee; father of two children: Kathleen Elizabeth and James Edward; practicing attorney, Decatur, Ga.; member: Georgia and American bar associations, Phi Delta Phi legal fraternity, Omicron Delta Kappa national leadership fraternity and Kappa Alpha Order, Civitan Club, National Council of Y.M.C.A.; trustee of Emory University; elected to six terms in the State house of representatives from DeKalb County; elected to 89th Congress, November 3, 1964, from newly created Fourth District.

FIFTH DISTRICT.—FULTON COUNTY, except southeastern border. Population (1960), 398,763.

CHARLES LONGSTREET WELTNER, Democrat, of Atlanta, Ga.; born in Atlanta, Ga., December 17, 1927, son of Philip Weltner and Mrs. Sally Hull Weltner (deceased); Oglethorpe University (A.B.) 1948, Columbia University School of Law (LL.B.) 1950; served on active duty as first lieutenant U.S. Army for 2 years; Presbyterian; practicing attorney; married to the former Betty Jean Center; father of four children; elected to the 88th Congress November 6, 1962; reelected to the 89th Congress.

SIXTH DISTRICT.—Counties: Bibb, Butts, Carroll, Clayton, Coweta, Fayette, Heard, Henry, Jones, Lamar, Meriwether, Monroe, Pike, Spalding, Troup, and Upson (16 counties). Population (1960), 455,575.

JOHN JAMES FLYNT, Jr., Democrat, of Griffin, Ga.; born in Griffin, Spalding County, Ga., November 8, 1914, son of John James Flynt, Sr., and Susan Banks Flynt, both deceased; educated in the public schools of Griffin, Ga., and Georgia Military Academy; graduated the University of Georgia, A. B. 1936; attended Emory University Law School: graduated George Washington University Law School, Washington, D.C., LL. B. 1940; admitted to practice before all courts; assistant United States attorney, northern district of Georgia; member of house of representatives, State of Georgia, 1947–48; solicitor general, Griffin Judicial Circuit (Fayette, Pike, Spalding, and Upson Counties), January 1, 1949, to November 2, 1954; president, Solicitors General Association of Georgia, 1950–51; president, Georgia Bar Association, 1954–55; member, Griffin Circuit, Georgia, and American Bar Association; served in the United States Army during World War II from March 22, 1941, to December 12, 1945; awarded Bronze Star Medal for meritorious service in Normandy and Northern France; graduated from Command and General Staff School and Air Corps Advanced Flying School, Brooks Field, Tex.; Colonel United States Army Reserve; Methodist (chairman of Board of Stewards), Mason; Shriner (Yaarab Temple); American Legion (40 and 8); V. F. W.; Kiwanis; Woodmen of the World; B. P. O. E.; SAE Fraternity; Phi Delta Phi legal fraternity; married Miss Patricia Bradley of Dalton, Ga., February 7, 1942; and they have three children—Susan Banks Flynt, John James Flynt 3d, and Crisp Bradley Flynt; elected to the 83d Congress in special election; reelected to the 84th, 85th, 86th, 87th, 88th, and 89th Congresses.

SEVENTH DISTRICT.—Counties: Bartow, Catoosa, Chattooga, Cobb, Dade, Douglas, Floyd, Gordon, Haralson, Murray, Paulding, Polk, Walker, and Whitfield (14 counties). Population (1960), 450,740.

JOHN WILLIAM DAVIS, Democrat, of Summerville, Ga., born September 12, 1916, in Rome, Ga.; attended the public schools; graduated from the University of Georgia, A.B. degree in 1937 and LL.B. degree in 1939; practiced law in Rome 1939–42; during World War II served 3½ years in the U.S. Army, assigned to the Counter Intelligence Corps, serving for a time in South America; in 1946 moved to Summerville, Ga., and continued the practice of law; solicitor general of the Rome Circuit, December 27, 1950, to January 1, 1953; judge of Lookout Mountain Judicial Circuit for six years, January 1, 1955, until his resignation December 31, 1960; married the former Vivian Hawkins of Walker County, Ga.; three children—Katherine DeLay, John W., Jr., and Mary Ellen; elected to the 87th Congress November 8, 1960; reelected to the 88th and 89th Congresses.

EIGHTH DISTRICT.—Counties: Appling, Atkinson, Bacon, Ben Hill, Berrien, Bleckley, Brantley, Camden, Charlton, Clinch, Coffee, Cook, Dodge, Echols, Glynn, Irwin, Jeff Davis, Lanier, Lowndes, Pierce, Telfair, Ware, Wayne, and Wilcox (24 counties). Population (1960), 338,948.

JAMES RUSSELL TUTEN, Democrat, of Brunswick, Ga.; born on Appling County farm July 23, 1911; educated in Appling County public schools, South Georgia College, Douglas, Ga., and Georgia Southern College, Statesboro, Ga.; farmer, teacher, bricklayer, businessman, and building contractor; Baptist; deacon, First Baptist Church in Brunswick, Ga., 11 years; chairman of board of deacons 2 years; chairman board of trustees, Brewton Parker College; Mason; York Rite and Scottish Rite bodies; Shriner, past district master of 11th Masonic District of Georgia, and past grand marshal of Grand Lodge of Georgia; Order of the Eastern Star; member, Gridiron Secret Society of University of Georgia and Brunswick-Glynn County Chamber of Commerce; Kiwanian; Brunswick City Commissioner 1956–62; mayor of Brunswick 1958 and 1962; married to the former Hazel Wicker of Appling County, Ga.; four sons—James, John, Ernest, and Mark; elected to the 88th Congress November 6, 1962; reelected to the 89th Congress; member of House Committee on Public Works.

NINTH DISTRICT.—Counties: Banks, Barrow, Cherokee, Dawson, Elbert, Fannin, Forsyth, Franklin, Gilmer, Gwinnett, Habersham, Hall, Hart, Jackson, Lumpkin, Madison, Pickens, Rabun, Stephens, Towns, Union, and White (22 counties). Population (1960), 329,738.

PHILLIP MITCHELL LANDRUM, Democrat, of Jasper, Ga.; born September 10, 1909, in Martin, Stephens County, Ga.; lawyer; attended Mercer University; graduate of Piedmont College and Atlanta Law School; served approximately 3 years in United States Army Air Force in World War II; former assistant attorney general of the State of Georgia; served as executive secretary to the Governor of Georgia; married Miss Laura Brown, of Dewey Rose, Ga.; two children—Phillip, Jr., age 26, and Susan, age 19; elected to the 83d Congress November 4, 1952; reelected to the 84th, 85th, 86th, 87th, 88th, and 89th Congresses.

TENTH DISTRICT.—COUNTIES: Baldwin, Clarke, Columbia, Glascock, Greene, Hancock, Jasper, Jefferson, Lincoln, McDuffie, Morgan, Newton, Oconee, Oglethorpe, Putnam, Richmond, Taliaferro, Walton, Warren, Washington, and Wilkes (21 counties). Population (1960), 408,823.

ROBERT GRIER STEPHENS, JR., Democrat, of Athens, Ga.; born in Atlanta, Ga., August 14, 1913, son of Dr. Robert Grier and Martha Lucy (Evans) Stephens; educated in the Atlanta public schools; was graduated from Boys' High School in 1931 and the University of Georgia (A.B. degree) in 1935; attended the University of Hamburg, Germany, on an exchange student scholarship; taught history and political science at the University of Georgia 1936–40; received the M.A. degree in 1937 and law degree, cum laude, in 1941; during World War II served in the U.S. Army for 4½ years in the States and in Germany, the last assignment before separation was on the legal staff of Mr. Justice Robert Jackson at the Nuremberg trials of Nazi war criminals; returned to Athens, Ga., and engaged for 15 years in general practice of law from 1946 to 1961; city attorney of Athens 1947–50; member of State senate 1951–53 and member of State house of representatives 1953–59; married the former Grace Winston of Clarke County in 1938; four children, Grace Winston, Robert Grier III, Mary Winston, and Lawton Evans; elder of the Presbyterian Church; member of American Legion, VFW, Elks, Kiwanis (lieutenant-governor), Woodmen, Phi Beta Kappa, Phi Kappa Phi, Phi Delta Phi legal fraternity, Kappa Alpha Order, and ODK; elected to 87th Congress November 8, 1960; reelected to the 88th and 89th Congresses.

HAWAII

(Population (1960), 632,772)

SENATORS

HIRAM LEONG FONG, Republican, of Honolulu, Hawaii; born in Honolulu, October 1, 1907; attorney and businessman; corporation president of Finance Factors, Grand Pacific Life Insurance, Finance Realty, Finance Home Builders, Finance Investment, Finance Factors Building, Finance Factors Foundation, and Market City; operates banana farm in Honolulu; attended Kalihiwaena Grammar School, St. Louis College, and McKinley High School; University of Hawaii, B.A., LL.D. (honorary); member Phi Beta Kappa; Harvard Law School, LL.B.; Tufts University, LL.D. (honorary); Lafayette College, LL.D. (honorary), Elector, Hall of Fame for Great Americans; 14 years in Legislature of the Territory of Hawaii; 6 years as speaker and 4 years as vice speaker; delegate to the Republican National Conventions 1952, 1956, 1960, and 1964; vice president of Territorial Constitutional Convention, 1950; judge advocate of the Seventh Fighter Command of the Seventh Air Force with rank of major in World War II; presently colonel, U.S. Air Force Reserve; married to Ellyn Lo; 4 children, Hiram, Jr., Rodney, Merie-Ellen, and Marvin-Allan; elected to the United States Senate July 28, 1959, for the term beginning August 21, 1959, and ending January 3, 1965; reelected November 3, 1964, for the term ending January 3, 1971.

DANIEL KEN INOUYE, Democrat, of Honolulu, Hawaii; born in Honolulu, September 7, 1924; A.B. degree in government and economics, University of Hawaii, 1950; J.D. degree, George Washington University Law School, 1952; majority leader, Territorial house of representatives, 1954–58; Territorial senate, 1958–59; enlisted as private, 442d Infantry Regimental Combat Team, 1943; battlefield commission, second lieutenant, 1944; served in France and Italy; retired captain, U.S. Army; Methodist; married the former Margaret Shinobu Awamura of Honolulu; one son, Daniel Ken Inouye, Jr.; elected July 28, 1959, to the 86th Congress; reelected to the 87th Congress; elected to the United States Senate November 6, 1962, for the term ending January 3, 1969.

REPRESENTATIVES

AT LARGE.—Population (1960), 632,772.

SPARK MASAYUKI MATSUNAGA, Democrat, of Honolulu, Hawaii; born Kukuiula, Kauai, Hawaii, October 8, 1916; graduate, Kauai High School, 1933; University of Hawaii (with Phi Kappa Phi, Pi Gamma Mu, Real Dean honors), 1941, Ed. B.; Harvard Law School, 1951, LL.B. (Ames semifinalist in oral advocacy); postgraduate studies, Northwestern University Traffic Institute, 1957, and Lawyers Post Graduate Clinics of Chicago, Ill., 1958; University ROTC cadet major, commissioned second lieutenant, U.S. Army Reserve, June 1941; volunteered for active service, U.S. Army, July 1941; as original member of Nisei 100th Infantry Battalion Separate (later 1st Bn., 442d Regimental Combat Team) served in North Africa and Europe; twice wounded in battle; released as captain, December 1945; now lieutenant colonel in Reserve; awarded Bronze Star Medal, Purple Heart Medal with Oak Leaf Cluster, Army Commendation Medal, combat and expert infantry badges, American Defense Service Medal with metal clasp, American Campaign Medal, Asiatic-Pacific Campaign Medal with one battle star, European-African-Middle Eastern Campaign Medal with four battle stars; worked way through high school as stevedore and warehouseman and through college as laboratory helper; veterans' counselor, U.S. Department of the Interior, December 1945 to July 1947; Chief, Priority Division, War Assets Administration, July 1947 to August 1948; assistant public prosecutor,

Honolulu, 1952–54; entered private law practice 1954; member, Territorial legislature, 1954–59; house majority leader, 1959; candidate for Lieutenant Governor of Hawaii, 1959; married Helene Hatsumi Tokunaga, 1948; five children: Karen, Keene, Diane, Merle, Matthew; member Hawaii Statehood Delegation to Congress, 1950, 1954; American and Hawaii Bar Associations; past commander, Disabled American Veterans; past president, Club 100; director, Lions Club; board chairman, YMCA; director, Society for Crippled Children and Adults, Honolulu Community Theater, and other civic and community associations; president, Democratic Precinct Club; county committeeman; district councilman; delegate to county and State conventions, 1962–64; elected to 88th Congress November 1962; reelected to the 89th Congress 1964.

PATSY TAKEMOTO MINK, Democrat, of Waipahu, Hawaii; born in Paia, Maui, Hawaii, December 6, 1927; graduate of Maui High School (student body president) 1944; attended Wilson College, Chambersburg, Pa. (1946), and University of Nebraska (1947), University of Hawaii (B.A.) 1948, and University of Chicago Law School (J.D.) in 1951; married to John Francis Mink; one daughter, Gwendolyn; attorney at law; lecturer, University of Hawaii 1952–56 and 1959–62; attorney for Territorial Legislature, 1955; member, Hawaii House of Representatives 1956 and 1958; member, Hawaii State Senate 1958–59 and 1962–64; member Democratic Party since 1953; charter president, Young Democrats of Oahu, 1954; delegate to National Democratic Convention and the Platform Committee in 1960; delegate to National Young Democrats Convention in 1957, 1959, and 1961; vice president, National Young Democrats of America 1957–59; director, Lanakila Crafts, eleemosynary organization to help handicapped; director Hawaii Chapter, American Association for the United Nations; member NAACP; former director, Hawaii Association to Help Retarded Children and Rural YMCA chapter, Oahu; elected to the 89th Congress November 3, 1964.

IDAHO

(Population (1960), 667,191)

SENATORS

FRANK CHURCH, Democrat, of Boise, Idaho; born July 25, 1924, at Boise; attended public schools; A. B., LL. B., Stanford University; enlisted as private in United States Army during World War II and commissioned as officer on 20th birthday, serving with Military Intelligence in China, Burma, and India; engaged in private law practice in Boise; married to former Bethine Clark, daughter of United States District Judge and former Idaho Governor Chase A. Clark; two sons: Forrest, 16, and Clark, 7; two terms Department Judge Advocate, Idaho Department of the American Legion; State chairman Crusade for Freedom, 1954–55; State chairman, Young Democrats of Idaho, 1952–54; Keynoter, Democratic National Convention, 1960; elected to the United States Senate on November 6, 1956; reelected November 6, 1962.

LEN B. JORDAN, Republican, of Boise, Idaho; rancher, businessman; born in Mount Pleasant, Utah, May 15, 1899; attended the public and high schools at Enterprise, Oreg.; enlisted in the U.S. Army during World War I, was commissioned, and discharged as a second lieutenant; entered the University of Oregon in 1919 and worked his way with part-time campus jobs and summer jobs and graduated in 1923 with A.B. degree; married the former Grace Edgington of Hood River, Oreg., on December 30, 1924; three children—Joseph, Stephen, and Patricia (Mrs. Charles Storey); member of Idaho Legislature in 1947; Governor of Idaho, 1951–55; member of the International Joint Commission 1955–57; member of the International Development Advisory Board 1958–59; is a trustee of the Boise Methodist Church, a Mason, and a member of Rotary International; appointed to the United States Senate August 6, 1962, to fill the vacancy caused by the death of Henry C. Dworshak and elected November 6, 1962, for remainder of term, ending January 3, 1967; is a member of the Interior and Insular Affairs Committee, the Labor and Public Welfare Committee, and the Joint Economic Committee.

REPRESENTATIVES

FIRST DISTRICT.—COUNTIES: Adams, Benewah, Boise, Bonner, Boundary, Canyon, Clearwater, Custer, Gem, Idaho, Kootenai, Latah, Lemhi, Lewis, Nez Perce, Payette, Shoshone, Valley, and Washington (19 counties). Population (1960), 257,242.

COMPTON IGNATIUS WHITE, JR., Democrat, of Clarkfork, Bonner County, Idaho; born in Spokane, Wash., December 19, 1920; livestock breeder; also actively engaged in mining and logging; son of the late Compton I. White, Sr., who was a member of 73d through 79th and 81st Congresses from the First District of Idaho, and Josephine Elizabeth Bunn White, residents of Clarkfork, Idaho; educated in the public schools of Clarkfork, Idaho, and Washington, D.C.; George Washington University, Washington, D.C.; University of Idaho, Moscow, Idaho; married Florence Eulalia Waddell of Athol, Idaho, November 19, 1948; six children—John Edward, born September 16, 1949; Michael Bowman, born November 20, 1950; Joel Patrick, born January 4, 1952; Christine Marie, born January 4, 1953; Harold Lewis, born January 29, 1954; and Daniel Paul, born April 29, 1955; member of school board and Clarkfork Board of Trustees, served two terms as chairman; also member Advisory Committee Kaniksu National Forest and various civic organizations; candidate for Democratic nomination to United States Senate from Idaho in 1960; mayor of Clarkfork 1958–62; elected to the 88th Congress November 6, 1962; reelected to the 89th Congress; member of Committee on Interior and Insular Affairs with subcommittee assignments to Mines and Mining, Irrigation and Reclamation and Public Lands and the Committee on Banking and Currency with subcommittee assignments to International Trade and International Finance.

SECOND DISTRICT.—COUNTIES: Ada, Bannock, Bear Lake, Bingham, Blaine, Bonneville, Butte, Camas, Caribou, Cassia, Clark, Elmore, Franklin, Fremont, Gooding, Jefferson, Jerome, Lincoln, Madison, Minidoka, Oneida, Owyhee, Power, Teton, and Twin Falls (25 counties) and part of Yellowstone National Park. Population (1960), 409,949.

GEORGE VERNON HANSEN, Republican, of Pocatello, Idaho; born in Tetonia, Idaho, September 14, 1930; graduated Teton High School, Driggs, Idaho, 1948; Ricks College, Rexburg, Idaho, B.A., 1956, with honors (history and Russian); Idaho State University, graduate work; Grimms Business College, Pocatello, Idaho, graduate in accounting; agent, life insurance; mayor of Alameda 1961–62; city commissioner of Pocatello 1962 to January 1965; past director of the Idaho Municipal League 1961 to 1963; past president of 20–30 Club; past director of Kiwanis; member of Chamber of Commerce, Farm Bureau, and American Legion; chairman, County Heart Fund; member of Church of Jesus Christ of Latter-Day Saints; chairman, vice chairman, publicity chairman, precinct committeeman of Bannock County Republican Central Committee; president, Bannock County Young Republican Club; married to the former Connie Camp of Malden, Mo.; five children, Steven George, James Vernon, Patricia Sue, William Dean, and Joanne; served in the U.S. Air Force 3½ years; U.S. Naval Reserve officer; candidate for U.S. Senate in 1962; elected to the 89th Congress November 3, 1964.

ILLINOIS

(Population (1960), 10,081,158)

SENATORS

PAUL H. DOUGLAS, Democrat, of Chicago, Ill.; born in Salem, Mass., March 26, 1892; A. B. Bowdoin College; Ph. D. Columbia University, 1921; recipient of numerous honorary degrees; married to Emily Taft Douglas, Congresswoman-at-large from Illinois, 79th Congress; father of Helen (Mrs. Paul Klein), John, Dorothea (Mrs. Robert John), Paul, and Jean (Mrs. Ned Bandler); member of Economics Department, University of Chicago, 1920–48; author of The Theory of Wages, Real Wages in the United States, and Social Security in the United States, etc.; president American Economic Association (1947); drafted first Illinois Old Age Pension Act and helped to draft Illinois' unemployment insurance law; adviser to Governor Roosevelt on New York's social security problems and helped to revise Federal Social Security Act in 1939; alderman from Fifth Ward, Chicago City Council, 1939–42; enlisted as a private in United States Marine Corps in May 1942; served with First Marine Division, advancing through ranks to rank of lieutenant colonel, twice wounded at Peleliu and Okinawa; awarded Bronze Star for "heroic achievement in action"; elected Senator on November 2, 1948, by plurality of 407,728, reelected November 2, 1954, by a majority of 240,655; reelected November 8, 1960, by a majority of 437,091.

EVERETT McKINLEY DIRKSEN, Republican, of Pekin, Ill.; born at Pekin, Ill., January 4, 1896; attended grade and high schools of Pekin and University of Minnesota College of Law; served in the United States Army, 1917–19, with 17 months' overseas service; commissioned from the ranks; member of the bar of the District of Columbia and Illinois; married and has one daughter, Mrs. Howard H. Baker, Jr.; elected to the 73d, 74th, 75th, 76th, 77th, 78th, 79th, and 80th Congresses; retired voluntarily on January 3, 1949; nominated for United States Senate in open primary April 11, 1950; elected to Senate November 7, 1950; renominated for Senate April 1956; reelected November 6 for second full term; renominated for Senate April 1962; reelected November 6, 1962, for third full term; honorary degrees; LL. D., Bradley University, Peoria, Ill.; Hope College, Holland, Mich.; Lincoln Memorial University, Harrogate, Tenn.; and DePaul University, Chicago, Ill.; member of American Legion, Veterans of Foreign Wars, Eagles, Elks, Moose, Masons, Shrine, and Eastern Star; reelected as minority leader for a fourth term on January 4, 1965; serves on Committee on Finance and Committee on Judiciary.

REPRESENTATIVES

FIRST DISTRICT.—CITY OF CHICAGO: That part of ward 2 south of the center line of 31st Street as extended; ward 3; that part of ward 4 north of the center line of east 46th Street as extended and that part west of the center line of south Cottage Grove Avenue; ward 6; that part of ward 8 west of the center line of south Stony Island Avenue as extended and that part north of the center line of east 99th Street as extended; ward 20; that part of ward 21 east and north of the line drawn from the intersection of the center lines of west 87th Street and south Stewart Avenue, south along the center line of south Stewart Avenue as extended to its intersection with the center line of west 99th Street, east along the center line of west 99th Street as extended to its intersection with the center line of south State Street. Population (1960), 397,324.

WILLIAM L. DAWSON, Democrat, of Chicago, Ill.; born in Albany, Ga.; was graduated from Albany (Ga.) Normal School and Fisk University with A. B. degree; attended Kent and Northwestern Schools of Law; during the First World War served as first lieutenant of the 365th Infantry, A. E. F.; attorney at law; State central committeeman, First Congressional District, 1930–32; alderman of the second ward, 1933–39; Democratic Committeeman from second ward since 1939; married Miss Nellie Brown of Washington, D. C.; two children, William L., Jr., and Barbara D. Morgan; secretary of Democratic Congressional Committee; vice chairman, Democratic National Committee; vice chairman, Cook County Central Committee; elected to the 78th Congress on November 3, 1942; reelected to the 79th, 80th, 81st, 82d, 83d, 84th, 85th, 86th, 87th, 88th, and 89th Congresses; during the 81st, 82d, 84th, 85th, 86th, 87th, and 88th Congresses served as chairman of the Government Operations Committee; and is presently serving as chairman of the Government Operations Committee and as a member of the House District Committee.

SECOND DISTRICT.—CITY OF CHICAGO: That part of ward 4 south of the center line of east 46th Street as extended and east of the center line of south Cottage Grove Avenue; wards 5 and 7; that part of ward 8 east of the center line of south Stony Island Avenue as extended and that part south of the center line of east 99th Street as extended; wards 9 and 10. Population (1960), 365,525.

BARRATT O'HARA, Democrat; born at St. Joseph, Mich., April 28, 1882; the oldest member of the House and the only Spanish War veteran in the Congress; son of the late Circuit Judge Thomas O'Hara and Mary (Barratt) O'Hara; educated at University of Missouri, Northwestern University, Chicago-Kent College of Law, LL. B., LL. D. (honorary, Shorter College-Jackson Seminary); married Florence M. Hoffman; children—Barratt, Jr., Lorence Hoffman, Howard Mears, Florence Frances Louise (deceased); as boy, accompanied General Ludlow and Admiral Walker on expedition through Nicaragua marking route for inter-oceanic canal, Smithsonian Institution party exploring jungles of Central America for fungus growth, and expedition of General Alexander in determination of boundary dispute between Nicaragua and Costa Rica; at 15, when sophomore in high school enlisted in 33d Michigan Volunteer Infantry and landed in Cuba 3 days after "Teddy" Roosevelt and Rough Riders, participated in siege of Santiago de Cuba and later was awarded the Order of Military Merit in White by the Republic of Cuba for services rendered the people of Cuba during their war for independence; at 20, was sporting editor of St. Louis (Mo.) Chronicle (Scripps-McRae) and at 21 was sporting editor of Hearst's Chicago American; later was Sunday editor of the Chicago Examiner and editor and publisher of the Chicago Magazine; at 30 was elected Lieutenant Governor of Illinois, the youngest in the State's history; chairman of Illinois Senate Vice and Wage Commission, which was responsible for the passage of the first State minimum-wage laws; while Acting Governor (in absence from State of Governor Dunne) served as member of Secretary Redfield's Federal board of inquiry into SS *Eastland* tragedy (capsizing July 23, 1915, in Chicago River, occasioning loss of 812 lives) and proposed legislation which, enacted by the Congress, has prevented similar catastrophes since that time; in 1917 became president of company with studios in Hollywood, an organization previously headed by David Wark Griffith, resigning on declaration of war with Germany to reenter military service; served in World War I with 319th Infantry, 80th Division, and later 12th Regular Army Division; at termination of hostilities resumed law practice in Chicago; defense counsel in many homicide trials with a record of never having a death sentence imposed; from 1932 to 1937 spoke nightly over WCFL radio station (American Federation of Labor) and was instrumental in effecting reforms in bankruptcy proceedings to bring relief to impoverished holders of real-estate bonds; from 1939 to 1948, and again in 1951 and 1952, was an attorney for the city of Chicago in traction reorganization and subway construction; Past Judge Advocate General, Veterans of Foreign Wars; one of the organizers of the American Legion in Illinois; member Chicago Press Veterans Association, Phi Gamma Delta, Phi Delta Phi, American Veterans Committee, United Spanish War Veterans, and 80th Division Veterans Association; author of From Figg to Johnson, Legislative Compendium, Defaulted Real Estate Bonds, and (with Marie Crowe) Who Made the Constitution?; elected to the 81st Congress and the 83d Congress; reelected to the 84th, 85th, 86th, 87th, 88th, and 89th Congresses; in 1964 receiving 107,795 votes to his Republican opponent's 52,416; member Committee on Foreign Affairs; chairman, subcommittee on Africa.

THIRD DISTRICT.—CITY OF CHICAGO: That part of ward 13 south of the center line of west 66th Street as extended; wards 16, 17, 18, and 19; that part of ward 21 west and south of the line drawn from the intersection of the center lines of west 87th Street and south Stewart Avenue, south along the center line of south Stewart Avenue as extended to its intersection with the center line of west 99th Street, east along the center line of west 99th Street as extended to its intersection with the center line of south State Street. COOK COUNTY: That part of the township of Worth located within the limits of the village of Evergreen Park. Population (1960), 426,070.

WILLIAM T. MURPHY, Democrat, Chicago, Ill.; born in Chicago, Ill.; married to the former Rose M. McInerney; children: William T., Jr.; John P., and Rosemary; Loyola University School of Law 1926, LL.B.; admitted to Illinois State Bar 1927 and U.S. Supreme Court 1944; member of Federal Bar Association; member of Delta Theta Phi Legal Fraternity; veteran World War I; member American Legion; delegate to Democratic National Convention 1944, 1948, 1952, and 1956; Democratic ward committeeman, 17th Ward, city of Chicago, 1940–63; member Chicago City Council 1935–59; chairman, Committee on Labor-Management 1940–47; chairman, Committee on Planning 1947–55; chairman, Committee on Planning and Housing 1955–59; member, Chicago Plan Commission 1947–59; member, Lambda Alpha Honorary Land Economics

Fraternity; licensed professional engineer; registered land surveyor; member, 86th, 87th, 88th, and 89th Congresses; member, House Foreign Affairs Committee; Subcommittee on Africa; member, Canada-United States Interparliamentary Group 1961–64, fourth, fifth, sixth, and seventh sessions, Ottawa-Washington, D.C.; awarded Tenth Commemorative Medal in 1964 by Assembly of Captive Nations.

FOURTH DISTRICT.—COOK COUNTY: Townships of Bloom, Bremen, Calumet, Lemont, Lyons, Orland, Palos, Rich, Thornton, and Worth, except that part of the township of Worth located within the limits of the village of Evergreen Park. Population (1960), 516,624.

EDWARD J. DERWINSKI, Republican, of South Holland, Ill.; born September 15, 1926, in Chicago; attended Mount Carmel High School and Loyola University, Chicago (B. Sc. History); veteran World War II, Army, Infantry, Pacific Theater; served one term in Illinois General Assembly as State representative of the 24th District, 1957–58; president of the West Pullman Savings & Loan Association; religion, Roman Catholic; member of Knights of Columbus, Polish Roman Catholic Union, Moose, Kiwanis, American Legion, VFW, Polish Legion of American Veterans (past post commander, past State vice commander), Amvets, Polish National Alliance, Polish Highlanders (national director), Catholic War Veterans; selected by the Chicago Junior Association of Commerce and Industry as one of Chicago's Ten Outstanding Young Men for 1959 and 1961; married to Patricia Van Der Giessen; one daughter, Maureen Sue; elected to the 86th Congress; reelected to the 87th, 88th, and 89th Congresses.

FIFTH DISTRICT.—CITY OF CHICAGO: That part of ward 11 south of the center line of west 31st Street as extended; ward 12; that part of ward 13 north of the center line of west 66th Street as extended; wards 14 and 15; that part of ward 23 south of the Illinois and Michigan Canal. COOK COUNTY: That part of the township of Stickney located south of west 65th Street as extended. Population (1960), 351,023.

JOHN C. KLUCZYNSKI, Democrat, of Chicago, Ill.; born February 15, 1896; educated in public and parochial schools; served overseas with the Eighth Field Artillery in World War I; married to Stephanie Estelle Polowy; elected to the Illinois State Legislature in 1932, serving 16 consecutive years; elected in 1948 to State senate; resigned in December 1949 to become candidate for Representative in Congress; elected to 82d Congress on November 7, 1950, and reelected to each succeeding Congress; member of House Public Works Committee; chairman of subcommittee on Roads; also member of Small Business Committee; owns and operates Syrena Restaurant & Caterers, 4270 Archer Avenue, Chicago, Ill.; residence: 2450 West 55th Street, Chicago, Ill. and Army-Navy Club, Washington, D.C.

SIXTH DISTRICT.—CITY OF CHICAGO: Ward 22, precincts 1 to 73, all; ward 23, precincts 24, 25, 31, 33, 34, 41, 43 to 46, 54, 57, and 59; ward 24, precincts 1 to 58, all; ward 29, precincts 1 to 64, all; ward 30, precincts 21 to 48, 58 to 61, 64, 65, 66, 73, 74 and 75; ward 37, precincts 15, 24, 26, 27, 46 to 68, 71, 72, 73, and 75 to 78; and Stickney, precincts 1 to 8, all; total precincts, 288. Population (1960), 278,703.

DANIEL J. RONAN, Democrat, of Chicago, Ill.; born in Chicago July 13, 1914; graduated St. Ignatius in 1933, Loyola University in 1938; majored in economics and political history; postgraduate work at Loyola 1939–41 and 1947–48; served in Army Air Force Communications as a cryptographer in China-Burma-India Theater in 1942; worked for Sanitary District 1934–48; served as State representative 1948–52; served as alderman 1951–64; acting ward committeeman in 1959, and elected in 1960 and reelected in 1964; member of the Chicago Plan Commission; not married; elected to the 89th Congress November 3, 1964.

SEVENTH DISTRICT.—CITY OF CHICAGO: Ward 1; that part of ward 2 north of the center line of 31st Street as extended; that part of ward 11 north of the center line of west 31st Street; wards 25 to 28. Population (1960), 393,209.

FRANK ANNUNZIO, Democrat, of Chicago, Ill.; born in Chicago, Ill., January 12, 1915; while attending school worked in a polishing and plating shop and an ornamental iron shop; graduated from Crane Technical High School, DePaul University, B.S. degree and a master's degree in education; vocational instructor while attending college; taught civics and history at Harper High School 1940–42; married the former Angeline Alesia; three daughters; assistant supervisor of the National Defense Program at Austin High School 1942 and 1943, educational representative of the United Steelworkers of America 1943–48; director of labor, State of Illinois, 1948–52; one of the pioneers in organizing the C.Y.O.; went into privately owned business in 1954; elected to the 89th Congress November 3, 1964.

EIGHTH DISTRICT.—CITY OF CHICAGO: That part of ward 30 north of the center line of west Kinzie Street as extended; wards 31 to 34; that part of ward 35 south and east of the line drawn from the intersection of the center lines of west Diversey Avenue and north Long Avenue, east along the center line of west Diversey Avenue to its intersection with the center line of north Pulaski Road, north along the center line of north Pulaski Road to its intersection with the center line of west Addison Street; ward 36; that part of ward 37 north of the center line of west Kinzie Street as extended, and that part of ward 40 south of the thread of the north branch of the Chicago River. Population (1960), 483,537.

DAN ROSTENKOWSKI, Democrat, of Chicago, Ill.; educated in St. John's Military Academy and Loyola University; served as State representative in the 68th General Assembly and as State senator from the 33d senatorial district in the 69th and 70th General Assemblies; served 2 years in the Infantry in Korea; former president of the Automobile Salesman Association; member of—Knights of Columbus, Veterans of Foreign Wars, Northwest Town Kiwanis Club, Loyal Order of Moose; chairman of Finance Committee Boy Scout Drive, 1959–60; regional chairman, March of Dimes, 1960–61; married LaVerne Pirkins and has four daughters; elected delegate to the Democratic National Convention in 1960 and 1964; elected to the 86th Congress on November 4, 1958; re-elected to the 87th, 88th, and 89th Congresses.

NINTH DISTRICT.—CITY OF CHICAGO: Wards 42 to 44, 46, 48, and 49. Population (1960), 428,202.

SIDNEY R. YATES, Democrat, of Chicago, Ill.; born in Chicago, Ill., August 27, 1909; educated in public elementary and high school in Chicago; received the degree of Bachelor of Philosophy from the University of Chicago in 1931 and the degree of Doctor of Jurisprudence from the University of Chicago in 1933; served in the United States Navy for 26 months; released from active duty with the rank of lieutenant; practicing attorney since 1933; assistant attorney for Illinois State bank receiver, 1935–37; assistant attorney general attached to Illinois Commerce Commission as traction attorney, 1937–40; editor of "Bulletin of Decalogue Society of Lawyers," 1947; married Adeline J. Holleb of Chicago in 1935; has one son, Stephen R. Yates, age 24; member of American Bar Association, American Veterans' Committee, Chicago Bar Association, Illinois State Bar Association, Chicago Council on Foreign Relations, City Club of Chicago, Decalogue Society of Lawyers; elected to the 81st Congress on November 2, 1948; reelected to the 82d, 83d, 84th, 85th, 86th, and 87th Congresses; U.S. representative to Trusteeship Council of the United Nations with rank of Ambassador, 1963–64; elected to the 89th Congress November 3, 1964.

TENTH DISTRICT.—CITY OF CHICAGO: That part of ward 38 west of the Des Plaines River, and that part of Du Page County which is located in the city of Chicago. COOK COUNTY: Townships of Berwyn, Cicero, Leyden, Maine, Oak Park, Proviso, River Forest, Riverside, and that part of Chicago O'Hare International Airport which is located in the township of Elk Grove. Population (1960), 552,582.

HAROLD R. COLLIER, Republican, of Berwyn, Ill.; born December 12, 1915, at Lansing, Mich.; resident of the 10th District for 38 years; attended the public schools; graduated from the J. Sterling Morton High School in 1932; attended Morton Junior College and entered Lake Forest College on a grant-in-aid scholarship in 1934, leaving in midyear 1937 to become editor of the Berwyn Beacon; employed in editorial department of Suburban Life Publications 1938 to 1941; in 1940 went with the Match Corporation of America, Chicago, Ill., in the sales promotion department and after 3 years was promoted to personnel manager; in 1952 went with the McAlear Manufacturing Co., of Chicago, Ill., as advertising and public relations director; elected alderman of Berwyn City Council in 1951; was a candidate in 1952 primary for secretary of state; president of the Berwyn Public Health Board; served three terms as secretary-treasurer of Cook County Supervisors Association; chairman of the First Senatorial District Republican Committee; secretary of the Third Legislative District Republican Committee; member of: Berwyn Lodge Loyal Order of Moose, Riverside Drive Improvement Association, Lake Forest College Alumni Association, Berwyn-Cicero University Club, and the First Methodist Church of Berwyn; married to the former Carol Jean Bangert; three children—Calvin, 23; Lynne, 21; Harold Paul, 19; elected to the 85th Congress November 6, 1956; reelected to the 86th, 87th, 88th, and 89th Congresses.

ELEVENTH DISTRICT.—CITY OF CHICAGO: That part of ward 35 north and west of the line drawn from the intersection of the center lines of west Diversey Avenue and north Long Avenue, east along the center line of west Diversey Avenue to its intersection with the center line of north Pulaski Road, north along the center line of north Pulaski Road to its intersection with the center line of west Addison Street; that part of ward 38 east of the Des Plaines River; ward 39; that part of ward 40 north of the thread of the north branch of the Chicago River; wards 41, 45, and 47. COOK COUNTY: Township of Norwood Park. Population (1960), 433,491.

ROMAN C. PUCINSKI, Democrat, of Chicago, Ill.; born May 13, 1919; educated in Chicago public schools; attended Northwestern University and John Marshall Law School in Chicago; has been a staff reporter and writer for the Chicago Sun-Times for the past 20 years before being elected to Congress; served in World War II, enlisting as a private in the 106th Cavalry; was honorably discharged with the rank of captain; served with 20th Global (Superfort) Air Force; led his bomber group on the first B–29 bombing raid over Tokyo in 1944 and subsequently flew 48 missions over Japan; awarded the Distinguished Flying Cross and Air Medal with Clusters; served as chief investigator for a select committee of Congress which investigated the mass murder by the Communists of 15,000 Polish army officers in World War II; Roman Catholic; married to Aurelia Bordin of Chicago, Ill.; has two children; elected to the 86th Congress on November 4, 1958; reelected to the 87th, 88th, and 89th Congresses; member of House Committee on Education and Labor; chairman of special Subcommittee on a National Research Data Processing and Information Retrieval Center; chairman of special task force to study labor dispute involving the nuclear ship N.S. *Savannah*.

TWELFTH DISTRICT.—COUNTIES: Boone, Lake, and McHenry (3 counties). Population (1960), 398,192.

ROBERT McCLORY, Republican, of Lake Bluff, Ill.; born in Riverside, Ill., January 31, 1908; educated public schools, L'Institut Sillig, Vevey, Switzerland; Dartmouth College, LL. B. degree from Chicago-Kent College of Law, 1932; U.S. Marine Corps Reserve 1933–37; engaged in practice of law in State and Federal courts in Cook and Lake Counties, Ill., from 1932; elected house of representatives, Illinois General Assembly, 1950; elected Illinois State Senate 1952, and reelected 1956 and 1960; married to the former Audrey B. Vasey of Toronto, Canada; one daughter, Beatrice (Mrs. Andre Donald Etienne); two sons, Michael and Oliver; member Chicago, Lake County, Illinois State, and American Bar Associations, Law Club of Chicago; elected to the 88th Congress November 6, 1962; reelected to the 89th Congress.

THIRTEENTH DISTRICT.—COOK COUNTY: Townships of Barrington, Evanston, Hanover, New Trier, Niles, Northfield, Palatine, Schaumburg, and Wheeling; that portion of the township of Elk Grove not included within the limits of the city of Chicago. CITY OF CHICAGO: Ward 50. Population (1960), 503,435.

DONALD RUMSFELD, Republican, of Glenview, Ill.; born in Evanston, Ill., July 9, 1932; attended Winnetka public schools; graduated Princeton University, 1954, in politics; served as a naval aviator and flight instructor until 1957; married the former Joyce Pierson of Wilmette; two daughters, Valerie and Marcy; administrative assistant to former Congressman David Dennison, Ohio, 1958; on staff of Congressman Robert Griffin, Michigan, in 1959; was associated with A. G. Becker & Co., Inc., Chicago investment bankers, as registered representative, 1960–62; member Presbyterian Church; elected to the 88th Congress November 6, 1962; reelected to the 89th Congress.

FOURTEENTH DISTRICT.—WILL COUNTY. DU PAGE COUNTY: That portion not included in the city of Chicago. Population (1960), 505,076.

JOHN N. ERLENBORN, Republican, of Elmhurst, Ill.; born in Chicago, Ill., February 8, 1927; lifelong resident of the 14th Congressional District; graduated Immaculate Conception High School, Elmhurst, 1944; served with the U.S. Navy in World War II; undergraduate Notre Dame, Indiana State Teachers College, University of Illinois, and Loyola of Chicago; graduated Loyola of Chicago LL.B. 1949; engaged in the practice of law in Elmhurst, Ill., law firm of Erlenborn, Bauer and Hotte; married to the former Dorothy Fisher of Glen Ellyn May 10, 1952; three children, Debra, Paul, and David; assistant State's attorney 1950–52, Du Page County, Illinois; member of Du Page County, Illinois, and American Bar Associations; State representative (36th District) 1957–65; elected to the 89th Congress November 3, 1964.

FIFTEENTH DISTRICT.—COUNTIES: De Kalb, Grundy, Kane, Kendall, and La Salle (5 counties). Population (1960), 410,650.

CHARLOTTE T. REID, Republican, of Aurora, Ill.; born September 27, 1913, in Kankakee, Ill.; attended public schools of Aurora and Illinois College at Jacksonville, Ill.; under the name of Annette King, served as staff vocalist on NBC and appeared as a vocalist for 3 years on Don McNeill's radio program; active in civic and political affairs; married to Frank R. Reid, Jr. (now deceased), in 1938; two sons, Frank R. Reid III and Edward Thompson Reid; and two daughters, Patricia (Mrs. George Lindner) and Susan Reid; elected to the 88th Congress November 6, 1962; reelected to the 89th Congress.

SIXTEENTH DISTRICT.—COUNTIES: Carroll, Jo Daviess, Ogle, Stephenson, Whiteside, and Winnebago (6 counties).   Population (1960), 395,293.

JOHN B. ANDERSON, Republican, of Rockford, Ill.; born in Rockford, Ill., February 15, 1922; graduated from Rockford Central High School in 1939; A.B. and J.D. degrees from the University of Illinois; LL.M. degree from Harvard Law School; while at Harvard served on the faculty of Northeastern University School of Law, Boston, Mass.; admitted to practice before the Supreme Court of Illinois in 1946; during World War II enlisted in the U.S. Army and served in the Field Artillery for 2½ years, 10 months of which were spent overseas in four major campaigns in the European Theater of Operations; member of the U.S. State Department's Career Diplomatic Service in 1952 and then sent abroad and stationed in West Berlin for 2½ years as an adviser on the staff of the U.S. High Commissioner for Germany; engaged in practice of law in 1955; State's attorney of Winnebago County 1956–60; married to Keke Machakos; four children, Eleanora, John, Jr., Diane, and Karen Beth; member of Winnebago County Bar Association, American Legion, the University Club of Rockford, and the First Evangelical Free Church of Rockford of which he was a former trustee; member of Board of Education of Trinity College, Chicago; elected to the 87th Congress November 8, 1960; reelected to the 88th and 89th Congresses.

SEVENTEENTH DISTRICT.—COUNTIES: Ford, Iroquois, Kankakee, Livingston, McLean, Vermilion, and Woodford (7 counties).   Population (1960), 387,204.

LESLIE C. ARENDS, Republican, of Melvin, Ill., born at Melvin, Ill.; attended grade and high schools at Melvin, Ill., and Oberlin College, Oberlin, Ohio; LL. D. degree from Illinois Wesleyan University; married and has one daughter, Letty; served in the United States Navy during World War I, charter member of Melvin Post, No. 642, American Legion, serving as post commander, county commander, and seventeenth district commander; member of Ford County Farm Bureau; Methodist; 33d degree Mason; member of board of directors, Illinois Wesleyan University; actively engaged in banking and farming since 1920; elected to the 74th Congress on November 6, 1934; reelected to the 75th, 76th, 77th, 78th, 79th, 80th, 81st, 82d, 83d, 84th, 85th, 86th, 87th, 88th, and 89th Congresses; elected Republican Whip in 1943.

EIGHTEENTH DISTRICT.—COUNTIES: Bureau, Lee, Marshall, Peoria, Putnam, Stark, and Tazewell (7 counties).   Population (1960), 391,232.

ROBERT H. MICHEL, Republican, of Peoria, Ill.; born March 2, 1923, in Peoria, Ill.; graduate of Peoria Public Schools and Bradley University, B.S. 1948, business administration; distinguished Alumnus Award 1961; served in the enlisted ranks during World War II as combat infantryman in England, France, Belgium, and Germany; wounded by machine-gun fire and discharged as a disabled veteran after being awarded the Bronze Star, Purple Heart, and four battle stars; administrative assistant to predecessor, Congressman Harold Velde, during his service in the House from 1949 through 1956; elected to 85th, 86th, 87th, 88th, and 89th Congresses; delegate 1964 Republican National Convention; member of: American Legion, VFW, DAV, Amvets, Military Order Purple Heart, Peoria Association of Commerce, Ad Club, Cosmopolitan International, Orpheus Club, Creve Coeur Council Boy Scouts, YMCA, Order of Ahepa, Sigma Nu and Pi Kappa Delta fraternities; married former Corinne Woodruff, December 26, 1948; four children—Scott (14), Bruce (13), Laurie (11), Robin (10); residing at 1029 North Glenwood, Peoria, Ill.

NINETEENTH DISTRICT.—COUNTIES: Fulton, Henderson, Henry, Knox, Mercer, Rock Island, and Warren (7 counties). Population (1960), 350,515.

GALE SCHISLER, Democrat, of London Mills, Ill.; born on a farm in Indian Point Township, Knox County, Ill., March 2, 1933; attended Indian Point schools; graduated Abingdon High School in 1951; worked in a pottery and canning factory before going to Western Illinois University at Macomb for two quarters, majoring in agriculture; served in the U.S. Air Force, training for B–29 and B–26 gunnery, serving in the United States and France, 1952–55; married Carolyn K. Cochran of Galesburg in 1957; three children; returned to Western Illinois University to continue education and graduated, B.S., in March 1959; began teaching at London Mills Junior High School in 1959, principal 1960–64; during summer 1960–62 attended Northeast Missouri State Teachers College at Kirksville and earned a M.A. degree in school administration; Mason; member of American Legion, I.E.A., N.E.A., Junior High Principals Association, and Spoon River Valley Teacher's Association; elected to the 89th Congress November 3, 1964.

TWENTIETH DISTRICT.—COUNTIES: Adams, Brown, Calhoun, Cass, Greene, Hancock, Jersey, McDonough, Macoupin, Morgan, Pike, Sangamon, Schuyler, and Scott (14 counties). Population (1960), 445,443.

PAUL FINDLEY, Republican, of Pittsfield, Ill.; born June 23, 1921, in Jacksonville, Ill.; graduated from Illinois College, A.B. degree; Phi Beta Kappa; engaged in the printing and publishing business and publisher of two weekly newspapers; married to the former Lucille Gemme; two children, Craig and Diane; veteran World War II (Guam invasion, Japan); elected to the 87th Congress November 8, 1960; reelected to 88th and 89th Congresses; member, Committee on Agriculture, Committee on Education and Labor, Republican Project Committee on NATO Unity; member, board of trustees of Illinois College, Jacksonville, Ill.; member, board of directors, Federal Union, Inc., Washington, D.C.; past director, Illinois Press Association; past president, Pittsfield Industrial Development Association; member, Lions Club, American Legion, Veterans of Foreign Wars, Congregational Church.

TWENTY-FIRST DISTRICT.—COUNTIES: Alexander, Franklin, Gallatin, Hamilton, Hardin, Jackson, Jefferson, Johnson, Massac, Monroe, Perry, Pope, Pulaski, Randolph, Saline, Union, White, and Williamson (18 counties). Population (1960), 363,196.

KENNETH J. GRAY, Democrat, of West Frankfort, Ill.; born at West Frankfort, Ill., November 14, 1924; educated in the West Frankfort and Pope County elementary schools and graduated from the West Frankfort Community High School; also attended Army Advanced School during World War II; married to the former June Croslin of West Frankfort in 1943; one daughter, Diann; engaged in the automobile business since graduation from high school; also operated an air service at Benton, Ill., for 6 years; licensed pilot; served in the Army and Air Forces during World War II, 2 years of which was in overseas combat service in Italy, North Africa, Corsica, and southern France; active in civic affairs since his discharge from service in 1945; member of the Baptist Church, American Legion, Forty and Eight, Veterans of Foreign Wars, Kiwanis Club, Elks, Eagles, Past Commanders Club of the American Legion; State vice president of the Illinois Junior Chamber of Commerce 1953–54; one of the founders of the Walking Dog Foundation for the Blind, 1950, a nonprofit organization formed to train guide dogs and present them to blind persons free of charge; licensed auctioneer; elected to the 84th Congress November 2, 1954; reelected to the 85th Congress November 6, 1956; reelected to 86th Congress November 4, 1958; reelected to the 87th Congress November 8, 1960; reelected to 88th Congress November 6, 1962; reelected to 89th Congress November 3, 1964.

TWENTY-SECOND DISTRICT.—COUNTIES: Champaign, De Witt, Douglas, Logan, Macon, Mason, Menard, Moultrie, and Piatt (9 counties). Population (1960), 373,881.

WILLIAM L. SPRINGER, Republican, of Champaign-Urbana, Ill.; born April 12, 1909, at Sullivan, Ind., and educated in the public schools of Sullivan; graduated DePauw University, 1931, A. B., and from the University of Illinois Law School, 1935, LL. B.; Millikin University, 1953, LL. D. (hon.); practiced law at Champaign-Urbana; member, Champaign County, Illinois State, and American Bar Associations and the American Juridical Society; state's attorney of Champaign County 1940–42; served in the United States Navy 1942–45: county judge of Champaign County 1946–50; married Elsie Mattis in 1942 and they have three children, Katherine, Ann, and Georgia; elected to the 82d Congress November 7, 1950; reelected to the 83d, 84th, 85th, 86th, 87th, 88th, and 89th Congresses; home address: 900 West Park Street, Champaign; Washington address: 16 West Lenox Street, Chevy Chase, Md.

TWENTY-THIRD DISTRICT.—COUNTIES: Bond, Christian, Clark, Clay, Clinton, Coles, Crawford, Cumberland, Edwards, Effingham, Edgar, Fayette, Jasper, Lawrence, Marion, Montgomery, Richland, Shelby, Wabash, Washington, and Wayne (21 counties). Population (1960), 443,553.

GEORGE EDWARD SHIPLEY, Democrat, of Olney, Ill.; born in Richland County, Ill., April 21, 1927; graduated from Olney High School; attended Georgetown University; chief deputy sheriff of Richland County 1950–54; sheriff of Richland County 1954–58; served in the United States Marine Corps for 3 years and was discharged in 1947, with service in the South Pacific; owner of a restaurant in Olney; married Ann Watson and they have four children; elected to the 86th Congress on November 4, 1958; reelected to the 87th, 88th, and 89th Congresses.

TWENTY-FOURTH DISTRICT.—COUNTIES: Madison and St. Clair (2 counties). Population (1960), 487,198.

CHARLES MELVIN PRICE, Democrat, of East St. Louis, Ill.; born in East St. Louis, Ill., January 1, 1905; educated in the parochial schools of East St. Louis, St. Louis (Mo.) University High School, and prelegal at St. Louis (Mo.) University; newspaper correspondent (East St. Louis, Ill., Journal, St. Louis, Mo., Globe-Democrat, sports editor East St. Louis News-Review); former member of National Baseball Writers' Association; member of St. Clair County Board of Supervisors, 1929–31; secretary to former Congressman Edwin M. Schaefer, March 4, 1933, to January 3, 1943; married Garaldine M. Freelin, of Moberly, Mo., July 7, 1952; one son, William Melvin; member of American Legion, AMVETS, Knights of Columbus, Loyal Order of Moose, Eagles, Elks, Ancient Order of Hibernians, and the National Press Club; elected to the 79th and each succeeding Congress.

INDIANA

(Population (1960), 4,662,498)

SENATORS

VANCE HARTKE, Democrat, of Evansville, Ind.; born in Stendal, Pike County, Ind., May 31, 1919, son of the late Hugo Hartke and Ida Egbert Hartke; educated in Stendal public schools; graduated from Evansville College with A.B. degree; captain of the basketball team; president Student Government Association; member Lamba Chi Alpha; graduated from Indiana University Law School with J. D. degree; double scholarship winner; editor Indiana Law Journal; Phi Delta Phi and Tau Kappa Alpha (honoraries); veteran of Navy and Coast Guard service in World War II; including supply and purchasing duties at Underwater Sound Laboratory at New London, Conn.; attorney, Evansville, Ind., 1948–58; deputy prosecuting attorney, Vanderburgh County, Ind., 1950–51; Mayor of Evansville, Ind., 1956–58; member: Wabash Valley Association, Ohio Valley Improvement Association, Exchange Club, Central Turners, St. Paul's Lutheran Church, Lutheran Laymen's League; director, Evansville's Future, Inc.; married Martha Tiernan of Richmond, Ind., in June 1943; seven children; elected to the United States Senate on November 4, 1958; reelected November 3, 1964.

BIRCH BAYH, Democrat, of Terre Haute, Ind.; born January 22, 1928, in Terre Haute, Ind.; B.S. from Purdue University, School of Agriculture, 1951; studied government and social studies at Indiana State College; J.D. from Indiana University School of Law; served with U.S. Army in Europe; elected to four terms in Indiana House of Representatives; served as speaker for one term and as minority leader for two terms; member of Centenary Methodist Church in Terre Haute; married to the former Marvella Hern, Enid, Okla.; father of one son, Evan, age 9; elected to the United States Senate November 6, 1962, for the term beginning January 3, 1963.

REPRESENTATIVES

FIRST DISTRICT.—LAKE COUNTY. Population (1960), 513,269.

RAY J. MADDEN, Democrat, of Gary, Ind.; born in Waseca, Minn.; attended the public schools and was graduated from Sacred Heart Academy, Waseca, Minn., and from Creighton University, Omaha, Nebr., with LL. B. degree; elected municipal judge of Omaha, Nebr.; served in the Armed Forces during the First World War; city comptroller of Gary, Ind., 1935–38; treasurer of Lake County, Ind., 1938–42; member of the American Legion; attorney; elected to the 78th, 79th, 80th, 81st, 82d, 83d, 84th, 85th, 86th, 87th, 88th, and 89th Congresses.

SECOND DISTRICT.—COUNTIES: Benton, Carroll, Cass, Fulton, Jasper, Kosciusko, Newton, Porter, Pulaski, Starke, Tippecanoe, and White (12 counties). Population (1960), 357,309.

CHARLES A. HALLECK, Republican, of Rensselaer, was born in Jasper County, Ind., August 22, 1900, and has resided there all his life; attended grade and high schools in Rensselaer; was graduated from Indiana University with an A.B. degree in 1922 and with an LL. B. degree in 1924; elected a member of Phi Beta Kappa and Order of the Coif, and is also a member of Beta Theta Pi and Phi Delta Phi; served in World War I and is a member of the American Legion; married to Blanche White, of Indianapolis, and they have two children, Charles W. and Mrs. Walter R. Litchfield; was elected prosecuting attorney of the Jasper-Newton circuit in 1924, and was reelected four times; was elected to the 74th Congress at a special election held on January 29, 1935; reelected to the 75th and succeeding Congresses; majority leader in 80th and 83d Congresses; minority leader in 86th, 87th, and 88th Congresses.

THIRD DISTRICT.—Counties: Elkhart, La Porte, Marshall, and St. Joseph (4 counties). Population (1960), 472,958.

JOHN BRADEMAS, Democrat, of South Bend, Ind.; born in Mishawaka, Ind., March 2, 1927; graduate of South Bend Central High School; B. A. magna cum laude, 1949, Harvard University (Veterans National Scholar, Phi Beta Kappa); D. Phil. 1954, Oxford University (Rhodes Scholar for Indiana); served in the U.S. Navy, 1945–46; assistant professor of political science, St. Mary's College, Notre Dame, Ind.; executive assistant to Adlai E. Stevenson, 1955–56; during 1955, legislative assistant to United States Senator Pat McNamara of Michigan, and administrative assistant to Representative Thomas Ludlow Ashley of Ohio; member: First Methodist Church of South Bend; Portage Lodge, No. 675, F. & A. M.; Ahepa; Eagles; Moose; American Legion; elected to the 86th Congress on November 4, 1958; reelected to the 87th, 88th, and 89th Congresses.

FOURTH DISTRICT.—Counties: Adams, Allen, De Kalb, Lagrange, Noble, Steuben, Wells, and Whitley (8 counties). Population (1960), 390,010.

E. ROSS ADAIR, Republican, of Fort Wayne, Ind.; born at Albion, Noble County, Ind., December 14, 1907, son of Edwin L. and Alice Prickett Adair; grade and high school at Albion, graduating in 1924; Hillsdale (Mich.) College, A. B. 1928; the George Washington University Law School, LL. B. 1933; practicing attorney and probate commissioner of Allen County prior to election to Congress; called to active duty as a second lieutenant, QMC-Reserve, in September 1941, serving until October 1945; presently holding the rank of lieutenant colonel, Judge Advocate Reserve; awarded battle stars for the Normandy, Northern France, Ardennes, Rhine and Central European campaigns; married Marian Wood of Hillsdale, Mich., July 21, 1934; two children, Mrs. Caroline Adair Dimmers and Stephen Wood Adair; trustee, Hillsdale College; member of Methodist Church, Masonic bodies, Loyal Order of Moose, Elks, American Legion, Veterans of Foreign Wars, Delta Sigma Phi (past national president), Phi Alpha Delta, Allen County, Ind., and American Bar Associations; elected to 82d Congress on November 7, 1950; reelected to the 83d, 84th, 85th, 86th, 87th, 88th, and 89th Congresses.

FIFTH DISTRICT.—Counties: Blackford, Clinton, Grant, Howard, Huntington, Jay, Madison, Miami, Tipton, and Wabash (10 counties). Population (1960), 459,473.

J. EDWARD ROUSH, Democrat, of Huntington, Ind.; born in Barnsdall, Okla., September 12, 1920; has resided in Huntington County, Ind., since 1924; attended the elementary schools; was graduated from Huntington High School in 1938; Huntington (Ind.) College with A.B. degree, and Indiana University School of Law in 1949 with LL.B. degree; lawyer; served one term in Indiana Legislature in 1949; elected prosecuting attorney of Huntington County in 1954 for a 4-year term; served as an Infantry officer during World War II with approximately 4 years of service; was recalled into the Army in 1950, serving as a Counter Intelligence Corps agent; member of the Board of Education of the Church of the United Brethren in Christ; member of the Board of Trustees of Huntington College; member: Huntington County Bar Association (past president), Indiana State Bar Association, and American Bar Association; married the former Pauline Borton of Fayette, Ohio, and has four children; elected to the 86th Congress on November 4, 1958; reelected to the 87th, 88th, and 89th Congresses.

SIXTH DISTRICT.—Counties: Boone, Fountain, Hamilton, Hendricks, Montgomery, Parke, Putnam, Vermillion, Vigo, and Warren (10 counties). Population (1960), 333,783.

RICHARD LOWELL ROUDEBUSH, Republican of Noblesville, Ind.; born on a farm near Noblesville January 18, 1918; attended the schools of Hamilton County; graduated from Butler University in 1941, B.S. degree; during World War II served in the U.S. Army as a demolition specialist for the Ordnance Department in the Middle East, North African, and Italian Campaigns; awarded five battle stars; partner in the Roudebush Commission Co., handling livestock at the Indianapolis stockyards; married the former Marjorie Elliott of Indianapolis; one daughter, Karen and one son, Roy L.; member of the Veterans of Foreign Wars, serving as National Commander in 1957; American Legion, Disabled American Veterans, Masonic Lodge, Scottish Rite, Shrine, Flying Farmers, Indianapolis Livestock Exchange, 376th Bomb Group Veterans Association,

Elks Lodge, Sigma Chi, Kiwanis, Farm Bureau, Civil War Centennial Commission, and the Refuge Christian Church; elected to the 87th Congress November 8, 1960; reelected to the 88th and 89th Congresses; committee assignment: House Committee on Science and Astronautics, Manned Space Flight Subcommittee, and House District Committee.

SEVENTH DISTRICT.—Counties: Clay, Daviess, Gibson, Greene, Johnson, Knox, Martin, Monroe, Morgan, Owen, and Sullivan (11 counties). Population (1960), 329,213.

WILLIAM GILMER BRAY, Republican, Martinsville, Ind.; born Mooresville, Ind., June 17, 1903, the son of Gilmer and Dorcas (Mitchel) Bray; reared on a farm near Mooresville; graduated from Mooresville High School 1920; received LL. B. from Indiana University School of Law in 1927; served two terms as prosecuting attorney in Morgan County; returned to private practice in Martinsville; married Esther Debra of Warren, Ind., in 1930; one son, Richard, born March 1, 1934; an Army Reserve officer, was called to active duty June 25, 1941, with the rank of captain; served with tank units throughout the Pacific campaign, receiving the Silver Star; after the war, was transferred to Military Government and served 9 months in Korea as deputy property custodian; released from active duty in November 1946 with the rank of colonel and returned to private law practice in Martinsville; member of Friends Church, Masonic orders, Kiwanis Club, Acacia fraternity, Elks, Moose, Eagles, American Legion, and Veterans of Foreign Wars; elected to the 82d Congress on November 7, 1950; reelected to the 83d, 84th, 85th, 86th, 87th, 88th, and 89th Congresses.

EIGHTH DISTRICT.—Counties: Clark, Crawford, Dubois, Floyd, Harrison, Perry, Pike, Posey, Spencer, Vanderburgh, and Warrick (11 counties). Population (1960), 423,929.

WINFIELD K. DENTON, Democrat, of Evansville, Ind.; born October 28, 1896, and resided there throughout his entire life; practiced law since 1922; served as prosecutor of Vanderburgh County for two terms, and three terms in the Indiana State Legislature, during which time was minority leader in the 1941 session and caucus chairman in the 1939 session; appointed to the State Budget Committee by both Governors Townsend and Schricker; married Grace Abernethy, December 27, 1927; three daughters: Mrs. Beth Bamberger, Columbus, Ind.; Mary, Evansville, Ind.; and Mrs. David Ong, Cleveland, Ohio; member of the American Legion, Veterans of Foreign Wars; a Mason (32d degree K.T., Shriner), Elk, and Phi Kappa Psi Fraternity; enlisted as a private in World War I, was commissioned a second lieutenant as an aviator, and saw service in France; entered World War II when 46 years of age as a major and was promoted to lieutenant colonel, serving in the Judge Advocate General's office and assigned to the Air Corps; graduated from DePauw University in 1919 with A. B. degree, and from Harvard Law School in 1922, with LL. B. degree; is a member of the Trinity Methodist Church, Evansville, Ind.; elected to the 81st, 82d, 84th, 85th, 86th, 87th, 88th, and 89th Congresses.

NINTH   DISTRICT.—Counties: Bartholomew, Brown, Dearborn, Franklin, Jackson, Jefferson, Jennings, Lawrence, Ohio, Orange, Ripley, Scott, Switzerland, and Washington (14 counties). Population (1960), 290,596.

LEE HERBERT HAMILTON, Democrat, of Columbus, Ind.; born in Daytona Beach, Fla., April 20, 1931; graduated, Central High School, Evansville, Ind., 1948; from DePauw University (A.B., cum laude) in 1952; Goethe University, Frankfurt on Main, Germany, on scholarship for study and travel 1952–53; and Indiana University School of Law, J.D. 1956; married the former Nancy Ann Nelson August 21, 1954; three children, Tracy Lynn, Deborah Lee, and Douglas Nelson; practicing attorney in Columbus, Ind.; instructor in contracts and negotiables at American Banking Institute; member of Indiana, Illinois, and American bar associations; treasurer, Bartholomew County Young Democrats 1960–63 and president 1963–64; member of First Methodist Church in Columbus and active in church, civic, and community affairs; member of Rotary Club; received Distinguished Service Award, Junior Chamber of Commerce, in 1962; elected to the 89th Congress November 3, 1964.

TENTH DISTRICT.—COUNTIES: Decatur, Delaware, Fayette, Hancock, Henry, Randolph, Rush, Shelby, Union, and Wayne (10 counties). Population (1960), 394,391.

RALPH HARVEY, Republican, of Henry County, Ind., was born August 9, 1901, on a farm near Mount Summit; after being graduated from Mount Summit High School, earned a B.S.A. degree at Purdue University, and returned to his home community to serve as a vocational agricultural instructor from 1923 to 1928; an active farmer, he is married (Charline Bowers), and is a member of the Christian Church, Masonic orders, Kiwanis Club, Alpha Gamma Rho, the Indiana Farm Bureau; entered politics as a county councilman appointed to succeed his father and twice was elected to the office; in 1942, was elected to the House of Representatives of the Indiana General Assembly, and served in the sessions of 1943, 1945, and 1947; in a special election, November 4, 1947, was elected to the 80th Congress; reelected to the 81st, 82d, 83d, 84th, and 85th Congresses; elected to the 87th Congress November 8, 1960; reelected to the 88th and 89th Congresses.

ELEVENTH DISTRICT.—MARION COUNTY. Population (1960), 697,567.

ANDREW JACOBS, JR., Democrat, of Indianapolis, Ind.; born in Indianapolis, February 24, 1932; graduated from Shortridge High School, Indianapolis, 1949; active duty U.S. Marine Corps, 1950–52, with Infantry company in Korea in 1951, discharged as private first class; B.S. degree from Indiana University, 1955; LL.B. degree from Indiana University, 1958; practicing attorney since 1958; member, Indianapolis Bar Association; member, Indiana House of Representatives, 1959–60; member, American Legion; member, SS. Peter and Paul Cathedral; unmarried; elected to 89th Congress November 3, 1964.

IOWA

(Population (1960), 2,757,537)

SENATORS

BOURKE BLAKEMORE HICKENLOOPER, Republican, of Cedar Rapids, Linn County, Iowa; born in Blockton, Taylor County, Iowa, July 21, 1896, son of Nathan O. and Margaret A. (Blakemore) Hickenlooper; graduated Blockton High School, 1914; graduated Iowa State College, B. S.; Law School, University of Iowa, J. D.; honorary degrees, Parsons College, LL. D., and Loras College, LL. D.; Elmira College, D. C. L.; Upper Iowa University, LL. D.; first officers' training camp, Fort Snelling, Minn., 1917; served in Three Hundred and Thirty-ninth Field Artillery in United States and France until spring of 1919; practiced law, Cedar Rapids, Iowa, beginning 1922; elected to Iowa Legislature (house) 1934; reelected 1936; elected Lieutenant Governor of Iowa, 1938; reelected 1940; elected Governor of Iowa, November 1942; married Verna E. Bensch, of Lansing, Iowa, 1927; two children, Mrs. Russell Oberlin, and David B.; member various fraternal and professional organizations and Methodist Church; elected to the United States Senate in November 1944; reelected November 1950; reelected November 1956; reelected November 1962.

JACK RICHARD MILLER, Republican, of Sioux City, Iowa; born in Chicago, Ill., June 6, 1916; moved from Wilmette, Ill., to Sioux City with parents in 1932 and to Bedford, Iowa, in 1937; A.B. (cum laude) Creighton University, 1938; M.A. (K. of C. Fellow) Catholic University, 1939; LL.B. Columbia University School of Law, 1946; postgraduate work, State University of Iowa College of Law, 1946; LL.D. (honorary) Parsons College, 1962; served with U.S. Air Force from January 1942 to January 1946, attaining rank of lieutenant colonel, service including Air Force Headquarters, Washington, D.C., faculty of U.S. Army Command and General Staff College, Fort Leavenworth, Kans., and China-Burma-India Theater of Operations; admitted to Iowa and Nebraska bars, 1946, and United States Supreme Court and District of Columbia bars, 1949; attorney, office of chief counsel, Internal Revenue Service, Washington, D.C., 1947 and 1948; professorial lecturer in taxation, George Washington University, 1948; assistant professor of law, University of Notre Dame College of Law, 1948 and 1949; private practice as tax lawyer and farm tax writer, Sioux City, Iowa, 1949–60; member of Iowa House of Representatives, 1955 and 1956, and of Iowa Senate, 1957–60; member of Catholic Church, Rotary, American Legion, Veterans of Foreign Wars, Moose, Eagles, Elks, Knights of Columbus, John Carroll Society (board of governors), Izaak Walton League, U.C.T., Air Force Association, R.O.A., Iowa and American bar associations, and American Law Institute (life); colonel in U.S. Air Force Reserve; married Isabelle (Jerry) Browning of Windber, Pa., at Bolling Field, D.C., 1942; four children—Janice (Mrs. John Flanagan), Judy, Jimmy, and Jaynie; elected to United States Senate November 8, 1960, for 6-year term beginning January 3, 1961; member of Committee on Agriculture, Committee on Armed Services, Joint Senate-House Economic Committee, and Special Committee on Problems of the Aging.

REPRESENTATIVES

FIRST DISTRICT.—COUNTIES: Cedar, Des Moines, Henry, Iowa, Jefferson, Johnson, Lee, Louisa, Muscatine, Scott, Van Buren, and Washington (12 counties). Population (1960), 403,048.

JOHN RICHARD SCHMIDHAUSER, Democrat, of Iowa City, Iowa; born in the Bronx, New York, January 3, 1922; attended the public schools of New York and Maryland; served as an enlisted man in the U.S. Navy including duty on the aircraft carrier U.S.S. *Bon Homme Richard* in the Philippine campaign, the Battle of Okinawa, and the final assault on Japan under Admiral Halsey, August 1941 to December 1945; graduated from the University of Delaware (B.A.) 1949; the University of Virginia (M.A.) 1952, and the University of Virginia (Ph. D.) 1954; professor of constitutional law at State University of Iowa 1954–64; married; six children, four boys and two girls; precinct committeeman and Democratic county chairman of Johnson County, Iowa; member of the American Association of University Professors, the American Political Science Association, the Izaak Walton League, and the Unitarian Church; elected to the 89th Congress November 3, 1964.

SECOND DISTRICT.—COUNTIES: Allamakee, Buchanan, Clayton, Clinton, Delaware, Dubuque, Fayette, Jackson, Jones, Linn, and Winneshiek (11 counties). Population (1960), 442,406.

JOHN C. CULVER, Democrat, of Marion, Iowa; born in Rochester, Minn., August 8, 1932; attended Johnson School and graduated from Franklin High School, Cedar Rapids, 1950; A.B. (cum laude) Harvard College 1954; Lionel de Jersey Harvard Scholar, Emmanuel College, Cambridge University; served 39 months in U.S. Marine Corps, captain USMCR; LL.B. Harvard 1962; law firm, McGuire, Bernau & Culver, Cedar Rapids; married to former Ann Cooper of Cedar Rapids, Iowa; three children—Christina, Rebecca, and Catherine; served as dean of men of the Harvard University Summer School 1960; member county and state bar associations; Presbyterian; served as legislative assistant to Senator Edward M. Kennedy 1962–63; elected to 89th Congress November 3, 1964.

THIRD DISTRICT.—COUNTIES: Black Hawk, Bremer, Butler, Cerro Gordo, Chickasaw, Floyd, Franklin, Grundy, Hamilton, Hancock, Hardin, Howard, Mitchell, Winnebago, Worth, and Wright (16 counties). Population (1960), 403,442.

H. R. GROSS, Republican, of Waterloo, Iowa; born, Arispe, Iowa, June 30, 1899, and raised on a farm; education, rural schools, University of Missouri School of Journalism; profession, newspaper reporter and editor from 1921 to 1935; radio news commentator from 1935 to 1948; military service, Mexican Border Service 1916, American Expeditionary Forces World War I; member Presbyterian Church, Masonic Lodge, Elks, American Legion, Veterans of Foreign Wars; married to Hazel E. Webster, Cresco, Iowa, June 29, 1929; two sons, Phil and Alan; elected to the 81st Congress on November 2, 1948; reelected to the 82d, 83d, 84th, 85th, 86th, 87th, 88th, and 89th Congresses.

FOURTH DISTRICT.—COUNTIES: Appanoose, Benton, Clarke, Davis, Decatur, Jasper, Keokuk, Lucas, Mahaska, Marion, Marshall, Monroe, Poweshiek, Ringgold, Tama, Union, Wapello, Warren, and Wayne (19 counties). Population (1960), 366,119.

BERT ANDREW BANDSTRA, Democrat, of Pella, Iowa; born on a farm between Eddyville and Albia, January 25, 1922, and in 1925 moved to another farm in Mahaska County near Taintor; attended Taintor Independent School and New Sharon High School; enlisted as a seaman in the U.S. Navy in March 1942, served in the Solomon Islands and Okinawa campaigns, received the Presidential Unit Citation, and was honorably discharged as a second class petty officer in December 1945; resumed education and graduated from Central College at Pella (B.A. degree cum laude in 1950) and from the University of Michigan (LL.B. degree in 1953); married Theressa Van Wyngarden August 24, 1950; two sons, Bruce Alan and Thomas Anno; was admitted to the bar in 1953 and commenced practice of law in Pella, Iowa; Marion County attorney January 1955 to June 1959; member of the Marion County Bar Association, the Iowa State Bar Association, the American Legion, and the Christian Reformed Church; assistant to Congressman Neal Smith January 1959 to February 1964; elected to the 89th Congress November 3, 1964.

FIFTH DISTRICT.—COUNTIES: Boone, Polk, Story, and Webster (4 counties). Population (1960), 391,489.

NEAL SMITH, Democrat, of Altoona, Iowa; born March 23, 1920, at Hedrick, Iowa; married Beatrix Havens; two children, Douglas and Sharon; farmer and lives on farm near Altoona, Iowa; engaged in the practice of law in Des Moines, Iowa—clients included about 50 school boards in Iowa; graduated Drake University Law School; attended Missouri University College of Liberal Arts and Syracuse University Schools of Public and Business Administration; 4–H Club member and leader for 10 years; has farmed for himself since 1937 except for time in armed services and some of the time in college; spent 4 years in World War II; citations include 9 battle stars, Air Medal, 4 Oak Leaf Clusters, and Order of the Purple Heart; elected National President Young Democratic Clubs of America 1953—served usual 2-year term 1953 to 1955; former chairman, Polk County Board of Social Welfare (a nonpaying civic board which distributed several million dollars per year to needy families and elder citizens); former assistant county attorney for Polk County, Iowa; member of Disabled American Veterans, Masonic Order, and various farm, school, and service organizations; elected to 86th Congress, November 4, 1958; reelected to the 87th, 88th, and 89th Congresses.

SIXTH DISTRICT.—COUNTIES: Buena Vista, Calhoun, Cherokee, Clay, Dickinson, Emmet, Humboldt, Ida, Kossuth, Lyon, O'Brien, Osceola, Palo Alto, Plymouth, Pocahontas, Sac, Sioux, and Woodbury (18 counties). Population (1960), 397,877.

STANLEY LLOYD GREIGG, Democrat, of Sioux City, Iowa; born in Ireton, Sioux County, Iowa, May 7, 1931; moved to Hawarden, Iowa, in 1938 and to Sioux City in 1941; graduated from East High School in 1950, from Morningside College (B.A.) in 1954, receiving a fellowship to Syracuse University and studied at Maxwell Graduate School of Citizenship and Public Affairs; while working for a master's degree at Syracuse served on the dean of men's staff; served in the U.S. Navy 1957 to 1959; returned to Morningside College in 1959 and named dean of men; elected to Sioux City Council in 1961 and selected as mayor in 1964; affiliated with many civic and fraternal organizations; member of the Lutheran Church; elected to the 89th Congress November 3, 1964.

SEVENTH DISTRICT.—COUNTIES: Adair, Adams, Audubon, Carroll, Cass, Crawford, Dallas, Fremont, Greene, Guthrie, Harrison, Madison, Mills, Monona, Montgomery, Page, Pottawattamie, Shelby, and Taylor (19 counties). Population (1960), 353,156.

JOHN ROBERT HANSEN, Democrat, of Manning, Iowa; born in Manning, August 24, 1901, son of Herman P. and Laura Karstens Hansen; graduated from Manning High School; attended State University of Iowa 1919–21; married the former Mary Louise Osthoff of Lincoln, Nebr., June 21, 1928; two sons, Robert and John; president and general manager of Dultmeier Manufacturing Co., Manning, Iowa, 1932–62; president of Dultmeier Sales, Omaha, Nebr., 1934–57 and a major partner since 1957; member of—National Farm Equipment Manufacturers Association, Manning General Hospital Board, Masons, Order of Eastern Star, Rotary International, Presbyterian Church (ordained elder), Lions, Manning Chamber of Commerce, Alpha Sigma Phi, Iowa Welfare Association, and Iowa Mental Health Association; Carroll County Democratic chairman 1944–52; Sixth District Democratic chairman 1953–57; alternate delegate to Chicago Convention 1944 and delegate to Philadelphia Convention in 1948; member of Iowa Commission for Interstate Affairs 1959–61, Executive Council Governor's Alcoholism Commission, and State Board of Control 1957–60; nominee for Lieutenant Governor 1960; area manager, U.S. Savings Bond Division of Treasury Department, 1962–64; past member, Southwest Iowa Council Boy Scouts of America, Carroll County Defense Savings Bond Staff, and Carroll County Red Cross Board; elected to the 89th Congress November 3, 1964.

KANSAS

(Population (1960), 2,178,611)

SENATORS

FRANK CARLSON, Republican, of Concordia, Kans.; farmer-stockman; born January 23, 1893, at Concordia, Kans.; attended rural schools, Concordia High School, Concordia Normal and Business College, and Kansas State College; World War veteran; member of Kansas Legislature 1929 and 1931 sessions; chairman of Republican State Committee 1932; member of Masonic bodies and the Baptist Church; married August 26, 1919; one daughter, Eunice Marie; elected from the Sixth Congressional District, Kansas, to the 74th Congress on November 6, 1934; reelected to the 75th, 76th, 77th, 78th, and 79th Congresses; elected Governor of Kansas November 5, 1946; reelected November 2, 1948; served as a member of the State and Federal Affairs Committee of the Hoover Committee for Reorganization of the Executive Branch of the Government; chairman of the Interstate Oil Compact Commission 1949; chairman of the National Governors' Conference 1949; chairman, Council of State Governments 1950; vice chairman, President's National Safety Conference 1950; received honorary degrees of doctor of laws from Bob Jones University in 1951, from Springfield College, Springfield, Mass., in 1953, and from William Jewell College, Liberty, Mo., in 1955; honorary degree, doctor of laws, from St. Benedict's College, Atchison, Kans., 1961; honorary degree, doctor of laws, Kansas State University, Manhattan, Kans., 1962; president of the International Council for Christian Leadership; member of the board of governors of the Menninger Foundation, Topeka, Kans., the Institute of Logopedics, Wichita, Kans., and the Agricultural Hall of Fame, 1964 United States Delegate to United Nations; elected to the Senate November 7, 1950, for unexpired term; elected to the Senate November 7, 1950, for regular term ending January 3, 1957; reelected November 6, 1956, for regular term ending January 1963; reelected November 6, 1962, for regular term ending January 3, 1969; member of Post Office and Civil Service, Finance, Foreign Relations, and Joint Committee on Internal Revenue Taxation.

JAMES BLACKWOOD PEARSON, Republican, of Prairie Village, Kans.; born in Nashville, Tenn., May 7, 1920; moved with his family to Virginia; attended Virginia schools; graduated from the University of Virginia Law School in 1950; attended Duke University 1940–42; interrupted schooling to serve as a Navy pilot based at Olathe, Kans., Naval Air Station 1943–46; married the former Martha Mitchell of Johnson City, Kans., in 1946; four children—Jimmy, Tommy, Billy, and Laura Alice; admitted to the bar in 1950 and began practice at Mission, Kans., in 1950; city attorney for Westwood, Fairway, and Lenexa 1952–61; assistant county attorney 1952–54; probate judge of Johnson County 1954–56; member of the State senate 1956–60; was not a candidate for reelection; returned to law practice; was the State campaign manager for Governor Anderson's successful race in 1960 and served as State Republican chairman for a short term thereafter; appointed to the United States Senate January 31, 1962, to fill the vacancy caused by the death of Senator Andrew F. Schoeppel and elected November 6, 1962, for the term ending January 3, 1967.

REPRESENTATIVES

FIRST DISTRICT.—COUNTIES: Barber, Barton, Cheyenne, Clark, Cloud, Comanche, Decatur, Edwards, Ellis, Ellsworth, Finney, Ford, Gove, Graham, Grant, Gray, Greeley, Hamilton, Harper, Haskell, Hodgeman, Jewell, Kearny, Kingman, Kiowa, Lane, Lincoln, Logan, Meade, Mitchell, Morton, Ness, Norton, Osborne, Ottawa, Pawnee, Phillips, Pratt, Rawlins, Reno, Republic, Rice, Rooks, Rush, Russell, Saline, Scott, Seward, Sheridan, Sherman, Smith, Stafford, Stanton, Stevens, Thomas, Trego, Wallace and Wichita (58 counties). Population (1960), 539,592.

ROBERT J. DOLE, Republican, of Russell, Kans.; born in Russell, July 22, 1923, son of Doran R. and Bina Dole; graduate of Russell High School 1941; Washburn Municipal University, Topeka, Kans., A.B. 1952 and LL.B. in 1952; also undergraduate work at University of Kansas and University of Arizona; married Phyllis E. Holden of Concord, N.H.; one daughter, Robin; during World War II served as a combat Infantry officer in Italy with the 10th Mountain Division; wounded twice and was hospitalized more than 39 months; awarded Bronze Star with

Cluster for heroic achievement; member of State house of representatives, 1951 session; served four terms as Russell County attorney 1953–61; engaged in the private practice of law in Russell, Kans., since 1953; member of the Methodist Church, Masonic Lodge, Isis Shrine, American Legion, VFW, Kappa Sigma Fraternity, Kiwanis, Elks, and the 4–H Fair Association; elected to the 87th Congress November 8, 1960; reelected to the 88th and 89th Congresses.

SECOND DISTRICT.—Counties: Atchison, Brown, Clay, Doniphan, Geary, Jackson, Leavenworth, Marshall, Nemaha, Pottawatomie, Riley, Shawnee, Wabaunsee, Washington, and all that portion of Wyandotte County lying outside the boundaries of the city of Kansas City, as of April 21, 1961. Population (1960), 445,193.

CHESTER L. MIZE, Republican, of Atchison, Kans.; born in Atchison December 25, 1917; attended the public schools; student at the School of Business Administration, University of Kansas, 1935–39; joined the U.S.N.R. in 1940; served in the U.S. Navy during World War II, South Pacific Theater, 1941–45; returned to civilian life as a lieutenant commander in the U.S.N.R.; married the former Betty Muchnic of Atchison, Kans.; three children, David, Ann, and Janet; treasurer of Blish, Mize & Silliman Hardware Co. 1945–51; vice president of Valley Co., Inc., general investment company, 1951–64; owned and operated a cattle ranch in New Mexico and a farm in Atchison County, Kans.; past president of University of Kansas Alumni Association, past chairman of the Greater University Fund (University of Kansas); member, University of Kansas Athletic Board and the Advisory Board of the School of Business Administration (University of Kansas); past member of the board of the Atchison public school system; vestryman of the Trinity Episcopal Church; chairman, board of trustees, Mount St. Scholastica of Atchison; chairman of Atchison County Savings Bond Drives for several years; member of American Legion, V.F.W., Kansas Farm Bureau, Elks, Kansas Chamber of Commerce, and Phi Delta Theta; elected to the 89th Congress November 3, 1964.

THIRD DISTRICT.—Counties: Anderson, Douglas, Franklin, Jefferson, Johnson, Linn, Miami, and the city of Kansas City in Wyandotte County as its boundaries were constituted on April 21, 1961. Population (1960), 378,834.

ROBERT F. ELLSWORTH, Republican, of Lawrence, Kans.; born June 11, 1926, in Lawrence, Kans.; attended public schools of Lawrence; B.S. degree in mechanical engineering, University of Kansas; LL. B., University of Michigan; admitted to the bar in 1949 and began practice of law in Springfield, Mass.; in 1953 and 1954 was legal assistant for maritime affairs to vice chairman, Federal Maritime Board, U.S. Department of Commerce; since 1954 engaged in private practice of law in Lawrence, Kans.; admitted to practice law in the highest state courts of Massachusetts and Kansas, U.S. Patent Office, U.S. Treasury Department, U.S. District Court, U.S. Supreme Court; faculty, University of Kansas School of Business, in 1956 and 1957; married to the former Vivian Sies; one son, Robert William; one daughter, Ann Elizabeth; lieutenant commander, USNR, active duty World War II and Korean Conflict; member American Legion, Veterans of Foreign Wars, Optimist Club, Beta Theta Pi, Phi Delta Phi; Episcopalian; elected to 87th Congress November 8, 1960; reelected to the 88th and 89th Congresses.

FOURTH DISTRICT.—Counties: Chase, Dickinson, Harvey, McPherson, Marion, Morris, and Sedgwick (7 counties). Population (1960), 441,409.

GARNER E. SHRIVER, Republican, of Wichita, Kans.; born July 6, 1912, in Towanda, Kans.; attended the public schools of Towanda and Wichita; moved to Wichita in 1925; graduate of University of Wichita in 1934 (postgraduate study at University of Southern California in 1936) and Washburn Law School, LL.B. degree, in 1940; married Martha Jane Currier in 1941; three children— Mrs. Kay Leroux, David, and Linda; worked for Fox-Vliet Drug Co., of Wichita 1934–36; instructor in English speech, South Haven High School, South Haven, Kans., in 1936 and 1937; engaged in law practice since 1940; during World War II served for 3 years in the U.S. Navy as an enlisted man and officer; State representative, 1947–51 and State senator 1953–60; member of American, Kansas and

Wichita bar associations, Veterans of Foreign Wars, American Legion, National Sojourners, Albert Pike Masonic Lodge, Wichita Consistory, DeMolay Legion of Honor, and College Hill Methodist Church; elected to the 87th Congress November 8, 1960; reelected to the 88th and 89th Congresses.

FIFTH DISTRICT.—Counties: Allen, Bourbon, Butler, Chautauqua, Cherokee, Coffey, Cowley, Crawford, Elk, Greenwood, Labette, Lyon, Montgomery, Neosho, Osage, Sumner, Wilson, and Woodson (18 counties). Population (1960), 373,583.

JOE SKUBITZ, Republican, of Pittsburg, Kans.; born in Frontenac, Crawford County, Kans., son of Joe Skubitz and Mary Youvan; attended grade school in Ringo, Kans.; high school in Girard and Frontenac, Kans.; graduate of Kansas State College, Pittsburg, Kans., receiving B.S. and M.S. degrees; attended law school at Washburn University, Topeka, Kans., and received LL.B. degree from George Washington University, Washington, D.C.; licensed to practice law in Kansas and the District of Columbia; received special citation from Kansas State College, Pittsburg, Kans.; served as administrative assistant to Senators Clyde M. Reed and Andrew F. Schoeppel; married Mary Jess McClellan, daughter of Dr. George B. and Lillian McClellan, Weir, Kans., September 27, 1930; one son, Dan Joseph Skubitz, who married Betty Mayhew; two granddaughters, Danette and Suzanne; elected to the 88th Congress November 6, 1962; reelected to the 89th Congress.

KENTUCKY

(Population (1960), 3,038,156)

SENATORS

JOHN SHERMAN COOPER, Republican, of Somerset, Ky.; born Somerset, Pulaski County, Ky., August 23, 1901, son of John Sherman and Helen Gertrude (Tartar) Cooper; married Lorraine Rowan Shevlin in 1955; educated public schools in Somerset; Centre College, 1918–19; Yale College, A.B., 1923; Harvard Law School, 1923–25; honorary degrees: LL.D., Centre College, University of Kentucky, Georgetown College, Berea College, Eastern Kentucky State College, Yale University; L.H.D., Lincoln Memorial University; D.C.L., Nasson College, Maine; served as member Lower House, Kentucky Legislature; two terms as county judge, Pulaski County, Ky., circuit judge, 28th Judicial District, Ky.; elected United States Senate 1946 to fill unexpired term; defeated 1948; elected 1952 to fill unexpired term; defeated 1954; elected 1956 to fill unexpired term; reelected 1960 for term ending January 1967; member of Committees on Agriculture and Forestry, Public Works, Small Business, and Rules and Administration; member, 1964, The President's Commission on the Assassination of President John F. Kennedy; served as U.S. delegate to 1949–50–51 sessions of General Assembly of United Nations; adviser to Secretary of State Dean Acheson, London and Brussels meetings, 1950, NATO Council of Ministers; appointed by President Eisenhower Ambassador to India and Nepal January 1955, served until August 1956, resigned to become candidate for U.S. Senate; veteran World War II; enlisted as private, U.S. Army, 1942; received Officers Candidate School commission as second lieutenant, 1943; served Third U.S. Army from July 1944 in Normandy, France, Luxembourg, German campaigns; awarded Bronze Star Medal; after close of war, at Munich, headed reorganization German judicial system of Bavaria; discharged as captain February 1946; member law firm of Gardner, Morrison & Rogers, Washington, D.C., 1949–51; member of American Bar and Kentucky Bar Associations; Yale University Council; board of trustees Centre College, Ky.; American Legion; Veterans of Foreign Wars; Rotary International; Beta Theta Pi; Baptist.

THRUSTON B. MORTON, Republican, of Louisville, Ky.; born in Louisville, Ky., August 19, 1907; was graduated from Yale University in 1929 with A.B. degree; formerly chairman of the board, Ballard & Ballard Co., Inc., Louisville, Ky.; former director of various civic organizations and business enterprises; 51 months active duty in the United States Navy; married Belle Clay Lyons of Louisville, Ky., in 1931; two sons, both married; four grandchildren; elected to the 80th Congress on November 5, 1946; reelected to the 81st and 82d Congresses; Assistant Secretary of State from January 1953 to March 1956; elected to United States Senate on November 6, 1956; reelected November 6, 1962; chairman of the Republican National Committee, 1959–61; chairman of the Republican Senatorial Campaign Committee, 1963–; member of Finance and Commerce Committees; member Republican Policy Committee.

REPRESENTATIVES

FIRST DISTRICT.—COUNTIES: Allen, Ballard, Butler, Caldwell, Calloway, Carlisle, Christian, Crittenden, Fulton, Graves, Hickman, Livingston, Logan, Lyon, McCracken, Marshall, Muhlenberg, Simpson, Todd, and Trigg (20 counties). Population (1960), 350,839.

FRANK A. STUBBLEFIELD, Democrat, of Murray, Ky.; born in Murray, Ky., April 5, 1907; graduated from Murray High School and from the University of Kentucky College of Commerce with B. S. degree; retail drug business; member of the Kentucky Railroad Commission since 1951; married; three daughters; elected to the 86th Congress on November 4, 1958; reelected to the 87th, 88th, and 89th Congresses.

SECOND DISTRICT.—COUNTIES: Barren, Breckinridge, Daviess, Edmonson, Grayson, Hancock, Hart, Henderson, Hopkins, McLean, Meade, Metcalfe, Ohio, Union, Warren, and Webster (16 counties). Population (1960), 357,627.

WILLIAM H. NATCHER, Democrat, of Bowling Green, Warren County, Ky.; born in Bowling Green, Ky.; educated in the public schools of Bowling Green, Ky., and high school at Ogden Preparatory Department; A.B., degree, Western Kentucky State College, Bowling Green, Ky.; LL.B. degree, Ohio State University, Columbus, Ohio; married to Miss Virginia Reardon, of Bowling Green, Ky., on June 17, 1937; two daughters: Celeste White, 25, and Louise Lewter, 21; practicing attorney, Bowling Green, Ky., since March 18, 1934; Federal conciliation commissioner 1936–37 for Western District of Kentucky; elected county attorney of Warren County in 1937 and served three 4-year terms; elected Commonwealth attorney of the 8th Judicial District, composed of Allen and Warren Counties, in 1951 and served until August 15, 1953, having been elected to Congress; Baptist; member of Kiwanis club, Odd Fellows, American Legion Post 23, and 40 and 8 Mammoth Cave Voiture 1146; past president of the Bowling Green Bar Association; past president of the Young Democratic Clubs of Kentucky, 1941–46; during World War II served in the United States Navy from October 1942 to December 1945; elected to the 83d Congress August 1, 1953; reelected to 84th, 85th, 86th, 87th, 88th, and 89th Congresses; member, Committee on Appropriations; home address, 638 East Main, Bowling Green, Ky.; district office: 414 East 10th Street.

THIRD DISTRICT.—JEFFERSON COUNTY. Population (1960), 610,947.

CHARLES ROWLAND PEASLEE FARNSLEY, Democrat, of Louisville, Ky.; born in Louisville March 28, 1907, son of Burrel Hopson and Anna May (Peaslee) Farnsley; LL.B., University of Louisville, 1930, A.B. 1942, LL.D. (hon. causa) 1950; LL.D. (hon. causa) Wesleyan University, Middletown, Conn., 1959; lawyer; married Nancy Hall Carter, February 27, 1937; children—Mrs. Robert Bird, Jr., Mrs. Ronald Gascoyne, Alexander Farnsley IV, Burrel Charles Peaslee, Douglass Charles Ellerbe; practiced law, 1930–48 and 1954–64; trustee, University of Louisville, 1946–48 and secretary, board of trustees, 1947–48; curator, Transylvania University, Lexington, Ky., 1947–58; member, Kentucky Legislature, 1936–40; mayor, city of Louisville, 1948–54; member, board of trustees, Louisville Free Public Library, 1943–48; president, Louisville Philharmonic Society, 1948; member, Society Colonial Wars, Delta Upsilon, Omicron Delta Kappa, Episcopalian, Mason; clubs: Louisville Country, Pendennis, Wynn Stay, Filson, Harmony Landing (Louisville), National Democratic, Century, Grolier (N.Y.C.); elected to the 89th Congress November 3, 1964.

FOURTH DISTRICT—COUNTIES: Anderson, Boone, Bullitt, Campbell, Carroll, Gallatin, Green, Hardin, Kenton, Larue, Marion, Mercer, Nelson, Oldham, Shelby, Spencer, Taylor, Trimble, and Washington (19 counties). Population (1960), 478,783.

FRANK CHELF, Democrat, of Lebanon, Ky.; born in Elizabethtown, Ky., September 22, 1910; parents, Judge Weed S. Chelf and Hallie Wrather Chelf; at death of parents, was placed in Masonic Widows and Orphans Home of Kentucky; attended St. Mary's College, St. Mary, Ky., and Centre College, Danville, Ky.; received LL.B. degree, Cumberland University, Lebanon, Tenn.; married Louise Rash, North Middletown, Ky.; children—Caroline, Bonnie, and Frank, Jr.; elected prosecuting attorney, Marion County, three consecutive 4-year terms; took leave of absence and served in World War II with U.S. Army Air Forces; was a major when retired for physical disability; member, Phi Delta Theta, American Legion (40 and 8), V. F. W., Knights Templar, Eastern Star; served as chairman special House judiciary subcommittee that investigated Department of Justice in 1952; elected to 79th Congress; reelected continuously since; member, Judiciary Committee.

FIFTH DISTRICT.—COUNTIES: Adair, Bell, Casey, Clay, Clinton, Cumberland, Estill, Harlan, Jackson, Knox, Laurel, Leslie, McCreary, Monroe, Owsley, Pulaski, Rockcastle, Russell, Wayne, and Whitley (20 counties). Population (1960), 365,140.

TIM LEE CARTER, Republican, of Tompkinsville, Ky.; born in Tompkinsville, Ky., September 2, 1910, son of James Clark and Idru Tucker Carter; educated in public schools of Tompkinsville, Ky.; A.B., Western Kentucky State College, 1934; M.D., University of Tennessee, 1937; interned U.S. Marine Hospital and Chicago Maternity Center; volunteered for military service World War II, served 42 months as combat medic; captain, 38th Infantry Division; received Combat Medical Badge and Bronze Star Medal; married the former Kathleen Bradshaw of Tompkinsville; one son; practicing physician; member Kentucky and American Medical Associations, Kentucky and American Academy of General Practice; American Legion, V.F.W., 32d Degree Mason, Shriner; elected to the 89th Congress November 3, 1964.

SIXTH DISTRICT.—Counties: Bourbon, Boyle, Bracken, Clark, Fayette, Franklin, Garrard, Grant, Harrison, Henry, Jessamine, Lincoln, Madison, Montgomery, Nicholas, Owen, Pendleton, Powell, Robertson, Scott, and Woodford (21 counties). Population (1960), 411,545.

JOHN CLARENCE WATTS, Democrat, of Jessamine County, Ky.; born Nicholasville, Ky., July 9, 1902; graduate Nicholasville High School, 1921; A. B. and LL. B. University of Kentucky 1925, 1927; lawyer, farmer, and banker; police judge, city of Nicholasville 1929–33; county attorney, Jessamine County, Ky., 1933–45; member and majority leader, house of representatives, Kentucky State Legislature, 1947–48; commissioner of motor transportation, Commonwealth of Kentucky, 1948–51; county chairman, Democratic Party, Jessamine County, Ky., 28 years; elected to 82d Congress, special election April 14, 1951; reelected each subsequent Congress; member, Committee on Ways and Means; married Miss Nora Wilburn, Lexington, Ky.; one daughter, Lillian Frances, age 16.

SEVENTH DISTRICT.—Counties: Bath, Boyd, Breathitt, Carter, Elliott, Fleming, Floyd, Greenup, Johnson, Knott, Lawrence, Lee, Letcher, Lewis, Magoffin, Martin, Mason, Menifee, Morgan, Perry, Pike, Rowan, and Wolfe (23 counties). Population (1960), 463,275.

CARL D. PERKINS, Democrat, of Hindman, Knott County, Ky.; born in Hindman, Ky., October 15, 1912, where he still resides; son of J. E. and Dora Calhoun Perkins; educated in the Knott County grade schools and Hindman High School; attended Caney Junior College; studied law at Jefferson School of Law, Louisville, Ky., graduating in 1935 and began practice of law; married Miss Verna Johnson, of Knott County, Ky.; one son, Carl Christopher, born August 6, 1954; member of the American Legion and Masons; Baptist; served an unexpired term in 1939 as commonwealth attorney from thirty-first judicial district; member of Kentucky General Assembly from the ninety-ninth district in 1940; elected Knott County attorney in 1941 and reelected in 1945; resigned January 1, 1948, to become counsel for department of highways, Frankfort, Ky.; served in World War II, and saw service in European theater, participating in battles of northern France, the Ardennes, the Rhineland, and central Europe; elected on November 2, 1948, to the 81st Congress; reelected to the 82d, 83d, 84th, 85th, 86th, 87th, 88th, and 89th Congresses.

LOUISIANA

(Population (1960), 3,257,022)

SENATORS

ALLEN JOSEPH ELLENDER, Democrat, of Houma, La.; born in Montegut, Terrebonne Parish, La., September 24, 1890; lawyer and farmer; graduate of St. Aloysius College, New Orleans, La., and Tulane University of Louisiana, at New Orleans, with degrees of M. A. and LL. B.; married to Miss Helen Calhoun Donnelly (died September 30, 1949); one son, Allen J., Jr.; served in World War I; city attorney of Houma, 1913–15; district attorney, Terrebonne Parish, 1915–16; delegate to Constitutional Convention of Louisiana in 1921; member of the house of representatives of Louisiana, 1924–36; floor leader, 1928–32, during administration of the late Huey P. Long, Governor; speaker of the house of representatives, 1932–36; Democratic nominee for United States Senator from Louisiana, and elected without opposition in the general election held on November 3, 1936, for the term ending January 3, 1943; reelected November 3, 1942, in the general election, without opposition, for the term ending January 3, 1949; reelected without opposition in the general election held on November 2, 1948, for the term ending January 3, 1955; again reelected without opposition in the general election held on November 2, 1954, for the term ending January 3, 1961; reelected November 8, 1960, for the term ending January 3, 1967; Democratic national committeeman from Louisiana, 1939–40.

RUSSELL B. LONG, Democrat; born in Shreveport, La., November 3, 1918, of Huey P. and Rose McConnell Long; attended public schools in Shreveport, Baton Rouge, and New Orleans, La.; graduate of Louisiana State University, B. A. degree in 1941, LL. B. degree in 1942; lawyer; admitted to Louisiana bar in June 1942; member of Delta Kappa Epsilon, Omicron Delta Kappa, Order of the Coif, Tau Kappa Alpha, Phi Delta Phi, Lions, Elks, and American Legion; lieutenant, United States Naval Reserve; veteran of World War II; married Katherine Hattic; two daughters, Rita Katherine and Pamela Rust; elected to United States Senate on November 2, 1948, to fill unexpired term of the late John H. Overton; reelected November 7, 1950, for 6-year term beginning January 3, 1951; reelected November 6, 1956, without opposition, for the 6-year term beginning January 3, 1957; reelected November 6, 1962, for the 6-year term beginning January 3, 1963; elected Assistant Majority Leader, January 4, 1965.

REPRESENTATIVES

FIRST DISTRICT.—CITY OF NEW ORLEANS: Wards 3 to 9 and 15. PARISHES: Plaquemines and St. Bernard. Population (1960), 449,491.

F. EDWARD HÉBERT (pronounced "A-Bear"), Democrat, of New Orleans, La., was born in New Orleans, La., October 12, 1901; educated in the public and parochial elementary schools, Jesuit High School, and Tulane University of New Orleans; newspaperman on the New Orleans States and New Orleans Times-Picayune; city editor of the New Orleans States; elected successively to the 77th through the 89th Congresses.

SECOND DISTRICT.—CITY OF NEW ORLEANS: Wards 1, 2, 10 through 14, 16, and 17. PARISHES: Jefferson, St. Charles, St. James, and St. John the Baptist. Population (1960), 499,561.

HALE BOGGS, Democrat, of New Orleans, La.; born on February 15, 1914, on the Mississippi Gulf Coast; educated in the public and parochial schools of Jefferson Parish, La., and was graduated from Tulane University with B.A. degree in 1935 and LL. B. degree in 1937; served as youngest Democrat in the 77th Congress and was a member of the Banking and Currency Committee; served in World War II as an officer in the United States Naval Reserve and United States Maritime Service; separated from the service in January 1946; nominated to the 80th Congress on September 10, 1946; member of the Beta Theta Pi academic fraternity, the Omicron Delta Kappa leadership fraternity, the Phi Beta Kappa scholastic fraternity, the New Orleans, Louisiana, and

American Bar Associations, the Roman Catholic Church, the New Orleans Association of Commerce, the Sons of the American Revolution, Society of Colonial Wars, the American Legion, AMVETS, Catholic War Veterans, and the Knights of Columbus; married to Miss Corinne Morrison Claiborne of New Roads and New Orleans, La.; three children—Mrs. Paul Sigmund, Thomas Hale, Jr., and Corinne Claiborne; elected to the 80th Congress on November 5, 1946; reelected to each succeeding Congress; appointed to the Committee on Ways and Means January 1, 1949; American delegate to Interparliamentary Union since 1948, now vice president of American group; chairman, Committee on Elections, 82d Congress and ranking minority member, 83d Congress; chairman, Special Subcommittee on Narcotics, 83d Congress; chairman, Subcommittee on Foreign Trade Policy, 84th and succeeding Congresses, chairman, Subcommittee on Highway Financing, 84th Congress; appointed to Joint Economic Committee 85th Congress; vice chairman, Democratic National Committee, 1954 to date; member of the President's Commission on the Assassination of President Kennedy; parliamentarian, Democratic National Convention, 1964; Deputy Democratic Whip, 85th, 86th, and first session, 87th Congresses; Democratic Whip since second session, 87th Congress.

THIRD DISTRICT.—PARISHES: Assumption, Iberia, Lafayette, Lafourche, St. Martin, St. Mary, Terrebonne, and Vermilion (8 parishes). Population (1960), 387,207.

EDWIN E. WILLIS, Democrat, of St. Martinville, La.; born October 2, 1904; lawyer; married to Estelle Bulliard; one child, Bob Willis; elected to State Senate in January 1948; elected to 81st Congress November 2, 1948; reelected to 82d, 83d, 84th, 85th, 86th, 87th, 88th, and 89th Congresses.

FOURTH DISTRICT.—PARISHES: Bienville, Bossier, Caddo, Claiborne, De Soto, Red River, and Webster (7 parishes). Population (1960), 391,541.

JOE D. WAGGONNER, JR., Democrat, of Plain Dealing, La.; born September 7, 1918, near Plain Dealing, Bossier Parish, in Northwest Louisiana, son of the late Elizzibeth Johnston and Joe D. Waggonner, Sr., descendants of Anglo-Saxon stock which settled North Louisiana prior to the Civil War; graduated from Plain Dealing High School; B.A. degree, Louisiana Polytechnic Institute, Ruston, La.; elected Bossier Parish School Board, 1954; elected president of same board, 1956; reelected member, 1960; elected member, Louisiana State Board of Education (Third Public Service Commission District) 1960; elected president, United Schools Committee of Louisiana, 1961; president, Louisiana School Boards Association, 1961; served as lieutenant commander, U.S. Navy, in World War II and as same rank from May 1951 to November 1952 during Korean Conflict; operator of wholesale petroleum products distribution agency for North Bossier Parish; Methodist, charge lay leader of Plain Dealing Methodist Church; Mason; member El Karubah Shrine, Shreveport; Elk; member American Legion and 40 & 8; member, Lions Club and Kappa Sigma Social fraternity; married December 14, 1942, to former Miss Mary Ruth Carter; two children, David, 15, and Carol Jean, 19; elected to the 87th Congress December 19, 1961, to fill the vacancy caused by the death of Overton Brooks; reelected to the 88th and 89th Congresses without opposition.

FIFTH DISTRICT.—PARISHES: Caldwell, Catahoula, Concordia, East Carroll, Franklin, Jackson, Lincoln, Madison, Morehouse, Ouachita, Richland, Tensas, Union, and West Carroll (14 parishes). Population (1960), 345,013.

OTTO ERNEST PASSMAN, Democrat, of Monroe, La.; born on a farm in Washington Parish, near Franklinton, La., June 27, 1900, of Irish-French-Holland Dutch extraction; married; owner of Passman Wholesale Equipment Co. and of Passman Investment Co., Monroe, La.; served as officer in U.S. Navy during World War II; member, First Baptist Church, Monroe, La.; past State Commander, American Veterans of World War II, Inc.; member, American Legion; 33d degree Scottish Rite Mason; member, Red Cross of Constantine of York Rite of Freemasonry; past Grand Master, Grand Lodge of the State of Louisiana, Free and Accepted Masons; elected on November 5, 1946, to the 80th Congress; reelected to the 81st, 82d, 83d, 84th, 85th, 86th, 87th, 88th, and 89th Congresses.

SIXTH DISTRICT.—PARISHES: Ascension, East Baton Rouge, East Feliciana, Iberville, Livingston, Pointe Coupee, St. Helena, St. Tammany, Tangipahoa, Washington, West Baton Rouge, and West Feliciana (12 parishes). Population (1960), 536,029.

JAMES HOBSON MORRISON, Democrat, of Hammond, La.; born in Hammond, La., December 8, 1908; attended the public schools; was graduated from Tulane University in 1935 with LL. B. degree; admitted to the bar in 1934 and commenced practice in Hammond, La.; married Miss Marjorie Abbey, of Webb, Miss., February 14, 1940; two children, Hobson and Benjamin; elected to the 78th Congress on November 3, 1942; reelected to the 79th, 80th, 81st, 82d, 83d, 84th, 85th, 86th, 87th, 88th, and 89th Congresses.

SEVENTH DISTRICT.—PARISHES: Acadia, Allen, Beauregard, Calcasieu, Cameron, Evangeline, Jefferson Davis, and St. Landry (8 parishes). Population (1960), 384,330.

T. ASHTON THOMPSON, Democrat, of Ville Platte, Evangeline Parish, La.; born March 31, 1916, son of C. A. Thompson, deceased, and Rosa Soileau Thompson, attended public school in Ville Platte; married former Leatrice D. Soileau; attended Louisiana State University and completed course in higher accounting; religion, Catholic; entered State government service in 1934; was traveling auditor for the Louisiana Highway Commission; transferred to staff of State Department of Finance in 1940; assisted in State reorganization plan; veteran of World War II; served 3½ years in United States Air Force; captain, U.S. Air Force Reserve; appointed State budget officer and financial adviser to the Louisiana Legislature, and designed and installed a complete accounting system for all State agencies; author of legislation for State employees retirement system and subsequently elected twice to 4-year terms as chairman of board of trustees of that system; member of National Association of State Budget Officers and National Committee on Governmental Accounting; appointed to National Finance Committee of AMVETS in 1948 and devised first budget and accounting system for that organization; member of the American Legion; represented United States Department of State in Louisiana in training of foreign representatives in principles of democracy; represented Louisiana at the national assembly of the States in the development of the civil defense program; elected to the 83d Congress on November 4, 1952; reelected to the 84th, 85th, 86th, 87th, 88th, and 89th Congresses.

EIGHTH DISTRICT.—PARISHES: Avoyelles, Grant, La Salle, Natchitoches, Rapides, Sabine, Vernon, and Winn (8 parishes). Population (1960), 263,850.

SPEEDY O. LONG, Democrat, of Jena, La.; attorney at law; born in Tullos, La Salle Parish, La., June 16, 1928; son of Felix F. and Verda Pendarvis Long; attended public schools in La Salle and Winn Parishes, graduating from Winnfield High School, Winnfield, La., in 1945; served in U.S. Regular Navy for 22 months; graduated from Northeast Junior College, Monroe, La., 1950; received B.A. degree from Northwestern State College at Natchitoches, La., 1951; recalled to active duty, U.S. Navy, during Korean conflict; received LL.B. degree from Louisiana State University Law School, February of 1959; practices law in Jena, La.; served 8 years in Louisiana State Senate from May 1956 to May 1964; member of Louisiana Bar Association and American Bar Association of Louisiana; member and former president of 28th Judicial District Bar Association of Louisiana; member of American Legion; 32d degree Mason and Shriner; member of Jena and Louisiana Junior Chambers of Commerce; honorary chapter farmer, La Salle Parish Future Farmers of America; member of First Baptist Church of Jena, La.; married Florence Marie Theriot of Golden Meadow, La.; two children, Felix Paul and David Theriot; elected to the 89th Congress November 3, 1964.

MAINE

(Population (1960), 969,265)

SENATORS

MARGARET CHASE SMITH, Republican.

EDMUND S. MUSKIE, Democrat, of Waterville, Maine; born in Rumford, Maine, March 28, 1914; married to former Jane F. Gray; five children: Stephen Oliver, Ellen, Melinda, Martha, and Edmund S., Jr.; lawyer; member of house of representatives 93d, 94th, and 95th Maine legislatures; Governor of Maine from January 6, 1955 to 1959; elected to United States Senate to serve from January 1959 to January 1965; reelected November 3, 1964; during World War II served in the U.S. Naval Reserve.

REPRESENTATIVES

FIRST DISTRICT.—Counties: Cumberland, Kennebec, Knox, Lincoln, Sagadahoc, Waldo, and York (7 counties). Population (1960), 463,800.

STANLEY R. TUPPER, Republican, of Boothbay Harbor, Maine; born January 25, 1921; married to former Esther McKown; one child, Stanley, Jr.; lawyer; served in U.S. Navy during World War II; member and chairman Board of Selectmen Boothbay Harbor, Maine, 1948–50; elected to 96th Maine Legislature 1952; Commissioner of Sea and Shore Fisheries for State of Maine 1953–57; elected to 87th Congress November 8, 1960; reelected to the 88th and 89th Congresses.

SECOND DISTRICT.—Counties: Androscoggin, Aroostook, Franklin, Hancock, Oxford, Penobscot, Piscataquis, Somerset, and Washington (9 counties). Population (1960), 505,465.

WILLIAM DODD HATHAWAY, Democrat, of Auburn, Maine; born in Cambridge, Mass., February 21, 1924; educated in Boston elementary and high schools; served on active duty with Army Air Force 1942–46; enlisted as private and discharged as captain; navigator on Liberator bomber; shot down over Ploesti and was prisoner of war in Roumania for 3 months; graduate of Harvard College in 1949 and Harvard Law School in 1953; admitted to the bar and began practice of law in Lewiston, Maine, in 1953; assistant county attorney, Androscoggin County, 1955–57; hearing examiner for the State Liquor Commission, 1957–61; member of—American, State, and County bar associations; Maine Medical-Legal Society; Board of Directors of the Lewiston-Auburn chapter of the American Red Cross, and the Board of Directors of the Lewiston-Auburn Association for Retarded Children; division chairman of Lewiston-Auburn United Fund; Episcopalian; married August 21, 1945, to Mary Lee Bird of Akron, Ohio; one daughter, Susan Louise, one son, Fred William; elected to the 89th Congress November 3, 1964.

MARYLAND

(Population (1960), 3,100,689)

SENATORS

DANIEL BAUGH BREWSTER, Democrat, of Towson, Md.; born in Baltimore County, Md., November 23, 1923; educated in Gilman School; St. Paul's, Concord, N.H.; Princeton University; Johns Hopkins University; Law School, University of Maryland, LL. B. degree in 1949; enlisted in the United States Marine Corps in 1942; served 2 years in South Pacific as troop commander in Raider Battalion; Guam and Okinawa invasions; wounded; awarded Purple Heart; Gold Star in lieu of second Purple Heart; Bronze Star; and now lieutenant colonel, United States Marine Corps Reserve; admitted to the bar in 1949; elected to the Maryland House of Delegates in 1950, reelected in 1954 and served as vice chairman of Judiciary Committee 1954–58; owns and operates grain and cattle farm near Glyndon, in Baltimore County; married; two sons—Daniel B., Jr., and Gerry Leiper; member—American Bar Association, Maryland State Bar Association, Baltimore County Bar Association; former president, Maryland State Fair and Agricultural Society; elected to the 86th Congress on November 4, 1958; reelected to the 87th Congress; member of House Armed Services Committee; elected to the United States Senate November 6, 1962, for the term expiring January 3, 1969.

JOSEPH DAVIES TYDINGS, Democrat, of Havre de Grace, Md.; born in Ashville, N.C., May 4, 1928, son of the late Millard E. Tydings, former Senator from Maryland; attended Aberdeen public schools, McDonogh School (1946), University of Maryland (1950), and University of Maryland Law School (1953); president, Young Democratic Clubs of Maryland 1953–55; member of State house of delegates 1955–61; United States district attorney for Maryland 1961–63; senior warden, St. John's Episcopal Church, Havre de Grace, since 1961; chairman, Maryland Chapter National Multiple Sclerosis Society, 1961; president, Junior Bar Association of Baltimore City 1962–63; member, Metropolitan Board of Directors YMCA 1961–64; married to the former Virginia Campbell; three children, Mary Campbell, Millard, and Emlen; elected to the United States Senate November 3, 1964, for the term commencing January 3, 1965.

REPRESENTATIVES

AT LARGE.—Population (1960), 3,100,689.

CARLTON R. SICKLES, Democrat, of Lanham, Md.; born June 15, 1921, in Hamden, Conn.; married to the former Simone Shornick of Shanghai, China; one daughter; Georgetown College of Arts and Sciences, B.S.S. cum laude 1943; Georgetown Law School, LL.B. 1948; lawyer, 1949–; adjunct professor, Georgetown University Law School; officer, Carday Associates, Inc.; during World War II, 1943–46, U.S. Army, Infantry, service in United States, India, and China; and in Korean War, 1951–52, U.S. Air Force, Office of Special Investigations, service in United States; served as delegate, Maryland House of Delegates, 1955–62; member of many local political, business, service, and civic organizations; member of American Bar, District of Columbia Bar, and Prince Georges Bar associations; elected to the 88th Congress November 6, 1962; reelected to the 89th Congress.

FIRST DISTRICT.—COUNTIES: Caroline, Cecil, Dorchester, Kent, Queen Annes, Somerset, Talbot, Wicomico, and Worcester (9 counties). Population (1960), 243,570.

ROGERS CLARK BALLARD MORTON, Republican, of Easton, Md; born in Louisville, Ky., September 19, 1914; farmer-businessman, Talbot County, Easton, Md.; broad experience in business management, labor relations, and the Armed Services; president, major business concern at 33; served in the U.S. Army during World War II, first as an enlisted man, ending the war a captain; member of the Civilian Advisory Board of the Air Training Command of the Air Force; graduate of Yale University; married Anne Jones in 1939; one son, David, and one daughter, Anne; Episcopalian; elected to the 88th Congress November 6, 1962; reelected to the 89th Congress November 3, 1964.

SECOND DISTRICT.—Counties: Baltimore, Carroll, and Harford (3 counties). Population (1960), 621,935.

CLARENCE DICKINSON LONG, Democrat, of Ruxton, Md.; born in South Bend, Ind., December 11, 1908; received B.A. from Washington and Jefferson College, 1932, and M.A. in 1933; M.A. from Princeton University in 1935 and Ph. D. in 1938; served in the U.S. Navy as a lieutenant in World War II; professor of economics at the Johns Hopkins University since 1946 (on leave 1963–64); associate task force director of the first Hoover Commission in 1948; senior staff member of the Council of Economic Advisers to the President 1953–54 and 1956–57; acting chairman of the Democratic State Central Committee of Maryland 1961–62; author of seven books and many articles on unemployment, wages, labor force, and economic fluctuations; married to the former Susanna Larter; two children, Clarence Dickinson 3d and Susanna Elizabeth; elected to the 88th Congress November 6, 1962; reelected to the 89th Congress.

THIRD DISTRICT.—City of Baltimore: Wards 1 to 8; ward 18, precincts 3 to 9; wards 22 to 24; ward 26, precincts 1 to 34; ward 27, precinct 1. Population (1960), 258,826.

EDWARD A. GARMATZ, Democrat, of Baltimore, Md.; born in Baltimore, Md., February 7, 1903; attended the public schools and the Polytechnic Institute; married to Ruth Burchard; engaged in the electrical business; associated with the Maryland State Racing Commission for 3 years; served as police magistrate 1944–47; elected to the 80th Congress July 15, 1947, to fill the vacancy caused by the resignation of Thomas D'Alesandro; reelected to the 81st and each succeeding Congress.

FOURTH DISTRICT.—City of Baltimore: Wards 9 to 14; ward 17; ward 18, precincts 1 and 2; wards 19 and 20; ward 27, precincts 37 to 56 and 76 to 80. Population (1960), 283,320.

GEORGE H. FALLON, Democrat, of Baltimore, Md.; born in the city of Baltimore, July 24, 1902, the son of the late Lawrence Fallon, Sr., and Mary Dempsey Fallon; educated in the public schools and Calvert Business College, Johns Hopkins University (night); married Miss Willa Virginia Thomas in 1929 and they have one child, Mary Joyce; elected to Democratic State Central Committee of Baltimore in 1938, served as chairman; elected to the Baltimore City Council in 1939; reelected in 1943; elected to the 79th Congress on November 7, 1944; reelected to the 80th, 81st, 82d, 83d, 84th, 85th, 86th, 87th, 88th, and 89th Congresses.

FIFTH DISTRICT.—Counties: Anne Arundel, Calvert, Charles, Howard, Prince Georges, and St. Marys (6 counties). City of Baltimore: Ward 25, precincts 12 to 19. Population (1960), 711,045.

HERVEY GILBERT MACHEN, Democrat, of Hyattsville, Md.; born in Washington, D.C., October 14, 1916; educated in Prince Georges County public schools; received LL.B. and LL.M. degrees from Southeastern University; joined the Coast Artillery in April 1941 and was honorably discharged as a captain in February 1946; married; five children; elected to State house of delegates in 1954 and reelected in 1958 and 1962; served as assistant State attorney for Prince Georges County and as city attorney for Cheverly and Hyattsville; member of the Prince Georges Chamber of Commerce, Terrapin Club, Almas Temple Shrine, Kiwanis, Moose Lodge, Episcopal Church, Caravan Club, Mount Herman Lodge; director of the Citizens Bank of Maryland and of the Maryland Home Title Co.; former vice chairman of the State Democratic State Central Committee, an organizer and first president of Young Democrats of Prince Georges, and served as vice president of the Young Democrats of Maryland; elected to the 89th Congress November 3, 1964.

SIXTH DISTRICT.—Counties: Allegany, Frederick, Garrett, Montgomery, and Washington (5 counties). Population (1960), 608,666.

CHARLES McC. MATHIAS, Jr., Republican, of Frederick, Md.; born in Frederick on July 24, 1922; educated in public schools of Frederick; Haverford College, B.A. degree 1944; Yale University (V–12); University of Maryland, LL.B. degree in 1949; enlisted as an apprentice seaman in 1942; commissioned an ensign in 1944; sea duty in Pacific Ocean Area 1944–46; now lieutenant commander, USNR; admitted to the Maryland bar in 1949 and to the U.S. Supreme Court bar in 1954; assistant attorney general of Maryland in 1953 and 1954; city attorney of Frederick, Md., 1954–59; elected to Maryland House of Delegates 1958; member of House Judiciary Committee in 1959 and 1960; married Ann Hickling Bradford of Cambridge, Mass., November 8, 1958; two sons, Charles Bradford and Robert Fiske; member of All Saints' Episcopal Church; elected to the 87th Congress November 8, 1960; reelected to the 88th and 89th Congresses.

SEVENTH DISTRICT.—CITY OF BALTIMORE: Wards 15, 16, and 21; ward 25, precincts 1 to 11; ward 26, precincts 35 to 45; ward 27, precincts 2 to 36, 57 to 75 and 81 to 105; and ward 28. Population (1960), 373,327.

SAMUEL N. FRIEDEL, Democrat, of Baltimore, Md.; born in Washington, D. C., April 18, 1898; attended public schools of Baltimore and business college; married the former Regina Bradley Johnson; elected to the house of delegates of the Maryland State Legislature in 1935, serving from 1935 to 1939 as a member of the ways and means committee; in 1939 was elected to the city council of Baltimore to fill the unexpired term of a vacancy in the first district; reelected in 1939 and again in 1943; while a member of the city council served as chairman of the budget and finance committee; elected in 1951 to the Baltimore City Council representing the fifth district and was chairman of the ways and means committee; elected to the 83d Congress November 4, 1952, from the new Seventh Congressional District of Maryland; reelected to the 84th, 85th, 86th, 87th, 88th, and 89th Congresses.

MASSACHUSETTS

(Population (1960), 5,148,578)

SENATORS

LEVERETT SALTONSTALL, Republican, of Dover, Mass.; born in Chestnut Hill (Newton), Mass., September 1, 1892; Noble and Greenough School; Harvard College, A. B., 1914; Harvard University Law School, LL. D., 1917; married Alice Wesselhoeft, of Jaffrey, N. H., June 27, 1916; children, Leverett, Jr. (first lieutenant, U. S. Army, discharged), Rosalie (deceased), Emily B. (Rm. 1/c U. S. N. R. WAVES, discharged), Peter B. (killed in action, sergeant, U. S. Marines), William L. (Quartermaster 3/c U. S. N. R., discharged), and Susan; served as first lieutenant, Three Hundred and First Field Artillery, 1917–18 (5 months' service in France); attorney at law; member of board of aldermen, Newton, 1920–22; assistant district attorney of Middlesex County, 1921–22; member, Massachusetts House of Representatives, 1923–36; speaker of the House for 8 years of service; director of first Greater Boston Community Fund Drive, 1938; elected Governor of Massachusetts in 1938; reelected in 1940 and 1942; chairman, New England Governors' Conference, 1939–44; chairman, National Governors' Conference, 1944; served three terms as member of Board of Overseers at Harvard: 1928–34, 1935–41, 1943–49; was president in 1943–49; elected to the United States Senate on November 7, 1944, for the unexpired term of Senator Henry Cabot Lodge, Jr. (resigned), ending January 3, 1949; reelected in 1948, 1954, and again in 1960 for the term ending January 3, 1967.

EDWARD MOORE KENNEDY, Democrat, of Boston, Mass.; born in Brookline, Mass., February 22, 1932, son of Joseph P. and Rose Kennedy; Milton Academy, 1950; Harvard College, A.B., 1954; International Law School, The Hague, Holland, 1958; University of Virginia Law School, LL.B., 1959; married Virginia Joan Bennett of Bronxville, N.Y., November 29, 1958; two children, Kara and Edward M., Jr.; enlisted in the U.S. Army as a private and served in France and Germany from June 1951 to March 1953; chairman of the American Cancer Crusade in Massachusetts, 1961; member of board of trustees, Boston University; advisory board, Emmanuel College; president of the Joseph P. Kennedy, Jr., Foundation; assistant district attorney of Suffolk County; elected to the U.S. Senate November 6, 1962, to fill unexpired term of his brother, John F. Kennedy; reelected November 3, 1964.

REPRESENTATIVES

FIRST DISTRICT.—BERKSHIRE COUNTY: Cities of North Adams and Pittsfield. Towns of Adams, Alford, Becket, Cheshire, Clarksburg, Dalton, Egremont, Florida, Great Barrington, Hancock, Hinsdale, Lanesborough, Lee, Lenox, Monterey, Mount Washington, New Ashford, New Marlborough, Otis, Peru, Richmond, Sandisfield, Savoy, Sheffield, Stockbridge, Tyringham, Washington, West Stockbridge, Williamstown, and Windsor. FRANKLIN COUNTY: Towns of Ashfield, Bernardston, Buckland, Charlemont, Colrain, Conway, Deerfield, Erving, Gill, Greenfield, Hawley, Heath, Leverett, Leyden, Monroe, Montague, New Salem, Northfield, Orange, Rowe, Shelburne, Shutesbury, Sunderland, Warwick, Wendell, and Whately. HAMPDEN COUNTY: Cities of Holyoke and Westfield. Towns of Blandford, Chester, Granville, Montgomery, Russell, Southwick, and Tolland. HAMPSHIRE COUNTY: City of Northampton. Towns of Amherst, Chesterfield, Cummington, Easthampton, Goshen, Hadley, Hatfield, Huntington, Middlefield, Pelham, Plainfield, Southampton, Westhampton, Williamsburg, and Worthington. WORCESTER COUNTY: Towns of Athol, Petersham, Phillipston, Royalston, and Templeton. Population (1960), 376,336.

SILVIO O. CONTE, Republican, of Pittsfield, Mass.; born in Pittsfield November 9, 1921, son of Mr. and Mrs. Ottavio Conte; attended public schools in Pittsfield and the Pittsfield Vocational High School, graduating in 1940; machinist at General Electric Co. in Pittsfield before joining Seabees in World War II; served in Southwest Pacific; attended Boston College and Boston College Law School, graduating in 1949; admitted to the bar same year; in November 1950 elected to the Massachusetts State Senate; served as Senator from Berkshire District 1951–58; served as chairman of Senate committees on Constitutional Law, Insurance, Judiciary, and as chairman of Legislative Research Council, Special Commission Investigating Health and Welfare Trust Funds, Commission on Fish and Game, Commission Investigating Accident and Health Insurance,

Commission Investigating the Increase in Tank-Wagon Prices of Gasoline and Fuel Oil, Commission Studying Blue Cross-Blue Shield, Commission Investigating Discriminatory Practices in Fraternities and Societies in Massachusetts Colleges and Universities; selected by Massachusetts Junior Chamber of Commerce as outstanding young man of the year in 1954; member of platform committee at the Republican National Convention in 1960 and 1964; director of the Pittsfield Girls' Club; director of Hillcrest Hospital; member of Berkshire Bar Association, Massachusetts Bar Association, Federal Bar Association; maintains congressional office at 7 North Street, Pittsfield, Mass.; married to the former Corinne Duval, four children; elected to the 86th Congress November 4, 1958; reelected to the 87th, 88th, and 89th Congresses.

SECOND DISTRICT.—HAMPDEN COUNTY: Cities of Chicopee and Springfield. Towns of Agawam, Brimfield, East Longmeadow, Hampden, Holland, Longmeadow, Ludlow, Monson, Palmer, Wales, West Springfield, and Wilbraham. HAMPSHIRE COUNTY: Towns of Belchertown, Granby, South Hadley, and Ware. WORCESTER COUNTY: Towns of Brookfield, East Brookfield, North Brookfield, Sturbridge, Warren, and West Brookfield. Population (1960), 388,578.

EDWARD P. BOLAND, Democrat, of Springfield, Mass.; elected to 83d and reelected to 84th, 85th, 86th, 87th, 88th, and 89th Congresses.

THIRD DISTRICT.—MIDDLESEX COUNTY: City of Marlborough. Towns of Acton, Ashby, Ayer, Boxborough, Dunstable, Groton, Holliston, Hudson, Littleton, Maynard, Natick, Pepperell, Sherborn, Shirley, Stow, Townsend, Tyngsborough, and Westford. NORFOLK COUNTY: Towns of Bellingham, Franklin, Medway, and Millis. WORCESTER COUNTY: Cities of Fitchburg, Gardner, and Leominster. Towns of Ashburnham, Barre, Berlin, Blackstone, Bolton, Charlton, Clinton, Douglas, Dudley, Hardwick, Harvard, Hopedale, Hubbardston, Lancaster, Leicester, Lunenburg, Mendon, Milford, Millbury, Millville, New Braintree, Northbridge, Oakham, Oxford, Paxton, Princeton, Rutland, Southbridge, Spencer, Sterling, Sutton, Upton, Uxbridge, Webster, Westminster, and Winchendon. Population (1960), 441,558.

PHILIP JOSEPH PHILBIN, Democrat, of Clinton, Mass.; born in Clinton, Mass., May 29, 1898; educated at Clinton public and high schools, Harvard College, A. B. course, class of 1920, and Columbia University Law School, class of 1924, LL. B. degree; practicing attorney, businessman, and farmer; former secretary, campaign manager, and personal representative for United States Senator David I. Walsh; former special counsel, United States Senate Committee on Education and Labor; former referee, United States Department of Labor; former member, advisory board, Massachusetts Unemployment Compensation Commission; present chairman of Town of Clinton Finance Committee; married Miss Lillan Sundberg (deceased); two children, Mrs. Albert R. Scansaroli (Mary Ellen Bamby Philbin) and Ann Blenda; veteran of First World War; elected to the 78th Congress on November 3, 1942; reelected to the 79th, 80th, 81st, 82d, 83d, 84th, 85th, 86th, 87th, 88th, and 89th Congresses.

FOURTH DISTRICT.—MIDDLESEX COUNTY: City of Waltham. Towns of Ashland, Framingham, Hopkinton, Sudbury, Watertown, Wayland, and Weston. WORCESTER COUNTY: City of Worcester. Towns of Auburn, Boylston, Grafton, Holden, Northborough, Shrewsbury, Southborough, Westborough, and West Boylston. Population (1960), 444,069.

HAROLD D. DONOHUE, Democrat, of Worcester, Mass.; born in Worcester, Mass., June 18, 1901; attended the schools of that city; was graduated from the Northeastern University School of Law in 1925; was admitted to the Massachusetts Bar in February 1926 and practiced law in the city of Worcester since; entered the United States Navy in December 1942 and was separated from the service in December 1945 with the rank of lieutenant commander; single; served in the Worcester city government for a period of 10 years; elected to the 80th Congress on November 5, 1946; reelected to the 81st, 82d, 83d, 84th, 85th, 86th, 87th, 88th, and 89th Congresses.

FIFTH DISTRICT.—ESSEX COUNTY: City of Lawrence, and town of Andover. MIDDLESEX COUNTY: Cities of Lowell, Melrose, and Woburn. Towns of Bedford, Billerica, Burlington, Carlisle, Chelmsford, Concord, Dracut, Lexington, Lincoln, North Reading, Reading, Stoneham, Tewksbury, Wilmington, and Winchester. Population (1960), 450,716.

F. BRADFORD MORSE, Republican, of Lowell, Mass.; born in Lowell August 7, 1921; attended Lowell public schools, Boston University, B.S., 1948;

LL.B., 1949; married Vera Francesca Cassilly of Harford County, Md., May 7, 1955; daughter, Susanna Francesca Morse, born February 17, 1961; son, Anthony Bradford Morse, born March 8, 1963; served in Army of the United States, 1942–46; attorney-at-law; law clerk to chief justice of the Supreme Judicial Court of Massachusetts, 1949; faculty member, Boston University School of Law, 1949–53; member of Lowell City Council, 1952–53; attorney, U.S. Senate Committee on Armed Services, 1953–54; executive secretary and chief assistant to Senator Leverett Saltonstall, 1955–58; deputy administrator of Veterans Affairs for the United States, 1958–60; member United States-Mexican Interparliamentary Group; member, International Parliamentary Union; sponsor, the Atlantic Council; congressional adviser to Inter-American Economic and Social Council; member, American Bar Association; American Legion; Veterans of Foreign Wars; Sigma Alpha Epsilon; Elks; trustee, Dana Hall Schools, Wellesley, Mass.; elected to the 87th Congress November 8, 1960; reelected to the 88th and 89th Congresses; member, Committee on Foreign Affairs.

SIXTH DISTRICT.—Essex County: Cities of Beverly, Gloucester, Haverhill, Lynn, Newburyport, Peabody, and Salem. Towns of Amesbury, Boxford, Danvers, Essex, Georgetown, Groveland, Hamilton, Ipswich, Manchester, Marblehead, Merrimac, Methuen, Middleton, Nahant, Newbury, North Andover, Rockport, Rowley, Salisbury, Swampscott, Topsfield, Wenham, and West Newbury. Population (1960), 452,956.

WILLIAM HENRY BATES, Republican, of Salem, Mass.; born in Salem, Mass., April 26, 1917, son of Mrs. Nora Jennings Bates and the late Hon. George J. Bates; educated in Salem schools, Worcester Academy, Brown University, and the Harvard Graduate School of Business Administration; married Miss Pearle Jean Dreyer in 1943, and they have one daughter, Susan; in naval service more than 9 years, resigning commission as lieutenant commander, United States Navy, when elected to the 81st Congress in a special election held February 14, 1950; reelected to the 82d, 83d, 84th, 85th, 86th, 87th, 88th, and 89th Congresses.

SEVENTH DISTRICT.—Essex County: Towns of Lynnfield and Saugus. Middlesex County: Cities of Everett, Malden, and Medford. Towns of Arlington, Belmont, and Wakefield. Suffolk County: Cities of Chelsea and Revere, and town of Winthrop. Population (1960), 392,350.

TORBERT HART MACDONALD, Democrat, of Malden, Mass.; born in Boston, Mass., June 6, 1917, son of John G. Macdonald and Harriet Hart; graduate of Malden public schools, Medford High School, Andover Academy, Harvard College (1940), Harvard Law School (1943) (1946); married to Phyllis Brooks; four children, Torbert Hart, Jr., Laurie, Brian, and Robin; member of the Massachusetts and Federal bars; admitted to practice before the United States Supreme Court; veteran of World War II, having served as P.T. boat commander in Southwest Pacific; received Silver Star Medal and Presidential Citation; practicing attorney; former member of National Labor Relations Board for New England area; former legal assistant to Eric Johnston; member Harvard Varsity Club; majority whip for New England area; awarded Order of Merit, Commendatore Rank, by the Republic of Italy; appointed to the Third Mexico-United States Interparliamentary Conference, March 1963; delegate to the National Democratic Conventions, 1956, 1960, and 1964; member Boston, Federal, and Massachusetts Bar Associations; was elected to the 84th Congress November 2, 1954; reelected to the 85th, 86th, 87th, 88th, and 89th Congresses.

EIGHTH DISTRICT.—Middlesex County: Cities of Cambridge and Somerville. Norfolk County: Town of Brookline. Suffolk County: City of Boston: Wards 1 to 3, 21, and 22. Population (1960), 420,596.

THOMAS P. O'NEILL, Jr., Democrat, of Cambridge, Mass.; born December 9, 1912; son of Thomas P. O'Neill and Rose Anne (Tolan) O'Neill; educated St. John's High School and Boston College, A.B. 1936; engaged in the insurance business; married Mildred Anne Miller June 17, 1941; five children: Rosemary, Thomas 3d, Susan, Christopher, and Michael Tolan; member Cambridge School Committee 1946 and 1947; member of Massachusetts Legislature 1936–52, serving as minority leader 1947 and 1948 and as speaker of the house 1948–52; elected to the 83d Congress November 4, 1952; reelected to 84th, 85th, 86th, 87th, 88th, and 89th Congresses.

NINTH DISTRICT.—SUFFOLK COUNTY: City of Boston: Wards 4 to 17, 19, and 20. Population (1960) 478,962.

JOHN W. McCORMACK, Democrat, of Dorchester; born in South Boston; lawyer; educated in the Boston public schools; married to M. Harriet Joyce of South Boston; member of the constitutional convention, 1917–18; member of the Massachusetts House of Representatives 1920, 1921, and 1922, and the Massachusetts Senate 1923, 1924, 1925, and 1926, the last 2 years as Democratic leader; Member 70th Congress, filling unexpired term of the late James A. Gallivan; Member of 71st, 72d, 73d, 74th, 75th, 76th, 77th, 78th, and 79th Congresses; majority leader; Member 80th Congress, Democratic whip; Member 81st and 82d Congresses, majority leader; Member 83d Congress, Democratic whip; Member 84th, 85th, 86th, and first session 87th Congresses, majority leader, and second session of 87th, 88th, and 89th Congresses, Speaker; World War I veteran; awarded honorary degrees of LL.D. by Boston University, Boston, Mass.; Holy Cross College, Worcester, Mass.; Boston College, Chestnut Hill, Mass.; Villanova College, Villanova, Pa.; Tufts College, Medford, Mass.; Providence College, Providence, R.I.; Stonehill College, North Easton, Mass.; Georgetown University, Washington, D.C.; Catholic University of America, Washington, D.C.; Suffolk University, Boston, Mass.; and Staley College, Brookline, Mass.; member of Order of Malta First Class; awarded the "Peace Medal" of the Third Order of Saint Francis; Knight Commander, Order of St. Gregory the Great, with star; commander, Legion of Honor, Republic of the Philippines; Bellarmine Medal, Bellarmine College, 1957, Bellarmine College, Louisville, Ky.; Cardinal Gibbons Medal, Catholic University of America, Washington, D.C., November 1963; commander, Order of Duarte Sanches Y Mella, Dominican Republic; Grand Officer, Order of Merito Della Republica (Italy); Titular De La Cruz De Aloy Alfaro (Panama); Grand Commander of the Royal Order of the Phoenix, with Star (Greece); member, Knights of Columbus; elected Speaker, second session 87th, 88th and 89th Congresses.

TENTH DISTRICT.—BRISTOL COUNTY: Cities of Attleboro, Fall River, and Taunton. Towns of Berkley, Dighton, Easton, Freetown, Mansfield, North Attleboro, Norton, Raynham, Rehoboth, Seekonk, Somerset, and Swansea. MIDDLESEX COUNTY: City of Newton. NORFOLK COUNTY: Towns of Dover, Foxborough, Medfield, Needham, Norfolk, Plainville, Walpole, Wellesley, Westwood, and Wrentham. Population (1960), 456,308.

JOSEPH WILLIAM MARTIN, JR., Republican, of North Attleboro, Mass.; born November 3, 1884; educated in the public schools of North Attleboro; honorary degrees: LL. D., Tufts College, Medford, Mass.; LL. D., Pennsylvania Military College, Chester, Pa.; D. C. L., Boston University, Boston, Mass.; LL. D., Stonehill College, North Easton, Mass.; LL. D., Dartmouth College, Hanover, N. H.; LL. D., Syracuse University, Syracuse, N. Y.; master of science, Bradford Durfee Technical Institute, Fall River, Mass.; M. S. B. A., Bryant College, Providence, R. I.; Doctor of Jurisprudence, Portia Law School; Doctor of Laws, New England College; publisher of Evening Chronicle, North Attleboro, and Franklin Sentinel, Franklin, Mass.; member Massachusetts House of Representatives, 1912–14; member Massachusetts State Senate, 1914–17; chairman, Massachusetts Street Railway Investigating Committee, 1917; chairman, Massachusetts Republican Legislative Campaign Committee, 1917; Harding-Coolidge presidential elector, 1920; executive secretary, Republican State committee, 1922–25; delegate to Republican National Conventions of 1916, 1936, 1940, 1944, 1948, and 1952; permanent chairman of the Republican National Conventions of 1940, 1944, 1948, 1952, and 1956; chairman, Republican Congressional Campaign Committee in 1938; member of the Republican National Committee, 1936–40; chairman, Republican National Committee from July 1940 to November 1942; in 1924 elected Member of the 69th and each succeeding Congress, including the 89th; elected minority leader 76th to 85th Congresses except the 80th and 83d, in which he was elected Speaker.

ELEVENTH DISTRICT.—NORFOLK COUNTY: City of Quincy. Towns of Avon, Braintree, Canton, Dedham, Holbrook, Milton, Norwood, Randolph, Sharon, Stoughton, and Weymouth. PLYMOUTH COUNTY: City of Brockton. SUFFOLK COUNTY: City of Boston: Ward 18. Population (1960), 441,180.

JAMES A. BURKE, Democrat, of Milton, Mass.; born March 30, 1910, at Boston, Mass.; educated in the Boston public schools, Lincoln Preparatory, and Suffolk University; married to the late Margaret E. Grant of Hyde Park, Mass.; former Registrar of vital statistics for the city of Boston; during World War II, special agent in the Counter-Intelligence, attached to the 77th Infantry Division in the South Pacific; awarded four battle stars and other decorations; served as a member of the Massachusetts General Court for 10 years; assistant majority leader in the Massachusetts House of Representatives 4 years; house chairman of World War II Veterans Problems and Korean Veterans Commission; member of committees on Cities, Counties, Mercantile Affairs, Pensions, Old Age, and House Rules Committee; 4 years vice chairman of the Massachusetts Democratic State Committee; elected to the 86th Congress November 4, 1958; member, Committee on Banking and Currency; reelected to the 87th, 88th, and 89th Congresses; member, Committee on Ways and Means.

TWELFTH DISTRICT.—BARNSTABLE COUNTY: Towns of Barnstable, Bourne, Brewster, Chatham, Dennis, Eastham, Falmouth, Harwich, Mashpee, Orleans, Provincetown, Sandwich, Truro, Wellfleet, and Yarmouth. BRISTOL COUNTY: City of New Bedford. Towns of Acushnet, Dartmouth, Fairhaven, and Westport. DUKES COUNTY: Towns of Chilmark, Edgartown, Gay Head, Gosnold, Oak Bluffs, Tisbury, and West Tisbury. NANTUCKET COUNTY: Town of Nantucket. NORFOLK COUNTY: Town of Cohasset. PLYMOUTH COUNTY: Towns of Abington, Bridgewater, Carver, Duxbury, East Bridgewater, Halifax, Hanover, Hanson, Hingham, Hull, Kingston, Lakeville, Marion, Marshfield, Mattapoisett, Middleborough, Norwell, Pembroke, Plymouth, Plympton, Rochester, Rockland, Scituate, Wareham, West Bridgewater, and Whitman. Population (1960), 404,969.

HASTINGS KEITH, Republican, of West Bridgewater, Mass.; son of Honorable and Mrs. Roger Keith, born in Brockton, Mass., November 22, 1915; graduated from Brockton High School, Deerfield Academy, and the University of Vermont with a B.S. degree; a member of: Sigma Phi, Masons, Kiwanis Club, Elks, American Legion, V.F.W.; member of Aircraft Owners and Pilots Association; chartered life underwriter by profession; served as an agent and district manager for the Equitable Life Assurance Society in Boston; partner in firm of Roger Keith & Sons, general insurance; served overseas with the Army during World War II; is a colonel in the organized Reserves; married to the former Louise Harriman of Norfolk, Va., August 31, 1943, and they have two daughters: Helen Harriman Keith, born September 15, 1944; and Carolyn Louise Keith, born July 2, 1947; Congregationalist; first political office was in the State senate, 1953–56; elected to the 86th Congress, November 4, 1958; reelected to the 87th, 88th, and 89th Congresses; member Committee on Interstate and Foreign Commerce and Subcommittee on Commerce and Finance; member Committee on Merchant Marine and Fisheries and Subcommittees on Oceanography and Fisheries and Wildlife Conservation; and House Republican Policy Committee.

MICHIGAN

(Population (1960), 7,823,194)

SENATORS

PATRICK V. McNAMARA, Democrat, of Detroit, Mich.; born in North Weymouth, Mass., October 4, 1894; engaged in construction industry, and active in civic and labor affairs; appointed Detroit Area Rent Director of Office of Price Administration 1942; elected Detroit City Council 1946; elected Detroit Board of Education 1949; married Mary L. Mattee, of Calumet, Mich.; two children, Mrs. Mary Jane Ballard and Patrick V. McNamara 3d; elected to the United States Senate for the term beginning January 3, 1955; reelected in 1960 for the term ending January 3, 1967.

PHILIP A. HART, Democrat, of Mackinac Island, Mich.; born December 10, 1912, at Bryn Mawr, Pa.; Georgetown University, A.B. cum laude, 1934; University of Michigan Law School, J.D., 1937; U.S. Army, 1941–46, with Fourth Infantry Division, wounded in D-Day assault on Utah Beach, Normandy; Michigan Corporation and Securities Commissioner, 1949–50; director, O.P.S., 1951; U.S. Attorney for Eastern Michigan, 1952: legal adviser to Governor Williams, 1953–54; elected Lieutenant Governor, 1954, reelected 1956; trustee and past president of Michigan Bar Foundation; married Jane C. Briggs, of Detroit, in 1943; four sons and four daughters; elected to the U.S. Senate November 4, 1958; reelected November 3, 1964.

REPRESENTATIVES

FIRST DISTRICT.—CITY OF DETROIT: Wards 1 to 10, 12 to 14, 16, 18, and city of Highland Park. Population (1960), 416,667.

JOHN CONYERS, JR., Democrat, of Detroit, Mich.; born May 16, 1929, in Detroit, Mich., son of John and Lucille Conyers; educated in Detroit public school system; graduated from Wayne State University (B.A. 1957); graduated from Wayne State Law School (LL. B. June 1958); served as officer in the U.S. Army Corps of Engineers, served 1 year in Korea; awarded combat and merit citations; unmarried; executive board member of Detroit Chapter NAACP and American Civil Liberties Union; chairman of Police Relations Committee of Cotillion Club; engaged in many civil rights and labor activities; secretary, 15th Congressional District Democratic organization; legislative assistant to Congressman John D. Dingell December 1958 to May 1961; elected to 89th Congress November 3, 1964.

SECOND DISTRICT.—COUNTIES: Lenawee, Livingston, Monroe, and Washtenaw; and the townships of Plymouth and Northville and the city of Plymouth in Wayne County. Population (1960), 414,385.

WESTON EDWARD VIVIAN, Democrat, of Ann Arbor, Mich.; born in Newfoundland, Canada, October 25, 1924; moved to the United States September 5, 1929; enlisted man and officer, U.S. Navy, 1943–46; graduated from Union College, Schenectady, N.Y., B.S., in 1945; from Massachusetts Institute of Technology, M.S., in 1949, and from the University of Michigan, Ph. D., in 1959; married the former Anne Biggs of Lapeer, Mich., in 1946; four children, Byron, Alice, Leslie, and Sarah; attends Unitarian Church; scientist, electronics engineer, and businessman; past lecturer at the University of Michigan; consultant for various firms and institutions; one of the founders in 1960, and, until election to Congress, a vice president and member of the board of directors of Conductron Corporation, Ann Arbor, Mich.; member, American Physical Society and NAACP; past member, Board of Ann Arbor United Fund, and Board of Michigan United Fund; chairman of Ann Arbor City Democratic Committee in 1959 and 1960; elected to the 89th Congress November 3, 1964.

THIRD DISTRICT.—Counties: Barry, Calhoun, Eaton, Kalamazoo, and Clinton, except the townships of Bath and DeWitt. Population (1960), 416,580.

PAUL H. TODD, Jr., Democrat, of Kalamazoo, Mich.; born in Kalamazoo September 22, 1921; graduated from Cornell University, B.S., class of 1943; founder of Kalamazoo Spice Extraction Co.; married to the former Ruth Newell; four children; member, American Economic Association, American Farm Economic Association, American Chemical Society, and Institute of Food Technologists; elected to the 89th Congress November 3, 1964.

FOURTH DISTRICT.—Counties: Allegan, Berrien, Branch, Cass, Hillsdale, St. Joseph, and Van Buren (7 counties). Population (1960), 404,898.

EDWARD HUTCHINSON, Republican, of Fennville, Mich.; born in Fennville, Mich., October 13, 1914; graduated from Fennville High School and the University of Michigan, A.B. 1936, LL.B. 1938; attorney; married; enlisted as private, Army of the United States, in January 1941; served as noncommissioned officer in 14th Coast Artillery and captain, Transportation Corps; discharged in April 1946; elected to Michigan House of Representatives in 1946 and 1948; State senator 1951–60; delegate and vice president, Michigan Constitutional Convention of 1961–62; elected to the 88th and 89th Congresses.

FIFTH DISTRICT.—Counties: Ionia and Kent (2 counties). Population (1960), 406,319.

GERALD R. FORD, Republican, of Grand Rapids, Mich.; born in Omaha, Nebr., July 14, 1913; attended Grand Rapids public schools; graduated Grand Rapids South High School 1931; graduated from University of Michigan with B. A. degree 1935 and from Yale University Law School with LL. B. degree 1941; admitted to Michigan bar in 1941; served 47 months in United States Navy in World War II; Grand Rapids Junior Chamber of Commerce Distinguished Service Award 1947; United States Junior Chamber of Commerce Distinguished Service Award 1949; married to Elizabeth Bloomer; three sons—Michael Gerald, John Gardner, and Steven Meigs, and one daughter, Susan Elizabeth; elected to the 81st Congress on November 2, 1948; reelected to the 82d, 83d, 84th, 85th, 86th, 87th, 88th, and 89th Congresses. *

SIXTH DISTRICT.—Counties: Ingham, Jackson, and Shiawassee and the townships of Bath and DeWitt in Clinton County. Population (1960), 408,117.

CHARLES E. CHAMBERLAIN, Republican, of East Lansing, Mich.; born July 22, 1917, Locke Township, Ingham County, Mich.; attended Lansing public schools; University of Virginia, B.S. in commerce, major in accounting, 1941; LL.B. 1949; admitted to Virginia bar and Michigan bar, 1949; served 4 years in World War II, commanding officer of vessels in both Atlantic and Pacific theaters; commander, U.S. Coast Guard Reserve; Internal Revenue agent, U.S. Treasury Department, 1946–47; city attorney of East Lansing, legal counsel to Michigan Senate Judiciary Committee, 1953–54; prosecuting attorney of Ingham County, 1955–56; married Charlotte Mary Craney of Norwich, Conn., 1943; three children: Charlotte Ellen, 1946, Christine Clark, 1951, Charles, Jr., 1954; member of Kiwanis, American Legion, Veterans of Foreign Wars, Reserve Officers Association, Lansing Chamber of Commerce, Michigan State Bar, American Bar Association, and Sons of the American Revolution; elected to 85th Congress November 6, 1956; reelected to 86th, 87th, 88th, and 89th Congresses.

SEVENTH DISTRICT.—Counties: Genesee and Lapeer (2 counties). Population (1960), 416,239.

JOHN C. MACKIE, Democrat, of Flint, Mich.; born in Toronto, Canada, June 1, 1920; moved with his family to Detroit in 1924; graduated from Detroit's Southeastern High School, attended Lawrence Institute of Technology, and graduated from Michigan State University (C.E.) in 1942; employed on airplane engine design in Detroit; enlisted in 1943 in U.S. Army Air Force; studied math and meteorology at New York University and served in the Pacific theater as an aircraft control officer until discharged as first lieutenant in 1946; worked in the Flint area for a Detroit engineering firm 1946 to 1952; in 1952 organized the Flint Surveying & Engineering Co. which was sold in 1957; married the former Kathleen Flood of Toronto in 1943; three daughters, Anne, Margaret, and Lora; elected Genesee County surveyor three times; elected State Highway Commissioner of Michigan in 1957 and reelected in 1961; registered professional engineer and land surveyor; member, Michigan Society of Planning Officials, Michigan Engineering

Society, Society of Automotive Engineers, Michigan Society of Registered Land Surveyors; Tau Beta Pi; past president (1963) of the American Association of State Highway Officials; elected to the 89th Congress November 3, 1964.

EIGHTH DISTRICT.—COUNTIES: Huron, Saginaw, St. Clair, Sanilac, and Tuscola (5 counties). Population (1960), 407,578.

JAMES HARVEY, Republican, of Saginaw, Mich.; born July 4, 1922, in Iron Mountain, Mich.; enrolled in the University of Michigan in 1940 but studies were interrupted by 3 years of service in the U.S. Air Force; in 1946 enrolled in the University of Michigan Law School and graduated in 1948, LL.B. degree; commenced the practice of law in Saginaw in 1949; served as assistant city attorney 1949–53, city councilman 1955–57, county supervisor 1955–57, and mayor 1957–59; Saginaw Junior Chamber of Commerce Distinguished Service Award 1957; one of Five Outstanding Young Men of Michigan 1957; married the former June Collins of Detroit, Mich.; two children, Diane and Thomas; elected to the 87th Congress November 8, 1960; reelected to the 88th and 89th Congresses.

NINTH DISTRICT.—COUNTIES: Benzie, Grand Traverse, Lake, Leelanau, Manistee, Mason, Muskegon, Newaygo, Oceana, Ottawa, and Wexford (11 counties). Population (1960), 404,789.

ROBERT P. GRIFFIN, Republican, of Traverse City, Mich.; born in Michigan November 6, 1923, son of J. A. and Beulah M. Griffin; educated in public schools of Garden City and Dearborn, Mich.; graduate of Central Michigan College with A.B. and B.S. degrees; graduate of University of Michigan Law School with J.D. degree; honorary LL.D. Central Michigan University, 1963; served as enlisted man in 71st Infantry Division during World War II, 14 months overseas; practiced law in Traverse City, Mich., 1950–56; named one of the Ten Outstanding Young Men of the Nation in 1959 by the United States Junior Chamber of Commerce; member of American Bar Association, Michigan State Bar Association, Kiwanis Club, American Legion; married to former Marjorie J. Anderson of Ludington; four children; elected to 85th Congress November 6, 1956; reelected to 86th, 87th, 88th, and 89th Congresses.

TENTH DISTRICT.—COUNTIES: Alcona, Antrim, Arenac, Bay, Clare, Crawford, Gladwin, Gratiot, Iosco, Isabella, Kalkaska, Mecosta, Midland, Missaukee, Montcalm, Ogemaw, Osceola, Oscoda, and Roscommon (19 counties). Population (1960), 403,263.

ELFORD A. CEDERBERG, Republican, of Bay City, Mich.; born in Bay City March 6, 1918, son of Swedish immigrant; attended Bay City schools and Bay City Junior College; entered the Army in April 1941; commissioned a captain in 1943; participated in the Normandy invasion and fought in France and Germany; received five campaign battle stars and Bronze Star Medal during war service; following World War II became manager of Nelson Manufacturing Co., Bay City; married; two children; elected mayor of Bay City in 1949, reelected in 1951; member of Evangelical Church, Lions Club, B. P. O. E., Odd Fellows, Masons, American Legion, and Veterans of Foreign Wars; elected to the 83d, 84th, 85th, 86th, 87th, 88th, and 89th Congresses.

ELEVENTH DISTRICT.—COUNTIES: Alger, Alpena, Baraga, Charlevoix, Cheboygan, Chippewa, Delta, Dickinson, Emmet, Gogebic, Houghton, Iron, Keweenaw, Luce, Mackinac, Marquette, Menominee, Montmorency, Ontonagon, Otsego, Presque Isle, and Schoolcraft (22 counties). Population (1960), 403,507.

RAYMOND FRANCIS CLEVENGER, Democrat, of Sault Ste. Marie, Mich.; born in Chicago, Ill., June 6, 1926; graduated from high school in 1944; served in the U.S. Army Medical Corps July 1944 to July 1946; attended Roosevelt University in Chicago, the London School of Economics and Political Science (University of London, England), B.A. degree from Roosevelt University in 1949 and LL.B. degree from University of Michigan in 1952; worked at various jobs while attending school; married the former Francile M. Corbat of Oxford, Mich., in 1948; five children, Phil, Diane, Jeffrey, John, and Sue Ann; began the practice of law in Sault Ste. Marie in 1953; admitted to practice in Michigan, Illinois, and before the Federal courts; commissioner of Michigan Corporation and Securities Commission 1961–63; appointed Circuit Court Commissioner in Chippewa County and later elected 1958 to 1960; served as acting municipal judge in the Sault; member of the Sault Industrial Development Commission and the Sault Park Commission; one of the founders of the Sault Community Council for Youth Work; active in both partisan and nonpartisan politics since 1950; elected to the 89th Congress November 3, 1964.

TWELFTH DISTRICT.—MACOMB COUNTY and Precincts 93, 105, 106 and 107 in ward 21, City of Detroit. Population (1960), 411,800.

JAMES G. O'HARA, Democrat, of Utica, Mich.; born in Washington, D.C., November 8, 1925, has lived in Michigan since 1939; graduate of University of Michigan, A.B. and LL.B.; attorney at law; World War II veteran; married Susan Puskas; seven children; elected to 86th Congress November 4, 1958, and to subsequent Congresses.

THIRTEENTH DISTRICT.—CITY OF DETROIT: Ward 1, precincts 1, 3 to 10, 12 to 18, and 20; ward 2, precincts 1 to 9; ward 4, precincts 2 to 9; ward 5, precincts 1 to 10; ward 6, precincts 1 to 9; ward 8, precincts 2 to 6 and 8 to 12; ward 9, precincts 1 and 6 to 15; ward 10, precincts 1 to 15; ward 11, precincts 1 to 14; ward 12, precincts 1 to 7 and 9 to 15; ward 13, precincts 1 to 15 and 17 to 19; ward 14, precincts 7, 10, 13, and 16; ward 15, precincts 1 and 3 to 18; ward 17, precincts 1 to 28; ward 19, precincts 1 to 3 and 5 to 24; and ward 21, precincts 1 to 19, 22 to 24, 28 to 31, 110 to 120, and 123. Population (1960), 416,452.

CHARLES C. DIGGS, JR., Democrat, of Detroit, Mich.; born in Detroit December 2, 1922; attended the public schools of Detroit and the University of Michigan in 1940, 1941, and 1942; enrolled at Fisk University, Nashville, Tenn., in the fall of 1942 and while a student there entered the United States Army as a private February 19, 1943, and was discharged as a second lieutenant June 1, 1945; furthered his education at Wayne University in Detroit and graduated in June 1946; mortician and business executive; married to the former Anna Johnston, an attorney; father of 4 children; member of the State senate 1951–54; elected to the 84th Congress November 2, 1954, and reelected to succeeding Congresses.

FOURTEENTH DISTRICT.—CITY OF DETROIT: Portions of wards 9, 13, 15, 17, 19, and 21; cities of Grosse Pointe, Grosse Pointe Farms, Grosse Pointe Park, Grosse Pointe Woods, Hamtramck, and Harper Woods; township of Grosse Pointe, in Wayne County. Population (1960), 417,026.

LUCIEN NORBERT NEDZI, Democrat, of Detroit, Mich.; born May 28, 1925; graduated from Hamtramck High School in 1943; University of Michigan, economics, A.B. degree, 1948; University of Detroit Law School, 1949; University of Michigan Law School, LL.B. degree, 1951; veteran World War II, with 20 months of overseas duty in the Philippines and Japan; served in the Korean War; admitted to the Michigan bar in January 1952 and engaged in the practice of law to date; Wayne County Public Administrator 1955; delegate to the Democratic National Convention in 1960; U.S. delegate to Interparliamentary Union; member of numerous community, fraternal, and legal organizations; married to Margaret Garvey; has four children: Lucien A., Bridget K., Brendan T., and Gretchen T.; member of the Catholic Church; elected to the 87th Congress on November 7, 1961, to fill the vacancy caused by the resignation of Thaddeus M. Machrowicz; reelected to the 88th and 89th Congresses.

FIFTEENTH DISTRICT.—The townships of Canton, Dearborn, Huron, Nankin, Romulus, Sumpter, Taylor, and Van Buren; the cities of Allen Park, Belleville, Dearborn Heights, Garden City, Inkster, Lincoln Park, Melvindale, and Wayne, all in Wayne County. Population (1960), 414,015.

WILLIAM DAVID FORD, Democrat, of Taylor, Mich.; born in Detroit, Mich., August 6, 1927; educated Henry Ford Trade School, Melvindale High School, Wayne University, University of Denver (B.S. and LL.B.); served in the U.S. Navy 1944–46 and U.S. Air Force Reserve 1950–58 and discharged as first lieutenant (legal officer); wife's name, Corinne H. Ford; three children, William D., Jr., Margaret, and John; attorney for 13 years; justice of the peace, Taylor Township, 1955–57; city attorney, Melvindale, Mich., 1957–59; attorney, Taylor Township 1957–64; Constitutional Convention delegate, 19th Representative District, in 1961–62; member State senate 1962 to 1964; member 16th District Democratic Organization, member of executive board 1959–64, corresponding secretary 1960–62; member Taylor Township Democratic Club, vice chairman and chairman of executive board; precinct delegate of the Democratic Party; member of—Taylor Township Businessmen's Association, Phi Delta Phi, Michigan Bar Association, Downriver Bar Association, American Bar Association, National Institute of Municipal Law Officers, and Rotary International; Distinguished Service Award, Junior Chamber of Commerce, in 1962; elected to the 89th Congress November 3, 1964.

SIXTEENTH DISTRICT.—CITY OF DETROIT: Parts of Wards 14, 16, and 18, all of Ward 20; cities of Dearborn, Ecorse, Gibraltar, River Rouge, Riverview, Rockwood, Southgate, Trenton, and Wyandotte; villages of Flat Rock and Woodhaven; townships of Brownstown and Grosse Ile. Population (1960), 414,872.

JOHN D. DINGELL, Democrat, of Dearborn, Mich.; born in Colorado Springs, Colo., July 8, 1926, to John D. Dingell, Sr., and the former Grace B.

Bigler, both deceased; married Helen Patricia Henebry on June 25, 1952, and they have three children, John David III, born August 9, 1954; Christopher Dennis, born February 23, 1957; and Jeanne Patricia, born October 8, 1963; graduated from Georgetown University and Georgetown University Law School; World War II veteran; worked as research assistant to United States District Judge Theodore Levin; served as assistant prosecuting attorney of Wayne County; practicing attorney, member of the bar of Michigan and the District of Columbia; ran for Congress to succeed his late father, who had represented the 15th District since its creation in 1932; elected to the 84th Congress December 1955; reelected to the 85th, 86th, 87th, and 88th Congresses; elected to the 89th Congress from the new 16th District created from portions of the former 15th and 16th Districts; member of the Polish Legion of American Veterans, Veterans of Foreign Wars, American Legion, Knights of Columbus, Polish National Alliance, Polish Roman Catholic Union, and Dearborn Chamber of Commerce; serves on Committee on Interstate and Foreign Commerce, Committee on Merchant Marine and Fisheries, and Select Committee on Small Business.

SEVENTEENTH DISTRICT.—Ward 22 in the city of Detroit, and that part of Detroit's 16th Ward east of Meyers which is bounded on the east by Livernois, on the north by Eight Mile, and on the south by the Pennsylvania Railroad tracks. Population (1960), 415,948.

MARTHA W. GRIFFITHS, Democrat, of Detroit, Mich.; born in Pierce City, Mo.; graduated, A. B., University of Missouri, and LL. B., University of Michigan Law School; member of the Michigan Legislature 1949–52; recorder and judge of Recorder's Court 1953; husband, Hicks G. Griffiths; elected to the 84th and succeeding Congresses.

EIGHTEENTH DISTRICT.—The cities of Berkley, Birmingham, Bloomfield Hills, Clawson, Ferndale, Hazel Park, Huntington Woods, Lathrup Village, Madison Heights, Oak Park, Pleasant Ridge, Royal Oak, Southfield, and Troy; the townships of Addison, Avon, Bloomfield, Oakland, Pontiac, Royal Oak, and Southfield, all in Oakland County. Population (1960), 417,174.

WILLIAM S. BROOMFIELD, Republican, of Royal Oak, Mich.; born in Royal Oak, son of Dr. S. C. and Fern Broomfield on April 28, 1922; graduated from Royal Oak High School in June 1940, and attended Michigan State University; in 1951, married Jane Thompson of Oak Park, Ill.; three daughters— Susan, Nancy, and Barbara Ann; member of First Presbyterian Church of Royal Oak; Berkley Lodge No. 536, F. & A. M.; Royal Oak Chapter No. 167, R.A.M.; Pontiac Commandery No. 2, Moslem Temple of Detroit; Greater Farmington Shrine Club; Greater North Woodward Optimist Club; life member of Optimist International; Royal Oak Hi-Twelve Club; Berkley Lions Club; Odd Fellows; honorary member of Royal Oak Kiwanis Club; honorary member of Metropolitan Club of America, Spirit 22, B.P.O. Elks Lodge No. 2169; elected to the Michigan House of Representatives in 1948, 1950, 1952, and was elected speaker pro tem in 1953 (the youngest man to hold such office in Michigan history); elected to the State senate in 1954; elected to the 85th Congress on November 6, 1956; reelected to the 86th, 87th, 88th, and 89th Congresses; member of Committee on Foreign Affairs.

NINETEENTH DISTRICT.—The townships of Brandon, Commerce, Farmington, Groveland. Highland, Holly, Independence, Lyon, Milford, Novi, Orion, Oxford, Rose, Springfield, Waterford, West Bloomfield, and White Lake; the cities of Farmington, Keego Harbor, Pontiac, South Lyon, Sylvan Lake, Walled Lake, and Wixom, all in Oakland County; that portion of the city of Northville lying in Oakland County; the township of Redford and the city of Livonia in Wayne County, and that portion of the city of Northville lying in Wayne County. Population (1960), 414,389.

BILLIE SUNDAY FARNUM, Democrat, of Drayton Plains, Mich.; born in Saginaw, Mich., April 11, 1916; raised in a farm community at Watrousville, Mich.; graduated from Vassar (Mich.) High School in 1933, continued education in Civilian Conservation Corps, and with special courses; worked for Pontiac Motor Co. in Pontiac, Mich., in 1936; held various UAW–CIO union offices from steward to international representative; consultant and adviser to civic bodies, boards, and commissions; appointed fair commissioner and helped to rejuvenate historic Michigan State Fair; administrative aide to former Senator Blair Moody 1952–54; assistant secretary of state of Michigan 1955; deputy secretary of state of Michigan 1957–60; auditor general of Michigan 1961–64; married the former Maxine DeCoe; three sons, Eugene, Norman, and Ronald; five grandchildren; served Michigan Democratic Party from precinct delegate to deputy state chairman, 1960–61; member of Congregational Church, Masons, Shrine, Elks, Eagles, Boy Scout organizations, and PTA; elected to the 89th Congress November 3, 1964.

MINNESOTA

(Population (1960), 3,413,864)

SENATORS

EUGENE J. McCARTHY, Democrat-Farmer-Labor, of St. Paul, Minn.; born in Watkins, Minn., March 29, 1916; graduated from St. John's University, College-ville, Minn., in 1935, from the University of Minnesota at Minneapolis with M. A. degree; taught social science in high schools for 5 years; professor of economics and education at St. John's University 1940–42; civilian technical assistant in the Military Intelligence Division, War Department; married Abigail Quigley in 1945; they have three daughters and one son—Ellen Anne, Mary Abigail, Margaret Alice, and Michael Benet; acting chairman of sociology department of St. Thomas College 1946; chairman of the Ramsey County Democratic Farmer-Labor Party in 1948; delegate at large to the Democratic National Convention in 1948; elected to the 81st, 82d, 83d, 84th, and 85th Congresses; elected as United States Senator for a 6-year term beginning January 3, 1959; reelected November 3, 1964; member of Senate Committees on Finance and Agriculture and Forestry; in 1959 and 1960 chairman of the Senate Special Committee on Unemployment Problems; author of the book *Frontiers in American Democracy* (1960), *Dictionary of American Politics* (1962), and *A Liberal Answer to the Conservative Challenge* (1964).

WALTER F. MONDALE, Democrat-Farmer-Labor, of Minneapolis, Minn.; born in Ceylon, Minn., January 5, 1928; son of the Rev. and Mrs. Sigvaard Mondale; attended Minnesota public schools, Macalester College, St. Paul, Minn., the University of Minnesota, B.A., and the University of Minnesota Law School, LL.B.; served as member of the Minnesota Law Review; married to Joan Adams, St. Paul; two sons and one daughter, Theodore, Eleanor Jane, and William; appointed attorney general, State of Minnesota, in May 1960; elected attorney general in November 1960, and reelected in 1962; while attorney general served as member of the President's Consumer Advisory Council, member of executive board of National Association of Attorneys General, chairman of National Association of Attorneys General Committee on Consumer and Investor Protection, chairman of Midwest Regional Association of Attorneys General; appointed to United States Senate, December 30, 1964, to fill unexpired term of Hon. Hubert H. Humphrey of Minnesota.

REPRESENTATIVES

FIRST DISTRICT.—COUNTIES: Dakota, Dodge, Fillmore, Freeborn, Goodhue, Houston, Mower, Olmsted, Rice, Steele, Wabasha, and Winona (12 counties). Population (1960), 438,835.

ALBERT HAROLD QUIE, Republican, of Dennison, Minn.; born near Dennison, Minn., September 18, 1923; attended the public schools; Navy pilot World War II; graduated from St. Olaf College, Northfield, Minn., with B.A. degree in political science, in 1950; married to Miss Gretchen Hansen, of Minneapolis, Minn., June 6, 1948; five children: Frederic, 15; Jennifer, 13; Daniel, 11; Joel, 9; and Benjamin, 3; farmer; former school board member and soil conservation district director; the recipient of the Distinguished Service Award of the Northfield, Minn., Junior Chamber of Commerce and the "Young Man of the Year" citation from the Minnesota Junior Chamber of Commerce; the recipient of the distinguished alumnus award of St. Olaf College; elected State senator in 1954; elected to the 85th Congress February 18, 1958, in a special election; reelected to the 86th, 87th, 88th, and 89th Congresses; member of the Committee on Agriculture and Education and Labor.

SECOND DISTRICT.—COUNTIES: Blue Earth, Brown, Carver, Cottonwood, Faribault, Jackson, LeSueur, McLeod, Martin, Murray, Nicollet, Nobles, Pipestone, Rock, Scott, Sibley, Waseca, and Watonwan (18 counties). Population (1960), 375,475.

ANCHER NELSEN, Republican, of Hutchinson, Minn.; born in Renville County, Minn., October 11, 1904; high-school graduate; farmer; served on local township and school boards; State senator for McLeod County from 1935 to 1948; Lieutenant Governor for the State of Minnesota in 1952; administrator of the National Rural Electrification program 1953–56; wife: Ilo; children: Richard, Bruce, and Miriam; elected to the 86th Congress on November 4, 1958; reelected to the 87th, 88th, and 89th Congresses.

THIRD DISTRICT.—ANOKA COUNTY. HENNEPIN COUNTY: That part outside the city of Minneapolis. Population (1960), 445,898.

CLARK MacGREGOR, Republican, of Plymouth, Minn.; born in Minneapolis, Minn., July 12, 1922, son of William E. and Edith Clark MacGregor; educated Minneapolis public schools, graduating covaledictorian from Washburn High School; academic scholarship to Dartmouth College, class of 1944, A.B. degree with honors; 3 years' service in United States Army in World War II, commissioned directly in the field in Burma while serving with Office of Strategic Services; LL.B. degree from University of Minnesota, 1948; practicing trial lawyer, 1948–60, partner in King & MacGregor; married Barbara Porter Spicer; three daughters, Susan, Laurie, and Eleanor; member of Bethlehem Presbyterian Church; director of Hennepin County community chest; member of American Legion; member VFW; elected to the 87th Congress November 8, 1960; reelected to the 88th and 89th Congresses.

FOURTH DISTRICT.—COUNTIES: Ramsey and Washington (2 counties). Population (1960), 474,957.

JOSEPH E. KARTH, Democrat-Farmer-Labor, of St. Paul, Minn.; born in New Brighton, Ramsey County, Minn., August 26, 1922; was educated in Ramsey County elementary schools and North St. Paul High School; attended the University of Nebraska School of Engineering; after completing 2 years of college courses in engineering, education was interrupted by a call to combat duty, during service in the European Theater of Operations received a recommendation for a battlefield commission; employed by the Minnesota Mining and Manufacturing Co.; international representative of the OCAW–AFL–CIO for 10 years; member of the Minnesota House of Representatives from 1950 through 1958; and during special session of 1958 was voted "Outstanding Legislator"; member: V. F. W., American Legion, Indianhead Council of the Boy Scouts, the First Presbyterian Church of White Bear Lake, Minn.; married the former Charlotte Nordgren and they have three sons; elected to the 86th Congress on November 4, 1958; reelected to the 87th, 88th, and 89th Congresses.

FIFTH DISTRICT.—HENNEPIN COUNTY: CITY OF MINNEAPOLIS. Population (1960), 482,872.

DONALD MacKAY FRASER, Democrat-Farmer-Labor, of Minneapolis, Minn.; attorney and former State senator 1954–62; born in Minneapolis, February 20, 1924; educated in Minneapolis public schools and University of Minnesota, B.A., cum laude, 1944, while in Naval ROTC, LL.B. 1948; served in Pacific Theater, World War II, as radar officer; active in D.F.L. party since 1947; secretary, Minnesota delegation to Democratic National Convention, 1960; chairman, Minnesota Citizens for Kennedy, 1960; former president, Minneapolis Foreign Policy Association; secretary and vice chairman, Minneapolis Citizens' League; vice chairman, Minneapolis Citizens' Committee on Public Education; served on boards of Legal Aid Society and University of Minnesota Law Alumni Association; married to former Arvonne Skelton; six children; partner in firm of Lindquist, Fraser & Magnuson; elected to the 88th Congress November 6, 1962; reelected to the 89th Congress.

SIXTH DISTRICT.—COUNTIES: Benton, Big Stone, Chippewa, Crow Wing, Kandiyohi, Lac qui Parle, Lincoln, Lyon, Meeker, Mille Lacs, Morrison, Redwood, Renville, Sherburne, Stearns, Stevens, Swift, Wright, and Yellow Medicine (19 counties). Population (1960), 420,235.

ALEC GEHARD OLSON, Democrat-Farmer-Labor, of Montevideo, Minn.; born September 11, 1930, in Mamre Township, Kandiyohi County, Minn.; attended public schools and graduated from Willmar High School, Willmar, Minn., in 1948; actively engaged in farming 1948–55; employed as a full-time insurance representative in 1955 and progressed from local agent to district supervisor, the position held when employment was terminated to run for Congress in 1962; held various elective offices in the D.F.L. party in Minnesota for the past 10 years, the most recent being 7th District D.F.L. chairman for 4 years prior to congressional redistricting in Minnesota; married to the former Janice Albrecht of Paynesville, Minn.; four children; elected to the 88th Congress November 6, 1962; reelected to the 89th Congress.

SEVENTH DISTRICT.—COUNTIES: Becker, Beltrami, Cass, Clay, Clearwater, Douglas, Grant, Hubbard, Kittson, Lake of the Woods, Mahnomen, Marshall, Norman, Otter Tail, Pennington, Polk, Pope, Red Lake, Roseau, Todd, Traverse, Wadena, and Wilkin (23 counties). Population (1960), 377,675.

ODIN LANGEN, Republican, Kennedy, Minn.; born January 5, 1913, in Minneapolis; graduate, Kennedy high school; 2 years' study, Dunwoody Industrial Institute; married Lillian Clauson of Kennedy; one daughter, Lois; two sons, Wayne and Lynden; active farmer; 15 years with the national farm program, Kittson County; served as chairman of Production and Marketing Administration; past president Kennedy School Board and Parent-Teacher Association; past chairman Red River Farmers Club and Red River Town Board; member of Masons, Lions, Lutheran Church in America (formerly Augustana); member of church's National Board of Social Ministry; State representative from 67th District, 1951–58; committee work in Agriculture, Education, State Taxation; vice chairman, Minnesota House Education Committee; minority leader of Minnesota House 1957–58; elected to U.S. House of Representatives 1958; reelected 1960, 1962, 1964; committee assignment, Appropriations.

EIGHTH DISTRICT.—COUNTIES: Aitkin, Carlton, Chisago, Cook, Isanti, Itasca, Kanabec, Koochiching, Lake, Pine, and St. Louis (11 counties). Population (1960), 397,917.

JOHN A. BLATNIK, Democrat-Farmer-Labor, of Chisholm, Minn.; born in Chisholm, Minn., August 17, 1911; attended Chisholm public schools; Winona State Teachers College, Minnesota, B. E. degree, 1935; University of Chicago; graduate work in Public Administration, University of Minnesota 1941–42; school teaching and administration, 8 years; elected to Minnesota State Senate in 1940; reelected in 1942; World War II; veteran 3½ years in Army Air Corps Intelligence and Office of Strategic Services; 18 months overseas in Italy and northern Yugoslavia; awarded Bronze Star Medal with Oak Leaf Cluster and Air Medal; discharged from service January 1946 as paratrooper captain; married to Gisela Hager in 1955; one son, Thomas H., and two daughters, Stephanie and Valerie; elected to 80th Congress November 5, 1946; reelected to 81st, 82d, 83d, 84th, 85th, 86th, 87th, 88th, and 89th Congresses.

MISSISSIPPI

(Population (1960), 2,178,141)

SENATORS

JAMES OLIVER EASTLAND, Democrat, of Doddsville, Miss.; born in Doddsville, Miss., November 28, 1904; Methodist; attended the University of Mississippi, Vanderbilt University, and the University of Alabama; moved to Forest, Miss., in 1905 and was reared in Scott County, Miss.; studied law, was admitted to the bar in 1927, and commenced practice in Forest, Miss.; also engaged in farming; member of the State house of representatives from Scott County, Miss., 1928–32; married Elizabeth Coleman in 1932; three daughters, Nell, Ann, and Sue, and one son, Woods Eugene; moved to Sunflower County, Miss., in 1934; appointed to the United States Senate to fill the vacancy caused by the death of Hon. Pat Harrison, and served from June 30, 1941, to September 28, 1941, when a duly elected successor qualified; elected to the United States Senate on November 3, 1942, for the term beginning January 3, 1943; unopposed for the term beginning January 3, 1949; reelected for term beginning January 1955; reelected for term beginning January 3, 1961.

JOHN CORNELIUS STENNIS, Democrat, of De Kalb, Miss., was born in Kemper County, Miss., August 3, 1901, the son of Hampton Howell and Cornelia (Adams) Stennis; B. S. degree. Mississippi State University, 1923; LL. B. degree, University of Virginia Law School, 1928; LL.D., Millsaps College, 1957; LL.D., University of Wyoming, 1962; member of Phi Beta Kappa, Phi Alpha Delta (legal), and Alpha Chi Rho fraternities; Presbyterian, Mason, Lion, member of Farm Bureau, Mississippi and American Bar Associations; past president, State 4–H Club Advisory Council; elected Mississippi House of Representatives 1928–32; elected district prosecuting attorney, Sixteenth Judicial District, 1931 and 1935; appointed circuit judge, 1937, and elected 1938, 1942, 1946; elected United States Senator November 4, 1947; reelected 1952, 1958, and 1964; member, Appropriations Committee, Armed Services Committee, and Aeronautical and Space Sciences Committee; chairman, Preparedness Investigating Subcommittee; married Coy Hines, 1929; two children, John Hampton and Mrs. Samuel Syme; a granddaughter, Jane Grey Syme, and a grandson, John Stennis Syme.

REPRESENTATIVES

FIRST DISTRICT.—COUNTIES: Alcorn, Attala, Calhoun, Chickasaw, Choctaw, Clay, Itawamba, Lee, Lowndes, Monroe, Noxubee, Oktibbeha, Pontotoc, Prentiss, Tishomingo, Webster, and Winston (17 counties). Population (1960), 364,963.

THOMAS GERSTLE ABERNETHY, Democrat, of Okolona, Miss.; born in Eupora, Webster County, Miss., May 16, 1903, the son of Thomas Franklin and Minnie Jinkins Abernethy; educated in the public schools of Eupora, Miss., the University of Alabama, Cumberland University (LL. B. 1924), and the University of Mississippi; admitted to bar in July 1924 and entered practice of law at Eupora, Miss., 1925; served as mayor of town of Eupora, 1927–29; moved to Okolona, Miss., in July 1929, where he has continued his practice; elected district attorney of the Third Judicial District of Mississippi, 1935, and reelected without opposition, 1939; Methodist, Mason, Shriner, Lambda Chi Alpha and Alpha Kappa Psi fraternities; married July 5, 1936, to Miss Alice Margaret Lamb, of State College, Miss.; two daughters, Margaret Gail, married to Arthur Warren Doty, and Alice Kay, and one son, Thomas Gerstle, Jr.; elected November 3, 1942, to the 78th Congress; reelected to the 79th, 80th, 81st, 82d, 83d, 84th, 85th, 86th, 87th, 88th, and 89th Congresses.

SECOND DISTRICT.—COUNTIES: Benton, Bolivar, Carroll, Coahoma, DeSoto, Grenada, Holmes, Humphreys, Issaquena, Lafayette, Leflore, Marshall, Montgomery, Panola, Quitman, Sharkey, Sunflower, Tallahatchie, Tate, Tippah, Tunica, Union, Washington, and Yalobusha (24 counties). Population (1960), 608,441.

JAMIE L. WHITTEN, Democrat, of Charleston, Miss.; born at Cascilla, Miss., April 18, 1910; married to Miss Rebecca Thompson, of Saltillo, Miss., June 20, 1940; two children, James Lloyd, born March 5, 1942, and Beverly Rebecca, born January 14, 1946; member Presbyterian Church, Masonic Order, Rotarian, Phi Alpha Delta (legal fraternity), and Beta Theta Pi; educated in the public schools of Cascilla and Charleston, Miss.; attended both literary and law departments of the University of Mississippi, being admitted to the bar in 1932 with honors and has since practiced law at Charleston, Miss.; served 1 year as school principal, 1930–31; elected to the Mississippi House of Representatives when 21 years of age and served one session; elected district attorney of the seventeenth district of Mississippi at the age of 23; reelected district attorney twice and served in that capacity until elected to the 77th Congress at a special election held on November 4, 1941, to fill the vacancy caused by the resignation of Hon. Wall Doxey; reelected to the 78th, 79th, 80th, 81st, 82d, 83d, 84th, 85th, 86th, 87th, 88th, and 89th Congresses.

THIRD DISTRICT.—COUNTIES: Adams, Amite, Claiborne, Copiah, Franklin, Hinds, Jefferson, Lincoln, Pike, Walthall, Warren, Wilkinson, and Yazoo (13 counties). Population (1960), 460,100.

JOHN BELL WILLIAMS, Democrat, of Raymond, Miss.; born on December 4, 1918, in Raymond, Miss., the son of G. K. and Maude Williams; veteran of World War II; prosecuting attorney of Hinds County, Mississippi, from May 20, 1944, to October 1, 1946; married to Elizabeth Ann Wells, of Raymond, Miss.; three children; Baptist, Mason; elected to 80th and succeeding Congresses.

FOURTH DISTRICT.—COUNTIES: Clarke, Jasper, Kemper, Lauderdale, Leake, Madison, Neshoba, Newton, Rankin, Scott, Simpson, and Smith (12 counties). Population (1960), 295,072.

PRENTISS LAFAYETTE WALKER, Republican, of Mize, Miss.; born in Smith County, Miss., August 23, 1918; attended grade school 12 years and college 2 years; president of Walker Egg Farms, Inc., in Mize, Miss.; past State president Mississippi State Fox Hunters Association; member of Governor's staff and on the Executive Committee of the State Game and Fish Commission under Governor Barnett; deacon in Baptist Church; past master Masonic Lodge; veteran of World War II; married to the former Dimple Marie Howell; two children, Jan Walker Magee and Treta Walker; elected to the 89th Congress November 3, 1964.

FIFTH DISTRICT.—COUNTIES: Covington, Forrest, George, Greene, Hancock, Harrison, Jackson, Jefferson Davis, Jones, Lamar, Lawrence, Marion, Pearl River, Perry, Stone, and Wayne (16 counties). Population (1960), 449,565.

WILLIAM MEYERS COLMER, Democrat, of Pascagoula, Miss.; elected to the 73d Congress on November 8, 1932, reelected to the 74th and succeeding Congresses; sponsor and chairman of the Special Committee on Post-War Economic Policy and Planning in 78th and 79th Congresses; member of the House Rules Committee and National Forest Reservation Commission.

MISSOURI

(Population (1960), 4,319,813)

SENATORS

STUART SYMINGTON, Democrat, of Richmond Heights, St. Louis, Mo., 63117; born June 26, 1901, in Amherst, Mass.; attended public schools in Baltimore, Md.; enlisted in the Army at 17; Yale, 1919–23; started in steel business as a molder; married to Evelyn Wadsworth, daughter of Senator James W. Wadsworth; two sons, Stuart and James; became president of Emerson Electric Manufacturing Co. of St. Louis; entered Government service July 16, 1945, serving successively as chairman of Surplus Property Board; Assistant Secretary of War for Air; Secretary of the Air Force; chairman of National Security Resources Board; Administrator, Reconstruction Finance Corporation; Episcopalian; Mason; elected United States Senator for Missouri on November 4, 1952; reelected November 4, 1958; reelected November 3, 1964, for term ending January 3, 1971.

EDWARD V. LONG, Democrat, of Clarksville, Mo.; born in Lincoln County, Mo., July 18, 1908; married to Florence Secor; one daughter, Ann Garner Long; educated public schools of Lincoln County, Culver-Stockton College and University of Missouri; practicing attorney; admitted to Missouri bar in 1936; elected prosecuting attorney of Pike County in 1937 and served two terms; president of Pike County Young Democratic Club 1940–44; city attorney of Bowling Green, 1941–45; elected to Missouri Senate 1945; majority floor leader of Missouri Senate, 65th General Assembly, and president pro tem 68th General Assembly; elected Lieutenant Governor of Missouri November 6, 1956, and renominated Democratic candidate for Lieutenant Governor in 1960; resigned as Lieutenant Governor September 23, 1960, to accept appointment as United States Senator, filling vacancy created by death of Senator Thomas C. Hennings, Jr.; elected United States Senator, special election, November 8, 1960, to unexpired term of Senator Hennings, ending January 3, 1963; reelected to full term on November 6, 1962, expiring January 3, 1969; district governor of Rotary International in 1942 and 1943; director of Rotary International 1950–52; member of Baptist Church; Phoenix Lodge No. 136; Ancient Free and Accepted Masonry; St. Louis Consistory No. 1; 33d degree Mason; Moolah Temple, Royal Arch Mason, Ascalon Commandery; Order of the Eastern Star; Independent Order of Odd Fellows, Elks, Sons of the American Revolution; member Pike County Bar Association, Missouri and Federal bar; resides Brookhill Farm, Clarksville, Mo.

REPRESENTATIVES

FIRST DISTRICT.—City of St. Louis: Wards 1 to 5, 19 to 22, and 27. St. Louis County: Townships of Florissant, Normandy, St. Ferdinand, and Washington. Population (1960), 466,482.

FRANK M. KARSTEN, Democrat, of St. Louis, Mo.; born January 7, 1913; attended elementary schools and high school in St. Louis and National University in Washington, D.C., receiving degree of LL.B.; member of the bar of the District of Columbia; admitted to practice before Supreme Court of the United States; served as congressional secretary to the late Representative John J. Cochran of the 13th Congressional District of Missouri from 1934 until 1946, during which time he also served as Chief of Staff for two congressional committees, the House Committee on Expenditures in the Executive Departments which was renamed the House Government Operations Committee, and the House Committee on Accounts; married Miss Opal Osborn, of Washington, D.C., and has two children, a daughter, LaVerne, and a son, Frank, Jr.; member of the Episcopal Church; first elected November 6, 1946, to the 80th Congress and has served continuously since that date; Assistant Majority Whip, member of the Committee on Ways and Means, United States Territorial Expansion Memorial Commission, and Migratory Bird Conservation Commission.

SECOND DISTRICT.—St. Louis County: Townships of Airport, Bonhomme, Clayton, Concord, Creve Coeur, Gravois, Hadley, Jefferson, Lemay, Lincoln, Meramec, and Midland. Population (1960), 506,854.

THOMAS B. CURTIS, Republican, 462 Florence Avenue, Webster Groves, St. Louis, Mo.; born in St. Louis, Mo., May 14, 1911; educated in Webster Groves public schools; A. B., Dartmouth College, 1932; M. A. (honorary) Dartmouth College, 1951; LL. B., Washington University Law School, 1935; Westminster College, LL.D. 1962; admitted to the bar of Missouri, 1934; member of Biggs, Hensley, Hughes, Curtis & Biggs; engaged in the general practice of law; member of the Board of Election Commissioners, St. Louis County, 1942; member of the St. Louis County Republican Central Committee, 1946–50; member of the State Board of Law Examiners, 1948–50; life trustee of Dartmouth College; member, board of trustees, William Woods College; served in the United States Navy from April 8, 1942, to December 21, 1945; married to Susan Ross Chivvis; five children: Elizabeth, Leland, Allan, Charles, and Jonathan; elected to the 82d Congress, November 7, 1950; reelected to the 83d, 84th, 85th, 86th, 87th, 88th, and 89th Congresses; member, Ways and Means Committee and Joint Economic Committee; represents St. Louis County; District office: Suite 201, 34 North Brentwood, Clayton, Mo., 63105.

THIRD DISTRICT.—City of St. Louis: Wards 6 to 18, 23 to 26, and 28. Population (1960), 480,222.

LEONOR KRETZER SULLIVAN (Mrs. John B. Sullivan), Democrat, of St. Louis, Mo.; widow of Representative John Berchmans Sullivan who was serving his fourth term as Representative from the 11th District at the time of his death on January 29, 1951; born in St. Louis, Mo., one of nine children; educated in public and private schools in St. Louis and attended Washington University at night; was director of a St. Louis business training school prior to marriage; served as administrative assistant to her husband during his terms in Congress; a Roman Catholic; member of the St. Louis League of Women Voters and the American Legion Auxiliary of Quentin Roosevelt Post No. 1; elected to the 83d Congress on November 4, 1952, by a majority of some 50,000 votes over her Republican opponent who had been selected at a special election held on March 9, 1951, to fill the vacancy caused by the death of her husband; is the first woman to be elected to Congress from the State of Missouri; reelected to the 84th, 85th, 86th, 87th, 88th, and 89th Congresses; home address—St. Louis, Mo.

FOURTH DISTRICT.—City of Kansas City: Wards 15, 17, and 23 and all that part of ward 24 lying east of U.S. Highway No. 71, and all of Jackson County outside the corporate limits of Kansas City, except that portion lying between the south line of Jackson County and the south city limits of Kansas City, and being west of U.S. Highway No. 71. Counties: Bates, Cass, Henry, Johnson, Lafayette, Pettis, and Vernon. Population (1960), 418,981.

WILLIAM J. RANDALL, Democrat, of Independence, Mo.; born, Independence, Mo., July 16, 1909; graduated William Chrisman High School, Junior College of Kansas City, Mo., University of Missouri, Kansas City School of Law, University of Kansas City; admitted to Missouri bar in 1936; veteran of World War II with service in Amphibious Unit in the Southwest Pacific and the Philippines; elected in 1946 as judge of the Jackson County Court and reelected to six additional 2-year terms; elected March 3, 1959, as Member of Congress, Fourth Missouri District, to fill the unexpired term of the late George H. Christopher; reelected to the 87th, 88th, and 89th Congresses; wife, Margaret L. Randall; one daughter, Mary Randall Wilson (Mrs. Garland Wilson III); member, Committee on Armed Services and Committee on Government Operations.

FIFTH DISTRICT.—City of Kansas City: Wards 1 to 14, 16, 18 to 20, and 22; all that part of ward 24 lying west of U.S. Highway No. 71, and all that part of Jackson County lying between the south line of Jackson County and the south city limits of Kansas City, and being west of U.S. Highway No. 71. Population (1960), 378,499.

RICHARD BOLLING, Democrat, of Kansas City, Mo.; born May 17, 1916, in New York City; B.A. and M.A., University of the South, Sewanee, Tenn., and further graduate work, Vanderbilt University, Nashville, Tenn.; teacher and coach, Sewanee Military Academy, Sewanee, Tenn.; veterans adviser and director of student activities, University of Kansas City, Kansas City, Mo.; volunteered as private in Army, 1941; served more than 5 years, over 4 of which were overseas in Australia, New Guinea, Philippines, and Japan; last assignment was as assistant to General MacArthur's chief of staff; awarded Legion of Merit and Bronze Star; discharged as lieutenant colonel; married to Jim Grant Bolling; three children; elected to 81st Congress, November 2, 1948; reelected to 82d, 83d, 84th, 85th, 86th, 87th, 88th, and 89th Congresses; member of Joint Economic Committee and House Committee on Rules.

SIXTH DISTRICT.—COUNTIES: Andrew, Atchison, Buchanan, Caldwell, Carroll, Chariton, Clay, Clinton, Daviess, DeKalb, Gentry, Harrison, Holt, Linn, Livingston, Nodaway, Platte, Ray, and Worth (19 counties).   Population (1960), 388,486.

W. R. HULL, JR., Democrat, of Weston, Mo.; born in Weston, Platte County, Mo., April 17, 1906; widower; children, Mrs. Susan Hudson and W. R. Hull 3d; elected to the 84th Congress November 2, 1954; reelected to the 85th, 86th, 87th, 88th, and 89th Congresses.

SEVENTH DISTRICT.—COUNTIES: Barry, Barton, Benton, Cedar, Christian, Dade, Dallas, Douglas, Greene, Hickory, Jasper, Lawrence, McDonald, Newton, Ozark, Polk, St. Clair, Stone, Taney, Webster, and Wright (21 counties).   Population (1960), 436,933.

DURWARD GORHAM HALL, Republican, of Springfield, Mo.; born in Cassville, Mo., September 14, 1910; educated in Greenwood High School, Southwest Missouri State College, 1926, Drury College, 1930, A.B., and Rush Medical College, 1934, M.D.; married the former Mary Elizabeth Turner of Springfield, Mo., September 6, 1931; one daughter, Mrs. Monty Ellison; chief surgeon with Smith-Glynn-Callaway Clinic; in general practice for 5 years; during World War II served for 7 years in the U.S. Army as chief of personnel service in Office of Surgeon General and as colonel with Legion of Honor; awarded commendation ribbon and two palms; member of U.S. Army Reserve; specialist in general surgery since 1947; fellow, American College of Surgeons, 1942; diplomat, American Board of Surgery, 1948; delegate to American Medical Association and alternate delegate to World Medical Association; Congressional adviser, XVth World Health Assembly, Geneva, Switzerland, 1962; past President of Rotary, local Chamber of Commerce, local council of B.S.A., State Chamber of Commerce, and member of executive committee of Region 8 B.S.A.; member of University Heights Baptist Church; elected to the 87th Congress November 8, 1960; reelected to the 88th and 89th Congresses.

EIGHTH DISTRICT.—COUNTIES: Boone, Camden, Carter, Cole, Cooper, Crawford, Dent, Howard, Iron, Jefferson, Laclede, Madison, Maries, Miller, Moniteau, Morgan, Phelps, Pulaski, Reynolds, Saline, Shannon, Texas, Washington, and Wayne (24 counties).   Population (1960), 452,385.

RICHARD H. ICHORD, Democrat, of Houston, Mo.; born June 27, 1926, in Licking, Texas County, Mo.; attended the public schools; upon graduation from high school he enlisted in the U.S. Navy Air Corps and served for 2 years in the Pacific area in the Naval Air Transport Service; married the former Vera Rodgers, of Licking, Mo.; two children, Richard 3d and Pamela; graduated from the University of Missouri, B.S. degree in 1949; member of Phi Eta Sigma, Delta Sigma Pi, Alpha Pi Zeta, and Beta Gamma Sigma; taught business law and accounting at the University of Missouri; received LL.B. degree in 1952 from University of Missouri; member of Phi Delta Phi; was admitted to the Missouri bar and commenced the private practice of law in Houston; member of the State house of representatives 1952–60; was elected speaker pro tem in 1957 and speaker in 1959; member of the Baptist Church, Veterans of Foreign Wars, Lions Club, American Legion, Independent Order of Odd Fellows, and the Masons; elected to the 87th Congress November 8, 1960; served on Committee on Interior and Insular Affairs and Committee on Post Office and Civil Service; reelected to the 88th Congress in 1962; served on Armed Services Committee and Un-American Activities Committee; reelected to the 89th Congress in 1964.

NINTH DISTRICT.—COUNTIES: Adair, Audrain, Callaway, Clark, Franklin, Gasconade, Grundy, Knox, Lewis, Lincoln, Macon, Marion, Mercer, Monroe, Montgomery, Osage, Pike, Putnam, Ralls, Randolph, St. Charles, Schuyler, Scotland, Shelby, Sullivan, and Warren (26 counties).   Population (1960), 409,369.

WILLIAM LEONARD HUNGATE, Democrat, of Troy, Mo.; born in Benton, Ill., December 14, 1922; attended public schools in Bowling Green, Mo., Central Methodist College, and the University of Michigan; graduated from Missouri University A. B. 1943 and Harvard Law School LL.B. 1948; married the former Dorothy Nell Wilson; two children, David and Kay; admitted to the Missouri, Illinois, and Federal bars and also to practice before the U.S. Supreme Court; past lieutenant governor of Kiwanis International, 1959; past president of Harvard Law School Association of Missouri, 1962–64; member of Christian Church, Veterans of Foreign Wars, American Legion, Masons, Shriners; researched with the American Bar Foundation into administration of criminal justice, 1956; elected to the 88th Congress November 3, 1964, to fill the vacancy caused by the death of Clarence Cannon; also elected to the 89th Congress.

TENTH DISTRICT.—Counties: Bollinger, Butler, Cape Girardeau, Dunklin, Howell, Mississippi, New Madrid, Oregon, Pemiscot, Perry, Ripley, St. Francois, Ste. Genevieve, Scott, and Stoddard (15 counties). Population (1960), 381,602.

PAUL C. JONES, Democrat, of Kennett, Mo., born March 12, 1901, in Kennett, Mo.; former member of the city council and mayor of Kennett; member for 12 years and president of the board of education in Kennett; 10 years' service in the Missouri legislature January 1935 to December 1944 (8 years in the State senate where he served as chairman of the appropriations committee); chairman of the State Highway Commission of Missouri from August 1945 to May 1948; directed the organization of the Sixth Missouri Infantry, Missouri State Guard, and for more than 5 years, from December 1940 until July 1946, served as commanding officer of that volunteer regiment; married Ethel Rockholt August 2, 1923, and they have three children, Mrs. Joe D. (Betty Anne) Cash, Paul C. Jones, Jr., and Mrs. Tom B. (Nell) Mobley; for more than 20 years member of the official board of the Christian Church, and superintendent of the Sunday school; copublisher of the Dunklin Democrat for more than 25 years until February 1, 1953; general manager of radio station KBOA since its opening in July 1947; past district governor of Lions International; Mason; graduate of the school of journalism, University of Missouri, B.J., 1923; president Mississippi Valley Flood Control Association, 1958-60; elected November 2, 1948, to unexpired term in the 80th Congress; reelected to the 81st, 82d, 83d, 84th, 85th, 86th, 87th, 88th, and 89th Congresses.

MONTANA

(Population (1960), 674,767)

SENATORS

MICHAEL J. MANSFIELD, Democrat, Missoula, Mont.; born March 16, 1903; enlisted in the United States Navy, World War I, at 14 years of age; subsequently enlisted in United States Army and United States Marine Corps; worked as miner and mining engineer in Butte, Mont., 1922–30; attended Montana School of Mines and Montana State University and received B.A. and M.A. degrees from latter in 1933 and 1934; professor of Latin American and Far Eastern history at Montana University 1933–43; married Maureen Hayes of Butte, Mont.; one daughter, Anne; elected to 78th and served through 82d Congresses; elected to United States Senate on November 4, 1952, for the term commencing January 3, 1953; reelected in 1958 for the term ending January 3, 1965; reelected in 1964 for the term ending January 3, 1971.

LEE METCALF, Democrat, of Helena, Mont.; lawyer; born in Stevensville, Mont., January 28, 1911; married to Donna Hoover of Wallace, Idaho, 1938; have a foster son Jerry; elected associate justice Montana Supreme Court, 1946; member of House of Representatives in 83d, 84th, 85th, and 86th Congresses; elected to United States Senate November 3, 1960.

REPRESENTATIVES

FIRST DISTRICT.—COUNTIES: Beaverhead, Broadwater, Deer Lodge, Flathead, Gallatin, Granite, Jefferson, Lake, Lewis and Clark, Lincoln, Madison, Mineral, Missoula, Powell, Ravalli, Sanders, and Silver Bow (17 counties). Population (1960), 274,194.

ARNOLD OLSEN, Democrat, of Helena, Mont.; born in Butte, Mont., December 17, 1916, son of Anna Olsen and the late Albert Olsen; attended the Butte public schools, the Montana School of Mines, and received law degree from Montana State University Law School; World War II served 4 years overseas duty U.S. Navy; married the former Margaret Williams of Butte, Mont.; three children—Margaret Rae, 19; Anna Kristine, 15; and Karen Synneve, 12; began the practice of law in Butte in 1940; attorney general of Montana 8 years; president law office in Helena; member of Methodist Church, Phi Delta Phi, American Legion, Veterans of Foreign Wars, American Veterans of World War II, Silver Bow Lodge 48 AF & AM, Scottish Rite, and Bagdad Temple of the Shrine, Scandinavian Fraternity of America, Elks, and Eagles; elected to the 87th Congress November 8, 1960; reelected to 88th and 89th Congresses; member Public Works Committee; Post Office and Civil Service Committee, and Chairman Subcommittee on Census and Government Statistics.

SECOND DISTRICT.—COUNTIES: Big Horn, Blaine, Carbon, Carter, Cascade, Chouteau, Custer, Daniels, Dawson, Fallon, Fergus, Garfield, Glacier, Golden Valley, Hill, Judith Basin, Liberty, McCone, Meagher, Musselshell, Park, Petroleum, Phillips, Pondera, Powder River, Prairie, Richland, Roosevelt, Rosebud, Sheridan, Stillwater, Sweet Grass, Teton, Toole, Treasure, Valley, Wheatland, Wibaux, and Yellowstone (39 counties), and part of Yellowstone and Glacier National Parks. Population (1960), 400,573.

JAMES FRANKLIN BATTIN, Republican, of Billings, Mont.; born February 13, 1925, in Wichita, Kans.; moved with family to Montana in November 1929; educated in public schools of Billings; upon completion of high school enlisted in the U.S. Navy for 3 years of service, with 2½ years overseas in the Pacific Theater; awarded two battle stars for action at Saipan and Okinawa; graduated in prelaw course from Montana State University Teachers College at Billings and LL.B. in 1951 from George Washington University, Washington, D.C.; married the former Barbara Choate; children—Loyce, Patricia, and James Franklin, Jr.; practiced law for 1 year in Washington, D.C., then returned to Billings to continue in law; served as deputy county attorney, secretary-counsel to City-County Planning Board, assistant city attorney, and city attorney; served in the State house of representatives; member of the Congregational Church, Masons, Shrine, DeMolay Legion of Honor, American Legion, and the junior and senior Chambers of Commerce; active in politics since 1950 and served as chairman of the Yellowstone County Young Republicans in 1954; elected to the 87th Congress November 8, 1960; reelected to the 88th and 89th Congresses; served on Judiciary Committee 87th Congress and Foreign Affairs Committee 88th and 89th Congresses.

NEBRASKA

(Population (1960), 1,411,330)

SENATORS

ROMAN LEE HRUSKA, Republican, of Omaha, Nebr.; born in David City, Nebr., August 16, 1904; son of Joseph C. and Caroline L. Hruska; attended the public schools; University of Omaha; University of Chicago Law School, 1927 and 1928; Creighton University College of Law, Omaha, LL. B. 1929; Creighton University LL. D. (hon.); Doane College (Nebr.) LL. D. (hon.); Coe College (Iowa) Doctor of Humanities (hon.); general practice of law in Omaha; married Miss Victoria E. Kuncl of Omaha, 1930; three children, Roman L., Jr., Quentin J., and Jana L.; member Nebraska State and American Bar Associations, Kiwanis, Shrine, Unitarian Church; University of Omaha Board of Regents 1950–57; national vice president and general counsel Western Bohemian Fraternal Association (Cedar Rapids, Iowa); past president Nebraska Fraternal Congress; 1944–52 Board of County Commissioners, Douglas County, Nebr., served as chairman 1945–52; member Advisory Committee to Nebraska Board of Control, 1947–52; president, Nebraska Association of County Officials 1950–51; vice president, National Association of County Officials, 1951 and 1952; elected to the 83d Congress November 4, 1952; elected to the United States Senate November 2, 1954, to complete unexpired term; reelected November 4, 1958 and November 3, 1964.

CARL T. CURTIS, Republican, of Minden, Nebr.; born near Minden, Kearney County, Nebr., March 15, 1905; attended Nebraska Wesleyan; lawyer; married Miss Lois Wylie-Atwater, of Minden, Nebr., June 6, 1931; one daughter, Mrs. Clara Mae Hopkins, and one son, Carl T. Curtis, Jr. (Tom); elected to the House of Representatives for the 76th through the 83d Congresses; served in the United States Senate since January 1, 1955; present term ends January 3, 1967; home address, Minden, Nebr.

REPRESENTATIVES

FIRST DISTRICT.—COUNTIES: Burt, Butler, Cedar, Colfax, Cuming, Dakota, Dixon, Dodge, Fillmore, Gage, Jefferson, Johnson, Knox, Lancaster, Madison, Nemaha, Otoe, Pawnee, Pierce, Platte, Polk, Richardson, Saline, Saunders, Seward, Stanton, Thayer, Thurston, Wayne, and York (30 counties). Population (1960), 530,507.

CLAIR ARMSTRONG CALLAN, Democrat, of Odell, Nebr.; born in Odell, March 20, 1920; attended the public schools and graduated from Peru State College, B.A.; married the former Joyce Stark in 1942; two children, John and Catherine; Naval officer in World War II, serving on a destroyer in Pacific theater; engaged as a farmer and stockman, and also in hardware, farm implement, and fertilizer business; lay leader in Methodist Church; member of Odell Village Board, Odell School Board, Gage County School Reorganization Board, Gage County Fair Board, and Gage County Extension Board; chairman of Governor's Committee on State Government Reorganization Board and the Nebraska Power Review Board; member of American Legion, Veterans of Foreign Wars, Masonic Lodge, Shrine, Beatrice Optimists Club, I.O.O.F., Elks, Odell Commercial Club, and American Aberdeen Angus Association; elected to the 89th Congress November 3, 1964.

SECOND DISTRICT.—COUNTIES: Cass, Douglas, Sarpy, and Washington (4 counties). Population (1960), 404,695.

GLENN C. CUNNINGHAM, Republican, of Omaha, Nebr.; born in Omaha, Nebr., September 10, 1912, son of George and Emma Cunningham; attended South Omaha High School; graduated from the University of Omaha with an A. B. degree in 1935; married Janis Thelen of Omaha, Nebr., in July 1941; six children, Glenn, Jr., Judy, Mary, Jimmy, David, and Ann Melissa; spent all adult life in civic and governmental work; served as executive secretary, Omaha Junior Chamber of Commerce from 1936 to 1940; from 1940 to 1941 served as manager of the Convention Bureau, Omaha Chamber of Commerce; from 1942 to 1947 served as manager, Omaha Safety Council; appointed to the Omaha City Council in 1947 and served until 1948 as superintendent of Department of Fire Protection and Water Supply for city of Omaha; elected mayor of Omaha 1948, reelected mayor of Omaha in 1951 having served a total of 6 years; appointed Nebraska State director, Savings Bonds Division, U.S. Treasury Department, 1954 and served in that capacity until April 1956; elected to Omaha Board of Education in 1946 and served as president of the Omaha Junior Chamber of Commerce in 1945; named Nebraska's Outstanding Young Man in 1946; is a member of the Legion of Honor, Order of DeMolay; member of Episcopal Church; Pi Kappa Alpha; Eagles; elected 2d District delegate to Republican National Conventions, 1948 and 1952; elected to 85th Congress November 6, 1956; reelected to the 86th, 87th, 88th, and 89th Congresses.

THIRD DISTRICT.—COUNTIES: Adams, Antelope, Arthur, Banner, Blaine, Boone, Box Butte, Boyd, Brown, Buffalo, Chase, Cherry, Cheyenne, Clay, Custer, Dawes, Dawson, Deuel, Dundy, Franklin, Frontier, Furnas, Garden, Garfield, Gosper, Grant, Greeley, Hall, Hamilton, Harlan, Hayes, Hitchcock, Holt, Hooker, Howard, Kearney, Keith, Keya Paha, Kimball, Lincoln, Logan, Loup, McPherson, Merrick, Morrill, Nance, Nuckolls, Perkins, Phelps, Red Willow, Rock, Scotts Bluff, Sheridan, Sherman, Sioux, Thomas, Valley, Webster, and Wheeler (59 counties).   Population (1960), 476,128.

DAVID THOMAS MARTIN, Republican, of Kearney, Nebr.; born in Kearney; July 9, 1907; attended the public schools in Kearney and Dartmouth College, married Margaret Taylor of Taylorville, Ill.; three children, David K., Patricia Maloney, and John L.; engaged in retail lumber business in Kearney; Presbyterian, Elk, Shriner; chairman, Nebraska State Republican Committee, 1949–54; member Republican National Committee, 1952–54; elected to the 87th Congress November 8, 1960; reelected to the 88th and 89th Congresses.

NEVADA

(Population (1960), 285,278)

SENATORS

ALAN BIBLE, Democrat, of Reno, Nev.; born in Lovelock, Nev., November 20, 1909, son of J. H. and Isabel (Welsh) Bible; married Loucile Jacks; children— Debra (Mrs. Robert Watkins), Paul Alfred, William Alan, and David Milton; A. B., University of Nevada, 1930; LL. B., Georgetown University School of Law, 1934; admitted to the Nevada State Bar, 1935; appointed, then elected district attorney of Storey County (Virginia City), 1935; elected attorney general of Nevada in 1942; reelected in 1946; served as president and vice president of National Association of Attorneys General; private practice of law under firm name of Bible, McDonald, & Carano, Reno, from January 1951; member of American Bar Association, Nevada State Bar Association; Methodist, Mason, Eagle, Lambda Chi Alpha fraternity; elected to the United States Senate November 2, 1954, to fill the unexpired term of late Senator Pat McCarran; reelected November 6, 1956; reelected November 6, 1962.

HOWARD WALTER CANNON, Democrat, of Las Vegas, Nev.; born St. George, Utah, son of Walter and Leah (Sullivan) Cannon; B.E. degree at Arizona State Teachers College, Flagstaff, Ariz., 1933; LL.B. at University of Arizona, 1937; honorary doctor of laws, Arizona State College, 1962; elected county attorney of Washington County, Utah, 1940; military service, 1941–46; awards include Distinguished Flying Cross, Air Medal with two Oak Leaf Clusters, Purple Heart, European Theater Ribbon with eight Battle Stars, and the French Croix de Guerre with Silver Star; 20 months overseas, shot down over Holland and evaded capture for 42 days before reaching allied lines; brigadier general in the Air Force Reserve, and has flown over a score of different planes, including the F–100 series (supersonic jets) and the B–58 Hustler; member, Nevada, Utah, and Arizona bars; firm, Hawkins, Cannon & Hawkins; elected Las Vegas city attorney, June 1949, reelected three consecutive terms; former president Clark County Chamber of Commerce; elected to United States Senate on Democratic ticket, November 4, 1958, for term ending January 3, 1965; reelected November 3, 1964; member of following Senate committees: Armed Services, Aeronautical and Space Sciences, Commerce, Rules and Administration; chairman, Subcommittee on Privileges and Elections; Senate advisor to United Nations Committee on Peaceful Uses of Outer Space; chairman, Military Committee, NATO Parliamentarians Conference; member, Reserve Officers Association, Air Force Association, International Counselor of Lions International, B.P.O. Elks, American Legion, Disabled American Veterans, and Veterans of Foreign Wars; religious affiliation is with the Church of Jesus Christ of Latter-Day Saints; married to Dorothy Pace; they have two children, Nancy Lee and Alan Howard.

REPRESENTATIVE

AT LARGE.—Population (1960), 285,278.

WALTER S. BARING, Democrat, of Reno, Nev.; born in Goldfield, Nev., September 9, 1911; was graduated from Reno High School in 1929 as a gold medal honor student; was graduated from the University of Nevada in 1934, with a B. S. degree and a B. A. degree; holds a high-school teacher's certificate; elected chairman Democratic Central Committee of Washoe County in 1936; was elected assemblyman from Washoe County to the Nevada State Legislature in 1936; was reelected in 1942; resigned in order to enlist in the United States Navy; served for 3 years; member Reno Lodge No. 13, F. & A. M.; member thirty-second degree Scottish Rite; member of Kerak Temple of the Shrine; member of Adah Chapter No. 4, Order of Eastern Star; member of the Fraternal Order of Eagles; member of the American Legion, Darrell Dunkle Post No. 1, Reno, Nev.; charter member Reno Sertoma Club; elected Councilman, Sixth Ward, Reno City Council in 1947; engaged in furniture business in Reno; Protestant; married to Geraldine Buchanan January 31, 1942; has four children,

Walter Stephan Baring 3d, William Robert Baring, John Buchanan Baring, and Thomas Jefferson Baring; elected to the 81st Congress on November 2, 1948; reelected to the 82d Congress November 7, 1950; elected to the 85th Congress November 6, 1956; reelected to the 86th Congress November 4, 1958; reelected to the 87th Congress November 8, 1960; reelected to the 88th Congress November 6, 1962; reelected to the 89th Congress November 3, 1964.

NEW HAMPSHIRE

(Population (1960), 606,921)

SENATORS

NORRIS COTTON, Republican, of Lebanon, N.H.; born Warren, N.H., May 11, 1900; educated Phillips Exeter Academy, Wesleyan University, George Washington University Law School; lawyer, firm of Cotton, Tesreau & Stebbins, Lebanon, N.H.; married in 1927 to Ruth Isaacs, of Union City, Tenn.; secretary to U.S. Senator George Moses, 1924–28; county attorney for Grafton County; justice, Municipal Court of Lebanon; majority leader, and later speaker New Hampshire House of Representatives; elected to the 80th Congress on November 5, 1946; reelected to the 81st, 82d, and 83d Congresses; elected to the United States Senate November 2, 1954, to complete the term of the late Senator Charles W. Tobey ending January 3, 1957; reelected November 6, 1956, for the term ending January 3, 1963; reelected November 6, 1962, for the term ending January 3, 1969; member of committees on Appropriations, Commerce, Small Business, and Republican Policy.

THOMAS JAMES McINTYRE, Democrat, of Laconia, N.H.; born in Laconia, February 20, 1915; attended public and parochial schools of Laconia; graduated from the Manlius School in 1933, Dartmouth College in 1937, and Boston University Law School in 1940; served during World War II, 1942–46, 376th Infantry, 94th Division, Third Army; awarded four battle stars, Combat Infantry Badge, and Bronze Star with oak leaf cluster for meritorious achievement; retired as major of Infantry; mayor of Laconia 1949–51; Laconia City Solicitor 1953; candidate for Congress in 1954; delegate to Democratic National Convention 1956; chairman of Laconia Democratic City Committee and Belknap County Democratic Committee; married to the former Myrtle Ann Clement (New Hampshire Democratic National Committeewoman 1952–56); one daughter, Martha Grey McIntyre; honorary president, board of trustees, Taylor Home for Aged 1954–62; director Laconia Industrial Development Corporation 1962; president Belknap County Bar Association 1961–63; member of Chamber of Commerce, Kiwanis, Knights of Columbus, Veterans of Foreign Wars, American Legion, Catholic War Veterans, Grange, and New Hampshire Bar Association; elected to the United States Senate November 6, 1962, to fill the vacancy caused by the death of Styles Bridges, in the term ending January 3, 1967.

REPRESENTATIVES

FIRST DISTRICT.—Counties: Belknap, Carroll, Rockingham, and Strafford. Hillsboro County: City of Manchester; towns of Bedford, Goffstown, Merrimack, Hudson, Litchfield, and Pelham. Merrimack County: Towns of Allenstown, Canterbury, Chichester, Epsom, Hooksett, Loudon, Northfield, Pembroke, and Pittsfield. Population (1960), 331,818.

J. OLIVA HUOT, Democrat, of Laconia, N.H.; born in Laconia August 11, 1917; educated Sacred Heart Parochial School and Laconia High School; supervisor of tabulating department in charge of data processing equipment for Scott & Williams, Inc., 1935–56; advertising manager, Laconia Evening Citizen, 1956; general manager, Lakes Region Trader, a weekly published by the Citizens Publishing Co., 1959; married the former Irene R. Fournier; one son, David; member Sacred Heart Church in Laconia; member, Kiwanis, Chamber of Commerce, Knights of Columbus, Laconia St. Jean-Baptiste Society, Elks, Lakes Region Sled Dog Association, Moose, Alpine Snowshoe Club of Manchester (life), and New England Daily Newspaper Association; engaged in Red Cross, Cancer, United Fund drives, Boy Scout work, community, civic, and religious activities; served 6-year term on Laconia Board of Education; elected mayor Laconia in 1959 and again in 1961; nominee for Congress in 1962; delegate to Democratic National Convention in 1964; elected to the 89th Congress November 3, 1964.

SECOND DISTRICT.—COUNTIES: Cheshire, Coos, Grafton, and Sullivan. HILLSBORO COUNTY: City of Nashua; towns of Amherst, Antrim, Bennington, Brookline, Deering, Francestown, Greenfield, Greenville, Hancock, Hillsboro, Hollis, Lyndeboro, Mason, Milford, Mount Vernon, New Boston, New Ipswich, Peterborough, Sharon, Temple, Weare, Wilson, and Windsor. MERRIMACK COUNTY: Cities of Concord and Franklin; towns of Andover, Boscawen, Bow, Bradford, Danbury, Dunbarton, Henniker, Hill, Hopkinton, Newbury, New London, Salisbury, Sutton, Warner, Webster, and Wilmot. Population (1960), 275,103.

JAMES C. CLEVELAND, Republican, of New London, N.H.; born in Montclair, N.J., June 13, 1920, son of Dr. and Mrs. Mather Cleveland; attended public schools, Deerfield Academy, Colgate University, magna cum laude, and Yale Law School; enlisted December 1941, served overseas in the Pacific for 40 months with the 40th Infantry Division; Field Artillery forward observer, air observer; and battery commander; received Bronze Star for valor as a forward observer at Fort Stotsenberg, Philippine Islands, discharged as a captain, Field Artillery, recalled to overseas duty during the Korean War; graduated Yale Law School in 1948; opened law offices in Concord and New London in spring of 1949; partner in firm of Cleveland & Bass, founded in 1960 and later changed to Cleveland, Waters & Bass in 1962; organizer, incorporator, officer, and director of New London Trust Co.; trustee, Colgate University, Hamilton, N.Y.; incorporator and director of King Ridge Ski Area; director of other business, charitable, and educational organizations; member of American Legion, V.F.W., Franklin Rotary Club, Masons, Elks, Eagles, Grange, New London Outing Club, and Phi Beta Kappa; married to former Hilary Paterson of Andover, N.H., December 9, 1950; four children—Cotton Mather, James Colby, David Paterson, and Lincoln Mather; member of the New Hampshire State Senate 1950–62, serving as majority floor leader during Gregg and Dwinell administrations; elected to the 88th Congress November 6, 1962; reelected to the 89th Congress.

NEW JERSEY

(Population (1960), 6,066,782)

SENATORS

CLIFFORD P. CASE, Republican, of Rahway, N. J.; born in Franklin Park, N.J., April 16, 1904, son of the Rev. Clifford P. Case and Jeannette McAlpin Benedict; married Ruth M. Smith of Linden, N.J., on July 13, 1928, and they have two daughters: Mary Jane (Mrs. William M. Weaver) and Ann (Mrs. John C. Holt); a son, Clifford P. 3d; and seven grandchildren; residence, 1128 Bryant Street, Rahway, N.J.; attended public schools in Poughkeepsie, N.Y., and was graduated from Rutgers University with A. B. degree in 1925 and from Columbia University with LL. B. degree in 1928; received honorary LL. D. from Rutgers University, 1955; honorary LL. D. from Middlebury College, 1956; honorary LL. D. from Rollins College in 1957; honorary LL. D. from Rider College in 1959; honorary LL. D. from Bloomfield College, 1962; was admitted to the New York bar in 1928 and practiced in New York City from 1928 to 1939 as an associate, and from 1939 to 1953 as a member of the law firm of Simpson, Thatcher & Bartlett; from August 1953 to March 1954 was president of The Fund for the Republic, created and financed by The Ford Foundation; member of the Rahway Common Council, 1938–42, and of the New Jersey House of Assembly, 1943–44; served as a Member of the House of Representatives from the Sixth New Jersey District (Union County), 1945–53; trustee of Rutgers University from 1945 to 1959; trustee of New Jersey Society for Crippled Children and Adults; director, N.J. chapter, Arthritis and Rheumatism Foundation; director, American Institute for Retarded Children; trustee, Rahway (N.J.) Chapter, American Red Cross; member, Sponsors Committee, Woodrow Wilson Foundation; member, Associate and Advisory Committee to Special Committee on Atomic Attack of American Bar Association; member, board of trustees, Roper Public Opinion Research Center at Williams College; member of Council on Foreign Relations; New York City, County, State, and American Bar Associations; Delta Upsilon, Phi Delta Phi, and Phi Beta Kappa Fraternities; Rahway Lodge No. 1075, B.P.O. Elks; and the Second Presbyterian Church, Rahway, N.J.; elected to the United States Senate on November 2, 1954, for the term beginning January 3, 1955; reelected in 1960 for the term ending January 3, 1967.

HARRISON ARLINGTON WILLIAMS, Jr., Democrat; residence, 231 Elizabeth Avenue, Westfield, N. J.; born December 10, 1919, in Plainfield; was graduated from Oberlin College, A.B. 1941, and Columbia Law School, LL. B. 1948; attended Georgetown University School of Foreign Service; awarded LL.D. from Rutgers University; attorney at law practicing in New Jersey; married Nancy S. McGlone in 1948; five children: Nancy, Peter, Wendy, Jonathan, and Nina; served 4 years in the Naval Reserve; Navy pilot; elected to the 83d Congress November 3, 1953; reelected to the 84th Congress November 2, 1954; elected to United States Senate November 4, 1958; reelected November 3, 1964; member of the New Jersey Tercentenary Celebration Commission, the Woodrow Wilson Memorial Commission, the Advisory Committee of the Unitarian Laymen's League, the New Jersey Bar Association, the Executive Committee of the Democratic National Committee's Nationalities Division, and the Elks; received an honorary doctor of laws degree at Rutgers, the State University, in June 1960; in February 1963 was the first recipient of the Father Raymond A. McGowan Award, presented by the National Council for the Spanish-Speaking.

REPRESENTATIVES

FIRST DISTRICT.—COUNTIES: Camden, Gloucester, and Salem (3 counties). Population (1960), 585,586.

WILLIAM T. CAHILL, Republican, of Collingswood, N. J.; born in Philadelphia, Pa., June 25, 1912; graduate of Camden Catholic High School, 1929; St. Joseph's College, 1933, and Rutgers Law School, 1937; has an A. B. and

LL. B. degree; counselor at law; served as city prosecutor of the city of Camden; first assistant prosecutor of the county of Camden, deputy attorney general of the State of New Jersey, special agent of the Federal Bureau of Investigation, and member of the New Jersey Legislature; married the former Elizabeth B. Myrtetus and they have eight children; elected to the 86th Congress on November 4, 1958; reelected to the 87th, 88th, and 89th Congresses.

SECOND DISTRICT.—COUNTIES: Atlantic, Cape May, and Cumberland (3 counties). Population (1960), 316,285.

THOMAS C. McGRATH, JR., Democrat, of Margate City, N.J., born April 22, 1927, in Philadelphia, Pa.; attended public and parochial schools; graduated from St. Joseph's Preparatory School, Philadelphia, in 1944; majored in the classics; studied chemical engineering at the University of Notre Dame for 1 year, leaving to serve in the U.S. Navy as an enlisted man in World War II; in 1945 was appointed to the United States Naval Academy at Annapolis, Md., and graduated with the class of 1950; served in the Atlantic and Pacific Fleets 1950–54, winning five battle stars while serving on the U.S.S. *Missouri* during the Korean fighting; qualified for command at sea, having served as acting commanding officer of LSM 397; lieutenant, USNR; graduated, University of Pennsylvania Law School 1954–57, LL.B. degree; practiced law in Philadelphia with the law firm of Dechert, Price & Rhoads 1957–63; a proctor in admiralty, also admitted to practice before the Supreme Courts of the United States, New Jersey, and Pennsylvania; member of the law firm of McGahn & McGrath, with offices in Atlantic City, N.J.; member of the American, New Jersey, and Pennsylvania bar associations; served New Jersey law clerkship in the office of the attorney general of New Jersey and was appointed a deputy attorney general, serving as counsel to the Division of Shell Fisheries, Division of Pensions, Department of Agriculture, Department of Labor and Industry, and Department of Banking and Insurance; married to the former Betty Butler and resides at 110 South Kenyon Avenue, Margate City, N.J.; member of the Blessed Sacrament Church in Margate; elected to the 89th Congress November 3, 1964.

THIRD DISTRICT.—COUNTIES: Monmouth and Ocean (2 counties). Population (1960), 442,642.

JAMES J. HOWARD, Democrat, of Wall Township, N.J.; born in Irvington, N.J., July 24, 1927, son of George P. and Bernice M. Howard; graduate of St. Rose School, Belmar, N.J., Asbury Park High School, St. Bonaventure University, Olean, N.Y. (B.A. 1952), Rutgers University (M. Ed. 1958); teacher and acting principal in Wall Township school system 1952–64; served as president of the Monmouth County Education Association and as member of the Delegate Assembly of the New Jersey Education Association; member of the National Education Association; past commodore of the Shark River Yacht Club; served with the United States Navy during World War II (South Pacific); married to the former Marlene Vetrano of Asbury Park, N.J.; three children, Kathleen, Lenore, and Marie; elected to the 89th Congress on November 3, 1964.

FOURTH DISTRICT.—COUNTIES: Burlington and Mercer (2 counties). Population (1960), 490,891.

FRANK THOMPSON, JR., Democrat, of Trenton, N. J.; born in Trenton, N. J., July 26, 1918; educated in the Trenton parochial and public schools, Wake Forest College, North Carolina, and Wake Forest Law School; member of law firm of Thompson & Convery, practicing at 122 West State Street, Trenton, N. J.; active in civic and veterans affairs; member of the American Veterans' Committee, the American Legion, and the V. F. W.; entered the United States Navy in 1941 and served until 1948; commanded the U. S. S. *LCI* (L) *428* and *LCI* (Rocket) Squadrons *63* and *48*; received three combat decorations for action at Iwo Jima and Okinawa; was commanding officer of USNR Battalion 4–22 and on January 1, 1952, completed a 17-month tour of active duty on the staff of the commander, Eastern Sea Frontier; married to Evelina Van Metre of Washington, D.C.; two daughters, Anne Gleaves and Evelina Porter Thompson; elected to the general assembly in 1949 and reelected in 1951 and 1953; served as assistant minority leader in 1950, the first person to hold that office, and minority leader in 1954; chairman, National Voters Registration Committee for the 1960 Presidential Campaign; elected to the 84th Congress November 2, 1954; reelected to the 85th, 86th, 87th, 88th, and 89th Congresses.

FIFTH DISTRICT.—Counties: Morris and Somerset (2 counties). Population (1960), 405,533.

PETER H. B. FRELINGHUYSEN, Republican, of Morristown, N. J.; born January 17, 1916; education: Princeton University, B. A. 1938, magna cum laude in history; Yale Law School, LL. B. 1941; during World War II served for 3 years in United States Naval Reserve; released to inactive duty with commission of lieutenant; on the staff of Foreign Affairs Task Force of Hoover Commission, 1948; director Trust Co. of Morris County; married Beatrice S. Procter, September 7, 1940; five children, Peter, Beatrice, Rodney, Adaline, and Frederick; elected to the 83d Congress November 4, 1952; reelected to the 84th, 85th, 86th, 87th, 88th, and 89th Congresses.

SIXTH DISTRICT.—Union County. Population (1960), 504,255.

FLORENCE P. DWYER, Republican, of Elizabeth, N. J.; born in Reading, Pa.; former State legislation chairman of New Jersey Business and Professional Women; member of the New Jersey Legislature, 1950 through 1956; husband, M. Joseph Dwyer; one son, graduate of U. S. Naval Academy, class of 1956; elected to the 85th Congress November 6, 1956; reelected to 86th, 87th, 88th, and 89th Congresses; member of House Government Operations and Banking and Currency Committees; member of Advisory Commission on Intergovernmental Relations.

SEVENTH DISTRICT.—Counties: Hunterdon, Sussex, and Warren. Passaic County: Borough of Ringwood and township of West Milford. Bergen County: Boroughs of Allendale, East Paterson, Emerson, Fairlawn, Franklin Lakes, Glen Rock, Hillsdale, Hohokus, Lodi, Maywood, Midland Park, Montvale, Oakland, Oradell, Paramus, Park Ridge, Ramsey, River Edge, Saddle River, Upper Saddle River, Waldwick, Westwood, and Woodcliff Lake; townships of Mahwah, Ridgewood (Ridgewood Village), River Vale, Rochelle Park, Saddle Brook, South Hackensack, Washington, and Wyckoff; cities of Garfield and Hackensack. Population (1960), 555,555.

WILLIAM BECK WIDNALL, Republican, of Saddle River, N. J.; born in Hackensack, N. J., March 17, 1906; Episcopalian; educated in the Hackensack public schools; graduated from Brown University, Ph. B., in 1926 and from the New Jersey Law School (now part of Rutgers University), LL. B., in 1931; profession is law; married Marjorie Soule in 1933 and has two children—Barbara and William S.; member of Bergen County Bar Association; member of the New Jersey House of Assembly 1946–49 and reelected for 1950 and 1951; elected to the 81st Congress in a special election held February 6, 1950; reelected to the 82d, 83d, 84th, 85th, 86th, 87th, 88th, and 89th Congresses.

EIGHTH DISTRICT.—Passaic County: Boroughs of Bloomingdale, Haledon, Hawthorne, North Haledon, Pompton Lakes, Prospect Park, Totowa, Wanaque, and West Paterson; townships of Little Falls and Wayne; cities of Clifton, Passaic, and Paterson. Population (1960), 394,279.

CHARLES S. JOELSON, Democrat, of Paterson, N.J.; born in Paterson January 27, 1916; attended local grammar schools and graduated from Montclair Academy; B.A. degree from Cornell University in 1937 and elected to membership in Phi Beta Kappa in junior year; LL.B. degree from Cornell in 1939; was admitted to the bar and began practice in 1940; enlisted in the U.S. Navy in 1942 and assigned to duties in the Far Eastern Branch of the Division of Naval Intelligence; city counsel of Paterson 1949–52; New Jersey chairman of the National Institute of Municipal Law Offices in 1952; became New Jersey deputy attorney general in 1954 and served until 1956, then served for 2 years as acting prosecutor of Passaic County; director of criminal investigation for the entire State of New Jersey 1958–60; married; one daughter, Susan; elected to the 87th Congress November 8, 1960; reelected to the 88th and 89th Congresses; serves on Appropriations Committee.

NINTH DISTRICT.—Bergen County: Boroughs of Alpine, Bergenfield, Bogota, Carlstadt, Cliffside Park, Closter, Cresskill, Demarest, Dumont, East Rutherford, Edgewater, Englewood Cliffs, Fairview, Fort Lee, Harrington Park, Hasbrouck Heights, Haworth, Leonia, Little Ferry, Moonachie, New Milford, North Arlington, Northvale, Norwood, Old Tappan, Palisades Park, Ridgefield, Rockleigh, Rutherford, Tenafly, Teterboro, Wallington, and Wood-Ridge; city of Englewood; townships of Lyndhurst, Ridgefield Park, and Teaneck. Hudson County: Township of North Bergen and town of Guttenberg. Population (1960), 451,126.

HENRY HELSTOSKI, Democrat, of East Rutherford, N.J.; born in Wallington, Bergen County, N.J., March 21, 1925; during World War II served in the U.S. Air Force in control nets system 1943 to 1945; management consultant in advertising 1962 to 1964; attended Paterson State College and graduated from Montclair State College, M.A. degree in 1949; teacher, high-school principal, and superintendent of schools 1949 to 1962; councilman of East Rutherford, N.J., in 1956 and served as mayor 1957–64; charter member of New Jersey Teachers Vets Association and member of N.E.A. and New Jersey Teachers Association; active in many civic, fraternal, veteran, and professional organizations; elected to the 89th Congress November 3, 1964.

TENTH DISTRICT.—ESSEX COUNTY: City of Newark, North Ward, districts 1 to 47; East Ward, districts 16 to 26 and 28; West Ward, districts 1 to 10; borough of Glen Ridge; towns of Belleville, Bloomfield, and Nutley. HUDSON COUNTY: Borough of East Newark; towns of Harrison and Kearny. Population (1960), 303,979.

PETER WALLACE RODINO, JR., Democrat, of 205 Grafton Avenue, Newark, N. J.; born June 7, 1909, in Newark, N. J.; lawyer; one of first enlisted men to be commissioned overseas; served with First Armored Division and Military Mission Italian Army; discharged April 1946 as captain; spearheaded drive against communism in the April 1948 elections in Italy; U.S. Bronze Star and other decorations; holds knighthood in the Sovereign Military Order of Malta; Knight Commander, Order of Merit, Italian Republic; Star of Solidarity, Italian Republic; knighted by former King Umberto of Italy, Knight of the Order Crown of Italy, Knight of St. Maurizio e Lazzaro; Italian Cross of Merit and other various foreign decorations; awards and citations from Veterans of Foreign Wars, AMVETS, Catholic War Veterans; past national chairman, Columbus Foundation, Inc.; honorary life member of Unico; recipient of 1964 Bill of Rights Award for distinguished public service in the field of Government; married to the former Marianna Stango; two children, Margaret Ann and Peter 3d; elected to the 81st Congress on November 2, 1948; reelected to the 82d, 83d, 84th, 85th, 86th, 87th, 88th, and 89th Congresses; U.S. Delegate to NATO Parliamentarian's Conference; U.S. Delegate to Intergovernmental Committee for European Migration.

ELEVENTH DISTRICT.—ESSEX COUNTY: City of Newark, West Ward, districts 11 to 44; Central Ward, districts 1 to 28, 32, and 33; South Ward, districts 47, 48, and 49; cities of East Orange and Orange; village of South Orange and the town of West Orange. Population (1960), 308,660.

JOSEPH GEORGE MINISH, Democrat, of West Orange, N.J.; born September 1, 1916, in Throop, Pa., son of George and Angelina Minish; attended elementary schools in Throop, Pa.; graduate of Dunmore High School, Pennsylvania; served as trustee, Essex County Welfare Federation for 6 years; vice chairman, 2 years; executive secretary of CIO, Essex-West Hudson Council, 7 years; secretary-treasurer, AFL–CIO, Essex-West Hudson Labor Council; member of the Newark Committee on Economic Development, Mental Health Association of Essex County, and the executive committee of the Green Acres Citizens Group; World War II veteran; member of Knights of Columbus Council No. 150, Newark, N.J., and of West Orange Lodge No. 1590, B.P.O. Elks; married the former Theresa La Capra; three children—George, James, and Joyce; elected to the 88th Congress November 6, 1962; reelected to the 89th Congress.

TWELFTH DISTRICT.—ESSEX COUNTY: City of Newark, South Ward, districts 1 to 46; East Ward, districts 1 to 15, 27, and 29 to 35; Central Ward, districts 29 to 31; boroughs of Caldwell, Essex Fells, North Caldwell, Roseland, Verona, and West Caldwell; towns of Irvington and Montclair; townships of Caldwell, Cedar Grove, Livingston, Maplewood, and Millburn. Population (1960), 361,993

PAUL KREBS, Democrat, of Livingston, N.J.; born in New York City May 26, 1912; formal education ended at high-school level but through a program of self-education and experience became a popular lecturer before many groups and on radio and television; engaged in welfare, civic, educational, labor, and political activities and served as a member and officer of many organizations in these fields; married to the former Peggy Thompson of East Orange, N.J.; member of the executive committee of the Essex County Democratic Committee; served as shop steward, secretary, and director of political action and education for the United Auto Workers, regional area 9, covering New Jersey; elected to the 89th Congress November 3, 1964.

THIRTEENTH DISTRICT.—HUDSON COUNTY: City of Bayonne; city of Jersey City: ward A, ward B; ward C, districts 17 to 40; ward E, districts 1 to 15; and ward F. Population (1960), 256,977.

CORNELIUS E. GALLAGHER, Democrat, of Bayonne, N.J.; born on March 2, 1921; a practicing lawyer; served on faculty of Rutgers University; graduated from John Marshall College and John Marshall College of Law, LL. B., cum laude; postgraduate studies at New York University; schooling was interrupted by 5 years' service in World War II; during World War II was a captain, commanded an Infantry Rifle Company in General Patton's Third Army in Europe, was wounded three times and holds eight decorations; recalled and served 1 year during Korean War; is a member of the law firm of Dembe, Dembe & Gallagher, a director of and counsel to the Broadway National Bank; elected to the Hudson County Board of Freeholders in 1953 and resigned to accept appointment as commissioner of New Jersey Turnpike Authority, later serving as vice chairman; has lectured and written articles on toll highways; member of the Hudson County Democratic Executive Committee since 1950 and served as a delegate to the 1952, 1956, 1960, and 1964 National Democratic Conventions; received award of National Council of Christians and Jews; member of the American, New Jersey, and Hudson County Bar Associations, American Legion, Knights of Columbus, and Elks; is married to former Claire Richter of Bayonne, they have four children: Diane, Christine, Patrice, and Briget; elected to the 86th Congress November 4, 1958; reelected to the 87th, 88th, and 89th Congresses; member House Foreign Affairs Committee and chairman, United States and Canadian Interparliamentary Group; adviser to United States Delegation to the Disarmament Conference; member House Government Operations Committee and chairman of Special Subcommittee Investigating Invasion of Privacy.

FOURTEENTH DISTRICT.—HUDSON COUNTY: City of Jersey City: ward C, districts 1 to 16; ward D; ward E, districts 16 to 33; cities of Hoboken and Union City; towns of Secaucus and West New York; township of Weehawken. Population (1960), 255,165.

DOMINICK V. DANIELS, Democrat, of Jersey City, N. J.; born in Jersey City, N. J., October 18, 1908; educated in the Jersey City public schools; attended Fordham University and graduated in 1929 from Rutgers University (N. J.) Law School, receiving LL. B. degree; admitted to New Jersey bar in 1930 and has since been engaged in the general practice of law; now senior member of the law firm of Daniels, Colello & Daniels of 591 Summit Avenue, Jersey City, N.J.; married Camille Curcio in 1935 and has two children, Dolores and Barbara; appointed magistrate of the Jersey City Municipal Court in May 1952, reappointed in 1955, and subsequently appointed presiding magistrate; president of Jersey City Lions Club from 1949 to 1950; president of the Dante Alighieri Society of Jersey City, Inc., from 1954 to 1957; Jersey City chairman of Po Valley Flood Relief Committee; vice chairman of the Jersey City Civil Rights Committee from 1952 to 1955; member of University Club of Hudson County, Hudson County Bar Association, New Jersey Bar Association, Benevolent Protective Order of Elks, Knights of Columbus (Council 137), fourth degree; elected to the 86th Congress November 4, 1958; reelected to the 87th, 88th, and 89th Congresses; member of Education and Labor Committee and the Post Office and Civil Service Committee and the following subcommittees: Retirement, Insurance and Health Benefits (chairman); Postal Operations, Postal Rates, and Postal Facilities and Modernization.

FIFTEENTH DISTRICT.—MIDDLESEX COUNTY. Population (1960), 433,856.

EDWARD JAMES PATTEN, Democrat, of Perth Amboy, N.J.; born in Perth Amboy, August 22, 1905; graduated from Newark State College, Rutgers Law School, LL.B., and Rutgers University, B.S. Ed.; member of Eagles, Moose, Elks, Kiwanis, Knights of Columbus, National Conference of Christians and Jews, Chamber of Commerce, and NAACP; lawyer, 1927; teacher public schools, 1927–34; mayor of the city of Perth Amboy, 1934–40; county clerk of Middlesex County, 1940–54; campaign manager for Robert B. Meyner, 1953 and 1957; secretary of state of the State of New Jersey, 1954–62; president, Salvation Army Board; past president of the Middlesex Bar Association; chairman of the Middlesex County Democratic Committee, 1934–36; member of the Democratic State Committee and member of American Judicature Society; recipient of "Outstanding Citizenship" award from American Heritage Foundation and B'nai B'rith's "Brotherhood" award; married February 22, 1936, to Anna Quigg of South Amboy, N.J.; one daughter, Catherine M.; elected to the 88th Congress November 6, 1962; reelected to the 89th Congress.

NEW MEXICO

(Population (1960), 951,023)

SENATORS

CLINTON P. ANDERSON, Democrat, of Albuquerque, N. Mex.; born at Centerville, S. Dak., October 23, 1895; was educated at Dakota Wesleyan University and University of Michigan; general insurance business; married; two children; president, Rotary International, 1932–33; treasurer of State of New Mexico, 1933–34; administrator, New Mexico Relief Administration, 1935; field representative, Federal Emergency Relief Administration, 1935–36; chairman and executive director, Unemployment Compensation Commission of New Mexico, 1936–38; managing director, United States Coronado Exposition Commission, 1939–40; elected to 77th, 78th, and 79th Congresses; appointed Secretary of Agriculture June 30, 1945; resigned May 10, 1948, to enter Democratic primary for United States Senator; elected on November 2, 1948, to the United States Senate; reelected in 1954 and again in 1960 for the term ending January 3, 1967.

JOSEPH M. MONTOYA, Democrat, of Santa Fe, N. Mex.; born in Sandoval County, N. Mex., September 24, 1915; attended Regis College in Denver, Colo., and Georgetown University Law School in Washington, D. C., receiving LL. B. in 1938; a lawyer by profession; actively engaged in various business enterprises; elected to New Mexico House of Representatives in 1936 at age of 21 while still in college; reelected in 1938 and named majority floor leader; elected as youngest member of State senate in 1940 and named majority whip; reelected to State senate in 1944 and named chairman, Senate Judiciary Committee; was elected Lieutenant Governor in 1946 and reelected in 1948; in 1952 again was elected to the State senate; in 1954 was returned to the office of Lieutenant Governor, and reelected in 1956; married Della Romero and they have three children—Joseph II, Patrick, and Linda; delegate, Interparliamentary Conference, Warsaw, Poland, 1959; U. S. member of Executive Committee, Inter-American Parliamentary Organization; National co-chairman, Viva Kennedy Clubs, 1960; elected to the 85th Congress in special election April 9, 1957, to fill the vacancy caused by the death of Antonio M. Fernandez; reelected to the 86th, 87th, and 88th Congresses; elected to the United States Senate November 3, 1964, to fill the unexpired term of Dennis Chavez and also elected to the full term ending January 3, 1971.

REPRESENTATIVES

AT LARGE.—Population (1960), 951,023.

THOMAS G. MORRIS, Democrat, of Tucumcari, N. Mex.; born in Eastland County, Tex., August 20, 1919; graduate of University of New Mexico, class of 1948, receiving a B. S. degree in civil engineering; married Corinne Stevens and they have one son, Thomas G. Morris 2d, 9 years of age, and one daughter, Elizabeth Jane, 2 years; served in the United States Navy as an enlisted man from November 12, 1937, to March 22, 1944; engaged in farming and ranching business in Quay County, New Mexico; elected to the New Mexico House of Representatives and served continuously from January 1953 to December 31, 1958; chairman of the New Mexico Interstate Streams Commission; member of Veterans of Foreign Wars, D. A. V., American Legion, New Mexico Farm and Livestock Bureau, National Reclamation Association, New Mexico Cattle Growers Association, B. P. O. E., Lions International; elected to the 86th Congress on November 4, 1958; reelected to the 87th, 88th, and 89th Congresses.

E. S. JOHNNY WALKER, Democrat, of Santa Fe, N. Mex.; born in Fulton, Ky., June 18, 1911; resident of New Mexico 38 years; graduate Albuquerque High School, attended University of New Mexico, and the National University in Washington, D.C.; veteran of World War II, and served in North African and European theaters of operation; member of the Veterans of Foreign Wars, the American Legion, and Elks; served two terms in the New Mexico House of Representatives (majority whip); chairman, Ways and Means Committee; 8 years (four terms) commissioner, State Land Office (only commissioner ever elected four terms to Land Office); commissioner of the Bureau of Revenue (New Mexico); organizer and first director of the Oil and Gas Accounting Commission; served as member of the Oil Conservation Commission, the State Forestry Commission, the Oil and Gas Accounting Commission, and the State Investment Council; married; wife, Polly; two children, Janet and Stephen Michael (University of New Mexico); private enterprises include the Johnny Walker Enterprises, part owner Free Fraser Pharmacy, and the Adobe Motel in Santa Fe; elected to the 89th Congress November 3, 1964.

NEW YORK

(Population (1960), 16,782,304)

SENATORS

JACOB K. JAVITS, Republican, of New York City; born on the lower East Side of New York City, May 18, 1904; after working several years and taking supplementary night courses at Columbia University was graduated from New York University (Law School) in 1926; admitted to the bar in 1927; honorary LL. D. degrees from New York University, Lincoln University, Long Island University, Hartwick College, Yeshiva University, Hebrew Union College, Pace College, Ithaca College; before Pearl Harbor was a special assistant to the Chief of Chemical Warfare Service, U.S. Army; remained in that service until March 1942, when he went into the Army as a major and became assistant to the Chief of Operations of Chemical Warfare; served in the European Theater of Operations in 1943 and in the Pacific in 1944; received the Legion of Merit and Army Commendation Ribbon; discharged as a lieutenant colonel in June 1945 and resumed the practice of law; married Marion Ann Borris in 1947; three children: Joy, age 17; Joshua, age 15; and Carla, age 9; member of American Legion, Veterans of Foreign Wars, and Jewish War Veterans; served in the 80th, 81st, 82d, and 83d Congresses from Washington Heights and Inwood District of New York City; elected attorney general of New York in 1954 for a 4-year term; elected to the United States Senate on November 6, 1956, for the term ending 1963; reelected November 6, 1962, for the term ending 1969.

ROBERT FRANCIS KENNEDY, Democrat, of Glen Cove, N.Y.; born Boston, Mass.; November 20, 1925; graduated Milton Academy, Milton, Mass.; B.A. Harvard University, 1948; LL.B. University of Virginia Law School, 1951; LL.D. (honorary) Assumption College, Mount St. Mary's College, Tufts University, Fordham University, Nihon University, Manhattan College, University of the Philippines, Marquette University; Ph.D. (honorary) Free University of Berlin; Catholic; married to Ethel Skakel; children: Kathleen Hartington, Joseph Patrick, Robert Francis, David Anthony, Mary Courtney, Michael LeMoyne, Mary Kerry, Christopher George, and Matthew Maxwell Taylor; president of the Foundation for All Africa; member of the Advisory Council for the Law School of the University of Notre Dame; member of the Board of Visitors, University of Virginia Law School; member of the American Bar Association, Federal Bar Association, Veterans of Foreign Wars, American Legion; author of "The Enemy Within," "Just Friends and Brave Enemies," and "Pursuit of Justice"; admitted to Massachusetts State Bar, 1951; admitted to practice before the United States Supreme Court, 1955; served in the U.S. Navy 1944–46; correspondent Boston Post, Arab-Israel War, 1948; attorney, Criminal Division, Department of Justice, 1951–52; campaign manager for Congressman John F. Kennedy's election to U.S. Senate (1952); assistant counsel, Senate Permanent Subcommittee on Investigations (1953); assistant counsel, Hoover Commission (1953); chief counsel to the Minority Senate Permanent Subcommittee on Investigations (1954); chief counsel and staff director, Senate Permanent Subcommittee on Investigations (1955); chief counsel Senate Select Committee on Improper Activities in the Labor or Management Field (1957–60); campaign manager for President Kennedy's election to the Presidency; Attorney General of the United States, January 21, 1961 to September 3, 1964; elected to the U.S. Senate November 3, 1964, for the term commencing January 3, 1965.

REPRESENTATIVES

FIRST DISTRICT.—SUFFOLK COUNTY: That part consisting of the towns of Smithtown, Islip, Brookhaven, Riverhead, Southampton, Southold, East Hampton, Shelter Island, Gardiner's Island, Fisher's Island, Shinnecock Indian Reservation, and all islands within the above-mentioned townships. Population (1960), 398,254.

OTIS G. PIKE, Democrat, of Riverhead, L.I., N.Y.; born in Riverhead August 31, 1921; graduated from Princeton University, A.B., Columbia University,

LL. B., and Adelphi University, LL. D.; attorney; married Doris A. Orth; three children, Lois, Douglas, and Robert; served in World War II as a Marine Corps dive bomber pilot in Solomon Islands and as a night fighter pilot at Peleliu and Okinawa, with occupation forces at Peking, North China; flew 120 combat missions; awarded 5 air medals; vice president of Long Island Home, Ltd., Amityville, N.Y., past director of Central Suffolk Hospital, Riverhead, N.Y.; justice of peace of the town of Riverhead 1954–60; member of First Congregational Church, Rotary Club, V.F.W., American Legion, Suffolk County Bar Association, and F. & A.M.; elected to the 87th Congress November 8, 1960; reelected to the 88th Congress November 6, 1962; reelected to the 89th Congress November 3, 1964.

SECOND DISTRICT.—SUFFOLK COUNTY: That part consisting of the towns of Huntington and Babylon. NASSAU COUNTY: That part beginning at a point in the town of Oyster Bay where the Northern State Parkway intersects the dividing line between the county of Suffolk and the county of Nassau, thence westerly along Northern State Parkway to the Wantagh Oyster Bay Expressway, thence southerly to Phipps Lane, to Wallace Drive (Edgemere Road), to Wantagh Oyster Bay Expressway, to Old Country Road, to Farmers Plain Avenue (Grohman Road), to Plain Hay Path, to Plainview Road, to Bethpage State Parkway, to Central Park Avenue, to Bethpage State Parkway, to Southern State Parkway, to a point where Southern State Parkway and the northwest village line of the village of Massapequa Park intersects, thence southerly along said village line of the village of Massapequa Park to Jerusalem Avenue, thence westerly along Jerusalem Avenue to the dividing line between the town of Oyster Bay and the town of Hempstead, thence southerly along said dividing line to the waters of the Atlantic Ocean, thence easterly through the waters of the Atlantic Ocean to the dividing line between the county of Nassau and the county of Suffolk, thence northerly along the dividing line between the county of Nassau and the county of Suffolk to the place of beginning. Population (1960), 372,645.

JAMES R. GROVER, JR., Republican, of Babylon, N.Y.; born March 5, 1919, in Babylon, N.Y.; graduate of St. Joseph's Elementary School, Babylon High School, Hofstra College, and Columbia Law School; during World War II served overseas in the Coast Artillery and the Air Force in China Theater and was discharged with rank of captain; married the former Mary Fullerton of Babylon and they have four children—Nancy, Jean, Bobby, and Jill; member of the New York State Assembly, 1957–62; attorney, with law offices in Babylon, N.Y.; served as special counsel for the town of Babylon; member of Lions Club, Knights of Columbus, Holy Name Society, Veterans of Foreign Wars, American Legion, American Red Cross, and Babylon Yacht Club; elected to the 88th Congress November 6, 1962; reelected to the 89th Congress.

THIRD DISTRICT.—NASSAU COUNTY: That part beginning at a point in the town of Oyster Bay where the Northern State Parkway intersects the dividing line between the county of Suffolk and the county of Nassau, thence westerly along Northern State Parkway to the Wantagh Oyster Bay Expressway, thence southerly to Phipps Lane, to Wallace Drive (Edgemere Road), to Southern Parkway, to Wantagh Oyster Bay Expressway, to Old Country Road, to Farmers Plain Avenue (Grohman Road), to Plain Hay Path, to Plainview Road, to Bethpage State Parkway, to Bethpage Turnpike (Hempstead Turnpike), thence westerly along Bethpage Turnpike (Hempstead Turnpike) to the intersection of Bethpage Turnpike (Hempstead Turnpike) and the town line of Oyster Bay and the town line of Hempstead, thence northerly, westerly and northwesterly along the town lines of the town of Oyster Bay and the town of Hempstead and said town lines of the town of Oyster Bay and the town of North Hempstead extended to the waters of Hempstead Harbor, thence through the waters of Hempstead Harbor, Long Island Sound, Cold Spring Harbor to the northern dividing line between the county of Suffolk and the county of Nassau and thence southerly along said dividing line between the county of Suffolk and the county of Nassau to the place of beginning, also including the town of North Hempstead and the city of Glen Cove. Population (1960), 399,067.

LESTER LIONEL WOLFF, Democrat, Great Neck, N.Y.; born in New York City January 4, 1919; married the former Blanche Silver; two children, Bruce and Diane; educated New York University, 1939, marketing major and lecturer 1939–41; head of Marketing Department of Collegiate Institute 1945–49; major, public relations officer, squad commander, C.A.P., U.S.A.F. Auxiliary; chairman of the board of Coordinated Marketing Agency and member of the board of Noramco (Dugan's) and the Madison Life Insurance Co.; served as television moderator and producer of Between the Lines 1948–60 and as producer for Showcase and the Wendy Barrie Show 1955–58; member of U.S. Trade Mission to the Philippines in 1962 and to Malaysia and Hong Kong in 1963; chairman, Advisory Committee of the Subcommittee on Consumers Study by the House of Representatives, 1957; trustee, National Jewish Hospital at Denver and Deborah Hospital; elected to the 89th Congress November 3, 1964.

FOURTH DISTRICT.—NASSAU COUNTY: That part beginning at a point where the village line of the village of Valley Stream intersects the county line of the county of Queens and the county of Nassau, thence easterly along the village of Valley Stream's northern boundary, to the westerly boundary of the village of Malverne, thence northerly and easterly along said boundary of the village of Malverne to Southern State Parkway, thence easterly along Southern State Parkway to Jerusalem Avenue to the westerly border line of the village of Massapequa Park, thence northerly along said village line to Southern State Parkway, thence westerly to Bethpage State Parkway, to Bethpage Turnpike (Hempstead Turnpike), thence westerly along Bethpage Turnpike (Hempstead Turnpike) to the town line of the town of Oyster Bay and the town of Hempstead, thence northerly and westerly along the town line of Oyster Bay, the town of Hempstead, and the town of North Hempstead, to the dividing line between the town of Hempstead, the town of North Hempstead, the county of Nassau and the county of Queens, thence southerly along the dividing line of the county of Nassau and the county of Queens to the place of beginning. Population (1960), 393,811.

JOHN W. WYDLER, Republican, of Garden City, L.I., N.Y.; born June 9, 1924, in Brooklyn, N.Y.; attended the West School of Long Beach, Long Beach High School, and Brown University; enlisted in the U.S. Air Force as a private during the Second World War and was promoted to sergeant in a chemical weapons company assigned to the China-Burma-India Theater; was discharged in 1945; joined the Air Force Reserve and served as a lieutenant in the Judge Advocate's Office; resumed studies at Brown University and was named to Phi Beta Kappa in his junior year; at the completion of junior year was accepted at Harvard Law School; was a member of the Harvard Law School Forum, graduated in 1950; admitted to the New York State Bar in 1950; in the U.S. Attorney's Office from 1953–59 where he prosecuted criminal cases for 3 years and handled civil cases for 3 years; appointed in 1959 to the New York State Investigation Commission to probe New York City school construction irregularities; entered private practice in 1959 as an associate of A. A. Forman, 150 Old Country Road, Mineola, L.I., N.Y.; married the former Brenda O'Sullivan in October 1959; one son, Christopher John, born September 5, 1960; attends the Cathedral of the Incarnation in Garden City, is a charter member of the Bishop's Men and Men's Association; member of the American Legion, Veterans of Foreign Wars, Lions Club, Order of AHEPA, Sigma Chi Fraternity, District Attorney's Association, Federal and Nassau County bar associations, Protestant Lawyers' Association, Masons, Elks; member at-large of the Boy Scouts of America; is a Republican executive committeeman; elected to the 88th Congress November 6, 1962; reelected to the 89th Congress.

FIFTH DISTRICT.—NASSAU COUNTY: That part beginning at a point where the village line of the village of Valley Stream intersects the county line of the county of Queens and the county of Nassau, thence easterly along the village of Valley Stream's northern boundary, to the westerly boundary of the village of Malverne, thence northerly and easterly along said boundary of the village of Malverne to Southern State Parkway, thence easterly along Southern State Parkway to Jerusalem Avenue and the dividing line between the town of Oyster Bay and the town line of the town of Hempstead, thence southerly along said dividing line of the town of Oyster Bay and the town of Hempstead, to the Atlantic Ocean, and thence through the waters of the Atlantic Ocean, Reynolds' Channel, to the dividing line between the county of Nassau and the county of Queens, thence northerly along said dividing line between the county of Nassau and the county of Queens to the place of beginning, also the city of Long Beach. Population (1960), 403,178.

HERBERT TENZER, Democrat, of Lawrence, Long Island, N.Y.; born in New York, N.Y., November 1, 1905; educated at P.S. 34, Manhattan (1919), Stuyvesant High School (1923), and New York University Law School (1927); senior partner in New York law firm; director, New York County Lawyers' Association; director, New York University Law Alumni Association; 1960 presidential elector, New York State; during past 25 years served as board chairman or officer of various business, banking and real estate companies; trustee of Candy Workers' Local 452, pension and welfare funds; founder, UJA of Greater New York; president, Fight for Sight; chairman, South Shore, Albert Einstein College of Medicine; former chairman, Rescue Children, Inc.; board member, Chronic Disease Hospital; past president, Congregation Beth Sholom, Lawrence; Mason; Knights of Pythias; B'nai B'rith; married to Florence R. Novor, Philadelphia; two children, Diane and Barry; elected to the 89th Congress November 3, 1964.

SIXTH DISTRICT.—QUEENS COUNTY: That part beginning at a point where Linden Boulevard intersects the county line between Queens County and Nassau County, thence westerly along Linden Boulevard to Springfield Boulevard, to Murdock Avenue, to Colfax Street, to Hollis Avenue, to Jamaica Avenue to Merrick Boulevard, to Archer Avenue, to VanWyck Expressway, to Atlantic Avenue, to 127th Street to Atlantic Avenue, to Woodhaven Boulevard, to Park Lane South, to 98th Street (Diamond Street), to Woodhaven Boulevard, to Myrtle Avenue, to 80th Street, to Metropolitan Avenue, to 69th Avenue, to Burns Street, to Union Turnpike, to Queens Boulevard, to Main Street, to 85th Drive, to 144th Street, to 85th Avenue, to 148th Street, to 84th Drive, to Smedley Street, to Grand Central Parkway, to 164th Street, to Union Turnpike, thence easterly along Union Turnpike to Hollis Court Boulevard, to Richland Avenue, to Peck Avenue, to Bell Boulevard, to Kingsbury Avenue, to Springfield Boulevard, to 69th Avenue, to Cloverdale Boulevard, to Horace Harding Expressway, thence westerly along Horace Harding Expressway to Peck Avenue, to Fresh Meadow Lane, to North Hempstead Turnpike, to Main Street, to Horace Harding Expressway, to Rodman Street, thence northerly along Rodman Street to North Hempstead Turnpike, and 133d Street, thence along 133d Street to Elder Avenue, to Peck Avenue, to Main Street, to Elder Avenue, to Kissena Boulevard, to 145th Avenue, to Parsons Boulevard, thence northerly to Bayside Avenue, thence easterly along Bayside Avenue to Bayside Lane, to Francis Lewis Boulevard, to 24th Road, to Utopia Parkway, to 24th Avenue, to 201st Street, to 23d Avenue, to 207th Street, to 26th Avenue, to Bell Boulevard, to 24th Avenue, thence easterly along 24th Avenue and 24th Avenue Extended to and through the waters of Little Neck Bay to the county line between Queens County and Nassau County, thence southerly along said county lines of the county of Queens and the county of Nassau to the place of beginning. Population (1960), 417,367.

SEYMOUR HALPERN, Republican, of Forest Hills, N.Y.; born in New York City, November 19, 1913; son of former State Assemblyman Ralph and Mrs. Halpern; graduate of Richmond Hill High School; attended Seth Low College of Columbia University; engaged in the insurance business; vice president, John C. Paige & Co., Inc.; reporter for the Long Island Daily Press, 1931–32; feature writer for the Chicago Herald-Examiner, 1932–33; staff assistant to Mayor Fiorello H. LaGuardia, 1937; assistant to the president, New York City Council, 1938–40; elected to New York State Senate, 1940; served seven consecutive terms, through 1954; chairman, Senate Committee on Civil Service, 1941–44; chairman, Senate Committee on Public Institutions, 1945; chairman, Senate Committee on Motor Vehicles and Transportation, 1946–47; chairman, Joint Legislative Committee on Motor Vehicle Problems, 1948–54; member, Temporary State Commission to Revise the Civil Service Law, 1952–54; member, Mayor's Committee on Courts, 1956–58; member, national panel, American Arbitration Association; director, National Aeronautics Association; member, National Executive Council, Zionist Organization of America; director, Association for Cultural Exchange; honorary member, Mayor's Committee on Intergroup Relations; member, National Council, Foundation for the Jewish National Fund; member, Executive Board, Citizens Union, 1954–58; director, Queens Mental Health Society; member, Advisory Board, National Association for the Prevention of Juvenile Delinquency; member, The New York Regional Advisory Board, Anti-Defamation League of B'nai B'rith; chairman of the board, National Family Council on Drug Addiction; director, Queens Hospital Center Cancer Research Society; member, Advisory Council National Committee on Playgrounds for Young America; advisory board member, New York State Association for Mental Health; member, board of directors, North Queens Child Guidance Center; charter member, U.S. Capitol Historical Society; sponsor of The City of Hope, the Association of Health of Retarded Children, the New York Child Foundation; former Queens chairman, United Cerebral Palsy, the Greater New York Fund and the Child Service League; member, executive committee, Queens Division, Federation of Jewish Philanthropies; chairman, board of sponsors, Queens Symphony Orchestra; charter member, Queens Botanical Society; member, Capitol Hill Club, National Republican Club, Queens County Republican Committee, BPO Elks; named Outstanding Native-born New Yorker of the Year by New York Society of the City of New York, 1953; honorary member, New York University Law Alumni; recipient of VFW Achievement Medal, 1954, and New York State JWV's first Public Service Award, 1958; New York State VFW Human Rights Award, 1964; Federation of 213 Housing Co-ops; Distinguished Service Award, 1964; Assembly of Captive Nations' Tenth Anniversary Commemorative Medal, 1964; married December 27, 1959, to Barbara Olsen of Flushing; elected to 86th Congress November 4, 1958; reelected to the 87th, 88th, and 89th Congresses; member of Banking and Currency Committee, Veterans Affairs Committee, and the Franklin D. Roosevelt Memorial Commission.

SEVENTH DISTRICT.—QUEENS COUNTY: That part beginning at a point where Linden Boulevard intersects the county line between Queens County and Nassau County, thence westerly along Linden Boulevard to Springfield Boulevard, to Murdock Avenue, to Colfax Street, to Hollis Avenue, to Jamaica Avenue, to Merrick Boulevard, to Archer Avenue, to VanWyck Expressway, to Atlantic Avenue, to 127th Street, to Atlantic Avenue, to Woodhaven Boulevard, to Park Lane South, to 98th Street (Diamond Street), to Woodhaven Boulevard, to Myrtle Avenue, to 80th Street, to Cooper Avenue, to 73d Place, to Metropolitan Avenue, to 74th Street, to Juniper Boulevard South, to 71st Street, to Lutheran Avenue, to the intersection of Eliot Avenue, Lutheran Avenue and 75th Street, thence along 75th Street, to Caldwell Avenue, to 71st (Mazeau) Street, to Midtown Highway, to Grand Avenue, thence westerly along Grand Avenue to the dividing line between Queens County and Kings County and thence southerly along said dividing line to the waters of Jamaica Bay, thence easterly through the waters of Jamaica Bay, Grassy Bay and Head of Bay Inlet to the dividing line between the county of Queens and county of Nassau, thence northerly along said dividing line to the place of beginning. Population (1960), 459,844.

JOSEPH PATRICK ADDABBO, Democrat, of 132–43 86th Street, Ozone Park, N.Y.; born March 17, 1925, in Queens, N.Y., son of Dominick and Anna Addabbo; attended P.S. 66, Boys' High School in Brooklyn, City College for 2 years, and graduated St. John's Law School, LL.B. degree; married the former Grace Salamone; three children, Dominic, Dina, and Joseph; engaged in the general practice of law in Ozone Park; active in civic and community affairs; member of Queens County Bar Association; delegate to Judicial Convention; elected to the 87th Congress November 8, 1960; reelected to the 88th and 89th Congresses.

EIGHTH DISTRICT.—QUEENS COUNTY: That part beginning at a point where 23d Avenue extended intersects the waters of Flushing Bay, thence southwesterly along 23d Avenue Extended and 23d Avenue to Grand Central Parkway, to 94th Street, to 30th Avenue, to 93d Street, to Northern Boulevard, to Junction Boulevard, to 57th Avenue, to 99th Street, to 63d Road, to the intersection of Junction Boulevard, Queens Boulevard, 63d Road and 63d Drive, thence northwesterly along Queens Boulevard to 51st Avenue, to 69th Street, to the intersection of Midtown Highway, Grand Avenue and 69th Street, thence along Midtown Highway to 71st (Mazeau) Street, to Caldwell Avenue, to 75th Street, to the intersection of Eliot Avenue, 75th Street and Lutheran Avenue, thence southerly along Lutheran Avenue, to 71st Street, to Juniper Boulevard South, to 74th Street, to Metropolitan Avenue, to 73d Place, to Cooper Avenue, to 80th Street, to Metropolitan Avenue, to 69th Avenue, to Burns Street, to Union Turnpike, to Queens Boulevard, to Main Street, to 85th Drive, to 144th Street, to 85th Avenue to 148th Street, to 84th Drive, to Smedley Street, to Grand Central Parkway, to 164th Street, to Union Turnpike, thence easterly along Union Turnpike to Hollis Court Boulevard, to Richland Avenue, to Peck Avenue, to Bell Boulevard, to Kingsbury Avenue, to Springfield Boulevard, to 69th Avenue, to Cloverdale Boulevard, to Horace Harding Expressway, thence westerly along Horace Harding Expressway to Peck Avenue, to Fresh Meadow Lane, to North Hempstead Turnpike, to Main Street, to Horace Harding Expressway, to Rodman Street, thence northerly along Rodman Street to the intersection of North Hempstead Turnpike and 133d Street, thence along 133d Street to Elder Avenue, to Peck Avenue, to Main Street, to Elder Avenue, to Kissena Boulevard to 45th Avenue, to Parsons Boulevard, thence northerly to Bayside Avenue, thence easterly along Bayside Avenue to Bayside Lane, to Francis Lewis Boulevard, to 24th Road, to Utopia Parkway, to 24th Avenue, to 201st Street, to 23d Avenue, to 207th Street, to 26th Avenue, to Bell Boulevard, to 24th Avenue, thence easterly along 24th Avenue and 24th Avenue Extended to and through the waters of Little Neck Bay to the county line between Queens County and Nassau County, thence northerly through the waters of Little Neck Bay, East River and Flushing Bay to the place of beginning. Population (1960), 432,776.

BENJAMIN S. ROSENTHAL, Democrat, of Elmhurst, Long Island, N.Y.; born in New York City, N.Y., June 8, 1923; educated in the public schools of the city of New York; attended Long Island University and City College; LL.B. Brooklyn Law School (1949), LL. M. New York University (1952); married Lila Moskowitz, two children—Debra and Edward; attorney; admitted to New York bar 1949; admitted to practice before United States Supreme Court 1954; member of firm of Peirez, Karmiol & Rosenthal, 60–10 Roosevelt Avenue, Woodside, Long Island, N.Y.; served in United States Army March 1943 to January 1946, 18 months in Iceland; elected as Democrat-Liberal to the 87th Congress in special election February 20, 1962, to fill the vacancy caused by resignation of Lester Holtzman; reelected to the 88th and 89th Congresses.

NINTH DISTRICT.—QUEENS COUNTY: That part beginning at a point where 23d Avenue extended intersects the waters of Flushing Bay, thence southwesterly along 23d Avenue Extended and 23d Avenue, to Grand Central Parkway, to 94th Street, to 30th Avenue, to 93d Street, to Northern Boulevard, to Junction Boulevard, to 57th Avenue, to 99th Street, to 63d Road, to the intersection of Junction Boulevard, Queens Boulevard, 63d Road and 63d Drive, thence northwesterly along Queens Boulevard to 51st Avenue, to 69th Street, to the intersection of Midtown Highway, Grand Avenue and 69th Street, thence westerly along Grand Avenue to the dividing line between the county of Queens and the county of Kings, thence northerly along said dividing line between the county of Queens, and the county of Kings to Newtown Creek, to East River, to East Channel, to Hell Gate, to Riker's Island Channel, to East River and Flushing Bay to the place of beginning. Population (1960), 428,700.

JAMES J. DELANEY, Democrat, of Long Island City, N. Y.; born in New York, N. Y., March 19, 1901; member of law firm of Danahy & Delaney, 44 Court Street, Brooklyn, N. Y.; assistant district attorney for 9 years in the district attorney's office, Queens County, N. Y.; married; one son, Patrick; elected to the 79th Congress on November 7, 1944; elected to the 81st Congress on November 2, 1948; reelected to the 82d, 83d, 84th, 85th, 86th, 87th, 88th, and 89th Congresses.

TENTH DISTRICT.—QUEENS COUNTY: That part beginning at a point where the county line of the county of Kings and the county of Queens are intersected by Rockaway Inlet, thence easterly and northerly along said county line of the county of Kings and the county of Queens to a point where said county line of the county of Kings and the county of Queens are intersected by the waters of Jamaica Bay and Grassy Bay, thence easterly through the waters of Jamaica Bay, Grassy Bay and Mott Basin to the dividing line between the county of Queens and the county of Nassau, thence easterly and southerly along said dividing line of the county of Queens and the county of Nassau to the waters of the Atlantic Ocean, thence westerly through the waters of the Atlantic Ocean and Rockaway Inlet to the place of beginning. KINGS COUNTY: That part of the borough of Brooklyn beginning at a point where Flatbush Avenue Extended southward intersects the waters of Rockaway Inlet, thence northwesterly along Flatbush Avenue Extended and Flatbush Avenue to Fillmore Avenue, to Avenue T, to East 69th Street, to Avenue K, to Ralph Avenue, thence southerly to Avenue M, to East 58th Street, to Avenue L, East 45th Street, to Avenue K, to Troy Avenue, to Avenue H, to Schenectady Avenue, to Glenwood Road, to East 46th Street, to Farragut Road, to Schenectady Avenue, to Foster Avenue, to East 45th Street, to Avenue D, to Troy Avenue, to Cortelyou Road, to Schenectady Avenue, to Church Avenue, to East 53d Street, to Linden Boulevard, to East 52d Street, to Lenox Road, to Utica Avenue, to Winthrop Street, to Schenectady Avenue, to Lefferts Avenue, to Troy Avenue, to East New York Avenue, to Albany Avenue, to Empire Boulevard, to Troy Avenue, to Eastern Parkway, to Albany Avenue, to St. Johns Place, to Kingston Avenue, to Atlantic Avenue, to Brooklyn Avenue, to Fulton Street, to Marcy Avenue, to Monroe Street, to Bedford Avenue, to Myrtle Avenue, to Broadway, to Lafayette Avenue, to Stuyvesant Avenue, to Fulton Street, to Stone Avenue, to East New York Avenue, to Hopkinson Avenue, to East 98th Street, to Ditmas Avenue, to Rockaway Parkway, thence along Rockaway Parkway and Rockaway Parkway Extended, to the waters of Jamaica Bay, thence southerly and westerly through the waters of Jamaica Bay to the place of beginning, also including the islands in Jamaica Bay within the borough of Brooklyn. Population (1960), 422,745.

EMANUEL CELLER, Democrat; born in Brooklyn, N. Y., May 6, 1888; attended the public schools; was graduated from the Boys' High School of Brooklyn, in 1906, from Columbia College, New York City, in 1910, and from the Columbia University Law School, New York City, in 1912; admitted to the bar and commenced practice in New York City in 1912; elected as a Democrat to the 68th Congress, November 7, 1922; reelected to each succeeding Congress; chairman of the House Committee on the Judiciary; married and has two daughters—Judith S., and Jane B., married to Sydney B. Wertheimer; home address is 9 Prospect Park West, Brooklyn, N. Y.; Washington address, the Mayflower.

ELEVENTH DISTRICT.—KINGS COUNTY: That part of the Borough of Brooklyn beginning at a point where Stockholm Street intersects the dividing line between the county of Kings and the county of Queens, thence southwesterly along Stockholm Street, to Wilson Avenue, to DeKalb Avenue, to Evergreen Avenue, to Stockholm Street, to Bushwick Avenue, to Kossuth Place to Lafayette Avenue, to Stuyvesant Avenue, to Fulton Street, to Stone Avenue, to East New York Avenue, to Hopkinson Avenue, to East 98th Street, to Ditmas Avenue, to Rockaway Parkway, thence along Rockaway Parkway and Rockaway Parkway Extended, to the waters of Jamaica Bay, thence easterly through the waters of Jamaica Bay to the dividing line between the county of Kings and the county of Queens, thence northerly and westerly along said dividing line as it twists and turns to the place of beginning. Population (1960), 403,790.

EUGENE J. KEOGH, Democrat, of Brooklyn, N. Y.; elected consecutively since 1936.

TWELFTH DISTRICT.—KINGS COUNTY: That part of the Borough of Brooklyn beginning at a point where 23d Avenue, Avenue M, and Dahill Road intersect, thence northerly along Dahill Road to 58th Street, to 18th Avenue, to 59th Street, to Fort Hamilton Parkway, to 51st Street, to 8th Avenue, to 37th Street, to Fort Hamilton Parkway, to McDonald Avenue (Gravesend Avenue), to Greenwood Avenue, to Prospect Park Southwest, to Parkside Avenue, to Ocean Avenue, to Washington Avenue, to Eastern Parkway, to Underhill Avenue, to Prospect Place, to Vanderbilt Avenue, to Atlantic Avenue, to Cumberland Street, to Green Avenue, to Vanderbilt Avenue, to Gates Avenue, to Washington Avenue, to Lafayette Avenue, to Bedford Avenue, to Monroe Street, to Marcy Avenue, to Fulton Street, to Brooklyn Avenue, to Atlantic Avenue, to Kingston Avenue, to St. Johns Place, to Albany Avenue, to Eastern Parkway, to Troy Avenue, to Empire Boulevard, to Albany Avenue, to East New York Avenue, to Troy Avenue, to Lefferts Avenue, to Schenectady Avenue, to Winthrop Street, to Utica Avenue, to Lenox Road, to East 52d Street, to Linden Boulevard, to East 53d Street, to Church Avenue, to Schenectady Avenue, to Cortelyou Road, to Canarsie Avenue, to Tilden Avenue, to Flatbush Avenue, to Beverly Road, to Coney Island Avenue, to Ditmas Avenue, to Flatbush Avenue, to Newkirk Avenue, to Brooklyn Avenue, to Foster Avenue, to East 37th Street, to Farragut Road, thence westerly to Flatbush Avenue, to Glenwood Road, to Nostrand Avenue, to Avenue K, to East 15th Street, to Avenue L, to Coney Island Avenue, to Avenue K, to East 9th Street, to Avenue M, thence westerly to the place of beginning. Population (1960), 471,001.

EDNA F. KELLY, Democrat, of Brooklyn, N. Y.; born August 20, 1906, at East Hampton, N. Y., daughter of the late Patrick J. and Mary Ellen Flannery; educated at East Hampton High School and Hunter College, New York City, N. Y.; majored in history and economics; graduated in 1928 with B. A. degree; elected in 1944 a member of the executive committee of the Democratic Party of Kings County, N. Y., from Eighteenth Assembly District and continuously reelected to date; appointed associate research director of the Democratic Party in the New York State Legislature in 1943; designated chief research director in 1944 and served in that capacity until her election on November 8, 1949, to the second session of the 81st Congress; reelected to the 82d, 83d, 84th, 85th, 86th, 87th, 88th, and 89th Congresses; is Democratic National Committeewoman, State of New York; chairman, Subcommittee on Europe, Committee on Foreign Affairs; delegate to 18th General Assembly of the United Nations; is the widow of the late City Court Justice of the City of New York, Edward L. Kelly; has two children, William E. Kelly 2d, who served with the United States Coast Guard as ensign, and Maura Patricia Kelly, has eight grandchildren; Edward, William, Robert, Richard, Ellen, Elizabeth Ann, Elaine Mary Kelly, and Michael Bruce; home address, 1247 Carroll Street, Brooklyn, N.Y., 11213.

THIRTEENTH DISTRICT.—KINGS COUNTY: That part of the Borough of Brooklyn beginning at a point where Plumb 1st Street Extended intersects the waters of Sheepshead Bay, thence northerly along Plumb 1st Street Extended to Emmons Avenue, to Bedford Avenue, to Shore Parkway, to Bragg Street, to Avenue W, to Knapp Street, to Whitney Avenue, to Gerritsen Avenue, to Avenue U, to East 28th Street, to Avenue T, to East 27th Street, to Avenue S, to Brown Street, to Gerritsen Avenue, to Nostrand Avenue, to Kings Highway, to East 29th Street, to Avenue K, to East 15th Street, to Avenue L, to Coney Island Avenue, to Avenue K, to East 9th Street, to Avenue M, to Dahill Road, to 58th Street, to 18th Avenue, to 59th Street, to New Utrecht Avenue, to 14th Avenue, to 71st Street, to 16th Avenue, to 86th Street, to Bay 8th Street, thence southerly along Bay 8th Street and Bay 8th Street Extended to the waters of Gravesend Bay, thence southerly and easterly through the waters of Gravesend Bay, Lower Bay, Rockaway Inlet, Sheepshead Bay, to the place of beginning. Population (1960), 455,172.

ABRAHAM J. MULTER, Democrat, of New York; born in New York City December 24, 1900; resides at 1397 East 21st Street, Brooklyn, N.Y., with his wife, Bertha L.; two children, Robert K. and Howard C.; attended City College of New York; received LL. B. and LL. M. degrees from Brooklyn Law School; awarded LL. D. by Yeshiva University; admitted to New York State Bar 1923; admitted to practice in all New York State and Federal Courts; member of New York State Democratic Committee and Kings County Executive Committee; trustee, director, and member of many educational, charitable, fraternal, civic, and religious organizations; senior member of the law firm of Multer, Nova & Seymour, 120 Broadway, New York City; elected to the 80th Congress on November 4, 1947; reelected to each succeeding Congress; Democratic Whip for Zone 2; ranking member of Banking and Currency Committee; member of Small Business Committee, District Committee, and Joint Committee on Defense Production.

FOURTEENTH DISTRICT.—KINGS COUNTY: That part of the borough of Brooklyn beginning at a point where Bayridge Avenue extended westward intersects the waters of The Narrows, thence easterly along Bayridge Avenue Extended and Bayridge Avenue to Shore Parkway, thence northerly along Shore Parkway to Ridge Boulevard, to 2d Avenue, thence northerly along 2d Avenue to 65th Street, to 3d Avenue, to 60th Street, to 4th Avenue, to 24th Street, to 5th Avenue, to Prospect Expressway, to 4th Avenue, to 9th Street, to 5th Avenue, to Carroll Street, to 6th Avenue, to Prospect Place, to 5th Avenue, to St. Mark's Place, to 4th Avenue, to Flatbush Avenue, to State Street, to Hicks Street, to Joralemon Street, to the center line of the Brooklyn-Queens connecting highway, to Cranberry Street, to Fulton Street, to Prospect Street, to Pearl Street, to New Street, to Jay Street, to Fulton Street, to DeKalb Avenue, to South Oxford Street, to Lafayette Avenue, to Vanderbilt Avenue, to DeKalb Avenue, to Washington Avenue, to Lafayette Avenue, to Bedford Avenue, thence along Bedford Avenue, to Myrtle Avenue, thence easterly along Myrtle Avenue to Broadway, to the intersection of Lafayette Avenue, Broadway and Kossuth Place, thence northerly along Kossuth Place to Bushwick Avenue, to Stockholm Street, to Evergreen Avenue, to DeKalb Avenue, to Wilson Avenue, to Stockholm Street, to the dividing line between the county of Kings and the county of Queens, thence northerly along said dividing line of the county of Kings and the county of Queens to the waters of Newtown Creek, the East River, Buttermilk Channel, Upper Bay, Gowanus Bay, and The Narrows to the place of beginning. Population (1960), 463,957.

JOHN J. ROONEY, Democrat, of Brooklyn, N.Y., born of immigrant parents in the district which he represents and in which his family has lived for over 90 years, on November 29, 1903; education: St. Paul's Parochial School, St. Francis Preparatory and College, Fordham University School of Law, class of 1925; attorney; assistant district attorney of Kings County (Brooklyn) from January 1, 1940, to June 5, 1944; married Catherine Kramm Curran of Washington, D. C., and has four sons, John James, Jr., Edward Patrick, Arthur Patrick Curran, and William Edward Curran, and a daughter, Mary Ann (Mrs. Michael G. Farrell); knight commander with star, Ecclesiastic Order of St. Gregory the Great, past exalted ruler of Brooklyn Lodge No. 22, B. P. O. Elks; past New York State vice president of Ancient Order of Hibernians in America; past president, St. Patrick Society of Brooklyn; life member, Columbus Council No. 126, Knights of Columbus; honorary member, Sgt. Harry Wm. Steneck Post No. 601, Veterans of Foreign

Wars; member Committee on Appropriations; chairman of Subcommittee on Appropriations for State, Justice, Commerce, the Judiciary and related agencies: as member Committee on Military Affairs visited Western and Italian fronts November and December 1944; official observer, first Bikini Atom Test; official observer, Japanese Peace Conference, 1951; chairman of the Democratic Caucus, 84th Congress; elected consecutively from the 78th to the 89th Congresses, inclusive.

FIFTEENTH DISTRICT.—KINGS COUNTY: That part of the borough of Brooklyn beginning at a point where Bayridge Avenue Extended westward intersects the waters of The Narrows, thence easterly along Bayridge Avenue Extended and Bayridge Avenue, to Shore Parkway, thence northerly along Shore Parkway to Ridge Boulevard, to 2d Avenue, thence northerly along 2d Avenue to 65th Street, to 3d Avenue, to 60th Street, to 4th Avenue, to 24th Street, to 5th Avenue, to Prospect Expressway, to 4th Avenue, to 9th Street, to 5th Avenue, to Carroll Street, to 6th Avenue, to Prospect Place, to 5th Avenue, to St. Mark's Place, to 4th Avenue, to Flatbush Avenue, to State Street, to Hicks Street, to Joralemon Street, to the center line of the Brooklyn-Queens connecting highways, to Cranberry Street, to Fulton Street, to Prospect Street, to Pearl Street, to New Street, to Jay Street, to Fulton Street, to DeKalb Avenue, to South Oxford Street, to Lafayette Avenue, to Vanderbilt Avenue, to DeKalb Avenue, to Washington Avenue, to Gates Avenue, to Vanderbilt Avenue, to Green Avenue, to Cumberland Street, to Atlantic Avenue, to Vanderbilt Avenue, to Prospect Place, to Underhill Avenue, to Eastern Parkway, to Washington Avenue, to the intersection of Washington Avenue, Empire Boulevard and Ocean Avenue, thence westerly and southerly along Ocean Avenue, to Parkside Avenue, to Prospect Park Southwest, to Greenwood Avenue, to McDonald Avenue (Gravesend Avenue), to Fort Hamilton Parkway, to 37th Street, to 8th Avenue, to 51st Street, to Fort Hamilton Parkway, to 57th Street, to New Utrecht Avenue, to 14th Avenue, to 71st Street, to 16th Avenue, to 86th Street, to Bay 8th Street, thence southerly along Bay 8th Street and Bay 8th Street Extended to the waters of Gravesend Bay, thence northwesterly through the waters of Gravesend Bay and The Narrows to the place of beginning. Population (1960), 350,635.

HUGH L. CAREY, Democrat, of Brooklyn, N.Y.; born in Brooklyn April 11, 1919, son of Dennis J. and Margaret Collins Carey; graduated from St. Augustine's Elementary and High Schools; St. John's College, interrupted for military service; received LL.B. from St. John's Law School, 1951, member of Phi Delta Phi; admitted New York State Bar 1951; married the former Helen Owen; parents of Alexandria, Christopher, Susan, Peter, Hugh, Jr., Michael, Donald, Marianne, Nancy, Helen, Bryan, Paul, and Kevin; enlisted 101st Cavalry, New York National Guard; commissioned in Infantry via O.C.S.; saw combat with 104th Division in France, Belgium, Holland, Germany; rose to lieutenant colonel; decorations include Bronze Star, Croix de Guerre with Silver Star, Combat Infantry Award; member, board of directors of Gallaudet College, board of trustees of the League School, board of directors of St. Vincent's Home for Boys, Boy Scouts of America Finance Campaign; member 1st New York Cavalry Post American Legion, V.F.W., C.W.V., and Columbus Council K. of C.; elected to the 87th, 88th, and 89th Congresses; member of the Education and Labor Committee, the Interior and Insular Affairs Committee, and Board of Visitors to the U.S. Merchant Marine Academy.

SIXTEENTH DISTRICT.—RICHMOND COUNTY and the islands therein. KINGS COUNTY: That part of borough of Brooklyn beginning at a point where Flatbush Avenue Extended southward intersects the waters of Rockaway Inlet, thence northwesterly along Flatbush Avenue Extended and Flatbush Avenue to Fillmore Avenue, to Avenue T, to East 69th Street, to Ralph Avenue, thence southerly to Avenue M, to East 58th Street, to Avenue L, to East 45th Street, to Avenue K, to Troy Avenue, to Avenue H, to Schenectady Avenue, to Glenwood Road, to East 46th Street, to Farragut Road, to Schenectady Avenue, to Foster Avenue, to East 45th Street, to Avenue D, to Troy Avenue, to Cortelyou Road, to Canarsie Avenue, to Tilden Avenue, to Flatbush Avenue, to Beverly Road, to Coney Island Avenue, to Ditmas Avenue, thence easterly to Flatbush Avenue, to Newkirk Avenue, to Brooklyn Avenue, to Foster Avenue, to East 37th Street, to Farragut Road, to Flatbush Avenue, to Glenwood Road, to Nostrand Avenue, to Avenue K, to East 29th Street, to Kings Highway, to Nostrand Avenue, to Gerritsen Avenue, to Brown Street, to Avenue S, to East 27th Street, to Avenue T, to East 28th Street, to Avenue U, to Gerritsen Avenue, to Whitney Avenue, to Knapp Street, to Avenue W, to Bragg Street, to Shore Parkway, to Bedford Avenue, to Emmons Avenue, thence easterly along Emmons Avenue to Plumb 1st Street, thence southerly along Plumb 1st Street and Plumb 1st Street Extended to the waters of Sheepshead Bay and through the waters of Sheepshead Bay and Rockaway Inlet to the place of beginning. Population (1960), 352,901.

JOHN MICHAEL MURPHY, Democrat, of Staten Island, N.Y.; born in Staten Island, August 3, 1926, son of Frank and Florence Murphy; educated Public School No. 19, Staten Island, La Salle Military Academy, Oakdale, L.I., Amherst College, Amherst, Mass., and the U.S. Military Academy, West Point, N.Y.; B.S. degree in civil engineering; enlisted in U.S. Army in August 1944 as a private, promoted to corporal, and commissioned second lieutenant in May 1945; appointed to West Point in 1946; after graduation went to Korea and served as platoon leader, company commander, and intelligence officer in the 9th Infantry Regiment; promoted to first lieutenant in 1950 and captain in 1953;

awarded Distinguished Service Cross, Bronze Star with V and Oak Leaf Cluster, Commendation Ribbon with Oak Leaf Cluster, Combat Infantry Badge, Parachute Badge, Korean Service Medal with six battle stars and Chungmu Distinguished Service Medal; discharged from service as a captain in July 1956 to engage in private business; general manager for Frank Murphy, contract carrier of Staten Island 1956–62; member board of directors, Empire State Highway Transportation Association in 1960; president, Cleveland General Transport Co., Inc., 1957; married the former Patricia Hart of Staten Island; three children—Deirdre, John, and Eve; a Catholic; member of American Legion, V.F.W., Knights of Columbus, and many community, political, and Army organizations; elected to the 88th Congress November 6, 1962; reelected to the 89th Congress.

SEVENTEENTH DISTRICT.—NEW YORK COUNTY: That part beginning at a point where East 14th Street Extended intersects the waters of the East River, thence westerly along East 14th Street Extended and East 14th Street to 1st Avenue, to East 19th Street, to 3d Avenue, through Cooper's Square, to the Bowery, to Great Jones Street (West 3d Street), to The Avenue of the Americas (6th Avenue), to West 4th Street, to Christopher Street, to Bleecker Street, to Abbington Square, thence northerly along Eighth Avenue, to West 14th Street, to 7th Avenue, to West 34th Street, to 8th Avenue, to West 54th Street, to 9th Avenue, thence northerly along 9th Avenue and Columbus Avenue, to West 73d Street, to Central Park West, to the intersection of Cathedral Parkway, Central Park West and West 110th Street, thence easterly along West 110th Street to 5th Avenue, thence southerly along 5th Avenue to East 98th Street, to Madison Avenue, to East 97th Street, to Park Avenue, to East 96th Street, to Lexington Avenue, to East 91st Street, to 3d Avenue, to East 89th Street, to East End Avenue, thence northerly along East End Avenue and East End Avenue Extended to the waters of the East River, thence through the waters of the East River and the East River Channel to the place of beginning including Welfare Island. Population (1960), 382,320.

JOHN V. LINDSAY, Republican, of New York City, N. Y.; born in New York City, November 24, 1921; graduated from the Buckley School, New York City, 1935; St. Paul's School, Concord, N. H., 1940; Yale University, B. A. degree, 1944; Yale Law School, LL. B. degree, 1948; admitted to the New York bar, 1949; United States Supreme Court bar, 1955; District of Columbia bar, 1956; executive assistant to the Attorney General of the United States, January 1955 to January 1957; joined the Navy in May 1943, destroyer officer aboard U. S. S. *Swanson* DD 443, participating in landings at Sicily, 7th Fleet landings at Biak, Hollandia, Admiralty Islands; Carrier Task Group 38.4 during Philippine invasion; discharged March 1946 as lieutenant (sg.); married to the former Mary Harrison; three daughters and one son; member of St. James Episcopal Church; member, Association of the Bar of the City of New York, American Bar Association, New York State Bar Association, Council on Foreign Relations, and Citizens Committee for Children of New York City, Inc.; board member, Freedom House; elected to the Yale Corporation in 1964; elected chairman of the Political Committee of the NATO Parliamentarians Conference 1964; elected to the 86th Congress on November 4, 1958; reelected to the 87th, 88th, and 89th Congresses.

EIGHTEENTH DISTRICT.—NEW YORK COUNTY: That part beginning at a point where West 165th Street Extended easterly intersects the waters of the Harlem River, thence westerly along West 165th Street Extended and West 165th Street to Edgecombe Avenue, to St. Nicholas Place, to West 150th Street, to Amsterdam Avenue, thence southerly along Amsterdam Avenue to West 122d Street, to Morningside Drive, to Cathedral Parkway, thence easterly along Cathedral Parkway and West 110th Street to Fifth Avenue, thence southerly along 5th Avenue to East 98th Street, to Madison Avenue, to East 97th Street, to Park Avenue, to East 96th Street, to Lexington Avenue, to East 91st Street, to Third Avenue, to East 89th Street, to East End Avenue, thence northerly along East End Avenue and East End Avenue Extended to the waters of the Harlem River and through the waters of the Harlem River, Hell Gate, East River, Harlem River, to the place of beginning, including Randall's Island, Ward's Island, and Mill Rock. Population (1960), 431,330.

ADAM C. POWELL, Democrat, of New York City; born in New Haven, Conn., November 29, 1908; education: B. A. degree, Colgate University, 1930, M. A. degree, Columbia University, 1932; D. D. degree, Shaw University, 1934; 1947, LL. D., Virginia Union University; minister of the Abyssinian Baptist Church; councilman of the city of New York, 1941; vice president of World Association of Parliamentarians for World Government; reelected in 1953, 1954, and 1956; decorated by His Imperial Majesty, Haile Selassie, Knight Commander, Golden Cross of the Order of Ethiopia in 1954; attended 1955 Asian-African Conference, Bandung, Indonesia, as an unofficial observer; author, Marching Blacks, Dial Press, 1945; married M. Yvette Diago, December 15, 1960; son, Adam Clayton Powell 3d, born July 17, 1946; son born on May 27, 1962, Adam Clayton Powell-Diago; elected to the 79th Congress, November 7, 1944; reelected to the 80th, 81st, 82d, 83d, 84th, 85th, 86th, 87th, 88th, and 89th Congresses.

NINETEENTH DISTRICT.—NEW YORK COUNTY: That part beginning at a point where East 14th Street Extended intersects the waters of the East River, thence westerly along East 14th Street extended and East 14th Street, to 1st Avenue, to East 19th Street, to 3d Avenue, through Cooper's Square to the Bowery, to Great Jones Street (West 3rd Street), to The Avenue of the Americas (6th Avenue), to West 4th Street, to Christopher Street, to Bleecker Street, to Abbington Square, thence northerly along 8th Avenue, to West 14th Street, to 7th Avenue, to West 34th Street, to 8th Avenue, to West 54th Street, to 9th Avenue, thence northerly along 9th Avenue and Columbus Avenue, to West 73d Street, to Central Park West, to West 86th Street, thence westerly along West 86th Street and West 86th Street Extended to the waters of the Hudson River, thence southerly through the waters of the Hudson River, New York Bay, Buttermilk Channel, the East River to the place of beginning, including Governor's Island, Bedloe's Island, and Ellis Island. Population (1960), 445,175.

LEONARD FARBSTEIN, Democrat, of New York City; born in New York City (Manhattan), N.Y.; attended the public schools and graduated from the High School of Commerce; attended evening classes at City College of New York; graduated from New York University Law School with an LL. B. degree and was admitted to the bar licensed to practice in the State and Federal courts; has represented the Fourth Assembly District of Manhattan in the State Legislature; during World War II served in the United States Coast Guard Reserve; was a member of the Temporary Commission on the Courts, State Judicial Conference, and State Judicial Council; vice chairman of the East River Day Camp, a philanthropic organization; consultant to the Lower East Side Neighborhood Association and on the Manhattan Council of the Boy Scouts of America; Knights of Pythias (past chancellor); B'nai B'rith; the American Jewish Congress; Lower East Side Democratic Association; East Side Chamber of Commerce; Grand Street Boys; Bialystoker Synagogue, serving as trustee and director of Downtown Talmud Torah; member of the American Judicature Society; New York County Lawyers Association; New York State and American Bar Associations, and the Association of the Bar of the City of New York; elected to the 85th Congress on November 6, 1956; reelected to the 86th, 87th, 88th, and 89th Congresses.

TWENTIETH DISTRICT.—NEW YORK COUNTY: That part beginning at a point where West 165th Street Extended easterly intersects the waters of the Harlem River, thence westerly along West 165th Street Extended and West 165th Street to Edgecombe Avenue, to St. Nicholas Place, to West 150th Street, to Amsterdam Avenue, thence southerly along Amsterdam Avenue to West 122d Street, to Morningside Drive, to Cathedral Parkway, to Central Park West, to West 86th Street, thence along West 86th Street Extended to the waters of the Hudson River, thence northerly through the waters of the Hudson River, Harlem River, to the dividing line between the county of Bronx and the county of New York, thence northerly, easterly and southerly along said dividing line to the waters of the Harlem River, thence southerly through the waters of the Harlem River to the place of beginning. Population (1960), 439,456.

WILLIAM F. RYAN, Democrat-Liberal, of New York City; born June 28, 1922, in Albion, N.Y.; son of Bernard Ryan, former presiding judge, New York State Court of Claims, now retired, and Harriet Fitts; graduated from Princeton University, A.B., and from Columbia University, LL. B.; veteran World War II, first lieutenant, Field Artillery; Philippines campaigns and Japanese occupation, 32d Infantry Division; attorney; assistant district attorney, New York County, 1950–57; president, New York Young Democratic Club, Inc., 1955–56; a founding member Riverside Democrats, Inc.; founder, New York Democratic Reform Movement; Democratic leader, Seventh Assembly District, New York County, 1957–61; married Priscilla Marbury; four children—William, Jr., Priscilla, Virginia, Catherine; elected to the 87th Congress November 8, 1960; reelected to the 88th and 89th Congresses.

TWENTY-FIRST DISTRICT.—BRONX COUNTY: That part beginning at a point where East 140th Street Extended eastward intersects the waters of the East River, thence westerly along East 140th Street Extended and East 140th Street to Locust Avenue, to East 141st Street, to St. Ann's Avenue, to East 159th Street, to Eagle Avenue, to East 163d Street, to 3d Avenue, to East 167th Street, to Fulton Avenue, to Cross Bronx Expressway, thence westerly along the Cross Bronx Expressway to Grand Concourse, to East 181st Street, thence westerly along East 181st Street, and West 181st Street, to University Avenue, thence southerly along University Avenue, to West Burnside Avenue, to Sedgwick Avenue, to West Tremont Avenue, thence westerly along West Tremont Avenue and West Tremont Avenue Extended to the waters of the Harlem River, thence southerly and easterly through the waters of the Harlem River and the East River to the place of beginning. Population (1960), 361,069.

JAMES H. SCHEUER, Democrat, of the Bronx, N.Y.; born in New York City February 6, 1920; A.B. Swarthmore College, LL.B. Columbia Law School, and a degree in industrial administration from Harvard Graduate School of Business Administration; served as a flight instructor in the U.S. Army 1943–45; served as an economist for the U.S. Foreign Economic Administration 1945 to 1946 and as a member of the legal staff for the Office of Price Stabilization 1951 to 1957; wife's name is Emily; four children; president, Citizens' Housing and Planning Council of New York City; board member, National Housing Conference; member of Bar Association of City of New York and of the National Panel of Arbitrators of the American Arbitration Association; director of the Bronx Boys

Club; member of the board of directors Bronx Chapter National Conference of Christians and Jews; delegate to four United Nations conferences on housing and urban problems and human rights; writer and lecturer; developer of residential communities in eight cities under the Federal Urban Renewal program; elected to the 89th Congress November 3, 1964.

TWENTY-SECOND DISTRICT.—BRONX COUNTY: That part beginning at a point where East 140th Street Extended eastward intersects the waters of the East River, thence westerly along East 140th Street Extended and East 140th Street to Locust Avenue, to East 141st Street, to St. Ann's Avenue, to East 159th Street, to Eagle Avenue, to East 163d Street, to 3d Avenue, to East 167th Street, to Fulton Avenue, to Cross Bronx Expressway, thence westerly along the Cross Bronx Expressway, to Grand Concourse, thence northerly along the Grand Concourse to East Tremont Avenue, thence easterly along East Tremont Avenue to Bronx Park Avenue, to East 177th Street, thence easterly to the intersection of East 177th Street, Bronx River Parkway southerly extension and Cross Bronx Expressway, thence easterly along the Cross Bronx Expressway, to Beach Avenue, to Mansion Street, to St. Lawrence Avenue, to East Tremont Avenue, to White Plains Road, thence southerly along White Plains Road, to Westchester Avenue, to and southerly around Hugh J. Grant Circle to Westchester Avenue, to Olmstead Avenue, to Newbold Avenue, to the intersection of Newbold Avenue, Cross Bronx Expressway and Pugsley Avenue, thence easterly along Cross Bronx Expressway to Gleason Avenue, thence westerly along Gleason Avenue to Beach Avenue, to Watson Avenue, to Leland Avenue, to Bruckner Boulevard North, to White Plains Road, to Bruckner Boulevard South, to Olmstead Avenue to Quimby Avenue, to Pugsley Avenue, to Seward Avenue, to Castle Hill Avenue, to Cincinnatus Avenue, to Havemeyer Avenue, to Lacombe Avenue, to Newman Avenue, to Seward Avenue, to Thieriot Avenue, to Lafayette Avenue, to Rosedale Avenue, to Randall Avenue, to Commonwealth Avenue, to Lacombe Avenue, thence westerly along Lacombe Avenue to Bronx River Parkway, to Randall Avenue and Randall Avenue Extended westerly and southerly to the waters of the Bronx River, thence southerly and westerly through the waters of the Bronx River and East River to the place of beginning, also including North Brother Island, South Brother Island and Riker's Island. Population (1960), 359,751.

JACOB H. GILBERT, Democrat, of the Bronx, N.Y.; born in the Bronx, in the Congressional District he now represents, June 17, 1920; attended the public schools of New York City, James Monroe High School, St. John's College, and St. John's Law School; was admitted to the bar in 1944 and is licensed to practice in the State and Federal Courts; is engaged in the practice of law with offices at 267 Fifth Avenue, New York City; appointed an assistant corporation counsel of the City of New York and served from January 1949 to December 1950; served in the State Assembly 1951–54; member of the State Senate from 1955 to March 1960; elected as a Democrat to the Eighty-Sixth Congress on March 8, 1960, in a special election; member of the Pondiac Democratic Club, Bronx County Bar Association, Federal Bar Association of New York, New Jersey, and Connecticut, A.F. of L.–C.I.O., South Bronx Community Council, Advisory Board of Community Center P.S. 65, B'nai B'rith, Zionist Organization of America, American Jewish Congress, National Democratic Club, Bronx Chamber of Commerce, Bronx Lions Club, Elks Bronx Lodge No. 871; married to the former Irma Steuer; they have three children, Miriam Sharon, Sandra, and Samuel Stephen; reelected to the 87th, 88th, and 89th Congresses.

TWENTY-THIRD DISTRICT.—BRONX COUNTY: That part beginning at a point where the Major Deegan Expressway intersects the dividing line between the county of Bronx and the county of Westchester, thence southerly along Major Deegan Expressway to East 233d Street, to Webster Avenue, to East Gun Hill Road, to Reservoir Place, to Reservoir Oval East, to Bainbridge Avenue, to East Mosholu Parkway South, to East 204th Street, to Villa Avenue, to Van Cortlandt Avenue, to Jerome Avenue, thence southerly along Jerome Avenue, to Bedford Park Boulevard, to the Grand Concourse, to East 199th Street, to Valentine Avenue, to East 197th Street, to Briggs Avenue, to East Kingsbridge Road, to East Fordham Road, thence easterly along East Fordham Road to Washington Avenue, thence southerly through Flood Square to 3d Avenue, to East 184th Street, to Crescent Avenue, to East 187th Street, to Southern Boulevard, to East Fordham Road, thence easterly along East Fordham Road to Boston Road, to Pelham Parkway North, to Bronx Park East, to Rosewood Street, to White Plains Road, to East Gun Hill Road, to Holland Avenue, to East 211th Street, to Carlisle Place, to East 213th Street, to Barnes Avenue, to East 213th Street, to Bronxwood Avenue, to Tilden Street, to East 212th Street, to Paulding Avenue, to East Gun Hill Road, to Laconia Avenue, to Granada Place, to Baychester Avenue, thence southeasterly along Baychester Avenue to Needham Avenue, to East 224th Street, to Schieffelin Avenue, to East 222d Street, to Mickle Avenue, to Needham Avenue, to Eastchester Road, to Boston Road, to East Gun Hill Road, to Bouck Avenue, to Adee Avenue, to Yates Avenue, to Burke Avenue, to Bronxwood Avenue, to Arnow Avenue, to Williamsbridge Road, to Boston Road, to Astor Avenue, to Bronxwood Avenue, to Mace Avenue, to Williamsbridge Road, to Pelham Parkway South, to Esplanade South, to Paulding Avenue, to Lydig Avenue, to Colden Avenue, to Bogart Avenue, thence southerly along Bogart Avenue to Brady Avenue, to Antin Place, to Bronxdale Avenue, to Hunt Avenue, to Sagamore Street, to Amethyst Street, to Rhinelander Avenue, to Unionport Road, to Morris Park Avenue, to East Tremont Avenue, thence westerly along East Fremont Avenue to the Grand Concourse, to West 181st Street, to University Avenue, to West Burnside Avenue, to Sedgwick Avenue, to West Tremont Avenue, thence westerly along West Tremont Avenue and West Tremont Avenue Extended to the waters of the Harlem River, thence northerly through the waters of the Harlem River to the dividing line between the county of Bronx and the county of New York, thence northerly, westerly, and southerly along said dividing line to the waters of the Harlem River, thence westerly through the waters of the Harlem River and the Hudson River to a point where the boundary line between the county of Bronx and the county of Westchester extended westerly intersect the waters of the Hudson River, thence easterly along the said dividing line between the county of Bronx and the county of Westchester to the place of beginning. Population (1960), 353,809.

JONATHAN B. BINGHAM, Democrat, of the Bronx, N.Y.; born in New Haven, Conn., April 24, 1914, son of the late Senator Hiram Bingham of Connecticut; attended Groton School and graduated from Yale University (Phi Beta Kappa) in 1936 and received law degree in 1939; was admitted to the bar in 1940 and has practiced law in New York City; member of various bar associations; member of Judiciary Committee of New York City Bar Association; special correspondent for the New York Herald Tribune in 1935 and 1938 in Europe, the USSR, and the Far East; during World War II enlisted as a private and was discharged as a captain in Military Intelligence; married to the former June Rossbach; four children—Sherrell (Mrs. James E. Bland), June Mitchell, Timothy W., and Claudia R.; special assistant to an Assistant Secretary of State in 1945 and 1946; assistant director, Office of International Security Affairs in 1951; deputy and acting administrator, Technical Cooperation Administration 1951–53; secretary to Governor Averell Harriman of New York 1955–58; U.S. representative on the Economic and Social Council of the United Nations with the rank of Ambassador and as principal adviser to Ambassador Adlai E. Stevenson in economic and social affairs; member of the U.S. delegation to four United Nations General Assemblies 1961–63; U.S. representative on the United Nations Trusteeship Council with the rank of Minister in 1961 and 1962 and served as president of the Council in 1962; member and officer of many boards and civic and county organizations and is the recipient of awards from various organizations; elected to the 89th Congress November 3, 1964.

TWENTY-FOURTH DISTRICT.—Bronx County: That part beginning at a point where the Major Deegan Expressway intersects the dividing line between the county of Bronx and the county of Westchester, thence southerly along Major Deegan Expressway to East 233d Street, to Webster Avenue, to East Gun Hill Road, to Reservoir Place, to Reservoir Oval East, to Bainbridge Avenue, to East Mosholu Parkway South, to East 204th Street, to Villa Avenue, to Van Cortlandt Avenue, to Jerome Avenue, thence southerly along Jerome Avenue, to Bedford Park Boulevard, to The Grand Concourse, to East 199th Street, to Valentine Avenue, to East 197th Street, to Briggs Avenue, to East Kingsbridge Road, to East Fordham Road, thence easterly along East Fordham Road to Washington Avenue, thence southerly through Flood Square to 3d Avenue, to East 184th Street to Crescent Avenue, to East 187th Street, to Southern Boulevard, to East Fordham Road, thence easterly along East Fordham Road to Boston Road, to Pelham Parkway North, to Bronx Park East, to Rosewood Street, to White Plains Road, to East Gun Hill Road, to Holland Avenue, to East 211th Street, to Carlisle Place, to East 213th Street, to Barnes Avenue, to East 213th Street, to Bronxwood Avenue, to Tilden Street, to East 212th Street, to Paulding Avenue, to East Gun Hill Road, to Laconia Avenue, to Granada Place, to Baychester Avenue, thence southeasterly along Baychester Avenue to Needham Avenue, to East 224th Street, to Schieffelin Avenue, to East 222d Street, to Mickle Avenue, to Needham Avenue, to Eastchester Road, to Boston Road, to East Gun Hill Road, to Bouck Avenue, to Adee Avenue, to Yates Avenue, to Burke Avenue, to Bronxwood Avenue, to Arnow Avenue, to Williamsbridge Road, to Boston Road, to Astor Avenue, to Bronxwood Avenue, to Mace Avenue, to Williamsbridge Road, to Pelham Parkway South, to Esplanade South, to Paulding Avenue, to Lydig Avenue, to Colden Avenue, to Bogart Avenue, thence southerly along Bogart Avenue, to Brady Avenue, to Antin Place, to Bronxdale Avenue, to Hunt Avenue, to Sagamore Street, to Amethyst Street, to Rhinelander Avenue, to Unionport Road, to Morris Park Avenue, to East Tremont Avenue, to Bronx Park Avenue, to East 177th Street, thence easterly to the intersection of East 177th Street, Bronx River Parkway Southerly Extension and Cross Bronx Expressway, thence easterly along the Cross Bronx Expressway to Beach Avenue, to Mansion Street, to St. Lawrence Avenue, to East Tremont Avenue, to White Plains Road to Westchester Avenue, to and southerly around Hugh J. Grant Circle to Westchester Avenue, to Olmstead Avenue, to Newbold Avenue, to the intersection of Newbold Avenue, Cross Bronx Expressway and Pugsley Avenue, thence easterly along Cross Bronx Expressway to Gleason Avenue, thence westerly along Gleason Avenue to Beach Avenue, to Watson Avenue, to Leland Avenue, to Bruckner Boulevard North, to White Plains Road, to Bruckner Boulevard South, to Olmstead Avenue, to Quimby Avenue, to Pugsley Avenue, to Seward Avenue, to Castle Hill Avenue, to Cincinnatus Avenue, to Havemeyer Avenue, to Lacombe Avenue, to Newman Avenue, to Seward Avenue, to Thieriot Avenue, to Lafayette Avenue, to Rosedale Avenue, to Randall Avenue, to Commonwealth Avenue, to Lacombe Avenue, thence westerly along Lacombe Avenue to Bronx River Parkway, to Randall Avenue, and Randall Avenue Extended westerly and southerly to the waters of the Bronx River, thence southerly and northerly through the waters of the Bronx River, East River, Long Island Sound to the dividing line between the county of Bronx and the county of Westchester, thence westerly along the said dividing line to the place of beginning, also including Hunters Island, Hog Island, Middle Reef Island, East Nonations Island, South Nonations Island, Machaux Island, the Blauzes, Hart Island, High Island, Chimney Sweeps, Twin Islands, Rat Island, Green Flats Island, Big Tom Island, Cuban Ledge Island, City Island, and any other island not aforementioned. Population (1960), 350,186.

PAUL A. FINO, Republican; born in the Bronx, December 15, 1913; graduated P. S. 75 and James Monroe High School in the Bronx; attended St. John's University and, after 2 years, studied law at St. John's School of Law; graduated with the degree of LL. B.; was the recipient of two scholastic awards and was also a member of St. John's Debating Society; admitted to the bar of the State of New York in 1938; from March 1943 to December 1944 was an assistant attorney general of the State of New York attached to the Labor Bureau and later in charge of the Criminal Division of the Education Bureau; from January 1945 to May 1950 was New York State senator representing the 27th senatorial district; appointed by the mayor of the city of New York on June 1, 1950, to the Municipal Civil Service Commission, but resigned December 31, 1952, to assume his congressional seat; unanimously elected on January 26, 1961, Republican county chairman of Bronx County; is engaged in the practice of law with offices at 80 Broad Street, New York City; member of the Bronx County Bar Association, Royal Arcanum, Columbus Alliance, Bronx Lodge of Elks, 10th A.D. Republican Club, K. of C. Wakefield Council, and other civic and fraternal organizations; married to the former Esther C. Liquori; they have two children, Lucille and Paul, Jr.; elected to the 83d Congress on November 4, 1952; reelected to the 84th, 85th, 86th, 87th, 88th, and 89th Congresses; resides at 1518 Fielding Street, Bronx, New York.

TWENTY-FIFTH DISTRICT.—PUTNAM COUNTY. WESTCHESTER COUNTY: That part consisting of the city of Yonkers and the city of Peekskill and the towns of Greenburgh, Eastchester, Mt. Pleasant, Ossining, and Cortlandt. Population (1960), 438,409.

RICHARD LAWRENCE OTTINGER, Democrat, of Pleasantville, N.Y.; born January 27, 1929; attended Scarsdale public schools and Loomis School, Windsor, Conn.; Cornell University, B.A., 1950; Harvard Law School, LL.B. 1953; Georgetown University, graduate study in international law, 1960–61; U.S. Air Force, 1953–55 emerging as captain; was admitted to the New York bar in the 1955, U.S. Court of Appeals, Second Circuit, 1960, and the U.S. Supreme Court, 1960; married to the former Betty Ann Schneider of Louisville, Ky.; four children, Ronald, Randall, Lawrence, and Jenny Louise; practiced international and corporate law 1955–60; contract manager for International Cooperation Administration 1960–61; a founder and second staff member of the Peace Corps, serving as director of programs for the West Coast of South America 1961–64, member of American, Inter-American, International, New York City, County and State, Westchester County, and Yonkers bar associations; member of board of directors of U.S. Association of the United Nations, Westchester Children's Association, board of trustees of Jewish Board of Guardians, board of directors of Linden Hill School, United Cerebral Palsy Association; member of Westchester County Association, Bronxville American Legion Post No. 464, American Civil Liberties Union, Golden Retriever Club of America, and Long Island Retriever Field Trial Club; former trustee of Harvard Law School Association of New York City; elected to the 89th Congress November 3, 1964.

TWENTY-SIXTH DISTRICT.—WESTCHESTER COUNTY: That part consisting of the cities of White Plains, Mt. Vernon, New Rochelle, Rye and the towns of Yorktown, Somers, North Salem, Mamaroneck, Scarsdale, Lewisboro, Bedford, Poundridge, Pelham, New Castle, North Castle, Rye, and Harrison. Population (1960), 402,204.

OGDEN ROGERS REID, Republican, of Purchase, N.Y.; born in New York City, June 24, 1925; enlisted, private, U.S. Army 1943, discharged first lieutenant 1946, captain USAR, Inactive; first president 11th Airborne Division Association; A.B., Yale, 1949; married Mary Louise Stewart July 9, 1949; children—Stewart, Michael, William, Elisabeth, and Ogden Mills; president New York Herald Tribune, Societe Anonyme, 1953–58; president and editor, New York Herald Tribune, Inc., 1955–59; director, Panama Canal Company, 1956–59; United States Ambassador to Israel, 1959–61; Governor Rockefeller's cabinet, 1961–62; chairman, New York State Commission for Human Rights, 1961–62; chairman, New York State International Official Visitors Office, 1962; director, Massachusetts Mutual Life Insurance Company; elder, Rye Presbyterian Church, Rye, N.Y.; trustee, Hampton Institute; Long Island University; director, Atlantic Council of the United States; member, Advisory Council, School of International Affairs, Columbia University; Council on Foreign Relations; vice president, National Institute of Social Sciences; member, Lay Advisory Board, St. Agnes Hospital (White Plains, N.Y.); Chevalier of the Legion of Honor, July 1957; Cruseiro do Sul, Brazil, September 1956; honorary LL.D., Adelphi College and the Jewish Theological Seminary of America; honorary Doctor of Hebrew Letters, Dropsie College; fellow of Brandeis University and Bar-Ilan University, Israel; elected to the 88th Congress November 6, 1962; reelected to the 89th Congress.

TWENTY-SEVENTH DISTRICT.—COUNTIES: Delaware, Orange, Rockland, and Sullivan (4 counties). Population (1960), 409,349.

JOHN GOODCHILD DOW, Democrat, of Grand View, N.Y.; born in New York City May 6, 1905; graduated from Harvard College, A.B., and Columbia University, M.A.; systems analyst for large corporations; married; four children; served as director of Rockland County Mental Health Drive, P.T.A. official, Civil Defense director in Grand View, zoning official in Grand View, Orangetown Democratic committeeman (chairman); elected to the 89th Congress November 3, 1964.

TWENTY-EIGHTH DISTRICT.—COUNTIES: Columbia, Dutchess, Greene, Schoharie, and Ulster (5 counties). Population (1960), 396,122.

JOSEPH Y. RESNICK, Democrat, of Ellenville, N.Y.; born in Ellenville July 13, 1924; received an education in electronics; during World War II served as radio officer in the U.S. Merchant Marine; married the former Ruth Lehrer; four children, Jeffrey, Debbie, Todd, and David; religion, Jewish; founder and chairman of the board of Channel Master Corp.; engaged in electronics and plastic research and development; charter founder of Eleanor Roosevelt Memorial Foundation; member of the board of St. Cabrini Home, Inc.; member Ellenville School Board two terms; elected to the 89th Congress November 3, 1964.

TWENTY-NINTH DISTRICT.—COUNTIES: Albany and Schenectady. RENSSELAER COUNTY: That part in the city of Troy consisting of wards 1 to 4, 6 to 9, 11 and 12. Population (1960), 452,826.

LEO WILLIAM O'BRIEN, Democrat, of Albany, N.Y.; born in Buffalo, N.Y., September 21, 1900; graduate of Niagara University in 1922; newspaperman from 1922–52; as radio and television commentator won national awards in 1950 and 1951; honorary degrees from University of Alaska, University of Niagara, and Siena College; member of Alaska International Rail and Highway Commission; House floor manager for Alaska and Hawaii statehood bills; married Mabel Jean of Cambridge, Mass., in 1925; one son, Robert; elected to the 82d Congress on April 1, 1952; reelected to the 83d, 84th, 85th, 86th, 87th, 88th, and 89th Congresses.

THIRTIETH DISTRICT.—COUNTIES: Clinton, Essex, Fulton, Hamilton, Saratoga, Warren, and Washington. RENSSELAER COUNTY: Part of. Population (1960), 460,748.

CARLETON JAMES KING, Republican, of Saratoga Springs, N.Y.; born in Saratoga Springs, June 15, 1904; educated in the public schools; graduated from Union University with LL.B. degree in 1926; engaged in practice of law in the firm of King, Duval & Murphy, Saratoga Springs, N.Y.; member of county and State bar associations; admitted to practice before United States Supreme Court; acting City Judge, city of Saratoga Springs, 1936–41; Assistant District Attorney, Saratoga County, 1942–50, and District Attorney from 1950 until resignation December 31, 1960; president, New York State District Attorneys' Association in 1955; president, Saratoga County Bar Association in 1959 and 1960; married Constance M. Roddy of Brooklyn, N.Y.; two children, Lt. Carleton J. King, Jr., U.S. Navy, and Mrs. James A. Murphy, Jr.; elected to the 87th Congress November 8, 1960; reelected to the 88th and 89th Congresses.

THIRTY-FIRST DISTRICT.—COUNTIES: Franklin, Jefferson, Lewis, Oswego, and St. Lawrence (5 counties). Population (1960), 353,183.

ROBERT CAMERON McEWEN, Republican, of Ogdensburg, N.Y.; born in Ogdensburg January 5, 1920; attended the Ogdensburg public schools, the Mount Hermon School, the University of Vermont, the Wharton School of Finance of the University of Pennsylvania, and was graduated from the Albany Law School; married the former Anita Sharples of Ogdensburg; two children, Nancy and Mary; veteran of World War II, serving 3½ years in the Army Air Force, and was discharged as a sergeant; member of American Legion, Veterans of Foreign Wars, Masons, and Elks; member of New York State Senate 1954–64; elected to the 89th Congress November 3, 1964.

THIRTY-SECOND DISTRICT.—COUNTIES: Herkimer, Madison, and Oneida (3 counties). Population (1960), 385,406.

ALEXANDER PIRNIE, Republican, of 12 Slaytonbush Lane, Utica, N. Y.; born April 16, 1903, in Pulaski, N. Y., graduate of Pulaski Academy, Cornell University, A. B., and Cornell Law School, LL. B.; admitted to the bar in 1926 and began practice of law with Miller, Hubbell & Evans, Utica, now designated Evans, Pirnie & Burdick; military career began in 1924, when commissioned second lieutenant, Infantry, Officers Reserve Corps; volunteered for active duty December 4, 1942, in World War II; was successively promoted to rank of colonel in the Judge Advocate General's Corps; served overseas in the European theater on staff assignments; awarded Bronze Star and Legion of Merit; member of Liberty Lodge, No. 959, F.A.A.M.; the Yahnundasis Scottish Rite bodies; past potentate of Ziyara Temple A.A.O.M.S; member of the American and New York State Bar Associations; past president Judge Advocates Association; past president of the Oneida County Bar Association; past president of the Cornell Law Association and presently serving on Cornell Law School Council; wife,

Mildred S. Pirnie; sons: Lt. Bruce R. Pirnie, on duty with the U.S. Army, and Douglas J. Pirnie, a student at Cornell University; elected to the 86th Congress November 4, 1958; member of Agriculture Committee; reelected to the 87th, 88th, and 89th Congresses; member of Armed Services Committee.

THIRTY-THIRD DISTRICT.—COUNTIES: Broome, Chemung, Tioga, and Tompkins (4 counties). Population (1960), 415,333.

HOWARD WINFIELD ROBISON, Republican, of Owego, N. Y.; born in Owego, N. Y., October 30, 1915; educated at Cornell University, Ithaca, N. Y., A. B. 1937 and LL. B. 1939; profession, attorney at law; served in the United States Army, Counter Intelligence Corps, 1942–46; married to Gertrude L. Frederick in Endicott, N. Y., November 1, 1946; served as county attorney, Tioga County, N. Y., 1946–58; elected to the 85th Congress in a special election January 14, 1958, to fill the vacancy caused by resignation of Sterling Cole; reelected to the 86th, 87th, 88th, and 89th Congresses.

THIRTY-FOURTH DISTRICT.—ONONDAGA COUNTY. Population (1960), 423,023.

JAMES MICHAEL HANLEY, Democrat, of Syracuse, N.Y.; born in Syracuse July 19, 1920; graduated from St. Lucy's Academy; Catholic; member of St. Patrick's Church; funeral director, firm of Callahan-Hanley-Mooney Funeral Home; veteran; served in the U.S. Army, World War II; married the former Rita Ann Harrington of Syracuse August 12, 1950; two children, Christine Mary and Peter J.; member of Chamber of Commerce, American Legion, Knights of Columbus (grand knight), B.P.O. Elks, Syracuse Liederkranz, Ancient Order of Hibernians, Boys Town, Army and Navy Union, Onondaga Chapter Help for Retarded Children, Antique Auto Club of America, Holy Name Society, Order of the Alhambra, West End Social Club, St. Mary's Men's Club, Syracuse Police Benevolent Association (honorary), and national, State, and local funeral directors associations; executive secretary of Onondaga County Democratic Committee; active in civic, church, fraternal, political, and veterans' affairs; elected to the 89th Congress November 3, 1964.

THIRTY-FIFTH DISTRICT.—COUNTIES: Cayuga, Chenango, Cortland, Montgomery, Ontario, Otsego Seneca, and Yates (8 counties). Population (1960), 386,148.

SAMUEL S. STRATTON, Democrat, of Amsterdam, N.Y.; born in Yonkers, N.Y., September 27, 1916; educated in the public schools of Schenectady and Rochester, N.Y., and at Blair Academy, Blairstown, N.J.; graduated from the University of Rochester, A.B., 1937; Haverford College, M.A., 1938; Harvard University, M.A., 1940; married to former Joan Harris Wolfe; they have five children; secretary to Congressman Thomas H. Eliot of Massachusetts, 1940–42; deputy secretary general, Far Eastern Commission, Washington, D.C., 1946–48; city councilman, Schenectady, N.Y., 1949–53; mayor of Schenectady 1955–58; commissioned an ensign in the United States Naval Reserve, June 26, 1942; twice awarded the Bronze Star; recalled to active duty during the Korean emergency, 1951–53; currently holds rank of captain in the Naval Reserve; trustee, University of Rochester; member of Psi Upsilon fraternity, Phi Beta Kappa, Reserve Officers Association, United States Naval Institute, Navy League, Masons, Eagles, American Legion, Veterans of Foreign Wars, Amvets, and the Presbyterian Church; elected to the 86th Congress, November 4, 1958; reelected to the 87th, 88th, and 89th Congresses; member Armed Services Committee.

THIRTY-SIXTH DISTRICT.—WAYNE COUNTY. MONROE COUNTY: That part within and bounded by a line beginning at a point where the waters of the Genesee River and Charlotte Harbor intersect the waters of Lake Ontario, thence running in a southerly direction through the waters of Charlotte Harbor and the Genesee River to a point where the Genesee River intersects the city line, thence easterly and northerly along said city line as it winds and turns to the intersection of the city line and the waters of Lake Ontario, and thence through the waters of Lake Ontario to the place of beginning, together with the towns of Brighton, Henrietta, Irondequoit, Mendon, Penfield, Perinton, Pittsford, and Webster. Population (1960), 410,943.

FRANK HORTON, Republican, of Rochester, N.Y.; born in Cuero, Tex., December 12, 1919; graduate of Louisiana State University, 1941, B.A., and Cornell University Law School, 1947, LL.B.; married Marjorie Wilcox of Interlaken, N.Y.; two sons, Frank, 17, and Steven, 12; attorney; member of firm of Moser, Johnson & Reif; entered active duty with U.S. Army, June 1941, as second lieutenant and released to inactive duty, August 1945, as major; service in North Africa and Italy from November 1942 to August 1945; member, Order of the Coif; Phi Kappa Phi; Monroe County, New York State and American Bar Associations; Veterans of Foreign Wars; American Legion; Reserve Officers Association; master, Seneca Lodge No. 920, F. & A.M., 1962; president, Masonic Service Bureau, 1955–56; director, Masonic Service Bureau; member, Rochester Consistory, Scottish Rite; Damascus Temple, Shrine; Hamilton Chapter No. 62, R.A.M.; Doric Council No. 19, R. & S.M.; Monroe Commandery No. 12, Knights Templar; past president, Federation of Bar Associations of Western New York; secretary, Rochester Bar Association 1953–57; elder and trustee, Central Presbyterian Church; member, Legislative Committee of Rochester Presbytery and New York Synod; coowner of Camp Pathfinder, Algonquin Park, Ontario, Canada; active in Civil Defense and Boy Scout work; former president, Rochester Community Baseball, Inc.; former executive vice president of International Baseball League and attorney for the league; member, Rochester City Council, 1955–61; elected to the 88th Congress November 6, 1962; reelected to the 89th Congress.

THIRTY-SEVENTH DISTRICT.—COUNTIES: Genesee, Livingston, Orleans, and Wyoming. MONROE COUNTY: That part within and bounded by a line beginning at a point where the waters of the Genesee River and Charlotte Harbor intersect the waters of Lake Ontario, thence running in a southerly direction through the waters of Charlotte Harbor and the Genesee River to a point where the Genesee River intersects the city line, thence westerly and northerly along said city line as it winds and turns to the intersection of the city line and the waters of Lake Ontario, and thence through the waters of Lake Ontario to the place of beginning, together with the towns of Chili, Clarkson, Gates, Greece, Hamlin, Ogden, Parma, Riga, Rush, Sweden, and Wheatland. Population (1960), 410,432.

BARBER BENJAMIN CONABLE, JR., Republican, of Alexander, N.Y.; born in Warsaw, N.Y., November 2, 1922; graduated from Cornell University, A.B., 1942, and Cornell Law School, LL.B., 1948; served in the Marine Corps during World War II and in the Korean conflict; now lieutentnt colonel in Marine Corps Reserve; admitted to the bar in 1948 and engaged in the practice of law in Buffalo, N.Y.; in 1952 entered into law partnership with his father in Batavia, N.Y.; member of the State senate 1963 and 1964; married to former Charlotte Williams of Buffalo, N.Y.; four children; active worker in Republican Party affairs since 1953; member of American Legion and Veterans of Foreign Wars; engaged in community, civic, and welfare activities; elected to the 89th Congress November 3, 1964.

THIRTY-EIGHTH DISTRICT.—COUNTIES: Allegany, Cattaraugus, Chautauqua, Schuyler, and Steuben (5 counties). Population (1960), 382,277.

CHARLES E. GOODELL, Republican, of Jamestown, N.Y.; born in Jamestown, N. Y., March 16, 1926; graduated from Jamestown High School and Williams College; elected to Phi Beta Kappa in junior year and received a bachelor of arts degree cum laude; LL.B. degree from the Yale University School of Law in 1951; recipient of a Ford Foundation faculty scholarship at Yale while teaching at Quinnipiac College in New Haven; received a master's degree from the Yale University Graduate School of Government in 1952; former partner in law firm, Jamestown, N.Y.; on August 28, 1954, married the former Jean Rice of Buffalo, a registered nurse and graduate of Millard Fillmore School of Nursing; five sons: William Rice, born November 28, 1955; Timothy Bartlett, born May 10, 1957; Roger Stokoe, born February 19, 1959; Michael Charles Ellsworth, born June 10, 1960; and Jeffrey Harris, born August 17, 1962; U.S. Navy in World War II and U.S. Air Force during the Korean conflict; played college baseball and football, and semiprofessional baseball in the Jamestown area; was a congressional liaison assistant for the Department of Justice for the period 1954–55; served as chairman of the Governmental Affairs Committee and member of the board of directors of the Jamestown area Chamber of Commerce; member of Ellicott Town Board, 1958; former Sunday-school teacher, lay reader, and associate vestryman at St. Luke's Episcopal Church in Jamestown; elected chairman of the Chautauqua County Republican Committee in September 1958; elected to the 86th Congress in a special election May 26, 1959, to fill the seat left vacant by the late Honorable Daniel A. Reed; reelected to successive Congresses.

THIRTY-NINTH DISTRICT.—ERIE COUNTY: That part beginning at a point where Starin Avenue intersects the dividing line between the city of Buffalo and the town of Tonawanda, thence southerly along Starin Avenue to Taunton Place, to Standish Road, to Parkside Avenue, to North Drive, to Sterling Avenue, to Taunton Place, to Norwalk Avenue, to Linden Avenue, to Parkside Avenue, to Amherst Street, to Nottingham Terrace, to Elmwood Avenue, to Lafayette Avenue, to Main Street, to LeRoy Avenue, to Kensington Avenue, to the east city line, thence northerly, and westerly along said city line to the place of beginning; also that part of the city of Lackawanna described as follows: Beginning at a point where South Park Avenue intersects the city lines of the city of Buffalo and the city of Lackawanna, thence southerly along South Park Avenue, to Nason Parkway, to Electric Avenue, to Ridge Road, to Franklin Street, to Prospect Place, to Center Street, to Kirby Avenue, to Electric Avenue, to the intersection of Electric Avenue, the south city line of the city of Lackawanna and the town line of Hamburg, thence easterly, northerly and westerly along said Lackawanna city line to the place of beginning; also including the towns of Amherst, Clarence, Newstead, Cheektowaga, Lancaster, Alden, Marilla, Elma, West Seneca, Hamburg, Orchard Park, Aurora, Wales, Holland, Colden, Boston, Eden, Evans, Brant, North Collins, Collins, Concord, Sardinia and that part of the Cattaraugus Indian Reservation within Erie County. Population (1960), 436,243.

RICHARD DEAN McCARTHY, Democrat, of Buffalo, N.Y.; born in Buffalo September 24, 1927; graduated from Canisius High School and Canisius College, A.B.; graduate work at the University of Buffalo, Cornell University, and Harvard University; served in U.S. Navy in South Pacific, 1945–46 and U.S. Army in Far East, 1950–52; married in 1957 to the former Gail E. Coughlin of South Buffalo; five children: Maura, Brendan, Deirde, Dean, and Barry; former newsman and public relations executive; director of public relations for the National Gypsum Co., 1956–64; president, Niagara Frontier Chapter, Public Relations Society of America; past vice president, Greater Buffalo Development Foundation; member, Central Park Association, Buffalo Philharmonic Orchestra Society, Buffalo Area Chamber of Commerce, Frontier Press Club, Buffalo and Erie County Historical Society, and Troop 1 Post, American Legion; attends St. Mark's Catholic Church; elected to the 89th Congress November 3, 1964.

FORTIETH DISTRICT.—NIAGARA COUNTY. ERIE COUNTY: That part beginning at a point where Starin Avenue intersects the dividing line between the city of Buffalo and the town of Tonawanda, thence southerly along Starin Avenue to Taunton Place, to Standish Road, to Parkside Avenue, to North Drive, to Sterling Avenue, to Taunton Place, to Norwalk Avenue, to Linden Avenue, to Parkside Avenue, to Amherst Street, to Nottingham Terraco, to Elmwood Avenue, thence northerly to Amherst Street, to Reservation Street, to Grote Street, to Howell Street, to Amherst Street, to Thompson Street, to Hamilton Street, thence westerly along Hamilton Street and Hamilton Street Extended to the waters of the Niagara River, thence northerly through the waters of the Niagara River to a point where Vulcan Street Extended southwesterly intersects the waters of the Niagara River, thence northeasterly along Vulcan Street and Vulcan Street Extended and the dividing line between the city of Buffalo and the town of Tonawanda to the place of beginning, also including the towns of Tonawanda, Grand Island, city of Tonawanda, and the Tonawanda Indian Reservation. Population (1960), 435,282.

HENRY P. SMITH III, Republican, of North Tonawanda, N.Y.; born in North Tonawanda September 29, 1911; attended the public schools, Nichols School of Buffalo, Dartmouth College, A.B. in 1933, and Cornell Law School, LL.B. in 1936; engaged in the practice of law in Ithaca, N.Y., until 1941 and since then in North Tonawanda; elected mayor in November 1961 and resigned in January 1963 to accept appointment as Niagara County judge for 1 year; married the former Helen Elliott Belding; three daughters, Susan (Mrs. Walter G. McConnell), Lucinda, and Christiana; former president of the Chamber of Commerce; trustee, drive chairman, and president of the United Community Fund; member of Selective Service System Board 81; member and president of the Rotary Club; director of the Beeman Foundation in Niagara Falls; elder of North Presbyterian Church; selected by the Chamber of Commerce as Tonawanda's Citizen of the Year in 1963; elected to the 89th Congress November 3, 1964.

FORTY-FIRST DISTRICT.—ERIE COUNTY: That part beginning at a point within the city of Buffalo where Hamilton Street Extended intersects the waters of the Niagara River, thence easterly along Hamilton Street Extended and Hamilton Street to Thompson Street, to Amherst Street, to Howell Street, to Grote Street, to Reservation Street, to Amherst Street, to Elmwood Avenue, to Lafayette Avenue, to Main Street, to LeRoy Avenue, to Kensington Avenue, to the east city line of the city of Buffalo, thence southerly and westerly along said city line and city line extended to the waters of Lake Erie, thence northerly through the waters of Buffalo Harbor, Lake Erie and Niagara River to the place of beginning including Squaw Island; also that part of the city of Lackawanna described as follows: Beginning at a point where South Park Avenue intersects the city lines of the city of Buffalo and the city of Lackawanna, thence southerly along South Park Avenue to Nason Parkway, to Electric Avenue, to Ridge Road, to Franklin Street, to Prospect Place, to Center Street, to Kirby Avenue, to Electric Avenue, to the intersection of Electric Avenue, the south city line of the city of Lackawanna and the town line of Hamburg, thence westerly, northerly and easterly along the city line of the city of Lackawanna to the place of beginning. Population (1960), 435,432.

THADDEUS J. DULSKI, Democrat-Liberal, of Buffalo, N.Y.; born September 27, 1915; attended Canisius College and University of Buffalo; accountant and tax consultant; appointed to the Bureau of Internal Revenue, Treasury Department, in 1940; resigned in 1947 to enter private practice; veteran of World War II;

recalled to Government service in 1951 to serve as special agent in the Price Stabilization Administration; in 1953 elected Walden district councilman for two terms and in 1957 elected councilman-at-large of the city of Buffalo for a 4-year term, serving as member of Finance Council Committee; chairman of the Taxation Council Committee and Wage Classification Council Committee; married; five children; elected to the 86th Congress on November 4, 1958, reelected to the 87th, 88th, and 89th Congresses.

NORTH CAROLINA

(Population (1960), 4,556,155)

SENATORS

SAM J. ERVIN, JR., Democrat, born at Morganton, N.C., September 27, 1896; graduated from University of North Carolina with A.B. degree, 1917, and Harvard Law School with LL.B. degree, 1922; granted these honorary degrees: LL.D., University of North Carolina, 1951, LL.D., Western Carolina College, 1955, and D.P.A., Suffolk University, 1957; served in France with First Division in First World War; twice wounded in battle, twice cited for gallantry in action, and awarded French Fourragere, Purple Heart with Oak Leaf Cluster, Silver Star, and Distinguished Service Cross; subsequently served in National Guard; admitted to North Carolina Bar, 1919; practiced law at Morganton from 1922 until present except during service on the bench; representative from Burke County in North Carolina Legislature, 1923, 1925, 1931; chairman, Burke County Democratic Executive Committee, 1924; member North Carolina State Democratic Executive Committee, 1930–37; judge, Burke County Criminal Court, 1935–37; judge, North Carolina Superior Court, 1937–43; member North Carolina State Board of Law Examiners, 1944–46; representative from the Tenth North Carolina District in the 79th Congress, 1946–47; chairman, North Carolina Commission for the Improvement of the Administration of Justice, 1947–49; associate justice, North Carolina Supreme Court, February 3, 1948, until June 11, 1954, when he qualified as a U.S. Senator from North Carolina under appointment of Governor William B. Umstead as a successor to the late Clyde R. Hoey; returned to the U.S. Senate by the people of North Carolina at the election of 1954, 1956, and 1962 for additional terms ending on January 2, 1969; delegate to Democratic National Conventions, 1956, 1960; trustee, Morganton Graded Schools (1927–30), University of North Carolina (1932–35, 1945–46), and Davidson College (1948–58); chosen Morganton's Man of the Year, 1954; Grand Orator, the Grand Lodge of Masons of North Carolina, 1963; director, First National Bank of Morganton; member, American Bar Association, American Judicature Society, North Carolina Bar Association, North Carolina State Bar, Farm Bureau, Grange, Morganton Chamber of Commerce, Newcomen Society, North Carolina Wildlife Association, American Legion, Disabled American Veterans, Legion of Valor, Society of the First Division, Veterans of Foreign Wars, Veterans of the First World War, Royal Arch Masons, Royal and Select Masters, Knights Templar, Scottish Rite Masons 33d Degree, Shriners, Ahepa, Dokies, Junior Order, Knights of Pythias, Moose, American Historical Association, Burke County Historical Society, North Carolina Society for the Preservation of Antiquities, North Carolina Folklore Society, North Carolina Literary and Historical Association, Roanoke Island Historical Association, Society of the Cincinnati, Society of Mayflower Descendants (State Governor, 1950–52), Sons of the American Revolution, South Carolina Historical Society, Southern Historical Association, Southern Political Science Association, Western North Carolina Historical Association, Morganton Kiwanis Club, General Alumni Association of the University of North Carolina (President, 1947–48), Morganton Presbyterian Church (elder); cited by North Carolina Department of American Legion for "devotion to the Constitution," Patriotic Order of Sons of America for "great and inspiring public services," General Convention of the United Daughters of the Confederacy for "defense of constitutional rights," awarded the Cross of Military Service by the United Daughters of the Confederacy, the Good Citizenship Medal by the Sons of the American Revolution, the Distinguished Citizenship Certificate by the North Carolina Citizens Association, and the Patriotic Service Medal by the American Coalition of Patriotic Societies; married Margaret Bruce Bell of Concord, N.C., June 18, 1924; three children, Sam J. Ervin III, Mrs. Gerald M. Hansler, and Mrs. Hallett S. Ward, Jr.

B. EVERETT JORDAN, Democrat, of Saxapahaw, N. C.; born September 8, 1896, in Ramseur, N. C., son of the Rev. Henry Harrison and Annie Elizabeth Sellers Jordan; student at Rutherford College, N. C., Preparatory School, 1912–13, and at Trinity College, 1914–15; married Katherine McLean of Gastonia, N. C., November 29, 1924; children: Benjamin Everett, Rose Ann Gant, and John McLean; served with Tank Corps, U. S. Army, 1918–19, with occupation forces in Germany in 1919; organized Sellers Manufacturing Co., 1927, and has served as secretary-treasurer and general manager since and is an official in several other textile manufacturing companies; chairman of the North Carolina Democratic Executive Committee, 1949–54; Democratic National Committeeman from North Carolina, 1954–58; member of North Carolina Medical Care Commission, 1945–51; member of North Carolina Peace Officers Benefit and Retirement Commission, 1943–58; officer of the Alamance County TB Association and the Alamance County Red Cross; chairman, Board of Trustees, Alamance County General Hospital; trustee, Duke University, American University, and Elon College; member of Rotary Club and Masonic Order; Alamance County Man of the Year, 1955; Methodist lay leader, 1935–40; chairman, Methodist Board of Stewards, 1930–50; adult Bible class teacher, 1927–28; vice president, Board of Methodist Colleges, 1952–56; appointed to the United States Senate April 19, 1958, to fill the vacancy caused by the death of W. Kerr Scott, and elected November 4, 1958, for the term ending January 3, 1961; reelected November 8, 1960, for the term ending January 3, 1967.

REPRESENTATIVES

FIRST DISTRICT.—COUNTIES: Beaufort, Bertie, Camden, Chowan, Currituck, Dare, Gates, Hertford, Hyde, Martin, Pasquotank, Perquimans, Pitt, Tyrrell, and Washington (15 counties). Population (1960), 277,861.

HERBERT COVINGTON BONNER, Democrat, of Washington, N. C.; born in Washington, N. C.; son of Herbert M. and Hannah Hare Bonner; married to Eva Hassell Hackney, of Washington, N. C.; sergeant, Company I, Three Hundred and Twenty-second Infantry; served overseas with the Eighty-first Division during World War I; Episcopalian; Elk; Mason; Shriner; elected November 5, 1940, to the Seventy-sixth Congress to fill the unexpired term of Hon. Lindsay C. Warren, who resigned to become Comptroller General of the United States; also elected on the above date to the 77th Congress; reelected to the 78th, 79th, 80th, 81st, 82d, 83d, 84th, 85th, 86th, 87th, 88th, and 89th Congresses.

SECOND DISTRICT.—COUNTIES: Edgecombe, Franklin, Greene, Halifax, Lenoir, Northampton, Vance Warren, and Wilson (9 counties). Population (1960), 350,135.

L. H. FOUNTAIN, Democrat, of Tarboro, N.C.; born in village of Leggett, Edgecombe County, N.C., April 23, 1913; son of the late Sallie (Barnes) and Lawrence H. Fountain; educated in public schools of Edgecombe County and at University of North Carolina—A. B. and LL. B. degrees; married Christine Dail of Mount Olive, N. C.; one daughter, Nancy Dail Fountain; member local, State, and National Bar Associations, Kiwanis, Elks, and Moose Clubs; former Jaycee; reading clerk North Carolina State Senate 1936–41; World War II veteran of 4 years service; North Carolina State Senator 1947–52; Presbyterian elder; member, executive committee, East Carolina Council Boy Scouts of America; member, board of trustees, Saint Andrews Presbyterian College, Laurinburg, N.C.; elected to 83d Congress; reelected to 84th, 85th, 86th, 87th, 88th, and 89th Congresses; chairman, Intergovernmental Relations Subcommittee of Committee on Government Operations, member, Foreign Affairs Committee, and chairman, Near East Subcommittee thereof.

THIRD DISTRICT.—COUNTIES: Carteret, Craven, Duplin, Harnett, Jones, Onslow, Pamlico, Pender, Sampson, and Wayne (10 counties). Population (1960), 430,360.

DAVID NEWTON HENDERSON, Democrat, of Wallace, N.C.; born on a farm near Hubert, Onslow County, N.C., April 16, 1921, son of I. N. and Virginia Boney Henderson; graduated from Wallace High School in 1938, Davidson College, B.S., 1942, and University of North Carolina Law School, LL.B., in 1949; began practice of law in Wallace in 1949; commissioned a second lieutenant in the U.S. Air Corps as a Reserve graduate of Davidson College in 1942; served overseas in India, China, and Okinawa, and discharged as a major, U.S. Air Force, in 1946; married the former Mary Knowles of Wallace and has three sons, David Bruce, Wiley Bryant, and Wimbric Boney; assistant general counsel to the Committee on Education and Labor, U.S. House of Representatives 1951–52; solicitor of Duplin County General Court 1954–58 and judge from December 1958 to December 1960; member of the Presbyterian Church, Masons, American Legion, Veterans of Foreign Wars, Duplin County Bar Association, Wallace Squadron Civil Air Patrol, and the Lions Club; elected to the 87th Congress November 8, 1960; re-elected to the 88th and 89th Congresses; assigned to Public Works Committee and Post Office and Civil Service Committee; chairman, Subcommittee on Manpower Utilization.

FOURTH DISTRICT.—COUNTIES: Chatham, Davidson, Johnston, Nash, Randolph, and Wake (6 counties). Population (1960), 460,795.

HAROLD DUNBAR COOLEY, Democrat, of Nashville, N.C., son of the late Roger A. Pryor Cooley and Hattie Davis Cooley; born July 26, 1897; attended the public schools of Nash County, the law schools of the University of North Carolina and Yale University; licensed to practice law in 1918; served in the Naval Aviation Flying Corps during World War I; Presidential elector in 1932; president, Nash County Bar Association 1933; member: Nash-Rocky Mount, N.C., Bar Association, North Carolina State Bar Association, American Bar Association, and American Judicature Society; member of Junior Order United American Mechanics, Phi Delta Theta fraternity, and Phi Delta Phi national law fraternity; member of Baptist Church; married Miss Madeline Matilda Strickland in 1923, and is father of two children—a son, Roger A. Pryor Cooley 2d, and a daughter, Hattie Davis Cooley Lawrence; elected to the 73d Congress July 7, 1934; reelected to each succeeding Congress; chairman House Committee on Agriculture, 81st, 82d, 84th, 85th, 86th, 87th, 88th, and 89th Congresses; member of the Executive Committee and the Council of the Interparliamentary Union and past president of the American group; consultant and congressional adviser to United Nations Educational, Scientific and Cultural Organization; member of the Select Committee on Economic Aid to European Countries (Herter Committee), 80th Congress.

FIFTH DISTRICT.—COUNTIES: Caswell, Forsyth, Granville, Person, Rockingham, Stokes, Surry, and Wilkes (8 counties). Population (1960), 454,261.

RALPH JAMES SCOTT, Democrat, of Danbury, N.C.; born in Surry County, N.C., October 15, 1905; educated in Pinnacle High School, Stokes County, and Wake Forest College; LL. B. degree; licensed to practice law, 1930; member North Carolina House of Representatives, 1937; elected Solicitor, 21st District, 1938, 1942, 1946, 1950, and 1954; married Miss Verna Denny, November 30, 1929; two children—Patricia and Nancy; Baptist, Mason, Shriner, Elk; elected to the 85th Congress on November 6, 1956; reelected to the 86th, 87th, 88th, and 89th Congresses; member of Education and Labor Committee.

SIXTH DISTRICT.—COUNTIES: Alamance, Durham, Guilford, and Orange (4 counties). Population (1960), 487,159.

HORACE ROBINSON KORNEGAY, Democrat, of Greensboro, N.C.; born in Asheville, N.C., March 12, 1924; son of Marvin Earl Kornegay and the late Blanche Person Robinson Kornegay; educated in the public schools of Greensboro; Wake Forest College B.S. degree and Wake Forest College School of Law LL.B. degree; served in the U.S. Army 1943–46; awarded Purple Heart, Bronze Star, and two Campaign Stars; licensed to practice law in North Carolina in 1949, before the Supreme Court of North Carolina, and the United States Supreme Court; elected district solicitor (prosecuting attorney) for twelfth district of North Carolina in 1954 and 1958; member Greensboro Bar Association, North Carolina Bar Association, American Bar Association, American Judicature Society, and the Federal Bar Association; American Legion, Veterans of Foreign Wars, AMVETS and honorary member of British Legion; North Carolina Society of Sons of the American Revolution; Masonic Order, Scottish Rite and Shriner; member Alpha Sigma Phi, social fraternity, Phi Delta Phi, legal fraternity, and Omicron Delta Kappa, honorary fraternity, member, Board of Visitors, Wake Forest Law School; life-long member of West Market Street Methodist Church of Greensboro and former member of the official board; married Annie Ben Beale and have three children, Horace Robinson Kornegay, Jr., Kathryn Elder Kornegay, and Martha Beale Kornegay; elected to the 87th Congress to represent the Sixth District of North Carolina on November 8, 1960; reelected to the 88th and 89th Congresses; member Interstate and Foreign Commerce and Veterans Affairs committees.

SEVENTH DISTRICT.—Counties: Bladen, Brunswick, Columbus, Cumberland, Hoke, New Hanover, Robeson, and Scotland (8 counties). Population (1960), 448,933.

ALTON ASA LENNON, Democrat, of Wilmington, N. C.; born in Wilmington, N.C., August 17, 1906; graduate of New Hanover High School, Wilmington, N. C., and Wake Forest College; began practice of law in 1929, immediately after receiving law degree from Wake Forest College and passing the North Carolina State Bar; married Karine Welch on October 12, 1933; two children—Mrs. Lewis R. Frost III, and Alton Yates Lennon; served 8 years as judge, New Hanover County Recorder's Court; served two terms (1947 and 1951) as Ninth District senator in the North Carolina General Assembly; appointed by Gov. William B. Umstead to the United States Senate on July 10, 1953, succeeding the late Willis Smith; sworn in on July 15, 1953; elected to the 85th, 86th, 87th, 88th, and 89th Congresses.

EIGHTH DISTRICT.—Counties: Anson, Lee, Lincoln, Mecklenburg, Montgomery, Moore, Richmond, and Union (8 counties). Population (1960), 491,461.

CHARLES RAPER JONAS, Republican, of Lincolnton, N. C.; born in Lincoln County, N. C., December 9, 1904; son of Charles A. and Rosa P. Jonas; University of North Carolina, A. B., 1925; J. D., 1928; married Annie Elliott Lee; children: Charles, Jr., age 23 and Richard Elliott, age 21; practicing lawyer since 1928; active duty in A US 1940–46; president North Carolina Bar Association 1946–47; member: Lincoln County, North Carolina, and American Bar Associations; Chi Phi, Phi Delta Phi, Order of the Coif, American Legion; Methodist; Rotarian; elected to the 83d Congress November 4, 1952; reelected to the 84th, 85th, 86th, 87th, 88th, and 89th Congresses.

NINTH DISTRICT.—Counties: Alexander, Alleghany, Ashe, Cabarrus, Caldwell, Davie, Iredell, Rowan, Stanly, Watauga, and Yadkin (11 counties). Population (1960), 404,093.

JAMES THOMAS BROYHILL, Republican, of Lenoir, N.C.; born in Lenoir, August 19, 1927; attended public schools; graduated from University of North Carolina, business administration, B.S. 1950; associated with Broyhill Furniture Factories of Lenoir 1945–62, in sales, sales promotion, personnel, manufacturing, and administration; married to the former Louise Robbins of Durham, N.C.; three children, one daughter and two sons; Sunday school teacher and member of First Baptist Church of Lenoir; chosen Young Man of the Year for 1957 by Junior Chamber of Commerce for distinguished service to his city and county; member of Masons, Oasis Temple of the Shrine, Chamber of Commerce, Northwest North Carolina Development Association, and the North Carolina Forestry Association; elected to the 88th Congress November 6, 1962; reelected to the 89th Congress; member of Interstate and Foreign Commerce, Communications and Power Subcommittee.

TENTH DISTRICT.—Counties: Avery, Burke, Catawba, Cleveland, Gaston, Mitchell, and Rutherford (7 counties). Population (1960), 390,020.

BASIL LEE WHITENER, Democrat, of Gastonia, N. C.; born in York County, S. C.; son of Laura Barrett Whitener and the late Levi Whitener; attended public schools in Gaston County; graduated from Lowell High School in 1931, and from Rutherford College in 1933; attended the University of South Carolina 1933–35; graduated from Duke University with LL. B. degree in 1937, Honorary Doctor of Laws, Belmont Abbey College, 1960; was admitted to the North Carolina bar in August 1937; admitted to District of Columbia bar on June 4, 1959; organizer and first president, Gastonia Junior Chamber of Commerce, 1938; vice president, North Carolina Junior Chamber of Commerce 1940–41, and president, April 1941–April 1942; member of North Carolina House of Representatives, 1941 session, renominated in 1942, but resigned to enter the United States Navy; instructor in commercial law, Belmont Abbey College, Belmont, N.C., 1939–41; married Harriet Priscilla Morgan, of Union, S.C., and they have four children: John Morgan Whitener, born October 25, 1945; Laura Lee Whitener, born August 15, 1950; Basil Lee Whitener, Jr., born October 16, 1952; and Barrett Simpson Whitener, born June 6, 1960; served as gunnery officer in the Navy during World War II, being separated from service in November 1945 with rank of lieutenant; appointed solicitor, 14th Solicitorial District in January 1946; nominated in May 1946 for solicitor and elected in November

1946; reelected in 1950 and 1954; member of the First Methodist Church in Gastonia, having served on the official board; Kiwanis; Elks; American Legion; 40 and 8; Veterans of Foreign Wars; 32d degree Mason; York and Scottish Rite bodies; Shriner; president, North Carolina Young Democrats, 1946–47; delegate to the Democratic National Conventions, 1948 and 1960; permanent chairman, Young Democratic National Convention, Chattanooga, Tenn., in November 1949; president of Gaston County Bar Association, 1950; member: North Carolina and American Bar Associations; General Statutes Commission, 1946; Commission To Study Improvement of Administration of Justice, 1947–49, by virtue of appointment of Governor; and Judicial Conference of Fourth Federal Judicial Circuit; member North Carolina Tercentenary Commission; elected to the 85th Congress on November 6, 1956; reelected to 86th, 87th, 88th, and 89th Congresses; member of Judiciary and District of Columbia Committees.

ELEVENTH DISTRICT.—COUNTIES: Buncombe, Cherokee, Clay, Graham, Haywood, Henderson, Jackson, McDowell, Macon, Madison, Polk, Swain, Transylvania, and Yancey (14 counties). Population (1960), 361,077.

ROY A. TAYLOR, Democrat, of Black Mountain, N.C.; born in Vader, Wash., January 31, 1910; educated in the public schools of Buncombe County, N.C., Asheville-Biltmore College, Maryville College, and Asheville University Law School; admitted to the bar in January 1936; Navy combat veteran of World War II; discharged with rank of lieutenant; served as commanding officer of L.S.T.; member of Lions Club, district governor in 1952; representative in North Carolina General Assembly in 1947, 1949, 1951, and 1953; deacon in Baptist Church; Buncombe County attorney 1949–60; member of board of trustees of Asheville-Biltmore College 1949–60; married Evelyn Reeves; two children, Alan and Toni; elected to the 86th Congress June 25, 1960, to fill the vacancy caused by the death of David M. Hall; reelected to the 87th, 88th, and 89th Congresses.

NORTH DAKOTA

(Population (1960), 632,446)

SENATORS

MILTON R. YOUNG, Republican, of La Moure, N. Dak.; born December 6, 1897, in Berlin, N. Dak.; attended the La Moure County public schools and was graduated from La Moure High School in 1915; attended North Dakota State Agricultural College and Graceland College at Lamoni, Iowa; was actively engaged in the operation of his farm near Berlin, N. Dak., until his appointment to the United States Senate; member of school, township, and county AAA boards; elected to house of representatives of North Dakota State Legislature in 1932; elected to State senate of North Dakota in 1934 and served continuously until his resignation March 14, 1945; elected president pro tempore 1941; majority floor leader 1943; married Malinda V. Benson of La Moure, N. Dak., July 7, 1919; three sons—Wendell M., Duane C., and John M.; appointed to the United States Senate March 12, 1945, by Gov. Fred G. Aandahl to fill the vacancy caused by the death of John Moses; elected at special election June 25, 1946, for term ending January 3, 1951; reelected to full 6-year terms in general election November 7, 1950, on November 6, 1956, and November 6, 1962; in all statewide elections, both primary and general, he only lost three counties of the 53 in entire State; served as secretary to the Senate Republican Conference Committee since 1948; second ranking Republican member of Appropriations Committee and Agriculture and Forestry Committee.

QUENTIN N. BURDICK, Democrat, endorsed by Nonpartisan League, of Fargo, N. Dak.; born Munich, N. Dak., June 19, 1908; public school education; B.A. and LL.B. degrees, University of Minnesota; lawyer; married; elected to 86th Congress November 4, 1958; elected to the United States Senate June 28, 1960, to fill out the unexpired term of 4½ years of the late Senator William Langer; reelected to full 6-year term November 3, 1964.

REPRESENTATIVES

FIRST DISTRICT.—COUNTIES: Barnes, Benson, Cass, Cavalier, Dickey, Eddy, Goster, Grand Forks, Griggs, La Moure, Nelson, Pembina, Pierce, Ramsey, Ransom, Richland, Rolette, Sargent, Steele, Stutsman, Towner, Traill, and Walsh (23 counties). Population (1960), 333,290.

MARK ANDREWS, Republican, of Mapleton, N. Dak.; farmer; born May 19, 1926; attended public schools; enlisted U.S. Army 1944; received appointment to West Point; received degree in agricultural engineering at North Dakota State University in 1949; married to Mary Willming; children, Mark III, Sarah, and Karen; former director, Garrison Conservancy District; past president, North Dakota Crop Improvement Association; former North Dakota Republican national committeeman; member, American Legion, DAV, Elks, Masonic bodies, Shrine; elected to 88th Congress October 22, 1963, to fill the vacancy caused by the death of Hjalmar Nygaard; reelected to the 89th Congress.

SECOND DISTRICT.—COUNTIES: Adams, Billings, Bottineau, Bowman, Burke, Burleigh, Divide, Dunn, Emmons, Golden Valley, Grant, Hettinger, Kidder, Logan, McHenry, McIntosh, McKenzie, McLean, Mercer, Morton, Mountrail, Oliver, Renville, Sheridan, Sioux, Slope, Stark, Ward, Wells, and Williams (30 counties). Population (1960), 299,156.

ROLLAND REDLIN, Democrat, of Crosby, N. Dak.; born in Lambert, Mont., February 29, 1920; educated in grade school in Lambert, high school in Minneapolis, Minn., the University of Washington, and extension courses at Minot (N. Dak.) State Teachers College; engaged in farming; married the former Christine Nesje of Crosby; three daughters, Ilene, Jeannette, and Lisa and two sons, Daniel and Steven; nominee for State house of representatives in 1952; elected to the State senate in 1958 and reelected in 1962; elected to the 89th Congress November 3, 1964.

OHIO

(Population (1960), 9,706,397)

SENATORS

FRANK J. LAUSCHE, Democrat, of Cleveland, Ohio; born in Cleveland, November 14, 1895; graduate, John Marshall Law School; named judge of the municipal court, Cleveland, 1932; elected municipal judge in 1933; in 1935 was elected common pleas judge; served as mayor of Cleveland 1941–44; served as Governor of Ohio for five terms; degrees: doctor of laws from Kenyon College, Dennison University, Ohio Wesleyan University, Miami University of Ohio, Ashland College, Defiance College, Washington and Jefferson College, Oberlin College, Western Reserve University, and Ohio University; doctor of public service degree from Rio Grande College; LL.B., LL.M., and LL.D. from John Marshall School of Law; Akron University, Doctor of Laws; Marietta College, Doctor of Laws; Tiffin Business College, Doctor of Commercial Science; member of Delta Theta Phi, Phi Sigma Kappa, and Omicron Delta Kappa fraternities; Centennial Award from Northwestern University; Veterans Award for 1958 of the Joint Veterans Commission of Cuyahoga; recipient also of Good Citizenship Medal of the Society of the Sons of the American Revolution, and the Certificate of Merit from the American Veterans of World War II; was elected to the United States Senate in 1956 for term ending January 3, 1963; reelected November 6, 1962, for term ending January 3, 1969; married Jane Sheal of Cleveland, Ohio, in 1928.

STEPHEN M. YOUNG, Democrat, Cleveland, Ohio; trial lawyer; attended Kenyon College and Western Reserve University; received degree of LL.B. from Western Reserve University; master civil law (honorary), Kenyon College; LL.D. (honorary), Central State College; Chubb fellow, Yale University; elected Congressman at Large to 73d, 74th, 77th, and 81st Congresses; and to the United States Senate, November 4, 1958; reelected November 3, 1964; member of the Senate Committees on Aeronautical and Space Sciences, Armed Services, Public Works, chairman of the Subcommittee on Public Buildings and Grounds, and member of Special Committee on Aging; previously served two terms in Ohio General Assembly; chief criminal prosecuting attorney of Cuyahoga County; member of Ohio Commission on Unemployment Insurance; served in field artillery in World War I; served for 37 months in World War II, combat service in North Africa and with Fifth Army in Italy; in 1945, after armistice, was Allied Military Governor of the Province of Reggio Emilia, Italy; decorations: Bronze Star; European-African-Middle Eastern Theater Campaign Medal, four battle stars; Commendation of General Mark W. Clark; World War II Victory Medal; Order of the Crown of Italy; past president of the War Veterans Bar Association of Cleveland and of the Cuyahoga County Bar Association.

REPRESENTATIVES

AT LARGE.—Population (1960), 9,706,397.

ROBERT E. SWEENEY, Democrat, of Bay Village, Ohio; born in Cleveland, Ohio, November 4, 1924, son of the late Martin L. Sweeney, former Congressman from Ohio; educated at St. Ignatius High School, Cleveland, Ohio; Georgetown University, Washington, D.C.; Baldwin-Wallace College, Berea, Ohio; Cleveland-Marshall Law School, Cleveland, Ohio, LL.B. degree; veteran of World War II; practicing attorney in Cleveland 1951–64; former assistant director of law of the city of Cleveland and former special counsel to the attorney general of Ohio; Democratic nominee for attorney general of Ohio in 1962; member of Cleveland, Cuyahoga, and Ohio State bar associations; member of St. Raphael's Church and the Cleveland Athletic Club; elected to the 89th Congress November 3, 1964.

FIRST DISTRICT.—HAMILTON COUNTY: City of Cincinnati, wards 1 to 6; ward 7, except precincts J, U, W, and CC; wards 8 and 9; ward 10, except precincts I, K, L, N, O, and U; ward 11, precincts A, P, Q, T, U, and Y; ward 12, precincts A, N, P, Q, V, W, and Y; wards 13 and 14; ward 15, except precincts A and B; ward 16, except precincts A, C, E, F, H, I, J, L, M, N, Y, Z, and AA; ward 17, precincts B, D, E, M, S, T, V, W, and X; ward 23, precinct T; ward 24, precincts A, B, C, H, I, J, Q, S, and T; townships of Anderson, Columbia, Elmwood, and Symmes; all of city of Norwood; all of city of St. Bernard, village of Silverton, precincts A, B, C, D, E, and F. Population (1960), 375,753.

JOHN JOYCE GILLIGAN, Democrat, of Cincinnati, Ohio; born in Cincinnati March 22, 1921, son of Harry J. Gilligan and Blanche Joyce; educated at St. Xavier High School, University of Notre Dame (B.A. 1943), and University of Cincinnati (M.A. 1947); during World War II served as a lieutenant (j.g.) in U.S. Naval Reserve, 27 months as a destroyer gunnery officer in Atlantic, Mediterranean, and Pacific theaters, and awarded three area campaign ribbons, five battle stars, two naval unit citations, and a Silver Star for gallantry at Okinawa; married the former Mary Kathryn Dixon June 28, 1945; four children: Donald, Kathleen, John, and Ellen; instructor in literature at Xavier University 1948–53; elected at-large city councilman in 1953 and reelected five additional terms; candidate for Democratic nomination, Ohio Congressman-at-Large, in 1962; member of Bentley Post American Legion, Catholic Interracial Council (past president), Central Psychiatric Clinic (board member), Budget Review Committee, United Appeal, Playhouse-in-the-Park (board member), Babies Milk Fund (board member), and Better Housing League (advisory board member); elected to the 89th Congress November 3, 1964.

SECOND DISTRICT.—HAMILTON COUNTY: City of Cincinnati, ward 7, precincts J, U, W, and CC; ward 10, precincts I, K, L, N, O, and U; ward 11, all except A, P, Q, T, U, and Y; ward 12, all except A, N, P, Q, V, W, and Y; ward 15, precincts A and B; ward 16, precincts A, C, E, F, H, I, J, L, M, N, Y, Z, and AA; ward 17, all except B, D, E, M, S, T, V, W, and Z; wards 18, 19, 20, 21, 22; ward 23, all except T; ward 24, all except A, B, C, H, I, J, Q, S, and T; wards 25 and 26; cities of Cheviot, Deer Park, Lincoln Heights, Lockland, Mount Healthy, North College Hill, Reading, and Wyoming; townships of Colerain, Crosby, Deer Park, Delhi, Green, Harrison, Miami, Lockland, Reading, Springfield, Sycamore, and Whitewater; village of Silverton, precincts G, H, I, and J. Population (1960), 488,368.

DONALD D. CLANCY, Republican, of Cincinnati, Ohio; born July 24, 1921, in Cincinnati; educated at Elder High School, prelaw course at Xavier University, and LL.B., University of Cincinnati Law School in 1948; engaged in the practice of law; married Betty Jane Mangeot; three children, Kathy, Patricia, and Danny; elected member of Cincinnati council for five 2-year terms; mayor of Cincinnati, two terms, 1957–60; elected to the 87th Congress November 8, 1960; reelected to the 88th and 89th Congresses.

THIRD DISTRICT.—COUNTIES: Butler and Montgomery (2 counties). Population (1960), 726,156.

RODNEY MARVIN LOVE, Democrat, of Dayton, Ohio; born in Dayton July 18, 1908; graduated from Steele High School in 1926, Ohio State University B.A. 1930, and University of Dayton Law School LL.B. 1933; attorney at law; married the former Margaret Sullivan of Dayton; two children, Nancy (Mrs. Larry R. Cleaves) and Robert; chief deputy in Probate Court 1941–45; appointed judge in 1945; elected to the unexpired term in 1946 and reelected in 1948 and 1954; resigned from the bench in 1960 to reenter private practice; former president of the Dayton Bar Association; former member of the executive committee of the Ohio State Bar Association; past president of the Ohio Association of Probate Court Judges; member of boards of the Ohio Mental Health Association, Inc., the Mental Health Association of Montgomery County, and the Adult Psychiatric Clinic; past president and district governor of Sertoma Club International; past president and member of the board of trustees of the Ohio Soldiers and Sailors Home in Xenia; member of Miami Valley Lodge No. 660, Scottish Rite, 32d degree; the Council for Retarded Children; Dayton Council on World Affairs; Gem City Democratic Club and the American Bar Association; elected to the 89th Congress November 3, 1964.

FOURTH DISTRICT.—COUNTIES: Allen, Auglaize, Darke, Mercer, Miami, Preble, and Shelby (7 counties). Population (1960), 356,994.

WILLIAM M. McCULLOCH, Republican, of Piqua, Ohio; lawyer; member, Ohio State and American Bar Associations; member Ohio House of Representatives six terms, serving as minority (Republican) leader, 1936–39, and as Speaker for three terms; World War II veteran; married Mabel Harris in 1925; two daughters, Nancy and Ann; elected to the 80th Congress on November 4, 1947; reelected to each succeeding Congress.

FIFTH DISTRICT.—COUNTIES: Defiance, Fulton, Henry, Ottawa, Paulding, Putnam, Van Wertz, Williams, and Wood (9 counties). Population (1960), 298,051.

DELBERT L. LATTA, Republican, of Bowling Green, Ohio; born in Weston, Wood County, Ohio, March 5, 1920; attended North Baltimore, Ohio, and McComb, Ohio, public schools; graduate of McComb (Ohio) High School; member of McComb Church of Christ; A.B. and LL.B. degrees from Ohio Northern University; attorney; represented nine northwestern Ohio counties in the Ohio Senate for three terms; married to the former Rose Mary Kiene, of Pandora, Putnam County, Ohio; two children, Rose Ellen and Robert Edward; elected to the 86th Congress on November 4, 1958; reelected to the 87th, 88th, and 89th Congresses; member House Agriculture Committee; member of the following subcommittees: Livestock and Feed Grains; Tobacco; Equipment Supplies and Manpower; Family Farms; Wheat; Select Committee on Export Control, 87th Congress; Battle of Lake Erie Sesquicentennial Celebration Commission, 88th Congress.

SIXTH DISTRICT.—COUNTIES: Adams, Brown, Clermont, Fayette, Highland, Pickaway, Pike, Ross, and Scioto (9 counties). Population (1960), 380,847.

WILLIAM H. HARSHA, Republican, of Portsmouth, Ohio; born January 1, 1921, in Portsmouth; graduate of Portsmouth High School; A.B. degree, Kenyon College; LL.B. degree, Western Reserve University; attorney at law; member of Presbyterian Church; married to the former Rosemary Spellerberg; four sons— Bill, Mark, Bruce, and Brian; served in the Marine Corps during World War II; assistant city solicitor for Portsmouth 1947–51; Scioto County prosecutor 1951–55; member of Exchange Club, Elks, P.E.R., Masons, Y.M.C.A., Business and Professional Men's Club, American Legion, Disabled American Veterans, 40 & 8, Ohio State Bar Association, and Portsmouth Bar Association; admitted to practice before the United States Supreme Court; life member of Amateur Trapshooting Association; active sportsman and hobbies are fishing and hunting; past director of Scioto County chapter of Red Cross; past director, Scioto County Cancer Society; past chairman, Scioto County T.B. and Health Association; elected to the 87th Congress November 8, 1960; reelected to the 88th and 89th Congresses.

SEVENTH DISTRICT.—COUNTIES: Champaign, Clark, Clinton, Greene, Logan, Madison, Union, and Warren (8 counties). Population (1960), 435,621.

CLARENCE J. BROWN, Republican, Blanchester, Ohio; born in Blanchester; son of Owen and Ellen B. Brown; married Ethel McKinney July 15, 1916 (deceased January 20, 1965); three children, Betty Jean, now Mrs. L. M. Dearing; Dorothy Lucille, now Mrs. Robert A. Haines, and Clarence J., Jr.; graduated Blanchester High School and Washington & Lee University, Lexington, Va.; honorary degree, Wilmington College, Wilmington, Ohio; publisher, several Ohio newspapers; president of the Brown Publishing Co., printers and publishers; farm operator; Lieutenant Governor of Ohio 1919–23; Secretary of State of Ohio 1927–33; Republican nominee for Governor of Ohio 1934; delegate to various Republican National Conventions; Republican National Committeeman for Ohio 1944–64; chairman, executive committee of the Republican National Committee 1945–48; campaign director, Republican National Committee, 1946; author of the legislation creating both the first and second Commissions on the Organization of the Executive Branch of the Government (the Hoover Commissions), and served as member of both Commissions; ranking member of the House Committee on Rules; ranking member Committee on Government Operations; chairman, Ohio Republican Delegation, U.S. House of Representatives; O.D.K. and Sigma Delta Chi; member all Masonic bodies, including 33°; elected to the 76th, 77th, 78th, 79th, 80th, 81st, 82d, 83d, 84th, 85th, 86th, 87th, 88th, and 89th Congresses.

EIGHTH DISTRICT.—COUNTIES: Crawford, Hancock, Hardin, Marion, Morrow, Seneca, and Wyandot (7 counties). Population (1960), 290,694.

JACKSON E. BETTS, Republican, of Findlay, Ohio; born May 26, 1904, in Findlay, Ohio; graduate of Kenyon College, A. B. degree (cum laude), and Yale School of Law, LL.B. degree; honorary degrees: M.A., Kenyon College, Gambier, Ohio; LL.D., Ohio Northern University, Ada, Ohio, and LL.D., Heidelberg College, Tiffin, Ohio; lawyer; prosecuting attorney, Hancock County, Ohio, 1933–37; member of the Ohio General Assembly 1937–47; speaker of the House of

Representatives of Ohio 1945 and 1946; member of American, Ohio, and Findlay Bar Associations; married June 12, 1934, to Martha Neeley; one daughter, Nancy Lou (Mrs. David C. Bowman); elected to the 82d Congress November 7, 1950; reelected to the 83d, 84th, 85th, 86th, 87th, 88th, and 89th Congresses.

NINTH DISTRICT.—LUCAS COUNTY. Population (1960), 456,931.

THOMAS LUDLOW ASHLEY, Democrat, of Waterville, Ohio; born in Toledo, Ohio, January 11, 1923, son of Meredith and Alida Ashley and great grandson of James M. Ashley, Civil War Congressman and Governor of the Territory of Montana 1869–70; attended the public schools and the Kent School in Kent, Conn., 1939 to 1942; served in the Armed Forces during World War II and was assigned to the Pacific Theater of Operations 1943–45; after discharge from the service resumed studies and graduated from Yale University, B. A. degree, in 1948; became associated with the Toledo Publicity and Efficiency Commission in 1948 and studied law in evening classes at University of Toledo Law School; graduated from Ohio State University, LL. B. degree, in 1951; was admitted to the bar in 1951 and commenced the practice of law in Whitehouse, Ohio, and also was associated with father and brother in Toledo; in 1952 joined the staff of Radio Free Europe, serving in Europe as codirector of the press section and later as assistant director of special projects, resigning March 1, 1954; elected to the 84th Congress November 2, 1954; reelected to the 85th, 86th, 87th, 88th, and 89th Congresses.

TENTH DISTRICT.—COUNTIES: Athens, Fairfield, Gallia, Hocking, Jackson, Lawrence, Meigs, and Vinton (8 counties). Population (1960), 274,441.

WALTER H. MOELLER, Democrat, of Lancaster, Ohio; born near Indianapolis, Ind., March 15, 1910; attended local elementary and high schools; graduated from Concordia College and Seminary, Springfield, Ill., in 1935; earned A. B. degree at Defiance College and M. S. degree in education at Indiana University; spent 22 years in the ministry of the Lutheran Church, 15 of which were spent in Ohio; served 10 years as an instructor in English composition, German, and sociology at Giffen Junior College in Van Wert; farm reared and a farm owner; past member: board of directors of Fairfield County Y.M.C.A.; Phi Delta Kappa, scholastic fraternity in education; Kiwanis Club (past president); Institute of Human Relations; married Lenora Rafferty, a graduate of Butler University, in Indianapolis; one daughter Janeen (Mrs. John Arguelles); elected to the 86th Congress on November 4, 1958; reelected to the 87th Congress; elected to the 89th Congress November 3, 1964.

ELEVENTH DISTRICT.—COUNTIES: Ashtabula, Geauga, Lake, Portage, and twenty townships in Trumbull County. Population (1960), 512,022.

JOHN WILLIAM STANTON, Republican, of Painesville, Ohio; born in Painesville February 20, 1924; graduated from Culver Military Academy, Culver, Ind., in 1942; turned down an appointment to West Point to enter the School of Foreign Service at Georgetown University, Washington, D.C., in July 1942; left studies to enter the U.S. Army in December 1942; served overseas in the Pacific theater for 33 months and discharged as a captain January 1, 1946; awarded Bronze Star with Oak Leaf Cluster, the Purple Heart, the Presidential Unit Citation, and three major campaign ribbons; reentered Georgetown University, majored in government and economics, and received B.S. degree in 1949; past president of Painesville Chamber of Commerce, past exalted ruler of BPO Elks, past president of Painesville Exchange Club, charter member of Painesville Junior Chamber of Commerce; member of American Legion, Knights of Columbus (fourth degree), and St. Mary's Catholic Church; engaged in automobile retail business since 1948; Lake County commissioner 1956–64; elected to the 89th Congress November 3, 1964.

TWELFTH DISTRICT.—FRANKLIN COUNTY. Population (1960), 682,962.

SAMUEL LEEPER DEVINE, Republican, of Columbus, Ohio; born in South Bend, Ind., December 21, 1915; educated in Columbus, Grandview, and Upper Arlington public schools; Colgate University; Ohio State University; University of Notre Dame, LL. B., cum laude, 1940; appointed special agent, Federal Bureau of Investigation, U. S. Department of Justice, in 1940 and resigned October 15, 1945, to resume practice of law; served three terms in the Ohio Legislature, 1951–55; prosecuting attorney, Franklin County, Ohio, June 1955 through December 1958; former chairman of the Ohio Un-American Activities Commission; married Betty Galloway and they have three daughters—Lois, in college; Joyce, in high school, and Carol in high school; elected to the 86th Congress on November 4, 1958; reelected to the 87th, 88th, and 89th Congresses.

THIRTEENTH DISTRICT.—Counties: Erie, Huron, Lorain, and Sandusky (4 counties). Population (1960), 389,312.

CHARLES ADAMS MOSHER, Republican, of Oberlin, Ohio; born in DeKalb County, Ill., May 7, 1906; graduated from Oberlin College, A.B., cum laude, 1928; married Harriet Johnson, 1929; son, Frederic A., and daughter, Mary Jane; employed on daily newspapers in Illinois and Wisconsin 1929–38; president of Oberlin Printing Co., and publisher of Oberlin News-Tribune, 1940–62; member of Oberlin City Council, 1945–50; member of Ohio Senate five terms, 1951–60; vice chairman, Ohio School Survey Commission, 1954–55; Ohio Legislative Service Commission, 1955–59; member, Oberlin College Board of Trustees, January 1, 1964–; elected to the 87th Congress November 8, 1960; reelected to the 88th and 89th Congresses.

FOURTEENTH DISTRICT.—Counties: Medina and Summit (2 counties). Population (1960), 578,884.

WILLIAM HANES AYRES, Republican, of Akron, Ohio; born in Eagle Rock, Va., February 5, 1916; graduate of Western Reserve University (Adelbert College), B. A. degree, June 1936; president of William H. Ayres, Inc.; served as private in United States Army, honorable discharge December 17, 1945; married Mary Helen Coventry; three children, Virginia, Frank, and Judy; elected to the 82d Congress November 7, 1950; reelected to the 83d, 84th, 85th, 86th, 87th, 88th, and 89th Congresses.

FIFTEENTH DISTRICT.—Counties: Guernsey, Monroe, Morgan, Muskingum, Noble, Perry, and Washington (7 counties). Population (1960), 236,288.

ROBERT THOMPSON SECREST, Democrat, of Senecaville, Ohio; born at Senecaville, Ohio, on January 22, 1904; attended the public schools; A.B. degree Muskingum College in 1926; LL.B. degree, Washington (D.C.) College of Law in 1938; work completed for M.A. degree in political science at Columbia University in 1943; graduate Naval School of Military Government at Columbia University; completed course British School of Civil Affairs, Wimbledon, England; honorary degree, Bliss College, 1963; principal of Senecaville High School 1926–31; superintendent of schools, Murray City, Ohio, 1931–32; member of the Ohio Legislature 1931–32; elected to the U.S. House of Representatives and served from January 3, 1933, until his resignation in 1942 to join the U.S. Navy where he served until March 1, 1946, with rank of commander; served in England, Africa, Italy, and 1 year on Admiral Nimitz's staff in the Pacific as military government officer; again elected to the House of Representatives and served from January 3, 1949, until his resignation September 26, 1954; former past commander and life member of Senecaville American Legion Post 747; life member AMVETS and regular veterans association; member 40 & 8 and V.F.W.; member of the board of trustees of Muskingum College; member of Federal Trade Commission 1954–61; director of commerce, State of Ohio, January 15, 1962, to August 31, 1962; elected to the 88th Congress November 6, 1962; reelected to the 89th Congress.

SIXTEENTH DISTRICT.—Counties: Stark, Tuscarawas, and Wayne (3 counties). Population (1960), 492,631.

FRANK T. BOW, Republican, of Canton, Ohio; born in Canton, Ohio, February 20, 1901, where he has since resided; attended grade schools in Canton and Plain Township, Stark County, Ohio; attended University School, Cleveland, Ohio; Culver Military Academy, Culver, Ind., and received his legal education at Ohio Northern University, Ada, Ohio; was admitted to the bar of Ohio in 1923; served as general counsel to Subcommittee on Expenditures in the Eightieth Congress and general counsel of Select Committee To Investigate the Federal Communications Commission, Eightieth Congress; served as war correspondent, World War II, with Ohio's Thirty-seventh Division in the Philippines; married

Caroline C. Denzer May 12, 1923; has two sons, Robert Lee Bow and Joseph Withrow Bow; LL.D. (honorary) Ohio Northern University, June 4, 1961; LL.D. (honorary) Mount Union College June 2, 1963; regent, Smithsonian Institution; elected to the 82d Congress on November 7, 1950; reelected to the 83d, 84th, 85th, 86th, 87th, 88th, and 89th Congresses.

SEVENTEENTH DISTRICT.—Counties: Ashland, Coshocton, Delaware, Holmes, Knox, Licking, and Richland (7 counties). Population (1960), 375,504.

JOHN MILAN ASHBROOK, Republican, of Johnstown, Ohio; born in Johnstown September 21, 1928; graduate of Johnstown High School in 1946, with honors at Harvard University. A.B., in 1952, and Ohio State Law School, LL.B., in 1955; received Honorary LL.D. at Ashland College, 1963; practicing attorney and publisher of the Johnstown Independent, a weekly newspaper; member 101st and 102d Ohio General Assemblies; former Young Republican national chairman, 1957–59; married Joan Needels July 3, 1948; father of three daughters, Barbara, Laura, and Madeline; served in U.S. Navy; elected to the 87th Congress November 8, 1960; reelected to the 88th and 89th Congresses.

EIGHTEENTH DISTRICT.—Counties: Belmont, Carroll, Columbiana, Harrison, and Jefferson (5 counties). Population (1960), 328,921.

WAYNE L. HAYS, Democrat, of Flushing, Ohio; lifelong resident of Belmont County; graduate Ohio State University, 1933; additional work Duke University, 1935; former teacher of history and public speaking; mayor of Flushing, Ohio, three terms, 1939–45; Ohio State senator one term, 1941–42; member Officers' Reserve Corps, United States Army, 1933–42; volunteered for active duty World War II December 8, 1941; honorably discharged in August 1942; Belmont County commissioner, 1945–49; married Martha Judkins; one child, Martha Brigitta Hays; chairman of board of directors of the Citizens National Bank, offices in Flushing and St. Clairsville, Ohio; owner of Green Acres Farm, Belmont, Ohio, breeding Angus cattle and Tennessee Walking Horses; in 1956 elected president of the NATO Parliamentarians' Conference for 1956 and 1957; elected to the 81st Congress on November 2, 1948; reelected to succeeding Congresses.

NINETEENTH DISTRICT.—Mahoning County and five townships in Trumbull County. Population (1960), 378,122.

MICHAEL JOSEPH KIRWAN, Democrat, of Youngstown, Ohio; elected to the 75th and each succeeding Congress.

TWENTIETH DISTRICT.—City of Cleveland: Wards 1 to 9; ward 21, north of St. Clair Avenue, precincts A (one-half only), P, Y, Z, AA, and BB; wards 23, 31 to 33; Bratenahl, Brooklyn, and Parma. Population (1960), 465,341.

MICHAEL A. FEIGHAN, Democrat, Cleveland, Ohio; son of John T. Feighan Sr. (deceased), and Mary English Feighan; graduate of Princeton University, A.B. degree; graduate of Harvard Law School, LL.B degree; member of Ohio State Legislature, 1937–40; minority floor leader, 1939–40; married Florence Mathews; two children—William Mathews Feighan, Ohio State Representative, and Fleur M. Feighan; elected to the 78th Congress on November 3, 1942; reelected to succeeding Congresses; honorary LL.D. degree in political science from University of Munich, 1955; Testimonial Citation, Committee of Representatives of Non-Russian Nations Enslaved by the Soviet Union, 1955; member of the American delegation to the Interparliamentary Union Conference 1958 and 1960; three times awarded "Vigilant Patriot Honor Plaque" by All-American Conference to Combat Communism, 1959, 1962, and 1963; received Freedom Award for "distinguished leadership in combating Communism" from The Order of Lafayette, New York, 1964; awarded 10th Anniversary Commemorative Medal by the Assembly of Captive European Nations; chairman of the Subcommittee on Immigration and Nationality of the Committee on the Judiciary; chairman of the Joint Committee on Immigration and Nationality Policy.

TWENTY-FIRST DISTRICT.—CITY OF CLEVELAND: Wards 10 to 17; ward 21, south of St. Clair Avenue, precincts A (one-half only), B to O, Q to X, and CC; wards 22, 24, 25, 28 to 30; Garfield Heights and Newburg Heights. Population (1960), 421,804.

CHARLES A. VANIK, Democrat, of Cleveland, Ohio; born in the city of Cleveland, Cuyahoga County, Ohio, April 7, 1913; graduate of Adelbert College of Western Reserve University and the Western Reserve University School of Law; married Betty Best in 1945; one daughter, Phyllis, and one son, John; elected member of the Cleveland City Council in 1938; elected member of the Ohio State Senate in 1940; elected member of the Cleveland Board of Education in 1941; member of the United States Naval Reserve as an ensign, 1942, with amphibious forces Atlantic Fleet and Pacific Fleet until released to inactive duty December 1945 as lieutenant; appointed member Cleveland Library Board January 1946; elected judge, Cleveland Municipal Court, 1947; reelected to full term in 1949; elected to the 84th Congress November 2, 1954; reelected to 85th, 86th, 87th, 88th, snd 89th Congresses.

TWENTY-SECOND DISTRICT.—CITY OF CLEVELAND: Wards 18 to 20, 26, and 27; Cleveland Heights, East Cleveland, Euclid, Gates Mills, Highland Heights, Lyndhurst, Mayfield Heights, Mayfield Village, Richmond Heights, and South Euclid. Population (1960), 357,998.

FRANCES P. BOLTON, Republican, of Lyndhurst (suburb of Cleveland), Ohio; born in Cleveland, Ohio; married in 1907; three sons, Charles B., Kenyon C., and Oliver P.; active for many years in public health nursing and nursing education, social service, and education; honorary degrees, LL. D., Colgate University, 1940; LL. D., Ohio Wesleyan University, 1942; LL. D., Western College for Women, 1957; L. H. D., Baldwin-Wallace College, 1944; Doctor of Humanities, Western Reserve University, 1944; LL. D., Kenyon College, Gambier, Ohio, 1947; LL. D., Wooster College, Wooster, Ohio, 1948; LL. D., Fenn College, 1953; LL. D., Oberlin College, 1953; and LL. D., Heidelberg College, 1954; L. H. D., Tuskegee, 1957; Lake Erie College, 1959; and John Carroll University, 1959; LL.D., University of Maine, 1960; Republican State Central Committee, 1938–40; vice chairman, National Republican Program Committee, 1938–40; United States delegate to eighth session of United Nations General Assembly (1953); elected to the 76th Congress to fill the unexpired term of her husband, Chester C. Bolton, at a special election held on February 27, 1940; reelected to the 77th, 78th, 79th, 80th, 81st, 82d, 83d, 84th, 85th, 86th, 87th, 88th, and 89th Congresses; member, Committee on Foreign Affairs; headed Special Study Mission to Africa in fall of 1955, visiting 24 countries; one of four official United States delegates to Ghana independence ceremonies in March 1957; delegate, British-American Parliamentary Conference at Hamilton, Bermuda, 1961.

TWENTY-THIRD DISTRICT.—CUYAHOGA COUNTY: Bay Village, Beachwood Village, Bedford, Bentleyville, Berea, Brecksville, Broadview Heights, Brooklyn Heights, Brookpark, Chagrin Falls, Chagrin Falls Township, Cuyahoga Heights, Fairview Park, Glenwillow, Hunting Valley, Independence, Lakewood, Linndale. Maple Heights, Middleburgh Heights, Moreland Hills, North Olmsted, North Royalton, Oakwood Village, Olmsted Falls, Olmsted Township, Orange Village, Parkview, Parma Heights, Pepper Pike, Riveredge Township, Rocky River, Seven Hills, Shaker Heights, Solon, Strongville, University Heights, Valley View, Walton Hills, Warrensville Heights, Warrensville Township, Westlake, Westview, and Woodmere. Population (1960), 402,752.

WILLIAM E. MINSHALL, Republican, of Lakewood, Ohio; born in East Cleveland, Ohio, October 24, 1911; attended the public schools of East Cleveland, University School, Shaker Heights, Ohio, and the University of Virginia; graduated from the Cleveland Law School, LL. B. degree, and was admitted to the bar in 1940; married the former Frances Smith; three sons, William Edwin III, Werner Ellis, and Peter Charles; member of the 93d Ohio General Assembly 1939–40; during World War II enlisted in December 1940 as a private in the United States Army and served in the European theater, G–2 Section, Headquarters III Corps, and was honorably discharged as a lieutenant colonel in March 1946; after separation from the service engaged in private practice of law; general counsel to Maritime Administration, 1953–54; elected to the 84th Congress November 2, 1954; reelected to the 85th, 86th, 87th, 88th, and 89th Congresses; member Committee on Appropriations, subcommittees Defense and Foreign Operations; member of Board of Visitors to U.S. Military Academy 1961–62; Board of Visitors, U.S. Naval Academy, 1963.

OKLAHOMA

(Population (1960), 2,328,284)

SENATORS

A. S. MIKE MONRONEY, Democrat, of Oklahoma City, Okla.; born in Oklahoma City, March 2, 1902; educated in the public schools and the University of Oklahoma, B. A., 1924; married; son, Michael Monroney; served 5 years as political writer of the Scripps-Howard Oklahoma News in Oklahoma City; elected to the 76th Congress; reelected to the 77th, 78th, 79th, 80th, and 81st Congresses; served as vice chairman of the Joint Committee on the Organization of Congress during the 79th Congress; coauthor with Senator Robert M. La Follette of legislative reorganization bill of 1946; winner of 1945 Collier's award for "Distinguished Congressional Service" in House of Representatives; awarded 1961 Wright Brothers' Memorial Trophy for public service in aviation; member of Phi Gamma Delta, Sigma Delta Chi, and Phi Beta Kappa fraternities; elected to the United States Senate November 7, 1950; reelected November 6, 1956, and November 6, 1962.

FRED R. HARRIS, Democrat, of Lawton, Okla.,; born in Walters, Okla., November 13, 1930; educated in Walters public schools; B.A. degree in political science and history, 1952, and LL.B. degree "with distinction", 1954, both from the University of Oklahoma; selected for membership in Phi Beta Kappa and as outstanding law student; engaged in private practice of law until November 1964; served as member of Oklahoma State Senate 1956 to 1964; received Oklahoma Junior Chamber of Commerce "Outstanding Young Man of Oklahoma" award, 1959; married to former LaDonna Crawford of Walters; three children, Kathryn, Byron, and Laura; member Phi Alpha Delta legal fraternity, Masonic Lodge, First Baptist Church of Lawton, Okla., Oklahoma and American bar associations; elected to the United States Senate, November 3, 1964, to fill the unexpired term of Robert S. Kerr, ending January 3, 1967.

REPRESENTATIVES

FIRST DISTRICT.—COUNTIES: Alfalfa, Garfield, Grant, Kay, Major, Noble, Pawnee, Tulsa, Woods, and Woodward (10 counties). Population (1960), 521,542.

PAGE BELCHER, Republican, of Enid, Okla., was born in Jefferson, Okla., April 21, 1899, on the claim his father took in the opening of the Cherokee Strip; attended high school at Jefferson and Medford; attended college at Friends University, Wichita, Kans., and University of Oklahoma; LL.D. Oklahoma City University (honorary); made college letters in football, basketball, baseball, and track; served as court clerk, Garfield County; member of board of education; State president, United War Chest of Oklahoma; chairman of Red Cross; president, Enid Kiwanis Club; commander of American Legion; president, Great Salt Plains Council Boy Scouts, composed of eleven counties in northwest Oklahoma; municipal judge, city of Enid; member at large, National Council Boy Scouts of America; was awarded Silver Beaver by Boy Scouts of America for distinguished service to boyhood, the highest award given by a Boy Scout Council; is now a member of Garfield County Bar, Oklahoma Bar Association, Enid Chamber of Commerce, Enid Kiwanis Club, American Legion, I. O. O. F., and the Methodist Church; practicing attorney in Enid, Okla.; admitted to practice law before Oklahoma Supreme Court, United States District Court, United States Circuit Court of Appeals, and United States Supreme Court; political affiliations: Eighth District chairman 10 years, State executive secretary of Republican Party, Ross Rizley's campaign manager for Congress, and secretary to Ross Rizley during first term in Washington; married, and has a son, Page Belcher, Jr., who is a lawyer and is now practicing law with him; a daughter, Carol, whose husband, Clyde V. Collins, is also practicing law with him; and 7 grandchildren; elected to the 82d Congress November 7, 1950; reelected to the 83d, 84th, 85th, 86th, 87th, 88th, and 89th Congresses; member of Committee on Agriculture, Republican Policy Committee, and Committee on Committees.

SECOND DISTRICT.—COUNTIES: Adair, Cherokee, Craig, Delaware, Haskell, McIntosh, Mayes, Muskogee, Nowata, Okmulgee, Osage, Ottawa, Rogers, Sequoyah, Wagoner, and Washington (16 counties). Population (1960), 368,976.

ED EDMONDSON, Democrat, of Muskogee, Okla.; born in Muskogee, April 7, 1919; educated in Muskogee public schools; A. B. from University of Oklahoma in 1940; LL. B. from Georgetown University Law School in 1947; served with FBI, 1940–43; United States Navy, 1943–46; married Miss June Maureen Pilley in 1944; four sons, James Edmond, William Andrew, John Martin, Brian Thomas, and one daughter, June Ellen; admitted to practice of law in District of Columbia and Oklahoma in 1947; elected county attorney of Muskogee County, Okla., 1948; reelected 1950; member, American Legion, Veterans of Foreign Wars, First Presbyterian Church of Muskogee, Okla., Masonic Lodge, Elks, Kiwanis, Phi Delta Phi legal fraternity, Phi Beta Kappa, and Phi Gamma Delta; elected to the 83d Congress November 4, 1952; reelected to the 84th, 85th, 86th, 87th, 88th, and 89th Congresses.

THIRD DISTRICT.—COUNTIES: Atoka, Bryan, Carter, Choctaw, Johnston, Latimer, Le Flore, Love, McCurtain, Marshall, Murray, Pittsburg, and Pushmataha (13 counties). Population (1960), 227,692.

CARL BERT ALBERT, Democrat, of McAlester, Okla.; born in McAlester, May 10, 1908; oldest of five children of Ernest Homer and Leona Ann (Scott) Albert; University of Oklahoma, A. B.; Rhodes Scholar, Oxford University, B. A., B. C. L.; Oklahoma City University, LL. D. (honorary); Oklahoma Hall of Fame; World War II service; lawyer; married Mary Harmon of Columbia, S. C., daughter of David Henry and Mary Isabelle (Strange) Harmon; two children, Mary Frances and David Ernest; elected to 80th and succeeding Congresses; Democratic Whip, 84th, 85th, 86th, and first session 87th Congresses; Majority Leader, second session 87th and 88th Congresses.

FOURTH DISTRICT.—COUNTIES: Coal, Creek, Hughes, Lincoln, Logan, Okfuskee, Payne, Pontotoc, Pottawatomie, and Seminole (10 counties). Population (1960), 252,208.

TOM STEED, Democrat, of Shawnee, Okla.; born on a farm near Rising Star, Tex., March 2, 1904; served 20 years as newspaperman on Oklahoma dailies, including 4 years as managing editor of Shawnee News and Star; enlisted October 29, 1942, as private in Antiaircraft Artillery, released from active duty in May 1944, with rank of second lieutenant; joined Office of War Information July 1, 1944, and served in information division in India-Burma theater until December 1945; married February 26, 1923, to Hazel Bennett; one son, Richard N., Navy veteran; another son, Second Lieutenant Roger Steed, U. S. M. C., killed in line of duty as fighter pilot in China in May 1947; elected to the 81st Congress on November 2, 1948; reelected to 82d, 83d, 84th, 85th, 86th, 87th, 88th, and 89th Congresses.

FIFTH DISTRICT.—COUNTIES: Canadian, Cleveland, Garvin, McClain, and Oklahoma (5 counties). Population (1960), 552,863.

JOHN JARMAN, Democrat, of Oklahoma City, Okla.; born July 17, 1915; education: B. A. degree from Yale University in 1937; LL. B. degree from Harvard Law School in 1941; also attended Westminster College in Fulton, Mo., 2 years prior to attending Yale University; lawyer; member of house of representatives and State senate of Oklahoma Legislature; enlisted and served 47 months in Army during World War II, being honorably discharged December 11, 1945; married Ruth Bewley and has three children: Jay, 20 years; Susie, 17 years; and Steve, 11 years; elected to the 82d Congress November 7, 1950; reelected to the 83d, 84th, 85th, 86th, 87th, 88th, and 89th Congresses.

SIXTH DISTRICT.—COUNTIES: Beaver, Beckham, Blaine, Caddo, Cimarron, Comanche, Cotton, Custer, Dewey, Ellis, Grady, Greer, Harmon, Harper, Jackson, Jefferson, Kingfisher, Kiowa, Roger Mills, Stephens, Texas, Tillman, and Washita (23 counties). Population (1960), 405,003.

JED JOHNSON, JR., Democrat, of Chickasha, Okla.; born in Washington, D.C., December 27, 1939, son of Beatrice Luginbyhl Johnson and the late Jed Joseph Johnson, Congressman from Oklahoma's 6th District 1927–47; attended the public schools in Chickasha; served as congressional page; graduated from Capitol Page School; elected student body president and named one of the three outstanding senior men in his class, graduating in Government from the University of Oklahoma in 1961; appointed national field representative for college division of the American Association for the United Nations; delegate to International Student Movement for the United Nations Conference, Lund, Sweden, September 1961; elected president of the United States Youth Council; U.S. observer at 5th All-Indian Youth Congress, Tirupathi, India, September, 1962; led U.S. youth delegation visit to West Africa in June-July, 1963; appointed a member of the United States Commission for UNESCO; member of board of directors of the United States Committee for the United Nations and served 3 years as non-governmental observer at the United States Mission to the United Nations; elected to the 89th Congress November 3, 1964.

OREGON

(Population (1960), 1,768,687)

SENATORS

WAYNE LYMAN MORSE, Democrat, of Eugene, Oreg., lawyer, farmer, and educator; was born near Madison, Wis., October 20, 1900; received Ph. B. degree, University of Wisconsin, 1923, M. A. degree, 1924; LL. B. degree, University of Minnesota, 1928; J. D. degree, Columbia University, 1932; completed 4-year advanced military training course, University of Wisconsin, 1919–23; LL. D., Cornell College, 1946; LL. D. 1947, Drake University, and College of South Jersey; LL. D. 1952, Centre College of Kentucky; D. Jr. Sc., Suffolk University, Boston, Mass., 1961; LL. D. American International College, Springfield, Mass., 1962; distinguished service award, University of Oregon, 1963; held reserve commission as second lieutenant, Field Artillery, U.S. Army, 1923–30; taught argumentation at University of Wisconsin and University of Minnesota and was appointed assistant professor of law at University of Oregon in 1929; dean and professor of law, 1931–44; chairman, President's Railway Emergency Board, 1941; public member, National War Labor Board, 1942–44; member United States delegation to United Nations, 1960; chairman, President's Special Board on Atlantic and Gulf Coast Maritime Industry Dispute, 1963; married Miss Mildred Downie in 1924 and they have three daughters—Mrs. Hugh Campbell, Jr., Mrs. Wade Eaton, and Mrs. John Bilich; Congregationalist; elected to the United States Senate on November 7, 1944, for the term ending January 3, 1951; reelected November 7, 1950, for the term ending January 3, 1957; reelected November 6, 1956, for the term ending January 3, 1963; reelected November 6, 1962, for the term ending January 3, 1969.

MAURINE BROWN NEUBERGER, Democrat, of Portland, Oreg.; born in Cloverdale, Tillamook County, Oreg.; attended Oregon public schools, Oregon College of Education at Monmouth, and University of Oregon; graduate work, University of California at Los Angeles; taught for 12 years in public schools of Milton-Freewater, Newberg, and Portland, Oreg.; married the late Richard Lewis Neuberger, December 20, 1945, in Missoula, Mont.; married Dr. Philip Solomon, July 11, 1964; member of Oregon House of Representatives 1951–55; chairman of House Education Committee, 1953 session of Oregon Legislature; writer and photographer; Unitarian; member board of directors of American Association for the United Nations; member of President's Commission on Status of Women; elected on November 8, 1960, to the United States Senate for the balance of the unexpired term of the late Senator Richard L. Neuberger, and for the 6-year term ending January 3, 1967.

REPRESENTATIVES

FIRST DISTRICT.—COUNTIES: Benton, Clackamas, Clatsop, Columbia, Lincoln, Marion, Polk, Tillamook, Washington, and Yamhill (10 counties). Population (1960), 517,678.

WENDELL WYATT, Republican, of Astoria, Oreg.; born in Eugene, Oreg., June 15, 1917; attended grade school in Eugene, Jefferson High School in Portland, Oreg., and University of Oregon in Eugene, LL. B. in 1941; attorney at law, practicing in Astoria; member, board of bar governors, Oregon State Bar, 1952–55; president, Clatsop County Bar Association, 1950; delegate, house of delegates, American Bar Association, 1960; chairman, Oregon State Republican Central Committee, 1955–57; married; wife's name Faye L. Wyatt; five children, Sandi Hill, Larry D. Hill, Ann Wyatt, Jane Wyatt, and Bill Wyatt; elected to the 88th Congress November 3, 1964, to fill the vacancy caused by the death of Walter Norblad; also elected to the 89th Congress.

SECOND DISTRICT.—Counties: Baker, Crook, Deschutes, Gilliam, Grant, Harney, Hood River, Jefferson, Klamath, Lake, Malheur, Morrow, Sherman, Umatilla, Union, Wallowa, Wasco, and Wheeler (18 counties). Population (1960), 265,164.

AL ULLMAN, Democrat, of Baker, Oreg.; born in Great Falls, Mont., March 9, 1914; A.B., Whitman College, Walla Walla, Wash., in political science, 1935; taught in Port Angeles, Wash., High School 2 years; M.A. in public law from Columbia University, New York City, 1939; served in World War II as communications officer afloat in South and Southwest Pacific; married Anita Curfman, 1941; three children; member of First Presbyterian Church of Baker; Beta Theta, Pi; elected to 85th Congress, November 6, 1956; reelected to 86th, 87th, 88th, and 89th Congresses; served on Interior Committee and National Outdoor Recreation Review Commission; since 1961 a member of Ways and Means Committee and Democratic Committee on Committees.

THIRD DISTRICT.—County: Multnomah. Population (1960), 522,813.

EDITH GREEN, Democrat, of Portland, Oreg.; born in Trent, S. Dak. January 17, 1910; attended Salem schools and Willamette University; bachelor of science degree from University of Oregon; graduate work at Stanford University; two sons, James S. Green and Richard Green and three grandchildren; teacher; commercial radio work; director of public relations for Oregon Education Association; honorary degrees: Doctor of laws, doctor of humanities, doctor of humane letters; honored by the YWCA and National Council of Jewish Women; Annual B'nai B'rith Brotherhood Award, 1956; "Woman of the Year" Award, American Veterans Auxiliary, 1958; distinguished service awards of the American College Public Relations Association and the National Association of Colored Women's Clubs; United States delegate to Interparliamentary Conference in Switzerland sponsored by American Friends Committee, 1958; delegate to NATO Conference in London, 1959; delegate-at-large to Democratic National Convention, 1956; first woman chairman of State Democratic delegation to presidential nominating convention, 1960, and seconded John F. Kennedy's successful nomination; member First Christian Church, League of Women Voters, Urban League, United Nations Association, American Federation of Radio Artists; member of U.S. National Committee to UNESCO and of two commissions of the National Council of Churches; elected to the 84th Congress, 1954; reelected to the 85th, 86th, 87th, 88th, and 89th Congresses.

FOURTH DISTRICT.—Counties: Coos, Curry, Douglas, Jackson, Josephine, Lane, and Linn (7 counties). Population (1960), 463,032.

ROBERT BLACKFORD DUNCAN, Democrat, of Medford, Oreg.; born in Normal, Ill., December 4, 1920; raised in Bloomington, Ill., and attended grade and high school there; graduated Illinois Wesleyan University, B.A. 1942; attended University of Alaska 1939–40 and took correspondence courses from the University of California in 1940; during World War II served in the U.S. Naval Air Force 1942–45; presently lieutenant commander in the Naval Reserve; returned to studies and graduated University of Michigan Law School, LL.B. 1948; worked as a seaman in the Merchant Marine, in the gold fields of Alaska, for hybrid seed corn company in Illinois, for a bank in Chicago, and as an insurance adjuster; passed the bar in October 1948 and practiced law continuously in Medford in all U.S. and State courts until becoming a Congressman; married the former Marijane Dill; seven children—Nancy, Angus, David, James, Laurie, Bonnie Dee, and Jeannie Elizabeth; nominated in 1954 (write-in) for State legislature but declined for business reasons; elected to the State legislature in 1956, 1958, and 1960, serving two terms as Speaker and on occasion as acting Governor; member: the Methodist Church; American, Oregon, and Jackson County bar associations; National Association of Claimant's Compensation Attorneys; Jackson County Chamber of Commerce; the Elks Club; advisory board of the Salvation Army; the board of directors of Mercy Flights, and in other public and community organizations; elected to the 88th Congress November 6, 1962; reelected to the 89th Congress;

PENNSYLVANIA

(Population (1960), 11,319,366)

SENATORS

JOSEPH S. CLARK, Democrat, of Philadelphia, Pa.; born in Philadelphia, Pa., October 21, 1901; Harvard College, 1923, B. S. magna cum laude; University of Pennsylvania Law School, 1926, LL. B.; married Noel Hall, two children; lawyer; Colonel, Army Air Force 1941–45, China-Burma-India Theater; elected city controller of Philadelphia, 1949; elected mayor of Philadelphia, 1951; LL.D. (honorary) Temple University, 1952; LL. D. (honorary) Harvard University, 1952; LL. D. (honorary) Drexel Institute of Technology, 1957; Philadelphia Award (Bok), 1956; L.H.D. (honorary) Lincoln University 1961; D.C.L. (honorary) Susquehanna University, 1961; LL. D. (honorary) University of Pennsylvania, 1963; elected to the United States Senate November 6, 1956, for the term expiring January 3, 1963; reelected November 6, 1962, for the term ending January 3, 1969.

HUGH SCOTT, Republican, of Philadelphia, Pa.; lawyer, Philadelphia; elected 77th Congress, reelected seven additional terms; member, House minority policy committee; member, Board of Visitors, Naval Academy, 1948; chairman, Board of Visitors, U.S. Merchant Marine Academy, 1959; Board of Visitors, Coast Guard Academy, 1963; author, "Scott on Bailments" (1931), "How To Go Into Politics" (1949), and numerous articles in national magazines; national chairman, Republican Party, 1948–49; Eisenhower personal staff, 1952; chairman, Eisenhower Headquarters Committee, 1952; general counsel, Republican National Committee, 1955–60; member, United States Delegation to United Nations Social, Educational, and Cultural Organizations, 1954, 1956; Commonwealth Conference, Australia, 1959; NATO Parliamentary Conference, 1961; active duty, United States Naval Reserve, in World War II as a lieutenant; last rank, captain; active service with North Atlantic Patrol, Occupation of Iceland and Pacific area, including Occupation of Japan; duty aboard carrier *Valley Forge* in Korean War, August and September 1950; in summer of 1944 enlisted incognito as a merchant seaman on a tanker carrying high octane gasoline to Great Britain; A.B., Randolph-Macon College, 1919; LL.B., University of Virginia, 1922; LL.D., Randolph-Macon; L.H.D., La Salle College; LL.D., Dickinson College; LL.D., Temple University; Pub. Adm. D., Suffolk University; LL.D., Ursinus College; LL.D., Washington and Jefferson; LL.D., Lebanon Valley College; Litt. D., Philadelphia College of Osteopathy; LL.D., Philadelphia Textile Institute; Sc. D., Delaware Valley College; LL.D., Lincoln University; also attended University of Pennsylvania; member American Legion; VFW; AMVETS; Sons of the Revolution; Society of the Cincinnati; P.O.S. of A.; Capitol Press Club, Pa.; Friendly Sons of St. Patrick; Alpha Chi Rho (national president 1942–46); Phi Beta Kappa, Tau Kappa Alpha and Phi Alpha Delta fraternities; Philadelphia Cricket Club; Germantown Lions Club; Army and Navy Club, Washington; honorary alumnus, Philadelphia Textile Institute; married to Marian Huntington Chase, an alumna of Germantown Friends School; one daughter, Marian Scott Concannon; Episcopalian; elected United States Senator November 1958; reelected November 3, 1964.

REPRESENTATIVES

FIRST DISTRICT.—CITY OF PHILADELPHIA: Wards 1 to 4, 26, 36, 39, 40, 46, 48, 51 and 60. Population (1960), 418,192.

WILLIAM A. BARRETT, Democrat, of Philadelphia, Pa.; was graduated from Brown Preparatory School and St. Joseph's College, Philadelphia, Pa.; real estate broker; three children; elected to the 79th Congress on November 7, 1944; elected to the 81st, 82d, 83d, 84th, 85th, 86th, 87th, 88th, and 89th Congresses.

SECOND DISTRICT.—CITY OF PHILADELPHIA: Wards 7 to 10, 15, 24, 27, 29, 30, 32, 34, 44, and 52. Population (1960), 397,995.

ROBERT N. C. NIX, Democrat, of Philadelphia, Pa.; born in Orangeburg, S.C.; married; one son, Robert Nix, Jr.; member, legal firm Nix and Nix; graduated from Townsend Harris Hall High School, New York City; Lincoln University, Chester County, Pa., and University of Pennsylvania Law School; practicing lawyer since 1925; admitted to practice in all courts of Philadelphia County, Superior and Supreme of the Commonwealth of Pennsylvania, also U.S. District and Circuit Courts in Eastern Pennsylvania; was special deputy attorney general of Pennsylvania, assigned to Escheats Division, State Department of Revenue and special assistant deputy attorney general of Commonwealth 1934–38; member of Philadelphia Bar Association, Philadelphia Lawyers Club, Pyramid Club of Philadelphia, Omega Psi Phi Fraternity (University of Pennsylvania Chapter), Benevolent Protective Order of Elks, NAACP, YMCA, American Woodman, Philadelphia Citizens Committee Against Juvenile Delinquency and Its Causes, White Rock Baptist Church, Philadelphia, Pa., for 25 years and member of the deacon board for 6 years; elected 44th Ward executive committeeman, 9th division, in 1932 and reelected for 26 years to date; ward committee chairman 1950–58; unanimously elected Democratic ward leader of 32d Ward in 1958; member of Policy Committee, Philadelphia Democratic Campaign Committee, and co-chairman of Inter-Relations Committee of Democratic Campaign Committee since 1953; delegate to Democratic National Convention in Chicago in 1956; elected assistant treasurer of Democratic County Committee June 14, 1958; elected to the 85th Congress in a special election May 20, 1958, to fill vacancy caused by resignation of Earl Chudoff; reelected to the 86th, 87th, 88th, and 89th Congresses.

THIRD DISTRICT.—CITY OF PHILADELPHIA: Wards 5, 6, 11 to 14, 16 to 21, 28, 31, 37, 38, 47, and 59 Population (1960), 406,993.

JAMES ALOYSIUS BYRNE, Democrat, of Philadelphia, Pa.; born in Philadelphia, Pa., June 22, 1906; was graduated from St. Joseph's Prep School in 1925 and attended St. Joseph's College for 2 years; funeral director; served as United States marshal for eastern district of Pennsylvania; chief disbursing officer for State Treasury, Commonwealth of Pennsylvania; member of Pennsylvania State Legislature 1950–52; married M. Virginia Mullin, June 7, 1939; no children; elected to the 83d Congress November 4, 1952; reelected to the 84th, 85th, 86th, 87th, 88th, and 89th Congresses.

FOURTH DISTRICT.—CITY OF PHILADELPHIA: Wards 22, 35, 42, 50, 53, 56 to 58. Population (1960), 387,156.

HERMAN TOLL, Democrat, of Philadelphia, Pa.; received LL.B. degree from Temple University School of Law, and was business manager and note editor of the Temple Law Quarterly and a member of the Blue Key National Honor Society; practicing attorney in Philadelphia since 1930; elected to the General Assembly from the 16th Legislative District in Philadelphia in 1950; reelected in 1952, 1954, and 1956; board member Jewish Home for the Aged; board member of Northeast Neighborhood Centre; trustee of College of Podiatry at St. Luke's and Children's Medical Center; member: Personal Aid Bureau of the Jewish Family Service, Pennsylvania Prison Society, Fellowship Commission and Fellowship House, Employment Practices and Opportunities Committee of Philadelphia Jewish Community Relations Council, Urban League of Philadelphia, Temple Judea Congregation and Men's Club, Philadelphia Bar Association, Pennsylvania Bar Association, American Bar Association; past president, Law Academy of Philadelphia; past president, Philadelphia Chapter, Federal Bar Association; past president, Amity Lodge, B'nai B'rith; board of directors: Philadelphia Chapter, American Jewish Committee; Delaware Valley Chapter, American Jewish Congress; and Anti-Defamation League; married to former Rose Ornstein; two sons: Sheldon S., age 24, and Gilbert E., age 21; elected to 86th Congress November 4, 1958; reelected to 87th, 88th, and 89th Congresses; member of the House Judiciary Committee and its subcommittees on Antitrust and Civil Rights, and Patents.

FIFTH DISTRICT.—CITY OF PHILADELPHIA: Wards 23, 25, 33, 41, 43, 45, 49, 54, and 55. Population (1960), 392,176.

WILLIAM JOSEPH GREEN, Democrat, of Philadelphia, Pa.; born June 24, 1938, in Philadelphia, Pa., the son of William J. Green, Jr., and Mary E. (Kelly) Green; attended St. Joseph's Prep; graduated from St. Joseph's College in 1960; attended Villanova Law School; married Patricia Anne Kirk; elected to the 88th Congress in a special election April 28, 1964, to fill the vacancy caused by the death of his father, William J. Green, Jr.; reelected to the 89th Congress.

SIXTH DISTRICT.—COUNTIES: Berks, Northumberland, and Schuylkill (3 counties). Population (1960), 552,579.

GEORGE MILTON RHODES, Democrat, of Reading, Pa.; born February 24, 1898, in Reading, Pa.; wife, Margie Seiverling; veteran World War I; worked as printer, business manager, labor editor; elected to the 81st Congress on November 2, 1948; reelected to the 82d, 83d, 84th, 85th, 86th, 87th, 88th, and 89th Congresses.

SEVENTH DISTRICT.—DELAWARE COUNTY. Population (1960), 553,154.

G. ROBERT WATKINS, Republican, of Birmingham Township, Delaware County, Pa.; born in Hampton, Va., May 21, 1902, one of four children; first business experience, when 9 years of age, was selling newspapers to the crews of vessels anchored in the harbor; learned the trade of ship fitter in Newport News, Va.; married the former Hilda Jane Smerbeck, of Pittsburgh, Pa.; two sons, Robert G. and Dwain Joseph; went to Chester, Pa., in 1920; organized and headed the Chester Stevedoring Co. until 1931; in 1932, with a partner, organized the Blue Line Transfer Co., operating hundreds of trucks to all points in the East; served 4-year term as sheriff of Delaware County; member of the State senate for three 4-year terms; served a 4-year term as county commissioner; lives on a 60-acre farm in Delaware County and has bred thoroughbred horses since 1937; elected to the 89th Congress November 3, 1964.

EIGHTH DISTRICT.—COUNTIES: Bucks and Lehigh (2 counties). Population (1960), 536,103.

WILLARD S. CURTIN, Republican, of Morrisville, Bucks County, Pa.; born in Trenton, N. J., November 28, 1905; a resident of Bucks County and presently residing in Lower Makefield Township; graduate of Morrisville High School, Penn State University, and University of Pennsylvania Law School; senior partner in the law firm of Curtin & Heefner, located in Morrisville; married Geraldine H. Curtin; two sons—Lawrence B. and Jeffrey; first assistant district attorney of Bucks County 1938–49; district attorney 1949 through 1953; Episcopalian; elected to the 85th Congress on November 6, 1956; reelected to the 86th, 87th, 88th, and 89th Congresses.

NINTH DISTRICT.—COUNTIES: Chester and Lancaster (2 counties). Population (1960), 488,967.

PAUL BARTRAM DAGUE, Republican, of Downingtown, Pa.; born in Whitford, Chester County, Pa.; graduated from Downingtown High School; special studies at West Chester State Teachers College, and electrical engineering at Drexel Institute at Philadelphia; sheriff of Chester County, Pa., 1944–46; served in World War I as a private first class in the United States Marine Corps; past department finance officer of the American Legion; member of Legion National Publications Commission, Masonic fraternity, honorary member Rotary International, and Central Presbyterian Church; married Mary Virginia Williams; elected to the 80th, 81st, 82d, 83d, 84th, 85th, 86th, 87th, 88th, and 89th Congresses.

TENTH DISTRICT.—COUNTIES: Bradford, Lackawanna, Sullivan, Susquehanna, Wayne, and Wyoming (6 counties). Population (1960), 373,894.

JOSEPH MICHAEL McDADE, Republican, of Scranton, Pa.; born in Scranton September 29, 1931, son of John B. and Genevieve McDade; attended St. Paul's School and Scranton Preparatory School; graduated with honors from the University of Notre Dame, 1953, B.A., major in political science; graduated from University of Pennsylvania 1956, LL.B. degree; clerkship in office of Chief

Federal Judge John W. Murphy, Middle District of Pennsylvania; engaged in general practice of law; served as city solicitor of City of Scranton, January 1962 to December 1962; married to former Mary Teresa O'Brien, Waverly, N.Y.; two children—Joseph, Aileen; member: James Wilson Law Club, Knights of Columbus, Elks Club, Scranton Chamber of Commerce, Mid-Valley Oldtimers Athletic Association, National Rifle Association; American, Pennsylvania and Lackawanna County Bar Associations; elected to the 88th Congress November 6, 1962; reelected to the 89th Congress.

ELEVENTH DISTRICT.—LUZERNE COUNTY. Population (1960), 346,972.

DANIEL J. FLOOD, Democrat, of Wilkes-Barre, Pa.; born in Hazleton, Pa., November 26, 1903; received early education in the public schools of Wilkes-Barre, Pa., and St. Augustine, Fla.; graduate of Syracuse University, A. B. and M. A. degrees, and later attended Harvard Law School and Dickinson School of Law, Carlisle, Pa., graduating in 1929 with LL. B. degrees; admitted to the bar of the various State and Federal courts in 1930; member of the bar, District of Columbia and of the United States Supreme Court; member of Luzerne County, Pa., Pennsylvania State and American Bar Associations; engaged in the practice of law since 1930; attorney for Home Owners' Loan Corporation, 1934-35; appointed deputy attorney general for the Commonwealth of Pennsylvania and counsel for Pennsylvania Liquor Control Board, 1935-39; director, Bureau of Public Assistance Disbursements, State Treasury, and executive assistant to State Treasurer, Commonwealth of Pennsylvania, 1941-44; married Catherine H. Swank on September 24, 1949; member of many local civic, fraternal, beneficial, and social societies; president, Wilkes-Barre Chamber of Commerce; chairman, United States Marine Corps Volunteer Reserve Committee; secretary, Democratic Society of Pennsylvania; member of the Board of Directors, Wyoming Valley Motor Club; member of the Board of Directors, Catholic Charities; member of Board of Trustees and Board of Governors of Welfare Federation; special master for Railroad Reorganization, United States Circuit Court; Honorary Doctor of Laws from Dickinson School of Law, Carlisle, Pa.; Member of the Board of Directors of Kingston National Bank, Kingston, Pa.; Member of the Board of Trustees, College Misericordia, Dallas, Pa.; elected to the 79th Congress, November 7, 1944; elected to the 81st Congress, November 2, 1948; elected to the 82d Congress, November 7, 1950; elected to the 84th Congress, November 2, 1954; reelected to the succeeding Congresses; former vice chairman of Special Committee To Investigate the Katyn Massacre (murder of Polish officers by Russians); present member of the Appropriations Committee, Department of Defense Subcommittee.

TWELFTH DISTRICT.—COUNTIES: Bedford, Blair, Franklin, Fulton, Huntingdon, Mifflin, and Somerset (7 counties). Population (1960), 439,745.

J. IRVING WHALLEY, Republican, of Windber, Somerset County, Pa.; attended local schools, Cambria Rowe Business College, and took many extension courses; actively engaged in the automobile, banking and coal businesses; married to the former Ruth Anderson, journalism and English instructor, Windber High School; they have two children, John and Ruth; member of the advisory board of Johnstown College, University of Pittsburgh; chairman of the Somerset County Redevelopment Authority and the Windber Planning Commission; served two terms in the State house of representatives and two terms in the State senate of Pennsylvania; elected to the 86th Congress November 8, 1960, to fill the vacancy caused by the death of Douglas H. Elliott and also elected to the 87th Congress; reelected to the 88th and 89th Congresses.

THIRTEENTH DISTRICT.—MONTGOMERY COUNTY. Population (1960), 516,682.

RICHARD SCHULTZ SCHWEIKER, Republican, of Worcester, Pa.; born in Norristown, Pa., June 1, 1926; attended Worcester elementary and junior high schools; graduated from Norristown Senior High School in 1944, valedictorian, and Pennsylvania State University, B.A. degree in 1950, Phi Beta Kappa; honorary Doctor of Laws, Ursinus College, 1963; during World War II enlisted in the U.S. Navy and served abroad an aircraft carrier; 10 years of business experience as a manufacturing and sales executive; married the former Claire Coleman of Springfield Township, Montgomery County, Pa.; one son, Malcolm, and one daughter, Lani Lynne; selected Outstanding Young Man of

Lansdale, 1954; selected outstanding Jaycee President in Pennsylvania, 1955: selected Outstanding Young Man of Pennsylvania by the Pennsylvania Jaycees, 1961; received Citizenship Citation for Meritorious Service from B'nai B'rith, 1961; received Annual Civic Service Award from the Eastern Montgomery County Professional Business Council, 1961; former chairman Red Cross, Heart Fund, Community Chest and others; trustee, Pennsylvania United Fund; director, North Penn United Fund; Boy Scouts of America General Nash District Executive Committee; former member Penn State Alumni Council; member of Central Schwenkfelder Church, serving on Board of Directors of Schwenkfelder Library; member, Lansdale Lions Club, Veterans of Foreign Wars, American Legion, Y.M.C.A., Navy League, Sons of the American Revolution, and the Pennsylvania Society; National Captive Nations Committee; past Republican Committeeman of Worcester-East, alternate delegate to 1952 and 1956 National Republican Conventions; president of Montgomery County Young Republican Club 1952-54; Republican Finance Committee in North Penn Area 1952-58; member of Montgomery County Republican Campaign Committee in 1956 and chairman in 1958; member of Republican State Executive Committee; elected to the 87th Congress, November 8, 1960; reelected to the 88th and 89th Congresses; member of Armed Services Committee; former member Committee on Government Operations; secretary of Pennsylvania Republican delegation.

FOURTEENTH DISTRICT.—ALLEGHENY COUNTY: City of Pittsburgh: Wards 1 to 14, and 21 to 27. Population (1960), 390,512.

WILLIAM S. MOORHEAD, Democrat, of Pittsburgh, Pa., born in Pittsburgh, Pa., on April 8, 1923; Yale University, 1944, B. A.; served in U. S. Navy (Pacific Theater), 1943-46, commissioned lieutenant (j. g.); Harvard Law School, 1949, LL. B. (cum laude); married Lucy Galpin, four children; lawyer; member of law firm of Moorhead & Knox; assistant city solicitor, city of Pittsburgh, 1954-57; member of Allegheny County Housing Authority, 1956-58; member Art Commission, city of Pittsburgh, 1958; member of board of trustees of Tuberculosis League of Pittsburgh, Pittsburgh Child Guidance Center, Shadyside Hospital (1956-60) and Western Pennsylvania Conservancy; member of American Legion, VFW, and AMVETS; elected to the 86th Congress on November 4, 1958; reelected to the 87th, 88th, and 89th Congresses; member Committee on Banking and Currency and Committee on Government Operations.

FIFTEENTH DISTRICT.—COUNTIES: Carbon, Monroe, Northampton, and Pike (4 counties). Population (1960), 303,026.

FRED B. ROONEY, Democrat, of Bethlehem, Pa.; born November 6, 1925, in Bethlehem, Northampton County, Pa., the son of Fred B. and Veronica K. (McGreevy) Rooney; attended the public schools; graduated from the Bethlehem High School in 1944 and from the University of Georgia at Athens in 1950; holds a degree in business administration; engaged in the real estate and insurance business (office address, 405 E. Fourth Street, Bethlehem, Pa., and home address, 326 Wyandotte Street, Bethlehem, Pa.); served in the United States Army during World War II from February 1944 to April 1946, with service in Europe as a paratrooper in the 515th Paratroop Infantry Regiment, 13th Airborne Division; member of the American Legion, Amvets, Veterans of Foreign Wars, Catholic War Veterans, and the Knights of Columbus (past grand Knight); served as president of and reorganized the Young Democratic Club of Northampton County; member of the Bethlehem Housing Authority; elected to two terms in the State senate and served from November 5, 1958, until his resignation August 6, 1963; elected to the 88th Congress in a special election July 30, 1963, to fill the vacancy caused by the death of Francis E. Walter; reelected to the 89th Congress; member of the Interstate and Foreign Commerce Committee.

SIXTEENTH DISTRICT.—COUNTIES: Dauphin, Juniata, Lebanon, and Perry (4 counties). Population (1960), 353,564.

JOHN CRAIN KUNKEL, Republican, of Harrisburg, Pa., where he was born July 21, 1898; son of John C. and Louisa Sergeant Kunkel; grandson of John C. Kunkel, a Member of the 34th and 35th Congresses; and great-grandson of John Sergeant, a Member of Congress for eight terms; great-grandson of Robert Whitehill, Member of Congress 9th through 13th Congresses; great-great-grandson of Jonathan Dickinson Sergeant, a Member of the Continental Congress; attended Harrisburg Academy, Phillips Academy, Andover, Mass., Yale University, and Harvard Law School; engaged in banking and farming; member of the Episcopal Church, American Legion, Lions Club, Elks, and I.O.O.F.; married to Katherine Smoot Kunkel on October 11, 1947; elected to the 76th, 77th, 78th, 79th, 80th, and 81st Congresses; elected to the 87th Congress May 16, 1961, to fill the vacancy caused by the death of Walter M. Mumma; reelected to the 88th and 89th Congresses.

SEVENTEENTH DISTRICT.—COUNTIES: Cameron, Centre, Clinton, Columbia, Lycoming, Montour, Potter, Snyder, Tioga, and Union (10 counties). Population (1960), 408,036.

HERMAN T. SCHNEEBELI, Republican, of Williamsport, Pa.; born in Lancaster, Pa., July 7, 1907; attended Lancaster Public Schools; was graduated from Mercersburg Academy in 1926, Dartmouth College in 1930, and Amos Tuck School (MCS) in 1931; commission distributor Gulf Oil Corp.; served in World War II, captain, Ordnance Department, from 1942 to 1946; served as president, United Fund; president, Y.W.C.A. trustees; member of board of managers of Williamsport Hospital, American Legion, Elks, Kiwanis Club, vestryman Episcopal Church; bank director; married to the former Mary Louise Meyer of Bellefonte, Pa.; two daughters, Marta and Susan; elected to the 86th Congress in a special election held April 26, 1960; reelected to the 87th, 88th, and 89th Congresses.

EIGHTEENTH DISTRICT.—COUNTY OF ALLEGHENY: Boroughs of Aspinwall, Avalon, Bell Acres, Bellevue, Ben Avon, Ben Avon Heights, Blawnox, Brackenridge, Bradford Woods, Cheswick, Church-ill, Edgewood, Edgeworth, Emsworth, Etna, Forest Hills, Fox Chapel, Franklin Park, Glenfield, Haysville, Leetsdale, Millvale, Monroeville, Oakmont, Osborne, Pitcairn, Plum, Sewickley, Sewickley Heights, Sewickley Hills, Sharpsburg, Springdale, Tarentum, Verona, West View, and Wilkinsburg. Townships of Aleppo, East Deer, Fawn, Frazer, Hampton, Harmar, Harrison, Indiana, Kilbuck, Leet, McCandless, Marshall, O'Hara, Ohio, Penn Hills, Pine, Reserve, Richland, Ross, Shaler, Springdale, West Deer, and Wilkins. Population (1960), 409,291.

ROBERT J. CORBETT, Republican, Ben Avon Heights, Pittsburgh, Pa.; born in Avalon (Pittsburgh), Pa., August 25, 1905; graduated Allegheny College in 1927, with A. B. degree; graduated University of Pittsburgh in 1929, with M. A. degree; Wallace Research Fellow in History (University of Pittsburgh) 1927–29; senior high-school instructor, Coraopolis, Pa., 1929–38; former publisher and editor of the North Pittsburgh Times; member of Bellevue Chamber of Commerce, Phi Delta Theta fraternity, Loyal Order of Moose, Elks, Eagles, Kiwanis, Lions, Phi Alpha Theta, Delta Sigma Rho; board of directors, Suburban General Hospital; married Ruth McClintock, of Ligonier, Pa.; one child, Eleanor Louise (Mrs. Donald F. Dunbar, of Pittsburgh, Pa.); elected to the 76th Congress on November 8, 1938; elected sheriff of Allegheny County (Pittsburgh), 1941; former chairman and now ranking chairman of the Pennsylvania Republican Congressional Campaign Committee; representative to the NATO Parliamentary Conference 1957, 1958, 1959; elected to the 79th Congress on November 7, 1944; reelected to the 80th, 81st, 82d, 83d, 84th, 85th, 86th, 87th, 88th, and 89th Congresses.

NINETEENTH DISTRICT.—COUNTIES: Adams, Cumberland, and York (3 counties). Population (1960), 415,058.

NATHANIEL NEIMAN CRALEY, JR., Democrat, of York Pa.; born November 17, 1927, in Red Lion, Pa.; attended Red Lion Elementary School, York Collegiate Institute, Taft School (Graduate), Watertown, Conn., and Gettysburg College (B.A. degree 1950); furniture manufacturer; member, house committee, York YMCA; member, York City Parking Authority; member and teacher, St. Paul's Lutheran Sunday School; past activities: charter member and treasurer, York County Planning Commission; member, Charter Study Committee, York City; director and past president, York County Heart Association; director and first vice president, York County Council of Community Services; director, York County Council for Human Relations; director, White Rose Motor Club (AAA); chairman, York County Democratic Committee; instructor, York Junior College (Economics and History); married; four children; elected to the 89th Congress November 3, 1964.

TWENTIETH DISTRICT.—ALLEGHENY COUNTY: City of Pittsburgh: Wards 15 to 18, and 29 to 31. Cities of Clairton, Duquesne, and McKeesport. Boroughs of Braddock, Braddock Hills, Chalfant, Dravosburg, East McKeesport, East Pittsburgh, Elizabeth, Glassport, Homestead, Liberty, Lincoln, Mount Oliver, Munhall, North Braddock, Port Vue, Rankin, Swissvale, that part of Trafford in Allegheny County, Turtle Creek, Versailles, Wall, West Homestead, West Mifflin, Whitaker, White Oak, and Wilmerding. Townships of Elizabeth, Forward, North Versailles, and South Versailles. Population (1960), 404,997.

ELMER J. HOLLAND, Democrat, of Pittsburgh, Pa.; born in Pittsburgh, Pa., son of Thomas and Margaret (Keelan) Holland; educated in the Pittsburgh public

schools, Duquesne University, and the University of Montpelier, France; graduate
Civil Affairs School (United States Army), University of Pittsburgh, and American
School Center, Shrivenham, England; served in World War I in the A. E. F.;
graduated from Saumur Artillery School, France, as lieutenant in the F. A.;
served in World War II as major in Allied Military Government in European
Theater of Operations; commander, Post 435, Veterans of Foreign Wars; member
of the American Legion; Member Local 1272, United Steelworkers of America,
AFL–CIO; married to the former Emily J. Wilson, of Pittsburgh; has two
daughters, Jane and Christine; served four terms in the house of representatives
(Pennsylvania); elected to the 77th Congress on May 19, 1942, to serve unexpired
term; did not run for reelection due to reapportionment; elected to the State
senate (Pennsylvania) in 1942; reelected in 1946, 1950, and 1954; elected to the
84th Congress on January 24, 1956, to fill the vacancy caused by the death of
Hon. Vera Buchanan; reelected to the 85th, 86th, 87th, 88th, and 89th Congresses.

TWENTY-FIRST DISTRICT.—WESTMORELAND COUNTY. Population (1960), 352,629.

JOHN H. DENT, Democrat, of Jeannette, Westmoreland County, Pa.; born in
Johnetta, Pa., March 10, 1908, the son of Samuel and Genevieve Dent; educated
in the public schools of Armstrong and Westmoreland Counties, the Great Lakes
Naval Aviation Academy, and through correspondence school courses; member
of the local council of United Rubber Workers from 1923 to 1937, serving as president of Local 18759 and the executive council, also member of the international
council; served from 1924 to 1928 in the U. S. Marine Air Corps; member of many
lodges and societies; has experience as a newspaperman and has contributed to
magazines and labor publications; married Miss Margaret R. Dent April 4, 1929;
one daughter, Patricia (Mrs. Donald Sarp), a son, John Frederick, a practicing
attorney in Westmoreland County, Pa., and six grandchildren: John Frederick,
Jao Carol, Melissa Ann, Tracy, Susan, and Jennifer Dent; elected to the Pennsylvania House of Representatives for one term, then elected to the State senate in 1936; reelected in 1940, 1944, 1948, 1952, and 1956; served as Pennsylvania
Democratic floor leader in the senate for 17 years; engaged as an executive with
coal and coke companies and building and transportation companies; student of
politics and social legislation; considered an authority on unemployment and
workmen's compensation laws and parliamentary and legislative procedures;
elected to the 85th Congress in a special election January 21, 1958, to fill
vacancy caused by death of Augustine B. Kelley; reelected to the 86th, 87th,
88th, and 89th Congresses.

TWENTY-SECOND DISTRICT.—COUNTIES: Armstrong, Cambria, and Indiana (3 counties). Population (1960), 358,173.

JOHN P. SAYLOR, Republican, of Johnstown, Cambria County, Pa.; born
July 23, 1908, in Conemaugh Township, Somerset County, Pa.; married; two
children; member Cambria County, Pennsylvania, and American Bar Associa-
tions; member of St. John's Evangelical and Reformed Church of Johnstown;
former lay member of Synodical Council, Pittsburgh Synod, Evangelical and
Reformed Church; lay delegate in 1957 to merger Synod of United Church of
Christ in Cleveland; past exalted ruler, Johnstown Lodge No. 175, BPOE; member
American Legion, Veterans of Foreign Wars, AMVETS; Mason; Shriner; member
many other civic, fraternal, social organizations; president, Johnstown Federal
Savings & Loan Association; member board of regents, Mercersburg Academy;
member, board of trustees of Massanutten Academy; enlisted in United States
Navy, August 6, 1943; active member Naval Reserve; received national award
from National Parks Association in 1954 for contributions to preservation of
national parks and monuments; received national award in 1958 for distinguished
service to conservation from six leading conservation organizations of United
States; received "Conservationist of the Year" award for 1964 by National Wildlife Federation; member of Outdoor Recreation Resources Review Commission;
member Public Land Law Review Commission; member Boone and Crockett
Club; member National Forest Reservation Commission; elected to 81st Congress
in special election held September 13, 1949; reelected to succeeding Congresses.

TWENTY-THIRD DISTRICT.—COUNTIES: Clarion, Clearfield, Elk, Forest, Jefferson, McKean, Ven-
ango, and Warren (8 counties). Population (1960), 372,941.

ALBERT W. JOHNSON, Republican, of Smethport, Pa.; born in Smethport,
April 17, 1906, the son of John A. and Edla (Ostrom) Johnson; graduate of
Smethport High School, attended Wharton School of the University of Penn-
sylvania, and graduated LL.B. John B. Stetson University Law School, Deland,

Fla.; member, Alpha Tau Omega; member of the McKean County and the Pennsylvania Bar Associations; and of the Bar of the Courts of McKean County, the Superior and Supreme Courts, and the United States District Court; married to the former Virginia Balsley and has four children; elected to the Pennsylvania House of Representatives in 1946; reelected in 1948, 1950, 1952, 1954, 1956, 1958, 1960, and 1962; in the Pennsylvania legislature was majority whip 1951; minority whip 1955; minority leader 1959 and 1961; majority leader 1953, 1957, and 1963; member of Joint State Government Commission, General State Authority, State Public School Building Authority, State Highway and Bridge Authority, Legislative Budget and Finance Committee, Committee on Interstate Cooperation, State Council of Civil Defense; chairman, House Committee on Rules; director, Smethport National Bank, 20 years; chairman of Pennsylvania Republican Platform Committee in 1958 and 1962; elected to the 88th Congress in special election November 5, 1963, to fill the unexpired term of Leon H. Gavin; reelected to the 89th Congress.

TWENTY-FOURTH DISTRICT.—COUNTIES: Crawford, Erie, and Mercer (3 counties). Population (1960), 456,157.

JOSEPH PHILLIP VIGORITO, Democrat, of Erie, Pa.; born in Niles, Ohio, November 10, 1918; graduated from Strong Vincent High School, Erie, Pa., in 1938; veteran of World War II, U.S. Army, April 1942 to August 1945, first lieutenant, awarded the Purple Heart; B.S. in economics, Wharton School of Finance, University of Pennsylvania, 1947; M.B.A., University of Denver, 1949; certified public accountant; assistant professor, Pennsylvania State University; married to the former Florence Hoppe; two children, Tina and Barbara; elected to the 89th Congress November 3, 1964.

TWENTY-FIFTH DISTRICT.—COUNTIES: Beaver, Butler, and Lawrence (3 counties). Population (1960), 434,552.

FRANK M. CLARK, Democrat, of Bessemer, Pa.; born in Bessemer, Pa., December 24, 1915; married Patricia Loy; two sons: Frank, Jr., age 19 and Kelly age 15; delegate to the NATO Conference in 1956 and 1960; delegate to the Interparliamentary Conference, 1957; attended International Christian Leadership Conference for Peace at The Hague in 1958 and Delegate to the International Highway Congress in 1959 and 1961; in 1963 member of delegation inspecting NATO bases; 1964 Delegate to the NATO Conference in Paris; major in Air Force Reserves; elected to the 84th Congress November 2, 1954; reelected to 85th, 86th, 87th, 88th, and 89th Congresses.

TWENTY-SIXTH DISTRICT.—COUNTIES: Fayette, Greene, and Washington (3 counties). Population (1960), 426,035.

THOMAS E. MORGAN, Democrat, of Fredericktown, Pa., born in Ellsworth, Pa., October 13, 1906; attended the public schools of Washington County, and was graduated from East Bethlehem Township High School at Fredericktown, Pa., in 1926; was graduated from Waynesburg College, Waynesburg, Pa., in 1930 with a bachelor of science degree; from Detroit College of Medicine and Surgery, Detroit, Mich., in 1933 with a bachelor of medicine degree, and from Wayne University in 1934, with a doctor of medicine degree; served internship at Grace Hospital, Detroit, Mich., and since that time has practiced medicine and surgery at Fredericktown, Pa.; married Winifred Stait of Portage la Prairie, Manitoba, Canada, August 26, 1937; they have one daughter, Mary Ann; excise member of Pennsylvania State Medical Society, American Medical Association, and numerous fraternal and civic organizations; elected to the 79th Congress on November 7, 1944; reelected to each succeeding Congress; acting chairman of House Foreign Affairs Committee second session 85th Congress; chairman of the Foreign Affairs Committee 86th, 87th, and 88th Congresses.

TWENTY-SEVENTH DISTRICT.—ALLEGHENY COUNTY: City of Pittsburgh: Wards 19, 20, 28, and 32. Boroughs of Baldwin, Bethel Park, Brentwood, Bridgeville, Carnegie, Castle Shannon, Coraopolis, Crafton, Dormont, Green Tree, Heidelberg, Ingram, Jefferson, that part of McDonald in Allegheny County, McKees Rocks, Oakdale, Pleasant Hills, Rosslyn Farms, Thornburg, West Elizabeth, and Whitehall. Townships of Baldwin, Collier, Crescent, Findlay, Kennedy, Moon, Mount Lebanon, Neville, North Fayette, Robinson, Scott, Snowden, South Fayette, Stowe, and Upper St. Clair. Population (1960), 423,787.

JAMES G. FULTON, Republican, of Dormont (Pittsburgh), Pa.; member of Science and Astronautics Committee; member of Foreign Affairs Committee

14 years (80th to 86th Congresses); son of James Ernest and Emilie Fetterman Fulton; grandson of Rev. Dr. John Lockhart Fulton and Judge Charles Sylvester Fetterman, families active since the 1700's in civic affairs in Western Penna. and South Hills section of Pittsburgh; graduate South Hills High School; Penn State, A.B.; Harvard Law School, LL.B.; 2 years Fine Arts Department of Carnegie Tech; owner Mount Lebanon News, Boro News, Chartiers Valley Times Progress, The News (South Hills), East Liberty Tribune, Pittsburgh, Pa., and News Progress, Washington County, Pa., farmer, lawyer, formerly partner, Pittsburgh banking law firm; member Allegheny Co. Board Law Examiners 1934–42; solicitor Dormont Borough; Pennsylvania State senator, 1939–40; lieutenant U.S. Naval Reserve on active duty in 1942; elected to the 79th Congress on November 7, 1944; returned from Pacific combat area to Congress, 1945; reelected ten times to date; member Board of Visitors, Annapolis Naval Academy, on appointment of Speaker, 1947; chairman, special subcommittee on displaced persons of the Foreign Affairs Committee, 80th Congress; United States delegate to United Nations Conference on Trade and Employment at Habana 1947–48, on appointment by President Truman; chairman subcommittee for Europe, of House Foreign Affairs Committee, 83d Congress; appointed U.S. Delegate to 14th General Assembly of United Nations by President Eisenhower, 1959; congressional adviser on space to U.S. mission at U.N. 1960–64; member American Judicature Society, American Academy of Political and Social Science; member American Rocket Society; member board of governors, National Rocket Club, 1959–62; congressional office address in Pittsburgh, 724 Fulton Building, phone Grant 1–0800; home address, 2850 Espy Avenue, Pittsburgh, Pa., 15216, and Golden Pheasant Farm, Mount Lebanon, Pittsburgh, Pa., 15228, phone Lehigh 1–1062, and 343–2339.

RHODE ISLAND

(Population (1960), 859,488)

SENATORS

JOHN O. PASTORE, Democrat, of Cranston, R. I.; lawyer; born in Providence, March 17, 1907; married Elena Caito in 1941; children, John O., Jr., Frances Elizabeth, and Louise Marie; member of the Rhode Island General Assembly, assistant attorney general, Lieutenant Governor, Governor, U. S. Senator since 1950; Northeastern University, LL. B.; honorary degrees: Providence College, Brown University, University of Rhode Island, Rhode Island College of Education, Rhode Island College of Pharmacy, Bryant College, Northeastern University, Salve Regina College, and New Bedford Institute of Technology; trustee of Brown University 1961–.

CLAIBORNE PELL, Democrat, of Newport, R.I.; born November 22, 1918, in New York City, son of Congressman Herbert Claiborne and Matilda (Bigelow) Pell; St. George's School, Middletown, R.I., 1933–36; Princeton University, 1940, A.B., cum laude; Columbia University, A.M.; married Nuala O'Donnell in December 1944; children: Herbert III, Christopher, Dallas, and Julia; business executive, investments; entered Coast Guard as enlisted man prior to World War II, discharged as lieutenant, now captain, USCGR; special assistant at San Francisco United Nations Conference; served 7 years in United States Foreign Service and in State Department; decorated by France, Italy, Portugal, and Knights of Malta; U.S. delegate to Intergovernmental Maritime Consultative Organization in London, 1959; until election in 1960, vice president of International Rescue Committee, member of National Council of Refugees, treasurer of American Immigration Conference; Democratic national registration chairman in 1956; chief delegation tally clerk, Democratic National Conventions, 1956 and 1960; consultant, Democratic National Committee, 1953–60; administrative assistant to Rhode Island Democratic State chairman in 1952 and 1954; was first unendorsed candidate to win statewide primary election in Rhode Island; elected November 8, 1960, to United States Senate for term ending January 3, 1967.

REPRESENTATIVES

FIRST DISTRICT.—COUNTIES: Bristol and Newport. PROVIDENCE COUNTY: City of Providence, representative districts, 1 to 7; cities of Central Falls, Pawtucket, Woonsocket; towns of Cumberland, East Providence, and Lincoln. Population (1960), 399,050.

FERNAND JOSEPH ST GERMAIN, Democrat, of Woonsocket, R.I.; born January 9, 1928, in Blackstone, Mass.; attended the parochial school; graduated from Our Lady of Providence Seminary High School in 1945, from Providence College, B. Phil., in 1948, and from Boston University Law School, LL.B., in 1955; enlisted in the U.S. Army in January 1949, served as a pharmacy and laboratory technician, and was honorably discharged in January 1952; captain, AF Reserve; member of the State house of representatives, 1952–60; admitted to the Rhode Island bar in 1956 and the Federal bar in 1957; engaged in the practice of law in Providence and Woonsocket; delegate to the Rhode Island Constitutional Convention in 1955; member of the Rhode Island and Woonsocket Bar Associations, the Young Democrats of Rhode Island, the Woonsocket Young Democrats (president), Nationalities Division, Democratic National Committee; First Representative District Committee of Woonsocket, and the American Legion; married the former Rachel O'Neill; two daughters; elected to the 87th Congress, November 8, 1960; reelected to the 88th and 89th Congresses.

SECOND DISTRICT.—COUNTIES: Kent and Washington. PROVIDENCE COUNTY: City of Providence, representative districts, 8 to 25; city of Cranston; towns of Burrillville, Foster, Glocester, Johnston, North Providence, North Smithfield, Scituate, and Smithfield. Population (1960), 459,706.

JOHN EDWARD FOGARTY, Democrat, of Harmony, R.I., elected in 1940; reelected to succeeding Congresses.

SOUTH CAROLINA

(Population (1960), 2,382,594)

SENATORS

OLIN D. JOHNSTON, Democrat, of Spartanburg, S. C.; born near Honea Path, Anderson County, S. C., November 18, 1896; father and mother were E. A. and Lelia (Webb) Johnston, of Anderson, S. C.; married Miss Gladys E. Atkinson, of Spartanburg, S. C., on December 27, 1924; three children, Olin D. Johnston, Jr., Sallie Leigh Johnston (now Mrs. Vernon R. Scott), and Gladys Elizabeth Johnston; Baptist denomination; was graduated from Spartanburg Junior College in 1915, from Wofford College with A. B. degree in 1921, and from the University of South Carolina with M. A. degree in 1923 and LL. B. degree in 1924; during the First World War served as sergeant, Company C, One Hundred and Seventeenth Engineers, Forty-second Division, serving 18 months overseas; received regimental citation; moved from Anderson to Spartanburg, S. C., in 1924; lawyer, firm of Johnston & Williams; successful lawyer in all courts, both State and Federal; member of the State house of representatives from Anderson County 1923-24 and from Spartanburg County 1927-30; Democratic national executive committeeman 1935-40 and 1944-48; candidate for Governor in 1930, leading field of eight candidates by 15,000 majority in first primary and in second primary missed nomination by less than a thousand votes; in 1934 led field of eight candidates by approximately 20,000 votes in first primary and in second primary defeated opponent by almost 35,000 majority; elected Governor for a second 4-year term in 1942; member of the American Legion, Forty and Eight, Veterans of Foreign Wars, and Disabled American Veterans; member of the Baptist Church and for many years interested in work of Baptist Young People; thirty-second degree Mason, Shriner, Optimist, member of Jr. O. U. A. M., Red Men, Woodmen of the World, Knights of Pythias, and B. P. O. Elks; elected to the United States Senate on November 7, 1944, for the term ending January 3, 1951; reelected on November 7, 1950, for the term ending January 3, 1957; reelected on November 6, 1956, for the term ending January 3, 1963; reelected November 6, 1962, for the term ending January 3, 1969.

STROM THURMOND, Republican, of Aiken, S.C.; attorney and farmer; born December 5, 1902, in Edgefield, S.C., son of John William and Eleanor Gertrude (Strom) Thurmond; married Jean Crouch of Elko, S.C., November 7, 1947 (dec. Jan. 6, 1960); 1923 graduate of Clemson College; studied law at night and admitted to South Carolina Bar 1930, and admitted to practice in all Federal Courts, including the U.S. Supreme Court; LL.D. degrees, Bob Jones U. (1948), Presbyterian Coll. (1960), Clemson Coll. (1961); D. Mil. Sc. degree, The Citadel (1961); agriculture teacher 1923-29; county superintendent of education 1929-33; city attorney and county attorney for several years; State Senator 1933-38; circuit judge 1938-46; Governor of South Carolina 1947-51, serving as chairman of Southern Governors' Conference 1950; practiced law in Aiken, S.C., 1951-55; volunteered for service in World War II the day war was declared against Germany, served with Headquarters First Army 1942-46, European and Pacific Theaters, participated in Normandy invasion with 82d Airborne Division; awarded 5 battle stars and 16 decorations, medals and awards, including the Legion of Merit, Bronze Star Medal with "V", Army Commendation Ribbon, Purple Heart, Presidential Distinguished Unit Citation, 3d Army Certificate of Achievement, OCAMG Certificate of Achievement, Belgian Order of the Crown, and French Croix de Guerre; major general in U.S. Army Reserve, past national president of Reserve Officers Association and Military Government Association; member Baptist Church, American Bar Association, and numerous defense, veterans, civic, fraternal, and farm organizations; Thurmond Hall (1939) at Winthrop Coll., streets in several S.C. cities, and new Edgefield County consolidated high school (1961) named in his honor; delegate to Democratic National Conventions in 1932, 1936, 1948, 1952, 1956, and 1960 (chairman of South Carolina delegation and national committeeman in 1948); States' Rights Democratic candidate for President of the United States in 1948, carrying 4 states and receiving 39 electoral votes; elected to the United States Senate November 2, 1954, as a write-in candidate, for the term ending January 3, 1961; resigned as United

States Senator April 4, 1956, to place the office in a primary, pursuant to a promise made to the people during the 1954 campaign; renominated and reelected to the Senate without opposition in 1956, resuming duties on November 7, 1956; renominated June 14, 1960, by 273,795 to 32,136 and reelected November 8, 1960, without opposition for the term ending January 3, 1967.

REPRESENTATIVES

FIRST DISTRICT.—COUNTIES: Allendale, Beaufort, Berkley, Charleston, Clarendon, Colleton, Dorchester, Hampton, and Jasper (9 counties). Population (1960), 421,478.

L. MENDEL RIVERS, Democrat, of Charleston, S. C.; born in Gumville, Berkeley County, S. C., September 28, 1905; educated in public schools, College of Charleston, and University of South Carolina; admitted to South Carolina bar in 1932; served in the South Carolina Legislature, 1933–36; 1936 to 1940, served as special attorney, United States Department of Justice; admitted to practice before Supreme Court of United States; member of Elks, a Mason, life member of Exchange Club, and member of Grace Episcopal Church, Charleston, S. C.; married Margaret Middleton of Charleston; elected to 77th Congress, November 5, 1940; reelected to all succeeding Congresses; chairman Armed Services Committee, 89th Congress.

SECOND DISTRICT.—COUNTIES: Aiken, Bamberg, Barnwell, Calhoun, Lexington, Orangeburg, Richland, and Sumter (8 counties). Population (1960), 531,555.

[Vacant.]

THIRD DISTRICT.—COUNTIES: Abbeville, Anderson, Edgefield, Greenwood, McCormick, Newberry, Oconee, Pickens, and Saluda (9 counties). Population (1960), 318,809.

WILLIAM JENNINGS BRYAN DORN, Democrat; born in Greenwood County, S. C., April 14, 1916, son of Pearl Griffith Dorn and the late T. E. Dorn; youngest member South Carolina House of Representatives 1939, 1940; youngest member South Carolina State Senate 1941, 1942; at age 24 was seated in South Carolina Senate by a special vote; in 1942 volunteered for the Army Air Force and resigned from the State Senate, serving for 3½ years; 18 months in Europe with Ninth Air Force; discharged as corporal; one of seven brothers in Armed Forces during World War II; elected to Congress in 1946 and became one of the youngest Members of the 80th Congress; in 1948 was runner up in a field of five for the United States Senate polling more than 83,000 votes; in 1950 was elected to the 82d Congress and without opposition to the succeeding Congresses; in 1948 married the former Mildred Johnson, of United States News & World Report; three daughters, Briana Pearl, Olivia Byrd, and Debbie Gail; two sons, William Jennings Bryan Dorn II and Johnson Griffith Dorn; home residence: Route 1, Greenwood, S.C.; occupation: farmer.

FOURTH DISTRICT.—COUNTIES: Greenville, Laurens, and Spartanburg (3 counties). Population (1960), 414,215.

ROBERT THOMAS ASHMORE, Democrat, of Greenville, S. C.; born February 22, 1904, on a farm in Greenville County, S. C., son of John Thomas and Lena Smith Ashmore; married to Willie Vance Linthicum of Atlanta, Ga.; one daughter,

Nancy Vance; attended public schools in Greenville and graduated from Furman University Law School in May 1927; obtained college education by working as farmhand, grocery clerk, and R. F. D. substitute mail carrier; practiced law in Greenville since January 1928; elected solicitor (prosecuting attorney) Greenville County in 1930, solicitor of the 13th Judicial Circuit of South Carolina (Greenville and Pickens Counties) in 1936, and reelected in 1940, 1944, 1948, and 1952, being unopposed in the last three elections; volunteered in the United States Army in December 1942, discharged in May 1946: holds rank of colonel in United States Army Reserves; long record of Baptist church work; served as director, vice president, and president of the Greenville Jaycees and was instrumental in organizing the State Junior Chamber of Commerce; was first president of the State Jaycees, and served as vice president of the United States Junior Chamber of Commerce; charter member and past president of the Greenville Exchange Club; member of the Junior Order of United American Mechanics, Elks, Odd Fellows, Woodmen of the World, American Legion, Reserve Officers Association, and Men's Garden Club of Greenville; elected to the 83d Congress June 2, 1953, to fill the vacancy caused by the death of Hon. Joseph R. Bryson; reelected to 84th, 85th, 86th, 87th, 88th, and 89th Congresses.

FIFTH DISTRICT.—COUNTIES: Cherokee, Chester, Chesterfield, Fairfield, Kershaw, Lancaster, Union, and York (8 counties). Population (1960), 302,235.

THOMAS SMITHWICK GETTYS, Democrat, of Rock Hill, S.C.; born at Rock Hill, York County, S.C., June 19, 1912, fourth of eight children of Maud Martin Gettys and the late John E. Gettys; educated in the public schools of Rock Hill, attended Clemson College, A.B. degree from Erskine College in 1933, and did graduate work at Duke University and Winthrop College; taught and coached at Rock Hill High School and served as principal of Central School; was secretary to Congressman James P. Richards, Fifth S.C. District, for seven years; postmaster at Rock Hill 1951–54; admitted to South Carolina Bar in 1953 and since 1954 has practiced law in State and Federal courts; is a member of York County, South Carolina, and American Bar Associations; married to Mary Phillips White of Chester, S.C., on December 9, 1947; two daughters—Julia Martin, born November 7, 1948, and Sara Elizabeth, born September 23, 1951; World War II Navy veteran with duty in forward combat areas of Pacific; member of American Legion, Veterans of Foreign Wars, Elks Club, lifelong active member of Associate Reformed Presbyterian Church of Rock Hill, former deacon, now elder; member and past president Rock Hill Chamber of Commerce, member and past president Rotary Club, member and past president Y.M.C.A. Board, past chairman United Fund Campaign, past member and chairman Board of Trustees, Rock Hill School District No. 3; elected November 3, 1964, to fill vacancy in 88th Congress and also elected to 89th Congress.

SIXTH DISTRICT.—COUNTIES: Darlington, Dillon, Florence, Georgetown, Horry, Lee, Marion, Marlboro, and Williamsburg (9 counties). Population (1960), 394,302.

JOHN L. McMILLAN, Democrat, of Florence, S.C., son of the late M. L. and Mary Alice Keith McMillan, Mullins, S.C.; educated Mullins High School, University of North Carolina, and South Carolina University Law School; selected on All-State College Football Team for 4 years, All-Southern for 1 year, and a member of the All Time Star Football team of South Carolina; member of Mullins Baptist Church, Masons, 40 and 8, Fred Sexton American Legion Post, Florence, S.C.; selected by Speaker of the House to represent Congress of the United States at Interparliamentary Union in London in 1960 and also to represent Congress at the Interparliamentary Union in Tokyo, Japan, in 1961; served as chairman, House District Committee, during the 79th Congress and again selected as its chairman for the 81st, 82d, 84th, 85th, 86th, 87th, 88th, and 89th Congresses; ranks number three on the 37 member House Agriculture Committee after the chairman and vice chairman; also chairman of Forestry Subcommittee and vice chairman of the Tobacco Subcommittee; elected to Congress in 1938 over five opponents, and reelected over one opponent in 1940 by a majority of 18,000 votes; reelected in 1942 over two opponents by a majority of 17,000 votes; reelected in 1944 without opposition; reelected in 1946 over two opponents with a majority of 20,000 votes; reelected without opposition in 1948, 1950, 1952, 1954, 1956, 1958, 1960, and 1962; defeated opponent by vote of 48,000 to 10,500; reelected 1964 by a vote of approximately 50,000 to 25,000 for Republican opponent.

SOUTH DAKOTA

(Population (1960), 680,514)

SENATORS

KARL E. MUNDT, Republican, of Madison, S. Dak.; born in Humboldt, S. Dak., June 3, 1900, the only son of F. J. and Rose E. Mundt, pioneer hardware merchants of that community; educated in the public schools of Humboldt, Pierre, and Madison, in South Dakota; A. B. from Carleton College, Northfield, Minn., 1923; A. M. from Columbia University, New York City, 1927; LL. D. (honorary degree) Rider College, Trenton, N. J., 1952; successively a school teacher and school superintendent in Bryant, S. Dak.; college speech and social science teacher in Eastern State Normal School, Madison, S. Dak.; farm operator and real estate and insurance business; appointed to South Dakota Game and Fish Commission (bipartisan) in 1931 for a 6-year term; one-time national vice president of Izaak Walton League; member of Delta Sigma Rho, Pi Kappa Delta, and Tau Kappa Alpha (honorary societies); cofounder and holder of membership certificate No. 1, of National Forensic League, of which he is now national president; editor of the Rostrum; associate editor, the Speaker; former editorial writer, Outdoor America; author of articles in Successful Farming, Collier's, U. S. News & World Report, The Christian Advocate, The Country Gentleman, Liberty magazine, Tomorrow, The Annals of the American Academy of Political and Social Science, Nation's Schools, Fairplay (London), and others; past governor, Minnesota-Dakotas District of Kiwanis International; member National Press Club and the University Club, Washington, D. C.; married in 1924 to Mary Moses of Northfield, Minn.; elected to the 76th Congress; reelected to the 77th, 78th, 79th, and 80th Congresses; elected to the United States Senate in 1948 for the term commencing January 3, 1949; reelected in 1954 and again in 1960 for the term ending January 3, 1967.

GEORGE McGOVERN, Democrat, of Mitchell, S. Dak.; born July 19, 1922, Avon, S. Dak.; B.A., Dakota Wesleyan University; Ph. D., Northwestern University; bomber pilot, World War II, Distinguished Flying Cross; professor of history and government, Dakota Wesleyan University; member, U.S. House of Representatives, 1957–61; special assistant to the President and Director of Food for Peace, 1961–62; married to the former Eleanor Stegeberg; five children; elected United States Senator November 6, 1962, for the term expiring January 3, 1969.

REPRESENTATIVES

FIRST DISTRICT.—COUNTIES: Aurora, Beadle, Bon Homme, Brookings, Brown, Brule, Buffalo, Campbell, Charles Mix, Clark, Clay, Codington, Davison, Day, Deuel, Douglas, Edmunds, Faulk, Grant, Hamlin, Hand, Hanson, Hughes, Hutchinson, Hyde, Jerauld, Kingsbury, Lake, Lincoln, McCook, McPherson, Marshall, Miner, Minnehaha, Moody, Potter, Roberts, Sanborn, Spink, Sully, Turner, Union, Walworth, and Yankton (44 counties). Population (1960), 497,669.

BENJAMIN REIFEL, Republican, of Aberdeen, S. Dak.; born in log cabin September 19, 1906, in Parmelee, S. Dak., to Sioux Indian mother and German-American father; graduated from South Dakota State University, B.S. degree in 1932, and Harvard University, master in public administration in 1950 and doctor of public administration in 1952; married Alice Johnson of Erwin, S. Dak., December 26, 1933; one daughter, Loyce (Mrs. Emery G. Anderson); Administrator in Bureau of Indian Affairs, U.S. Department of the Interior; U.S. Army officer, 1942–45; named Outstanding American Indian in 1956; Indian Council Fire Award, 1960; Boy Scout Silver Antelope Award for leadership, 1960; member, Committee of Seven, Episcopal Church in South Dakota; elected to the 87th Congress; reelected to the 88th and 89th Congresses.

SECOND DISTRICT.—COUNTIES: Bennett, Butte, Corson, Custer, Dewey, Fall River, Gregory, Haakon, Harding, Jackson, Jones, Lawrence, Lyman, Meade, Mellette, Pennington, Perkins, Shannon, Stanley, Todd, Tripp, Washabaugh, and Ziebach (23 counties). Population (1960), 182,845.

E. Y. BERRY, Republican, of McLaughlin, S. Dak.; born at Larchwood, Iowa, October 6, 1902; practicing lawyer, newspaper editor and publisher; attended Morningside College, Sioux City, Iowa, 2 years; graduated LL. B. University of South Dakota Law School, 1927; married Rose Hartinger in 1928; children, Robert E. Berry and Nila Lee Berry McCracken; served as States attorney and county judge Corson County; member State senate 1939 and 1941 legislative sessions; member Missouri River States Committee, 1940–43; editor S. Dak. Bar Association Journal, 1938–50; president of S. Dak. Press Association 1944–45: member, State Board of Regents of Education, 1946–50; elected to 82d Congress November 7, 1950; reelected to 83d, 84th, 85th, 86th, 87th, 88th, and 89th Congresses; member Lambda Chi Alpha, Delta Theta Phi, and Sigma Delta Chi fraternities; Mason, Commandery, Consistory, and Shrine; member, Committee on Interior and Insular Affairs and Committee on Foreign Affairs.

TENNESSEE

(Population (1960), 3,567,089)

SENATORS

ALBERT GORE, Democrat, Carthage, Tenn.; born December 26, 1907; B. S., LL. B.; married; one daughter, one son; elected to the 76th through 82d Congresses; elected to the Senate in 1952, 1958, and 1964.

ROSS BASS, Democrat, of Pulaski, Tenn.; son of Mrs. Ethel Shook Bass and the late Rev. W. A. Bass; born March 17, 1918, in Giles County, Tennessee; veteran of World War II; served as captain, Air Force, bombardier, European Theater of Operations; married former Miss Avanell Keith, Greenville, S.C.; resigned after 6½ years of service as postmaster, Pulaski, Tenn., to make race for Congress; elected to the 84th Congress November 2, 1954; reelected to the 85th, 86th, 87th, and 88th Congresses; elected to House Committee on Ways and Means, First Session, 88th Congress; elected to the United States Senate November 3, 1964, to fill the vacancy caused by the death of Estes Kefauver in the term expiring January 3, 1967; home address: East Jefferson Street, Pulaski, Tenn.

REPRESENTATIVES

FIRST DISTRICT.—COUNTIES: Carter, Claiborne, Cocke, Grainger, Greene, Hamblen, Hancock, Hawkins, Jefferson, Johnson, Sevier, Sullivan, Unicoi, and Washington (14 counties). Population (1960), 460,583.

JAMES H. (JIMMY) QUILLEN, Republican, of Kingsport, Tenn.; born near Gate City, Scott County, Va., January 11, 1916, son of Mrs. Hannah Chapman Quillen and the late John A. Quillen; moved to Kingsport at an early age; graduated from Dobyns-Bennett High School, Kingsport; honorary doctor of laws degree from Steed College of Technology, Johnson City; served in U.S. Navy in World War II; former newspaper publisher in Kingsport and Johnson City, Tenn.; married Cecile Cox of Kingsport in 1952; former president of real estate, mortgage loans and insurance businesses in Kingsport and Johnson City; Republican member of the Tennessee House of Representatives in 1955 and for three succeeding terms—1957, 1959, and 1961; minority floor leader 1959 Tennessee House of Representatives; nominated in 1957 and 1961 as Republican speaker of the Tennessee House of Representatives; member of Tennessee Legislative Council 1957, 1959, and 1961; delegate at large to the Republican National Convention in San Francisco in 1956; Junior Chamber of Commerce Young Man of the Year, Johnson City, Tenn., for 1942; director of the Kingsport National Bank, past president of Kingsport Lions Club; member of the Methodist Church, the American Legion, the Veterans of Foreign Wars, Lions, Elks, Moose, Commercial Travelers, Kingsport, and Johnson City Chamber of Commerce, Ridgefields Country Club; elected to the 88th Congress November 6, 1962; reelected to the 89th Congress.

SECOND DISTRICT.—COUNTIES: Anderson, Blount, Campbell, Knox, Loudon, Morgan, Roane, Scott, and Union (9 counties). Population (1960), 497,121.

JOHN JAMES DUNCAN, Republican, of Knoxville, Tenn.; born in Scott County, Tenn., March 24, 1919; served in the U.S. Army from May 1942 to December 1945; assistant attorney general 1947 to 1956; director of law, city of Knoxville, 1956 to 1959, elected mayor in 1959 and served in that capacity until elected to Congress; State commander of the American Legion in 1954; member of: Knoxville Chamber of Commerce; Knoxville Tourist Bureau; American, Tennessee, and Knoxville bar associations; VFW; Board of the Eastminster Presbyterian Church; married; four children; elected to the 89th Congress November 3, 1964.

THIRD DISTRICT.—Counties: Bledsoe, Bradley, Grundy, Hamilton, McMinn, Marion, Meigs, Monroe, Polk, Rhea, and Sequatchie (11 counties). Population (1960), 412,664.

WILLIAM EMERSON BROCK 3D, Republican, of Chattanooga, Tenn.; born in Chattanooga, November 23, 1930, son of William E., Jr., and Myra Kruesi Brock; attended Lookout Mountain (Tenn.) grade school and the McCallie School in Chattanooga; graduated from Washington and Lee University, Lexington, Va., in June 1953, B.S. in commerce, majoring in business administration; served in the U.S. Navy 1953–56, lieutenant (jg); joined USNR (ready) in 1956, present rank, lieutenant; was associated with Brock Candy Co., Chattanooga, Tenn., serving as vice president (marketing); married the former Laura Handly January 11, 1957; has two sons and one daughter—William E. Brock IV, born October 25, 1957; Oscar Handy Brock, born December 22, 1962; Laura Hutcheson Brock, born April 1, 1964; member of the Presbyterian Church and was a Sunday school teacher; member of many civic, business and political organizations, including Chattanooga Chamber of Commerce, Jaycees, Area Literacy Movement, 365 Club for Handicapped, S.A.E. fraternity; elected Tennessee Young Republican National Committeeman, April 1961; elected chairman, National Teen Committee, June 1961; elected to the 88th Congress November 6, 1962; reelected to the 89th Congress; elected Outstanding Young Republican for 1963; serves on Banking and Currency Committee, Congressional Campaign Committee, Conference Study Committee.

FOURTH DISTRICT.—Counties: Bedford, Cannon, Clay, Coffee, Cumberland, De Kalb, Fentress, Franklin, Jackson, Lincoln, Macon, Marshall, Moore, Overton, Pickett, Putnam, Rutherford, Smith, Trousdale, Van Buren, Warren, White, and Wilson (23 counties). Population (1960), 389,563.

JOE L. EVINS, Democrat, Smithville, Tenn.; born De Kalb County, Tenn., October 24, 1910, the son of James Edgar Evins and Myrtie Goodson Evins; attended public schools of De Kalb County; Vanderbilt University, A. B., 1933; Cumberland University, LL. B., 1934 and LL. D. (honorary) 1958; postgraduate work in law, George Washington University Law 1938–40; lawyer by profession; member legal staff and assistant secretary, Federal Trade Commission 1935–41; served in Army 4 years, 1942–46; 2 years overseas, European Theater of Operations; discharged as major; past chairman, De Kalb County Democratic Executive Committee; received Democratic nomination as State senator, Twelfth Senatorial District (Cannon, De Kalb, and Rutherford Counties) while serving in army overseas, but declined to accept the nomination during continuance of the war; married the former Ann Smartt, daughter of Judge and Mrs. R. W. Smartt, McMinnville, Tenn.; three daughters: Joanna (Mrs. Malcolm R. Carnahan); Jane, student, Vanderbilt University, Nashville; and Mary, student, Mount Vernon Seminary, Washington, D.C.; chairman of board, First National Bank, Smithville, Tenn., and other business interests; member of Tennessee and American Bar Associations, American Legion, Veterans of Foreign Wars, and various veterans, civic and service clubs, Cross of Military Service and Tennessee Colonel, Church of Christ, Phi Kappa Sigma and Phi Delta Phi fraternities; elected to the 80th Congress November 5, 1946; reelected to the 81st, 82d, 83d, 84th, 85th, 86th, 87th, 88th, and 89th Congresses; delegate to Democratic National Conventions 1948, 1952, 1956, 1960, and 1964; Tennessee State Campaign Director for Johnson-Humphrey, 1964; chairman Speaker's Committee on Personnel; and chairman House Select Committee on Small Business; member of subcommittees on Independent Offices and Public Works Appropriations; Committee on Appropriations.

FIFTH DISTRICT.—Davidson County. Population (1960), 399,743.

RICHARD HARMON FULTON, Democrat, of Nashville, Tenn.; born in Nashville, January 27, 1927, son of Lyle Houston and Labina Plummer Fulton; graduated from Nashville public schools and attended University of Tennessee at Knoxville; served in U.S. Navy, 1945–46; served as State senator in Tennessee General Assembly, representing Davidson County, 1959; real estate broker; 32d degree Mason, Shriner, and a Methodist; married to former Jewel Simpson; father of five children—Richard, Michael, Barry, Donna, and Linda; elected to the 88th Congress November 6, 1962; reelected to the 89th Congress.

SIXTH DISTRICT.—Counties: Cheatham, Dickson, Giles, Hickman, Houston, Humphreys, Lawrence, Lewis, Maury, Montgomery, Perry, Robertson, Stewart, Sumner, Wayne, and Williamson (16 counties). Population (1960), 324,357.

WILLIAM ROBERT ANDERSON, Democrat, of Waverly, Tenn.; born in Bakerville, June 17, 1921, son of David H. and Mary McKelvey Anderson; attended public schools in Waynesboro, Tenn., and Columbia Military Academy, Columbia, Tenn.; graduated from U.S. Naval Academy, 1942; participated in 11 submarine combat patrols in the Pacific; received Bronze Star and other combat awards; commanding officer of the *Nautilus*, first atomic submarine, 1957–59; made first transpolar voyage under ice; 1959–62 assistant to Vice Admiral H. G. Rickover and Secretaries of the Navy William B. Franke, John Connally, and Fred Korth; 1962, retired from active Navy duty; 1963, consultant to President Kennedy for the National Service Corps; author of two books; member of American Legion, VFW, and Explorers Club; sponsor of Society for Crippled Children and Adults; married to former Yvonne (Bonny) Etzel; two children, Michael and William R., Jr.; elected to 89th Congress November 3, 1964.

SEVENTH DISTRICT.—Counties: Benton, Carroll, Chester, Decatur, Fayette, Hardeman, Hardin, Henderson, Henry, McNairy, and Madison (11 counties). Population (1960), 232,652.

TOM MURRAY, Democrat, of Jackson, Tenn., was born in Jackson, Tenn., on August 1, 1894; graduated from Jackson High School, Union University (B. A. degree) and Cumberland University (LL. B. degree); taught in high school 2 years; served in the United States Army in World War I and was a member of the American Expeditionary Forces in France; after discharge from the Army in 1919, began the practice of law in Jackson, Tenn.; elected district attorney general for the Twelfth Judicial Circuit of Tennessee in 1922 and served until September 1933; resigned as district attorney to become associated with the office of the Solicitor of the Post Office Department in Washington; served with the Post Office Department until May 31, 1942; chairman of Democratic Executive Committee of Madison County, Tenn., from 1924 to 1933; former member of State Democratic Executive Committee of Tennessee; delegate to Democratic National Conventions in 1928, 1932, and 1936; served as commander of the John A. Deaver Post of the American Legion at Jackson and as vice commander of the Legion for the State of Tennessee; member of the Veterans of Foreign Wars and Sigma Alpha Epsilon Fraternity; single; elected to the 78th Congress on November 3, 1942; reelected to 79th, 80th, 81st, 82d, 83d, 84th, 85th, 86th, 87th, 88th, and 89th Congresses.

EIGHTH DISTRICT.—Counties: Crockett, Dyer, Gibson, Haywood, Lake, Lauderdale, Obion, Tipton, and Weakley (9 counties). Population (1960), 223,387.

ROBERT A. EVERETT, Democrat, of Union City, Tenn.; born in Obion County, Tenn., February 24, 1915, son of Mrs. Lelia Ashton Everett and the late Charlie Everett; attended the public schools of Obion County and graduated from Union City High School in 1932; graduated Murray State College, Murray, Ky., in 1936, and elected member Obion County Court the same year; elected circuit court clerk of Obion County in 1938; served in Army for 31 months, and upon release from service served as administrative assistant to Senator Tom Stewart in Washington until January 1949; administrative assistant to Governor Gordon Browning 1950–52; executive secretary of Tennessee County Services Association from January 1, 1954, to February 1, 1958; member of American Legion and Farm Bureau; member of Cumberland Presbyterian Church; elected to the 85th Congress February 1, 1958, to fill the unexpired term of the late Jere Cooper; reelected to the 86th, 87th, 88th, and 89th Congresses.

NINTH DISTRICT.—Shelby County. Population (1960), 627,019.

GEORGE WILLIAM GRIDER, Democrat, of Memphis, Tenn.; born in Memphis, October 1, 1912, son of John McGavock and Marguerite Samuels Grider; attended the public schools of Memphis, Memphis University School and Southwestern at Memphis; graduated from the United States Naval Academy (B.S.) in 1936 and the University of Virginia (LL.B.) in 1950; served in the United States Navy from 1936 to 1947; retired as a captain because of physical disability; commanded the submarines *Flasher* and *Cubera*; holds Navy Cross and other decorations for World War II service; coauthor, with Lydel Sims, of the book, "War Fish"; practiced law in Memphis from 1950 to 1964; appointed to City Planning Commission 1956–57; elected Shelby County Quarterly Court in 1959, resigned in 1964; married to the former Ann Curlin of Memphis in 1936; they have four children: Lt. (j.g.) George W. Grider, Jr., USN, Mrs. Gail Ann Grider Gurley, Sally Elizabeth Grider, and Wilson Northcross Grider; member of Methodist Church, Bar Association, Engineers Club, Navy League, American Legion, President's Council of Southwestern at Memphis, and Memphis Academy of Arts; helped found and served as officer or director of Shelby United Neighbors, Memphis Committee on Human Relations, Memphis Chapter of Tennessee Council of Human Relations, and served on local and national boards of USO; elected to the 89th Congress November 3, 1964.

TEXAS

(Population (1960), 9,579,677)

SENATORS

RALPH WEBSTER YARBOROUGH, Democrat, of Austin, Tex.; born at Chandler, Henderson County, Tex., June 8, 1903, seventh of 11 children of Charles Richard and Nannie Jane (Spear) Yarborough; graduated from Chandler public schools and Tyler, Tex., High School; attended Sam Houston State Teachers College, Huntsville, Tex., one term, and the U.S. Military Academy at West Point, N.Y., 1 year; taught 3 years in one- and two-teacher schools at Delta and Martin Springs, Henderson County, Tex.; served 3 years as enlisted man in 36th Division, Texas National Guard; worked passage to Europe, spent 1 year working and studying in Europe, most of this time in Germany (assistant secretary, American Chamber of Commerce, Berlin); worked in wheat fields of Oklahoma and in the boom oil field of Borger, Tex.; received LL.B. from the University of Texas Law School, 1927, with highest honors; practiced law at El Paso, Tex., 3 years; served as assistant attorney general of Texas, 1931–34; wrote Texas' first underground water conservation law, and saved oil and gas bonus and royalty interest for State Permanent School Fund on 3,901,000 acres of land in case of Magnolia Petroleum Company against Walker; on original board of directors of the Lower Colorado River Authority, 1935–36; lectured on land law at University of Texas Law School, 1935; district judge of the 53d Judicial District, Austin, 1936–41, and for three years was presiding judge, Third Administrative Judicial District (33 central Texas counties); in Army in World War II with the 97th Infantry Division in Europe in combat and with occupation forces in Japan; discharged a lieutenant colonel in 1946; member, 1947–51, Texas Board of Law Examiners; member (and a former president), Travis County Bar Association; member, El Paso Bar Association; member (and a former director), State Bar of Texas; member, American Bar Association, American Law Institute, American Judicature Society, National Legal Aid Association, American Political Science Association, American Legion, Veterans of Foreign Wars, Phi Delta Phi, Acacia, Order of the Coif, Loyal Order of Moose, the First Baptist Church of Austin, and is a Shriner and Mason; married Opal Warren of Pine Bluff, Ark., June 30, 1928; son, Richard, born October 20, 1931, married Ann McJimsey of Arlington, Va.; unsuccessful candidate Democratic nomination for Governor of Texas 1952, 1954, 1956; elected United States Senator in a special election held on April 2, 1957, to fill the vacancy caused by the resignation of Price Daniel for the term ending January 3, 1959; reelected November 4, 1958, and November 3, 1964; delegate, 51st Interparliamentary Union Conference at Brasilia, Brazil, 1962; delegate, Democratic National Convention, Atlantic City, 1964.

JOHN GOODWIN TOWER, Republican, of Wichita Falls, Tex.; born in Houston, Tex., September 29, 1925, son of the Reverend and Mrs. Joe Z Tower; veteran of World War II, serving three years in the Navy aboard an amphibious gunboat in the Western Pacific; B.A. degree in political science from Southwestern University, Georgetown, Tex., in 1948 and M.A. degree from Southern Methodist University in 1953; general full course, London School of Economics and Political Science in 1952; member of the faculty of Midwestern University, Wichita Falls, Tex., 1951–60; married the former Lou Bullington of Wichita Falls; three daughters—Penelope, 10, Marian, 9, Jeanne, 8; member of the Southwestern Social Science Association, Texas Historical Society, American Association of University Professors, American Political Science Association, Hansard Society (British), International Political Science Association, and Kappa Sigma Fraternity; in Wichita Falls is a member of the board of stewards of the First Methodist Church, the Chamber of Commerce, the University Kiwanis Club, the board of directors of the Wichita Falls Symphony Orchestra, and is founder and member of the board of the Wichita Falls Civic Playhouse; at age 35 was the youngest Senator in the 87th Congress, the first Republican to be elected to the Senate from Texas since Reconstruction, and the only Republican Senator ever elected by popular vote from any of the former Confederate States; led a field of 71 candidates in the special election held April 4, 1961, and elected in a runoff election on May 27; was sworn in June 15 to fill the vacancy caused by the resignation of Senator Lyndon B. Johnson, for the term ending January 3, 1967; is a member of the Banking and Currency, Labor and Public Welfare, Joint Committee on Defense Production, and the Civil War Centennial Commission.

REPRESENTATIVES

AT LARGE.—Population (1960), 9,579,677.

JOE RICHARD POOL, Democrat, of Dallas, Tex.; born in Tarrant County, Tex., February 18, 1911, son of William Wesley Pool and Bonnie Jean Pool; attended Texas University; graduated from Southern Methodist University, LL. B. degree in 1937; was admitted same year to the Texas bar; served with U.S. Army as special investigator, Air Corps Intelligence, 1943–45; elected to Texas House of Representatives 1952; served three terms; chairman of the House Investigating Committee; chairman of Motor Traffic Committee; also served on Appropriations, Revenue and Taxation, and State Affairs Committee; married in 1940 to Elizabeth Chambless; have four sons—Richard, a student at Southern Methodist University, 22 years old; Wesley, 14 years old; John, 12 years old; Joe, Jr., 9 years old; member of Texas Bar Association and Dallas Bar Association; life member of Dallas Chamber of Commerce; member of the Interstate Cooperation Commission 1952–56; vice chairman of Insurance Committee while in legislature, 1954–56; elected to the 88th Congress as Congressman at Large November 6, 1962; reelected to the 89th Congress.

FIRST DISTRICT.—COUNTIES: Bowie, Cass, Delta, Franklin, Harrison, Hopkins, Lamar, Marion, Morris, Red River, and Titus (11 counties). Population (1960), 245,942.

WRIGHT PATMAN, Democrat, of Texarkana, Tex.; born at Patman's Switch near Hughes Springs, Cass County, Tex., August 6, 1893; finished high school at Hughes Springs, 1912; received LL. B. degree, Cumberland University, 1916; United States Army, 1917–19, enlisted man and first lieutenant—machine gun officer; married Miss Merle Connor, of Winnsboro, Tex., February 14, 1919 (they have three sons, all having served in World War II); member of Texas Legislature for 4 years; district attorney, fifth judicial district of Texas, 5 years; elected in 1928 to the 71st Congress and reelected to each succeeding Congress; chairman of the Banking and Currency Committee of the House of Representatives, chairman of the Joint House and Senate Defense Production Committee, member of the House Select Committee on Small Business, and member of the House and Senate Joint Economic Committee; he and all members of his family affiliated with the First Baptist Church of Texarkana, Tex.; member of Masons, Elks, Eagles, Shrine, American Legion, Disabled American Veterans; associate member of National Press Club; member of State Bar Association and admitted to practice before Supreme Court of the United States.

SECOND DISTRICT.—COUNTIES: Hardin, Jasper, Jefferson, Liberty, Newton, Orange, Sabine, San Augustine, and Tyler (9 counties). Population (1960), 420,402.

JACK BROOKS, Democrat, of Beaumont, Tex.; born December 18, 1922, in Crowley, La.; attended Beaumont public schools; Lamar Junior College; University of Texas, B.J. 1943, LL.B. 1949; U.S. Marine Corps, World War II; member Texas Legislature, 1946–50; elected to 83d Congress November 4, 1952; reelected to succeeding Congresses; married Charlotte Collins December 15, 1960.

THIRD DISTRICT.—COUNTIES: Camp, Gregg, Panola, Rusk, Shelby, Smith, Upshur, Van Zandt, and Wood (9 counties). Population (1960), 293,942.

LINDLEY BECKWORTH, Democrat, of Gladewater, Tex., route 2; married Eloise Carter; 5 children—Gary, Carter, Mary, Linda, and John Barney; elected to 76th, 77th, 78th, 79th, 80th, 81st, 82d, 85th, 86th, 87th, 88th, and 89th Congresses.

FOURTH DISTRICT.—COUNTIES: Collin, Fannin, Grayson, Hunt, Kaufman, Rains, and Rockwall (7 counties). Population (1960), 216,371.

RAY ROBERTS, Democrat, of McKinney, Collin County, Tex.; was born in that county March 28, 1913, son of Roy C. Roberts and Margaret Emma Roberts; graduated from McKinney High School and attended Texas A. & M.,

North Texas State, and Texas University; served on staff of Speaker Sam Rayburn; married Elizabeth Bush; one daughter, Mrs. Tom Murray III; served in the Navy during World War II and holds rank of Captain in the Naval Reserve; member of Texas State Senate 1955–1962; elected to the 87th Congress in special election January 30 1962, to fill the unexpired term of Speaker Sam Rayburn; reelected to the 88th and 89th Congresses.

FIFTH DISTRICT.—DALLAS COUNTY. Population (1960), 951,527.

EARLE CABELL, Democrat, of Dallas, Tex.; born on a farm south of the Trinity River in Dallas County, October 27, 1906; graduated from North Dallas High School in 1925; attended Texas A. & M. and Southern Methodist University; with two brothers organized in 1932 Cabell's, Inc. (dairies and drive-in food stores) and served as secretary-treasurer, executive vice president, president, and chairman of the board; married the former Elizabeth Holder of Little Rock, Ark., in 1932; two children, Elizabeth Lee (Mrs. William Pulley) and Earle, Jr.; member and officer of various professional, civic, and philanthropic organizations; chairman of the board of Patio Party Products, Inc., Marshall, Tex., and of Trolex Corp., Dallas, Tex.; director and member of executive committee of Grand Avenue Bank & Trust Co., Dallas, Tex.; member of Dallas Country Club, Dallas Athletic Club, McKinney Club Lake, and City Club; mayor of Dallas from May 1, 1961, until his resignation February 3, 1964, to be candidate for Congress; elected to the 89th Congress November 3, 1964.

SIXTH DISTRICT.—COUNTIES: Brazos, Ellis, Freestone, Hill, Hood, Johnson, Leon, Limestone, Navarro, Robertson, and Somervell (11 counties). Population (1960), 248,149.

OLIN E. TEAGUE, Democrat, of College Station, Tex.; attended Texas Agriculture and Mechanical College 1928–32; worked way through college while employed with Post Office, Animal Husbandry Department, and the railroad; married former Freddie Dunman of Fort Worth, Tex.; three children—James M., John O., and Jill Virginia; employed in the United States Post Office at A. & M. College, College Station, Tex., from college days until October 1940, when he left his position as South Station superintendent to volunteer for Army service; previously served 3 years as enlisted man in National Guard; commissioned second lieutenant in Officers Reserve Corps on finishing Texas A. & M.; commanded First Battalion, Three Hundred and Fourteenth Infantry, Seventy-ninth Division; was in combat 6 months, wounded a number of times, decorated eleven times; spent 2 years in Army Hospital due to combat incurred wounds; discharged as colonel, Infantry, in September 1946 to take seat in Congress; awarded Silver Star with two clusters, Bronze Star with two clusters, Purple Heart with two clusters, Combat Infantryman's Badge, Army Commendation Ribbon, French Croix de Guerre with Palm; elected to the Seventy-ninth Congress on August 22, 1946; reelected to succeeding Congresses; chairman of Veterans' Affairs Committee in the 84th Congress and has held position in succeeding Congresses (this committee supervises the operation of the Veterans' Program, which is the third costliest expenditure of the Federal Budget); appointed as a member of the Board of Visitors to West Point in 1955; appointed to newly created Science and Astronautics Committee in 86th Congress; was member of the District of Columbia Committee until 86th Congress when he resigned to accept position on Science and Astronautics Committee; chairman of the Select Committee in the 82d Congress, which investigated the shortcomings of the World War II, G. I. Bill (it was through these investigations that he was able to author and sponsor the Korean War Veterans Bill that was made Public Law 550).

SEVENTH DISTRICT.—COUNTIES: Anderson, Angelina, Cherokee, Grimes, Henderson, Houston, Madison, Montgomery, Nacogdoches, Polk, San Jacinto, Trinity, and Walker (13 counties). Population (1960), 265,629.

JOHN DOWDY, Democrat, of Athens, Henderson County, Tex., born February 11, 1912; married Johnnie Deana (J. D.) Riley; one daughter, Carol Sue (Mrs. Forrest Earle Roberts, Jr.); one son, John (Skip), Jr., age 22; licensed to practice law in 1940; elected district attorney, Third Judicial District of Texas, in 1944, serving 1945–52, resigning the office when elected to fill a vacancy in the 82d Congress September 23, 1952; reelected to the 83d, 84th, 85th, 86th, 87th, 88th, and 89th Congresses.

EIGHTH DISTRICT.—HARRIS COUNTY: That part north of a line beginning at the point where U. S. Highway No. 290 intersects the county line between Harris and Waller Counties; thence along U. S. Highway No. 290 to the intersection of said highway with Post Oak Road; thence along said Post Oak Road to Buffalo Bayou; thence along said Bayou to Morgan's Point. Population (1960), 568,193.

ALBERT THOMAS, Democrat, of Houston, Tex.; born in Nacogdoches, Tex., April 12, 1898; degrees, A. B., Rice University and LL. B., University of Texas; lawyer; Methodist; World War I veteran; married; two daughters, Anne, married to Edward A. Lasater, and Lera; elected to 75th and succeeding Congresses; chairman, Independent Offices Appropriations; member, Department of Defense Appropriations; member, Joint Atomic Energy Committee.

NINTH DISTRICT.—COUNTIES: Austin, Brazoria, Calhoun, Chambers, Colorado, Fayette, Fort Bend, Galveston, Goliad, Jackson, Lavaca, Matagorda, Victoria, Waller, and Wharton (15 counties). Population (1960), 498,775.

CLARK WALLACE THOMPSON, Democrat, of Galveston, Tex.; born in La Crosse, Wis., August 6, 1896; moved to Oregon in 1901; attended the University of Oregon; enlisted in the Marine Corps in 1917; commissioned second lieutenant December 1918; moved to Galveston after the war; married Libbie Moody of Galveston; two children, Clark Wallace, Jr., and Libbie Thompson Stansell (deceased); has been in business in Galveston ever since, except while serving as a Member of the Seventy-third Congress in which he filled the unexpired term of the late Clay Stone Briggs and during the Second World War when he was on active duty with the Marine Corps from November 1940 to May 1946; retired as colonel in the Marine Corps Reserve; elected to the 80th Congress, August 23, 1947, to fill the unexpired term of the late J. J. Mansfield; reelected to 81st, 82d, 83d, 84th, 85th, 86th, 87th, 88th, and 89th Congresses.

TENTH DISTRICT.—COUNTIES: Bastrop, Blanco, Burleson, Burnet, Caldwell, Hays, Lee, Travis, Washington, and Williamson (10 counties). Population (1960), 353,454.

J. J. (JAKE) PICKLE, Democrat, of Austin, Tex.; born October 11, 1913, Roscoe, Nolan County, Tex., son of J. B. and Mary Pickle; educated in public schools of Big Spring, Tex.; graduate of the University of Texas, B.A. degree; area director, National Youth Administration, 1938–41, resigning to enter Navy during W.W. II, serving 3½ years in Pacific; after discharge from Navy entered radio business as one of coorganizers of Radio Station KVET, Austin, Tex.; later entered public relations and advertising business; director of Texas State Democratic Executive Committee 1957–60; appointed member Texas Employment Commission in 1961, resigning September 27, 1963, to be candidate for the Congress; elected in special election December 17, 1963, to the 88th Congress; reelected to the 89th Congress; married, 3 children, Peggy Pickle, Dick McCarroll, Graham McCarroll.

ELEVENTH DISTRICT.—COUNTIES: Bell, Bosque, Coryell, Falls, McLennan, and Milam (6 counties). Population (1960), 322,484.

WILLIAM ROBERT (BOB) POAGE, Democrat, of Waco, McLennan County, Tex., was born in that city on December 28, 1899, son of William A. and Helen Conger Poage; spent his childhood and received his first education in Throckmorton County, Tex.; attended Baylor University, the University of Colorado, and the University of Texas, receiving his A. B. and LL. B. degrees from Baylor; was admitted to the bar in 1924, and practiced in Waco until elected to Congress; member of the Texas House of Representatives, 1925–29, and of the Texas State Senate, 1931–37; member of the American Legion; married Frances L. Cotton, February 14, 1938; was elected to the 75th Congress in 1936 and reelected to each succeeding Congress; since 1947 has served as a member of the American delegation to the Interparliamentary Union; vice chairman, Committee on Agriculture.

TWELFTH DISTRICT.—TARRANT COUNTY. Population (1960), 538,495.

JAMES C. WRIGHT, JR., Democrat, of Fort Worth, Tex.; born December 22, 1922, in Fort Worth, Tex., son of James C. and Marie Lyster Wright; educated in public schools of Fort Worth and Dallas, Weatherford College, and University of Texas; enlisted as a private in the United States Army in December 1941, flew combat missions in B-24s in South Pacific, awarded D. F. C.; married Mary

Ethelyn Lemons of Dallas; four children—Jimmy, age 19; Virginia Sue, age 15; Patricia Kay, age 13; and Alicia Marie, 5; partner in trade extension and advertising firm; served in Texas Legislature and two terms as mayor of Weatherford; served during 1953 as president of League of Texas Municipalities; lay worker in Presbyterian Church; elected to the 84th Congress November 2, 1954; reelected to the 85th, 86th, 87th, 88th, and 89th Congresses.

THIRTEENTH DISTRICT.—Counties: Archer, Baylor, Clay, Cooke, Denton, Foard, Hardeman, Haskell, Jack, Kent, King, Knox, Montague, Stonewall, Throckmorton, Wichita, Wilbarger, Wise, and Young (19 counties). Population (1960), 326,781.

GRAHAM PURCELL, Democrat, of Wichita Falls, Tex.; son of Graham B. Purcell and Della Key Purcell; born in Archer City, Tex., on May 5, 1919; attended public schools in Archer City; graduated Texas A. & M. College with a B.S. degree in agriculture in 1946; received LL.B. degree from Baylor University Law School in 1949; entered United States Army in 1941; served in Africa and Italy; remained in the Active Reserves, now lieutenant colonel, Armor, U.S.A.R.; married Betty Smith of Tucson, Ariz., in 1943; three sons—Blaine, Kirk, and Blake; one daughter—Jannie; practicing attorney in Big Spring, Tex., and Wichita Falls, Tex., from 1949 until 1955; appointed judge of the 89th Judicial District of Texas in 1955; reelected twice to that position in Wichita County; also served as juvenile court judge of Wichita County; very active in work with juveniles, both as judge and civic worker; district chairman, Boy Scouts of America; honored twice as "Outstanding Citizen of Wichita Falls"; deacon in Fain Memorial Presbyterian Church of Wichita Falls; elected to 87th Congress in special election, January 27, 1962, from the 13th Congressional District of Texas; reelected to the 88th and 89th Congresses; appointed to National Commission on Food Marketing by Speaker of the House on July 20, 1964.

FOURTEENTH DISTRICT.—Counties: Aransas, Atascosa, Bee, Brooks, Comal, De Witt, Duval, Gonzales, Guadalupe, Jim Wells, Karnes, Kenedy, Kleberg, Live Oak, McMullen, Nueces, Refugio, San Patricio, and Wilson (19 counties). Population (1960), 539,262.

JOHN YOUNG, Democrat, of Corpus Christi, Tex.; born November 10, 1916; son of Phillip M. and Catherine Gaffney Young; family has been residents of South Texas since 1827; bachelor of arts, 1937, doctor of laws, 1961, St. Edward's University, Austin, Tex., the University of Texas, 1937–40; admitted to State Bar of Texas, 1940; married Jane Gallier of Houston, Tex.; five children—Catherine Gaffney, born May 28, 1951, Nancy Rae, born October 7, 1954, John, Jr., born February 23, 1957, Robert Harold, born March 15, 1959, and Mary Patricia, born August 22, 1963; former assistant district attorney, county attorney, and county judge, Nueces County, Tex.; served with U.S. Navy, World War II; elected to the 85th Congress and succeeding Congresses.

FIFTEENTH DISTRICT.—Counties: Cameron, Dimmit, Frio, Hidalgo, Jim Hogg, La Salle, Maverick, Medina, Starr, Webb, Willacy, Zapata, and Zavala (13 counties). Population (1960), 515,716.

ELIGIO DE LA GARZA, Democrat, of Mission, Tex.; born in Mercedes, Tex., September 22, 1927; educated at Mission High School, Edinburg (Tex.) Jr. College, and St. Mary's University, San Antonio, Tex.; LL.B., 1952, St. Mary's Law School; during World War II enlisted in the U.S. Navy, age 17; served in the U.S. Army, 37th Division Artillery, as an officer 1950 to 1952; graduated as second lieutenant St. Mary's ROTC and also graduated Artillery School, Ft. Sill, Okla.; attorney; member of firm of Rankin, Kern, Martinez & De La Garza in McAllen, Tex.; married the former Lucille Alamia of Edinburg, Tex.; three children: Jorge, Michael, and Angela; Catholic; served in the State house of representatives for 12 years; member of Mission, McAllen, and Rio Grande Valley chambers of commerce; American Legion, Catholic War Veterans (past national judge advocate), Kiwanis, International Good Neighbor Council, Texas Legislative Council, Council of State Governments (legislative branch), Border Development Committee, Delta Theta Phi, and the League of United Latin American Citizens; elected to the 89th Congress November 3, 1964.

SIXTEENTH DISTRICT.—Counties: Brewster, Crane, Crockett, Culberson, Ector, El Paso, Glasscock, Hudspeth, Jeff Davis, Loving, Midland, Pecos, Presidio, Reagan, Reeves, Terrell, Upton, Ward, and Winkler (19 counties). Population (1960), 573,438.

RICHARD CRAWFORD WHITE, Democrat, of El Paso, Tex.; born in El Paso April 29, 1923; educated in Dudley primary school, El Paso High School,

Citizen's Military Training Camp at San Antonio, Texas Western College, University of Texas (B.A. 1946), and University of Texas Law School (LL.D. 1949); was a member of Phi Alpha Delta and Sigma Alpha Epsilon; during World War II served in the U.S. Marines in the Pacific theater as a Japanese interpreter-rifleman in the campaigns of Bougainville, Guam, and Iwo Jima; awarded the Purple Heart; engaged in the practice of law since 1949; member of the State house of representatives 1955–58; married the former Katherine Huffman of Marshall, Tex.; three sons, Rodrick James, Richard Whitman, and Raymond Edward; member of St. Clements Episcopal Church, El Paso Chamber of Commerce, Sons of the Sun, Del Norte Club, Beloved Vagabonds, Texas University Ex-Students Association, El Paso Tennis Club, and El Paso Museum of Art; Merit Badge Counselor for the Boy Scouts and is associated with the Tri-Hi-Y legislative program; member of El Paso County Bar Association, State Bar of Texas, the American Bar Association, and is licensed to practice before the United States Supreme Court; engaged in many State, county, and community activities including politics, welfare, and historical matters; elected to the 89th Congress November 3, 1964.

SEVENTEENTH DISTRICT.—Counties: Callahan, Comanche, Eastland, Erath, Fisher, Hamilton, Jones, Nolan, Palo Pinto, Parker, Scurry, Shackelford, Stephens, and Taylor (14 counties). Population (1960), 287,889.

OMAR BURLESON, Democrat, of Anson, Tex.; born March 19, 1906, son of J. M. and Betty Burleson; wife, Ruth; lawyer; county attorney and county judge of Jones County; special agent of F.B.I.; 3 years in the United States Navy, World War II; elected to the 80th and succeeding Congresses.

EIGHTEENTH DISTRICT.—Counties: Armstrong, Briscoe, Carson, Castro, Childress, Collingsworth, Cottle, Dallam, Deaf Smith, Donley, Gray, Hall, Hansford, Hartley, Hemphill, Hutchinson, Lipscomb, Motley, Moore, Ochiltree, Oldham, Parmer, Potter, Randall, Roberts, Sherman, Swisher, and Wheeler (28 counties). Population (1960), 363,596.

WALTER E. ROGERS, Democrat, Pampa, Gray County, Tex.; born July 19, 1908, Texarkana, Ark.; education: McKinney, Tex., public schools, Austin College, Sherman, Tex., University of Texas Law School, Austin, Tex.; district attorney thirty-first district of Texas 1943–47; married Catherine R. (Jean) Daly of Pampa, Tex., 1936; six children: John Edward, Walter Edward 2d, Susan Daly, Thomas Kelley, Robert Joseph, and Mary Catherine; member of American Bar Association, State of Texas Bar Association, District of Columbia Bar; member Amarillo Club, Pampa Country Club, Pampa Rotary Club, Sigma Phi Epsilon, Burning Tree; elected to 82d Congress November 7, 1950; reelected to 83d, 84th, 85th, 86th, 87th, 88th, and 89th Congresses; Pampa, Tex., office address, 314 Hughes Building; Washington office address 1330 New House Office Building; Washington residential address, 6219 Kennedy Drive, Kenwood, Chevy Chase, Md.

NINETEENTH DISTRICT.—Counties: Andrews, Bailey, Borden, Cochran, Crosby, Dawson, Dickens, Floyd, Gaines, Garza, Hale, Hockley, Howard, Lamb, Lubbock, Lynn, Martin, Mitchell, Terry and Yoakum (20 counties). Population (1960), 424,774.

GEORGE H. MAHON, Democrat, Lubbock, Tex.; born September 22, 1900, near Haynesville, La., son of J. K. and Lola Brown Mahon; moved to Mitchell County, Tex., 1908; reared on a farm; attended rural school, graduated from Loraine High School; B. A., Simmons University, Abilene, 1924; LL. B., University of Texas, 1925; attended University of Minnesota in 1925; honorary LL.D. 1951 Waynesburg College, Pennsylvania; honorary LL.D. 1960 Wayland Baptist College, Plainview, Tex.; honorary LL.D. 1962 Texas Technological College, Lubbock, Tex.; honorary LL.D. 1964 Hardin-Simmons University, Abilene, Tex.; married Helen Stevenson, of Loraine, Tex., 1923; one daughter— Daphne, born 1927; elected county attorney, Mitchell County, 1926; appointed district attorney, thirty-second judicial district, 1927; elected district attorney 1928, 1930, 1932; received American Political Science Association Congressional Distinguished Service Award in 1963; elected in 1934 to 74th Congress and reelected to each succeeding Congress; became chairman of Appropriations Committee of the House of Representatives in 1964, continuing in that capacity in the 89th Congress.

TWENTIETH DISTRICT.—Bexar County. Population (1960), 687,151.

HENRY B. GONZALEZ, Democrat, of San Antonio, Tex.; born in San Antonio, Tex., May 3, 1916, son of original colonists of the State of Durango in northern Mexico, who fled their country as the result of the revolution and moved to San Antonio, Tex., in 1911; attended the San Antonio public schools, San Antonio College, University of Texas, and St. Marys University School of Law (LL.B.); first elected to public office in 1953; served 2 years on the San Antonio City Council, serving as mayor pro tem part of the second term; served as chief probation officer of Bexar County; worked for bilingual publications; elected to the State senate in 1956 and reelected in 1960; married Bertha Cuellar in 1940 and they have 4 boys and 4 girls; elected to the 87th Congress on November 4, 1961, to fill the unexpired term of Paul J. Kilday; reelected to the 88th and 89th Congress.

TWENTY-FIRST DISTRICT.—Counties: Bandera, Brown, Coke, Coleman, Concho, Edwards, Gillespie, Irion, Kendall, Kerr, Kimble, Kinney, Lampasas, Llano, McCulloch, Mason, Menard, Mills, Real, Runnels, San Saba, Schleicher, Sterling, Sutton, Tom Green, Uvalde, and Val Verde (27 counties). Population (1960), 262,742.

O. CLARK FISHER, Democrat, of San Angelo, Tex.; member House Armed Services Committee; elected to 78th and succeeding Congresses.

TWENTY-SECOND DISTRICT.—Harris County: That part south of a line beginning at the point where U. S. Highway No. 290 intersects the county line between Harris and Waller Counties; thence along U. S. Highway No. 290 to the intersection of said highway with Post Oak Road; thence along said Post Oak Road to Buffalo Bayou; thence along said Bayou to Morgan's Point. Population (1960), 674,965.

ROBERT (BOB) RANDOLPH CASEY, Democrat, of Houston, Tex.; born in Joplin, Mo., July 27, 1915, son of Sam R. and Mabel E. Casey; moved to Houston, Tex., in 1930, and graduated from San Jacinto High School; attended the University of Houston and the South Texas School of Law at night; was admitted to the State bar of Texas in 1940; opened law office in Alvin, Tex., and served as city attorney and also a member of the school board; returned to Houston as an assistant district attorney in Harris County, in charge of the civil department; in 1948 was elected to the State house of representatives and served in the regular and special sessions of the 51st Legislature; elected county judge of Harris County in 1950 for a 2-year term; reelected in 1952 and again in 1954 for a 4-year term; member, First Christian Church; married Hazel Marian Brann on August 13, 1935, and have 10 children—Hazel Mary, Robert, Jr., Catherine, Bonnie, Mike, Shawn, Bridget, Eileen, Timothy, and Kevin; elected from the newly created 22d district to the 86th Congress on November 4, 1958; reelected to the 87th, 88th, and 89th Congresses.

UTAH

(Population (1960), 890,627)

SENATORS

WALLACE FOSTER BENNETT, Republican, Salt Lake City, Utah; born, Salt Lake City, November 13, 1898; second lieutenant of Infantry, 1918; A. B., University of Utah, 1919; principal, San Luis Stake Academy, Manassa, Colo., 1919–20; board chairman, Bennett's, Salt Lake City; board chairman, Bennett Motor Co.; vice president, National Paint, Varnish & Lacquer Association, 1935–36; president, National Glass Distributors Association, 1937; president, Salt Lake Rotary Club, 1940; president, Salt Lake Community Chest, 1944–45; president, National Association of Manufacturers, 1949; member, Salt Lake Country Club, Alta Club, Timpanogos Club, and Rotary Club; member, L. D. S. (Mormon) Church; treasurer, L. D. S. Sunday School General Board since 1935; author: "Faith and Freedom," 1950, and "Why I Am a Mormon," 1958; married Frances Grant, 1922; five children—Wallace Grant, Rosemary (Mrs. Robert C. Fletcher), David Wells, Frances (Mrs. Lawrence S. Jeppson), and Robert Foster; elected to the United States Senate November 7, 1950; reelected November 6, 1956, and November 6, 1962.

FRANK EDWARD MOSS, Democrat, of Salt Lake City, Utah; born in Holladay, Utah, September 23, 1911, son of James E. and Maud Moss; attended the public schools and Granite High School; graduated from the University of Utah with B. A. degree in 1933 and from George Washington University Law School with J. D. degree in 1937; attorney for the Securities and Exchange Commission, Washington, D. C., from 1937 to 1939; elected Salt Lake City Judge in 1940 and reelected in 1945; elected Salt Lake County Attorney in 1950 and reelected in 1954; served 4 years during World War II as Judge Advocate in the European Theater with the Air Corps; holds commission of colonel, United States Air Force Reserve; member: Church of Jesus Christ of Latter Day Saints, the American Legion, Veterans of Foreign Wars, and Lions Club; served as president of the Utah State Association of County Officials, and two terms as president of the National District Attorney's Association; married Phyllis Hart, daughter of Charles H. Hart, former judge and church leader, in 1934, and they have four children; elected to the United States Senate on November 4, 1958, for the term expiring January 3, 1965; reelected November 3, 1964.

REPRESENTATIVES

FIRST DISTRICT.—Counties: Beaver, Box Elder, Cache, Carbon, Daggett, Duchesne, Emery, Garfield, Grand, Iron, Juab, Kane, Millard, Morgan, Piute, Rich, San Juan, Sanpete, Sevier, Summit, Uintah, Wasatch, Washington, Wayne, and Weber (25 counties). Population (1960), 317,973.

LAURENCE J. BURTON, Republican, of Ogden, Utah; born in Ogden, Utah, October 30, 1926; graduated from Ogden High School in 1944; enlisted in U.S. Navy Air Corps in January 1945 and was honorably discharged in July 1946; graduated from Weber College (associate degree) in 1948 and served as student body president; won national Phi Rho Pi debate championship; graduated University of Utah in 1951, B.S. degree in political science; served as public relations director and athletic manager at Weber College; served as regional four-state director for American College Public Relations Association 1954–55; edited national magazine of National Junior College Athletic Association 1951–61; M.S. degree in political science, Utah State University, in 1956; also postgraduate work at Georgetown and George Washington Universities, 1957–58; married in 1947 to the former Janice Shupe; four children—Carol (1949), Susan (1953), Sally (1956), and Laurence S. (1959); served as legislative assistant to former Utah Congressman Henry Aldous Dixon during 86th Congress 1957–58; served on faculty at Weber College as assistant professor of political science 1958–60; served as administrative assistant to Utah Governor George Dewey Clyde 1960–62; member L.D.S. (Mormon) Church, American Legion, and Kiwanis Club; elected to the 88th Congress November 6, 1962; reelected to the 89th Congress.

SECOND DISTRICT.—Counties: Davis, Salt Lake, Tooele, and Utah (4 counties).   Population (1960), 572,654.

DAVID S. KING, Democrat, of Salt Lake City, Utah; born in Salt Lake City, Utah, June 20, 1917, son of the late Senator William H. King; was reared in Washington, D.C.; graduated from the University of Utah, in Salt Lake City, receiving B.A. degree in economics in 1937; served for 2 years as a missionary for the Church of Jesus Christ of Latter-day Saints (Mormon) in Great Britain; graduated from Georgetown University School of Law, LL.B. degree; for 1 year served as law clerk to Justice Harold M. Stephens of the United States Court of Appeals for the District of Columbia; returned to Salt Lake City in 1943; served 2 years as counsel for the Utah State Tax Commission; private practice of law since 1945; assistant general superintendent of the Mutual Improvement Association for the Latter-day Saints Church; served as director of the Salt Lake City Junior Chamber of Commerce, and vice president and director of a finance company; taught commercial law in a local college for 10 years; married, and is the father of eight children; elected to the 86th Congress on November 4, 1958; reelected to the 87th and 89th Congresses.

VERMONT

(Population (1960), 389,881)

SENATORS

GEORGE DAVID AIKEN, Republican, of Putney, Vt.; born in Dummerston, Vt., August 20, 1892; married Beatrice M. Howard; four children—Dorothy Aiken Morse (Mrs. Harry), Marjorie Aiken Cleverley (Mrs. Harry Leighton), Howard Aiken (deceased), Barbara Aiken Jones (Mrs. Malcolm S.); elected town representative in 1931 and 1933; speaker of the house of representatives in 1933; Lieutenant Governor of Vermont in 1935, and Governor of Vermont in 1937 and 1939; elected to the United States Senate on November 5, 1940; reelected November 7, 1944; reelected November 7, 1950; reelected November 6, 1956; reelected November 6, 1962.

WINSTON L. PROUTY, Republican, of Newport, Vt.; businessman; mayor of Newport for three terms, 1938 to 1941; member of Vermont House of Representatives in 1941, 1945, and 1947, serving as speaker in 1947; chairman, Vermont State Water Conservation Board 1948 until May 1950; married Jennette Herbert Hall July 3, 1962; elected to the 82d Congress November 7, 1950; reelected to the 83d, 84th, and 85th Congresses; elected to the United States Senate November 4, 1958; reelected November 3, 1964.

REPRESENTATIVE

AT LARGE.—Population (1960), 389,881.

ROBERT THEODORE STAFFORD, Republican, of Rutland, Vt.; born in Rutland, August 8, 1913; educated in the public schools of Rutland; Middlebury (Vt.) College, B.S. degree in 1935; the University of Michigan; and Boston University Law School, LL.B. in 1938; honorary LL.D. from Boston University, Norwich University, and Middlebury College; Rutland City grand juror 1938–42; served on active duty in the U.S. Navy as a lieutenant commander during World War II, 1942–46, and in the Korean conflict, 1951–53; presently a captain in the Naval Reserve; Rutland County state's attorney 1947–51; deputy attorney general 1953–55; attorney general 1955–57; Lieutenant Governor 1957–59; Governor 1959–61; married to the former Helen Kelley of Bellows Falls, Vt.; four daughters; member of the Congregational Church, American Legion, V.F.W., Lions Club, Eagles, Elks, Masons, and the Vermont and Rutland County bar associations; elected to the 87th Congress November 8, 1960; reelected to the 88th and 89th Congresses.

VIRGINIA

(Population (1960), 3,966,949)

SENATORS

HARRY FLOOD BYRD, Democrat, of Berryville, Va.; in 1915 elected to senate of Virginia, in which he served until he was elected Governor of the Commonwealth for the term 1926–30; appointed to the United States Senate by Gov. John Garland Pollard on March 4, 1933; elected on November 7, 1933, for the unexpired term of Claude A. Swanson, resigned, and reelected for the full term on November 6, 1934; reelected November 5, 1940, without opposition in the Democratic primary and without Republican opposition in the general election; reelected November 5, 1946; reelected November 4, 1952; reelected November 4, 1958; reelected November 3, 1964; newspaper publisher, farmer, and applegrower.

A. WILLIS ROBERTSON, Democrat, of Lexington, Va., was educated in the public schools of Lynchburg and Rocky Mount, Va.; B. A., LL. B., and honorary LL.D. degrees, University of Richmond, and honorary LL.D. degrees, Washington and Lee University, and College of William and Mary; member, Pi Kappa Alpha, Omicron Delta Kappa, Phi Beta Kappa, Phi Alpha Delta law fraternity, Jamestowne Society, Sons of the American Revolution, and Society of the Cincinnati; admitted to the bar in 1908; member of State Senate for 6 years, 1916–22; Commonwealth's attorney for Rockbridge County for 6 years, 1922–28; chairman of commission of game and inland fisheries for 6 years, 1926–33; during World War I served in the United States Army from August 1917 to June 1919; married Gladys Churchill Willis, and they have two sons, A. Willis Robertson, Jr., and Marion Gordon Robertson; elected to the 73d Congress on November 8, 1932; reelected to the 74th and succeeding Congresses; elected to United States Senate November 5, 1946, for the unexpired term of the late Senator Carter Glass; reelected to the United States Senate November 2, 1948; reelected November 2, 1954, and November 8, 1960, for term ending January 3, 1967.

REPRESENTATIVES

FIRST DISTRICT.—Counties: Accomack, Charles City, Essex, Gloucester, James City, King and Queen, Mathews, Middlesex, New Kent, Northampton, and York. Cities: Hampton, Newport News, Williamsburg, and Virginia Beach. Population (1960), 422,624.

THOMAS N. DOWNING, Democrat, of Newport News, Va.; born in Newport News, Va., February 1, 1919, son of the late Dr. Samuel Downing of Newport News and Mrs. Joseph Phillips, now residing in Hampton, Va.; educated in the public schools and is a graduate of Newport News High School; received B. S. degree from Virginia Military Institute and law degree from the University of Virginia; practicing attorney with the firm of Downing & Andrews in Hampton, Va.; former substitute judge of the Municipal Court for the former City of Warwick, served in World War II as a combat troop commander of Mechanized Cavalry with Gen. George S. Patton's Third U. S. Army and commanded the first troops in the Third Army to invade Germany; received a Silver Star for gallantry in action in France; member and trustee of St. Stephen's Episcopal Church of Newport News; member—Newport News Bar Association (former president), Hampton Bar Association, Virginia State and American Bar Associations, Lions Club, American Legion, Veterans of Foreign Wars; member of board of trustees, Old Dominion College; married the former Virginia Dickerson Martin of Philadelphia, Pa., and they have one daughter, Susan Nelms Downing, and one son, Samuel Dickerson Martin Downing; elected to the 86th Congress on November 4, 1958; reelected to the 87th, 88th, and 89th Congresses.

SECOND DISTRICT.—NORFOLK COUNTY. CITIES: Norfolk, Portsmouth, and South Norfolk. Population (1960), 494,292.

PORTER HARDY, JR., Democrat, of Churchland, Chesapeake, Va.; businessman-farmer; born in Chesterfield County, Va., June 1, 1903; son of Reverend Porter and Jane (Mahood) Hardy; educated at Randolph-Macon Academy, Bedford, Va., and in the public schools of Virginia, graduating from Boykins High School in 1918; B. A., Randolph-Macon College, 1922; attended Graduate School Business Administration, Harvard University, 1923–24; First Citizen, Portsmouth, Va., 1952; LL. D., Randolph-Macon College, 1955; 1959 recipient, Commerce Builder Award of Hampton Roads Foreign Commerce Club; honorary member, Norfolk Rotary Club; Hampton Roads Post, American Society Military Engineers; Hampton Roads Maritime Association; Ahepa; Moose; Kappa Alpha (Southern) and Tau Kappa Alpha; Methodist Church; was married in 1939 to Miss Edna Lynn Moore, of Morristown, Tenn.; has two children, Lynn and Porter 3d; elected to 80th Congress November 5, 1946; reelected to 81st and each succeeding Congress.

THIRD DISTRICT.—COUNTIES: Chesterfield and Henrico. CITIES: Colonial Heights and Richmond. Population (1960), 418,081.

DAVID EDWARD SATTERFIELD III, Democrat, of Richmond, Va.; born in Richmond December 2, 1920; educated in the public schools, St. Christopher's Preparatory School, University of Richmond, and University of Virginia; married the former Anne E. Powell of Blackstone, Va.; two sons, David and John; during World War II served as a U.S. Navy carrier-based fighter pilot in the Pacific theater; served in the Naval Air Reserve since 1946, to Air Wing Staff 66, Naval Air Reserve Training Unit, NAF, presently holds rank of commander; attorney, firm of Satterfield, Haw, Anderson, Parkerson & Beazley; assistant United States attorney 1950–53; councilman, city of Richmond 1954–56; member State house of delegates 1960–64; member of Kiwanis, Reserve Officers Association, Naval Reserve Association, Navy League, Phi Gamma Delta, Phi Alpha Delta, Richmond and Virginia bar associations, Mason (32d degree), Acca Temple Shrine; former president and director of Richmond Area Heart Association and of the Consultation and Evaluation Clinic; former director of Thalhimer-Virginia Wildlife Exhibit; former counsel and director of Boys Club of Richmond; civilian adviser to the National Health Services; elected to the 89th Congress November 3, 1964.

FOURTH DISTRICT.—COUNTIES: Amelia, Appomattox, Brunswick, Buckingham, Cumberland, Dinwiddie, Greensville, Isle of Wight, Lunenburg, Mecklenburg, Nansemond, Nottoway, Powhatan, Prince Edward, Prince George, Southampton, Surry, and Sussex. CITIES: Franklin, Hopewell, Petersburg, and Suffolk. Population (1960), 352,157.

WATKINS M. ABBITT, Democrat, of Appomattox, Va.; born May 21, 1908; graduated from Appomattox Agricultural High School in 1925; attended Richmond College and received LL. B. degree from the T. C. Williams School of Law of the University of Richmond, 1931; passed State bar, December 1930; began practice of law at Appomattox in July 1931; married Miss Corinne Hancock, March 20, 1937; has three children, Mrs. Samuel Kerr, Watkins, Jr., and Corinne; Commonwealth attorney for Appomattox County, 1932–48; Democratic elector for the Fourth District of Virginia in 1944; member of Virginia Constitutional Convention of 1945 which extended right to vote to members of the Armed Forces; elected State Democratic chairman, 1964; member of Virginia and Fifth Judicial Circuit Court bar associations; director, Farmers National Bank; deacon, Liberty Baptist Church; elected to 80th Congress in special election on February 17, 1948, to fill vacancy caused by the death of the late Hon. Patrick Henry Drewry; reelected to 81st, 82d, 83d, 84th, 85th, 86th, 87th, 88th, and 89th Congresses.

FIFTH DISTRICT.—COUNTIES: Carroll. Charlotte, Franklin, Grayson, Halifax, Henry, Patrick, Pittsylvania, and Wythe. CITIES: Danville and Martinsville. Population (1960), 325,989.

WILLIAM MUNFORD TUCK, Democrat, of South Boston, Halifax County, Va.; born in Halifax County, Va., September 28, 1896; attended the College of William and Mary and Washington and Lee University; degrees: LL. B. and LL. D., Washington and Lee University, and also honorary degree of LL. D. from College of William and Mary, Hampden-Sydney College, and Elon College (N.C.); married Eva Lovelace Dillard February 26, 1928; member, House of Delegates of Virginia, 1924–32; Virginia State Senate, 1932–42; Lieutenant

Governor of Virginia, 1942–46; elected to the office of Governor of Virginia, November 1945, and served the term as Governor beginning January 1946 and ending January 1950; United States Marine, World War I; Virginia Democratic Elector-at-Large, 1936; former chairman, Virginia State Democratic Committee; member: Baptist Church, The American and Virginia Bar Associations, Sons of American Revolution, Sons of Confederate Veterans, Omicron Delta Kappa, Sigma Phi Epsilon, Phi Delta Phi, American Legion, 40 and 8, Masons (33d degree), B.P.O.E., Eagles, Woodmen of the World, Redmen, Moose, Lions, Ruritan, and others; elected to the 83d Congress at special election, April 14, 1953, to fill unexpired term of Representative Thomas B. Stanley, resigned; reelected to the 84th, 85th, 86th, 87th, 88th, and 89th Congresses.

SIXTH DISTRICT.—COUNTIES: Alleghany, Bedford, Botetourt, Campbell, Craig, Floyd, Montgomery, and Roanoke. CITIES: Clifton Forge, Covington, Lynchburg, Radford, and Roanoke. Population (1960), 378,864.

RICHARD H. POFF, Republican, of Radford, Va.; born, Radford, Va., October 19, 1923; reared in Christiansburg, Va.; undergraduate work at Roanoke College, Salem, Va.; World War II B–24 bomber pilot; married Jo Ann Ragen Topper, Christiansburg, Va., June 24, 1945; daughter, Rebecca Topper Poff, age 17; son, Thomas Randolph Poff, age 4; Richard H. Poff, Jr., age 2; University of Virginia Law School, LL. B. degree; Sigma Nu Phi legal fraternity; partner, Dalton, Poff & Turk, attorneys, Radford, Va.; member of Tyler Memorial Presbyterian Church, Junior Chamber of Commerce, Lions Club, 32d degree Mason, Moose, American Legion, VFW; elected 83d Congress November 4, 1952; reelected 84th, 85th, 86th, 87th, 88th, and 89th Congresses.

SEVENTH DISTRICT.—COUNTIES: Amherst, Augusta, Bath, Clarke, Frederick, Highland, Madison, Nelson, Page, Rappahannock, Rockbridge, Rockingham, Shenandoah, and Warren. CITIES: Buena Vista, Harrisonburg, Staunton, Waynesboro, and Winchester. Population (1960), 312,890.

JOHN O. MARSH, JR., Democrat, of Strasburg, Va.; born in Winchester, Va., August 7, 1926; attended public schools of Harrisonburg, Va., and Washington and Lee University, Lexington, Va. (LL.B.); admitted to Virginia Bar, 1952, and established law practice in Strasburg; married Glenn Ann Patterson of Kenbridge, Va., and Winston-Salem, N.C., and they have three children—John Robert, Rebecca Patterson, and Scot Wayland; veteran, World War II, commissioned in Army at 19, served with occupation forces, Germany; presently major, Virginia National Guard; completed Airborne Mobility Course, Fort Benning, Ga., 1964; formerly member, Shenandoah County (Va.) School Board, town attorney of New Market, Va., and town judge of Strasburg, Va.; active in Liberty Tree and other patriotic programs, cited by National Jaycees and Freedoms Foundation at Valley Forge; designated "Outstanding Young Man in Virginia— 1959" by Virginia Jaycees; awarded distinguished service medal, Department of Virginia, American Legion; elder and adult bible class leader, Strasburg Presbyterian Church; life member, Virginia Jaycees; member, American Legion, Veterans of Foreign Wars, Virginia State Bar, American Bar Association, National Guard Association of the United States, Virginia National Guard Association, Masonic Lodge, Phi Kappa Psi, Phi Delta Phi, and ODK; elected to the 88th Congress November 6, 1962; reelected to the 89th Congress.

EIGHTH DISTRICT.—COUNTIES: Albemarle, Caroline, Culpeper, Fauquier, Fluvanna, Goochland, Greene, Hanover, King George, King William, Lancaster, Loudoun, Louisa, Northumberland, Orange, Prince William, Richmond, Spotsylvania, Stafford, and Westmoreland. CITIES: Charlottesville and Fredericksburg. Population (1960), 357,461.

HOWARD WORTH SMITH, Democrat, of Broad Run, Va.; born at Broad Run, Va.; graduated from Bethel Military Academy in 1901; B. L., University of Virginia, in 1903; admitted to the bar in 1904, and practiced law until 1922, when accepted appointment as judge of the corporation court of Alexandria; resigned this position in 1928 to accept appointment as judge of the sixteenth judicial circuit of Virginia; resigned as judge in 1930 to run for Congress; Commonwealth's attorney of Alexandria from 1918 until he resigned to accept appointment on the bench in 1922; is chairman of the board of the Alexandria National Bank; engaged in farming and dairying; is married and has two children, Howard Worth Smith, Jr., and Mrs. Joe H. Tonahill; member of the Episcopal Church; belongs to the fraternal order of Elks, Masons, and Odd Fellows; elected to the 72d and each succeeding Congress; chairman, Committee on Rules.

NINTH DISTRICT.—COUNTIES: Bland, Buchanan, Dickenson, Giles, Lee, Pulaski, Russell, Scott, Smyth, Tazewell, Washington, and Wise. CITIES: Bristol and Norton. Population (1960), 364,973.

WILLIAM PAT JENNINGS, Democrat, of Marion, Va.; born on a farm in Camp, Smyth County, Va., August 20, 1919; graduated from Sugar Grove (Va.) High School 1937; B.S. degree, Virginia Polytechnic Institute, 1941; United States Army, July 1941, until discharged May 1946, a major; served in European Theater overseas and participated in five major battles; business and farm interests, Marion, Va.; sheriff of Smyth County, January 1948, through December 1954; married Annabelle Cox, Sugar Grove, Va.; four children: Grover C.; Pat, Jr.; Mary Ann; and Richard Joel; member First Methodist Church of Marion, Kiwanis, Masons, Shriners, American Legion, V.F.W., Elks, Alpha Zeta, Sigma Phi Epsilon, ODK, United States Army Reserves (Lt. Col.), board of directors, Bank of Marion; vice president, Marion Publishing Co.; elected to the 84th Congress, November 2, 1954; reelected to the 85th, 86th, 87th, 88th, and 89th Congresses; member of House Committee on Ways and Means.

TENTH DISTRICT.—COUNTIES: Arlington and Fairfax. CITIES: Alexandria, Falls Church, and Fairfax City. Population (1960), 539,618.

JOEL T. BROYHILL, Republican, of Arlington, Va.; born in Hopewell, Va., November 4, 1919, and attended public schools in Hopewell, Fork Union Military Academy, Fork Union, Va., and George Washington University, Washington, D. C.; entered the Army as an enlisted man in World War II, advanced to the rank of captain and was captured in the Battle of the Bulge while serving as a company commander in the 106th Infantry Division; following the war, returned to Virginia and resumed business career, becoming a partner and general manager in one of the major real estate and building firms in Northern Virginia; took an active part in many community and civic organizations in Arlington; served as president of the Arlington County Chamber of Commerce; chairman of the Arlington County Planning Commission; president of the Arlington Optimist Club; member of the Church Council of the Resurrection Lutheran Church of Arlington, and has taken a leading part in many fund drives for nonprofit organizations; is a member of the American Legion, Veterans of Foreign Wars, Disabled American Veterans, AMVETS, Masonic Fraternity, Loyal Order of Moose, Order of Elks, Order of Eagles, the Kappa Alpha Alumni Association, Izaak Walton League, the International Supreme Council of the Order of DeMolay, Friendship Veterans Fire Engine Company, and Mount Vernon Guard; has also been active in various business, professional, and Republican political organizations; married the former Miss Jane Marshall Bragg, and has three daughters, Nancy Pierce, Jane-Anne, and Jeanne Marie; elected to the 83d Congress November 4, 1952; reelected to the 84th, 85th, 86th, 87th, 88th, and 89th Congresses; became ranking minority member on the District of Columbia Committee and third in rank on the Post Office and Civil Service Committee, before election to the Ways and Means Committee on January 22, 1964; was reelected to the District of Columbia Committee as a second committee in January 1965; residence, 2551 North Vermont Street, Arlington, Va.

WASHINGTON

(Population (1960), 2,853,214)

SENATORS

WARREN G. MAGNUSON, Democrat, Seattle; born, Minnesota, 1905; entered University of Washington, graduating from the law school in 1929, entering the practice of law that year; served as special prosecuting attorney of King County, 1931; elected to the Washington State Legislature; served in the regular and special sessions of 1933; chairman of the Judiciary Committee; assistant United States district attorney, 1934; elected prosecuting attorney of King County, November 1934; member of American Legion and Veterans of Foreign Wars; served as lieutenant commander in U.S.N.R. in Pacific fleet; married Mrs. Jermaine Elliott Peralta October 4, 1964; elected to the 75th, 76th, 77th, and 78th Congresses; appointed to fill unexpired term of Senator Homer T. Bone December 15, 1944; elected to United States Senate November 7, 1944, for the full term ending January 3, 1951; reelected for the term ending January 3, 1957; reelected for the term ending January 3, 1963; reelected for the term ending January 3, 1969.

HENRY M. JACKSON, Democrat, of Everett, Wash., was born in that city May 31, 1912; attended the Everett public schools and graduated from the Everett High School; University of Washington Law School, LL. B., 1935; after being admitted to the bar in 1935, became associated in the practice of law with the law firm of Black & Rucker; elected prosecuting attorney of Snohomish County in 1938; married Helen Eugenia Hardin December 16, 1961; one daughter, Anna Marie Jackson, born February 7, 1963; chairman, Democratic National Committee, July 1960 to January 1961; elected to the 77th Congress, November 1940, and to each succeeding Congress including the 82d; elected to the United States Senate, November 4, 1952, for the term ending January 3, 1959; reelected to the United States Senate November 4, 1958, for the term ending January 3, 1965; reelected November 3, 1964, for the term ending January 3, 1971.

REPRESENTATIVES

FIRST DISTRICT.—Part of Kitsap County consisting of Bainbridge Island; part of King County not included in Districts 2 and 7. Population (1960), 420,548.

THOMAS M. PELLY, Republican, of Seattle, Wash.; born in Seattle, Wash., August 22, 1902; education: public schools of Seattle, and Hoosac School, Hoosick, N.Y.; Episcopalian; business career: Seattle National Bank 1921–30 (trust officer); left to become vice president of Lowman & Hanford Co., printers and stationers; president and general manager in 1937–55; director: Seattle Trust & Savings Bank; Olympia State Bank & Trust Co., and Northern Life Insurance Co.; president Seattle Chamber of Commerce 1949–51; married in 1927 to Mary Virginia Taylor, of Washington, D.C.; two children; elected to the 83d Congress November 4, 1952; reelected to the 84th, 85th, 86th, 87th, 88th, and 89th Congresses.

SECOND DISTRICT.—COUNTIES: Clallam, Island, Jefferson, San Juan, Skagit, Snohomish, and Whatcom. KING COUNTY: Precincts of Alderwood, Avondale, Baring, Bear Creek, Berlin, Carnation, Cherry Valley, Cleveland, Cottage Lake, Duvall, East Redmond, Happy Valley, Hollywood, Leota, Martin Creek, Novelty, Redmond No. 1, Redmond No. 2, Skykomish, Stillwater, Tolt, Vincent and York. Population (1960), 366,395.

LLOYD MEEDS, Democrat of Everett, Wash.; born in Dillon, Mont., December 11, 1927; as a youngster moved with parents to Monroe, Wash.; graduated from Monroe High School and entered the U.S. Navy in 1946; attended Everett Junior College and Gonzaga University School of Law (LL.B. 1958); admitted to Washington State Bar 1958; served as deputy prosecuting attorney in Spokane and Snohomish Counties; engaged in private practice of law in Everett, Wash., for 2 years in association of Hunter, Meeds & French; elected Snohomish County prosecuting attorney in 1962; married Barbara Jean Sladek of Monroe, Wash.; three children, Michael R., Marcia L., and Michelle Jean; member Kiwanis International, Fraternal Order of Eagles, Washington State Bar Association, and vice president Snohomish County Bar Association; former president Snohomish County Young Democrats and Gonzaga Law Young Democrats; elected to the 89th Congress November 3, 1964.

THIRD DISTRICT.—COUNTIES: Clark, Cowlitz, Grays Harbor, Lewis, Mason, Pacific, Skamania, Thurston, and Wahkiakum (9 counties).   Population (1960), 342,540.

JULIA BUTLER HANSEN, Democrat, of Cathlamet, Wash.; born in Portland, Oreg., June 14, 1907; graduate of the University of Washington, B.A. degree; manager of title insurance and casualty insurance business; writer; member of the State house of representatives from January 1939 to November 1960, serving as speaker pro tempore 1955–60; chairman, Highways Committee, 1949–53, 1955–60, Joint Fact Finding Committee on Highways, Streets, and Bridges, 1949–53, 1957–60, and Eleven Western States Highway Policy Committee 1951–60; married to Henry A. Hansen; one son, David K. Hansen; member Land Title Associations, State and national; Business and Professional Women's Clubs of Longview, Wash., and Washington State; Order of Eastern Star, Mt. Rainier Chapter; honorary State member, Delta Kappa Gamma; served in past years as Wahkiakum County Chairman of American Red Cross, Polio Foundation, Crusade for Freedom, War Fund; Washington State Secretary, War Fund; winner of Road Building (Washington State Chapter) Certificate of Merit; Washington State Outstanding Service Plaque; Good Roads Association Award (second such award given); member of Education Committee, Rules Committee, Washington State House of Representatives, 1951–57; elected to the 86th Congress, November 8, 1960, to fill the vacancy caused by the death of Russell V. Mack and also elected to the 87th Congress; reelected to the 88th and 89th Congresses; member of Appropriations Committee; former service on Education and Labor Committee, Veterans' Affairs Committee, and Committee on Interior and Insular Affairs.

FOURTH DISTRICT.—COUNTIES: Adams, Asotin, Benton, Columbia, Franklin, Garfield, Grant, Kittitas, Klickitat, Walla Walla, Whitman, and Yakima (12 counties).   Population (1960), 414,764.

CATHERINE MAY (maiden name Billie Barnes), Republican, of Yakima, Wash.; born in Yakima, Wash., May 18, 1914, daughter of Charles H. and Pauline V. Barnes; married James O. May, a real estate and insurance broker, and they have two children; member, St. Michaels Episcopal Church; Sunday-school teacher; attended grade school in Yakima; Washington Junior High School; graduated from Yakima High School and Yakima Valley Junior College (sociology course); 3 years at University of Washington; B.A. degree and 5-year education degree; studied speech at the University of Southern California, teacher of English in Chehalis High School for 4 years; women's editor and news broadcaster, station KMO, Tacoma, Wash.; writer and special events broadcaster, station KOMO–KJR, Seattle, Wash.; head of radio department, Strang & Prosser Advertising Agency, Seattle, Wash.; head of radio and motion picture department, Federal Insurance Co., Seattle, Wash.; writer and assistant to commentator Adelaide Hawley, National Broadcasting Co., New York, N. Y.; women's editor, station KIT, Yakima, Wash.; elected to Washington State Legislature in 1952 and served 6 years; office manager and medical secretary, Yakima Medical Center; served as vice chairman of Governor's State Wide Committee on Educational Television; member of Governor's Safety Council; member of Washington Association for Retarded Children; legislative representative for Yakima unit of Association for Retarded Children; member of Alpha Chi Omega; honorary member of Chinook Business and Professional Women; honorary member Altrusa Club; honorary member of Zonta Club; recipient of McCall magazine "Togetherness" award and Theta Sigma Phi Matrix Table award; recipient of "Woman of the Year" award Alpha Chi Omega; member, National Commission on Food Marketing; elected to the 86th Congress on November 4, 1958; reelected to the 87th, 88th, and 89th Congresses.

FIFTH DISTRICT.—COUNTIES: Chelan, Douglas, Ferry, Lincoln, Okanogan, Pend Oreille, Spokane, and Stevens (8 counties). Population (1960), 399,093.

THOMAS STEPHEN FOLEY, Democrat, of Spokane, Wash.; born in Spokane March 6, 1929, son of Hon. Ralph E. and Helen Foley; graduated from Gonzaga High School, the University of Washington (B.A. 1951), and the University of Washington Law School (LL.B. 1957); associated with the firm of Higgins & Foley in the practice of law in 1957; appointed deputy prosecuting attorney of Spokane County in 1958; instructor in constitutional law at Gonzaga University Law School; appointed assistant attorney general, State of Washington, 1960; served as assistant chief clerk and special counsel of the Committee on Interior and Insular Affairs of the United States Senate 1961–63; elected to the 89th Congress November 3, 1964.

SIXTH DISTRICT.—COUNTY of PIERCE and KITSAP COUNTY (except Bainbridge Island). Population (1960), 399,362.

FLOYD V. HICKS, Democrat, of Tacoma, Wash.; born in Prosser, Wash., May 29, 1915; attended the public schools of Prosser, Wash.; graduated, Central Washington State College, Ellensburg, Wash., B.Ed. 1938, took advanced work in education, Washington State University; school teacher and coach 1935 to 1942; veteran, 4 years in Air Force; graduated from University of Washington Law School, LL.B. 1948; admitted to the bar in March 1949 and practiced in Pierce County, Wash., since then; appointed Pierce County Superior Court Judge in 1961 and elected in 1962; wife, Jeanne; two daughters, Tracie and Betsie; elected to the 89th Congress November 3, 1964.

SEVENTH DISTRICT.—Approximately south half of King County, including south half of Seattle. Population (1960), 510,512.

BROCK ADAMS, Democrat, of Seattle, Wash.; born in Atlanta, Ga., January 13, 1927; United States district attorney for Western Washington 1961–64; attended public schools in Iowa, Oregon, and Seattle, Wash.; graduate of University of Washington, B.A. (summa cum laude), and Harvard Law School, LL.B., 1952; U.S. Navy 1944–46; lawyer; author, "Estate and Gift Taxation of the Marital Community" 1953; instructor, American Institute of Banking; member Phi Beta Kappa, Vestry Epiphany Episcopal Church; former Trustee University of Washington Alumni Association; president, Neighborhood Settlement House; trustee, Civic Unity Committee of city of Seattle; honored by receiving Distinguished Service Award, Seattle Junior Chamber of Commerce, 1961; married the former Mary Elizabeth Scott of Jacksonville, Fla., and they have three children, two sons and one daughter; elected to 89th Congress November 3, 1964.

WEST VIRGINIA

(Population (1960), 1,860,421)

SENATORS

JENNINGS RANDOLPH, Democrat, Elkins, Randolph County, W. Va.; born at Salem, W. Va., March 8, 1902, son of Ernest and Idell (Bingman) Randolph; graduated from Salem Academy, 1920, and Salem College, 1924; honorary doctorate degrees—law, Davis and Elkins College, 1939; letters, Southeastern University, 1940; aeronautical science, Salem College, 1943; humanities, West Virginia State College, 1964; married 1933 to Mary Katherine Babb; two sons, Jennings, Jr., and Frank; member Seventh Day Baptist Church; former newspaper and magazine editor; former college professor and university dean; former airline executive and transportation officer; member and director of organizations, societies, and foundations for education, business, civic, and service programs; elected U.S. House of Representatives 73d Congress; reelected six consecutive terms; elected delegate at large for West Virginia to Democratic National Conventions, 1948, 1952, 1956, and 1964; elected to U.S. Senate, 1958 to complete the term ending January 1961; reelected 1960, for the term ending January 3, 1967.

ROBERT C. BYRD, Democrat; LL.B. cum laude, American University; elected to West Virginia House of Delegates in 1946 and reelected in 1948; elected to West Virginia Senate in 1950 and elected to U.S. House of Representatives in 1952, 1954, and 1956; elected to U.S. Senate in 1958; elected delegate at large from West Virginia to the Democratic National Convention in 1960; reelected to U.S. Senate in 1964 by greatest vote every accorded a West Virginia candidate; member of Appropriations Committee, Armed Services Committee, and Committee on Rules and Administration.

REPRESENTATIVES

FIRST DISTRICT.—COUNTIES: Braxton, Brooke, Calhoun, Doddridge, Gilmer, Hancock, Harrison, Lewis, Marion, Marshall, Ohio, Taylor, and Wetzel (13 counties). Population (1960), 408,794.

ARCH ALFRED MOORE, JR., Republican, of Glendale, W. Va.; lawyer; born in Moundsville, W. Va., April 16, 1923, son of Arch A. and Genevieve (Jones) Moore; student Lafayette College 1943; A. B. West Virginia University 1948 and LL. B. 1951; married Shelley S. Riley August 11, 1949; children— Arch A., III, Shelley Wellons, and Lucy St. Clair; admitted to West Virginia Bar 1951, and since practiced in Moundsville; partner Moore & Moore; former member West Virginia House of Delegates; member West Virginia Bar Association, West Virginia State Bar, American Bar Association; veteran of World War II, European theater, infantryman, holder of the Purple Heart medal for wounds received in action; member of: American Legion, 40 & 8, Veterans of Foreign Wars, Loyal Order of Moose, Fraternal Order of Eagles, and Benevolent and Protective Order of Elks; Methodist; Rotarian; social fraternity, Beta Theta Pi; international legal fraternity, Phi Delta Phi; home: 507 Jefferson Avenue, Glendale, W. Va.; office, 511 Seventh Street, Moundsville, W. Va.; elected to the 85th Congress November 6, 1956; reelected to the 86th, 87th, 88th, and 89th Congresses; member of Committee on the Judiciary, Select Committee to Conduct a Study and Investigation of the Problems of Small Business, and Joint Committee on Immigration and Nationality Policy.

SECOND DISTRICT.—COUNTIES: Barbour, Berkeley, Grant, Greenbrier, Hampshire, Hardy, Jefferson, Mineral, Monongalia, Morgan, Pendleton, Pocahontas, Preston, Randolph, Tucker, Upshur, and Webster (17 counties). Population (1960), 329,612.

HARLEY O. STAGGERS, Democrat, of Keyser, Mineral County, W. Va., born in Keyser, W. Va., August 3, 1907, son of Jacob and Frances (Cumberledge) Staggers; attended public schools of Mineral County; graduated with an A. B. degree from Emory and Henry College in 1931; received honorary Doctor of Laws from Emory and Henry College in 1953; high-school coach and teacher for 2 years; head coach at Potomac State College, Keyser, W. Va., for 2 years; sheriff of Mineral County from 1937 to 1941; served in United States Naval Air Corps as a navigator; member of the American Legion; Veterans of Foreign Wars, Disabled American Veterans, AMVETS, Loyal Order of Moose, Lions, Elks, Knights of Pythias, and West Virginia Farm Bureau; past president of the West Virginia State Moose Association; former district governor of West Virginia Lions Clubs; married Mary V. Casey, of Keyser, W. Va.; father of six children, Margaret Ann, Mary Katherine, Frances Susan, Elizabeth Ellen, Harley O., Jr., and Daniel Casey; elected to the 81st Congress on November 2, 1948; reelected to the 82d, 83d, 84th, 85th, 86th, 87th, 88th, and 89th Congresses.

THIRD DISTRICT.—COUNTIES: Boone, Clay, Kanawha, Nicholas, and Raleigh (5 counties). Population (1960), 396,871.

JOHN M. SLACK, JR., Democrat, of Charleston, W. Va.; born in Charleston, March 18, 1915; educated in Charleston public schools and at Virginia Military Institute; married; one son; engaged in construction business; former member of Kanawha County Court; Presbyterian; Scottish Rite and York Rite Mason; Shriner; member: Exchange Club; Elks; Press Club of Charleston; elected to the 86th Congress on November 4, 1958; reelected to the 87th, 88th, and 89th Congresses; member House Committee on Appropriations, James Madison Memorial Commission, and United States-Canada Interparliamentary Group.

FOURTH DISTRICT.—COUNTIES: Cabell, Jackson, Lincoln, Logan, Mason, Pleasants, Putnam, Ritchie, Roane, Tyler, Wayne, Wirt, and Wood (13 counties). Population (1960), 422,046.

KEN HECHLER, Democrat, of Huntington, W. Va.; born September 20, 1914, two miles outside the town of Roslyn, Long Island; parents, Charles H. (deceased) and Catherine Hechler, born and brought up on farms in Missouri; grandfather, George Hechler, volunteered in Union Army at Parkersburg, W. Va., in 1861 and was mustered out as a corporal at Wheeling, W. Va., in 1865, having been wounded at Antietam and fighting in major battles; attended public schools, was graduated from Swarthmore College, 1935; received master's degree from Columbia University in 1936 with master's thesis entitled: "Will Roosevelt Be Reelected?" (last chapter: "Yes"); doctor of philosophy in government and American history, Columbia University, 1940; teacher of political science at Columbia, Princeton, and Marshall Universities; research assistant to Judge Samuel I. Rosenman and President Franklin D. Roosevelt on Roosevelt's public papers; in 1939, invited by Professor Raymond Moley, former Roosevelt brain-truster, to take over his classes at Barnard College; section chief, Bureau of the Census, 1940; personnel officer, Office for Emergency Management, 1941; administrative analyst, United States Bureau of the Budget, 1942 and 1946–47; United States Army private, Infantry, 1942; commissioned second lieutenant, Armored Force, 1943; assigned to European theater of operations as combat historian, 1944; five battle stars from Normandy to the Elbe; discharged as major; special assistant to President Harry S. Truman in the White House, 1949–53, traveling with President Truman on his "whistle-stop" tours from coast to coast; associate director, The American Political Science Association, 1953–56, developing congressional interne program to enable young journalists and political scientists to work in congressional office; research director of Stevenson-Kefauver campaign of 1956, traveling with candidates; invited to Marshall College (now Marshall University), Huntington, February 1957, for one-term assignment as associate professor of political science; administrative aide to United States Senator John A Carroll, summer of 1957; television commentator, WHTN–TV, Huntington; author of "Insurgency," a story of the House and Senate battles against "Uncle Joe" Cannon and Senator Nelson Aldrich; author of "The Bridge at Remagen," a factual account of first Rhine crossing in World War II; member, American Legion, Veterans of Foreign Wars, Elks, Civitans; personal motto: "Better to jump the gun than not to move when the gun goes off"; member, Trinity Episcopal Church; not yet married; chairman of Subcommittee on Advanced Research and Development, House Committee on Science and Astronautics; elected to 86th Congress on November 4, 1958, by 3,503 votes; reelected to the 87th Congress by 9,879 votes; reelected to the 88th Congress by 22,576 votes; reelected to the 89th Congress by 40,034 votes.

FIFTH DISTRICT.—COUNTIES: Fayette, McDowell, Mercer, Mingo, Monroe, Summers, and Wyoming (7 counties). Population (1960), 303,098.

JAMES KEE, Democrat, of Bluefield, W. Va.; born in Bluefield, April 15, 1917, son of the late Congressman John Kee and former Congresswoman Elizabeth Kee; educated in the public schools and Sacred Heart School in Bluefield; Greenbrier Military School, Lewisburg, W. Va.; Southeastern University School of Law, and the School of Foreign Service, Georgetown University, Washington, D.C.; Episcopalian; married to the former Helen Lee Chapman of Welch, W. Va.; three daughters; member: Washington Coal Club; West Virginia Lodge No. 269 B.P.O. Elks; honorary vice president of the Democratic Club of the District of Columbia; past national president of the Greenbriar Military School Alumni Association; past national president of the Conference of State Societies; served as chairman of the State Societies Participation Committee of the 1961 Kennedy-Johnson Inaugural Committee; president of the West Virginia Society of the District of Columbia (fourth term); former member of the Congressional Secretaries Club; in 1962 was chosen as the West Virginia Son of the Year by the Sons' and Daughters' Day Foundation, Inc., and in 1964 was selected as the West Virginian of the Year by the Democratic Club of the District of Columbia; chairman of the Legislative Commission and past department vice commander of the American Legion, Department of the District of Columbia; gold life member of the American Legion; past commander of Housing Post No. 66, the American Legion; past chairman of the Membership Commission of The American Legion of the District of Columbia; served 4 years as assistant to the Clerk of the U.S. House of Representatives; housing adviser to the former United States Housing Authority; served in the U.S. Army Air Force; also served as career foreign service staff officer of the U.S. Department of State with domestic and foreign duties; served as administrative assistant to Congresswoman Elizabeth Kee from January 1, 1953, to January 1965; elected to the 89th Congress November 3, 1964, by an overwhelming majority.

WISCONSIN

(Population (1960), 3,951,777)

SENATORS

WILLIAM PROXMIRE, Democrat, of Wisconsin; married to Ellen Hodges Sawall.

GAYLORD NELSON, Democrat, of Madison, Wis.; born June 4, 1916, in Clear Lake, a village in northwestern Wisconsin, son of Dr. Anton Nelson; attended San Jose State College in California, graduating in 1939; received law degree from the University of Wisconsin in 1942; in the U.S. Army for 46 months during World War II, serving in the Okinawa campaign; married Carrie Lee Dotson in 1947; elected to the Wisconsin Legislature in 1948; elected Governor of Wisconsin in 1958 and reelected in 1960; elected to the U.S. Senate November 6, 1962.

REPRESENTATIVES

FIRST DISTRICT.—COUNTIES: Kenosha, Racine, Rock, and Walworth (4 counties).   Population (1960), 408,677.

LYNN ELLSWORTH STALBAUM, Democrat, of Racine, Wis.; born on a farm in Waterford, Wis., May 15, 1920; educated in the public schools and graduated from the Racine County Agricultural School in 1936; with U.S. Department of Agriculture in Racine County 1936–44 and served as administrative officer from 1939; served in U.S. Navy on a destroyer 1944–46; feed salesman 1946–51; secretary-treasurer of the Racine Milk Producers Cooperative Association and manager of the Harmony Dairy Co. 1951–64; elected to the State senate in 1954 and reelected in 1958 and 1962; caucus chairman in 1957, 1959, and 1961; minority leader in 1963; member of Kiwanis, American Legion (past commander Waterford Post), and V.F.W. (charter member Wind Lake Post); married the former Alice Gunderson of Waterford, Wis.; children, two daughters and two sons; elected to the 89th Congress November 3, 1964.

SECOND DISTRICT.—COUNTIES: Columbia, Dane, Dodge, Green, and Jefferson (5 counties).   Population (1960), 397,918.

ROBERT WILLIAM KASTENMEIER, Democrat, of Watertown, Wis.; born at Beaver Dam, Wis., January 24, 1924; educated in the public schools of Beaver Dam, and the University of Wisconsin, LL. B., 1952; entered United States Army as a private in February 1943; served in the Philippines; discharged August 15, 1946, as a first lieutenant; War Department branch office director, claims service, in the Philippines, 1946 to 1948; since September 1952 has practiced law in Watertown, Wis.; member of Jefferson County, and Wisconsin Bar Associations; married to the former Dorothy Chambers of Nacogdoches, Tex.; three sons; justice of the peace for Jefferson and Dodge Counties 1955–58; served as Jefferson County Democratic Party chairman from 1953 to 1956; member of the State Democratic Central Committee in 1956; delegate to the Democratic National Convention in 1956; elected to the 86th Congress, November 4, 1958; reelected to the 87th, 88th, and 89th Congresses; member, House Committee on the Judiciary.

THIRD DISTRICT.—COUNTIES: Buffalo, Crawford, Grant, Iowa, Jackson, Juneau, La Crosse, Lafayette, Monroe, Pepin, Pierce, Richland, Sauk, Trempealeau, and Vernon (15 counties).   Population (1960), 382,818.

VERNON WALLACE THOMSON, Republican, of Richland Center, Wis.; born November 5, 1905, in Richland Center, the son of A. A. and Ella Wallace Thomson; graduated from Richland Center High School in 1923; attended Carroll College in Waukesha 1923–25; graduated from University of Wisconsin in 1927; taught at Viroqua High School 1927–29; entered the University of Wisconsin

Law School in 1929 and graduated, LL.B. degree, in 1932; worked as a substitute mail carrier, waiter, teacher, and basketball coach while attending school; assistant district attorney of Richland County 1933–35 and city attorney 1933–37 and 1942–44; mayor of Richland Center for more than three terms beginning in April 1944; served 11 years as president of the library board; member of Order of Coif, Chi Phi, Phi Delta Phi, Masons; member of the State assembly 1935–49 and served as speaker for three consecutive terms and Republican floor leader during the 1945, 1947, and 1949 sessions; member of Advisory Committee on Rules, Pleadings, Practice and Procedure, Wisconsin Supreme Court; secretary of Wisconsin Legislative Council; member of Wisconsin Judicial Council; State attorney general 1951–56; Governor of Wisconsin in 1957 and 1958; engaged in the private practice of law in Madison and Richland Center; delegate to four Republican National Conventions; served as executive secretary of the Young Republican Federation; elected to the 87th Congress November 8, 1960; reelected to the 88th and 89th Congresses; member House Committee on Foreign Affairs.

FOURTH DISTRICT.—Milwaukee County: City of Milwaukee, wards 8 (except Wood, Wis.), 11, 12, 14, 17, and 19; cities of Cudahy, St. Francis, South Milwaukee, and West Allis; towns of Franklin, Greenfield, and Oak Creek; and villages of West Milwaukee, Hales Corners, and Greendale. Population (1960), 397,333.

CLEMENT J. ZABLOCKI, Democrat, of Milwaukee, Wis.; born in Milwaukee, Wis., November 18, 1912; son of Mathew and Mary Jankowski Zablocki; graduate of Marquette University with a Ph. B. degree; graduate work in education at Marquette University; taught high school in Milwaukee; organist and choir director; married Miss Blanche M. Janic of Milwaukee, May 26, 1937; son, Joseph Paul; daughter, Jane Frances; elected State senator of the Third District of Wisconsin in 1942, reelected in 1946; elected to the 81st Congress on November 2, 1948; reelected to the 82d, 83d, 84th, 85th, 86th, 87th, 88th, and 89th Congresses.

FIFTH DISTRICT.—Milwaukee County: City of Milwaukee, ward 1, precincts 6 to 32; ward 2, precincts 9 to 33; wards 3 to 7; ward 8, precinct 10; ward 9, precincts 31 and 32; wards 10 and 13; ward 15, precincts 1 to 10 and 16; and ward 16. Population (1960), 399,528.

HENRY S. REUSS, Democrat, of Milwaukee, Wis.; born in Milwaukee, Wis., February 22, 1912; educated in Milwaukee schools, A. B. Cornell University, LL. B. Harvard Law School; lawyer; lecturer (University of Wisconsin, Milwaukee), and writer; author of "The Critical Decade," 1964; member of Milwaukee School Board, 1953–55; married to Margaret Magrath, 1942; four children—Christopher, Michael, Jacqueline, Anne; assistant corporation counsel, Milwaukee County, 1939–40; assistant general counsel OPA, Washington, D.C., 1941–42; entered United States Army as private, January 1943; commissioned second lieutenant, Infantry, at Fort Benning, Ga., November 1943; served in 63d and 75th Infantry Divisions 1943–45; chief, Price Control Branch, Office of Military Government for Germany, June–December 1945; awarded Bronze Star Medal for action at Rhine crossing and Bronze Battle Stars for Normandy, Northern France, and Central Germany; deputy general counsel, Marshall Plan, Paris, France, 1949; special prosecutor, Milwaukee County Grand Jury 1950; personal counsel to Secretary of State Fred Zimmerman in Reapportionment Case, Wisconsin Supreme Court, 1953; former president, White Elm Nursery Co., Hartland, Wis.; former director, Marshall and Ilsley Bank, Milwaukee, Wis., and Niagara Share Corporation, Buffalo, N.Y.; past president, Cornell Alumni Association of Wisconsin; vice president, Chi Psi Alumni Association; director, Children's Service Society; vice chairman, Junior Bar Association; chairman, Milwaukee County Bar Association's Constitution and Citizenship Committee; vice chairman, Foreign Policy Association; member, Milwaukee City Club; former member, Legal Advisory Committee National Resources Board, Washington, D.C.; member, Milwaukee Chapter National Institute for Infantile Paralysis; Board of Alumni Visitors, Harvard Law School, 1957–60; Board of Visitors, Cornell University; National Board, Youth Hostel Association; elected to the 84th Congress November 2, 1954; reelected to 85th, 86th, 87th, 88th, and 89th Congresses.

SIXTH DISTRICT.—Counties: Calumet, Fond du Lac, Green Lake, Ozaukee, Sheboygan, Washington, and Winnebago (7 counties). Population (1960), 391,743.

JOHN ABNER RACE, Democrat, of Fond du Lac, Wis.; born in Fond du Lac May 12, 1914; attended the public grade and high schools and the University of

Wisconsin; employed as a specialist at Giddings & Lewis Machine Tool Co. in Fond du Lac for 23 years; member of the State Coordinating Committee for Higher Education, the Wisconsin State Board of Vocational and Adult Education, the Fond du Lac District Comprehensive Mental Health Planning Committee, and is a director of Sheltered Workshop, Inc., of Fond du Lac; elected county supervisor in 1958 and reelected in 1960 and 1962; chairman Fond du Lac County Democratic Party for 7 years and vice chairman Sixth District Democratic Party for 4 years; candidate for Congress in 1962; married to the former Dorothea Schroeder; three daughters; elected to the 89th Congress November 3, 1964.

SEVENTH DISTRICT.—COUNTIES: Adams, Clark, Florence, Forest, Langlade, Lincoln, Marathon, Marquette, Menominee, Portage, Shawano, Taylor, Waupaca, Waushara, and Wood (15 counties). Population (1960), 387,077.

MELVIN R. LAIRD, Republican, of Marshfield, Wis.; born September 1, 1922; son of Melvin R. and Helen C. Laird; attended Marshfield grade schools and high school; B. A. degree, Carleton College, Northfield, Minn.; served in United States Navy, World War II, aboard destroyer *Maddox* in Task Force 58 and Pacific Third Fleet; elected Wisconsin State Senator 1946; reelected without opposition 1948; member, Wisconsin delegation, Republican National Convention 1948, 1952, 1956, and 1960; member, Republican National Convention Platform Committee 1952, 1956, and 1960; chairman, 1962 Joint Committee on Republican Principles; member of American Legion, 40 et 8, Veterans of Foreign Wars, Disabled American Veterans, Military Order of Purple Heart, F. & A.M., United Commercial Travelers, and B.P.O.E.; elder, First Presbyterian Church of Marshfield; married Barbara Masters of Indianapolis, Ind., on October 15, 1945; three children, John Osborne, Alison, and David; home address, 207 South Central Avenue, Marshfield, Wis.; elected to 83d Congress November 4, 1952; reelected to the 84th, 85th, 86th, 87th, 88th, and 89th Congresses; member, House Agricultural Committee 84th Congress; member, House Appropriations Committee 83d, 85th, 86th, 87th, 88th, and 89th Congresses; presently serving on following subcommittees: Defense, Health, Education, Welfare, and Labor; chairman, Republican Platform Committee, 1964; chairman, Republican Conference, 89th Congress.

EIGHTH DISTRICT.—COUNTIES: Brown, Door, Kewaunee, Manitowoc, Marinette, Oconto, and Outagamie (7 counties). Population (1960), 400,567.

JOHN W. BYRNES, Republican, of Green Bay, Wis.; born in Green Bay, June 12, 1913; received B. A. from University of Wisconsin, 1936, and LL. B. from University of Wisconsin Law School, 1938; appointed Special Deputy Commissioner Banking, Wisconsin, 1938–41; began practice of law, 1939; elected Wisconsin State Senate, 1940; named chairman of Senate Judiciary Committee and majority floor leader, 1943; elected to 79th Congress, 1944; reelected to all succeeding Congresses; elected to Committee on Ways and Means, 80th Congress; elected chairman, Republican Policy Committee, 86th Congress; married Barbara Preston, 1947; six children; home office address: 101 North Jefferson Street, Green Bay, Wis.

NINTH DISTRICT.—WAUKESHA COUNTY, PART of MILWAUKEE COUNTY—City of Milwaukee: Ward 18, parts of wards 1, 2, 9, and 15; cities of Glendale and Wauwatosa; villages of Bayside, Brown Deer, Fox Point, River Hills, Shorewood, and Whitefish Bay. Population (1960), 397,429.

GLENN R. DAVIS, Republican, of New Berlin, Wis.; born on a farm in the town of Vernon, Waukesha County, Wis., October 28, 1914; graduated from rural school at 11, Mukwonago High School at 15, and Platteville State Teachers College (B. Ed. degree) at 19; taught 2 years at secondary level at Cottage Grove, Wis., and 2 years at Waupun High School; graduated from the University of Wisconsin Law School in 1940; elected to the State assembly from the First Waukesha County District the same year and served in the 1941 session; served 3½ years active duty in the U.S. Naval Reserve, 32 months continuously aboard an aircraft carrier; married in 1942 to Dr. Kathryn McFarlane, Waukesha dentist; five children; elected to the 80th Congress at a special election April 22, 1947, to fill a vacancy caused by the death of Robert K. Henry; reelected to the 81st, 82d, 83d, and 84th Congresses; served on the Veterans Affairs Committee the first two terms, assigned to the Appropriations Committee at the beginning of the third term, and appointed a subcommittee chairman in the 83d Congress; chosen in 1948 as one of the Ten Outstanding Young Men of America by the National Junior Chamber of Commerce; practiced law in Waukesha since January 1957; elected to the 89th Congress November 3, 1964.

TENTH DISTRICT.—Counties: Ashland, Barron, Bayfield, Burnett, Chippewa, Douglas, Dunn, Eau Claire, Iron, Oneida, Polk, Price, Rusk, St. Croix, Sawyer, Vilas, and Washburn (17 counties). Population (1960), 389,675.

ALVIN E. O'KONSKI, Republican, of Mercer, Wis.; born on a farm in Kewaunee, Wis.; graduated from rural school and high school at Kewaunee; worked way through Wisconsin State College at Oshkosh, Wis., earning a bachelor of education degree; captain of debating team for 3 years and president of student body 2 years; majored in speech and political science; graduate work speech and political science majors at University of Wisconsin; captain, University of Wisconsin Big Ten Championship Debating Team; graduate work in speech major, University of Iowa; taught at Omro, Oconto, and Pulaski High Schools in Wisconsin; taught at Itasca Junior College in Minnesota, Oregon State College in Oregon, and University of Detroit in Michigan; married Veronica Hemming of Janesville, Wis.; former publisher of newspaper, Hurley, Wis.; former owner of WOSA and WLIN, radio stations at Wausau and Merrill, Wis.; president WAEO–TV Inc., Rhinelander, Wis.; ranked first among all Congressmen in American History test conducted by United Press; former president World Bill of Rights Association 1945; director World League to Stop Communism, 1947; present director Free World Forum; member of Katyn Massacre Committee 1952; voted most distinguished American for 1945 by Foreign Language Press for his work against communism; awarded Polonia Restitutia, highest medal of Free Poland; member of Armed Services Committee and District of Columbia Committee; also served as member of Veterans Affairs, Public Works, and Education and Labor Committees; elected in 1942 to 78th Congress, reelected each time since; dean of Wisconsin delegation now serving twelfth term; in spite of District voting Democratic by margins of two to one, wins on Republican ticket by margins of two to one.

WYOMING

(Population (1960), 330,066)

SENATORS

GALE WILLIAM McGEE, Democrat, of Laramie, Wyo.; born in Lincoln, Nebr., March 17, 1915; graduate of high school, Norfolk, Nebr., 1932; A. B., 1936, Nebraska State Teachers College, Wayne, Nebr.; M. A., 1939, University of Colorado at Boulder; Ph. D. 1947, University of Chicago; professor of American history: Crofton, Nebr., High School, 1936–37; Kearney, Nebr., High School, 1937–40; Nebraska Wesleyan University, 1940–43; Iowa State, at Ames, 1943–44; University of Notre Dame, 1944–45; University of Chicago, 1945–46; University of Wyoming since 1946; married Loraine Baker, of Pierson, Iowa, in 1939; two sons and two daughters; elected to the United States Senate on November 4, 1958, for the term ending January 3, 1965; reelected November 3, 1964.

MILWARD LEE SIMPSON, Republican, of Cody, Wyo.; born in Jackson, Wyo., November 12, 1897, son of William L. and Margaret Burnett Simpson; attended the public schools of Wood River, Meeteetse, and Cody, all in Wyoming; served U.S. Army, Infantry, second lieutenant, World War I; graduated University of Wyoming, B.S. 1921; held instructorship, political science, at University of Wyoming; attended Harvard University Law School 1921–25; admitted Wyoming Bar in 1926 and practiced in Cody until 1955; honorary LL.D. University of Wyoming in 1955; member Wyoming House of Representatives 1926–27; married Lorna Helen Kooi of Sheridan, Wyo., June 29, 1929; two sons, Peter Kooi Simpson and Alan Kooi Simpson; served as Governor of Wyoming 1955–59; resumed law practice in 1959; member of executive committee of Governor's Conference; appointed to board of trustees University of Wyoming in 1939 and served as president 1943–54; member National Association Governing Boards of State Universities and Allied Institutions in 1950 and served as president 1952–53; member of American, Wyoming, Fifth Judicial District, and Park County bar associations; member Episcopal Church, American Legion, 40 and 8, Rotary International, Masons, Elks, Eagles, and Moose; member and officer in county, State, and national mental health associations 1959–61; member National Council, Boy Scouts of America, 1937–; elected to the United States Senate November 6, 1962, to fill vacancy caused by death of Senator-elect Keith Thomson in the term ending January 3, 1967.

REPRESENTATIVE

AT LARGE.—Population (1960), 330,066.

TENO RONCALIO, Democrat, of Cheyenne, Wyo.; born Rock Springs, Wyo., March 23, 1916; LL.B., University of Wyoming, 1947; U.S. Senate employee under patronage of the late Joseph C. O'Mahoney, 1941, resigned to enlist in Infantry, World War II, served 3 years overseas in First Division in North Africa, Sicily, Europe; decorations include Silver Star; admitted to the bar of Wyoming 1947; deputy prosecuting attorney, Laramie County, Wyo., 1950–56; senior partner, law firm Roncalio, Graves & Smyth, Cheyenne, Wyo.; Chairman Wyoming Democratic State Central Committee 1957–61; Chairman of the Board, Cheyenne National Bank; member International Joint Commission, United States-Canada, 1961–64; married Cecelia Waters Domenico; four foster children, two sons, Teno Frank and John Waters; elected to the 89th Congress November 3, 1964.

COMMONWEALTH OF PUERTO RICO

(Population (1960), 2,349,544)

RESIDENT COMMISSIONER

SANTIAGO POLANCO-ABREU, Popular Democrat, of Isabela, Puerto Rico; born October 30, 1920, in Bayamon, P.R.; married Viola Orsini in 1944; no children; attended elementary and high school in Isabela, P.R.; B.A. and LL.B., University of Puerto Rico, 1943; president of the student council; practiced law in Isabela and San Juan; appointed legal adviser to the Tax Court of Puerto Rico, August 1943; elected to the house of representatives, Commonwealth of Puerto Rico, 1948, 1952, 1956, 1960; member of the Constitutional Convention of Puerto Rico, 1951–52; chairman, Committee of Finance; vice chairman, Committees on Interior Government, Appointments and Impeachment Proceedings, and member of the Committee of Rules and Calendar; appointed speaker of the house, January 17, 1963; member ex officio of all house committees; member of the American Bar Association, Bar Association of Puerto Rico, Puerto Rican Atheneum, Association of American Writers, Lions Club, and Pan American Gun Club; elected Resident Commissioner of Puerto Rico November 3, 1964, for a 4-year term.

STATE DELEGATIONS

STATE DELEGATIONS

Number which precedes name of Representative designates congressional district.   Democrats in roman; Republicans in *italics*

ALABAMA
SENATORS

Lister Hill   John J. Sparkman

REPRESENTATIVES
[Democrats, 3; Republicans, 5]

1. *Jack Edwards*
2. *William L. Dickinson*
3. George Andrews
4. *Glenn Andrews*
5. Armistead I. Selden, Jr.
6. *John H. Buchanan, Jr.*
7. *James D. Martin*
8. Robert E. Jones

ALASKA
SENATORS

E. L. Bartlett   Ernest Gruening

REPRESENTATIVE
[Democrat, 1]

At large—Ralph J. Rivers

ARIZONA
SENATORS

Carl Hayden   *Paul J. Fannin*

REPRESENTATIVES
[Democrats, 2; Republican, 1]

1. *John J. Rhodes*   2. Morris K. Udall   3. George F. Senner, Jr.

ARKANSAS
SENATORS

John L. McClellan   J. W. Fulbright

REPRESENTATIVES
[Democrats, 4]

1. E. C. Gathings   3. James W. Trimble   4. Oren Harris
2. Wilbur D. Mills

CALIFORNIA
SENATORS

Thomas H. Kuchel   *George Murphy*

REPRESENTATIVES
[Democrats, 23; Republicans, 15]

1. *Don H. Clausen*
2. Harold T. Johnson
3. John E. Moss
4. Robert L. Leggett
5. Phillip Burton
6. *William S. Mailliard*
7. Jeffery Cohelan
8. George P. Miller
9. Don Edwards
10. *Charles S. Gubser*
11. *J. Arthur Younger*
12. *Burt L. Talcott*
13. *Charles M. Teague*
14. *John F. Baldwin*
15. John J. McFall
16. B. F. Sisk
17. Cecil R. King
18. Harlan Hagen
19. Chet Holifield
20. *H. Allen Smith*
21. Augustus F. Hawkins
22. James C. Corman
23. *Del Clawson*
24. *Glenard P. Lipscomb*
25. Ronald Brooks Cameron
26. James Roosevelt
27. *Ed Reinecke*
28. *Alphonzo Bell*
29. George E. Brown, Jr.
30. Edward R. Roybal
31. Charles H. Wilson
32. *Craig Hosmer*
33. Ken W. Dyal
34. Richard T. Hanna
35. *James B. Utt*
36. *Bob Wilson*
37. Lionel Van Deerlin
38. John V. Tunney

187

COLORADO

SENATORS

Gordon Allott   *Peter H. Dominick*

REPRESENTATIVES
[Democrats, 4]

1. Byron G. Rogers   3. Frank E. Evans   4. Wayne N. Aspinall
2. Roy H. McVicker

CONNECTICUT

SENATORS

Thomas J. Dodd   Abraham A. Ribicoff

REPRESENTATIVES
[Democrats, 6]

1. Emilio Q. Daddario   3. Robert N. Giaimo   5. John S. Monagan
2. William L. St. Onge   4. Donald J. Irwin   6. Bernard F. Grabowski

DELAWARE

SENATORS

John J. Williams   *J. Caleb Boggs*

REPRESENTATIVE
[Democrat, 1]

At large—Harris B. McDowell, Jr.

FLORIDA

SENATORS

Spessard L. Holland   George A. Smathers

REPRESENTATIVES
[Democrats, 10; Republicans, 2]

1. Robert L. F. Sikes   5. A. Sydney Herlong, Jr.   9. Don Fuqua
2. Charles E. Bennett   6. Paul G. Rogers   10. Sam M. Gibbons
3. Claude Pepper   7. James A. Haley   11. *Edward J. Gurney*
4. Dante B. Fascell   8. D. R. (Billy) Matthews 12. *William C. Cramer*

GEORGIA

SENATORS

Richard B. Russell   Herman E. Talmadge

REPRESENTATIVES
[Democrats, 9; Republican, 1]

1. G. Elliott Hagan   5. Charles L. Weltner   8. J. Russell Tuten
2. Maston O'Neal   6. John J. Flynt, Jr.   9. Phil M. Landrum
3. *Howard H. Callaway*   7. John W. Davis   10. Robert G. Stephens,
4. James A. Mackay   Jr.

HAWAII

SENATORS

Hiram L. Fong   Daniel K. Inouye

REPRESENTATIVES (AT LARGE)
[Democrats, 2]

Spark M. Matsunaga   Patsy T. Mink

IDAHO

SENATORS

Frank Church   *Len B. Jordan*

REPRESENTATIVES

[Democrat, 1; Republican, 1]

1. Compton I. White, Jr.   2. *George V. Hansen*

ILLINOIS

SENATORS

Paul H. Douglas   *Everett McKinley Dirksen*

REPRESENTATIVES
[Democrats, 13; Republicans, 11]

1. William L. Dawson
2. Barratt O'Hara
3. William T. Murphy
4. *Edward J. Derwinski*
5. John C. Kluczynski
6. Daniel J. Ronan
7. Frank Annunzio
8. Dan Rostenkowski
9. Sidney R. Yates
10. *Harold R. Collier*
11. Roman C. Pucinski
12. *Robert McClory*
13. *Donald Rumsfeld*
14. *John N. Erlenborn*
15. *Charlotte T. Reid*
16. *John B. Anderson*
17. *Leslie C. Arends*
18. *Robert H. Michel*
19. Gale Schisler
20. *Paul Findley*
21. Kenneth J. Gray
22. *William L. Springer*
23. George E. Shipley
24. Melvin Price

INDIANA

SENATORS

Vance Hartke   Birch Bayh

REPRESENTATIVES
[Democrats, 6; Republicans, 5]

1. Ray J. Madden
2. *Charles A. Halleck*
3. John Brademas
4. *E. Ross Adair*
5. J. Edward Roush
6. *Richard L. Roudebush*
7. *William G. Bray*
8. Winfield K. Denton
9. Lee H. Hamilton
10. *Ralph Harvey*
11. Andrew Jacobs, Jr.

IOWA

SENATORS

Bourke B. Hickenlooper   *Jack Miller*

REPRESENTATIVES
[Democrats, 6; Republican, 1]

1. John R. Schmidhauser
2. John C. Culver
3. *H. R. Gross*
4. Bert Bandstra
5. Neal Smith
6. Stanley L. Greigg
7. John R. Hansen

KANSAS

SENATORS

Frank Carlson   *James B. Pearson*

REPRESENTATIVES

[Republicans, 5]

1. *Bob Dole* 3. *Robert F. Ellsworth* 5. *Joe Skubitz*
2. *Chester L. Mize* 4. *Garner E. Shriver*

KENTUCKY

SENATORS

John Sherman Cooper *Thruston B. Morton*

REPRESENTATIVES

[Democrats, 6; Republican, 1]

1. Frank A. Stubblefield 4. Frank Chelf 6. John C. Watts
2. William H. Natcher 5. *Tim Lee Carter* 7. Carl D. Perkins
3. Charles P. Farnsley

LOUISIANA

SENATORS

Allen J. Ellender   Russell B. Long

REPRESENTATIVES

[Democrats, 8]

1. F. Edward Hébert 4. Joe D. Waggonner, Jr. 7. T. Ashton Thompson
2. Hale Boggs 5. Otto E. Passman 8. Speedy O. Long
3. Edwin E. Willis 6. James H. Morrison

MAINE

SENATORS

Margaret Chase Smith Edmund S. Muskie

REPRESENTATIVES

[Democrat, 1; Republican, 1]

1. *Stanley R. Tupper* 2. William D. Hathaway

MARYLAND

SENATORS

Daniel B. Brewster Joseph D. Tydings

REPRESENTATIVES

[Democrats, 6; Republicans, 2]

At large—Carlton R. Sickles

1. *Rogers C. B. Morton* 4. George H. Fallon 7. Samuel N. Friedel
2. Clarence D. Long 5. Hervey G. Machen
3. Edward A. Garmatz 6. *Charles McC. Mathias, Jr.*

MASSACHUSETTS

SENATORS

Leverett Saltonstall   Edward M. Kennedy

REPRESENTATIVES

[Democrats, 7; Republicans 5]

1. *Silvio O. Conte*
2. Edward P. Boland
3. Philip J. Philbin
4. Harold D. Donohue
5. *F. Bradford Morse*
6. *William H. Bates*
7. Torbert H. Macdonald
8. Thomas P. O'Neill, Jr.
9. John W. McCormack
10. *Joseph W. Martin, Jr.*
11. James A. Burke
12. *Hastings Keith*

MICHIGAN

SENATORS

Pat McNamara   Philip A. Hart

REPRESENTATIVES

[Democrats, 12; Republicans, 7]

1. John Conyers, Jr.
2. Weston E. Vivian
3. Paul H. Todd, Jr.
4. *Edward Hutchinson*
5. *Gerald R. Ford*
6. *Charles E. Chamberlain*
7. John C. Mackie
8. *James Harvey*
9. *Robert P. Griffin*
10. *Elford A. Cederberg*
11. Raymond F. Clevenger
12. James G. O'Hara
13. Charles C. Diggs, Jr.
14. Lucien N. Nedzi
15. William D. Ford
16. John D. Dingell
17. Martha W. Griffiths
18. *William S. Broomfield*
19. Billie S. Farnum

MINNESOTA

SENATORS

Eugene J. McCarthy   Walter F. Mondale

REPRESENTATIVES

[Democrats, 4; Republicans, 4]

1. *Albert H. Quie*
2. *Ancher Nelsen*
3. *Clark MacGregor*
4. Joseph E. Karth
5. Donald M. Fraser
6. Alec G. Olson
7. *Odin Langen*
8. John A. Blatnik

MISSISSIPPI

SENATORS

James O. Eastland   John Stennis

REPRESENTATIVES

[Democrats, 4; Republican, 1]

1. Thomas G. Abernethy
2. Jamie L. Whitten
3. John Bell Williams
4. *Prentiss Walker*
5. William M. Colmer

MISSOURI

SENATORS

Stuart Symington   Edward V. Long

REPRESENTATIVES

[Democrats, 8; Republicans, 2]

1. Frank M. Karsten
2. *Thomas B. Curtis*
3. Leonor Kretzer (Mrs. John B.) Sullivan
4. Wm. J. Randall
5. Richard Bolling
6. W. R. Hull, Jr.
7. *Durward G. Hall*
8. Richard H. Ichord
9. William L. Hungate
10. Paul C. Jones

MONTANA

SENATORS

Mike Mansfield   Lee Metcalf

REPRESENTATIVES
[Democrat, 1; Republican, 1]

1. Arnold Olsen   2. *James F. Battin*

NEBRASKA

SENATORS

Roman L. Hruska   *Carl T. Curtis*

REPRESENTATIVES
[Democrat, 1; Republicans, 2]

1. Clair A. Callan   2. *Glenn Cunningham*   3. *David T. Martin*

NEVADA

SENATORS

Alan Bible   Howard W. Cannon

REPRESENTATIVE
[Democrat, 1]

At large—Walter S. Baring

NEW HAMPSHIRE

SENATORS

Norris Cotton   Thomas J. McIntyre

REPRESENTATIVES
[Democrat, 1; Republican, 1]

1. J. Oliva Huot   2. *James C. Cleveland*

NEW JERSEY

SENATORS

Clifford P. Case   Harrison A. Williams, Jr.

REPRESENTATIVES
[Democrats, 11; Republicans, 4]

1. *William T. Cahill*
2. Thomas C. McGrath, Jr.
3. James J. Howard
4. Frank Thompson, Jr.
5. *Peter H. B. Frelinghuysen*
6. *Florence P. Dwyer*
7. *William B. Widnall*
8. Charles S. Joelson
9. Henry Helstoski
10. Peter W. Rodino, Jr.
11. Joseph G. Minish
12. Paul J. Krebs
13. Cornelius E. Gallagher
14. Dominick V. Daniels
15. Edward J. Patten

NEW MEXICO

SENATORS

Clinton P. Anderson   Joseph M. Montoya

REPRESENTATIVES (AT LARGE)
[Democrats, 2]

Thomas G. Morris   E. S. Johnny Walker

NEW YORK

SENATORS

Jacob K. Javits   Robert F. Kennedy

REPRESENTATIVES
[Democrats, 27; Republicans, 14]

1. Otis G. Pike
2. *James R. Grover, Jr.*
3. Lester L. Wolff
4. *John W. Wydler*
5. Herbert Tenzer
6. *Seymour Halpern*
7. Joseph P. Addabbo
8. Benjamin S. Rosenthal
9. James J. Delaney
10. Emanuel Celler
11. Eugene J. Keogh
12. Edna F. Kelly
13. Abraham J. Multer
14. John J. Rooney
15. Hugh L. Carey
16. John M. Murphy
17. *John V. Lindsay*
18. Adam C. Powell
19. Leonard Farbstein
20. William F. Ryan
21. James H. Scheuer
22. Jacob H. Gilbert
23. Jonathan B. Bingham
24. *Paul A. Fino*
25. Richard L. Ottinger
26. *Ogden R. Reid*
27. John G. Dow
28. Joseph Y. Resnick
29. Leo W. O'Brien
30. *Carleton J. King*
31. *Robert C. McEwen*
32. *Alexander Pirnie*
33. *Howard W. Robison*
34. James M. Hanley
35. Samuel S. Stratton
36. *Frank Horton*
37. *Barber B. Conable, Jr.*
38. *Charles E. Goodell*
39. Richard D. McCarthy
40. *Henry P. Smith, 3d*
41. Thaddeus J. Dulski

NORTH CAROLINA

SENATORS

Sam J. Ervin, Jr.   B. Everett Jordan

REPRESENTATIVES
[Democrats, 9; Republicans, 2]

1. Herbert C. Bonner
2. L. H. Fountain
3. David N. Henderson
4. Harold D. Cooley
5. Ralph J. Scott
6. Horace R. Kornegay
7. Alton Lennon
8. *Charles R. Jonas*
9. *James T. Broyhill*
10. Basil L. Whitener
11. Roy A. Taylor

NORTH DAKOTA

SENATORS

Milton R. Young   Quentin N. Burdick

REPRESENTATIVES
[Democrat, 1; Republican, 1]

1. *Mark Andrews*   2. Rolland Redlin

OHIO

SENATORS

Frank J. Lausche   Stephen M. Young

REPRESENTATIVES

[Democrats, 10; Republicans, 14]

At large—Robert E. Sweeney

1. John J. Gilligan
2. *Donald D. Clancy*
3. Rodney M. Love
4. *William M. McCulloch*
5. *Delbert L. Latta*
6. *William H. Harsha*
7. *Clarence J. Brown*
8. *Jackson E. Betts*
9. Thomas L. Ashley
10. Walter H. Moeller
11. *J. William Stanton*
12. *Samuel L. Devine*
13. *Charles A. Mosher*
14. *William H. Ayres*
15. Robert T. Secrest
16. *Frank T. Bow*
17. *John M. Ashbrook*
18. Wayne L. Hays
19. Michael J. Kirwan
20. Michael A. Feighan
21. Charles A. Vanik
22. *Frances P. Bolton*
23. *William E. Minshall*

OKLAHOMA

SENATORS

A. S. Mike Monroney   Fred R. Harris

REPRESENTATIVES

[Democrats, 5; Republican, 1]

1. *Page Belcher*
2. Ed Edmondson
3. Carl Albert
4. Tom Steed
5. John Jarman
6. Jed Johnson, Jr.

OREGON

SENATORS

Wayne Morse   Maurine B. Neuberger

REPRESENTATIVES

[Democrats, 3; Republican, 1]

1. *Wendell Wyatt*
2. Al Ullman
3. Edith Green
4. Robert B. Duncan

PENNSYLVANIA

SENATORS

Joseph S. Clark   *Hugh Scott*

REPRESENTATIVES

[Democrats, 15; Republicans, 12

1. William A. Barrett
2. Robert N. C. Nix
3. James A. Byrne
4. Herman Toll
5. William J. Green
6. George M. Rhodes
7. *G. Robert Watkins*
8. *Willard S. Curtin*
9. *Paul B. Dague*
10. *Joseph M. McDade*
11. Daniel J. Flood
12. *J. Irving Whalley*
13. *Richard S. Schweiker*
14. William S. Moorhead
15. Fred B. Rooney
16. *John C. Kunkel*
17. *Herman T. Schneebeli*
18. *Robert J. Corbett*
19. N. Neiman Craley, Jr.
20. Elmer J. Holland
21. John H. Dent
22. *John P. Saylor*
23. *Albert W. Johnson*
24. Joseph P. Vigorito
25. Frank M. Clark
26. Thomas E. Morgan
27. *James G. Fulton*

RHODE ISLAND

SENATORS

John O. Pastore   Claiborne Pell

REPRESENTATIVES
[Democrats, 2]

1. Fernand J. St Germain   2. John E. Fogarty

SOUTH CAROLINA

SENATORS

Olin D. Johnston   *Strom Thurmond*

REPRESENTATIVES
[Democrats, 5; vacant 1]

1. L. Mendel Rivers   3. W. J. Bryan Dorn   5. Tom S. Gettys
2. [Vacant]   4. Robert T. Ashmore   6. John L. McMillan

SOUTH DAKOTA

SENATORS

Karl E. Mundt   George McGovern

REPRESENTATIVES
[Republicans, 2]

1. *Ben Reifel*   2. *E. Y. Berry*

TENNESSEE

SENATORS

Albert Gore   Ross Bass

REPRESENTATIVES
[Democrats, 6; Republicans, 3]

1. *James H. Quillen*   4. Joe L. Evins   7. Tom Murray
2. *John J. Duncan*   5. Richard H. Fulton   8. Robert A. Everett
3. *William E. Brock 3d* 6. William R. Anderson   9. George W. Grider

TEXAS

SENATORS

Ralph W. Yarborough   *John G. Tower*

REPRESENTATIVES
[Democrats, 23]

At large—Joe Pool

1. Wright Patman   9. Clark W. Thompson   17. Omar Burleson
2. Jack Brooks   10. J. J. (Jake) Pickle 18. Walter Rogers
3. Lindley Beckworth   11. W. R. Poage   19. George H. Mahon
4. Ray Roberts   12. James C. Wright, Jr. 20. Henry B. Gonzalez
5. Earle Cabell   13. Graham Purcell   21. O. C. Fisher
6. Olin E. Teague   14. John Young   22. Bob Casey
7. John Dowdy   15. Eligio de la Garza
8. Albert Thomas   16. Richard C. White

UTAH

SENATORS

Wallace F. Bennett   Frank E. Moss

REPRESENTATIVES
[Democrat, 1; Republican, 1]

1. *Laurence J. Burton*   2. David S. King

VERMONT

SENATORS

George D. Aiken   *Winston L. Prouty*

REPRESENTATIVE
[Republican, 1]

At large—*Robert T. Stafford*

VIRGINIA

SENATORS

Harry Flood Byrd   A. Willis Robertson

REPRESENTATIVES
[Democrats, 8; Republicans, 2]

1. Thomas N. Downing
2. Porter Hardy, Jr.
3. David E. Satterfield 3d
4. Watkins M. Abbitt
5. William M. Tuck
6. *Richard H. Poff*
7. John O. Marsh, Jr.
8. Howard W. Smith
9. W. Pat Jennings
10. *Joel T. Broyhill*

WASHINGTON

SENATORS

Warren G. Magnuson   Henry M. Jackson

REPRESENTATIVES
[Democrats, 5; Republicans, 2]

1. *Thomas M. Pelly*
2. Lloyd Meeds
3. Julia Butler Hansen
4. *Catherine May*
5. Thomas S. Foley
6. Floyd V. Hicks
7. Brock Adams

WEST VIRGINIA

SENATORS

Jennings Randolph   Robert C. Byrd

REPRESENTATIVES
[Democrats, 4; Republican, 1]

1. *Arch A. Moore, Jr.*
2. Harley O. Staggers
3. John M. Slack, Jr.
4. Ken Hechler
5. James Kee

WISCONSIN

SENATORS

William Proxmire   Gaylord Nelson

REPRESENTATIVES

[Democrats, 5; Republicans, 5]

1. Lynn E. Stalbaum
2. Robert W. Kastenmeier
3. *Vernon W. Thomson*
4. Clement J. Zablocki

5. Henry S. Reuss
6. John A. Race
7. *Melvin R. Laird*
8. *John W. Byrnes*

9. *Glenn R. Davis*
10. *Alvin E. O'Konski*

WYOMING

SENATORS

Gale W. McGee   *Milward L. Simpson*

REPRESENTATIVE

[Democrat, 1]

At large—Teno Roncalio

COMMONWEALTH OF PUERTO RICO

RESIDENT COMMISSIONER

Santiago Polanco-Abreu

CLASSIFICATION

SENATE		HOUSE	
Democrats	68	Democrats	294
Republicans	32	Republicans	140
		Vacant	1
Total	100	Total	435

ALPHABETICAL LIST

ALPHABETICAL LIST

NAME, DISTRICT, HOME ADDRESS, WASHINGTON RESIDENCE, AND PAGE ON WHICH BIOGRAPHY APPEARS

[The * designates those who are married; the † designates unmarried daughters; the ‖ designates those having other ladies with them]

THE SENATE

*HUBERT H. HUMPHREY, Vice President of the United States and President of the Senate, 3216 Coquelin Terrace, Chevy Chase, Md., 20015.

CARL HAYDEN, President pro tempore.

*FELTON M. JOHNSTON, Secretary, 2010 48th Street, 20007.

*JOSEPH C. DUKE, Sergeant at Arms, Sheraton-Park, 20008.

*FRANCIS R. VALEO, Secretary for the Majority, 3420 17th Street, 20010.

*†J. MARK TRICE, Secretary for the Minority, 5017 Worthington Drive, Westmoreland Hills, Md., 20016.

*Rev. FREDERICK BROWN HARRIS, D.D., Litt. D., LL.D. Chaplain, 4000 Cathedral Avenue, 20016.

(For office rooms and telephones see pp. 405-407)

[Democrats in roman (68); Republicans in *italics* (32); total, 100]

Name	Home address	Washington residence and ZIP code number	Biography
			Page
*Aiken, George D_____	Putney, Vt_____	The Carroll Arms, 20002.	168
*Allott, Gordon_____	Lamar, Colo_____	-----------------------	23
*Anderson, Clinton P_____	Albuquerque, N. Mex.	6 Wesley Circle, 20016_	102
*†Bartlett, E. L_____	Juneau, Alaska_____	2343 49th St., 20007___	7
*Bass, Ross_____	Pulaski, Tenn_____	4000 Mass. Ave., 20016.	155
*Bayh, Birch_____	Terre Haute, Ind____	4108 Woodacre Dr., McLean, Va., 22101.	51
*Bennett, Wallace F_____	Salt Lake City, Utah.	4201 Mass. Ave., 20016.	166
*Bible, Alan_____	Reno, Nev_____	9338 Harvey Rd., Silver Spring, Md., 20910.	93
*Boggs, J. Caleb_____	Wilmington, Del_____	-----------------------	28
*Brewster, Daniel B_____	Towson, Md_____	Senate Office Bldg_____	68
*Burdick, Quentin N_____	Fargo, N. Dak_____	35 E St., 20001_____	127
Byrd, Harry Flood_____	Berryville, Va_____	The Shoreham, 20008__	169
*Byrd, Robert C_____	Sophia, W. Va_____	-----------------------	176
*Cannon, Howard W_____	Las Vegas, Nev_____	10012 East Bexhill Dr., Kensington, Md., 20795.	93
*Carlson, Frank_____	Concordia, Kans_____	Sheraton-Park, 20008__	58
*Case, Clifford P_____	Rahway, N.J_____	2728 Dumbarton Ave., 20007.	97
*Church, Frank_____	Boise, Idaho_____	405 Senate Office Bldg.	41
*Clark, Joseph S_____	Philadelphia, Pa____	3318 R St., 20007_____	140
*Cooper, John Sherman____	Somerset, Ky_____	2900 N St., 20007_____	61

THE SENATE—Continued

(For office rooms and telephones see pp. 405-407)

Name	Home address	Washington residence and ZIP code number	Biography Page
*Cotton, Norris	Lebanon, N.H		95
*Curtis, Carl T	Minden, Nebr	6613 31st Pl., 20015	91
*Dirksen, Everett McKinley.	Pekin, Ill	Broad Run Farms, Sterling, Va., 22170.	43
*Dodd, Thomas J	West Hartford, Conn.	1407 31st St., 20007	26
*Dominick, Peter H	Englewood, Colo	1801 45th St., 20007	23
*Douglas, Paul H	Chicago, Ill	2909 Davenport St., 20008.	43
*Eastland, James O	Doddsville, Miss	5116 Macomb St., 20016.	84
Ellender, Allen J	Houma, La	3900 Conn. Ave., 20008.	64
*Ervin, Sam J., Jr	Morganton, N.C	110 Maryland Ave. NE., 20002.	122
*†Fannin, Paul J	Phoenix, Ariz	4501 Conn. Ave., 20008.	8
*Fong, Hiram L	Honolulu, Hawaii	5519 Uppingham St., Chevy Chase, Md., 20015.	39
*Fulbright, J. W	Fayetteville, Ark	2527 Belmont Rd., 20008.	10
*†Gore, Albert	Carthage, Tenn	Fairfax Hotel, 20008	155
*Gruening, Ernest	Juneau, Alaska	7926 West Beach Dr., 20012.	7
*Harris, Fred R	Lawton, Okla	1309 Ridge Rd., McLean, Va., 22101.	135
*Hart, Philip A	Mackinac Island, Mich.	2812 Calvert St., 20008	76
*Hartke, Vance	Evansville, Ind	1010 Kern's Ct., Falls Church, Va., 22044.	51
Hayden, Carl	Phoenix, Ariz		8
*Hickenlooper, Bourke B	Cedar Rapids, Iowa	5511 Cedar Pkwy., Chevy Chase, Md., 20015.	55
*Hill, Lister	Montgomery, Ala	3715 49th St., 20016	3
*Holland, Spessard L	Bartow, Fla	Sheraton-Park, 20008	29
*†Hruska, Roman L	Omaha, Nebr	2429 North Lincoln St., Arlington, Va., 22207.	91
*Inouye, Daniel K	Honolulu, Hawaii	5100 Dorset Ave., Chevy Chase, Md., 20015.	39
*†Jackson, Henry M	Everett, Wash	2500 Q St., 20007	173
*Javits, Jacob K	New York City, N.Y		104
*Johnston, Olin D	Spartanburg, S.C	3900 16th St., 20011	150
*Jordan, B. Everett	Saxapahaw, N.C	Calvert-Woodley Apts., 20008.	122
*Jordan, Len B	Boise, Idaho	100 Maryland Ave. NE., 20002.	41
*‖Kennedy, Edward M	Boston, Mass		71
*Kennedy, Robert F	Glen Cove, N.Y	McLean, Va., 22101	104
*†Kuchel, Thomas H	Anaheim, Calif	3118 Arizona Ave., 20016.	12
*Lausche, Frank J	Cleveland, Ohio	6916 Marbury Rd., Bethesda, Md., 20034.	128

THE SENATE—Continued

(For office rooms and telephones see pp. 405-407)

Name	Home address	Washington residence and ZIP code number	Biography
			Page
*†Long, Edward V_____	Clarksville, Mo_____	4201 Cathedral Ave., 20016.	86
*Long, Russell B_____	Baton Rouge, La____	Potomac Plaza Apts., 20037	64
*McCarthy, Eugene J____	St. Paul, Minn_____	5916 Bradley Blvd., Bethesda, Md., 20014.	81
*McClellan, John L_____	Camden, Ark_____	The Fairfax, 20008____	10
*McGee, Gale W_____	Laramie, Wyo_____	7205 Marbury Rd., Bethesda, Md., 20034.	183
*††McGovern, George____	Mitchell, S. Dak____	3214 Coquelin Ter., Chevy Chase, Md., 20015.	153
*†McIntyre, Thomas J___	Laconia, N.H_____	6104 Kennedy Dr., Chevy Chase, Md., 20015.	95
*McNamara, Pat_____	Detroit, Mich_____	_____	76
*Magnuson, Warren G____	Seattle, Wash_____	The Shoreham, 20008__	173
*†Mansfield, Mike_____	Missoula, Mont_____	_____	90
*Metcalf, Lee_____	Helena, Mont_____	453 1st St. SE., 20003__	90
*†*Miller, Jack*_____	Sioux City, Iowa____	5417 Kirkwood Dr., Bethesda, Md., 20016.	55
*Mondale, Walter F_____	Minneapolis, Minn___	7903 Rocton Ave., Chevy Chase, Md., 20015.	81
*Monroney, A. S. Mike___	Oklahoma City, Okla.	2760 32d St., 20008____	135
*†Montoya, Joseph M____	Santa Fe, N. Mex___	5403 Surrey, Chevy Chase, Md., 20015.	102
*Morse, Wayne_____	Eugene, Oreg_____	4000 Mass. Ave., 20016.	138
*Morton, Thruston B_____	Louisville, Ky_____	_____	61
*Moss, Frank E_____	Salt Lake City, Utah.	4715 Merivale Rd., Chevy Chase, Md., 20015.	166
*Mundt, Karl E_____	Madison, S. Dak____	122 Schotts Ct. NE., 20002.	153
*Murphy, George_____	Beverly Hills, Calif__	Jefferson Hotel, 20036__	12
*Muskie, Edmund S_____	Waterville, Maine___	5409 Albia Rd., 20016_	67
*Nelson, Gaylord_____	Madison, Wis_____	3812 Kenilworth Dr., Chevy Chase, Md., 20015.	179
*Neuberger, Maurine B___	Portland, Oreg_____	2775 Virginia Ave., 20037.	138
*†Pastore, John O_____	Cranston, R.I_____	2727 29th St., 20008___	149
*Pearson, James B_____	Prairie Village, Kans.	6919 Woodside Pl., Chevy Chase, Md., 20015.	58
*Pell, Claiborne_____	Newport, R.I_____	3425 Prospect St., 20007.	149
*Prouty, Winston L_____	Newport, Vt_____	2500 Q St., 20007_____	168
*Proxmire, William_____	Madison, Wis_____	3025 Ordway St., 20008.	179
*Randolph, Jennings_____	Elkins, W. Va_____	4608 Reservoir Rd., 20007.	176
*Ribicoff, Abraham A____	Hartford, Conn_____	3402 Q St., 20007_____	26

THE SENATE—Continued

(For office rooms and telephones see pp. 405–407)

Name	Home address	Washington residence and ZIP code number	Biography
			Page
*Robertson, A. Willis_____	Lexington, Va_____	_____	169
Russell, Richard B_____	Winder, Ga_____	_____	35
*Saltonstall, Leverett_____	Dover, Mass_____	2320 Tracy Pl., 20008__	71
*Scott, Hugh_____	Philadelphia, Pa____	3260 N St., 20007_____	140
*Simpson, Milward L_____	Cody, Wyo_____	4910 Hillbrook Lane, 20016.	183
*Smathers, George A_____	Miami, Fla_____	_____	29
Smith, Margaret Chase____	Skowhegan, Maine__	4311 Thornapple St., Chevy Chase, Md., 20015.	67
*Sparkman, John J_____	Huntsville, Ala_____	4928 Indian Lane, 20016.	4
*Stennis, John_____	De Kalb, Miss_____	3609 Cumberland St., 20008.	84
*Symington, Stuart_____	St. Louis, Mo_____	3263 N St., 20007_____	86
*Talmadge, Herman E____	Lovejoy, Ga_____	3131 Cleveland Ave., 20008.	35
Thurmond, Strom_____	Aiken, S.C_____	2475 Virginia Ave., 20037.	150
*Tower, John G_____	Wichita Falls, Tex___	5103 Moorland Lane, Bethesda, Md., 20014.	159
*Tydings, Joseph D_____	Havre de Grace, Md_	_____	68
*Williams, Harrison A., Jr_	Westfield, N.J_____	352 Senate Office Bldg_	97
*Williams, John J_____	Millsboro, Del_____	The Mayflower, 20036__	28
*Yarborough, Ralph W___	Austin, Tex_____	110 Maryland Ave. NE., 20002.	159
*Young, Milton R_____	La Moure, N. Dak__	2800 Quebec St., 20008_	127
*‖Young, Stephen M_____	Cleveland, Ohio_____	5160 Manning Pl., 20016.	128

THE HOUSE OF REPRESENTATIVES

*John W. McCormack, Speaker, Hotel Washington, 20004.
Ralph R. Roberts, Clerk, the Sheraton-Park, 20008.
Zeake W. Johnson, Jr., Sergeant at Arms, 100 Maryland Ave. NE., 20002.
*William M. Miller, Doorkeeper, 3119 North Harrison St., Arlington, Va., 22207.
*H. H. Morris, Postmaster, 3318 Ordway St., 20008.
‖Rev. Bernard Braskamp, D.D., Chaplain, 1421 Montague St., 20011.

(For office rooms and telephones, see pp. 408–415)

[Democrats in roman (294); Republicans in *italics* (140); vacant 1; total, 435]

Name and district	Home address	Washington residence and ZIP code number	Biography
			Page
*Abbitt, Watkins M. (4)	Appomattox, Va	Hotel Washington, 20004.	170
*†Abernethy, Thomas G. (1).	Okolona, Miss	6278 29th St., 20015	84
*Adair, E. Ross (4)	Fort Wayne, Ind	4000 Mass. Ave., 20016.	52
*Adams, Brock (7)	Seattle, Wash	3312 Cathedral Ave., 20008.	175
*Addabbo, Joseph P. (7)	Ozone Park, N.Y	1727 House Office Bldg.	108
*Albert, Carl (3)	McAlester, Okla	4614 Reno Rd., 20008	136
*Anderson, John B. (16)	Rockford, Ill	5616 Ogden Rd., 20016	48
*Anderson, William R. (6)	Waverly, Tenn	3006 P St., 20007	157
*Andrews, George (3)	Union Springs, Ala	Congressional Hotel, 20003.	5
*Andrews, Glenn (4)	Anniston, Ala	1000 6th St. SW., 20024	5
*Andrews, Mark (1)	Mapleton, N. Dak	3207 Brooklawn Ter., Chevy Chase, Md., 20015.	127
*†Annunzio, Frank (7)	Chicago, Ill	4000 Tunlaw Rd., 20007.	45
*Arends, Leslie C. (17)	Melvin, Ill	4815 Dexter St., 20007	48
*Ashbrook, John M. (17)	Johnstown, Ohio	8513 Hempstead Ave., Bethesda, Md., 20034.	133
Ashley, Thomas L. (9)	Waterville, Ohio	1722 House Office Bldg	131
*†Ashmore, Robert T. (4)	Greenville, S.C	220 C St. SE., 20003	151
*Aspinall, Wayne N. (4)	Palisade, Colo	4201 Cathedral Ave., 20016.	24
*†Ayres, William H. (14)	Akron, Ohio	4201 Cathedral Ave., 20016.	132
*Baldwin, John F. (14)	Martinez, Calif	5521 17th St. North, Arlington, Va., 22205.	15
*Bandstra, Bert (4)	Pella, Iowa		56
*Baring, Walter S. (At L.)	Reno, Nev	House Office Bldg	93
Barrett, William A. (1)	Philadelphia, Pa		140
*†Bates, William H. (6)	Salem, Mass	1701 Holly St., 20012	73
*Battin, James F. (2)	Billings, Mont	2636 South Lynn St., Arlington, Va., 22200.	90
*Beckworth, Lindley (3)	Gladewater, Tex	6108 29th St., 20015	160
*Belcher, Page (1)	Enid, Okla	Dorchester House, 20009.	135
*Bell, Alphonzo (28)	Los Angeles, Calif	3815 52d St., 20016	19
*Bennett, Charles E. (2)	Jacksonville, Fla	1314 Rusticway Lane, Falls Church, Va., 22044.	30
*Berry, E. Y. (2)	McLaughlin, S. Dak	118 Schotts Ct. NE., 20002.	154

THE HOUSE OF REPRESENTATIVES—Continued

(For office rooms and telephones, see pp. 408–415)

Name and district	Home address	Washington residence and ZIP code number	Biography
			Page
*Betts, Jackson E. (8)_____	Findlay, Ohio_____	301 G St. SW., 20024__	130
*†Bingham, Jonathan B. (23).	Bronx, N.Y._____		114
*Blatnik, John A. (8)_____	Chisholm, Minn_____	2900 North Kensington St., Arlington, Va., 22207.	83
*†Boggs, Hale (2)_____	New Orleans, La____	5315 Bradley Blvd., Bethesda, Md., 20014.	64
‖‖‖Boland, Edward P. (2)__	Springfield, Mass____		72
*Bolling, Richard (5)_____	Kansas City, Mo_____	307 Warrenton Dr., Silver Spring, Md., 20900.	87
Bolton, Frances P. (22)____	Cleveland, Ohio_____	2301 Wyoming Ave., 20008.	134
*Bonner, Herbert C. (1)__	Washington, N.C____	2601 Woodley Pl., 20008.	123
*Bow, Frank T. (16)_____	Canton, Ohio_____	4301 Mass. Ave., 20016.	132
Brademas, John (3)_____	South Bend, Ind___	3050 P. St., 20007_____	52
*Bray, William G. (7)_____	Martinsville, Ind____	200 C St. SE., 20003___	53
*Brock, William E., 3d (3)_	Lookout Mountain, Tenn.	3230 Woodley Rd., 20008.	156
*Brooks, Jack (2)_____	Beaumont, Tex_____	304 C St. NE., 20002__	160
*Broomfield, William S. (18).	Royal Oak, Mich____		80
Brown, Clarence J. (7)____	Blanchester, Ohio___	1401 House Office Bldg.	130
*Brown, George E., Jr. (29).	Monterey Park, Calif.	429 N St. SW., 20024__	19
*Broyhill, James T. (9)___	Lenoir, N.C_____	4211 Lawton St., McLean, Va., 22101.	125
*††Broyhill, Joel T. (10)__	Arlington, Va_____	2551 North Vermont St., Arlington, Va., 22207.	172
*Buchanan, John H., Jr. (6).	Birmingham, Ala____	Congressional Hotel, 20003.	5
Burke, James A. (11)_____	Milton, Mass_____	House Office Bldg_____	75
*Burleson, Omar (17)_____	Anson, Tex_____	2737 Devonshire Pl., 20008.	164
*Burton, Laurence J. (1)__	Ogden, Utah_____	9354 Reid Circle, Captain's Cove, Ft. Washington, Md.	166
*Burton, Phillip (5)_____	San Francisco, Calif.		13
*Byrne, James A. (3)_____	Philadelphia, Pa_____		141
*Byrnes, John W. (8)_____	Green Bay, Wis_____	1215 25th St. South, Arlington, Va., 22202.	181
*Cabell, Earle (5)_____	Dallas, Tex_____	1900 South Eads, Arlington, Va., 22202.	161
*†Cahill, William T. (1) __	Collingswood, N.J.__	1440 House Office Bldg.	97
*†Callan, Clair A. (1)_____	Odell, Nebr_____	1200 South Courthouse Rd., Arlington, Va., 22204.	91

THE HOUSE OF REPRESENTATIVES—Continued

(For office rooms and telephones, see pp. 408–415)

Name and district	Home address	Washington residence and ZIP code number	Biography
			Page
*Callaway, Howard H. (3)	Pine Mountain, Ga__	10822 Alloway St., Potomac, Md., 20854.	36
*Cameron, Ronald Brooks (25).	Whittier, Calif_____	5 Woodmont Rd., Alexandria, Va., 22307.	18
*Carey, Hugh L. (15)_____	Brooklyn, N.Y_____	----------------------	111
*Carter, Tim Lee (5) _____	Tompkinsville, Ky __	Congressional Hotel, 20003.	62
*Casey, Bob (22)_____	Houston, Tex_____	5406 Albia Rd., 20016__	165
*Cederberg, Elford A. (10)_	Bay City, Mich_____	1100 Sussex Pl., Alexandria, Va., 22307.	78
*Celler, Emanuel (10)____	Brooklyn, N.Y_____	The Mayflower, 20036_	109
*†Chamberlain, Charles E. (6).	East Lansing, Mich__	----------------------	77
*Chelf, Frank (4)_____	Lebanon, Ky_____	449 House Office Bldg__	62
*Clancy, Donald D. (2)____	Cincinnati, Ohio____	----------------------	129
*Clark, Frank M. (25)____	Bessemer, Pa_____	220 C St. SE., 20003___	147
*Clausen, Don H. (1)_____	Crescent City, Calif_	7777 Maple Ave., Takoma Park, Md., 20012.	12
*Clawson, Del (23)_____	Compton, Calif_____	4201 Mass. Ave., 20016_	18
*Cleveland, James C. (2)___	New London, N.H___	----------------------	96
*Clevenger, Raymond F. (11).	Sault Ste. Marie, Mich.	3336 Quesada St., 20015.	78
*Cohelan, Jeffery (7)_____	Berkeley, Calif_____	5609 Broad Branch, 20015.	14
*Collier, Harold R. (10)___	Berwyn, Ill_____	----------------------	46
*‖Colmer, William M. (5)_	Pascagoula, Miss____	----------------------	85
*Conable, Barber B., Jr. (37).	Alexander, N.Y_____	----------------------	119
*Conte, Silvio O. (1)_____	Pittsfield, Mass_____	5619 Lamar Rd., 20016_	71
Conyers, John Jr. (1)_____	Detroit, Mich_____	Congressional Hotel, 20003.	76
*†Cooley, Harold D. (4)__	Nashville, N.C_____	2601 Woodley Pl., 20008.	124
*Corbett, Robert J. (18)____	Pittsburgh, Pa_____	1111 House Office Bldg_	145
*†Corman, James C. (22)__	Van Nuys, Calif_____	1401 Knox Pl., Alexandria, Va., 22304.	18
*Craley, N. Neiman, Jr. (19).	York, Pa_____	----------------------	145
*Cramer, William C. (12)__	St. Petersburg, Fla__	6714 Joallen Dr., Falls Church, Va., 22041.	34
*Culver, John C. (2)_____	Marion, Iowa_____	4819 Dorset Ave., Chevy Chase, Md., 20015.	56
*Cunningham, Glenn (2)___	Omaha, Nebr_____	4920 Yorktown Blvd., Arlington, Va., 22207.	91
*Curtin, Willard S. (8)____	Morrisville, Pa_____	200 C St. SE., 20003___	142
*Curtis, Thomas B. (2)____	Webster Groves, Mo_	1135 16th St., 20036___	87
*Daddario, Emilio Q. (1)__	Hartford, Conn_____	2707 Dumbarton Ave., 20007.	26
*Dague, Paul B. (9) _____	Downingtown, Pa___	----------------------	142
*Daniels, Dominick V. (14).	Jersey City, N.J_____	237 House Office Bldg_	101

THE HOUSE OF REPRESENTATIVES—Continued

(For office rooms and telephones, see pp. 408-415)

Name and district	Home address	Washington residence and ZIP code number	Biography
			Page
*†*Davis, Glenn R.* (9)_____	New Berlin, Wis____	2729 South Grove St., Arlington, Va., 22202.	181
*Davis, John W. (7)_____	Summerville, Ga____	215 Forest Villa Lane, McLean, Va., 22101.	37
*Dawson, William L. (1)__	Chicago, Ill_____	1536 House Office Bldg_	43
*de la Garza, Eligio (15)___	Mission, Tex_____	_____	163
*Delaney, James J. (9)____	Long Island City, N.Y.	1135 16th St., 20036___	108
*Dent, John H. (21)_____	Jeannette, Pa_____	453 House Office Bldg__	146
*Denton, Winfield K. (8)__	Evansville, Ind_____	4818 Chevy Chase Blvd., Chevy Chase, Md., 20015.	53
*_Derwinski, Edward J._ (4)_	South Holland, Ill___	335 O St. SW., 20024__	45
*_Devine, Samuel L._ (12)___	Columbus, Ohio_____	_____	131
*_Dickinson, William L._ (2)_	Montgomery, Ala____	510 2d St. SE., 20003__	4
*Diggs, Charles C., Jr. (13).	Detroit, Mich_____	House Office Bldg_____	79
*Dingell, John D. (16)____	Dearborn, Mich_____	_____	79
*_Dole, Bob_ (1)_____	Russell, Kans_____	6815 Joallen Dr., Falls Church Va., 22041.	58
Donohue, Harold D. (4)__	Worcester, Mass____	House Office Bldg_____	72
*Dorn, W. J. Bryan (3)___	Greenwood, S.C_____	2030 Laburnum, McLean, Va., 22101.	151
*Dow, John G. (27)_____	Grandview, N.Y____	_____	116
*Dowdy, John (7)_____	Athens, Tex_____	House Office Bldg_____	161
*Downing, Thomas N. (1)_	Newport News, Va__	2000 Conn. Ave., 20008_	169
*Dulski, Thaddeus J. (41)_	Buffalo, N.Y_____	110 D St. SE., 20003___	120
*_Duncan, John J._ (2)_____	Knoxville, Tenn_____	Capitol Park Apts., 20024.	155
*Duncan, Robert B. (4)___	Medford, Oreg_____	914 Lakeview Dr., Falls Church, Va., 22041.	139
*_Dwyer, Florence P._ (6)___	Elizabeth, N.J_____	Congressional Hotel, 20003.	99
*†Dyal, Ken W. (33)_____	San Bernardino, Calif.	2901 South Grant St., Arlington, Va., 22202.	20
*Edmondson, Ed (2)_____	Muskogee Okla_____	_____	136
*Edwards, Don (9)_____	San Jose, Calif_____	_____	14
*_Edwards, Jack_ (1)_____	Mobile, Ala_____	6316 Newburn Dr., 20016.	4
*_Ellsworth, Robert F._ (3)__	Lawrence, Kans_____	11706 Admiral's Ct., Potomac, Md., 20854.	59
*_Erlenborn, John N._ (14)__	Elmhurst, Ill_____	1400 South Joyce St., Arlington, Va., 22207.	47
*Evans, Frank E. (3)_____	Pueblo, Colo_____	6648 32d St., 20015____	24
‖ Everett, Robert A. (8)___	Union City, Tenn____	Congressional Hotel, 20003.	157
*†Evins, Joe L. (4)_____	Smithville, Tenn____	5044 Klingle St., 20016_	156
*Fallon, George H. (4)____	Baltimore Md_____	_____	69
*Farbstein, Leonard (19)__	New York City, N.Y.	The Mayflower, 20036_	113
*Farnsley, Charles P. (3)__	Louisville, Ky_____	1205 South Washington St., Alexandria, Va., 22314.	62

THE HOUSE OF REPRESENTATIVES—Continued

(For office rooms and telephones, see pp. 408-415)

Name and district	Home address	Washington residence and ZIP code number	Biography
			Page
*Farnum, Billie S. (19) ____	Drayton Plains, Mich.	822 Hyde Rd., Silver Spring, Md., 20902.	80
*Fascell, Dante B. (4) ____	Miami, Fla _____	House Office Bldg _____	31
*†Feighan, Michael A. (20).	Cleveland, Ohio _____	4000 Cathedral Ave., 20016.	133
*Findley, Paul (20) _____	Pittsfield, Ill _____	1310 Normandy Lane, Falls Church, Va., 22042.	49
*Fino, Paul A. (24) _____	Bronx, N.Y _____	The Coronet, 20003 ____	115
*Fisher, O. C. (21) _____	San Angelo, Tex _____	Calvert-Woodley Apts., 20008.	165
*Flood, Daniel J. (11) ____	Wilkes-Barre, Pa ____	The Congressional, 20003.	143
*†Flynt, John J., Jr. (6) __	Griffin, Ga _____	309 Juniper Lane, Falls Church, Va., 22044.	37
*†Fogarty, John E. (2) ___	Harmony, R.I _____	_____	149
Foley, Thomas S. (5) _____	Spokane, Wash _____	430 M St. SW., 20024 __	175
*Ford, Gerald R. (5) _____	Grand Rapids, Mich_	514 Crown View Dr., Alexandria, Va., 22314.	77
*Ford, William D. (15) ___	Taylor, Mich _____	200 C St. SE., 20003 ___	79
*Fountain, L. H. (2) _____	Tarboro, N.C _____	400 Cathedral Ave., 20016.	123
*Fraser, Donald M. (5) ___	Minneapolis, Minn __	121 Hesketh St., Chevy Chase, Md., 20015.	82
*†Frelinghuysen, Peter H. B. (5).	Morristown, N.J ____	3014 N St., 20007 _____	99
*Friedel, Samuel N. (7) ___	Baltimore, Md _____	_____	70
Fulton, James G. (27) _____	Pittsburgh, Pa _____	_____	147
*Fulton, Richard H. (5) ___	Nashville, Tenn _____	310 1st St. SE., 20003___	156
*†Fuqua, Don (9) _____	Altha, Fla _____	2216 Traies Court, Alexandria, Va.	33
*Gallagher, Cornelius E. (13).	Bayonne, N.J _____	233 House Office Bldg_	100
*Garmatz, Edward A. (3)_	Baltimore, Md _____	_____	69
*†‖Gathings, E. C. (1) ____	West Memphis, Ark _	404 Villimay Blvd., Alexandria, Va., 22307.	10
*††Gettys, Tom S. (5) ____	Rock Hill, S.C _____	_____	152
*†Giaimo, Robert N. (3)__	North Haven, Conn_	1311 Delaware Ave. SW., 20024.	27
*Gibbons, Sam M. (10) ___	Tampa, Fla_____	4813 Loch Raven Dr., McLean, Va., 22101.	33
*Gilbert, Jacob H. (22) ___	Bronx, N.Y_____	_____	114
*Gilligan, John J. (1) _____	Cincinnati, Ohio_____	_____	129
*Gonzalez, Henry B. (20)_	San Antonio, Tex____	200 C St. SE., 20003___	165
*Goodell, Charles E. (38) __	Jamestown, N.Y ____	3842 Macomb St., 20016.	119
*Grabowski, Bernard F. (6).	Bristol, Conn_____	35 E St., 20001 _____	27
*†Gray, Kenneth J. (21) __	West Frankfort, Ill__	House Office Bldg _____	49
Green, Edith (3) _____	Portland, Oreg_____	_____	139
*Green, William J. (5) ____	Philadelphia, Pa ____	3267 N St., 20007_____	142
‖Greigg, Stanley L. (6) ____	Sioux City, Iowa ____	301 G St. SW., 20024__	57
*Grider, George W. (9) ___	Memphis, Tenn _____	_____	157
*Griffin, Robert P. (9)_____	Traverse City, Mich_	5702 Ogden St., 20016_	78

THE HOUSE OF REPRESENTATIVES—Continued

(For office rooms and telephones, see pp. 408-415)

Name and district	Home address	Washington residence and ZIP code number	Biography
			Page
*Griffiths, Martha W. (17)	Detroit, Mich	1600 South Joyce St., Arlington, Va., 22202.	80
*Gross, H. R. (3)	Waterloo, Iowa	1600 South Joyce St., Arlington, Va., 22202.	56
*Grover, James R., Jr. (2)	Babylon, N.Y	The Coronet, 20003	105
*Gubser, Charles S. (10)	Gilroy, Calif	House Office Bldg	14
*Gurney, Edward J. (11)	Winter Park, Fla	11 2d St. NE., 20002	33
*Hagan, G. Elliott (1)	Sylvania, Ga	6476 Little Falls Rd., Arlington, Va., 22213.	35
*Hagen, Harlan (18)	Hanford, Calif	8 North Garfield St., Arlington, Va., 22201.	16
*Haley, James A. (7)	Sarasota, Fla	20 5th St. SE., 20003	32
*Hall, Durward G. (7)	Springfield, Mo	200 C St. SE., 20003	88
*Halleck, Charles A. (2)	Rensselaer, Ind	4926 Upton St., 20016	51
*Halpern, Seymour (6)	Forest Hills, N.Y	The Congressional, 20003.	107
*Hamilton, Lee H. (9)	Columbus, Ind	4216 Peachtree Pl., Alexandria, Va.	53
*Hanley, James M. (34)	Syracuse, N.Y	2401 Calvert St., 20008	118
*Hanna, Richard T. (34)	Huntington Beach, Calif.	1702 Hamilton Dr., Mantua Hills, Va., 22030.	20
*Hansen, George V. (2)	Pocatello, Idaho	4330 26th St. North, Arlington, Va., 22207.	42
*Hansen, John R. (7)	Manning, Iowa	800 4th St. SW., 20024.	57
*Hansen, Julia Butler (3)	Cathlamet, Wash	3129 Dumbarton Ave., 20007.	174
*Hardy, Porter, Jr. (2)	Churchland, Chesapeake, Va.	502 Lloyds Lane, Alexandria, Va., 22302.	170
*Harris, Oren (4)	El Dorado, Ark	1627 Myrtle St., 20012.	11
*Harsha, William H. (6)	Portsmouth, Ohio	1404 Delf Dr., McLean, Va., 22101.	130
*Harvey, James (8)	Saginaw, Mich	7505 Leesburg Pl., Bethesda, Md., 20034.	78
*Harvey, Ralph (10)	New Castle, Ind	17 3d St. NE., 20002	54
*Hathaway, William D. (2).	Auburn, Maine	6707 Wemberly Way, McLean, Va., 22101.	67
*Hawkins, Augustus F. (21).	Los Angeles, Calif	125 North Carolina Ave. SE., 20003.	17
*Hays, Wayne L. (18)	Flushing, Ohio	1323 Barger Dr., Falls Church, Va., 22044.	133
*Hébert, F. Edward (1)	New Orleans, La	26 Cockrell Ave., Alexandria, Va., 22304.	64
Hechler, Ken (4)	Huntington, W. Va		177
Helstoski, Henry (9)	East Rutherford, N.J.		99
*Henderson, David N. (3)	Wallace, N.C	110 D St. SE., 20003	123
*†Herlong, A. Sydney, Jr. (5).	Leesburg, Fla	4201 Mass. Ave., 20016.	31

THE HOUSE OF REPRESENTATIVES—Continued

(For office rooms and telephones, see pp. 408-415)

Name and district	Home address	Washington residence and ZIP code number	Biography Page
*Hicks, Floyd V. (6)	Tacoma, Wash	221 5th St. SE., 20003	175
*Holifield, Chet (19)	Montebello, Calif	1200 North Nash St., Arlington, Va., 22209.	17
*††Holland, Elmer J. (20)	Pittsburgh, Pa		145
*Horton, Frank (36)	Rochester, N.Y	9607 Hillridge Dr., Kensington, Md., 20795.	118
*Hosmer, Craig (32)	Long Beach, Calif	5024 Van Ness St., 20016.	20
*†††Howard, James J. (3).	Wall Township, N.J.	5008 Townsend Way, Bladensburg, Md., 20710.	98
†‖Hull, W. R., Jr. (6)	Weston, Mo	1817 Plymouth St., 20012.	88
*Hungate, William L. (9)	Troy, Mo	220 C St. SE., 20003	88
*Huot, J. Oliva (1)	Laconia, N.H	2000 South Eads St., Arlington, Va., 22202.	95
*Hutchinson, Edward (4)	Fennville, Mich	3242 28th St. South, Alexandria, Va., 22302.	77
*Ichord, Richard H. (8)	Houston, Mo	220 C St. SE., 20003	88
*Irwin, Donald J. (4)	Norwalk, Conn		27
Jacobs, Andrew, Jr. (11)	Indianapolis, Ind	1200 North Nash St., Arlington, Va., 22209.	54
Jarman, John (5)	Oklahoma City, Okla.	1203 Glavis Rd., Falls Church, Va., 22044.	136
*Jennings, W. Pat (9)	Marion, Va	1108 House Office Bldg.	172
*Joelson, Charles S. (8)	Paterson, N.J		99
*Johnson, Albert W. (23)	Smethport, Pa	1440 N St., 20005	146
*Johnson, Harold T. (2)	Roseville, Calif	110 D St. SE., 20003	12
‖Johnson, Jed, Jr. (6)	Chickasha, Okla		136
*Jonas, Charles R. (8)	Lincolnton, N.C	2601 Woodley Pl., 20008.	125
*Jones, Paul C. (10)	Kennett, Mo	1111 Army-Navy Dr., Arlington, Va., 22202.	89
*Jones, Robert E. (8)	Scottsboro, Ala	4412 34th St. South, Arlington, Va., 22206.	6
*Karsten, Frank M. (1)	St. Louis, Mo	3407 North Edison St., Arlington, Va., 22207.	86
*Karth, Joseph E. (4)	St. Paul, Minn	4678 Leslie Ave., Temple Hills, Md., 20031.	82
*Kastenmeier, Robert W. (2).	Watertown, Wis	2401 North Quincy St., Arlington, Va., 22207.	179
*†Kee, James (5)	Bluefield, W. Va	5441 16th Ave., Hyattsville, Md., 20782.	178
*†Keith, Hastings (12)	West Bridgewater, Mass.	5906 Harwick Rd., Wood Acres, Md., 20016.	75

THE HOUSE OF REPRESENTATIVES—Continued

(For office rooms and telephones, see pp. 408–415)

Name and district	Home address	Washington residence and ZIP code number	Biography
			Page
†Kelly, Edna F. (12)	Brooklyn, N.Y		109
*†Keogh, Eugene J. (11)	Brooklyn, N.Y	The Mayflower, 20036	109
*King, Carleton J. (30)	Saratoga Springs, N.Y.	301 G St. SW., 20024	117
*King, Cecil R. (17)	Inglewood, Calif		16
*King, David S. (2)	Salt Lake City, Utah	9614 Dewmar La., Kensington, Md., 20795.	167
*Kirwan, Michael J. (19)	Youngstown, Ohio	House Office Bldg	133
*Kluczynski, John C. (5)	Chicago, Ill	Army-Navy Club, 20006.	45
*Kornegay, Horace R. (6)	Greensboro, N.C	110 D St. SE., 20003	124
*Krebs, Paul J. (12)	Livingston, N.J	239 House Office Bldg	100
*Kunkel, John C. (16)	Harrisburg, Pa	Westchester Apts., 20016.	144
*Laird, Melvin R. (7)	Marshfield, Wis	House Office Bldg	181
*†Landrum, Phil M. (9)	Jasper, Ga	110 Maryland Ave. NE., 20002.	37
*†Langen, Odin (7)	Kennedy, Minn	200 C St. SE., 20003	83
*Latta, Delbert L. (5)	Bowling Green, Ohio	Fairfax, Va., 22030	130
*‖‖Leggett, Robert L. (4)	Vallejo, Calif	6922 Pinetree Terrace, Falls Church, Va., 22041.	13
*Lennon, Alton (7)	Wilmington, N.C	220 C St. SE., 20003	125
*Lindsay, John V. (17)	New York City, N.Y	2618 30th St., 20008	112
*Lipscomb, Glenard P. (24).	Los Angeles, Calif		18
*‖Long, Clarence D. (2)	Ruxton, Md		69
*Long, Speedy O. (8)	Jena, La	5708 22d St. North, Arlington, Va., 22207.	66
*Love, Rodney M. (3)	Dayton, Ohio	1200 North Nash Ave., Arlington, Va., 22209.	129
*McCarthy, Richard D. (39).	Buffalo, NY	4818 Drummond Ave., Chevy Chase, Md., 20015.	120
*McClory, Robert (12)	Lake Bluff, Ill	321 Constitution Ave. NE., 20002.	47
*McCormack, John W. (9)	Dorchester, Mass	Hotel Washington, 20004.	74
*†McCulloch, William M. (4).	Piqua, Ohio	4000 Mass. Ave., 20016	129
*McDade, Joseph M. (10)	Scranton, Pa	1400 South Joyce St., Arlington, Va., 22202.	142
*McDowell, Harris B., Jr. (At L.).	Middletown, Del	457 House Office Bldg	28
*McEwen, Robert C. (31)	Ogdensburg, N.Y	7611 Riverdale Rd., Lanham, Md., 20801.	117
*McFall, John J. (15)	Manteca, Calif	1404 Trinity Dr., Alexandria, Va., 22314.	16
*McGrath, Thomas C., Jr. (2).	Margate City, N.J	Madison Hotel, 20005	98
*McMillan, John L. (6)	Florence, S.C		152
*†McVicker, Roy H. (2)	Wheat Ridge, Colo	201 I St. SW., 20024	24
*Macdonald, Torbert H. (7).	Malden, Mass		73

THE HOUSE OF REPRESENTATIVES—Continued

(For office rooms and telephones, see pp. 408–415)

Name and district	Home address	Washington residence and ZIP code number	Biography
			Page
*MacGregor, Clark (3)	Plymouth, Minn	8119 Thoreau Dr., Bethesda, Md., 20014.	82
*†Machen, Hervey G. (5)	Hyattsville, Md	4107 Hamilton St., Hyattsville, Md., 20781.	69
*†Mackay, James A. (4)	Atlanta, Ga	1239 Vermont Ave., 20005.	36
*Mackie, John C. (7)	Flint, Mich	-------------------	77
Madden, Ray J. (1)	Gary, Ind	100 Maryland Ave. NE., 20002.	51
*Mahon, George H. (19)	Lubbock, Tex	3700 Mass. Ave., 20016	164
*†Mailliard, William S. (6).	San Francisco, Calif	5016 Westpath Ter., Bethesda, Md., 20016.	13
*Marsh, John O., Jr. (7)	Strasburg, Va	-------------------	171
*Martin, David T. (3)	Kearney, Nebr	500 4th St. SE., 20003	92
*Martin, James D. (7)	Gadsden, Ala	10821 Stanmore Dr., 'Potomac Falls, Md., 20854.	6
Martin, Joseph W., Jr. (10).	North Attleboro, Mass.	Sheraton-Park, 20008	74
*Mathias, Charles McC., Jr. (6).	Frederick, Md	-------------------	69
*Matsunaga, Spark M. (At L.).	Honolulu, Hawaii	9307 East Parkhill Dr., Bethesda, Md., 20014.	39
*††Matthews, D. R. (Billy) (8).	Gainesville, Fla	401 Fontaine St., Alexandria Va., 22302.	32
*†May, Catherine (4)	Yakima, Wash	8102 Whittier Blvd., Bethesda, Md., 20034.	174
*Meeds, Lloyd (2)	Everett, Wash	1907 Glenbrook Rd., Fairfax, Va., 22030.	173
*Michel, Robert H. (18)	Peoria, Ill	Capital Park Towers, 20024.	48
*Miller, George P. (8)	Alameda, Calif	-------------------	14
*Mills, Wilbur D. (2)	Kensett, Ark	2701 Conn. Ave., 20008.	10
*Minish, Joseph G. (11)	West Orange, N.J	-------------------	100
*†‖‖Mink, Patsy T. (At L.)	Waipahu, Hawaii	1200 North Nash St., Arlington, Va., 22209.	40
*Minshall, William E. (23).	Lakewood, Ohio	8120 Kerry Lane, Chevy Chase, Md., 20015.	134
*†Mize, Chester L. (2)	Atchison, Kans	4836 Van Ness, 20016	59
*Moeller, Walter H. (10)	Lancaster, Ohio	435 New Jersey Ave. SE., 20003.	131
*Monagan, John S. (5)	Waterbury, Conn	5506 Edson La., Rockville, Md., 20852.	27
*Moore, Arch A., Jr. (1)	Glen Dale, W. Va	10801 Pleasant Hill Dr., Potomac, Md., 20854.	176
*Moorhead, William S. (14).	Pittsburgh, Pa	1321 31st St., 20007	144

THE HOUSE OF REPRESENTATIVES—Continued

(For office rooms and telephones, see pp. 408-415)

Name and district	Home address	Washington residence and ZIP code number	Biography
			Page
*†Morgan, Thomas E. (26).	Fredericktown, Pa___	502 House Office Bldg__	147
*Morris, Thomas G. (At L.).	Tucumcari, N. Mex__	_____	102
*Morrison, James H. (6)__	Hammond, La_____	2500 Q St., 20007_____	66
*Morse, F. Bradford (5)___	Lowell, Mass_____	5207 Westwood Dr., 20016.	72
*†Morton, Rogers C. B. (1)_	Easton, Md_____	749 3d St. SW., 20024__	68
*†Mosher, Charles A. (13)__	Oberlin, Ohio_____	3702 R St., 20007_____	132
*†Moss, John E. (3)_____	Sacramento, Calif___	715 South Royal St., Alexandria, Va., 22314.	13
*Multer, Abraham J. (13)_	Brooklyn, N.Y_____	12 2d St. NE., 20002___	110
*Murphy, John M. (16)___	Staten Island, N.Y__	_____	111
*†Murphy, William T. (3)_	Chicago, Ill_____	301 G St. SW., 20024__	44
Murray, Tom (7)_____	Jackson, Tenn_____	The Congressional, 20003.	157
*Natcher, William H. (2)__	Bowling Green, Ky__	4201 Mass. Ave., 20016_	62
*Nedzi, Lucien N. (14)____	Detroit, Mich_____	1811 Highwood Dr., McLean, Va., 22101.	79
*Nelsen, Ancher (2)_____	Hutchinson, Minn___	8202 Jefferson St., Bethesda, Md., 20034.	82
*Nix, Robert N. C. (2)____	Philadelphia, Pa_____	The Congressional, 20003.	141
*O'Brien, Leo W. (29)____	Albany, N.Y_____	2712 Wisconsin Ave., 20007.	117
†‖O'Hara, Barratt (2)____	Chicago, Ill_____	The Congressional, 20003.	44
*O'Hara, James G. (12)___	Utica, Mich_____	_____	79
*O'Konski, Alvin E. (10)__	Mercer, Wis_____	507 D St. SE., 20003___	182
*†Olsen, Arnold (1)_____	Helena, Mont_____	4244 50th St., 20016___	90
*Olson, Alec G. (6)_____	Montevideo, Minn___	341 Courtland Rd., Alexandria, Va., 22306.	83
*O'Neal, Maston (2)_____	Bainbridge, Ga_____	110 Maryland Ave. NE., 20002.	35
*†‡O'Neill, Thomas P., Jr. (8).	Cambridge, Mass____	University Club, 20036.	73
*Ottinger, Richard L. (25)_	Pleasantville, N.Y___	Dorchester House, 20009.	116
*Passman, Otto E. (5)____	Monroe, La_____	The Congressional, 20003.	65
*Patman, Wright (1)_____	Texarkana, Tex_____	114 Schott's Court NE., 20002.	160
*Patten, Edward J. (15)__	Perth Amboy, N.J___	440 House Office Bldg__	101
*Pelly, Thomas M. (1)____	Bainbridge Island, Wash.	2700 N St., 20007_____	173
*Pepper, Claude (3)_____	Miami, Fla_____	1661 Crescent Pl., 20009.	30
*Perkins, Carl D. (7)_____	Hindman, Ky_____	915 Clemson Dr., Alexandria, Va., 22307.	63
Philbin, Philip J. (3)_____	Clinton, Mass_____	Hotel Willard, 20004___	72
*†Pickle, J. J. (Jake) (10)_	Austin, Tex_____	2500 Q St., 20007_____	162
*Pike, Otis G. (1)_____	Riverhead, N.Y_____	_____	104
*Pirnie, Alexander (32)___	Utica, N.Y_____	200 C St. SE., 20003___	117

THE HOUSE OF REPRESENTATIVES—Continued

(For office rooms and telephones, see pp. 408–415)

Name and district	Home address	Washington residence and ZIP code number	Biography
			Page
*Poage, W. R. (11)_____	Waco, Tex_____	228 2d St. SE., 20003__	162
*†*Poff, Richard H.* (6)____	Radford, Va_____	5001 Kingston Dr., Annandale, Va., 22003.	171
*Pool, Joe (At L.)_____	Dallas, Tex_____	55 Gay Lane, Falls Church, Va., 22044.	160
*Powell, Adam C. (18)____	New York City, N.Y_	House Office Bldg_____	112
*Price, Melvin (24)_____	East St. Louis, Ill___	735 Lakeview Dr., Falls Church, Va., 22041.	50
*†Pucinski, Roman C. (11)	Chicago, Ill_____	263 G St. SW., 20024__	47
*Purcell, Graham (13)____	Wichita Falls, Tex___	4329 Old Mt. Vernon Rd., Alexandria, Va., 22309.	163
Quie, Albert H. (1)_____	Dennison, Minn_____	710 Burnt Mills Ave., Silver Spring, Md., 20901.	81
Quillen, James H. (1)____	Kingsport, Tenn____	110 D St. SE., 20003___	155
*Race, John A. (6)_____	Fond du Lac, Wis___	800 4th St. SW., 20024.	180
*Randall, Wm. J. (4)_____	Independence, Mo___	220 C St. SE., 20003___	87
*Redlin, Rolland (2)_____	Crosby, N. Dak_____	6104 Overlea Rd., 20016.	127
†*Reid, Charlotte T.* (15) ___	Aurora, Ill_____	1200 North Nash, Arlington, Va., 22209.	48
Reid, Ogden R. (26)_____	Purchase, N.Y_____	2901 Garfield Ter., 20008.	116
Reifel, Ben (1)_____	Aberdeen, S. Dak___	800 4th St. SW., 20024_	153
Reinecke, Ed (27)_____	Tujunga, Calif_____	_____	19
*Resnick, Joseph Y. (28)__	Ellenville, N.Y_____	Prospect House, Arlington, Va., 22209.	117
*Reuss, Henry S. (5)_____	Milwaukee, Wis_____	6448 Brooks Lane, 20016.	180
*Rhodes, George M. (6)___	Reading, Pa_____	5603 24th Ave. SE., 20031.	142
Rhodes, John J. (1)_____	Mesa, Ariz_____	5502 Pollard Rd., 20016.	8
*†Rivers, L. Mendel (1)___	Charleston, S.C_____	4109 Pine Tree Rd., McLean, Va., 22101.	151
*Rivers, Ralph J. (At L.) _	Fairbanks, Alaska___	2305 Wemberly Way, McLean, Va., 22101.	7
*Roberts, Ray (4)_____	McKinney, Tex_____	1308 Park Terrace Dr., Alexandria, Va., 22307.	160
Robison, Howard W. (33) _	Oswego, N.Y_____	3903 Franklin St., Kensington, Md. 20795.	118
*Rodino, Peter W., Jr. (10)_	Newark, N.J_____	1607 House Office Bldg.	100
*Rogers, Byron G. (1)____	Denver, Colo_____	_____	23
*Rogers, Paul G. (6)_____	West Palm Beach, Fla.	4200 Cathedral Ave., 20016.	32
*†Rogers, Walter (18)____	Pampa, Tex_____	6219 Kennedy Dr., Chevy Chase, Md., 20015.	164

THE HOUSE OF REPRESENTATIVES—Continued

(For office rooms and telephones, see pp. 408–415)

Name and district	Home address	Washington residence and ZIP code number	Biography
			Page
Ronan, Daniel J. (6)	Chicago, Ill	310 House Office Bldg	45
*†Roncalio, Teno (At L.)	Cheyenne, Wyo	3323 Reservoir Rd., 20007.	183
*Rooney, Fred B. (15)	Bethlehem, Pa	3267 N St., 20007	144
*Rooney, John J. (14)	Brooklyn, N.Y	3228 Woodley Rd., 20008.	110
*Roosevelt, James (26)	Los Angeles, Calif	4509 Frazier Lane, McLean, Va., 22101.	19
*Rosenthal, Benjamin S. (8).	Elmhurst, L.I., N.Y		108
*Rostenkowski, Dan (8)	Chicago, Ill	1721 House Office Bldg	46
*Roudebush, Richard L. (6)	Noblesville, Ind	200 C St. SE., 20003	52
*Roush, J. Edward (5)	Huntington, Ind	800 4th St. SW., 20024	52
*Roybal, Edward R. (30)	Los Angeles, Calif	9519 East Stanhope Rd., Kensington, Md., 20795.	20
*Rumsfeld, Donald (13)	Wilmette, Ill	3424 Reservoir Rd., 20007.	47
*Ryan, William F. (20)	New York City, N.Y	1517 House Office Bldg	113
*St Germain, Fernand J. (1).	Woonsocket, R.I		149
*St. Onge, William L. (2)	Putnam, Conn		26
*Satterfield, David E., 3d (3).	Richmond, Va		170
*Saylor, John P. (22)	Johnstown, Pa	House Office Bldg	146
*Scheuer, James H. (21)	Bronx, N.Y	201 I St. SW., 20024	113
*Schisler, Gale (19)	London Mills, Ill		49
*Schmidhauser, John R. (1).	Iowa City, Iowa	3808 Military Rd., 20015.	55
*††Schneebeli, Herman T. (17).	Williamsport, Pa	301 G St. SW., 20024	145
*Schweiker, Richard S. (13)	Worcester, Pa	4700 Ft. Sumner Dr., 20016	143
*Scott, Ralph J. (5)	Danbury, N.C	4828 Eastern La., Suitland, Md., 20023.	124
*Secrest, Robert T. (15)	Senecaville, Ohio	5105 Oakcrest, Dr., Oxon Hill, Md., 20021.	132
*Selden, Armistead I., Jr. (5).	Greensboro, Ala	1213 Lily Dhu Lane, Falls Church, Va., 22044.	5
*Senner, George F., Jr. (3)	Miami, Ariz	444 House Office Bldg	9
*Shipley, George E. (23)	Olney, Ill	510 Adelman Circle, Vienna, Va., 22180.	50
*Shriver, Garner E. (4)	Wichita, Kans	424 Crosswoods Dr., Falls Church, Va., 22044.	59
*Sickles, Carlton R. (At L.).	Lanham, Md		68
*Sikes, Robert L. F. (1)	Crestview, Fla	446 New Jersey Ave. SE., 20003.	29
*Sisk, B. F. (16)	Fresno, Calif	129 6th St. NE., 20002	16
*Skubitz, Joe (5)	Pittsburg, Kans	2537 34th St. SE., 20020.	60
*Slack, John M., Jr. (3)	Charleston, W. Va	410 South Pitt St., Alexandria, Va., 22314.	177
*Smith, H. Allen (20)	Glendale, Calif		17

THE HOUSE OF REPRESENTATIVES—Continued

(For office rooms and telephones, see pp. 408–415)

Name and district	Home address	Washington residence and ZIP code number	Biography Page
*†*Smith, Henry P., 3d* (40)	North Tonawanda, N.Y.	1618 32d St., 20007	120
*Smith, Howard W. (8)	Broad Run, Va	204 West Walnut St., Alexandria, Va., 22301.	171
*†Smith, Neal (5)	Altoona, Iowa	6705 Joallen Dr., Falls Church, Va., 22041.	56
*†† ‖‖‖*Springer, William L.* (22).	Champaign, Ill	16 West Lenox St., Chevy Chase, Md., 20015.	49
**Stafford, Robert T.* (At L.).	Rutland, Vt	213 Devon Dr., Falls Church, Va., 22042.	168
*†Staggers, Harley O. (2)	Keyser, W. Va	401 House Office Bldg.	177
*Stalbaum, Lynn E. (1)	Racine, Wis	6311 Blackwood Rd., Bethesda, Md., 20034.	179
Stanton, J. William (11)	Painesville, Ohio	1111 Army-Navy Dr., Arlington, Va., 22202.	131
*Steed, Tom (4)	Shawnee, Okla	Congressional Hotel, 20003.	136
*†Stephens, Robert G., Jr. (10).	Athens, Ga	815 South Fairfax St., Alexandria, Va., 22314.	38
*Stratton, Samuel S. (35)	Amsterdam, N.Y	8305 Fenway Rd., Bethesda, Md., 20034.	118
*Stubblefield, Frank A. (1).	Murray, Ky	4619 Albemarle St., 20016.	61
‖Sullivan, Leonor Kretzer (Mrs. John B.) (3).	St. Louis, Mo	River House, Arlington, Va., 22202.	87
*Sweeney, Robert E. (At L.).	Bay Village, Ohio		128
**Talcott, Burt L.* (12)	Salinas, Calif		15
*Taylor, Roy A. (11)	Black Mountain, N.C.	2601 Woodley Pl., 20008.	126
**Teague, Charles M.* (13)	Ojai, Calif	4000 Cathedral Ave., 20016.	15
*Teague, Olin E. (6)	College Station, Tex	6015 Mass. Ave., 20016	161
*Tenzer, Herbert (5)	Lawrence, N.Y		106
*†Thomas, Albert (8)	Houston, Tex	2901 34th St., 20008	162
*Thompson, Clark W. (9)	Galveston, Tex	3301 Mass. Ave., 20008	162
*†Thompson, Frank, Jr. (4).	Trenton, N.J	106 South Lee St., Alexandria, Va., 22314.	98
*Thompson, T. Ashton (7).	Ville Platte, La	1600 Kenwood Ave., Alexandria, Va. 22302.	66
**Thomson, Vernon W.* (3).	Richland Center, Wis.	4803 Kellogg Dr., McLean, Va., 22101.	179
*Todd, Paul H., Jr. (3)	Kalamazoo, Mich	3312 Newark St., 20008.	77
*Toll, Herman (4)	Philadelphia, Pa		141
*Trimble, James W. (3)	Berryville, Ark	110 Maryland Ave. NE., 20002.	10
*Tuck, William M. (5)	South Boston, Va	Congressional Hotel, 20003.	170
*Tunney, John V. (38)	Riverside, Calif	2422 Tracy Pl., 20008	21

THE HOUSE OF REPRESENTATIVES—Continued

(For office rooms and telephones, see pp. 408-415)

Name and district	Home address	Washington residence and ZIP code number	Biography Page
*Tupper, Stanley R. (1)	Boothbay Harbor, Maine.	101 G St. SW., 20024	67
*‖Tuten, J. Russell (8)	Brunswick, Ga	214 Noland St., Falls Church, Va., 22046.	37
*Udall, Morris K. (2)	Tucson, Ariz		8
*†Ullman, Al (2)	Baker, Oreg	4616 38th St. North, Arlington, Va., 22207.	139
*Utt, James B. (35)	Santa Ana, Calif	4600 Conn. Ave., 20008	21
*Van Deerlin, Lionel (37)	San Diego, Calif	5912 Rosemont Dr., McLean, Va., 22101.	21
*Vanik, Charles A. (21)	Cleveland, Ohio		134
*Vigorito, Joseph P. (24)	Erie, Pa	2521 Eliot Pl., Hillcrest Hgts., Md., 20031.	147
*Vivian, Weston E. (2)	Ann Arbor, Mich		76
*Waggonner, Joe D., Jr. (4).	Plain Dealing, La	1630 Courtland Rd., Alexandria, Va., 22306.	65
*†Walker, E. S. Johnny (At L.).	Santa Fe, N. Mex	301 G St. SW., 20024	102
*†Walker, Prentiss (4)	Mize, Miss	4000 David Lane, Alexandria, Va.	85
*Watkins, G. Robert (7)	West Chester, Pa	200 C St. SE., 20003	142
*Watts, John C. (6)	Nicholasville, Ky	3806 Canal Dr., McLean, Va., 22101.	63
*Weltner, Charles L. (5)	Atlanta, Ga	9712 Rutley Rd., Bethesda, Md., 20034.	36
*†Whalley, J. Irving (12)	Windber, Pa	200 C St. SE., 20003	143
*White, Compton I., Jr. (1).	Clark Fork, Idaho	1215 23d St. South, Arlington, Va., 22202.	41
*White, Richard C. (16)	El Paso, Tex	3311 Cleveland Ave., 20008.	163
*Whitener, Basil L. (10)	Gastonia, N.C		125
*†Whitten, Jamie L. (2)	Charleston, Miss	5804 Nebraska Ave., 20015.	85
*Widnall, William B. (7)	Saddle River, N.J	110 Schott's Court NE., 20002.	99
*Williams, John Bell (3)	Raymond, Miss	1001 26th Rd. South, Arlington, Va., 22202.	85
*Willis, Edwin E. (3)	St. Martinville, La	2500 Q St., 20007	65
*Wilson, Bob (36)	San Diego, Calif	9417 Falls Rd., Potomac, Md., 20854.	21
*Wilson, Charles H. (31)	Los Angeles, Calif	312 Randolph Dr., Annandale, Va., 22003.	20
*Wolff, Lester L. (3)	Kensington, N.Y		105
*Wright, James C., Jr. (12).	Fort Worth, Tex	3611 North Abingdon, Arlington, Va., 22207.	162
*Wyatt, Wendell (1)	Astoria, Oreg	400 River Towers Dr., Alexandria, Va.	138
*Wydler, John W. (4)	Garden City, N.Y	The Coronet, 20003	106
*Yates, Sidney R. (9)	Chicago, Ill		46

THE HOUSE OF REPRESENTATIVES—Continued

(For office rooms and telephones, see pp. 408–415)

Name and district	Home address	Washington residence and ZIP code number	Biography
			Page
*Young, John (14) _____	Corpus Christi, Tex__	4007 North Albemarle, McLean, Va., 22101.	163
*Younger, J. Arthur (11) __	San Mateo, Calif____	4501 Conn. Ave., 20008.	15
*Zablocki, Clement J. (4) __	Milwaukee, Wis_____	6812 Georgia St., Chevy Chase, Md., 20015.	180

RESIDENT COMMISSIONER

*Polanco-Abreu, Santiago [1] __	Isabela, P.R_____	2210 R St., 20008_____	184

[1] Popular Democrat.

TERMS OF SERVICE

TERMS OF SERVICE

TERMS OF SERVICE

EXPIRATION OF THE TERMS OF SENATORS

CLASS II.—SENATORS WHOSE TERMS OF SERVICE EXPIRE IN 1967

[33 Senators in this group: Democrats, 19; Republicans, 14]

Name	Party	Residence
Allott, Gordon	R.	Lamar, Colo.
Anderson, Clinton P	D.	Albuquerque, N. Mex.
Bartlett, E. L	D.	Juneau, Alaska.
Bass, Ross [1]	D.	Pulaski, Tenn.
Boggs, J. Caleb	R.	Wilmington, Del.
Case, Clifford P	R.	Rahway, N.J.
Cooper, John Sherman	R.	Somerset, Ky.
Curtis, Carl T	R.	Minden, Nebr.
Douglas, Paul H	D.	Chicago, Ill.
Eastland, James O	D.	Doddsville, Miss.
Ellender, Allen J	D.	Houma, La.
Harris, Fred R.[2]	D.	Lawton, Okla.
Jordan, B. Everett	D.	Saxapahaw, N.C.
Jordan, Len B	R.	Boise, Idaho.
McClellan, John L	D.	Camden, Ark.
McIntyre, Thomas J	D.	Laconia, N.H.
McNamara, Pat	D.	Detroit, Mich.
Metcalf, Lee	D.	Helena, Mont.
Miller, Jack	R.	Sioux City, Iowa.
Mondale, Walter F.[3]	D.	Minneapolis, Minn.
Mundt, Karl E	R.	Madison, S. Dak.
Neuberger, Maurine B	D.	Portland, Oreg.
Pearson, James B	R.	Prairie Village, Kans.
Pell, Claiborne	D.	Newport, R.I.
Randolph, Jennings	D.	Elkins, W. Va.
Robertson, A. Willis	D.	Lexington, Va.
Russell, Richard B	D.	Winder, Ga.
Saltonstall, Leverett	R.	Dover, Mass.
Simpson, Milward L	R.	Cody, Wyo.
Smith, Margaret Chase	R.	Skowhegan, Maine.
Sparkman, John J	D.	Huntsville, Ala.
Thurmond, Strom	R.	Aiken, S.C.
Tower, John G	R.	Wichita Falls, Tex.

[1] Elected Nov. 3, 1964, to fill unexpired term of Estes Kefauver.
[2] Elected Nov. 3, 1964, to fill unexpired term of Robert S. Kerr.
[3] Appointed Dec. 30, 1964, to fill unexpired term of Hubert H. Humphrey.

223

CLASS III.—SENATORS WHOSE TERMS OF SERVICE EXPIRE IN 1969

[34 Senators in this group: Democrats, 23; Republicans, 11]

Name	Party	Residence
Aiken, George D	R.	Putney, Vt.
Bayh, Birch	D.	Terre Haute, Ind.
Bennett, Wallace F	R.	Salt Lake City, Utah.
Bible, Alan	D.	Reno, Nev.
Brewster, Daniel B	D.	Towson, Md.
Carlson, Frank	R.	Concordia, Kans.
Church, Frank	D.	Boise, Idaho.
Clark, Joseph S	D.	Philadelphia, Pa.
Cotton, Norris	R.	Lebanon, N.H.
Dirksen, Everett McKinley	R.	Pekin, Ill.
Dominick, Peter H	R.	Englewood, Colo.
Ervin, Sam J., Jr	D.	Morganton, N.C.
Fulbright, J. W	D.	Fayetteville, Ark.
Gruening, Ernest	D.	Juneau, Alaska.
Hayden, Carl	D.	Phoenix, Ariz.
Hickenlooper, Bourke B	R.	Cedar Rapids, Iowa.
Hill, Lister	D.	Montgomery, Ala.
Inouye, Daniel K	D.	Honolulu, Hawaii.
Javits, Jacob K	R.	New York City, N.Y.
Johnston, Olin D	D.	Spartanburg, S.C.
Kuchel, Thomas H	R.	Anaheim, Calif.
Lausche, Frank J	D.	Cleveland, Ohio.
Long, Edward V	D.	Clarksville, Mo.
Long, Russell B	D.	Baton Rouge, La.
McGovern, George	D.	Mitchell, S. Dak.
Magnuson, Warren G	D.	Seattle, Wash.
Monroney, A. S. Mike	D.	Oklahoma City, Okla.
Morse, Wayne	D.	Eugene, Oreg.
Morton, Thruston B	R.	Glenview, Ky.
Nelson, Gaylord	D.	Madison, Wis.
Ribicoff, Abraham A	D.	Hartford, Conn.
Smathers, George A	D.	Miami, Fla.
Talmadge, Herman E	D.	Lovejoy, Ga.
Young, Milton R	R.	La Moure, N. Dak.

CLASS I.—SENATORS WHOSE TERMS OF SERVICE EXPIRE IN 1971

[33 Senators in this group: Democrats, 26; Republicans, 7]

Name	Party	Residence
Burdick, Quentin N	D.	Fargo, N. Dak.
Byrd, Harry Flood	D.	Berryville, Va.
Byrd, Robert C	D.	Sophia, W. Va.
Cannon, Howard W	D.	Las Vegas, Nev.
Dodd, Thomas J	D.	West Hartford, Conn.
Fannin, Paul J	R.	Phoenix, Ariz.
Fong, Hiram L	R.	Honolulu, Hawaii.
Gore, Albert	D.	Carthage, Tenn.
Hart, Philip A	D.	Lansing, Mich.
Hartke, Vance	D.	Evansville, Ind.
Holland, Spessard L	D.	Bartow, Fla.
Hruska, Roman L	R.	Omaha, Nebr.
Jackson, Henry M	D.	Everett, Wash.
Kennedy, Edward M	D.	Boston, Mass.
Kennedy, Robert F	D.	New York, N.Y.
McCarthy, Eugene J	D.	St. Paul, Minn.
McGee, Gale W	D.	Laramie, Wyo.
Mansfield, Mike	D.	Missoula, Mont.
Montoya, Joseph M	D.	Santa Fe, N. Mex.
Moss, Frank E	D.	Salt Lake City, Utah.
Murphy, George	R.	Beverly Hills, Calif.
Muskie, Edmund S	D.	Waterville, Maine.
Pastore, John O	D.	Providence, R. I.
Prouty, Winston L	R.	Newport, Vt.
Proxmire, William	D.	Madison, Wis.
Scott, Hugh	R.	Philadelphia, Pa.
Stennis, John	D.	De Kalb, Miss.
Symington, Stuart	D.	Creve Coeur, Mo.
Tydings, Joseph D	D.	Havre de Grace, Md.
Williams, Harrison A., Jr	D.	Westfield, N.J.
Williams, John J	R.	Millsboro, Del.
Yarborough, Ralph W	D.	Austin, Tex.
Young, Stephen M	D.	Cleveland, Ohio.

CONTINUOUS SERVICE OF SENATORS

Rank	Name	State	Beginning of present service
1	Hayden, Carl	Arizona	Mar. 4, 1927
2	Russell, Richard B	Georgia	Jan. 12, 1933
3	Byrd, Harry Flood	Virginia	Mar. 4, 1933
4	Ellender, Allen J	Louisiana	Jan. 3, 1937
5	Hill, Lister	Alabama	Jan. 11, 1938
6	Aiken, George D	Vermont	Jan. 10, 1941
7	Eastland, James O. [1]	Mississippi	Jan. 3, 1943
	McClellan, John L	Arkansas	
8	Magnuson, Warren G	Washington	Dec. 14, 1944
9	Fulbright, J. W	Arkansas	Jan. 3, 1945
	Hickenlooper, Bourke B	Iowa	
	Johnston, Olin D	South Carolina	
	Morse, Wayne	Oregon	
10	Saltonstall, Leverett	Massachusetts	Jan. 4, 1945
11	Young, Milton R	North Dakota	Mar. 12, 1945
12	Holland, Spessard L	Florida	Sept. 25, 1946
13	Robertson, A. Willis	Virginia	Nov. 6, 1946
	Sparkman, John J	Alabama	
14	Williams, John J	Delaware	Jan. 3, 1947
15	Stennis, John	Mississippi	Nov. 5, 1947
16	Long, Russell B	Louisiana	Dec. 31, 1948
	Mundt, Karl E	South Dakota	
17	Anderson, Clinton P	New Mexico	Jan. 3, 1949
	Douglas, Paul H	Illinois	
	Smith, Margaret Chase	Maine	
18	Carlson, Frank	Kansas	Nov. 29, 1950
19	Pastore, John O	Rhode Island	Dec. 19, 1950
20	Bennett, Wallace F	Utah	Jan. 3, 1951
	Dirksen, Everett McKinley	Illinois	
	Monroney, A. S. Mike	Oklahoma	
	Smathers, George A	Florida	
21	Kuchel, Thomas H	California	Jan. 2, 1953
22	Gore, Albert	Tennessee	Jan. 3, 1953
	Jackson, Henry M	Washington	
	Mansfield, Mike	Montana	
	Symington, Stuart	Missouri	
23	Ervin, Sam J., Jr	North Carolina	June 5, 1954
24	Cotton, Norris	New Hampshire	Nov. 8, 1954
	Hruska, Roman L	Nebraska	
25	Bible, Alan	Nevada	Dec. 2, 1954
26	Curtis, Carl T	Nebraska	Jan. 1, 1955

[1] Mr. Eastland also served in the Senate from June 30, 1941, to Sept. 28, 1941.

CONTINUOUS SERVICE OF SENATORS—Continued

Rank	Name	State	Beginning of present service
27	Allott, Gordon	Colorado	
	Case, Clifford P	New Jersey	Jan. 3, 1955
	McNamara, Pat	Michigan	
28	Cooper, John Sherman [2]	Kentucky	Nov. 7, 1956
	Thurmond, Strom [3]	South Carolina	
29	Church, Frank	Idaho	
	Clark, Joseph S	Pennsylvania	
	Lausche, Frank J	Ohio	Jan. 3, 1957
	Morton, Thruston B	Kentucky	
	Talmadge, Herman E	Georgia	
30	Javits, Jacob K	New York	Jan. 9, 1957
31	Yarborough, Ralph W	Texas	Apr. 29, 1957
32	Proxmire, William	Wisconsin	Aug. 28, 1957
33	Jordan, B. Everett	North Carolina	Apr. 19, 1958
34	Randolph, Jennings	West Virginia	Nov. 5, 1958
35	Bartlett, E. L	Alaska	
	Byrd, Robert C	West Virginia	
	Cannon, Howard W	Nevada	
	Dodd, Thomas J	Connecticut	
	Gruening, Ernest	Alaska	
	Hart, Philip A	Michigan	
	Hartke, Vance	Indiana	
	McCarthy, Eugene J	Minnesota	Jan. 3, 1959
	McGee, Gale W	Wyoming	
	Moss, Frank E	Utah	
	Muskie, Edmund S	Maine	
	Prouty, Winston L	Vermont	
	Scott, Hugh	Pennsylvania	
	Williams, Harrison A., Jr	New Jersey	
	Young, Stephen M	Ohio	
36	Fong, Hiram L	Hawaii	Aug. 21, 1959
37	Burdick, Quentin N	North Dakota	Aug. 8, 1960
38	Long, Edward V	Missouri	Sept. 23, 1960
39	Neuberger, Maurine B	Oregon	Nov. 9, 1960
40	Boggs, J. Caleb	Delaware	
	Metcalf, Lee	Montana	Jan. 3, 1961
	Miller, Jack	Iowa	
	Pell, Claiborne	Rhode Island	

[2] Mr. Cooper also served in the Senate from Nov. 6, 1946, to Jan. 3, 1949, and from Nov. 5, 1952, to Jan. 3, 1955.

[3] Mr. Thurmond also served in the Senate by appointment from Dec. 24, 1954, to Jan. 3, 1955; was elected Nov. 2, 1954, as a write-in candidate for the term ending Jan. 3, 1961, and served from Jan. 3, 1955, until his resignation Apr. 4, 1956; reelected Nov. 6, 1956, to fill the vacancy caused by his own resignation.

CONTINUOUS SERVICE OF SENATORS—Continued

Rank	Name	State	Beginning of present service
41	Tower, John G	Texas	June 15, 1961
42	Pearson, James B	Kansas	Jan. 31, 1962
43	Jordan, Len B	Idaho	Aug. 6, 1962
44	Kennedy, Edward M	Massachusetts	
	McIntyre, Thomas J	New Hampshire	Nov. 7, 1962
	Simpson, Milward L	Wyoming	
45	Bayh, Birch	Indiana	
	Brewster, Daniel B	Maryland	
	Dominick, Peter H	Colorado	
	Inouye, Daniel K	Hawaii	Jan. 3, 1963
	McGovern, George	South Dakota	
	Ribicoff, Abraham A	Connecticut	
46	Nelson, Gaylord	Wisconsin	Jan. 8, 1963
47	Bass, Ross [4]	Tennessee	
	Harris, Fred R.[5]	Oklahoma	Nov. 4, 1964
	Montoya, Joseph M.[6]	New Mexico	
48	Mondale, Walter F.[7]	Minnesota	Dec. 30, 1964
49	Murphy, George [8]	California	Jan. 1, 1965
50	Fannin, Paul J	Arizona	
	Kennedy, Robert F	New York	Jan. 3, 1965
	Tydings, Joseph D	Maryland	

[4] Elected Nov. 3, 1964, to fill unexpired term of Estes Kefauver.
[5] Elected Nov. 3, 1964, to fill unexpired term of Robert S. Kerr.
[6] Elected Nov. 3, 1964, to fill unexpired term of Dennis Chavez.
[7] Appointed Dec. 30, 1964, to fill unexpired term of Hubert H. Humphrey
[8] Appointed Jan. 1, 1965, to fill unexpired term of Clair Engle.

CONGRESSES IN WHICH REPRESENTATIVES HAVE SERVED, WITH BEGINNING OF PRESENT SERVICE

[*Elected to fill a vacancy; † resigned]

Name	State	District	Congresses (inclusive)	Beginning of present service
22 terms, consecutive				
Celler, Emanuel_____	N.Y___	10	68th to 89th_____	Mar. 4, 1923
21 terms, consecutive				
Martin, Joseph W., Jr____	Mass__	10	69th to 89th_____	Mar. 4, 1925
20 terms, consecutive				
McCormack, John W____	Mass__	9	*70th to 89th_____	Nov. 6, 1928
19 terms, consecutive				
Patman, Wright_____	Tex____	1	71st to 89th_____	Mar. 4, 1929
18 terms, consecutive				
Smith, Howard W_____	Va_____	8	72d to 89th_____	Mar. 4, 1931
17 terms, consecutive				
Colmer, William M_____	Miss___	5	73d to 89th_____	Mar. 4, 1933
Cooley, Harold D_____	N.C.___	4	*73d to 89th_____	July 7, 1934
16 terms, consecutive				
Arends, Leslie C_____	Ill_____	17	74th to 89th_____	Jan. 3, 1935
Halleck, Charles A_____	Ind____	2	*74th to 89th_____	Jan 29, 1935
Mahon, George H_____	Tex____	19	74th to 89th_____	Jan. 3, 1935
15 terms, consecutive				
Keogh, Eugene J_____	N.Y___	11	75th to 89th_____	Jan. 3, 1937
Kirwan, Michael J_____	Ohio___	19	75th to 89th_____	Jan. 3, 1937
Poage, W.R_____	Tex____	11	75th to 89th_____	Jan. 3, 1937
Thomas, Albert_____	Tex____	8	75th to 89th_____	Jan. 3, 1937
14 terms, consecutive				
Bolton, Frances P_____	Ohio___	22	*76th to 89th_____	Feb. 27, 1940
Bonner, Herbert C_____	N.C___	1	*76th to 89th_____	Nov. 5, 1940
Brown, Clarence J_____	Ohio___	7	76th to 89th_____	Jan. 3, 1939
Gathings, E. C_____	Ark____	1	76th to 89th_____	Jan. 3, 1939
McMillan, John L_____	S.C____	6	76th to 89th_____	Jan. 3, 1939
Mills, Wilbur D_____	Ark____	2	76th to 89th_____	Jan. 3, 1939

39-650°—65——17

SERVICE OF REPRESENTATIVES—Continued

Name	State	District	Congresses (inclusive)	Beginning of present service
13 terms, consecutive				
Fogarty, John E_____	R.I____	2	77th, †78th, 79th to 89th.	Jan. 3, 1945
Harris, Oren_____	Ark____	4	77th to 89th_____	Jan. 3, 1941
Hébert, F. Edward_____	La_____	1	77th to 89th_____	Jan. 3, 1941
King, Cecil R_____	Calif___	17	*77th to 89th_____	Aug. 25, 1942
Rivers, L. Mendel_____	S.C____	1	77th to 89th_____	Jan. 3, 1941
Sikes, Robert L. F_____	Fla____	1	77th, †78th, 79th to 89th.	Jan. 3, 1945
Whitten, Jamie L_____	Miss___	2	*77th to 89th_____	Nov. 4, 1941
12 terms, consecutive				
Abernethy, Thomas G____	Miss___	1	78th to 89th_____	Jan. 3, 1943
Andrews, George_____	Ala____	3	*78th to 89th_____	Mar. 14, 1944
Dawson, William L_____	Ill_____	1	78th to 89th_____	Jan. 3, 1943
Feighan, Michael A_____	Ohio___	20	78th to 89th_____	Jan. 3, 1943
Fisher, O. C_____	Tex____	21	78th to 89th_____	Jan. 3, 1943
Holifield, Chet_____	Calif___	19	78th to 89th_____	Jan. 3, 1943
Madden, Ray J_____	Ind____	1	78th to 89th_____	Jan. 3, 1943
Morrison, James H_____	La_____	6	78th to 89th_____	Jan. 3, 1943
Murray, Tom_____	Tenn__	7	78th to 89th_____	Jan. 3, 1943
O'Konski, Alvin E_____	Wis____	10	78th to 89th_____	Jan. 3, 1943
Philbin, Philip J_____	Mass__	3	78th to 89th_____	Jan. 3, 1943
Rooney, John J_____	N.Y___	14	*78th to 89th_____	June 6, 1944
12 terms, not consecutive				
Beckworth, Lindley_____	Tex____	3	76th to 82d, 85th to 89th.	Jan. 3, 1957
Corbett, Robert J_____	Pa_____	18	76th, 79th to 89th___	Jan. 3, 1945
11 terms, consecutive				
Byrnes, John W_____	Wis____	8	79th to 89th_____	Jan. 3, 1945
Chelf, Frank_____	Ky____	4	79th to 89th_____	Jan. 3, 1945
Fallon, George H_____	Md____	4	79th to 89th_____	Jan. 3, 1945
Fulton, James G_____	Pa_____	27	79th to 89th_____	Jan. 3, 1945
Miller, George P_____	Calif___	8	79th to 89th_____	Jan. 3, 1945
Morgan, Thomas E_____	Pa_____	26	79th to 89th_____	Jan. 3, 1945
Powell, Adam C_____	N.Y___	18	79th to 89th_____	Jan. 3, 1945
Price, Melvin_____	Ill_____	24	79th to 89th_____	Jan. 3, 1945
Teague, Olin E_____	Tex____	6	*79th to 89th_____	Aug. 24, 1946
Trimble, James W_____	Ark____	3	79th to 89th_____	Jan. 3, 1945

SERVICE OF REPRESENTATIVES—Continued

Name	State	District	Congresses (inclusive)	Beginning of present service
11 terms, not consecutive				
Boggs, Hale.............	La.....	2	77th, 80th to 89th...	Jan. 3, 1947
Thompson, Clark W......	Tex....	9	*73d, *80th to 89th..	Aug. 23, 1947
10 terms, consecutive				
Abbitt, Watkins M.......	Va.....	4	*80th to 89th........	Feb. 17, 1948
Albert, Carl.............	Okla...	3	80th to 89th........	Jan. 3, 1947
Blatnik, John A.........	Minn..	8	80th to 89th........	Jan. 3, 1947
Burleson, Omar.........	Tex....	17	80th to 89th........	Jan. 3, 1947
Dague, Paul B.........	Pa.....	9	80th to 89th........	Jan. 3, 1947
Donohue, Harold D.....	Mass..	4	80th to 89th........	Jan. 3, 1947
Evins, Joe L...........	Tenn..	4	80th to 89th........	Jan. 3, 1947
Garmatz, Edward A.....	Md....	3	*80th to 89th........	July 15, 1947
Hardy, Porter, Jr......	Va.....	2	80th to 89th........	Jan. 3, 1947
Jones, Paul C..........	Mo....	10	*80th to 89th........	Nov. 2, 1948
Jones, Robert E........	Ala....	8	*80th to 89th........	Jan. 28, 1947
Karsten, Frank M......	Mo....	1	80th to 89th........	Jan. 3, 1947
McCulloch, William M...	Ohio...	4	*80th to 89th........	Nov. 4, 1947
Multer, Abraham J......	N.Y...	13	*80th to 89th........	Nov. 4, 1947
Passman, Otto E........	La.....	5	80th to 89th........	Jan. 3, 1947
Williams, John Bell.....	Miss...	3	80th to 89th........	Jan. 3, 1947
10 terms, not consecutive				
Barrett, William A.......	Pa.....	1	79th, 81st to 89th...	Jan. 3, 1949
Delaney, James J........	N.Y...	9	79th, 81st to 89th...	Jan. 3, 1949
Secrest, Robert T.......	Ohio...	15	73d to 77th, 81st to 83d, 88th, and 89th.	Jan. 3, 1963
9 terms, consecutive				
Aspinall, Wayne N......	Colo...	4	81st to 89th........	Jan. 3, 1949
Bates, William H........	Mass...	6	*81st to 89th........	Feb. 14, 1950
Bennett, Charles E......	Fla....	2	81st to 89th........	Jan. 3, 1949
Bolling, Richard.........	Mo....	5	81st to 89th........	Jan. 3, 1949
Ford, Gerald R..........	Mich...	5	81st to 89th........	Jan. 3, 1949
Gross, H. R.............	Iowa...	3	81st to 89th........	Jan. 3, 1949
Hays, Wayne L..........	Ohio...	18	81st to 89th........	Jan. 3, 1949
Herlong, A. Sydney, Jr...	Fla....	5	81st to 89th........	Jan. 3, 1949
Kelly, Edna F...........	N.Y...	12	*81st to 89th........	Nov. 8, 1949
Perkins, Carl D.........	Ky....	7	81st to 89th........	Jan. 3, 1949
Rhodes, George M.......	Pa.....	6	81st to 89th........	Jan. 3, 1949
Rodino, Peter W., Jr.....	N.J....	10	81st to 89th........	Jan. 3, 1949
Saylor, John P..........	Pa.....	22	*81st to 89th........	Sept. 13, 1949
Staggers, Harley O......	W. Va.	2	81st to 89th........	Jan. 3, 1949
Steed, Tom.............	Okla...	4	81st to 89th........	Jan. 3, 1949

SERVICE OF REPRESENTATIVES—Continued

Name	State	District	Congresses (inclusive)	Beginning of present service
9 terms, consecutive—Con.				
Widnall, William B_____	N.J____	7	*81st to 89th_____	Feb. 6, 1950
Willis, Edwin E_____	La_____	3	81st to 89th_____	Jan. 3, 1949
Zablocki, Clement J_____	Wis____	4	81st to 89th_____	Jan. 3, 1949
9 terms, not consecutive				
Dorn, W. J. Bryan_____	S.C____	3	80th, 82d to 89th____	Jan. 3, 1951
Flood, Daniel J_____	Pa_____	11	79th, 81st, 82d, 84th to 89th.	Jan. 3, 1955
Harvey, Ralph_____	Ind____	10	*80th to 85th, 87th to 89th.	Jan. 3, 1961
Kunkel, John C_____	Pa_____	16	76th to 81st, *87th to 89th.	May 16, 1961
8 terms, consecutive				
Adair, E. Ross_____	Ind____	4	82d to 89th_____	Jan. 3, 1951
Ayres, William H_____	Ohio___	14	82d to 89th_____	Jan. 3, 1951
Belcher, Page_____	Okla___	1	82d to 89th_____	Jan. 3, 1951
Berry, E. Y_____	S. Dak_	2	82d to 89th_____	Jan. 3, 1951
Betts, Jackson E_____	Ohio___	8	82d to 89th_____	Jan. 3, 1951
Bow, Frank T_____	Ohio___	16	82d to 89th_____	Jan. 3, 1951
Bray, William G_____	Ind____	7	82d to 89th_____	Jan. 3, 1951
Curtis, Thomas B_____	Mo_____	2	82d to 89th_____	Jan. 3, 1951
Dowdy, John_____	Tex____	7	*82d to 89th_____	Sept. 23, 1952
Jarman, John_____	Okla___	5	82d to 89th_____	Jan. 3, 1951
Kluczynski, John C_____	Ill_____	5	82d to 89th_____	Jan. 3, 1951
O'Brien, Leo W_____	N.Y___	29	*82d to 89th_____	Apr. 1, 1952
Rogers, Byron G_____	Colo___	1	82d to 89th_____	Jan. 3, 1951
Rogers, Walter_____	Tex____	18	82d to 89th_____	Jan. 3, 1951
Springer, William L_____	Ill_____	22	82d to 89th_____	Jan. 3, 1951
Watts, John C_____	Ky____	6	*82d to 89th_____	Apr. 14, 1951
8 terms, not consecutive				
Denton, Winfield K_____	Ind____	8	81st, 82d, 84th to 89th.	Jan. 3, 1955
O'Hara, Barratt_____	Ill_____	2	81st, 83d to 89th____	Jan. 3, 1953
Yates, Sidney R_____	Ill_____	9	81st to 87th, and 89th.	Jan. 3, 1965
7 terms, consecutive				
Ashmore, Robert T_____	S.C____	4	*83d to 89th_____	June 2, 1953
Boland, Edward P_____	Mass __	2	83d to 89th_____	Jan. 3, 1953
Brooks, Jack_____	Tex____	2	83d to 89th_____	Jan. 3, 1953
Broyhill, Joel T_____	Va_____	10	83d to 89th_____	Jan. 3, 1953
Byrne, James A_____	Pa_____	3	83d to 89th_____	Jan. 3, 1953

SERVICE OF REPRESENTATIVES—Continued

Name	State	District	Congresses (inclusive)	Beginning of present service
7 terms, consecutive—Con.				
Cederberg, Elford A_____	Mich__	10	83d to 89th_____	Jan. 3, 1953
Edmondson, Ed_____	Okla___	2	83d to 89th_____	Jan. 3, 1953
Fino, Paul A_____	N.Y___	24	83d to 89th_____	Jan. 3, 1953
Flynt, John J., Jr_____	Ga____	6	*83d to 89th_____	Nov. 2, 1954
Fountain, L. H_____	N.C___	2	83d to 89th_____	Jan. 3, 1953
Frelinghuysen, Peter H. B_	N.J____	5	83d to 89th_____	Jan. 3, 1953
Friedel, Samuel N_____	Md____	7	83d to 89th_____	Jan. 3, 1953
Gubser, Charles S_____	Calif___	10	83d to 89th_____	Jan. 3, 1953
Hagen, Harlan_____	Calif___	18	83d to 89th_____	Jan. 3, 1953
Haley, James A_____	Fla____	7	83d to 89th_____	Jan. 3, 1953
Hosmer, Craig_____	Calif___	32	83d to 89th_____	Jan. 3, 1953
Jonas, Charles R_____	N.C___	8	83d to 89th_____	Jan. 3, 1953
Laird, Melvin R_____	Wis____	7	83d to 89th_____	Jan. 3, 1953
Landrum, Phil M_____	Ga____	9	83d to 89th_____	Jan. 3, 1953
Lipscomb, Glenard P_____	Calif___	24	*83d to 89th_____	Nov. 10, 1953
Mailliard, William S_____	Calif___	6	83d to 89th_____	Jan. 3, 1953
Matthews, D. R. (Billy)__	Fla____	8	83d to 89th_____	Jan. 3, 1953
Moss, John E_____	Calif___	3	83d to 89th_____	Jan. 3, 1953
Natcher, William H_____	Ky____	2	*83d to 89th_____	Aug. 1, 1953
O'Neill, Thomas P., Jr___	Mass__	8	83d to 89th_____	Jan. 3, 1953
Pelly, Thomas M_____	Wash__	1	83d to 89th_____	Jan. 3, 1953
Poff, Richard H_____	Va_____	6	83d to 89th_____	Jan. 3, 1953
Rhodes, John J_____	Ariz___	1	83d to 89th_____	Jan. 3, 1953
Selden, Armistead I., Jr__	Ala____	5	83d to 89th_____	Jan. 3, 1953
Sullivan, Leonor Kretzer (Mrs. John B.).	Mo____	3	83d to 89th_____	Jan. 3, 1953
Thompson, T. Ashton____	La_____	7	83d to 89th_____	Jan. 3, 1953
Tuck, William M_____	Va_____	5	*83d to 89th_____	Apr. 14, 1953
Utt, James B_____	Calif___	35	83d to 89th_____	Jan. 3, 1953
Wilson, Bob_____	Calif___	36	83d to 89th_____	Jan. 3, 1953
Younger, J. Arthur_____	Calif___	11	83d to 89th_____	Jan. 3, 1953
7 terms, not consecutive				
Baring, Walter S_____	Nev___	At L.	81st, 82d, 85th to 89th.	Jan. 3, 1957
Holland, Elmer J_____	Pa_____	20	*77th, *84th to 89th_	Jan. 24, 1956
6 terms, consecutive				
Ashley, Thomas L_____	Ohio___	9	84th to 89th_____	Jan. 3, 1955
Baldwin, John F_____	Calif___	14	84th to 89th_____	Jan. 3, 1955
Clark, Frank M_____	Pa_____	25	84th to 89th_____	Jan. 3, 1955
Cramer, William C_____	Fla____	12	84th to 89th_____	Jan. 3, 1955
Diggs, Charles C., Jr_____	Mich__	13	84th to 89th_____	Jan. 3, 1955
Dingell, John D_____	Mich__	16	*84th to 89th_____	Dec. 13, 1955
Fascell, Dante B_____	Fla____	4	84th to 89th_____	Jan. 3, 1955

SERVICE OF REPRESENTATIVES—Continued

Name	State	District	Congresses (inclusive)	Beginning of present service
6 terms, consecutive—Con.				
Gray, Kenneth J_____	Ill_____	21	84th to 89th_____	Jan. 3, 1955
Green, Edith_____	Oreg___	3	84th to 89th_____	Jan. 3, 1955
Griffiths, Martha W_____	Mich__	17	84th to 89th_____	Jan. 3, 1955
Hull, W. R., Jr_____	Mo____	6	84th to 89th_____	Jan. 3, 1955
Jennings, W. Pat_____	Va_____	9	84th to 89th_____	Jan. 3, 1955
Macdonald, Torbert H___	Mass__	7	84th to 89th_____	Jan. 3, 1955
Minshall, William E_____	Ohio___	23	84th to 89th_____	Jan. 3, 1955
Reuss, Henry S_____	Wis____	5	84th to 89th_____	Jan. 3, 1955
Rogers, Paul G_____	Fla_____	6	*84th to 89th_____	Jan. 11, 1955
Roosevelt, James_____	Calif___	26	84th to 89th_____	Jan. 3, 1955
Sisk, B. F_____	Calif___	16	84th to 89th_____	Jan. 3, 1955
Teague, Charles M_____	Calif___	13	84th to 89th_____	Jan. 3, 1955
Thompson, Frank, Jr_____	N.J____	4	84th to 89th_____	Jan. 3, 1955
Vanik, Charles A_____	Ohio___	21	84th to 89th_____	Jan. 3, 1955
Wright, James C., Jr_____	Tex____	12	84th to 89th_____	Jan. 3, 1955
6 terms, not consecutive				
Davis, Glenn R_____	Wis____	9	*80th to 84th, and 89th.	Jan. 3, 1965
5 terms, consecutive				
Broomfield, William S____	Mich__	18	85th to 89th_____	Jan. 3, 1957
Chamberlain, Charles E__	Mich__	6	85th to 89th_____	Jan. 3, 1957
Collier, Harold R_____	Ill_____	10	85th to 89th_____	Jan. 3, 1957
Cunningham, Glenn_____	Nebr___	2	85th to 89th_____	Jan. 3, 1957
Curtin, Willard S_____	Pa_____	8	85th to 89th_____	Jan. 3, 1957
Dent, John H_____	Pa_____	21	*85th to 89th_____	Jan. 21, 1958
Dwyer, Florence P_____	N.J____	6	85th to 89th_____	Jan. 3, 1957
Everett, Robert A_____	Tenn__	8	*85th to 89th_____	Feb. 1, 1958
Farbstein, Leonard_____	N.Y___	19	85th to 89th_____	Jan. 3, 1957
Griffin, Robert P_____	Mich__	9	85th to 89th_____	Jan. 3, 1957
Lennon, Alton_____	N.C___	7	85th to 89th_____	Jan. 3, 1957
McFall, John J_____	Calif___	15	85th to 89th_____	Jan. 3, 1957
Michel, Robert H_____	Ill_____	18	85th to 89th_____	Jan. 3, 1957
Moore, Arch A., Jr_____	W.Va__	1	85th to 89th_____	Jan. 3, 1957
Nix, Robert N. C_____	Pa_____	2	*85th to 89th_____	May 20, 1958
Quie, Albert H_____	Minn__	1	*85th to 89th_____	Feb. 18, 1958
Robison, Howard W_____	N.Y___	33	*85th to 89th_____	Jan. 14, 1958
Scott, Ralph J_____	N.C___	5	85th to 89th_____	Jan. 3, 1957
Smith, H. Allen_____	Calif___	20	85th to 89th_____	Jan. 3, 1957
Ullman, Al_____	Oreg___	2	85th to 89th_____	Jan. 3, 1957
Whitener, Basil L_____	N.C___	10	85th to 89th_____	Jan. 3, 1957
Young, John_____	Tex____	14	85th to 89th_____	Jan. 3, 1957

SERVICE OF REPRESENTATIVES—Continued

Name	State	District	Congresses (inclusive)	Beginning of present service
5 terms, not consecutive				
McDowell, Harris B., Jr__	Del____	At L.	84th, 86th to 89th___	Jan. 3, 1959
4 terms, consecutive				
Brademas, John_____	Ind____	3	86th to 89th_____	Jan. 3, 1959
Burke, James A_____	Mass__	11	86th to 89th_____	Jan. 3, 1959
Cahill, William T_____	N.J____	1	86th to 89th_____	Jan. 3, 1959
Casey, Bob_____	Tex____	22	86th to 89th_____	Jan. 3, 1959
Cohelan, Jeffery_____	Calif___	7	86th to 89th_____	Jan. 3, 1959
Conte, Silvio O_____	Mass__	1	86th to 89th_____	Jan. 3, 1959
Daddario, Emilio Q_____	Conn__	1	86th to 89th_____	Jan. 3, 1959
Daniels, Dominick V_____	N.J____	14	86th to 89th_____	Jan. 3, 1959
Derwinski, Edward J_____	Ill_____	4	86th to 89th_____	Jan. 3, 1959
Devine, Samuel L_____	Ohio___	12	86th to 89th_____	Jan. 3, 1959
Downing, Thomas N_____	Va_____	1	86th to 89th_____	Jan. 3, 1959
Dulski, Thaddeus J_____	N.Y___	41	86th to 89th_____	Jan. 3, 1959
Gallagher, Cornelius E___	N.J____	13	86th to 89th_____	Jan. 3, 1959
Giaimo, Robert N_____	Conn__	3	86th to 89th_____	Jan. 3, 1959
Gilbert, Jacob H_____	N.Y___	22	*86th to 89th_____	Mar. 8, 1960
Goodell, Charles E_____	N.Y___	38	*86th to 89th_____	May 26, 1959
Halpern, Seymour_____	N.Y___	6	86th to 89th_____	Jan. 3, 1959
Hansen, Julia Butler_____	Wash__	3	*86th to 89th_____	Nov. 8, 1960
Hechler, Ken_____	W. Va_	4	86th to 89th_____	Jan. 3, 1959
Johnson, Harold T_____	Calif___	2	86th to 89th_____	Jan. 3, 1959
Karth, Joseph E_____	Minn__	4	86th to 89th_____	Jan. 3, 1959
Kastenmeier, Robert W__	Wis____	2	86th to 89th_____	Jan. 3, 1959
Keith, Hastings_____	Mass__	12	86th to 89th_____	Jan. 3, 1959
Langen, Odin_____	Minn__	7	86th to 89th_____	Jan. 3, 1959
Latta, Delbert L_____	Ohio___	5	86th to 89th_____	Jan. 3, 1959
Lindsay, John V_____	N.Y___	17	86th to 89th_____	Jan. 3, 1959
May, Catherine_____	Wash__	4	86th to 89th_____	Jan. 3, 1959
Monagan, John S_____	Conn__	5	86th to 89th_____	Jan. 3, 1959
Moorhead, William S_____	Pa_____	14	86th to 89th_____	Jan. 3, 1959
Morris, Thomas G_____	N. Mex_	At L.	86th to 89th_____	Jan. 3, 1959
Murphy, William T_____	Ill_____	3	86th to 89th_____	Jan. 3, 1959
Nelsen, Ancher_____	Minn__	2	86th to 89th_____	Jan. 3, 1959
O'Hara, James G_____	Mich__	12	86th to 89th_____	Jan. 3, 1959
Pirnie, Alexander_____	N.Y___	32	86th to 89th_____	Jan. 3, 1959
Pucinski, Roman C_____	Ill_____	11	86th to 89th_____	Jan. 3, 1959
Randall, Wm. J_____	Mo____	4	*86th to 89th_____	Mar. 3, 1959
Rivers, Ralph J_____	Alaska_	At L.	86th to 89th_____	Jan. 3, 1959
Rostenkowski, Dan_____	Ill_____	8	86th to 89th_____	Jan. 3, 1959
Roush, J. Edward_____	Ind____	5	86th to 89th_____	Jan. 3, 1959

SERVICE OF REPRESENTATIVES—Continued

Name	State	District	Congresses (inclusive)	Beginning of present service
4 terms, consecutive—Con.				
Schneebeli, Herman T____	Pa_____	17	*86th to 89th_____	Apr. 26, 1960
Shipley, George E_____	Ill_____	23	86th to 89th_____	Jan. 3, 1959
Slack, John M., Jr_____	W. Va_	3	86th to 89th_____	Jan. 3, 1959
Smith, Neal_____	Iowa___	5	86th to 89th_____	Jan. 3, 1959
Stratton, Samuel S_____	N.Y___	35	86th to 89th_____	Jan. 3, 1959
Stubblefield, Frank A____	Ky____	1	86th to 89th_____	Jan. 3, 1959
Taylor, Roy A_____	N.C___	11	*86th to 89th_____	June 25, 1960
Toll, Herman_____	Pa_____	4	86th to 89th_____	Jan. 3, 1959
Whalley, J. Irving_____	Pa_____	12	*86th to 89th_____	Nov. 8, 1960
3 terms, consecutive				
Addabbo, Joseph P_____	N.Y___	7	87th to 89th_____	Jan. 3, 1961
Anderson, John B_____	Ill_____	16	87th to 89th_____	Jan. 3, 1961
Ashbrook, John M_____	Ohio___	17	87th to 89th_____	Jan. 3, 1961
Battin, James F_____	Mont__	2	87th to 89th_____	Jan. 3, 1961
Bell, Alphonzo_____	Calif___	28	87th to 89th_____	Jan. 3, 1961
Carey, Hugh L_____	N.Y___	15	87th to 89th_____	Jan. 3, 1961
Clancy, Donald D_____	Ohio___	2	87th to 89th_____	Jan. 3, 1961
Corman, James C_____	Calif___	22	87th to 89th_____	Jan. 3, 1961
Davis, John W_____	Ga____	7	87th to 89th_____	Jan. 3, 1961
Dole, Bob_____	Kans___	1	87th to 89th_____	Jan. 3, 1961
Ellsworth, Robert F_____	Kans___	3	87th to 89th_____	Jan. 3, 1961
Findley, Paul_____	Ill_____	20	87th to 89th_____	Jan. 3, 1961
Gonzalez, Henry B_____	Tex____	20	*87th to 89th_____	Nov. 4, 1961
Hagan, G. Elliott_____	Ga____	1	87th to 89th_____	Jan. 3, 1961
Hall, Durward G_____	Mo____	7	87th to 89th_____	Jan. 3, 1961
Harsha, William H., Jr___	Ohio___	6	87th to 89th_____	Jan. 3, 1961
Harvey, James_____	Mich___	8	87th to 89th_____	Jan. 3, 1961
Henderson, David N_____	N.C___	3	87th to 89th_____	Jan. 3, 1961
Ichord, Richard H_____	Mo____	8	87th to 89th_____	Jan. 3, 1961
Joelson, Charles S_____	N.J____	8	87th to 89th_____	Jan. 3, 1961
King, Carleton J_____	N.Y___	30	87th to 89th_____	Jan. 3, 1961
Kornegay, Horace R_____	N.C___	6	87th to 89th_____	Jan. 3, 1961
MacGregor, Clark_____	Minn__	3	87th to 89th_____	Jan. 3, 1961
Martin, David T_____	Nebr___	3	87th to 89th_____	Jan. 3, 1961
Mathias, Charles McC.,Jr_	Md____	6	87th to 89th_____	Jan. 3, 1961
Morse, F. Bradford_____	Mass___	5	87th to 89th_____	Jan. 3, 1961
Mosher, Charles A_____	Ohio___	13	87th to 89th_____	Jan. 3, 1961
Nedzi, Lucien N_____	Mich___	14	*87th to 89th_____	Nov. 7, 1961
Olsen, Arnold_____	Mont__	1	87th to 89th_____	Jan. 3, 1961
Pike, Otis G_____	N.Y___	1	87th to 89th_____	Jan. 3, 1961
Purcell, Graham_____	Tex____	13	*87th to 89th_____	Jan. 27, 1962
Reifel, Ben_____	S. Dak_	1	87th to 89th_____	Jan. 3, 1961
Roberts, Ray_____	Tex____	4	*87th to 89th_____	Jan. 30, 1962
Rosenthal, Benjamin S___	N.Y___	8	*87th to 89th_____	Feb. 20, 1962
Roudebush, Richard L___	Ind____	6	87th to 89th_____	Jan. 3, 1961

SERVICE OF REPRESENTATIVES—Continued

Name	State	District	Congresses (inclusive)	Beginning of present service
3 terms, consecutive—Con.				
Ryan, William F_____	N.Y___	20	87th to 89th_____	Jan. 3, 1961
St Germain, Fernand J____	R.I____	1	87th to 89th_____	Jan. 3, 1961
Schweiker, Richard S_____	Pa_____	13	87th to 89th_____	Jan. 3, 1961
Shriver, Garner E_____	Kans___	4	87th to 89th_____	Jan. 3, 1961
Stafford, Robert T_____	Vt_____	At L.	87th to 89th_____	Jan. 3, 1961
Stephens, Robert G., Jr__	Ga_____	10	87th to 89th_____	Jan. 3, 1961
Thomson, Vernon W_____	Wis____	3	87th to 89th_____	Jan. 3, 1961
Tupper, Stanley R_____	Maine _	1	87th to 89th_____	Jan. 3, 1961
Udall, Morris K_____	Ariz___	2	*87th to 89th_____	May 2, 1961
Waggonner, Joe D., Jr____	La_____	4	*87th to 89th_____	Dec. 19, 1961
3 terms, not consecutive				
King, David S_____	Utah___	2	86th, 87th, and 89th_	Jan. 3, 1965
Moeller, Walter H_____	Ohio___	10	86th, 87th, and 89th_	Jan. 3, 1965
2 terms, consecutive				
Andrews, Mark_____	N. Dak_	1	*88th and 89th_____	Oct. 22, 1963
Brock, William E., 3d____	Tenn _ _	3	88th and 89th_____	Jan. 3, 1963
Brown, George E., Jr_____	Calif___	29	88th and 89th_____	Jan. 3, 1963
Broyhill, James T_____	N.C___	9	88th and 89th_____	Jan. 3, 1963
Burton, Laurence J_____	Utah___	1	88th and 89th_____	Jan. 3, 1963
Burton, Phillip_____	Calif___	5	*88th and 89th_____	Feb. 18, 1964
Cameron, Ronald Brooks_	Calif___	25	88th and 89th_____	Jan. 3, 1963
Clausen, Don H_____	Calif___	1	*88th and 89th_____	Jan. 22, 1963
Clawson, Del_____	Calif___	23	*88th and 89th_____	June 11, 1963
Cleveland, James C_____	N.H___	2	88th and 89th_____	Jan. 3, 1963
Duncan, Robert B_____	Oreg___	4	88th and 89th_____	Jan. 3, 1963
Edwards, Don_____	Calif___	9	88th and 89th_____	Jan. 3, 1963
Fraser, Donald M_____	Minn _ _	5	88th and 89th_____	Jan. 3, 1963
Fulton, Richard H_____	Tenn _ _	5	88th and 89th_____	Jan. 3, 1963
Fuqua, Don_____	Fla____	9	88th and 89th_____	Jan. 3, 1963
Gettys, Tom S_____	S.C____	5	*88th and 89th_____	Nov. 3, 1964
Gibbons, Sam M_____	Fla____	10	88th and 89th_____	Jan. 3, 1963
Grabowski, Bernard F____	Conn _ _	6	88th and 89th_____	Jan. 3, 1963
Green, William J_____	Pa_____	5	*88th and 89th_____	Apr. 28, 1964
Grover, James R., Jr_____	N.Y___	2	88th and 89th_____	Jan. 3, 1963
Gurney, Edward J_____	Fla____	11	88th and 89th_____	Jan. 3, 1963
Hanna, Richard T_____	Calif___	34	88th and 89th_____	Jan. 3, 1963
Hawkins, Augustus F____	Calif___	21	88th and 89th_____	Jan. 3, 1963
Horton, Frank J_____	N.Y___	36	88th and 89th_____	Jan. 3, 1963
Hungate, William L_____	Mo____	9	*88th and 89th_____	Nov. 3, 1964
Hutchinson, Edward_____	Mich _ _	4	88th and 89th_____	Jan. 3, 1963
Johnson, Albert W_____	Pa_____	23	*88th and 89th_____	Nov. 5, 1963
Leggett, Robert L_____	Calif___	4	88th and 89th_____	Jan. 3, 1963
Long, Clarence D_____	Md____	2	88th and 89th_____	Jan. 3, 1963

SERVICE OF REPRESENTATIVES—Continued

Name	State	District	Congresses (inclusive)	Beginning of present service
2 terms, consecutive—con.				
McClory, Robert_____	Ill_____	12	88th and 89th_____	Jan. 3, 1963
McDade, Joseph M_____	Pa_____	10	88th and 89th_____	Jan. 3, 1963
Marsh, John O., Jr_____	Va_____	7	88th and 89th_____	Jan. 3, 1963
Matsunaga, Spark M_____	Hawaii_	At L.	88th and 89th_____	Jan. 3, 1963
Minish, Joseph G_____	N.J____	11	88th and 89th_____	Jan. 3, 1963
Morton, Rogers C. B_____	Md____	1	88th and 89th_____	Jan. 3, 1963
Murphy, John M_____	N.Y___	16	88th and 89th_____	Jan. 3, 1963
Olson, Alec G_____	Minn__	6	88th and 89th_____	Jan. 3, 1963
Patten, Edward J_____	N.J____	15	88th and 89th_____	Jan. 3, 1963
Pepper, Claude_____	Fla____	3	88th and 89th_____	Jan. 3, 1963
Pickle, J. J. (Jake)_____	Tex____	10	*88th and 89th_____	Dec. 21, 1963
Pool, Joe_____	Tex____	At L.	88th and 89th_____	Jan. 3, 1963
Quillen, James H_____	Tenn__	1	88th and 89th_____	Jan. 3, 1963
Reid, Charlotte T_____	Ill_____	15	88th and 89th_____	Jan. 3, 1963
Reid, Ogden R_____	N.Y___	26	88th and 89th_____	Jan. 3, 1963
Rooney, Fred B_____	Pa_____	15	*88th and 89th_____	July 30, 1963
Roybal, Edward R_____	Calif___	30	88th and 89th_____	Jan. 3, 1963
Rumsfeld, Donald_____	Ill_____	13	88th and 89th_____	Jan. 3, 1963
St. Onge, William L_____	Conn__	2	88th and 89th_____	Jan. 3, 1963
Senner, George F., Jr_____	Ariz___	3	88th and 89th_____	Jan. 3, 1963
Sickles, Carlton R_____	Md____	At L.	88th and 89th_____	Jan. 3, 1963
Skubitz, Joe_____	Kans__	5	88th and 89th_____	Jan. 3, 1963
Talcott, Burt L_____	Calif___	12	88th and 89th_____	Jan. 3, 1963
Tuten, J. Russell_____	Ga_____	8	88th and 89th_____	Jan. 3, 1963
Van Deerlin, Lionel_____	Calif___	37	88th and 89th_____	Jan. 3, 1963
Weltner, Charles L_____	Ga_____	5	88th and 89th_____	Jan. 3, 1963
White, Compton I., Jr____	Idaho__	1	88th and 89th_____	Jan. 3, 1963
Wilson, Charles H_____	Calif___	31	88th and 89th_____	Jan. 3, 1963
Wyatt, Wendell_____	Oreg___	1	*88th and 89th_____	Nov. 3, 1964
Wydler, John W_____	N.Y___	4	88th and 89th_____	Jan. 3, 1963
2 terms, not consecutive				
Irwin, Donald J_____	Conn__	4	86th and 89th_____	Jan. 3, 1965
1 term				
Adams, Brock_____	Wash__	7	89th_____	Jan. 3, 1965
Anderson, William R_____	Tenn__	6	89th_____	Jan. 3, 1965
Andrews, Glenn_____	Ala____	4	89th_____	Jan. 3, 1965
Annunzio, Frank_____	Ill_____	7	89th_____	Jan. 3, 1965
Bandstra, Bert_____	Iowa___	4	89th_____	Jan. 3, 1965
Bingham, Jonathan B____	N.Y___	23	89th_____	Jan. 3, 1965
Buchanan, John H., Jr___	Ala____	6	89th_____	Jan. 3, 1965
Cabell, Earle_____	Tex____	5	89th_____	Jan. 3, 1965
Callan, Clair A_____	Nebr___	1	89th_____	Jan. 3, 1965
Callaway, Howard H_____	Ga_____	3	89th_____	Jan. 3, 1965

SERVICE OF REPRESENTATIVES—Continued

Name	State	District	Congresses (inclusive)	Beginning of present service

1 term—Continued

Name	State	District	Congresses (inclusive)	Beginning of present service
Carter, Tim Lee	Ky	5	89th	Jan. 3, 1965
Clevenger, Raymond F	Mich	11	89th	Jan. 3, 1965
Conable, Barber B., Jr	N.Y	37	89th	Jan. 3, 1965
Conyers, John, Jr	Mich	1	89th	Jan. 3, 1965
Craley, N. Neiman, Jr	Pa	19	89th	Jan. 3, 1965
Culver, John C	Iowa	2	89th	Jan. 3, 1965
de la Garza, Eligio	Tex	15	89th	Jan. 3, 1965
Dickinson, William L	Ala	2	89th	Jan. 3, 1965
Dow, John G	N.Y	27	89th	Jan. 3, 1965
Duncan, John J	Tenn	2	89th	Jan. 3, 1965
Dyal, Ken W	Calif	33	89th	Jan. 3, 1965
Edwards, Jack	Ala	1	89th	Jan. 3, 1965
Erlenborn, John N	Ill	14	89th	Jan. 3, 1965
Evans, Frank E	Colo	3	89th	Jan. 3, 1965
Farnsley, Charles P	Ky	3	89th	Jan. 3, 1965
Farnum, Billie S	Mich	19	89th	Jan. 3, 1965
Foley, Thomas S	Wash	5	89th	Jan. 3, 1965
Ford, William D	Mich	15	89th	Jan. 3, 1965
Gilligan, John J	Ohio	1	89th	Jan. 3, 1965
Greigg, Stanley L	Iowa	6	89th	Jan. 3, 1965
Grider, George W	Tenn	9	89th	Jan. 3, 1965
Hamilton, Lee H	Ind	9	89th	Jan. 3, 1965
Hanley, James M	N.Y	34	89th	Jan. 3, 1965
Hansen, George V	Idaho	2	89th	Jan. 3, 1965
Hansen, John R	Iowa	7	89th	Jan. 3, 1965
Hathaway, William D	Maine	2	89th	Jan. 3, 1965
Helstoski, Henry	N.J	9	89th	Jan. 3, 1965
Hicks, Floyd V	Wash	6	89th	Jan. 3, 1965
Howard, James J	N.J	3	89th	Jan. 3, 1965
Huot, J. Oliva	N.H	1	89th	Jan. 3, 1965
Jacobs, Andrew, Jr	Ind	11	89th	Jan. 3, 1965
Johnson, Jed, Jr	Okla	6	89th	Jan. 3, 1965
Kee, James	W. Va	5	89th	Jan. 3, 1965
Krebs, Paul J	N.J	12	89th	Jan. 3, 1965
Long, Speedy O	La	8	89th	Jan. 3, 1965
Love, Rodney M	Ohio	3	89th	Jan. 3, 1965
McCarthy, Richard D	N.Y	39	89th	Jan. 3, 1965
McEwen, Robert C	N.Y	31	89th	Jan. 3, 1965
McGrath, Thomas C., Jr	N.J	2	89th	Jan. 3, 1965
McVicker, Roy H	Colo	2	89th	Jan. 3, 1965
Machen, Hervey G	Md	5	89th	Jan. 3, 1965
Mackay, James A	Ga	4	89th	Jan. 3, 1965
Mackie, John C	Mich	7	89th	Jan. 3, 1965
Martin, James D	Ala	7	89th	Jan. 3, 1965
Meeds, Lloyd	Wash	2	89th	Jan. 3, 1965
Mink, Patsy T	Hawaii	At L	89th	Jan. 3, 1965
Mize, Chester L	Kans	2	89th	Jan. 3, 1965

SERVICE OF REPRESENTATIVES—Continued

Name	State	District	Congresses (inclusive)	Beginning of present service
1 term—Continued				
O'Neal, Maston	Ga	2	89th	Jan. 3, 1965
Ottinger, Richard L	N.Y	25	89th	Jan. 3, 1965
Race, John A	Wis	6	89th	Jan. 3, 1965
Redlin, Rolland	N. Dak	2	89th	Jan. 3, 1965
Reinecke, Ed	Calif	27	89th	Jan. 3, 1965
Resnick, Joseph Y	N.Y	28	89th	Jan. 3, 1965
Ronan, Daniel J	Ill	6	89th	Jan. 3, 1965
Roncalio, Teno	Wyo	At L.	89th	Jan. 3, 1965
Satterfield, David E., 3d	Va	3	89th	Jan. 3, 1965
Scheuer, James H	N.Y	21	89th	Jan. 3, 1965
Schisler, Gale	Ill	19	89th	Jan. 3, 1965
Schmidhauser, John R	Iowa	1	89th	Jan. 3, 1965
Smith, Henry P., 3d	N.Y	40	89th	Jan. 3, 1965
Stalbaum, Lynn E	Wis	1	89th	Jan. 3, 1965
Stanton, J. William	Ohio	11	89th	Jan. 3, 1965
Sweeney, Robert E	Ohio	At L.	89th	Jan. 3, 1965
Tenzer, Herbert	N.Y	5	89th	Jan. 3, 1965
Todd, Paul H., Jr	Mich	3	89th	Jan. 3, 1965
Tunney, John V	Calif	38	89th	Jan. 3, 1965
Vigorito, Joseph P	Pa	24	89th	Jan. 3, 1965
Vivian, Weston E	Mich	2	89th	Jan. 3, 1965
Walker, E. S. Johnny	N. Mex	At L.	89th	Jan. 3, 1965
Walker, Prentiss	Miss	4	89th	Jan. 3, 1965
Watkins, G. Robert	Pa	7	89th	Jan. 3, 1965
White, Richard C	Tex	16	89th	Jan. 3, 1965
Wolff, Lester L	N.Y	3	89th	Jan. 3, 1965
RESIDENT COMMISSIONER				
Polanco-Abreu, Santiago	P.R		89th	Jan. 3, 1965

STANDING, SELECT, AND SPECIAL COMMITTEES AND STAFFS

COMMITTEES

STANDING COMMITTEES OF THE SENATE

[Democrats in roman, Republicans in *italics*]

Aeronautical and Space Sciences

(Meets Tuesday)

Clinton P. Anderson, of New Mexico.
Richard B. Russell, of Georgia.
Warren G. Magnuson, of Washington.
Stuart Symington, of Missouri.
John Stennis, of Mississippi.
Stephen M. Young, of Ohio.
Thomas J. Dodd, of Connecticut.
Howard W. Cannon, of Nevada.
Spessard L. Holland, of Florida.
Walter F. Mondale, of Minnesota.
Joseph D. Tydings, of Maryland.

Margaret Chase Smith, of Maine.
Bourke B. Hickenlooper, of Iowa.
Carl T. Curtis, of Nebraska.
Len B. Jordan, of Idaho.
George D. Aiken, of Vermont.

James J. Gehrig, Acting Staff Director

Agriculture and Forestry

(Meets first and third Wednesdays)

Allen J. Ellender, of Louisiana.
Olin D. Johnston, of South Carolina.
Spessard L. Holland, of Florida.
James O. Eastland, of Mississippi.
Herman E. Talmadge, of Georgia.
B. Everett Jordan, of North Carolina.
Eugene J. McCarthy, of Minnesota.
George McGovern, of South Dakota.
Ross Bass, of Tennessee.
Joseph M. Montoya, of New Mexico.

George D. Aiken, of Vermont.
Milton R. Young, of North Dakota.
John Sherman Cooper, of Kentucky.
J. Caleb Boggs, of Delaware.
Jack Miller, of Iowa.

Cotys M. Mouser, Chief Clerk

Appropriations

(Meets upon call of chairman)

Carl Hayden, of Arizona.
Richard B. Russell, of Georgia.
Allen J. Ellender, of Louisiana.
Lister Hill, of Alabama.
John L. McClellan, of Arkansas.
A. Willis Robertson, of Virginia.
Warren G. Magnuson, of Washington.
Spessard L. Holland, of Florida.
John Stennis, of Mississippi.
John O. Pastore, of Rhode Island.
A. S. Mike Monroney, of Oklahoma.
Alan Bible, of Nevada.
Robert C. Byrd, of West Virginia.
Gale W. McGee, of Wyoming.
Mike Mansfield, of Montana.
E. L. Bartlett, of Alaska.
William Proxmire, of Wisconsin.
Ralph W. Yarborough, of Texas.

Leverett Saltonstall, of Massachusetts.
Milton R. Young, of North Dakota.
Karl E. Mundt, of South Dakota.
Margaret Chase Smith, of Maine.
Thomas H. Kuchel, of California.
Roman L. Hruska, of Nebraska.
Gordon Allott, of Colorado.
Norris Cotton, of New Hampshire.
Clifford P. Case, of New Jersey.

Everard H. Smith, Chief Clerk

Armed Services

(Meets Thursday)

Richard B. Russell, of Georgia.
John Stennis, of Mississippi.
Harry Flood Byrd, of Virginia.
Stuart Symington, of Missouri.
Henry M. Jackson, of Washington.
Sam J. Ervin, Jr., of North Carolina.
Howard W. Cannon, of Nevada.
Robert C. Byrd, of West Virginia.
Stephen M. Young, of Ohio.
Daniel K. Inouye, of Hawaii.
Thomas J. McIntyre, of New Hampshire.
Daniel B. Brewster, of Maryland

Leverett Saltonstall, of Massachusetts.
Margaret Chase Smith, of Maine.
Strom Thurmond, of South Carolina.
Jack Miller, of Iowa.
John G. Tower, of Texas.

Charles B. Kirbow, Chief Clerk

Banking and Currency

(Meets second Tuesday)

A. Willis Robertson, of Virginia.
John J. Sparkman, of Alabama.
Paul H. Douglas, of Illinois.
William Proxmire, of Wisconsin.
Harrison A. Williams, Jr., of New Jersey.
Edmund S. Muskie, of Maine.
Edward V. Long, of Missouri.
Maurine B. Neuberger, of Oregon.
Thomas J. McIntyre, of New Hampshire.
Walter F. Mondale, of Minnesota.

Wallace F. Bennett, of Utah.
John G. Tower, of Texas.
Strom Thurmond, of South Carolina.
Bourke B. Hickenlooper, of Iowa.

Matthew Hale, Chief of Staff

Commerce

(Meets first and third Tuesdays)

Warren G. Magnuson, of Washington.
John O. Pastore, of Rhode Island.
A. S. Mike Monroney, Of Oklahoma.
Frank J. Lausche, of Ohio.
E. L. Bartlett, of Alaska.
Vance Hartke, of Indiana.
Gale W. McGee, of Wyoming.
Philip A. Hart, of Michigan.
Howard W. Cannon, of Nevada.
Daniel B. Brewster, of Maryland.
Maurine B. Neuberger, of Oregon.
Ross Bass, of Tennessee.

Norris Cotton, of New Hampshire.
Thruston B. Morton, of Kentucky.
Hugh Scott, of Pennsylvania.
Winston L. Prouty, of Vermont.
James B. Pearson, of Kansas.
Peter H. Dominick, of Colorado.

Edward Jarrett, Chief Clerk

District of Columbia

(Meets second Friday)

Alan Bible, of Nevada.
Wayne Morse, of Oregon.
Thomas J. McIntyre, of New Hampshire.
Robert F. Kennedy, of New York.
Joseph D. Tydings, of Maryland.

Winston L. Prouty, of Vermont.
Peter H. Dominick, of Colorado.

Chester H. Smith, Staff Director

Finance

(Meets Wednesday)

Harry Flood Byrd, of Virginia.
Russell B. Long, of Louisiana.
George A. Smathers, of Florida.
Clinton P. Anderson, of New Mexico.
Paul H. Douglas, of Illinois.
Albert Gore, of Tennessee.
Herman E. Talmadge, of Georgia.
Eugene J. McCarthy, of Minnesota.
Vance Hartke, of Indiana.
J. W. Fulbright, of Arkansas.
Abraham A. Ribicoff, of Connecticut.

John J. Williams, of Delaware.
Frank Carlson, of Kansas.
Wallace F. Bennett, of Utah.
Carl T. Curtis, of Nebraska.
Thruston B. Morton, of Kentucky.
Everett McKinley Dirksen, of Illinois.

Elizabeth B. Springer, Chief Clerk

Foreign Relations

(Meets Tuesday)

J. W. Fulbright, of Arkansas.
John J. Sparkman, of Alabama.
Mike Mansfield, of Montana.
Wayne Morse, of Oregon.
Russell B. Long, of Louisiana.
Albert Gore, of Tennessee.
Frank J. Lausche, of Ohio.
Frank Church, of Idaho.
Stuart Symington, of Missouri.
Thomas J. Dodd, of Connecticut.
George A. Smathers, of Florida.
Joseph S. Clark, of Pennsylvania.
Claiborne Pell, of Rhode Island.

Bourke B. Hickenlooper, of Iowa.
George D. Aiken, of Vermont.
Frank Carlson, of Kansas.
John J. Williams, of Delaware.
Karl E. Mundt, of South Dakota.
Clifford P. Case, of New Jersey.

Carl Marcy, Chief of Staff

Government Operations

(Meets first Thursday)

John L. McClellan, of Arkansas.
Henry M. Jackson, of Washington.
Sam J. Ervin, Jr., of North Carolina.
Ernest Gruening, of Alaska.
Edmund S. Muskie, of Maine.
Abraham A. Ribicoff, of Connecticut.
Fred R. Harris, of Oklahoma.
Robert F. Kennedy, of New York.
Lee Metcalf, of Montana.
Joseph M. Montoya, of New Mexico.

Karl E. Mundt, of South Dakota.
Carl T. Curtis, of Nebraska.
Jacob K. Javits, of New York.
Milward L. Simpson, of Wyoming.

Walter L. Reynolds, Chief Clerk

Interior and Insular Affairs

(Meets upon call of chairman)

Henry M. Jackson, of Washington.
Clinton P. Anderson, of New Mexico.
Alan Bible, of Nevada.
Frank Church, of Idaho.
Ernest Gruening, of Alaska.
Frank E. Moss, of Utah.
Quentin N. Burdick, of North Dakota.
Carl Hayden, of Arizona.
George McGovern, of South Dakota.
Gaylord Nelson, of Wisconsin.
Lee Metcalf, of Montana.

Thomas H. Kuchel, of California.
Gordon Allott, of Colorado.
Len B. Jordan, of Idaho.
Milward L. Simpson, of Wyoming.
Paul J. Fannin, of Arizona.

Jerry T. Verkler, Staff Director

Judiciary

(Meets Mondays)

James O. Eastland, of Mississippi.
Olin D. Johnston, of South Carolina.
John L. McClellan, of Arkansas.
Sam J. Ervin, Jr., of North Carolina.
Thomas J. Dodd, of Connecticut.
Philip A. Hart, of Michigan.
Edward V. Long, of Missouri.
Edward M. Kennedy, of Massachusetts.
Birch Bayh, of Indiana.
Quentin N. Burdick, of North Dakota.
Joseph D. Tydings, of Maryland.

Everett McKinley Dirksen, of Illinois.
Roman L. Hruska, of Nebraska.
Hiram L. Fong, of Hawaii.
Hugh Scott, of Pennsylvania.
Jacob K. Javits, of New York.

Joseph A. Davis, Chief Clerk

Labor and Public Welfare

(Meets second and fourth Thursdays)

Lister Hill, of Alabama.
Pat McNamara, of Michigan.
Wayne Morse, of Oregon.
Ralph W. Yarborough, of Texas.
Joseph S. Clark, of Pennsylvania.
Jennings Randolph, of West Virginia.
Harrison A. Williams, Jr., of New Jersey.
Claiborne Pell, of Rhode Island.
Edward M. Kennedy, of Massachusetts.
Gaylord Nelson, of Wisconsin.
Robert F. Kennedy, of New York.

Jacob K. Javits, of New York.
Winston L. Prouty, of Vermont.
Peter H. Dominick, of Colorado.
George Murphy, of California.
Paul J. Fannin, of Arizona.

Stewart E. McClure, Chief Clerk

Post Office and Civil Service

(Meets second and fourth Tuesdays)

Olin D. Johnston, of South Carolina.
A. S. Mike Monroney, of Oklahoma.
Ralph W. Yarborough, of Texas.
Jennings Randolph, of West Virginia.
Gale W. McGee, of Wyoming.
Daniel B. Brewster, of Maryland.
Vance Hartke, of Indiana.
Quentin N. Burdick, of North Dakota.

Frank Carlson, of Kansas.
Hiram L. Fong, of Hawaii.
J. Caleb Boggs, of Delaware.
Milward L. Simpson, of Wyoming.

William P. Gulledge, Staff Director

Donald Russell, S.C.

Public Works

(Meets first and third Fridays)

Pat McNamara, of Michigan.
Jennings Randolph, of West Virginia.
Stephen M. Young, of Ohio.
Edmund S. Muskie, of Maine.
Ernest Gruening, of Alaska.
Frank E. Moss, of Utah.
Lee Metcalf, of Montana.
B. Everett Jordan, of North Carolina.
Daniel K. Inouye, of Hawaii.
Birch Bayh, of Indiana.
Joseph M. Montoya, of New Mexico.
Fred R. Harris, of Oklahoma.

John Sherman Cooper, of Kentucky.
Hiram L. Fong, of Hawaii.
J. Caleb Boggs, of Delaware.
James B. Pearson, of Kansas.
George Murphy, of California.

Ron M. Linton, Chief Clerk

Rules and Administration

(Meets second and fourth Wednesdays)

B. Everett Jordan, of North Carolina.
Carl Hayden, of Arizona.
Howard W. Cannon, of Nevada.
Claiborne Pell, of Rhode Island.
Joseph S. Clark, of Pennsylvania.
Robert C. Byrd, of West Virginia.

Carl T. Curtis, of Nebraska.
John Sherman Cooper, of Kentucky.
Hugh Scott, of Pennsylvania.

Gordon F. Harrison, Staff Director

SELECT AND SPECIAL COMMITTEES OF THE SENATE

Democratic Policy Committee

Chairman.—Mike Mansfield, Senator from Montana.
Democratic Whip.—Russell B. Long, Senator from Louisiana.
Secretary, Democratic Conference.—George A. Smathers, Senator from Florida.
  Lister Hill, Senator from Alabama.
  Richard B. Russell, Senator from Georgia.
  Carl Hayden, Senator from Arizona.
  Warren G. Magnuson, Senator from Washington.
  John O. Pastore, Senator from Rhode Island.
  Stuart Symington, Senator from Missouri.

Republican Policy Committee

Chairman.—Bourke B. Hickenlooper, Senator from Iowa.
  Leverett Saltonstall, Senator from Massachusetts.
  Milton R. Young, Senator from North Dakota.
  Everett McKinley Dirksen, Senator from Illinois.
  Thomas H. Kuchel, Senator from California.
  Thruston B. Morton, Senator from Kentucky.
  Frank Carlson, Senator from Kansas.
  Norris Cotton, Senator from New Hampshire.
  Margaret Chase Smith, Senator from Maine.
  Karl E. Mundt, Senator from South Dakota.
  Clifford P. Case, Senator from New Jersey.
  John Sherman Cooper, Senator from Kentucky.
  Strom Thurmond, Senator from South Carolina.
  James B. Pearson, Senator from Kansas.

Select Committee on Small Business

Room 424, Senate Office Building. Phone, 225–5175 (Code 180)

Chairman.—John J. Sparkman, Senator from Alabama.
  Russell B. Long, Senator from Louisiana.
  George A. Smathers, Senator from Florida,
  Wayne Morse, Senator from Oregon.
  Alan Bible, Senator from Nevada.
  Jennings Randolph, Senator from West Virginia.
  E. L. Bartlett, Senator from Alaska.
  Harrison A. Williams, Jr., Senator from New Jersey.
  Fred R. Harris, Senator from Oklahoma.
  Gaylord Nelson, Senator from Wisconsin.
  Joseph M. Montoya, Senator from New Mexico.
  Leverett Saltonstall, Senator from Massachusetts.
  Jacob K. Javits, Senator from New York.
  John Sherman Cooper, Senator from Kentucky.
  Hugh Scott, Senator from Pennsylvania.
  Winston L. Prouty, Senator from Vermont.
  Norris Cotton, Senator from New Hampshire.
Staff Director and General Counsel.—Lewis G. Odom, Jr., 922 North Ashton Street, Alexandria, Va.
Assistant Staff Director.—Blake O'Connor, 1244 34th Street.
Associate General Counsel.—Robert R. Locklin, 216 Cyrus Place, Alexandria, Va.

249

Professional Staff Members.—James B. Cash, Jr., 4801 Kenmore Avenue, Alexandria, Va.; William T. McInarnay, 7700 Killebrew Drive, Annandale, Va.; Daniel T. Coughlin, 2727 29th Street; Benjamin Gordon, 2856 Davenport Street; Raymond D. Watts, 811 East Jefferson Street, Rockville, Md., 20852; Neal D. Peterson, 1400 South Joyce Street, Arlington, Va.; Ellis C. Stewart, 3269 South Stafford Street, Arlington, Va.; Herbert L. Spira, 1400 South Joyce Street, Arlington, Va.

Chief Clerk.—Elizabeth A. Byrne, 4201 Massachusetts Avenue, 20016.

Assistant Chief Clerk.—Gertrude C. Taylor, 5502 Montgomery Street, Chevy Chase, Md., 20015.

Clerical Assistants.—Rose Marie Fried, 301 G Street SW.; Elaine C. Dye, 6800 Algonquin Avenue, Bethesda, Md., 20034; Sandra K. Klatt, 3222 Ravensworth Place, Alexandria, Va.; Mary C. Tursi, 1600 South Joyce Street, Arlington, Va.; Anne E. Stanley, Theological Seminary, Alexandria, Va.; Faye P. Hewlett, 1015 North Pegram Street, Alexandria, Va.; C. Joel Janney, 41 Ivy Street SE., 20003.

Special Committee on Aging

Room G-233, Senate Office Building.   Phone, 225-5364

Chairman.—George A. Smathers, Senator from Florida.
Pat McNamara, Senator from Michigan.
Harrison A. Williams, Jr., Senator from New Jersey.
Maurine B. Neuberger, Senator from Oregon.
Wayne Morse, Senator from Oregon.
Alan Bible, Senator from Nevada.
Frank Church, Senator from Idaho.
Jennings Randolph, Senator from West Virginia.
Edmund S. Muskie, Senator from Maine.
Edward V. Long, Senator from Missouri.
Frank E. Moss, Senator from Utah.
Edward M. Kennedy, Senator from Massachusetts.
Ralph W. Yarborough, Senator from Texas.
Stephen M. Young, Senator from Ohio.
Everett McKinley Dirksen, Senator from Illinois.
Frank Carlson, Senator from Kansas.
Winston L. Prouty, Senator from Vermont.
Hiram L. Fong, Senator from Hawaii.
Gordon Allott, Senator from Colorado.
Jack Miller, Senator from Iowa.
James B. Pearson, Senator from Kansas.

Staff Director.—J. William Norman, Jr., 6907 Adelphi Road, Hyattsville, Md.; Minority Staff Director: John Guy Miller, 5830 Oregon Avenue.

Professional Staff Members.—Frank C. Frantz, 3917 Livingston Street; William E. Oriol, 504 D Street SE.; Minority Professional Staff Member: Gerald P. Nye, 6 Farmington Drive, Chevy Chase, Md.

Research Director.—Jay B. Constantine, 9407 Locust Hill Road, Bethesda, Md.; Research Assistant: Toby Berkman, 3422 Prospect Avenue.

Chief Clerk.—Patricia G. Slinkard, 804 Hillsboro Drive, Silver Spring, Md.; Minority Chief Clerk: Marion P. Keevers, 1112 16th Street.

Assistant Clerks.—Eleanore M. Putz, 2001 Columbia Pike, Arlington, Va.; Mary M. Keeley, 3509-A South Stafford Street, Arlington, Va.; Fran Adams, 1150 12th Street; Carolyn R. Hyder; Minority Assistant Clerk: Theresa G. Neises, 3030 O Street.

STAFFS OF SENATE COMMITTEES

Aeronautical and Space Sciences.—Acting staff director, James J. Gehrig, 519 Gatewood Drive, Alexandria, Va.; professional staff: Everard H. Smith, Jr., 3620 Edmunds Street; William J. Deachman, 1126 Lake Boulevard, Annandale, Va.; Dr. Glen P. Wilson, 433 New Jersey Avenue SE.; Craig Voorhees, 7313 Millwood Road, Bethesda, Md.; Sam Bouchard, assistant chief clerk, 231 Old Senate Office Building; Robert Resnick, editorial assistant, 1025 Cecil Place; Eilene Galloway, special consultant, 4612 29th Place; Col. Harry N. Tufts, USA., facilities assistant, 1519 23rd Street South, Arlington, Va.; clerical assistants: Rhea J. Bowman, 2727 29th Street; Donald H. Brennan, 7612 Loretto Street, Springfield, Va.; Mary Rita Robbins, 328 Sixth Street, SE.; Patricia A. Robinson, 3491 South Wakefield Street, Arlington, Va.; Ruby H. Sutton, 3701 16th Street; Carol L. Wilson, 3801 Connecticut Avenue.

Agriculture and Forestry.—Chief Clerk, Cotys M. Mouser, 7057 Western Avenue; counsel, Harker T. Stanton, 10400 Haywood Drive, Silver Spring, Md.; assistant chief clerk, James M. Kendall, 3017 North Pershing Drive, Arlington, Va.; economist, Henry J. Casso, Jr., 547 Dead Run Drive, McLean, Va.; clerical assistants: Betty McHale Mason, 312 Willington Drive, Silver Spring, Md.; Blanche M. O'Berg, 3900 16th Street; Helen A. Miller, 1400 South Joyce Street, Arlington, Va.

Appropriations.—Chief Clerk, Everard H. Smith, 3321 Rittenhouse Street; assistant chief clerk, Thomas J. Scott, 3129 Westover Drive SE.; assistant clerk, Francis S. Hewitt, 2550 South Joyce Street, Arlington, Va; professional staff members: Kenneth J. Bousquet, 6135 Lee Highway, Arlington, Va.; Elizabeth H. Brantley, 2480 16th Street; Robert B. Clark, 4424 Q Street; Earl W. Cooper, Mayo, Md.; Herman E. Downey, 6212 Allen Court SE.; Paul R. Eaton, 2611 Evans Drive, Silver Spring, Md.; Leonard E. Edwards, 919 Baylor Drive, Westgrove, Alexandria, Va.; Joe E. Gonzales, 5312 Ludlow Drive SE.; William J. Kennedy, 501 Ashford Road, Silver Spring, Md.; Edmund T. King, 452 Oakwood Street; Cecil C. McDaniel, 2480 16th Street; Neilson A. McGown, 124 Billings Drive., Annandale, Va.; Harold E. Merrick, 4500 Ellicott Street; Mamie L. Mizen, 3025 Ontario Road; Maurice P. Pujol, 1000 Lamberton Drive, Silver Spring, Md.; Vorley M. Rexroad, 222 Dale View Drive, McLean, Va.; Raymond L. Schafer, 5505 Cornish Road, Bethesda, Md., Walter J. Stewart, 129 North Carolina Avenue, SE.; John M. Witeck, 2629 North Greenbrier Street, Arlington, Va.; William W. Woodruff, 504 Empress Court, Waynewood, Alexandria, Va.; special counsel: Paul J. Cotter, 3803 Woodbine Street, Chevy Chase, Md.; Clerical assistants: Gloria Butland, 1441 35th Street SE.; Virginia D. Carroll, 4314 North Carlyn Springs Road, Arlington, Va.; Helen Dackis, 800 Fourth Street SW.; Mildred F. Groverman, 4520 Reno Road; Mary Lou Vaughan, 2828 Connecticut Avenue; Dorothy Ward, 8909 Sudbury Road, Silver Spring, Md.; secretary: Dorothy S. Winchester, 75 East Wayne Avenue, Silver Spring, Md.; clerical assistants: Richard H. Jackson, 1417 42d Street SE.; Espy H. Miller, 605 Girard Street NE.; minority counsel: Joseph L. Borda, 3745 McKinley Street; clerical assistant: Marion L. Auerbach, 2480 16th Street.

Armed Services.—Professional staff: William H. Darden, 7517 June Street, Springfield, Va.; T. Edward Braswell, Jr., 213 South Pitt Street, Alexandria, Va.; Gordon A. Nease, 3640 Tallwood Terrace, Falls Church, Va.; chief clerk, Charles B. Kirbow, 5131 East Avenue, McLean, Va.; assistant chief clerk, Herbert S. Atkinson, 1733 Queens Lane, Arlington, Va.; clerical assistants: Laurie C. Chiperfield, 6712 Bostwick Drive, Springfield, Va.; Maurine E. Dantzic, 8005 Eastern Avenue, Silver Spring, Md.; Mary E. Keough, 3130 Wisconsin Avenue; Mary M. Welker, 215 C Street SE.

251

Banking and Currency.—Chief of staff, Matthew Hale, 918 Timber Branch Parkway, Alexandria, Va.; minority clerk, John R. Evans, 3900 Tunlaw Road; Woodlief Thomas, 3804 Raymond Street, Chevy Chase, Md.; Charles L. Egenroad, 4507 41st Street North, Arlington, Va.; Reginald W. Barnes, 1005 24th Street; Jonathan Lindley, 211 Martha's Road, Alexandria, Va.; Paul M. Penick, 314½ A Street NE.; Olin Cavness, 5100 37th Place SE.; George E. Wiggins, 3022 Lake Avenue, Cheverly, Md.; Henrietta S. Chase, 2828 Connecticut Avenue; Pauline C. Beam, 4733 First Street SW.; Caro M. Pugh, 4701 Connecticut Avenue; Florence Barr, 1545 18th Street.

Commerce.—Chief clerk, Edward Jarrett, 6236 29th Street North, Arlington, Va.; assistant chief clerk, Ralph W. Horton, 5517 Glenwood Road, Bethesda, Md.; chief counsel, Gerald B. Grinstein, 2853 29th Street, 20008; assistant chief counsel, Jeremiah J. Kenney, Jr., 13114 Holdridge Road, Silver Spring, Md.

Democratic Conference of the Senate.—Professional staff: Steven Ebbin, 1816 Metzerott Road, Adelphi, Md.; Marc S. Fasteau, 1367 Massachusetts Avenue; Teddy Roe, 140 North Early Street, Alexandria, Va.; Grace G. Tully, 3000 Connecticut Avenue.

Democratic Policy Committee.—Chief clerk and counsel, Pauline R. Moore, 4301 Massachusetts Avenue; general counsel, Charles D. Ferris, 5602 Belfast Lane, Springfield, Va.; counsel, Richard E. Streeter, 5633 Sanger Avenue, Alexandria, Va.; assistant counsel, Mary Ann Sames, 103 G Street, SW.; secretarial staff: Marie Mathew, 800 Fourth Street SW.; Betty Jane Lustic, 3601 Fifth Street South, Arlington, Va.

District of Columbia.—Staff Director, Chester H. Smith, 205 Cyrus Place, Waynewood, Alexandria, Va., 22308; counsel, Fred L. McIntyre, 1510 Quebec Street, Hyattsville, Md.; assistant counsel, Robert T. Hall, 333 Pine Spring Road, Falls Church, Va.; professional staff member, Richard E. Judd, 4628 Albemarle Street; assistant clerks; Ruth W. Bryant, 4206 Wicomico Avenue, Beltsville, Md.; Arlene Williams, 3330 Curtis Drive, Hillcrest Heights, Md.; Betty Kraus, 1420 South Walter Reed Drive, Arlington, Va.; Guthrie S. Alvarez, 8128 15th Avenue, West Hyattsville, Md.

Finance.—Chief clerk, Elizabeth B. Springer, 2311 North Utah Street, Arlington, Va.; assistant chief clerk, Evelyn R. Thompson, 1914 Columbia Pike, Arlington, Va.; professional staff member: Thomas Vail, 535 North Longfellow Street, Arlington, Va.; clerical assistants: Betty Mae Tapy, 2122 Massachusetts Avenue; Sandra D. Everly, 1101 New Hampshire Avenue; document clerk, Jesse R. Nichols, 3644 Park Place.

Foreign Relations.—Chief of Staff, Carl Marcy, 2600 South Hayes Street, Arlington, Va.; Consultants: Pat M. Holt, 7510 Exeter Road, Bethesda, Md.; Chief Clerk, Darrell St. Claire, 4970 Linnean Ave NW.; Consultants: Donald G. Henderson, 3205 Gunston Road, Alexandria, Va.; Arthur M. Kuhl, 1200 South Court House Road, Arlington, Va.; Seth P. Tillman, 1807 37th Street; Norvill Jones, 48 Fort Williams Parkway, Alexandria, Va.; Assistant Chief Clerk, Morella R. Hansen, 2415 I Street; Staff Assistant, Milrae E. Jensen, River House, 1111 Army-Navy Drive, Arlington, Va.; Assistant Clerks: Varney Porter, 1300 30th Street; Penelope deB. Saffer, 3320-A South Wakefield Street, Arlington, Va.; Mildred Mitchel, 6445 Luzon Avenue; Carolyn F. Smith, 1707 Second Street; R. Patricia McMahon, 2417 I Street; Margaret C. Brown, 1330 New Hampshire Avenue; Mary N. McFall, 1869 Mintwood Place; Alice Fales, 80 Kalorama Circle; Elmira Vogtmann, The Dodge House; Charles L. Parks, 1667 35th Street; Phillip C. Dozier, 651 E Street SE; Gibson-Taylor Ahlgren, 101 North Carolina Avenue SE; Printing Clerk, Abner Kendrick, 8437 Ravenswood Road, Hyattsville, Md.

Government Operations.—Chief Clerk and staff director, Walter L. Reynolds, 4801 Connecticut Avenue, 20008; professional staff members, Glenn K. Shriver, 5415 Center Street, Chevy Chase, Md., 20015; Eli E. Nobleman, 3106 Brooklawn Terrace, Chevy Chase, Md., 20015; W. E. O'Brien, 2401 32d Street SE. 20020; James R. Calloway, 3111 Savoy Drive, Fairfax, Va.; staff editor: Arthur A. Sharp, 6130 Rivanna Drive, Springfield, Va., 22150; assistant chief clerk, Ann M. Grickis, 4301 Columbia Pike, Arlington, Va., 22204; clerical assistants: Ray Barnett, 2000 Connecticut Avenue, 20008; Yvonne Scott, 1500 Massachusetts Avenue, 20005; Anne Kalland, 907 Cottage Street, Vienna, Va., 22180; Dorothy Lang, 3012 South Grant Street, Arlington, Va, 22202.

Interior and Insular Affairs.—Staff director, Jerry T. Verkler, 8004 Greeley Boulevard, West Springfield, Va.; professional staff: Stewart French, chief counsel, 2228 Q Street; Laurence S. Frank, 5909 Taylor Road, Riverdale, Md.; James H. Gamble, 1306 Barger Drive, Falls Church, Va.; Richard N. Little, 4200 Cathedral Avenue; Roy M. Whitacre, 2900 St. Clair Drive SE.; clerical staff: Rosemary Donnelley, 4201 Cathedral Avenue; Jessie Mackenzie, 2801 Quebec Street; Ethel Schissell, 3906 Vernon View Drive, Alexandria, Va.; Betty Sutton, 5900 Paul Street, Alexandria, Va.

Judiciary.—Chief clerk, Joseph A. Davis, 127 Lynmoor Drive, Silver Spring, Md.; professional staff: Thomas B. Collins, 5306 Everest Drive SE.; George S. Green, 6001 Logan Way, Bladensburg, Md.; L. P. B. Lipscomb, 3619 Alabama Avenue SE.; Francis C. Rosenberger, 509 Fontaine Street, Alexandria, Va.; Robert B. Young, 5016 Hawthorne Place; clerical staff: Mildred E. Canon, 2423 North Powhatan Street, Arlington, Va.; C. D. Chrissos, 7505 Mansfield Drive, Camp Springs, Md.; Carrie Lee Conner, 3005 South Grant Street, Arlington, Va.; Katherine M. Ellis, 2416 Spring Lake Drive, Lutherville-Timonium, Md.; Beatrice Martin Gray, 2745 29th Street; Mary Rogers, 2141 I Street; Richard F. Wambach, 3059 Q Street.

Labor and Public Welfare.—Chief clerk, Stewart E. McClure, 3013 Dent Place; general counsel, John S. Forsythe, 1606 North Jefferson Street, Arlington, Va.; professional staff members: Frederick R. Blackwell, 17 D Street SW.; Robert W. Barclay, 10809 Clermont Avenue, Garrett Park, Md.; Charles Lee, 301 G Street SW.; Charles M. Johnston, 3167 Westover Drive SE.; William C. Smith, 6812 Lupine Lane, McLean, Va.; George Pazianos, 207 10th Street SE.; John Bruff, 4230 New Senate Office Building; minority professional staff members: Stephen Kurzman, 1250 28th Street; Roy Millenson, 7013 Amy Lane, Bethesda, Md.; assistant chief clerk, Marjorie Whittaker, 1710 Hobart Street; printing clerk, Stephen J. Coffey, 1703 East-West Highway, Silver Spring, Md.; clerical staff: Thelma Blankenship, 5250 Oak Crest Drive; Helyn Eagle, 509 Constitution Avenue NE.; Eleanor Forsythe, 113 Woodley Drive, Alexandria, Va.; Nina Fountain, 4153 Southern Avenue SE.; Sandra Garofoli, 539 Seventh Street SE.; Lucille Gould, 2511 Q Street; Delores Hampton, 4114 Davis Place; Vivien Harman, 802 Dale Drive, Silver Spring, Md.; Bobbie Paradise, 103 G Street SW.; Margaret Porcher, 149 Duddington Place SE.; Julie Weatherman, 3405 Prospect Street.

Post Office and Civil Service.—William P. Gulledge, staff director and counsel, Room 6215, Senate Office Building; professional staff members: Frank A. Paschal, 4201 Massachusetts Avenue; Richard G. Fuller, 907 Eldon Drive, Alexandria, Va.; LeGrand A. Rouse II, 5610 Nebraska Avenue; Harold F. Murph, 6204 Senate Office Building; legal assistant, David Minton, 2643 Powhatan Street, Arlington, Va.; clerical assistants: Betty C. Alexander, 5200 Oakcrest Drive, Oxen Hill, Md.; Dorothy G. Bell, 6209 43d Street, Riverdale, Md.; Gladys N. Johnston, 3900 16th Street; Innis E. McDonald, 3140 Wisconsin Avenue; June R. Moody, Room 6206 Senate Office Building; Ann Moore, 3711 Alabama Avenue SE.; Polly Sargent, 2480 16th Street; Margaret I. Shenk, 9113 Wellington Place, Lanham, Md.; Peggy L. Thornton, 5048 Silver Hill Court, Suitland, Md.

Public Works.—Ron M. Linton, chief clerk and staff director, 3346 Stuyvesant Place; Richard E. Gerrish, assistant chief clerk, 4301 Columbia Pike, Arlington, Va.; technical staff: John L. Mutz, 4200 Cathedral Avenue; Richard B. Royce, 11014 Kenilworth Avenue, Garrett Park, Md.; clerical staff: Frances T. Clark, 2401 Calvert Street, Apt. 814; Sylvia S. De Baun, 215 Constitution Avenue NE.; Kathaleen R. Edwards, 20 9th Street NE.; Joseph F. van Vladricken, professional staff member, 1009 Custis Drive, Falls Church, Va.; William E. Miron, Jr., professional staff member, 9702 Cable Drive, Kensington, Md.; Mary L. Burke, 2461 P Street; Mary L. Vasarhelyi, 2645 Naylor Road SE., Apt. 201; Alyce M. Thompson, 10916 Jarboe Court, Silver Spring, Md.

Republican Conference of the Senate.—Staff director, Fred B. Rhodes, Jr., 129 South Abingdon Street, Arlington, Va.; deputy staff director, Bryan F. LaPlante, 3555 Martha Custis Drive, Alexandria, Va.; professional staff: Martin J. Clancy, 5010 Hampden Lane, Bethesda, Md.; David Kammerman, 5009 Cathedral Avenue; Cordelia B. Makarius, 714 Janneys Lane, Alexandria, Va.; F. Clyde Wilkinson, 3030 North Quincy Street, Arlington, Va.; secretarial staff: Patricia L. Doolittle, 6235 Springhill Drive, Greenbelt, Md.; research librarian, E. Elizabeth Bryden, 3801 Connecticut Avenue.

Republican Policy Committee.—Staff director, Fred B. Rhodes, Jr., 129 South Abingdon Street, Arlington, Va.; deputy staff director, Bryan F. LaPlante, 3555 Martha Custis Drive, Alexandria, Va.; professional staff: Bruce R. Barr, 3910 Jenifer Street; Arthur E. Burgess, 1435 North Van Dorn Street, Alexandria, Va.; Winifrede B. DeWeese, 604 E Street SE.; William B. Hatch, 611 Crocus Drive, Rockville, Md.; Arthur E. Scott, Box 64, Centreville, Va.; Harold M. Templeman, 1118 South Thomas Street, Arlington, Va.; George R. Wallrodt, Jr., 10 Tenth Street NE.; secretarial staff: Alice A. Robinson, 431 North Armistead Street, Alexandria, Va.; Irene E. Semiklose, 2041–B 38th Street SE.; Eleanor A. Tehan, 3636 16th Street; Elizabeth Voth, 2037 38th Street SE.; T. Ave Rian, 4315 57th Avenue, Bladensburg, Md.

Rules and Administration.—Staff director, Gordon F. Harrison, 4310 Softwood Trail, McLean, Va.; chief counsel, Hugh Q. Alexander, 525 Monticello Boulevard, Alexandria, Va.; general counsel, Lennox P. McLendon, First and C Streets NE.; staff members: Walter L. Mote, 5214 53d Avenue, Camp Springs, Md.; John P. Coder, 8115 Manson Street, Hyattsville, Md.; Lewis B. Hastings, 9953 Moss Avenue, Silver Spring, Md.; Marian G. Moore, 610 Arlington Village, Arlington, Va.; Hildreth T. Sharp, 3636 16th Street; Ora Jean Hunt, 4620 Second Street South, Arlington, Va.

STANDING COMMITTEES OF THE HOUSE

[Democrats in roman; Republicans in *italics*]

Agriculture

(Meets first Tuesday)

Harold D. Cooley, of North Carolina.
W. R. Poage, of Texas.
E. C. Gathings, of Arkansas.
John L. McMillan, of South Carolina.
Thomas G. Abernethy, of Mississippi.
Watkins M. Abbitt, of Virginia.
Paul C. Jones, of Missouri.
Harlan Hagen, of California.
Frank A. Stubblefield, of Kentucky.
Graham Purcell, of Texas.
James H. Morrison, of Louisiana.
Alec G. Olson, of Minnesota.
Spark M. Matsunaga, of Hawaii.
Maston O'Neal, of Georgia.
Thomas S. Foley, of Washington.
Joseph Y. Resnick, of New York.
Lynn E. Stalbaum, of Wisconsin.
Eligio de la Garza, of Texas.
Joseph P. Vigorito, of Pennsylvania.
John C. Mackie, of Michigan.
Rolland Redlin, of North Dakota.
Bert Bandstra, of Iowa.
Stanley L. Greigg, of Iowa.
Clair A. Callan, of Nebraska.
Santiago Polanco-Abreu, of Puerto Rico.

Paul B. Dague, of Pennsylvania
Page Belcher, of Oklahoma.
Charles M. Teague, of California.
Albert H. Quie, of Minnesota.
Catherine May, of Washington.
Delbert L. Latta, of Ohio.
Ralph Harvey, of Indiana.
Paul Findley, of Illinois.
Bob Dole, of Kansas.
Laurence J. Burton, of Utah.
Prentiss Walker, of Mississippi.

Christine S. Gallagher, Clerk

Appropriations

(Meets upon call of chairman)

George H. Mahon, of Texas.
Albert Thomas, of Texas.
Michael J. Kirwan, of Ohio.
Jamie L. Whitten, of Mississippi.
George W. Andrews, of Alabama.
John J. Rooney, of New York.
John E. Fogarty, of Rhode Island.
Robert L. F. Sikes, of Florida.
Otto E. Passman, of Louisiana.
Joe L. Evins, of Tennessee.
Edward P. Boland, of Massachusetts.
William H. Natcher, of Kentucky.
Daniel J. Flood, of Pennsylvania.
Winfield K. Denton, of Indiana.
Tom Steed, of Oklahoma.
George E. Shipley, of Illinois.
John M. Slack, Jr., of West Virginia.
John J. Flynt, Jr., of Georgia.
Neal Smith, of Iowa.
Robert N. Giaimo, of Connecticut.
Julia Butler Hansen, of Washington.
Charles S. Joelson, of New Jersey.
Joseph P. Addabbo, of New York.
John J. McFall, of California.
W. R. Hull, Jr., of Missouri.
D. R. (Billy) Matthews, of Florida.
Jeffrey Cohelan, of California.
Thomas G. Morris, of New Mexico.
Edward J. Patten, of New Jersey.
Clarence D. Long, of Maryland.
John O. Marsh, Jr., of Virginia.
Robert B. Duncan, of Oregon.
Sidney R. Yates, of Illinois.
Billie S. Farnum, of Michigan.

Frank T. Bow, of Ohio.
Charles R. Jonas, of North Carolina.
Melvin R. Laird, of Wisconsin.
Elford A. Cederberg, of Michigan.
Glenard P. Lipscomb, of California.
John J. Rhodes, of Arizona.
William E. Minshall, of Ohio.
Robert H. Michel, of Illinois.
Silvio O. Conte, of Massachusetts.
Odin Langen, of Minnesota.
Ben Reifel, of South Dakota.
Glenn R. Davis, of Wisconsin.
Howard W. Robison, of New York.
Garner E. Shriver, of Kansas.
Joseph M. McDade, of Pennsylvania.
Mark Andrews, of North Dakota.

Kenneth Sprankle, Clerk

Armed Services

(Meets Tuesday)

L. Mendel Rivers, of South Carolina.
Philip J. Philbin, of Massachusetts.
F. Edward Hébert, of Louisiana.
Melvin Price, of Illinois.
O. C. Fisher, of Texas.
Porter Hardy, Jr., of Virginia.
Charles E. Bennett, of Florida.
James A. Byrne, of Pennsylvania.
Samuel S. Stratton, of New York.
Otis G. Pike, of New York.
Richard H. Ichord, of Missouri.
Lucien N. Nedzi, of Michigan.
Alton Lennon, of North Carolina.
Wm. J. Randall, of Missouri.
G. Elliott Hagan, of Georgia.
Charles H. Wilson, of California.
Robert L. Leggett, of California.
Donald J. Irwin, of Connecticut.
Jed Johnson, Jr., of Oklahoma.
Frank E. Evans, of Colorado.
Rodney M. Love, of Ohio.
Floyd V. Hicks, of Washington.
Hervey G. Machen, of Maryland.
Speedy O. Long, of Louisiana.
E. S. Johnny Walker, of New Mexico.
Santiago Polanco-Abreu, of Puerto Rico.

William H. Bates, of Massachusetts.
Leslie C. Arends, of Illinois.
Alvin E. O'Konski, of Wisconsin.
William G. Bray, of Indiana.
Bob Wilson, of California.
Charles S. Gubser, of California.
Charles E. Chamberlain, of Michigan.
Alexander Pirnie, of New York.
Durward G. Hall, of Missouri.
Donald D. Clancy, of Ohio.
Robert T. Stafford, of Vermont.
Richard S. Schweiker, of Pennsylvania.

John R. Blandford, Chief Counsel

Banking and Currency

(Meets first and third Tuesdays)

Wright Patman, of Texas.
Abraham J. Multer, of New York.
William A. Barrett, of Pennsylvania.
Leonor Kretzer (Mrs. John B.) Sullivan, of Missouri.
Henry S. Reuss, of Wisconsin.
Thomas L. Ashley, of Ohio.
William S. Moorhead, of Pennsylvania.
Robert G. Stephens, Jr., of Georgia.
Fernand J. St Germain, of Rhode Island.
Henry B. Gonzalez, of Texas.
Joseph G. Minish, of New Jersey.
Charles L. Weltner, of Georgia.
Richard T. Hanna, of California.
Bernard F. Grabowski, of Connecticut.
Compton I. White, Jr., of Idaho.
Tom S. Gettys, of South Carolina.
Paul H. Todd, Jr., of Michigan.
Richard L. Ottinger, of New York.
Earle Cabell, of Texas.
Thomas C. McGrath, of New Jersey.
John R. Hansen, of Iowa.
Frank Annunzio, of Illinois.

William B. Widnall, of New Jersey.
Paul A. Fino, of New York.
Florence P. Dwyer, of New Jersey.
Seymour Halpern, of New York.
James Harvey, of Michigan.
William E. Brock 3d, of Tennessee.
Burt L. Talcott, of California.
Del Clawson, of California.
Albert W. Johnson, of Pennsylvania.
J. William Stanton, of Ohio.
Chester L. Mize, of Kansas.

Paul Nelson, Acting Clerk and Staff Director

Committees of the House   257

District of Columbia
(Meets on call of chairman and first Monday)

John L. McMillan, of South Carolina.
Thomas G. Abernethy, of Mississippi.
Howard W. Smith, of Virginia.
William L. Dawson, of Illinois.
Abraham J. Multer, of New York.
John Dowdy, of Texas.
Basil L. Whitener, of North Carolina.
James W. Trimble, of Arkansas.
B. F. Sisk, of California.
Charles C. Diggs, Jr., of Michigan.
G. Elliott Hagan, of Georgia.
Don Fuqua, of Florida.
Donald M. Fraser, of Minnesota.
Carlton R. Sickles, of Maryland.
J. Oliva Huot, of New Hampshire.
George W. Grider, of Tennessee.
John Bell Williams, of Mississippi.

Ancher Nelsen, of Minnesota.
William L. Springer, of Illinois.
Alvin E. O'Konski, of Wisconsin.
William H. Harsha, of Ohio.
Charles McC. Mathias, Jr., of Maryland.
Frank Horton, of New York.
Richard L. Roudebush, of Indiana.
Joel T. Broyhill, of Virginia.

James T. Clark, Clerk

Education and Labor
(Second and fourth Thursdays)

Adam C. Powell, of New York.
Carl D. Perkins, of Kentucky.
Edith Green, of Oregon.
James Roosevelt, of California.
Frank Thompson, Jr., of New Jersey.
Elmer J. Holland, of Pennsylvania.
John H. Dent, of Pennsylvania.
Roman C. Pucinski, of Illinois.
Dominick V. Daniels, of New Jersey.
John Brademas, of Indiana.
James G. O'Hara, of Michigan.
Ralph J. Scott, of North Carolina.
Hugh L. Carey, of New York.
Augustus F. Hawkins, of California.
Carlton R. Sickles, of Maryland.
Sam M. Gibbons, of Florida.
William D. Ford, of Michigan.
William D. Hathaway, of Maine.
Patsy T. Mink, of Hawaii.
James H. Scheuer, of New York.
Lloyd Meeds, of Washington.

William H. Ayres, of Ohio.
Robert P. Griffin, of Michigan.
Albert H. Quie, of Minnesota.
Charles E. Goodell, of New York.
John M. Ashbrook, of Ohio.
Dave Martin, of Nebraska.
Alphonzo Bell, of California.
Paul Findley, of Illinois.
Ogden R. Reid, of New York.
Glenn Andrews, of Alabama.

Louise Maxienne Dargans, Chief Clerk

Foreign Affairs

(Meets Tuesday)

Thomas E. Morgan, of Pennsylvania.
Clement J. Zablocki, of Wisconsin.
Omar Burleson, of Texas.
Edna F. Kelly, of New York.
Wayne L. Hays, of Ohio.
Armistead I. Selden, Jr., of Alabama.
Barratt O'Hara, of Illinois.
L. H. Fountain, of North Carolina.
Dante B. Fascell, of Florida.
Leonard Farbstein, of New York.
Charles C. Diggs, Jr., of Michigan.
Lindley Beckworth, of Texas.
Harris B. McDowell, Jr., of Delaware.
William T. Murphy, of Illinois.
Cornelius E. Gallagher, of New Jersey.
Robert N. C. Nix, of Pennsylvania.
John S. Monagan, of Connecticut.
Donald M. Fraser, of Minnesota.
Ronald Brooks Cameron, of California.
Benjamin S. Rosenthal, of New York.
Edward R. Roybal, of California.
John C. Culver, of Iowa.
Lee H. Hamilton, of Indiana.
Roy H. McVicker, of Colorado.

Frances P. Bolton, of Ohio.
E. Ross Adair, of Indiana.
William S. Mailliard, of California.
Peter H. B. Frelinghuysen, of New Jersey.
William S. Broomfield, of Michigan.
J. Irving Whalley, of Pennsylvania.
H. R. Gross, of Iowa.
E. Y. Berry, of South Dakota.
Edward J. Derwinski, of Illinois.
F. Bradford Morse, of Massachusetts.
Vernon W. Thomson, of Wisconsin.
James G. Fulton, of Pennsylvania.

Boyd Crawford, Staff Administrator

Government Operations

(Meets third Wednesday)

William L. Dawson, of Illinois.
Chet Holifield, of California.
Jack Brooks, of Texas.
L. H. Fountain, of North Carolina.
Porter Hardy, Jr., of Virginia.
John A. Blatnik, of Minnesota.
Robert E. Jones, of Alabama.
Edward A. Garmatz, of Maryland.
John E. Moss, of California.
Dante B. Fascell, of Florida.
Henry S. Reuss, of Wisconsin.
John S. Monagan, of Connecticut.
Torbert H. Macdonald, of Massachusetts.
J. Edward Roush, of Indiana.
William S. Moorhead, of Pennsylvania.
Cornelius E. Gallagher, of New Jersey.
Wm. J. Randall, of Missouri.
Benjamin S. Rosenthal, of New York.
James C. Wright, Jr., of Texas.
Fernand J. St Germain, of Rhode Island.
David S. King, of Utah.
John G. Dow, of New York.
Henry Helstoski, of New Jersey.

Clarence J. Brown, of Ohio.
Florence P. Dwyer, of New Jersey.
Robert P. Griffin, of Michigan.
Ogden R. Reid, of New York.
Frank Horton, of New York.
Delbert L. Latta, of Ohio.
Donald Rumsfeld, of Illinois.
William L. Dickinson, of Alabama.
John N. Erlenborn, of Illinois.
Howard H. Callaway, of Georgia.
Edward J. Gurney, of Florida.

Christine Ray Davis, Staff Director

House Administration

(Meets second Wednesday)

Omar Burleson, of Texas.
Samuel N. Friedel, of Maryland.
Robert T. Ashmore, of South Carolina.
Wayne L. Hays, of Ohio.
Paul C. Jones, of Missouri.
Frank Thompson, Jr., of New Jersey.
Watkins M. Abbitt, of Virginia.
Joe D. Waggonner, Jr., of Louisiana.
Carl D. Perkins, of Kentucky.
John H. Dent, of Pennsylvania.
Sam M. Gibbons, of Florida.
Lucien N. Nedzi, of Michigan.
John Brademas, of Indiana.
John W. Davis, of Georgia.
Kenneth J. Gray, of Illinois.
Augustus F. Hawkins, of California.
Jonathan B. Bingham, of New York.

Glenard P. Lipscomb, of California.
Robert J. Corbett, of Pennsylvania.
Charles E. Chamberlain, of Michigan.
Charles E. Goodell, of New York.
Willard S. Curtin, of Pennsylvania.
Samuel L. Devine, of Ohio.
John N. Erlenborn, of Illinois.
William L. Dickinson, of Alabama.

Julian P. Langston, Chief Clerk

Interior and Insular Affairs

(Meets Wednesday or on call of chairman)

Wayne N. Aspinall, of Colorado.
Leo W. O'Brien, of New York.
Walter Rogers, of Texas.
James A. Haley, of Florida.
Ed Edmondson, of Oklahoma.
Walter S. Baring, of Nevada.
Ralph J. Rivers, of Alaska.
Roy A. Taylor, of North Carolina.
Harold T. Johnson, of California.
Hugh L. Carey, of New York.
Morris K. Udall, of Arizona.
Compton I. White, Jr., of Idaho.
Phillip Burton, of California.
David S. King, of Utah.
Walter H. Moeller, of Ohio.
John V. Tunney, of California.
Jonathan B. Bingham, of New York.
Thomas S. Foley, of Washington.
N. Neiman Craley, Jr., of Pennsylvania.
John A. Race, of Wisconsin.
Richard White, of Texas.
Teno Roncalio, of Wyoming.
Santiago Polanco-Abreu, of Puerto Rico.

John P. Saylor, of Pennsylvania.
E. Y. Berry, of South Dakota.
Craig Hosmer, of California.
Joe Skubitz, of Kansas.
Charlotte T. Reid, of Illinois.
Laurence J. Burton, of Utah.
Rogers C. B. Morton, of Maryland.
Wendell Wyatt, of Oregon.
George V. Hansen, of Idaho.
Henry P. Smith 3d, of New York.
Ed Reinecke, of California.

Nancy J. Arnold, Chief Clerk

Interstate and Foreign Commerce

(Second Tuesday or on call of chairman)

Oren Harris, of Arkansas.
Harley O. Staggers, of West Virginia.
Walter Rogers, of Texas.
Samuel N. Friedel, of Maryland.
Torbert H. Macdonald, of Massachusetts.
John Jarman, of Oklahoma.
Leo W. O'Brien, of New York.
John E. Moss, of California.
John D. Dingell, of Michigan.
Paul G. Rogers, of Florida.
Horace R. Kornegay, of North Carolina.
Lionel Van Deerlin, of California.
J. J. (Jake) Pickle, of Texas.
Fred B. Rooney, of Pennsylvania.
John M. Murphy, of New York.
David E. Satterfield 3d, of Virginia.
Daniel J. Ronan, of Illinois.
J. Oliva Huot, of New Hampshire.
James A. Mackay, of Georgia.
John J. Gilligan, of Ohio.
Charles P. Farnsley, of Kentucky.
John Bell Williams, of Mississippi.

William L. Springer, of Illinois.
J. Arthur Younger, of California.
Samuel L. Devine, of Ohio.
Ancher Nelsen, of Minnesota.
Hastings Keith, of Massachusetts.
Willard S. Curtin, of Pennsylvania.
Glenn Cunningham, of Nebraska.
James T. Broyhill, of North Carolina.
James Harvey, of Michigan.
Tim Lee Carter, of Kentucky.
Howard H. Callaway, of Georgia

W. E. Williamson, Clerk

Judiciary

(Meets Tuesday)

Emanuel Celler, of New York.
Michael A. Feighan, of Ohio.
Frank Chelf, of Kentucky.
Edwin E. Willis, of Louisiana.
Peter W. Rodino, Jr., of New Jersey.
Byron G. Rogers, of Colorado.
Harold D. Donohue, of Massachusetts.
Jack Brooks, of Texas.
William M. Tuck, of Virginia.
Robert T. Ashmore, of South Carolina.
John Dowdy, of Texas.
Basil L. Whitener, of North Carolina.
Herman Toll, of Pennsylvania.
Robert W. Kastenmeier, of Wisconsin.
Jacob H. Gilbert, of New York.
James C. Corman, of California.
William L. St. Onge, of Connecticut.
George F. Senner, Jr., of Arizona.
Don Edwards, of California.
William L. Hungate, of Missouri.
Herbert Tenzer, of New York.
John Conyers, Jr., of Michigan.
George W. Grider, of Tennessee.
Andrew Jacobs, Jr., of Indiana.

William M. McCulloch, of Ohio.
Richard H. Poff, of Virginia.
William C. Cramer, of Florida.
Arch A. Moore, Jr., of West Virginia.
John V. Lindsay, of New York.
William T. Cahill, of New Jersey.
Clark MacGregor, of Minnesota.
Charles McC. Mathias, Jr., of Maryland.
Carleton J. King, of New York.
Edward Hutchinson, of Michigan.
Robert McClory, of Illinois.

Bess E. Dick, Staff Director

Merchant Marine and Fisheries
(Meets Wednesday of each week)

Herbert C. Bonner, of North Carolina.
Edward A. Garmatz, of Maryland.
Leonor Kretzer (Mrs. John B.) Sullivan, of Missouri.
T. Ashton Thompson, of Louisiana.
Frank M. Clark, of Pennsylvania.
Thomas L. Ashley, of Ohio.
John D. Dingell, of Michigan.
Alton Lennon, of North Carolina.
Thomas N. Downing, of Virginia.
Bob Casey, of Texas.
James A. Byrne, of Pennsylvania.
Harlan Hagen, of California.
Edith Green, of Oregon.
Paul G. Rogers, of Florida.
Frank A. Stubblefield, of Kentucky.
John M. Murphy, of New York.
Jacob H. Gilbert, of New York.
J. Russell Tuten, of Georgia.
William L. St. Onge, of Connecticut.
John G. Dow, of New York.
Raymond F. Clevenger, of Michigan.

William S. Mailliard, of California.
Thomas M. Pelly, of Washington.
Stanley R. Tupper, of Maine.
Charles A. Mosher, of Ohio.
James R. Grover, Jr., of New York.
Rogers C. B. Morton, of Maryland.
Hastings Keith, of Massachusetts.
Jack Edwards, of Alabama.
G. Robert Watkins, of Pennsylvania.
Ed Reinecke, of California.

W. B. Winfield, Clerk

Post Office and Civil Service
(Meets first and third Thursdays)

Tom Murray, of Tennessee.
James H. Morrison, of Louisiana.
Thaddeus J. Dulski, of New York.
David N. Henderson, of North Carolina.
Arnold Olsen, of Montana.
Morris K. Udall, of Arizona.
Dominick V. Daniels, of New Jersey.
Lindley Beckworth, of Texas.
Harley O. Staggers, of West Virginia.
Robert N. C. Nix, of Pennsylvania.
Joe R. Pool, of Texas.
William J. Green, of Pennsylvania.
Spark M. Matsunaga, of Hawaii.
Paul J. Krebs, of New Jersey.
Raymond F. Clevenger, of Michigan.
James M. Hanley, of New York.
John V. Tunney, of California.

Robert J. Corbett, of Pennsylvania.
H. R. Gross, of Iowa.
Glenn Cunningham, of Nebraska.
Edward J. Derwinski, of Illinois.
Robert F. Ellsworth, of Kansas.
Albert W. Johnson, of Pennsylvania.
John H. Buchanan, Jr., of Alabama.
James T. Broyhill, of North Carolina.

Charles E. Johnson, Staff Director

Public Works

(Meets upon call of chairman)

George H. Fallon, of Maryland.
John A. Blatnik, of Minnesota.
Robert E. Jones, of Alabama.
John C. Kluczynski, of Illinois.
T. Ashton Thompson, of Louisiana.
James C. Wright, Jr., of Texas.
Kenneth J. Gray, of Illinois.
Frank M. Clark, of Pennsylvania.
Ed Edmondson, of Oklahoma.
Harold T. Johnson, of California.
W. J. Bryan Dorn, of South Carolina.
David N. Henderson, of North Carolina.
Arnold Olsen, of Montana.
J. Russell Tuten, of Georgia.
Ralph J. Rivers, of Alaska.
Ray Roberts, of Texas.
Robert A. Everett, of Tennessee.
Richard D. McCarthy, of New York.
James Kee, of West Virginia.
John R. Schmidhauser, of Iowa.
Robert E. Sweeney, of Ohio.
James J. Howard, of New Jersey.
Ken W. Dyal, of California.

William C. Cramer, of Florida.
John F. Baldwin, of California.
William H. Harsha, of Ohio.
John C. Kunkel, of Pennsylvania.
James R. Grover, Jr., of New York.
James C. Cleveland, of New Hampshire.
Don H. Clausen, of California.
Charles A. Halleck, of Indiana.
Charlotte T. Reid, of Illinois.
Robert C. McEwen, of New York.
James D. Martin, of Alabama.

Edward J. McNeal, Staff Director

Rules

(Meets upon call of chairman)

Howard W. Smith, of Virginia.
William M. Colmer, of Mississippi.
Ray J. Madden, of Indiana.
James J. Delaney, of New York.
James W. Trimble, of Arkansas.
Richard Bolling, of Missouri.
Thomas P. O'Neill, Jr., of Massachusetts.
B. F. Sisk, of California.
John Young, of Texas.
Claude Pepper, of Florida.

Clarence J. Brown, of Ohio.
H. Allen Smith, of California.
John B. Anderson, of Illinois.
David T. Martin, of Nebraska.
James H. Quillen, of Tennessee.

Thomas M. Carruthers, Counsel

Science and Astronautics

(Meets Tuesday)

George P. Miller, of California.
Olin E. Teague, of Texas.
Joseph E. Karth, of Minnesota.
Ken Hechler, of West Virginia.
Emilio Q. Daddario, of Connecticut.
J. Edward Roush, of Indiana.
Bob Casey, of Texas.
John W. Davis, of Georgia.
William F. Ryan, of New York.
Thomas N. Downing, of Virginia.
Joe D. Waggonner, Jr., of Louisiana.
Don Fuqua, of Florida.
Carl Albert, of Oklahoma.
Roy A. Taylor, of North Carolina.
George E. Brown, Jr., of California.
Walter H. Moeller, of Ohio.
William R. Anderson, of Tennessee.
Brock Adams, of Washington.
Lester L. Wolff, of New York.
Weston E. Vivian, of Michigan.
Gale Schisler, of Illinois.

Joseph W. Martin, Jr., of Massachusetts.
James G. Fulton, of Pennsylvania.
Charles A. Mosher, of Ohio.
Richard L. Roudebush, of Indiana.
Alphonzo Bell, of California.
Thomas M. Pelly, of Washington.
Donald Rumsfeld, of Illinois.
Edward J. Gurney, of Florida.
John W. Wydler, of New York.
Barber B. Conable, Jr., of New York.

Charles F. Ducander, Executive Director

Un-American Activities

(Meets first and third Wednesdays)

Edwin E. Willis, of Louisiana.
William M. Tuck, of Virginia.
Joe R. Pool, of Texas.
Richard H. Ichord, of Missouri.
George F. Senner, Jr., of Arizona.
Charles L. Weltner, of Georgia.

John M. Ashbrook, of Ohio.
Del Clawson, of California.
John H. Buchanan, Jr., of Alabama.

Francis J. McNamara, Director

Veterans' Affairs

(Meets upon call of chairman)

Olin E. Teague, of Texas.
W. J. Bryan Dorn, of South Carolina.
James A. Haley, of Florida.
Walter S. Baring, of Nevada.
Robert A. Everett, of Tennessee.
Thaddeus J. Dulski, of New York.
Harris B. McDowell, Jr., of Delaware.
Horace R. Kornegay, of North Carolina.
Ray Roberts, of Texas.
Robert T. Secrest, of Ohio.
George E. Brown, Jr., of California.
Charles H. Wilson, of California.
David E. Satterfield 3d, of Virginia.
Teno Roncalio, of Wyoming.
Henry Helstoski, of New Jersey.
Joseph Y. Resnick, of New York.
James M. Hanley, of New York.

E. Ross Adair, of Indiana.
William H. Ayres, of Ohio.
Paul A. Fino, of New York.
John P. Saylor, of Pennsylvania.
Charles M. Teague, of California.
Seymour Halpern, of New York.
Robert F. Ellsworth, of Kansas.
John J. Duncan, of Tennessee.

Oliver E. Meadows, Staff Director

Ways and Means

(Meets upon call of chairman)

Wilbur D. Mills, of Arkansas.
Cecil R. King, of California.
Hale Boggs, of Louisiana.
Eugene J. Keogh, of New York.
Frank M. Karsten, of Missouri.
A. Sydney Herlong, Jr., of Florida.
John C. Watts, of Kentucky.
Al Ullman, of Oregon.
James A. Burke, of Massachusetts.
Clark W. Thompson, of Texas.
Martha W. Griffiths, of Michigan.
W. Pat Jennings, of Virginia.
George M. Rhodes, of Pennsylvania.
Dan Rostenkowski, of Illinois.
Phil M. Landrum, of Georgia.
Charles A. Vanik, of Ohio.
Richard H. Fulton, of Tennessee.

John W. Byrnes, of Wisconsin.
Thomas B. Curtis, of Missouri.
James B. Utt, of California.
Jackson E. Betts, of Ohio.
Herman T. Schneebeli, of Pennsylvania.
Harold R. Collier, of Illinois.
Joel T. Broyhill, of Virginia.
James F. Battin, of Montana.

Leo H. Irwin, Chief Counsel

SELECT AND SPECIAL COMMITTEES OF THE HOUSE

Select Committee To Conduct a Study and Investigation of the Problems of Small Business

Phone, 225–5821 (Code 180)

Chairman.—Joe L. Evins, Representative from Tennessee.
  Wright Patman, Representative from Texas.
  Abraham J. Multer, Representative from New York.
  Tom Steed, Representative from Oklahoma.
  James Roosevelt, Representative from California.
  John C. Kluczynski, Representative from Illinois.
  John D. Dingell, Representative from Michigan.
  Neal Smith, Representative from Iowa.
  Charles L. Weltner, Representative from Georgia.
  Arch A. Moore, Jr., Representative from West Virginia.
  H. Allen Smith, Representative from California.
  Ralph Harvey, Representative from Indiana.
  Silvio O. Conte, Representative from Massachusetts.
  James T. Broyhill, Representative from North Carolina.
  Frank Horton, Representative from New York.
Staff Director.—Bryan Haskell Jacques, 4505 19th Street North, Arlington, Va.
General Counsel.—Richard L. Mitchell, College Park Towers, College Park, Md.
Clerk.—Myrtle Ruth Foutch, 103 G Street SW., 20024.
Minority Counsel.—John J. Williams, 4903 Fort Sumner Drive, 20016.

STAFFS OF HOUSE COMMITTEES

Agriculture.—Robert C. Bruce, 442 Vista Drive, Falls Church, Va., assistant counsel; Christine S. Gallagher, 2500 Q Street, 20007, clerk; Martha S. Hannah, 1639 Fitzgerald Lane, Alexandria, Va., staff assistant; John J. Heimburger, 2001 Columbia Pike, Arlington, Va., general counsel; Marjorie B. Johnson, 4147 Southern Avenue SE., staff assistant; Peggy J. Lamm, 110 D Street SE., staff assistant; Francis M. LeMay, 418 Constitution Avenue NE., staff consultant; George F. Misslbeck, 8002 Karl Road, Alexandria, Va., printing editor; Hyde H. Murray, 3511 Texas Avenue SE., assistant clerk; M. Allen Paul, 2500 Q Street, staff assistant; Betty Prezioso, 1600 South Joyce Street, Arlington, Va., staff assistant; Lydia Vacin, 1500 Massachusetts Avenue, staff assistant; Ruth Carolyn Windsor, Keystone Gardens, Forrestville, Md., staff assistant; Jane C. Wojcik, 532 20th Street, staff assistant.

Appropriations.—Clerk and staff director: Kenneth Sprankle, 5902 Welborn Drive, Wood Acres, Md., 20016; assistant clerk and staff director: Paul M. Wilson, 7602 Wildwood Drive, Takoma Park, Md.; staff members: Carson W. Culp, 4200 Dresden Street, Kensington, Md.; Jay B. Howe, 10230 New Hampshire Avenue, Hillandale, Silver Spring, Md.; Ross P. Pope, 723 South Lee Street, Alexandria, Va.; Robert M. Moyer, 505 Prosperity Avenue, Fairfax, Va.; Frank P. Sanders, 5310 Glenwood Road, Bethesda, Md.; Eugene B. Wilhelm, 1406 Highview Place, Falls Church, Va.; Robert P. Williams, 151 Sleepy Hollow Road, Falls Church, Va.; George E. Evans, 1211 La Ronde Court, Alexandria, Va.; Aubrey A. Gunnels, 1127 Aronow Drive, Falls Church, Va.; Robert L. Michaels, 205 Deerfield Court, Falls Church, Va.; G. Homer Skarin, 2907 North Greencastle Street, Arlington, Va.; Earl C. Silsby, 5907 Cranston Road, Wood Acres, Md., 20016; Lawrence C. Miller, 4214 Van Buren Street, University Park, Hyattsville, Md.; Francis G. Merrill, 4016 Sumner Road, Alexandria, Va.; Ralph Preston, 9223 Limestone Place, College Park, Md.; Keith F. Mainland, 508 Courtley Court, Fairfax, Va.

Armed Services.—Professional staff: John R. Blandford, chief counsel, 4520 39th Street North, Arlington, Va.; Philip W. Kelleher, counsel, 3 Shannon Court, Alexandria, Va.; Frank M. Slatinshek, counsel, 401 Belle Vista Drive, Alexandria, Va.; William H. Cook, counsel, 1600 South Joyce Street, Arlington, Va.; Earl J. Morgan, 7507 Whittier Boulevard, Bethesda, Md.; Ralph Marshall, 7517 Axton Street, Springfield, Va.; clerical staff: Oneta L. Stockstill, executive secretary, 417 First Street SE.; Berniece Kalinowski, secretary, 4000 Beecher Street; L. Louise Ellis, secretary, 2500 Wisconsin; Edna E. Johnson, 1200 North Nash Street, Arlington, Va.; Dorothy R. Britton, secretary, 5418 20th Street, Hyattsville, Md.; Doris L. Scott, secretary, 4301 Columbia Pike, Arlington, Va.; James A. Deakins, bill clerk, 17 Second Street NE.

Banking and Currency.—Acting clerk and staff director, Paul Nelson, 3195 Porter Street; professional staff member, John E. Barriere, 1207 Rippon Road, Alexandria, Va.; counsel, Alvin Lee Morse, 2418 North Dickerson, Arlington, Va.; minority staff member, Orman S. Fink, 824 North Abingdon Street, Arlington, Va.; administrative assistant, Jane M. Deem, 5415 Connecticut Avenue.

District of Columbia.—James T. Clark, clerk, 5600 Kirkside Drive, Chevy Chase, Md.; Hayden S. Garber, counsel, 4620 Careybrook Lane, Oxon Hill, Md.; Clayton D. Gasque, staff director, 445 House Office Building; Donald J. Tubridy, minority clerk, 1400 South Joyce Street, Arlington, Va.; Leonard O. Hilder, investigator, 4805 North Second Street, Arlington, Va.; Ellen M. Coxeter, assistant clerk, 445 House Office Building; Jean Quarles, assistant clerk, 1410 33d Street.

Education and Labor.—Professional Staff: Louise Maxienne Dargans, Chief Clerk; Russell Derrickson, Staff Director; Deborah Wolfe, Education Chief; Leon Abramson, Chief Counsel for Labor-Management; Philip Rodgers, Minority Clerk and Counsel; Charles Radcliffe, Minority Counsel for Education; Assistant Counsels: Donald Anderson, Michael Schwartz; Investigator: Odell Clark; Administrative Assistants: Donald Berens, Mary Shuler, Louise Wright, Jeanne Thomson, Corrine Huff; Secretaries: Aurora Harris, Goldie Baldwin; Messenger, John Warren.

Foreign Affairs.—Staff administrator and committee clerk, Boyd Crawford, 101 Idylwood Road, Falls Church, Va.; senior staff consultant, Roy J. Bullock, 8 North Oakland Street, Arlington, Va.; staff consultants: Albert C. F. Westphal, 4010 Warren Street; Franklin J. Schupp, 5165 Rockwood Parkway; Robert F. Brandt, 4616 Massachusetts Avenue; Harry C. Cromer, 8904 Charred Oak Drive, Bethesda, Md.; Philip B. Billings, 5703 Ridgefield Road; Marian A. Czarnecki, 1701 Juniper Street; Melvin O. Benson, 1301 Delaware Avenue SW.; senior staff assistant, June Nigh, 2004 Leesburg Pike, Falls Church, Va.; staff assistants: Helen C. Mattas, 2323 North 11th Street, Arlington, Va.; Helen L. Hashagen, 2800 Quebec Street, Mary Louise O'Brien, 5525 39th Street; Mary E. Medsger, 2520 Q Street; Doris B. McCracken, 2916 Russell Road, Alexandria, Va.; Jean E. Smith, 2500 Wisconsin Avenue; Robert J. Bowen, clerical assistant, 5207 Colonial Drive, Camp Springs, Md.

Government Operations.—Christine Ray Davis, staff director, 4805 Blagden Avenue; James A. Lanigan, general counsel, 3401 Porter Street; Miles Q. Romney, associate general counsel, 610 Lakeview Drive, Falls Church, Va.; staff members: Earle J. Wade, 4121 W Street; Dolores Fel'Dotto, 2480 16th Street; Ann E. McLachlan, 2480 16th Street; Patricia Maheux, 2604 Arcola Avenue, Silver Spring, Md.; Charlotte C. Bickett, 1636 Buchanan Street NE.; minority staff: John Philip Carlson, 111 Marlan Drive, Alexandria, Va.; Raymond T. Collins, 2109 Spencer Road, Silver Spring, Md.

House Administration.—Chief clerk, Julian P. Langston; assistant clerks: Marjorie Savage, 4108 Lee Highway, Arlington, Va.; Mary F. Stolle, 3032 N Street; Louis Silverman, 5441 16th Avenue, Hyattsville, Md.; David S. Wolman, 10616 Cavalier Drive, Silver Spring, Md., personnel analyst.

Interior and Insular Affairs.—Professional staff; Sidney L. McFarland, professional staff director and engineering consultant, 9417 Crosby Road, Silver Spring, Md.; T. Richard Witmer, counsel and consultant on national parks, 433 South Lee Street, Alexandria, Va.; John L. Taylor, consultant on Territorial and Indian Affairs, 7101 Bridle Path Lane, Rosemary Terrace, Hyattsville, Md.; Milton A. Pearl, 2317 Surrey Lane, Falls Church, Va., consultant on mining, minerals, and public lands; clerical staff: Nancy J. Arnold, chief clerk, 2420 Menokin Drive, Alexandria, Va.; Dixie S. Barton, clerk, 2400 Pennsylvania Avenue; Patricia A. Murray, clerk, 3607 N Street; Virginia Bedsole, clerk, 3906 Stratford Lane, Alexandria, Va.; Patricia B. Freeman, clerk, 4405 Windom Place; Susan A. Whitener, clerk, 2315 Pennsylvania Avenue.

Interstate and Foreign Commerce.—Clerk, W. E. Williamson, 912 Lakeview Drive, Falls Church, Va.; assistant clerks: Kenneth J. Painter, 12511 Atherton Drive, Wheaton, Md.; Marcella M. Fencl, 2725 39th Street; Joanne C. Neuland, 1901 Wyoming Avenue; Mildred H. Lang, 8617 Adams Drive, Fort Washington Forest, Md.; Mary Ryan, 8600 Carroll Avenue, Silver Spring, Md.; Elsie M. Karpowich, 5239 Ellis Street SE.; printing editor, Glenn L. Johnson, 1900 South Eads Street, Arlington, Va.; minority counsel, Lewis E. Berry, 4709 Warren Street; minority staff assistant, Marion M. Burson, 2422 North Underwood Street, Arlington, Va.; professional staff: Andrew Stevenson, coordinator, 9208 Jones Mill Road, Chevy Chase, Md.; Kurt Borchardt, 3339 Legation Street; James M. Menger, Jr., 2106 Marian Court, Falls Church, Va.; William J. Dixon, 3414 Belleview Avenue, Cheverly, Md.

Judiciary.—Staff director, Bess E. Dick, 2928 Ellicott Terrace; general counsel, William R. Foley, 420 Blue Bill Lane, Alexandria, Va.; professional staff: Stuart H. Johnson, Jr., 2710 Poplar Street; Murray Drabkin, 505 Franklin Street, Alexandria, Va.; Herbert Fuchs, 2220 49th Street; Garner J. Cline, 5225 Woodland Drive, Springfield, Va.; William H. Copenhaver, 1535 44th Street; law revision counsel, Charles J. Zinn, 2601 Woodley Place; assistant law revision counsel, Joseph Fischer, 208 Massachusetts Avenue NE; William P. Shattuck, 4815 16th Street North, Arlington, Va.; clerical staff: Carrie Lou Allen, 101 North Carolina Avenue SE.; Anne J. Berger, 800 Fourth Street SW.; Lorraine W. Beland, 4129 Manor Court; Gertrude C. Burak, 8500 16th Street, Silver Spring, Md.; Jane C. Caldwell, 2500 Wisconsin Avenue; Frances Christy, 5225 Woodland Drive, Springfield, Va.; Vera Goudelock, 101 Woodland Drive, Forest Heights, Md.

Merchant Marine and Fisheries.—Clerk, W. B. Winfield, 4809 V Street; professional staff: John M. Drewry, chief counsel, 2438 North Nottingham Street, Arlington, Va.; Counsel, Bernard J. Zincke, 203 Maryland Avenue NE.; assistant counsel, Ned P. Everett, 1400 South Joyce Street, Arlington, Va.; consultant, Paul S. Bauer, 4816 Tilden Street; assistant clerks: Frances Still, 702 South Royal, Street, Alexandria, Va.; Ruth E. Brookshire, 5017 Allan Road; secretaries: Vera A. Barker, 2823 Hillcrest Drive SE.; Edith W. Gordon, 6559 North 28th Street, Arlington, Va.

Post Office and Civil Service.—Charles E. Johnson, staff director, 1100 Kingwood Drive, Takoma Park, Md.; Bun Benton Bray, Jr., professional staff member, 108–B Van Winkle, Falls Church, Va.; John H. Martiny, Counsel, 6298 15th Road North, Arlington, Va.; William A. Irvine, professional staff member, Turkey Point, Edgewater, Md.; assistant clerks: Lillian H. Hanninen, 4151 Southern Avenue SE.; John B. Price, 2117 Observatory Place; Lucy K. Daley, 3210 Wisconsin Avenue; secretaries: Elsie Thornton, 7710 Maple Ave., Takoma Park, Md., Blanche M. Simons, 1127 West Wakefield Drive, Alexanderia, Va., Barbara M. Wells, 5425 Connecticut Avenue.

Public Works.—Edward J. McNeal, staff director, 1227 Northview Road, Baltimore, Md.; Richard J. Sullivan, chief counsel, 1555 South 28th Street, Arlington, Va.; Joseph R. Brennan, engineer-consultant, Hunting Towers, Alexandria, Va.; Clifton W. Enfield, minority counsel, 1706 Tilton Drive, Silver Spring, Md.; staff assistants: Helen A. Thompson, 5328 Goldsboro Road, Bethesda, Md.; Dorothy Beam, 4801 Connecticut Avenue; Erla S. Youmans, 4802 69th Avenue, Hyattsville, Md.; Meriam Buckley, 5483 30th Street.

Rules.—Counsel, Thomas M. Carruthers, Suite H–313, the Capitol; assistant counsel, Mary Spencer Forrest, 4416 34th Street South, Arlington, Va.; minority counsel, Robert D. Hynes, Jr., 508 Second Street SE.

270 *Congressional Directory*

Science and Astronautics.—Charles F. Ducander, executive director and chief counsel; John A. Carstarphen, Jr., chief clerk and counsel; Philip B. Yeager, counsel; Frank R. Hammill, Jr., counsel; W. H. Boone, chief technical consultant; Emily Dodson, secretary; Mary Ann Robert, secretary; Carol F. Rodgers, secretary; June C. Stafford, secretary; Elizabeth M. Fleming, secretary; investigating subcommittee: Richard P. Hines, staff consultant; Peter A. Gerardi, technical consultant; James E. Wilson, technical consultant; Harold A. Gould, technical consultant; Philip Dickinson, technical consultant; Joseph M. Felton, assistant counsel; Elizabeth S. Kernan, scientific research assistant; Katherine V. Flanigan, assistant clerk; Denis C. Quigley, publications clerk; Virginia Robison, secretary.

Un-American Activities.—Francis J. McNamara, director, 8040 Cindy Lane, Bethesda, Md., 20034; William Hitz, general counsel, 18 Hesketh Street, Chevy Chase, Md., 20015; Alfred M. Nittle, counsel, Melbourne House, 1315 16th Street.

Veterans' Affairs.—Professional staff: Oliver E. Meadows, staff director, 7115 Marlan Drive, Alexandria, Va.; Edwin B. Patterson, counsel, 5213 Elsmere Avenue, Bethesda, Md., Billy E. Kirby, 4409 Phyllis Street, Alexandria, Va.; clerical staff: George Fisher, 10403 Royalton Terrace, Silver Spring, Md; Helen A. Biondi, 12 Densmore Court, Alexandria, Va.; Alice V. Matthews, 1658 Irving Street; Carol A. Davis, 4169 Southern Avenue SE.; George Turner, 208 76th Street; minority staff: John R. Holden, 11100 Slye Court, Silver Spring, Md.

Ways and Means.—Chief counsel, Leo H. Irwin, 5508 24th Avenue SE., Hillcrest Heights, Md.; assistant chief counsel, John M. Martin, Jr., 910 Fort Hunt Road, Alexandria, Va.; professional staff: John Patrick Baker, 2713 South Inge Street, Arlington, Va.; Thomas P. Kerester, 8082 Glenister Drive, Springfield, Va.; staff assistants: Florence Burkett, 5609 18th Avenue, Hyattsville, Md.; Virginia Butler, 1600 South Joyce Street, Arlington, Va.; William C. Byrd, 3946 Suitland Road; Mary Daniel, 4804 West Avenue, Suitland, Md.; Grace G. Kagan, 821 Gregorio Drive, Silver Spring, Md.; June A. Kendall, 4809 Barrymore Drive, Oxon Hill, Md.; Max C. Mehlburger, 3001 Branch Avenue, Prince Georges County, Md.; Elizabeth M. Price, 2601 Woodley Place; Sue Huitt Ritner, 301 G Street SW.; Gloria Shaver, 2800 Woodley Road; Eileen Sonnett, 4208 Duncan Drive, Annandale, Va.; Irene Wade, Hamlet East, 5511 Sanger Avenue, Alexandria, Va.; document clerks: Hughlon Greene, 6219 Piney Branch Road; Walter B. Little, 1760 Corcoran Street; minority staff: counsel, William H. Quealy, 1625 35th Street; assistant counsel, Richard Wilbur, 2851 South Buchanan Street, Arlington, Va.; minority staff assistants: Dolores Rogers, 126 Sixth Street NE.; Susan A. Taylor, 2475 Virginia Avenue.

CONGRESSIONAL JOINT COMMITTEES, COMMISSIONS, AND BOARDS

CONGRESSIONAL JOINT COMMITTEES, COMMISSIONS, AND BOARDS

Joint Committee on Printing

Created by act of Aug. 3, 1846 (9 Stat. 114)

Room S-151, Capitol. Phone 225-5241 (Code 180)

Chairman.—Carl Hayden, Senator from Arizona.
Vice Chairman.—Omar Burleson, Representative from Texas.
  B. Everett Jordan, Senator from North Carolina.
  Hugh Scott, Senator from Pennsylvania.
  Wayne L. Hays, Representative from Ohio.
  Glenard P. Lipscomb, Representative from California.
Staff Director.—John F. Haley, 4018 Tenth Street NE., 20017.
Assistant Staff Director.—Paul C. Beach, 865 North Nottingham Street, Arlington, Va., 22205.
Administrative Assistant.—Elizabeth T. Anderson, 3512 Newton Place, Mount Rainier, Md., 20822.
Printing Technician.—J. H. McWhorter, 612 Philadelphia Avenue, Takoma Park, Md., 20012.
Clerk-Stenographer.—Rosemary S. Cribben, 4420 Briarwood Court North, Annandale, Va., 22003.
Editorial Assistants:
  Herbert V. Bibus, 9206 Flower Avenue, Silver Spring, Md., 20901.
  Paul L. Zenor, 4312 North Carlyn Spring Road, Arlington, Va., 22203.

CONGRESSIONAL RECORD INDEX OFFICE

Room 6304, Senate Building. Phone, 225-5268 (Code 180)

Chief Indexer.—C. J. Moore, 401 Mashie Drive SE., Vienna, Va.
Assistant Indexers:
  Dale E. Condon, 13205 Kara Lane, Silver Spring, Md.
  Alene D. Tayman, 3411 Otis Street, Mt. Rainier, Md.
  Elwin Skiles, Jr., 312 Marcy Avenue, Oxon Hill, Md.
  Robert L. Curtis, 3390 Highview Terrace SE.
History of Bills.—Evelyn Dyrenforth, 120 C Street NE.
Technical Assistants:
  George G. Kundahl, 6801 Meadow Lane, Chevy Chase, Md.
  William E. Deedrick, 2010 Hanover Street, Silver Spring, Md.

Commission for Extension of the United States Capitol

Created by Public Law 242, 84th Congress (69 Stat. 515-516)

Chairman.—John W. McCormack, Speaker of the House of Representatives.
  Hubert H. Humphrey, President of the Senate.
  Everett McKinley Dirksen, Minority Leader of the Senate.
  Gerald R. Ford, Minority Leader of the House of Representatives.
  J. George Stewart, Architect of the Capitol.

273

Senate Office Building Commission

Created by the Act of April 28, 1904 (33 Stat. 481), as amended by the Act of July 11, 1947 (61 Stat. 307), the Act of August 1, 1953 (67 Stat. 328), and the Act of August 3, 1956 (70 Stat. 966)

Chairman.—John J. Sparkman, Senator from Alabama.
Karl E. Mundt, Senator from South Dakota.
Gordon Allott, Senator from Colorado.
Edmund S. Muskie, Senator from Maine.
Stephen M. Young, Senator from Ohio.
Thruston B. Morton, Senator from Kentucky.
B. Everett Jordan, Senator from North Carolina.
Howard W. Cannon, Senator from Nevada.
Everett McKinley Dirksen, Senator from Illinois.

House Office Building Commission

Title 40, U. S. C. 175

Chairman.—John W. McCormack, Speaker of the House of Representatives.
Emanuel Celler, Representative from New York.
Charles E. Goodell, Representative from New York.

Joint Committee on Atomic Energy

Room H–403, Capitol.   Phone, 225–6171 (Code 180)

Room H–403, Capitol.   Phone, CApitol 4–3121 (Code 180), extension 6171

Chairman.—Chet Holifield, Representative from California.
Vice Chairman.—John O. Pastore, Senator from Rhode Island.
Members:
Melvin Price, Representative from Illinois.
Wayne N. Aspinall, Representative from Colorado.
Albert Thomas, Representative from Texas.
Thomas G. Morris, Representative from New Mexico.
Craig Hosmer, Representative from California.
William H. Bates, Representative from Massachusetts.
John B. Anderson, Representative from Illinois.
William M. McCulloch, Representative from Ohio.
Richard B. Russell, Senator from Georgia.
Clinton P. Anderson, Senator from New Mexico.
Albert Gore, Senator from Tennessee.
Henry M. Jackson, Senator from Washington.
Bourke B. Hickenlooper, Senator from Iowa.
George D. Aiken, Senator from Vermont.
Wallace F. Bennett, Senator from Utah.
Carl T. Curtis, Senator from Nebraska.
Executive Director.—John T. Conway.

Joint Committee on Defense Production

50 U. S. C. App. 2162

Room 459, Senate Office Building.   Phone, 224–3121 (Code 180), extensions 2337, 2338, and 2339

Chairman.—A. Willis Robertson, Senator from Virginia.
Vice Chairman.—Wright Patman, Representative from Texas.
Members:
John J. Sparkman, Senator from Alabama.
Paul H. Douglas, Senator from Illinois.
Wallace F. Bennett, Senator from Utah.
John G. Tower, Senator from Texas.
Abraham J. Multer, Representative from New York.
William A. Barrett, Representative from Pennsylvania.

Members—Continued
   William B. Widnall, Representative from New Jersey.
   Paul A. Fino, Representative from New York.
Staff.—Harold J. Warren, clerk and counsel; George T. Ault, professional staff; Ted B. O. Fertig, professional staff; Janice M. Maguire, secretary.

Joint Committee on Disposition of Executive Papers

Created by Public Law 115, 78th Congress

Room H–329, Capitol.   Phone, 225–2064 (Code 180)

Members:
   Olin D. Johnston, Senator from South Carolina.
   Frank Carlson, Senator from Kansas.
   Frank Thompson, Jr., Representative from New Jersey.
   Charles E. Chamberlain, Representative from Michigan.
Clerk.—Julian P. Langston.

Joint Committee on Immigration and Nationality Policy

Created by Public Law 414, 82d Congress

Room B–363, Rayburn Office Building.   Phone, 224–3121, extensions 7101–7102

Chairman.—Michael A. Feighan, Representative from Ohio.
Members:
   Emanuel Celler, Representative from New York.
   Frank Chelf, Representative from Kentucky.
   William M. McCulloch, Representative from Ohio.
   Arch A. Moore, Jr., Representative from West Virginia.
   James O. Eastland, Senator from Mississippi.
   Olin D. Johnston, Senator from South Carolina.
   John L. McClellan, Senator from Arkansas.
   Everett McKinley Dirksen, Senator from Illinois.
   [Vacancy.]
Staff Director.—Edward M. O'Connor.

Joint Committee on Internal Revenue Taxation

Created by Public Law 20, 69th Congress

Room 1011, Longworth House Office Building.   Phone, 225–3621 (Code 180)

Chairman.—Wilbur D. Mills, Representative from Arkansas.
Vice Chairman.—Harry Flood Byrd, Senator from Virginia.
Members:
   Cecil R. King, Representative from California.
   Hale Boggs, Representative from Louisiana.
   John W. Byrnes, Representative from Wisconsin.
   Thomas B. Curtis, Representative from Missouri.
   Russell B. Long, Senator from Louisiana.
   George A. Smathers, Senator from Florida.
   John J. Williams, Senator from Delaware.
   Frank Carlson, Senator from Kansas.
Chief of Staff.—Dr. Laurence N. Woodworth, 2810 Crest Avenue, Cheverly, Md.
Assistant Chief of Staff.—Lincoln Arnold, 1619 North Inglewood Street, Arlington, Va.
Administrative Assistant.—James M. LaMarche, 316 Anneliese Drive, Falls Church, Va.
Legal Staff:
   Legislative Counsel.—Nicholas A. Tomasulo, 707 3rd Street SW., 20024.
   Refund Counsel.—Robert R. Smyers, 4501 Clermont Place, Garrett Park, Md.
   Attorneys.—Robert J. Moody, 5922 Welborn Drive, 20016; Carl A. Nordberg, Jr., 8604 Piccadilly Place, Springfield, Va.; Harrison B. McCawley, 5012 24th Street SE., 20021; Herbert L. Chabot, 8508 16th Street, Silver Spring, Md.; James W. McBride, 518 First Street SE., 20003.

Legal Staff—Continued
  Economist.—Alan P. Murray, 3813 T Street 20007.
  Statistical Analysts.—James H. Symons, 1127 South Quincy Street, Arlington, Va.; Grace T. Gunn, 2420 39th Street.
  Statistical Clerks.—Anastasia F. Connaughton, 3540 39th Street; Joseph E. Fink, 4907 Iroquois Street, College Park, Md.
  Tax Consultants.—Russell M. Oram, 203 Oxford Street, Chevy Chase, Md.; P. W. Meekins, 2623 South Inge Street, Arlington, Va.
  Secretaries:
    Nicki Rae Fairfax, 4753 Branch Avenue, SE.; Cleo H. Fonelli, 5800 16th Street; Jacqueline S. Pfeiffer, Apt. 516, Robert Towers, 120 South Arlington Ridge Road, Arlington, Va.; Gloria J. McCabe, 5011 5013 Kerby Hill Road, Apt. 404, Oxon Hill, Md.; Joanne McDermott, 1524 North 16th Road, Arlington Va.; Ila Coe, 4516 Yuma Street, 20016; Mildred Feldt, 1034 Cherry Hill Lane; June M. Matthews, 309 South Maple Street, Fairfax, Va.; Blanche F. Nagro, 9913 East Light Drive, Silver Spring, Md.; Betty Balkum, 235 Second Street NE.

Joint Committee on the Library

2d Stat. ch. 37, sec. 5

Room H–329, Capitol.   Phone, 225-2064   (Code 180)

Chairman.—Omar Burleson, Representative from Texas.
Vice Chairman.—B. Everett Jordan, Senator from North Carolina.
Members:
  Paul C. Jones, Representative from Missouri.
  Frank Thompson, Jr., Representative from New Jersey.
  Glenard P. Lipscomb, Representative from California.
  Robert J. Corbett, Representative from Pennsylvania.
  Claiborne Pell, Senator from Rhode Island.
  Joseph S. Clark, Senator from Pennsylvania.
  John Sherman Cooper, Senator from Kentucky.
  Hugh Scott, Senator from Pennsylvania.
Chief Clerk.—Julian P. Langston.
Assistant Chief Clerk.—Gordon F. Harrison.

Joint Committee on Navajo-Hopi Indian Administration

Created by Public Law 474, 81st Congress

Clinton P. Anderson, Senator from New Mexico.
Alan Bible, Senator from Nevada.
Paul J. Fannin, Senator from Arizona.
James A. Haley, Representative from Florida.
Morris K. Udall, Representative from Arizona.
E. Y. Berry, Representative from South Dakota.

Joint Committee on Organization of the Congress

Created by Senate Concurrent Resolution 2, 89th Congress

A. S. Mike Monroney, Senator from Oklahoma.
John J. Sparkman, Senator from Alabama.
Lee Metcalf, Senator from Montana.
Karl E. Mundt, Senator from South Dakota.
Clifford P. Case, Senator from New Jersey.
J. Caleb Boggs, Senator from Delaware.
Ray J. Madden, Representative from Indiana.
Jack Brooks, Representative from Texas.
Ken Hechler, Representative from West Virginia.
Thomas B. Curtis, Representative from Missouri.
Robert P. Griffin, Representative from Michigan.
Durward G. Hall, Representative from Missouri.

Joint Committee on Reduction of Nonessential Federal Expenditures

Created by Public Law 250, 77th Congress (55 Stat. 726)

Room 329, Senate Office Building. Phone, 225-3750 (Code 180)

Chairman.—Harry Flood Byrd, Senator from Virginia.
Vice Chairman.—[Vacant.]
   Allen J. Ellender, Senator from Louisiana.
   Spessard L. Holland, Senator from Florida.
   Russell B. Long, Senator from Louisiana.
   John J. Williams, Senator from Delaware.
   Leverett Saltonstall, Senator from Massachusetts.
   George H. Mahon, Representative from Texas.
   Albert Thomas, Representative from Texas.
   Wilbur D. Mills, Representative from Arkansas.
   Cecil R. King, Representative from California.
   John W. Byrnes, Representative from Wisconsin.
   Frank T. Bow, Representative from Ohio.
   Henry H. Fowler, Secretary of the Treasury.
   Kermit Gordon, Director of the Budget.
Clerk.—Catherine F. Kolnacki.

Joint Committee To Commemorate the 100th Anniversary of the Second Inaugural of Abraham Lincoln

Created by Public Law 427, 88th Congress

Paul H. Douglas, Senator from Illinois.
Vance Hartke, Senator from Indiana.
Everett McKinley Dirksen, Senator from Illinois.
John Sherman Cooper, Senator from Kentucky.
Melvin Price, Representative from Illinois.
Winfield K. Denton, Representative from Indiana.
William G. Bray, Representative from Indiana.
Paul Findley, Representative from Illinois.

Joint Economic Committee

Created pursuant to Sec. 5(a) of Public Law 304, 79th Congress

Room G-133, New Senate Office Building. Phones: (Code 180) 225-5171; 225-5321 (publications)

Chairman.—Wright Patman, Representative from Texas.
Vice Chairman.—Paul H. Douglas, Senator from Illinois.
   Richard Bolling, Representative from Missouri.
   Hale Boggs, Representative from Louisiana.
   Henry S. Reuss, Representative from Wisconsin.
   Martha W. Griffiths, Representative from Michigan.
   Thomas B. Curtis, Representative from Missouri.
   William B. Widnall, Representative from New Jersey.
   Robert F. Ellsworth, Representative from Kansas.
   John Sparkman, Senator from Alabama.
   J. W. Fulbright, Senator from Arkansas.
   William Proxmire, Senator from Wisconsin.
   Herman E. Talmadge, Senator from Georgia.
   Jacob K. Javits, Senator from New York.
   Jack Miller, Senator from Iowa.
   Len B. Jordan, Senator from Idaho.
Executive Director.—James W. Knowles.
Deputy Director.—John R. Stark, 4815 Grantham Avenue, Chevy Chase, Md.
Senior Economist.—William H. Moore.
Economists.—Thomas H. Boggs, Jr., Gerald A. Pollack, Donald A. Webster (minority).
Financial Clerk.—Marian T. Tracy.
Administrative Clerk.—Hamilton D. Gewehr.
Assistant to Executive Director.—Hope G. Sham.
Secretaries.—Esther S. Hickey, William M. Woodard, Roberta S. Conner, Marguerite Fry, Patricia A. Goldman (minority).
Publications.—Frances Tillinghast.
Printing Assistant.—Christopher C. O'Malley.

Board of Visitors to the Military Academy

Title 10, U. S. C., Section 4355 (a)

Richard B. Russell, Senator from Georgia, ex officio.
E. L. Bartlett, Senator from Alaska.
John O. Pastore, Senator from Rhode Island.
J. Caleb Boggs, Senator from Delaware.
L. Mendel Rivers, Representative from South Carolina, ex officio.
Olin E. Teague, Representative from Texas.
William H. Natcher, Representative from Kentucky.
Glenard P. Lipscomb, Representative from California
Alexander Pirnie, Representative from New York.

Board of Visitors to the Naval Academy

Title 10, U. S. C., Section 6968 (a)

Richard B. Russell, Senator from Georgia, ex officio.
A. Willis Robertson, Senator from Virginia.
Gale W. McGee, Senator from Wyoming.
James B. Pearson, Senator from Kansas.
L. Mendel Rivers, Representative from South Carolina, ex officio.
Daniel J. Flood, Representative from Pennsylvania.
Samuel N. Friedel, Representative from Maryland.
William E. Minshall, Representative from Ohio.
Carleton J. King, Representative from New York.

Board of Visitors to the Air Force Academy

Title 10, U. S. C., Section 9355 (a)

Richard B. Russell, Senator from Georgia, ex officio.
Ralph W. Yarborough, Senator from Texas.
Daniel B. Brewster, Senator from Maryland.
Gordon Allott, Senator from Colorado.
L. Mendel Rivers, Representative from South Carolina, ex officio.
Byron G. Rogers, Representative from Colorado.
John J. Flynt, Jr., Representative from Georgia.
Melvin R. Laird, Representative from Wisconsin.
Burt L. Talcott, Representative from California.

Board of Visitors to the Coast Guard Academy

Title 14, U. S. C., Section 194 (a)

Warren G. Magnuson, Senator from Washington, ex officio.
Maurine B. Neuberger, Senator from Oregon.
Thomas J. Dodd, Senator from Connecticut.
Thruston B. Morton, Senator from Kentucky.
Herbert C. Bonner, Representative from North Carolina, ex officio.
William L. St. Onge, Representative from Connecticut.
Edward A. Garmatz, Representative from Maryland.
Alton Lennon, Representative from North Carolina.
Wendell Wyatt, Representative from Oregon.
James R. Grover, Jr., Representative from New York.

Board of Visitors to the Merchant Marine Academy

Title 46, U. S. C., Section 1126c

Warren G. Magnuson, Senator from Washington, ex officio.
Harrison A. Williams, Jr., Senator from New Jersey.
E. L. Bartlett, Senator from Alaska.
Winston L. Prouty, Senator from Vermont.

Herbert C. Bonner, Representative from North Carolina, ex officio.
Hugh L. Carey, Representative from New York.
Thomas N. Downing, Representative from Virginia.
William S. Mailliard, Representative from California.
John M. Murphy, Representative from New York.
Charles A. Mosher, Representative from Ohio.

Battle of New Orleans Sesquicentennial Celebration Commission

Created by Public Law 87-759, 87th Congress

5446-48 Interior Building. Phone, 343-2095 (Code 183, extension 2095)
1750 National Bank of Commerce Building, New Orleans, La., 70112. Phone, 525-4467

Chairman.—Maj. Gen. Edward S. Bres (Retired), 5325 38th Street NW., Washington, D.C., 20015, and 815 Dumaine Street, New Orleans, La., 70116.
Vice Chairman.—Mrs. Martha G. Robinson, 26 Audubon Place, New Orleans, La., 70118.
Executive Officer.—George B. Hartzog, Jr., Director, National Park Service, Department of the Interior, Washington, D.C., 20240.

MEMBERS

Allen J. Ellender, Senator from Louisiana.
Russell B. Long, Senator from Louisiana.
John Sherman Cooper, Senator from Kentucky.
Thruston B. Morton, Senator from Kentucky.
James O. Eastland, Senator from Mississippi.
John C. Stennis, Senator from Mississippi.
Albert Gore, Senator from Tennessee.
Ross Bass, Senator from Tennessee.
F. Edward Hébert, Representative from Louisiana.
William M. Colmer, Representative from Mississippi.
Thomas G. Abernathy, Representative from Mississippi.
Hale Boggs, Representative from Louisiana.
Robert A. Everett, Representative from Tennessee.
William H. Natcher, Representative from Kentucky.
James H. Quillen, Representative from Tennessee.
[Vacancy.]
Robert E. LeCorgne, Jr., National Bank of Commerce Building, New Orleans, La., 70112.
Raphael H. Morvant, Maritime Building, New Orleans, La., 70112.
Edwin M. Roy, 234 Mehle Avenue, Arabi, New Orleans, La.
Hugh M. Wilkinson, National Bank of Commerce Building, New Orleans, La., 70112.
George B. Hartzog, Jr., Director, National Park Service, Department of the Interior, Washington, D.C., 20240.

Civil War Centennial Commission

Created by Public Law 305, 85th Congress

1815 H Street. Phone, 382-1225 (Code 128, extension 21225)

Chairman.—Allan Nevins, Henry E. Huntington Library, San Marino, Calif.

MEMBERS

Lyndon B. Johnson, President of the United States, ex officio.
Hubert H. Humphrey, President of the Senate, ex officio.
John W. McCormack, Speaker of the House of Representatives, ex officio.
Clinton P. Anderson, Senator from New Mexico.
Hugh Scott, Senator from Pennsylvania.
John G. Tower, Senator from Texas.
Ralph W. Yarborough, Senator from Texas.

MEMBERS—continued

Emilio Q. Daddario, Representative from Connecticut.
[3 vacancies.]
Alvin L. Aubinoe, 10215 Old Georgetown Road, Bethesda, Md.
Mrs. Consuelo N. Bailey, Strong Building, Burlington, Vt.
Bruce Catton, 551 Fifth Avenue, New York, N.Y.
Dr. Avery O. Craven, 23 Circle Drive, Dune Acres, Chesterton, Ind.
Roy K. Davenport, Deputy Under Secretary of the Army (Personnel), The
    Pentagon, Washington, D.C., 20310.
W. Norman FitzGerald, Jr., 761 North Broadway, Milwaukee, Wis.
George B. Hartzog, Jr., Director, National Park Service, Department of the
    Interior, Washington, D.C., 20240.
Dr. John A. Krout, 385 Melrose Street, Tiffin, Ohio, 44883.
Dr. John W. Masland, Jr., Dartmouth College, Hanover, N.H.
David C. Mearns, Library of Congress, Washington, D.C.
Aksel Nielsen, 1711 California Street, Denver, Colo.
William S. Paley, Columbia Broadcasting System, Inc., 485 Madison Avenue,
    New York, N.Y.
Dr. Bell I. Wiley, Department of History, Emory University, Atlanta, Ga.

Corregidor-Bataan Memorial Commission

Created by Public Law 193, 83d Congress; amended by Public Law 298, 84th Congress,
Public Law 240, 88th Congress

Room 1154, Veterans Administration Building. Phone, DUpont 9-3953 (Code 148, extension 3953)

Chairman.—Hon. Emmet O'Neal, 2311 Connecticut Avenue, 20009.
Members:
  Gale W. McGee, Senator from Wyoming.
  Clifford P. Case, Senator from New Jersey.
  Daniel B. Brewster, Senator from Maryland.
  Armistead I. Selden, Jr., Representative from Alabama.
  William S. Mailliard, Representative from California.
  Robert L. F. Sikes, Representative from Florida.
  Frank Hewlett, Virginia.
  John H. Leims, Missouri.
  Emmet O'Neal, Kentucky.
Executive Director.—Capt. Samuel G. Kelly, USN (retired), 4000 Cathedral
    Avenue, 20016.

Franklin Delano Roosevelt Memorial Commission

Created by Public Law 372, 84th Congress

Room 1730, Longworth House Office Building. Phone, 225-5471 (Code 180)

Chairman.—Francis Biddle, 1669 31st Street, (phone, ADams 4-3560).
Secretary.—Eugene J. Keogh, Representative from New York.
Members:
  Clifford P. Case, Senator from New Jersey.
  Jacob K. Javits, Senator from New York.
  Maurine B. Neuberger, Senator from Oregon.
  Eugene J. McCarthy, Senator from Minnesota.
  James Roosevelt, Representative from California.
  Seymour Halpern, Representative from New York.
  [Vacancy.]
  Anna M. Rosenberg, of New York.
  Clark Clifford, of Washington, D.C.
  James H. Rowe, Jr., of Montana.

Lewis and Clark Trail Commission

Created by Public Law 630, 88th Congress

Room 5356, Department of the Interior Building, 20240

MEMBERS

Chairman.—Sherry R. Fisher, J. N. "Ding" Darling Foundation, Inc., 303 Fleming Building, Des Moines, Iowa.
Vice Chairman.—Marcus J. Ware, 1219 Idaho Street, Lewiston, Idaho, 83501.
Executive Officer.—Edward C. Crafts, Director, Bureau of Outdoor Recreation, Department of the Interior, Washington, D.C., 20240.
William E. Towell, Director, Conservation Commission, State of Missouri, Jefferson City, Mo., 65102.
Melvin O. Steen, Director, Game, Forestation and Parks Commission, Lincoln, Nebr.
Hon. John Anderson, Jr., Governor of Kansas, Topeka, Kans.
Curtis B. Mateer, executive vice president, Pierre National Bank, Pierre, S. Dak.
Paul A. Ewald, State Historical Society, Bismarck, N. Dak., 58501.
Orvin B. Fjare, State Advertising Director, Highway Commission, Helena, Mont.
Hon. Harold E. Hughes, Governor of Iowa, Des Moines, Iowa.
Hon. Mark O. Hatfield, Governor of Oregon, Salem, Oreg., 97310.
Lloyd R. Bell, Washington State Parks and Recreation Commission, 522 South Franklin, Olympia, Wash.
Hon. Thomas G. Morris, Representative from New Mexico.
Hon. Ralph J. Rivers, Representative from Alaska.
Hon. E. Y. Berry, Representative from South Dakota.
Hon. Joe Skubitz, Representative from Kansas.
Hon. Frank Church, Senator from Idaho.
Hon. Quentin N. Burdick, Senator from North Dakota.
Hon. Len B. Jordan, Senator from Idaho.
Hon. Milward L. Simpson, Senator from Wyoming.
John A. Baker, Assistant Secretary, U.S. Department of Agriculture.
Lowell K. Bridwell, Deputy Under Secretary for Transportation, U.S. Department of Commerce.
Stephen S. Jackson, Special Assistant to Assistant Secretary (Manpower), Department of Defense.
Joseph T. Ventura, Assistant to the Secretary, U.S. Department of Health, Education and Welfare.
Marshall N. Dana, 3070 NW. Front Avenue, Portland, Oreg., 97210.
John Kyl, KTVO Building, Ottumwa, Iowa.
Christopher D. Koss, 601 Grand Avenue, Des Moines, Iowa, 50309.

Marine Corps Memorial Commission

Created by Public Law 327, 80th Congress

Chairman.—Joseph J. McCarthy, 3130 Lake Shore Drive, Chicago, Ill.
Commissioners:
Raymond R. Wilkowski, 4513 West 100th Street, Oak Lawn, Ill.
Edward J. Barrett, 2440 Lakeview Avenue, Chicago, Ill.

Migratory Bird Conservation Commission

Created by act of February 18, 1929, 16 U.S.C. 715a

Room 1349, United States Department of the Interior Building

Phone, 343-4676 (Code 183, extension 4676)

Chairman.—Stewart L. Udall, Secretary of the Interior.
Orville L. Freeman, Secretary of Agriculture.
John T. Connor, Secretary of Commerce.
Roman L. Hruska, Senator from Nebraska.
Lee Metcalf, Senator from Montana.
Frank M. Karsten, Representative from Missouri.
Silvio O. Conte, Representative from Massachusetts.
Secretary.—Albert J. Rissman, 5 Overhill Road, Falls Church, Va.

James Madison Memorial Commission

Created by Public Law 417, 86th Congress (74 Stat. 37)

Room 432, Shoreham Building, 806 Fifteenth Street, 20005. Phone, DIstrict 7–2836

Chairman.—Dr. Harold W. Dodds, 87 College Road West, Princeton, N.J.
Chairman, Executive Committee.—Clinton M. Hester, Shoreham Building, Washington, D.C.
Members:
  Dr. Colgate W. Darden, Jr., National Bank of Commerce Building, Norfolk, Va.
  Dr. William T. Hutchinson, 1126 East 59th Street, Chicago, Ill.
  Howard W. Smith, Representative from Virginia.
  Arch A. Moore, Jr., Representative from West Virginia.
  John M. Slack, Jr., Representative from West Virginia.
  Glenn Andrews, Representative from Alabama.
  Wallace F. Bennett, Senator from Utah.
  Frank Carlson, Senator from Kansas.
  Spessard L. Holland, Senator from Florida.
  A. Willis Robertson, Senator from Virginia.

National Commission on Food Marketing

Created by Public Law 354, 88th Congress

General Services Regional Office Building, Seventh and D Streets SW.

Phone, WOrth 3–7308 (Code 13, extension 37308)

Chairman.—Phil S. Gibson (San Francisco Office), Federal Building, Box 36104, 450 Golden Gate Avenue, San Francisco, Calif., 94102.
Members:
  William M. Batten, New York City, N.Y.
  Elmer R. Kiehl, Columbia, Mo.
  Fred J. Marshall, Grove City, Minn.
  Albert K. Mitchell, Albert, N. Mex.
  Warren G. Magnuson, U.S. Senator from Washington.
  Gale W. McGee, U.S. Senator from Wyoming.
  Philip A. Hart, U.S. Senator from Michigan.
  Thruston B. Morton, U.S. Senator from Kentucky.
  Roman L. Hruska, U.S. Senator from Nebraska.
  Leonor K. Sullivan, U.S. Representative from Missouri.
  Graham Purcell, U.S. Representative from Texas.
  Benjamin S. Rosenthal, U.S. Representative from New York.
  Glenn C. Cunningham, U.S. Representative from Nebraska.
  Catherine May, U.S. Representative from Washington.
Executive Director.—George E. Brandow.
Assistant to the Executive Director.—Richard F. Ottman, 102 Windsor Road, Alexandria, Va.
General Counsel.—James E. Corkey, 118 Croton Drive, Alexandria, Va.
Project Leaders:
  Bakery and Cereal Products.—H. Wayne Bitting, 7400 Bybrook Lane, Chevy Chase, Md., 20015.
  Dairy Products.—Linley E. Juers.
  Fruits and Vegetables.—Marshall R. Godwin.
  Meats and Poultry.—Paul L. Farris, 58 G Street SW.
  Retailing.—Warren L. Sharfman, 2426 I Street.
Information Officer.—Ruth K. Holstein, 9215 Worth Drive, Silver Spring, Md.

National Fisheries Center and Aquarium Advisory Board

Created by Public Law 758, 87th Congress

Warren G. Magnuson, Senator from Washington.
Winston L. Prouty, Senator from Vermont.
Michael J. Kirwan, Representative from Ohio.
Jack Edwards, Representative from Alabama.

National Forest Reservation Commission

Created by act of March 1, 1911 (36 Stat. 962, 16 U.S.C. 513)

Room 3016, South Building, United States Department of Agriculture

Phone, DUdley 8–7401 (Code 111, extension 7401)

President.—Stephen Ailes, Secretary of the Army.
  Stewart L. Udall, Secretary of the Interior.
  Orville L. Freeman, Secretary of Agriculture.
  John Stennis, Senator from Mississippi.
  George D. Aiken, Senator from Vermont.
  William M. Colmer, Representative from Mississippi.
  John P. Saylor, Representative from Pennsylvania.
Secretary.—Russell P. McRorey, 412 Randolph Drive, Annandale, Va.

National Memorial Stadium Commission

Created by Public Law 523, 78th Congress

John Stennis, Senator from Mississippi.
Vance Hartke, Senator from Indiana.
Peter H. Dominick, Senator from Colorado.
Olin E. Teague, Representative from Texas.
Carlton R. Sickles, Representative from Maryland.
Don H. Clausen, Representative from California.

New Jersey Tercentenary Celebration Commission

Created by Public Law 683, 86th Congress

Harrison A. Williams, Jr., Senator from New Jersey.
Clifford P. Case, Senator from New Jersey.
A. Willis Robertson, Senator from Virginia.
George D. Aiken, Senator from Vermont.
Peter W. Rodino, Jr., Representative from New Jersey.
Frank Thompson, Jr., Representative from New Jersey.
William B. Widnall, Representative from New Jersey.
Florence P. Dwyer, Representative from New Jersey.

Permanent Committee for the Oliver Wendell Holmes Devise Fund

Created by act of Congress approved Aug. 5, 1955 (Public Law 246, 84th Congress), to administer Oliver
Wendell Holmes Devise Fund, established by same act

Chairman.—L. Quincy Mumford, Librarian of Congress, ex officio.
Appointive Members:
  Frederick D. G. Ribble, Dean, The Law School, University of Virginia,
    Charlottesville, Va.
  Ethan A. H. Shepley, Shepley, Kroeger, Fisse & Shepley, 319 North Fourth
    Street, St. Louis, 2, Mo.
  Jefferson B. Fordham, Dean, The Law School, University of Pennsylvania,
    Philadelphia, Pa.
  Harry Hunt Ransom, University of Texas, Austin, Tex.
Editor in Chief.—Paul A. Freund, The Law School, Harvard University, Cambridge, Mass.
Assistant Librarian, In Charge of Administrative Office for the Devise.—Mrs.
    Elizabeth E. Hamer, 6620 River Road, Bethesda, Md., 20034.

Public Land Law Review Commission

Created by Public Law 606, 88th Congress (78 Stat. 982)

Chairman.—(The Chairman of the Commission is to be elected as the nineteenth member by the present members but at the time the Directory went to press the call for the organization meeting had not been issued.)

Appointed by the President of the United States:
Laurance S. Rockefeller, of New York City, N.Y.
Governor Philip Hoff, of the State of Vermont.
H. Byron Mock, attorney, of Salt Lake City, Utah.
Mrs. John Glessner Lee, of Farmington, Conn.
Dr. Robert Emmet Clark, professor, Albuquerque, N. Mex.
Dr. Maurice Goddard, Secretary of Forests and Waters, State of Pennsylvania.
Appointed by the President of the Senate:
Henry M. Jackson, Senator from Washington.
Clinton P. Anderson, Senator from New Mexico.
Alan Bible, Senator from Nevada.
Thomas H. Kuchel, Senator from California.
Gordon Allott, Senator from Colorado.
Len B. Jordan, Senator from Idaho.
Appointed by the Speaker of the House of Representatives:
Wayne N. Aspinall, Representative from Colorado.
Leo W. O'Brien, Representative from New York.
Compton I. White, Jr., Representative from Idaho.
John P. Saylor, Representative from Pennsylvania.
Laurence J. Burton, Representative from Utah.
Rogers C. B. Morton, Representative from Maryland.

Saint Augustine Quadricentennial Commission

Created by Public Law 586, 87th Congress

Chairman.—Herbert E. Wolfe, Box 1361, St. Augustine, Fla.
Spessard L. Holland, Senator from Florida.
George A. Smathers, Senator from Florida.
D. R. (Billy) Matthews, Representative from Florida.
William C. Cramer, Representative from Florida.
Charles Patrick Clark (attorney at law), 500 World Center Building, Washington, D.C.
Henry Ford II, The Ford Motor Company, The American Road, Dearborn, Mich.
J. Peter Grace, W. R. Grace & Co., 7 Hanover Square, New York, N.Y.
Archbishop Joseph P. Hurley, Bishop of St. Augustine, Box 381, St. Augustine, Fla.
Dr. Edward H. Litchfield, Chancellor, University of Pittsburgh, Pittsburgh, Pa.
Executive Officer.—Conrad L. Wirth, United States Department of the Interior, National Park Service, Washington, D.C.
Acting Secretary and Director General.—Earle W. Newton, Box 484, St. Augustine, Fla. (phone, VA. 4–3356).

The Interparliamentary Union

49 Stat. 425, 22 U.S.C. 276

OFFICERS OF UNITED STATES GROUP FOR THE 89TH CONGRESS

President.—Herman E. Talmadge, Senator from Georgia.
Vice Presidents:
John Sparkman, Senator from Alabama.
Gordon Allott, Senator from Colorado.
Alexander Pirnie, Representative from New York.
Treasurer.—Paul C. Jones, Representative from Missouri.
Secretary.—Katharine St. George.

Executive Committee:
  Herman E. Talmadge, Senator from Georgia.
  John Sparkman, Senator from Alabama.
  Gordon Allott, Senator from Colorado.
  Alexander Pirnie, Representative from New York.
  Paul C. Jones, Representative from Missouri.
  Katharine St. George.
  W. Robert Poage, Representative from Texas.
  E. Ross Adair, Representative from Indiana.
  Thomas H. Kuchel, Senator from California.
Honorary Members:
  Homer Ferguson, Judge, Military Court of Appeals.
  Katharine St. George.
Permanent Executive Secretary.—Dr. George B. Galloway, Library of Congress, (phone, STerling 3–0400, extension 547).

United States-Puerto Rico Commission on the Status of Puerto Rico

1634 I Street NW. Phone, 382-8711 (Code 128, extension 28711)

MEMBERS

Appointed by the President:
  Chairman.—James H. Rowe, Jr., 3207 Highland Place, 20008.
  Brewster C. Denny, University of Washington, Seattle, Wash., 98105.
  Mrs. Patricia Roberts Harris, 2804 13th Street NE., 20017.
Appointed by the Congress:
  Senator Clinton P. Anderson from New Mexico.
  Senator Jacob K. Javits from New York.
  Representative Rogers C. B. Morton from Maryland.
  Representative Leo W. O'Brien from New York.
Appointed by the Governor of Puerto Rico as certified by:
  Popular Democratic Party—
    Teodoro Moscoso, Laguna Terrace Apts. 10D, San Juan, Puerto Rico.
    Senator Luis Muñoz Marín, Senate of the Commonwealth of Puerto Rico.
    Senator Luis A. Negrón Lopez, Senate of the Commonwealth of Puerto Rico.
  Statehood Republican Party—
    Luis A. Ferré, Box 1492, Ponce, Puerto Rico.
    Senator Miguel A. Garcia Mendez, Senate of the Commonwealth of Puerto Rico.
  Independista Party—
    Dr. Gilberto Concepcion de Gracia, Apartment 481, Rio Piedras, Puerto Rico.

STAFF

Executive Secretary.—Ben S. Stephansky, 3517 Cummings Lane, Chevy Chase, Md.
Special Counsel.—Arnold H. Leibowitz, 2801 McKinley Place NW., 20015.
Chief Economist.—Eugene R. Schlesinger, 7 Bruce Lane, Westport, Conn., 06880.
Program Officer.—Robert G. Flick, 1315 35th Street NW., 20007.
Administrative Officer.—Paul C. Krusekopf, 301 Center Street, Fairfax, Va.

United States Territorial Expansion Memorial Commission

48 Stat. 967

11 North Fourth Street, St. Louis, Mo. Phone, CEntral 1-5474

Chairman.—Clinton P. Anderson, Senator from New Mexico.
Vice Chairman.—Dean William W. Wurster, 1620 Montgomery Street, San Francisco, Calif.
Secretary.—Ronald J. Foulis, 1730 K Street NW., Suite 1100, Washington, D.C.
Appointed by the President of the United States:
  William W. Crowdus, 506 Olive Street, St. Louis, Mo., 63101.
  J. Lionberger Davis, Independence Drive, Princeton, N.J.
  Morton D. May, 601 Olive Street, St. Louis, Mo., 63101.

Appointed by the President of the Senate:
 Clinton P. Anderson, Senator from New Mexico.
 Wayne Morse, Senator from Oregon.
 Roman L. Hruska, Senator from Nebraska.
Appointed by the Speaker of the House:
 Frank M. Karsten, Representative from Missouri.
 Wayne L. Hays, Representative from Ohio.
 Glenn Cunningham, Representative from Nebraska.
Appointed by Jefferson National Expansion Memorial Association:
 Senator Harry F. Byrd, Senate Office Building, Washington, D. C.
 Chester C. Davis, 1605 Kensington Road, San Marino, Calif.
 Harold W. Dodds, 87 College Road West, Princeton, N.J.
 Judge James M. Douglas, 705 Olive Street, St. Louis, Mo., 63101.
 James M. Kemper, Commerce Trust Co., Kansas City, Mo.
 William W. Wurster, 1620 Montgomery Street, San Francisco, Calif.
Executive Committee:
 Judge James M. Douglas (chairman).
 William W. Crowdus.
 Chester C. Davis.
 J. Lionberger Davis.
 James M. Kemper.

Woodrow Wilson Memorial Commission

Created by Public Law 364, 87th Congress

Harrison A. Williams, Jr., Senator from New Jersey.
Clifford P. Case, Senator from New Jersey.
Cornelius E. Gallagher, Representative from New Jersey.
Peter H. B. Frelinghuysen, Representative from New Jersey.

COMMITTEE ASSIGNMENTS

COMMITTEE ASSIGNMENTS

ASSIGNMENTS OF SENATORS TO COMMITTEES

AIKEN _____ Aeronautical and Space Sciences.
Agriculture and Forestry.
Foreign Relations.
Joint Committee on Atomic Energy.

ALLOTT _____ Appropriations.
Interior and Insular Affairs.

ANDERSON _____ Aeronautical and Space Sciences, chairman.
Finance.
Interior and Insular Affairs.
Joint Committee on Atomic Energy.
Joint Committee on Navajo-Hopi Indian Administration.

BARTLETT _____ Appropriations.
Commerce.

BASS _____ Agriculture and Forestry.
Commerce.

BAYH _____ Judiciary.
Public Works.

BENNETT _____ Banking and Currency.
Finance.
Joint Committee on Atomic Energy.
Joint Committee on Defense Production.

BIBLE _____ District of Columbia, chairman.
Appropriations.
Interior and Insular Affairs.
Joint Committee on Navajo-Hopi Indian Administration.

BOGGS _____ Agriculture and Forestry.
Post Office and Civil Service.
Public Works.
Joint Committee on Organization of Congress.

BREWSTER _____ Armed Services.
Commerce.
Post Office and Civil Service.

BURDICK _____ Interior and Insular Affairs.
Judiciary.
Post Office and Civil Service.

BYRD of Virginia _____ Finance, chairman.
Armed Services.
Joint Committee on Reduction of Nonessential Federal Expenditures, chairman.
Joint Committee on Internal Revenue Taxation.

BYRD of West Virginia _____ Appropriations.
Armed Services.
Rules and Administration.

CANNON_____ Aeronautical and Space Sciences.
Armed Services.
Commerce.
Rules and Administration.

CARLSON_____ Finance.
Foreign Relations.
Post Office and Civil Service.
Joint Committee on Internal Revenue Taxation.
Joint Committee on Disposition of Executive Papers.

CASE_____ Appropriations.
Foreign Relations.
Joint Committee on Organization of Congress.

CHURCH_____ Foreign Relations.
Interior and Insular Affairs.

CLARK_____ Foreign Relations.
Labor and Public Welfare.
Rules and Administration.
Joint Committee on the Library.

COOPER_____ Agriculture and Forestry.
Public Works.
Rules and Administration.
Joint Committee on the Library.
Joint Committee To Commemorate the 100th
Anniversary of the Second Inaugural of Abraham
Lincoln.

COTTON_____ Appropriations.
Commerce.

CURTIS_____ Aeronautical and Space Sciences.
Finance.
Government Operations.
Rules and Administration.
Joint Committee on Atomic Energy.

DIRKSEN_____ Finance.
Judiciary.
Joint Committee on Immigration and Nationality
Policy.
Joint Committee To Commemorate the 100th
Anniversary of the Second Inaugural of Abraham
Lincoln.

DODD_____ Aeronautical and Space Sciences.
Foreign Relations.
Judiciary.

DOMINICK_____ Commerce.
District of Columbia.
Labor and Public Welfare.

DOUGLAS_____ Banking and Currency.
Finance.
Joint Committee on Defense Production.
Joint Committee To Commemorate the 100th
Anniversary of the Second Inaugural of Abraham
Lincoln.
Joint Economic Committee.

EASTLAND_____ Judiciary, chairman.
Agriculture and Forestry.
Joint Committee on Immigration and Nationality
Policy.

ELLENDER_____ Agriculture and Forestry, chairman.
Appropriations.
Joint Committee on Reduction of Nonessential Federal Expenditures.

ERVIN_____ Armed Services.
Government Operations.
Judiciary.

FANNIN_____ Interior and Insular Affairs.
Labor and Public Welfare.
Joint Committee on Navajo-Hopi Indian Administration.

FONG_____ Judiciary.
Post Office and Civil Service.
Public Works.

FULBRIGHT_____ Foreign Relations, chairman.
Finance.
Joint Economic Committee.

GORE_____ Finance.
Foreign Relations.
Joint Committee on Atomic Energy.

GRUENING_____ Government Operations.
Interior and Insular Affairs.
Public Works.

HARRIS_____ Government Operations.
Public Works.

HART_____ Commerce.
Judiciary.

HARTKE_____ Commerce.
Finance.
Post Office and Civil Service.
Joint Committee to Commemorate the 100th Anniversary of the Second Inaugural of Abraham Lincoln.

HAYDEN_____ Appropriations, chairman.
Interior and Insular Affairs.
Rules and Administration.
Joint Committee on Printing, chairman.

HICKENLOOPER_____ Aeronautical and Space Sciences.
Banking and Currency.
Foreign Relations.
Joint Committee on Atomic Energy.

HILL_____ Labor and Public Welfare, chairman.
Appropriations.

HOLLAND_____ Aeronautical and Space Sciences.
Agriculture and Forestry.
Appropriations.
Joint Committee on Reduction of Nonessential Federal Expenditures.

HRUSKA_____ Appropriations.
Judiciary.

INOUYE_____ Armed Services.
Public Works.

JACKSON_____ Interior and Insular Affairs, chairman.
Armed Services.
Government Operations.
Joint Committee on Atomic Energy.

JAVITS_____ Government Operations.
Judiciary.
Labor and Public Welfare.
Joint Economic Committee.

JOHNSTON_____ Post Office and Civil Service, chairman.
Agriculture and Forestry.
Judiciary.
Joint Committee on Disposition of Executive Papers.
Joint Committee on Immigration and Nationality Policy.

JORDAN of Idaho_____ Aeronautical and Space Sciences.
Interior and Insular Affairs.
Joint Economic Committee.

JORDAN of North Carolina__ Rules and Administration, chairman.
Agriculture and Forestry.
Public Works.
Joint Committee on the Library.
Joint Committee on Printing.

KENNEDY of Massachusetts_ Judiciary.
Labor and Public Welfare.

KENNEDY of New York_____ District of Columbia.
Government Operations.
Labor and Public Welfare.

KUCHEL_____ Appropriations.
Interior and Insular Affairs.

LAUSCHE_____ Commerce.
Foreign Relations.

LONG of Louisiana_____ Finance.
Foreign Relations.
Joint Committee on Internal Revenue Taxation.
Joint Committee on Reduction of Nonessential Federal Expenditures.

LONG of Missouri_____ Banking and Currency.
Judiciary.

MCCARTHY_____ Agriculture and Forestry.
Finance.

MCCLELLAN_____ Government Operations, chairman.
Appropriations.
Judiciary.
Joint Committee on Immigration and Nationality Policy.

MCGEE_____ Appropriations.
Commerce.
Post Office and Civil Service.

MCGOVERN_____ Agriculture and Forestry.
Interior and Insular Affairs.

MCINTYRE_____ Armed Services.
Banking and Currency.
District of Columbia.

McNAMARA_____ Public Works, chairman.
                        Labor and Public Welfare.

MAGNUSON_____ Commerce, chairman.
                        Aeronautical and Space Sciences.
                        Appropriations.

MANSFIELD_____ Appropriations.
                        Foreign Relations.

METCALF_____ Government Operations.
                        Interior and Insular Affairs.
                        Public Works.
                        Joint Committee on Organization of Congress.

MILLER_____ Agriculture and Forestry.
                        Armed Services.
                        Joint Economic Committee.

MONDALE_____ Aeronautical and Space Sciences.
                        Banking and Currency.

MONRONEY_____ Appropriations.
                        Commerce.
                        Post Office and Civil Service.
                        Joint Committee on Organization of Congress.

MONTOYA_____ Agriculture and Forestry.
                        Government Operations.
                        Public Works.

MORSE_____ District of Columbia.
                        Foreign Relations.
                        Labor and Public Welfare.

MORTON_____ Commerce.
                        Finance.

MOSS_____ Interior and Insular Affairs.
                        Public Works.

MUNDT_____ Appropriations.
                        Foreign Relations.
                        Government Operations.
                        Joint Committee on Organization of Congress.

MURPHY_____ Labor and Public Welfare.
                        Public Works.

MUSKIE_____ Banking and Currency.
                        Government Operations.
                        Public Works.

NELSON_____ Interior and Insular Affairs.
                        Labor and Public Welfare.

NEUBERGER_____ Banking and Currency.
                        Commerce.

PASTORE_____ Appropriations.
                        Commerce.
                        Joint Committee on Atomic Energy.

PEARSON_____ Commerce.
                        Public Works.

PELL_____ Foreign Relations.
                        Labor and Public Welfare.
                        Rules and Administration.
                        Joint Committee on the Library.

PROUTY_____ Commerce.
District of Columbia.
Labor and Public Welfare.

PROXMIRE_____ Appropriations.
Banking and Currency.
Joint Economic Committee.

RANDOLPH_____ Labor and Public Welfare.
Post Office and Civil Service.
Public Works.

RIBICOFF_____ Finance.
Government Operations.

ROBERTSON_____ Banking and Currency, chairman.
Appropriations.
Joint Committee on Defense Production, chairman.

RUSSELL_____ Armed Services, chairman.
Aeronautical and Space Sciences.
Appropriations.
Joint Committee on Atomic Energy.

SALTONSTALL_____ Appropriations.
Armed Services.
Joint Committee on Reduction of Nonessential
Federal Expenditures.

SCOTT_____ Commerce.
Judiciary.
Rules and Administration.
Joint Committee on the Library.
Joint Committee on Printing.

SIMPSON_____ Government Operations.
Interior and Insular Affairs.
Post Office and Civil Service.

SMATHERS_____ Finance.
Foreign Relations.
Joint Committee on Internal Revenue Taxation.

SMITH_____ Aeronautical and Space Sciences.
Appropriations.
Armed Services.

SPARKMAN_____ Banking and Currency.
Foreign Relations.
Joint Committee on Defense Production.
Joint Economic Committee.
Joint Committee on Organization of Congress.

STENNIS_____ Aeronautical and Space Sciences.
Appropriations.
Armed Services.

SYMINGTON_____ Aeronautical and Space Sciences.
Armed Services.
Foreign Relations.

TALMADGE_____ Agriculture and Forestry.
Finance.
Joint Economic Committee.

THURMOND_____ Armed Services.
Banking and Currency.

TOWER———————————— Armed Services.
Banking and Currency.
Joint Committee on Defense Production.

TYDINGS———————————— Aeronautical and Space Sciences.
District of Columbia.
Judiciary.

WILLIAMS of Delaware—————— Finance.
Foreign Relations.
Joint Committee on Internal Revenue Taxation.
Joint Committee on Reduction of Nonessential Federal Expenditures.

WILLIAMS of New Jersey——— Banking and Currency.
Labor and Public Welfare.

YARBOROUGH—————————— Appropriations.
Labor and Public Welfare.
Post Office and Civil Service.

YOUNG of North Dakota——— Agriculture and Forestry.
Appropriations.

YOUNG of Ohio—————————— Aeronautical and Space Sciences.
Armed Services.
Public Works.

ASSIGNMENTS OF REPRESENTATIVES AND RESIDENT COMMISSIONER TO COMMITTEES

ABBITT_____ Agriculture.
House Administration.

ABERNETHY_____ Agriculture.
District of Columbia.

ADAIR_____ Foreign Affairs.
Veterans' Affairs.

ADAMS_____ Science and Astronautics.

ADDABBO_____ Appropriations.

ALBERT_____ Majority Floor Leader.
Science and Astronautics.

ANDERSON of Illinois_____ Rules.
Joint Committee on Atomic Energy.

ANDERSON of Tennessee_____ Science and Astronautics.

ANDREWS, GEORGE_____ Appropriations.

ANDREWS, GLENN_____ Education and Labor.

ANDREWS of North Dakota_____ Appropriations.

ANNUNZIO_____ Banking and Currency.

ARENDS_____ Minority Whip.
Armed Services.

ASHBROOK_____ Education and Labor.
Un-American Activities.

ASHLEY_____ Banking and Currency.
Merchant Marine and Fisheries.

ASHMORE_____ House Administration.
Judiciary.

ASPINALL_____ Interior and Insular Affairs, chairman.
Joint Committee on Atomic Energy.

AYRES_____ Education and Labor.
Veterans' Affairs.

BALDWIN_____ Public Works.

BANDSTRA_____ Agriculture.

BARING_____ Interior and Insular Affairs.
Veterans' Affairs.

BARRETT_____ Banking and Currency.
Joint Committee on Defense Production.

297

BATES_____ Armed Services.
Joint Committee on Atomic Energy.

BATTIN_____ Ways and Means.

BECKWORTH_____ Foreign Affairs.
Post Office and Civil Service.

BELCHER_____ Agriculture.

BELL_____ Education and Labor.
Science and Astronautics.

BENNETT_____ Armed Services.

BERRY_____ Foreign Affairs.
Interior and Insular Affairs.
Joint Committee on Navajo-Hopi Indian Admin-
istration.

BETTS_____ Ways and Means.

BINGHAM_____ House Administration.
Interior and Insular Affairs.

BLATNIK_____ Government Operations.
Public Works.

BOGGS_____ Majority Whip.
Ways and Means.
Joint Economic Committee.
Joint Committee on Internal Revenue Taxation.

BOLAND_____ Appropriations.

BOLLING_____ Rules.
Joint Economic Committee.

BOLTON_____ Foreign Affairs.

BONNER_____ Merchant Marine and Fisheries, chairman.

BOW_____ Appropriations.
Joint Committee on Reduction of Nonessential
Federal Expenditures.

BRADEMAS_____ Education and Labor.
House Administration.

BRAY_____ Armed Services.
Joint Committee To Commemorate the 100th
Anniversary of the Second Inaugural of Abraham
Lincoln.

BROCK_____ Banking and Currency.

BROOKS_____ Government Operations.
Judiciary.
Joint Committee on Organization of Congress.

BROOMFIELD_____ Foreign Affairs.

BROWN of California_____ Science and Astronautics.
Veterans' Affairs.

BROWN of Ohio_____ Government Operations.
Rules.

BROYHILL of North Carolina_ Interstate and Foreign Commerce.
Post Office and Civil Service.

BROYHILL of Virginia_____ District of Columbia.
Ways and Means.

BUCHANAN_____ Post Office and Civil Service.
Un-American Activities.

BURKE_____ Ways and Means.

BURLESON_____ House Administration, chairman.
Foreign Affairs.
Joint Committee on the Library, chairman.
Joint Committee on Printing.

BURTON of California_____ Interior and Insular Affairs.

BURTON of Utah_____ Agriculture.
Interior and Insular Affairs.

BYRNE of Pennsylvania____ Armed Services.
Merchant Marine and Fisheries.

BYRNES of Wisconsin_____ Ways and Means.
Joint Committee on Internal Revenue Taxation.
Joint Committee on Reduction of Nonessential
Federal Expenditures.

CABELL_____ Banking and Currency.

CAHILL_____ Judiciary.

CALLAN_____ Agriculture.

CALLAWAY_____ Government Operations.
Interstate and Foreign Commerce.

CAMERON_____ Foreign Affairs.

CAREY_____ Education and Labor.
Interior and Insular Affairs.

CARTER_____ Interstate and Foreign Commerce.

CASEY_____ Merchant Marine and Fisheries.
Science and Astronautics.

CEDERBERG_____ Appropriations.

CELLER_____ Judiciary, chairman.
Joint Committee on Immigration and Nationality
Policy.

CHAMBERLAIN_____ Armed Services.
House Administration.
Joint Committee on Disposition of Executive
Papers.

CHELF_____ Judiciary.
Joint Committee on Immigration and Nationality
Policy.

CLANCY_____ Armed Services.

CLARK_____ Merchant Marine and Fisheries.
Public Works.

CLAUSEN, DON H_____ Public Works.

CLAWSON, DEL_____ Banking and Currency.
Un-American Activities.

CLEVELAND_____ Public Works.

CLEVENGER_____ Merchant Marine and Fisheries.
Post Office and Civil Service.

COHELAN_____ Appropriations.

COLLIER_____ Ways and Means.

COLMER_____ Rules.

CONABLE_____ Science and Astronautics.

CONTE_____ Appropriations.

CONYERS_____ Judiciary.

COOLEY_____ Agriculture, chairman.

CORBETT_____ House Administration.
Post Office and Civil Service.
Joint Committee on the Library.

CORMAN_____ Judiciary.

CRALEY_____ Interior and Insular Affairs.

CRAMER_____ Judiciary.
Public Works.

CULVER_____ Foreign Affairs.

CUNNINGHAM_____ Interstate and Foreign Commerce.
Post Office and Civil Service.

CURTIN_____ House Administration.
Interstate and Foreign Commerce.

CURTIS_____ Ways and Means.
Joint Economic Committee.
Joint Committee on Internal Revenue Taxation.
Joint Committee on Organization of Congress.

DADDARIO_____ Science and Astronautics.

DAGUE_____ Agriculture.

DANIELS_____ Education and Labor.
Post Office and Civil Service.

DAVIS of Georgia_____ House Administration.
Science and Astronautics.

DAVIS of Wisconsin_____ Appropriations.

DAWSON_____ Government Operations, chairman.
District of Columbia.

DE LA GARZA_____ Agriculture.

DELANEY_____ Rules.

DENT_____ Education and Labor.
House Administration.

DENTON_____ Appropriations.
Joint Committee To Commemorate the 100th Anniversary of the Second Inaugural of Abraham Lincoln.

DERWINSKI_____ Foreign Affairs.
Post Office and Civil Service.

DEVINE_____ House Administration.
Interstate and Foreign Commerce.

DICKINSON_____ Government Operations.
House Administration.

DIGGS_____ District of Columbia.
Foreign Affairs.

DINGELL_____ Interstate and Foreign Commerce.
Merchant Marine and Fisheries.

DOLE_____ Agriculture.

DONOHUE_____ Judiciary.

DORN_____ Public Works.
Veterans' Affairs.

DOW_____ Government Operations.
Merchant Marine and Fisheries.

DOWDY_____ District of Columbia.
Judiciary.

DOWNING_____ Merchant Marine and Fisheries.
Science and Astronautics.

DULSKI_____ Post Office and Civil Service.
Veterans' Affairs.

DUNCAN of Oregon_____ Appropriations.

DUNCAN of Tennessee_____ Veterans' Affairs.

DWYER_____ Banking and Currency.
Government Operations.

DYAL_____ Public Works.

EDMONDSON_____ Interior and Insular Affairs.
Public Works.

EDWARDS of Alabama_____ Merchant Marine and Fisheries.

EDWARDS of California_____ Judiciary.

ELLSWORTH_____ Post Office and Civil Service.
Veterans' Affairs.
Joint Economic Committee.

ERLENBORN_____ Government Operations.
House Administration.

EVANS_____ Armed Services.

EVERETT_____ Public Works.
Veterans' Affairs.

EVINS_____ Appropriations.

FALLON_____ Public Works, chairman.

FARBSTEIN_____ Foreign Affairs.

FARNSLEY_____ Interstate and Foreign Commerce.

FARNUM_____ Appropriations.

FASCELL_____ Foreign Affairs.
Government Operations.

FEIGHAN_____ Judiciary.
Joint Committee on Immigration and Nationality
Policy, chairman.

FINDLEY_____ Agriculture.
Education and Labor.
Joint Committee To Commemorate the 100th
Anniversary of the Second Inaugural of Abraham
Lincoln.

FINO_____ Banking and Currency.
Veterans' Affairs.
Joint Committee on Defense Production.

FISHER_____ Armed Services.

FLOOD_____ Appropriations.

FLYNT_____ Appropriations.

FOGARTY_____ Appropriations.

FOLEY_____ Agriculture.
Interior and Insular Affairs.

FORD, GERALD R_____ Minority Leader.

FORD, WILLIAM D_____ Education and Labor.

FOUNTAIN_____ Foreign Affairs.
Government Operations.

FRASER_____ District of Columbia.
Foreign Affairs.

FRELINGHUYSEN_____ Foreign Affairs.

FRIEDEL_____ House Administration.
Interstate and Foreign Commerce.

FULTON of Pennsylvania___ Foreign Affairs.
Science and Astronautics.

FULTON of Tennessee_____ Ways and Means.

FUQUA_____ District of Columbia.
Science and Astronautics.

GALLAGHER_____ Foreign Affairs.
Government Operations.

GARMATZ_____ Government Operations.
Merchant Marine and Fisheries.

GATHINGS_____ Agriculture.

GETTYS_____ Banking and Currency.

GIAIMO _____ Appropriations.

GIBBONS _____ Education and Labor.
House Administration.

GILBERT _____ Judiciary.
Merchant Marine and Fisheries.

GILLIGAN _____ Interstate and Foreign Commerce.

GONZALEZ _____ Banking and Currency.

GOODELL _____ Education and Labor.
House Administration.

GRABOWSKI _____ Banking and Currency.

GRAY _____ House Administration.
Public Works.

GREEN of Oregon _____ Education and Labor.
Merchant Marine and Fisheries.

GREEN of Pennsylvania ____ Post Office and Civil Service.

GREIGG _____ Agriculture.

GRIDER _____ District of Columbia.
Judiciary.

GRIFFIN _____ Education and Labor.
Government Operations.
Joint Committee on Organization of Congress.

GRIFFITHS _____ Ways and Means.
Joint Economic Committee.

GROSS _____ Foreign Affairs.
Post Office and Civil Service.

GROVER _____ Merchant Marine and Fisheries.
Public Works.

GUBSER _____ Armed Services.

GURNEY _____ Government Operations.
Science and Astronautics.

HAGAN of Georgia _____ Armed Services.
District of Columbia.

HAGEN of California _____ Agriculture.
Merchant Marine and Fisheries.

HALEY _____ Interior and Insular Affairs.
Veterans' Affairs.
Joint Committee on Navajo-Hopi Indian Adminis-
tration.

HALL _____ Armed Services.
Joint Committee on Organization of Congress.

HALLECK _____ Public Works.

HALPERN _____ Banking and Currency.
Veterans' Affairs.

HAMILTON _____ Foreign Affairs.

HANLEY	Post Office and Civil Service.
	Veterans' Affairs.
HANNA	Banking and Currency.
HANSEN of Idaho	Interior and Insular Affairs.
HANSEN of Iowa	Banking and Currency.
HANSEN of Washington	Appropriations.
HARDY	Armed Services.
	Government Operations.
HARRIS	Interstate and Foreign Commerce, chairman.
HARSHA	District of Columbia.
	Public Works.
HARVEY of Indiana	Agriculture.
HARVEY of Michigan	Banking and Currency.
	Interstate and Foreign Commerce.
HATHAWAY	Education and Labor.
HAWKINS	Education and Labor.
	House Administration.
HAYS	Foreign Affairs.
	House Administration.
	Joint Committee on Printing.
HÉBERT	Armed Services.
HECHLER	Science and Astronautics.
	Joint Committee on Organization of Congress.
HELSTOSKI	Government Operations.
	Veterans' Affairs.
HENDERSON	Post Office and Civil Service.
	Public Works.
HERLONG	Ways and Means.
HICKS	Armed Services.
HOLIFIELD	Government Operations.
	Joint Committee on Atomic Energy, chairman.
HOLLAND	Education and Labor.
HORTON	District of Columbia.
	Government Operations.
HOSMER	Interior and Insular Affairs.
	Joint Committee on Atomic Energy.
HOWARD	Public Works.
HULL	Appropriations.
HUNGATE	Judiciary.
HUOT	District of Columbia.
	Interstate and Foreign Commerce.
HUTCHINSON	Judiciary.

ICHORD	Armed Services. Un-American Activities.
IRWIN	Armed Services.
JACOBS	Judiciary.
JARMAN	Interstate and Foreign Commerce.
JENNINGS	Ways and Means.
JOELSON	Appropriations.
JOHNSON of California	Interior and Insular Affairs. Public Works.
JOHNSON of Oklahoma	Armed Services.
JOHNSON of Pennsylvania	Banking and Currency. Post Office and Civil Service.
JONAS	Appropriations.
JONES of Alabama	Government Operations. Public Works.
JONES of Missouri	Agriculture. House Administration. Joint Committee on the Library.
KARSTEN	Ways and Means.
KARTH	Science and Astronautics.
KASTENMEIER	Judiciary.
KEE	Public Works.
KEITH	Interstate and Foreign Commerce. Merchant Marine and Fisheries.
KELLY	Foreign Affairs.
KEOGH	Ways and Means.
KING of California	Ways and Means. Joint Committee on Internal Revenue Taxation. Joint Committee on Reduction of Nonessential Federal Expenditures.
KING of New York	Judiciary.
KING of Utah	Government Operations. Interior and Insular Affairs.
KIRWAN	Appropriations.
KLUCZYNSKI	Public Works.
KORNEGAY	Interstate and Foreign Commerce. Veterans' Affairs.
KREBS	Post Office and Civil Service.
KUNKEL	Public Works.
LAIRD	Appropriations.

LANDRUM	Ways and Means.
LANGEN	Appropriations.
LATTA	Agriculture. Government Operations.
LEGGETT	Armed Services.
LENNON	Armed Services. Merchant Marine and Fisheries.
LINDSAY	Judiciary.
LIPSCOMB	Appropriations. House Administration. Joint Committee on Printing. Joint Committee on the Library.
LONG of Louisiana	Armed Services.
LONG of Maryland	Appropriations.
LOVE	Armed Services.
McCARTHY	Public Works.
McCLORY	Judiciary.
McCORMACK	Speaker of the House.
McCULLOCH	Judiciary. Joint Committee on Atomic Energy. Joint Committee on Immigration and Nationality Policy.
McDADE	Appropriations.
McDOWELL	Foreign Affairs. Veterans' Affairs.
McEWEN	Public Works.
McFALL	Appropriations.
McGRATH	Banking and Currency.
McMILLAN	District of Columbia, chairman. Agriculture.
McVICKER	Foreign Affairs.
MACDONALD	Government Operations. Interstate and Foreign Commerce.
MACGREGOR	Judiciary.
MACHEN	Armed Services.
MACKAY	Interstate and Foreign Commerce.
MACKIE	Agriculture.
MADDEN	Rules. Joint Committee on Organization of Congress.

MAHON_____ Appropriations, chairman.
Joint Committee on Reduction of Nonessential Federal Expenditures.

MAILLIARD_____ Foreign Affairs.
Merchant Marine and Fisheries.

MARSH_____ Appropriations.

MARTIN of Alabama_____ Public Works.

MARTIN of Massachusetts___ Science and Astronautics.

MARTIN of Nebraska_____ Education and Labor.
Rules.

MATHIAS_____ District of Columbia.
Judiciary.

MATSUNAGA_____ Agriculture.
Post Office and Civil Service.

MATTHEWS_____ Appropriations.

MAY_____ Agriculture.

MEEDS_____ Education and Labor.

MICHEL_____ Appropriations.

MILLER_____ Science and Astronautics, chairman.

MILLS_____ Ways and Means, chairman.
Joint Committee on Internal Revenue Taxation, chairman.
Joint Committee on Reduction of Nonessential Federal Expenditures.

MINISH_____ Banking and Currency.

MINK_____ Education and Labor.

MINSHALL_____ Appropriations.

MIZE_____ Banking and Currency.

MOELLER_____ Interior and Insular Affairs.
Science and Astronautics.

MONAGAN_____ Foreign Affairs.
Government Operations.

MOORE_____ Judiciary.
Joint Committee on Immigration and Nationality Policy.

MOORHEAD_____ Banking and Currency.
Government Operations.

MORGAN_____ Foreign Affairs, chairman.

MORRIS_____ Appropriations.
Joint Committee on Atomic Energy.

MORRISON_____ Agriculture.
Post Office and Civil Service.

MORSE_____ Foreign Affairs.

MORTON_____ Interior and Insular Affairs.
Merchant Marine and Fisheries.

MOSHER_____ Merchant Marine and Fisheries.
Science and Astronautics.

MOSS_____ Government Operations.
Interstate and Foreign Commerce.

MULTER_____ Banking and Currency.
District of Columbia.
Joint Committee on Defense Production.

MURPHY of Illinois_____ Foreign Affairs.

MURPHY of New York_____ Interstate and Foreign Commerce.
Merchant Marine and Fisheries.

MURRAY_____ Post Office and Civil Service, chairman.

NATCHER_____ Appropriations.

NEDZI_____ Armed Services.
House Administration.

NELSEN_____ District of Columbia.
Interstate and Foreign Commerce.

NIX_____ Foreign Affairs.
Post Office and Civil Service.

O'BRIEN_____ Interior and Insular Affairs.
Interstate and Foreign Commerce.

O'HARA of Illinois_____ Foreign Affairs.

O'HARA of Michigan_____ Education and Labor.

O'KONSKI_____ Armed Services.
District of Columbia.

OLSEN of Montana_____ Post Office and Civil Service.
Public Works.

OLSON of Minnesota_____ Agriculture.

O'NEAL_____ Agriculture.

O'NEILL_____ Rules.

OTTINGER_____ Banking and Currency.

PASSMAN_____ Appropriations.

PATMAN_____ Banking and Currency, chairman.
Joint Committee on Defense Production.
Joint Economic Committee, chairman.

PATTEN_____ Appropriations.

PELLY_____ Merchant Marine and Fisheries.
Science and Astronautics.

PEPPER_____ Rules.

PERKINS_____ Education and Labor.
House Administration.

PHILBIN_____ Armed Services.

PICKLE_____ Interstate and Foreign Commerce.

PIKE_____ Armed Services.

PIRNIE_____ Armed Services.

POAGE_____ Agriculture.

POFF_____ Judiciary.

POLANCO-ABREU_____ Agriculture.
Armed Services.
Interior and Insular Affairs.

POOL_____ Post Office and Civil Service.
Un-American Activities.

POWELL_____ Education and Labor, chairman.

PRICE_____ Armed Services.
Joint Committee on Atomic Energy.
Joint Committee to Commemorate the 100th Anniversary of the Second Inaugural of Abraham Lincoln.

PUCINSKI_____ Education and Labor.

PURCELL_____ Agriculture.

QUIE_____ Agriculture.
Education and Labor.

QUILLEN_____ Rules.

RACE_____ Interior and Insular Affairs.

RANDALL_____ Armed Services.
Government Operations.

REDLIN_____ Agriculture.

REID of Illinois_____ Interior and Insular Affairs.
Public Works.

REID of New York_____ Education and Labor.
Government Operations.

REIFEL_____ Appropriations.

REINECKE_____ Interior and Insular Affairs.
Merchant Marine and Fisheries.

RESNICK_____ Agriculture.
Veterans' Affairs.

REUSS_____ Banking and Currency.
Government Operations.
Joint Economic Committee.

RHODES of Arizona_____ Appropriations.

RHODES of Pennsylvania___ Ways and Means.

RIVERS of Alaska_____	Interior and Insular Affairs. Public Works.
RIVERS of South Carolina___	Armed Services, chairman.
ROBERTS of Texas_____	Public Works. Veterans' Affairs.
ROBISON_____	Appropriations.
RODINO_____	Judiciary.
ROGERS of Colorado_____	Judiciary.
ROGERS of Florida_____	Interstate and Foreign Commerce. Merchant Marine and Fisheries.
ROGERS of Texas_____	Interior and Insular Affairs. Interstate and Foreign Commerce.
RONAN_____	Interstate and Foreign Commerce.
RONCALIO_____	Interior and Insular Affairs. Veterans' Affairs.
ROONEY of New York_____	Appropriations.
ROONEY of Pennsylvania___	Interstate and Foreign Commerce.
ROOSEVELT_____	Education and Labor.
ROSENTHAL_____	Foreign Affairs. Government Operations.
ROSTENKOWSKI_____	Ways and Means.
ROUDEBUSH_____	District of Columbia. Science and Astronautics.
ROUSH_____	Government Operations. Science and Astronautics.
ROYBAL_____	Foreign Affairs.
RUMSFELD_____	Government Operations. Science and Astronautics.
RYAN of New York_____	Science and Astronautics.
ST GERMAIN_____	Banking and Currency. Government Operations.
ST. ONGE_____	Judiciary. Merchant Marine and Fisheries.
SATTERFIELD_____	Interstate and Foreign Commerce. Veterans' Affairs.
SAYLOR_____	Interior and Insular Affairs. Veterans' Affairs.
SCHEUER_____	Education and Labor.
SCHISLER_____	Science and Astronautics.
SCHMIDHAUSER_____	Public Works.

SCHNEEBELI_____ Ways and Means.

SCHWEIKER_____ Armed Services.

SCOTT_____ Education and Labor.

SECREST_____ Veterans' Affairs.

SELDEN_____ Foreign Affairs.

SENNER_____ Judiciary.
Un-American Activities.

SHIPLEY_____ Appropriations.

SHRIVER_____ Appropriations.

SICKLES_____ District of Columbia.
Education and Labor.

SIKES_____ Appropriations.

SISK_____ District of Columbia.
Rules.

SKUBITZ_____ Interior and Insular Affairs.

SLACK_____ Appropriations.

SMITH of California_____ Rules.

SMITH of Iowa_____ Appropriations.

SMITH of New York_____ Interior and Insular Affairs.

SMITH of Virginia_____ Rules, chairman.
District of Columbia.

SPRINGER_____ District of Columbia.
Interstate and Foreign Commerce.

STAFFORD_____ Armed Services.

STAGGERS_____ Interstate and Foreign Commerce.
Post Office and Civil Service.

STALBAUM_____ Agriculture.

STANTON_____ Banking and Currency.

STEED_____ Appropriations.

STEPHENS_____ Banking and Currency.

STRATTON_____ Armed Services.

STUBBLEFIELD_____ Agriculture.
Merchant Marine and Fisheries.

SULLIVAN_____ Banking and Currency.
Merchant Marine and Fisheries.

SWEENEY_____ Public Works.

TALCOTT_____ Banking and Currency.

TAYLOR	Interior and Insular Affairs. Science and Astronautics.
TEAGUE of California	Agriculture. Veterans' Affairs.
TEAGUE of Texas	Veterans' Affairs, chairman. Science and Astronautics.
TENZER	Judiciary.
THOMAS	Appropriations. Joint Committee on Atomic Energy. Joint Committee on Reduction of Nonessential Federal Expenditures.
THOMPSON of Louisiana	Merchant Marine and Fisheries. Public Works.
THOMPSON of New Jersey	Education and Labor. House Administration. Joint Committee on Disposition of Executive Papers. Joint Committee on the Library.
THOMPSON of Texas	Ways and Means.
THOMSON of Wisconsin	Foreign Affairs.
TODD	Banking and Currency.
TOLL	Judiciary.
TRIMBLE	District of Columbia. Rules.
TUCK	Judiciary. Un-American Activities.
TUNNEY	Interior and Insular Affairs. Post Office and Civil Service.
TUPPER	Merchant Marine and Fisheries.
TUTEN	Merchant Marine and Fisheries. Public Works.
UDALL	Interior and Insular Affairs. Post Office and Civil Service. Joint Committee on Navajo-Hopi Indian Administration.
ULLMAN	Ways and Means.
UTT	Ways and Means.
VAN DEERLIN	Interstate and Foreign Commerce.
VANIK	Ways and Means.
VIGORITO	Agriculture.
VIVIAN	Science and Astronautics.
WAGGONNER	House Administration. Science and Astronautics.

WALKER of Mississippi____ Agriculture.

WALKER of New Mexico___ Armed Services.

WATKINS_____ Merchant Marine and Fisheries.

WATTS_____ Ways and Means.

WELTNER_____ Banking and Currency.
Un-American Activities.

WHALLEY_____ Foreign Affairs.

WHITE of Idaho_____ Banking and Currency.
Interior and Insular Affairs.

WHITE of Texas_____ Interior and Insular Affairs.

WHITENER_____ District of Columbia.
Judiciary.

WHITTEN_____ Appropriations.

WIDNALL_____ Banking and Currency.
Joint Economic Committee.
Joint Committee on Defense Production.

WILLIAMS_____ District of Columbia.
Interstate and Foreign Commerce.

WILLIS_____ Un-American Activities, chairman.
Judiciary.

WILSON, BOB_____ Armed Services.

WILSON, CHARLES H_____ Armed Services.
Veterans' Affairs.

WOLFF_____ Science and Astronautics.

WRIGHT_____ Government Operations.
Public Works.

WYATT_____ Interior and Insular Affairs.

WYDLER_____ Science and Astronautics.

YATES_____ Appropriations.

YOUNG_____ Rules.

YOUNGER_____ Interstate and Foreign Commerce.

ZABLOCKI_____ Foreign Affairs.

ADMINISTRATIVE ASSISTANTS
AND SECRETARIES

315

LIST OF SENATORS, ADMINISTRATIVE ASSISTANTS, AND SECRETARIES

Senator	Administrative Assistant	Secretary
Aiken (Vt.)		Lola Pierotti, 305 C St. NE., 20002.
Allott (Colo.)	A. H. Gallatin, 1150 12th St.	Caroline Browne, 2554 Naylor Rd. SE., 20020.
Anderson (N. Mex.)	Claude E. Wood, 4630 36th St. South, Arlington, Va., 22206.	Eloise De La O, 1801 Clydesdale Pl., 20009.
Bartlett (Alaska)	Mary Lee Council, 2801 Quebec St.	Mrs. Douglas Smith, 3326 South Wakefield St., Arlington, Va.
Bass (Tenn.)	John R. Stephens, 3316 R St.	Peggy Bryant, 2500 Q St.
Bayh (Ind.)	Robert J. Keefe, 100 North Linden St., Alexandria, Va.	Frances Voorde, 38A G St. SW.
Bennett (Utah)	Tom C. Korologos, 5521 Sanger Ave., No. 12, Alexandria, Va.	Keith H. Jaques, 3928 Livingston St., 20015.
Bible (Nev.)	Jack Carpenter, 145 Senate Office Bldg.	
Boggs (Del.)	James A. Flood, 5310 Colonial Dr. SE., 20031.	
Brewster (Md.)	William S. Townsend, 240 Senate Office Bldg.	John F. Sullivan, 240 Senate Office Bldg.
Burdick (N. Dak.)	Charles Plante, Route 1, Box 585A, Great Falls, Va.	Yvonne Beck, 35 E St.
Byrd (Va.)	M. J. Menefee, 209 Senate Office Bldg.	Meda V. Dick, General Scott Apts.
Byrd (W. Va.)	Perry W. Woofter	Ethel R. Low.
Cannon (Nev.)	John F. Conlon, 102 Schotts Court NE.	Chester B. Sobsey, 4410 Colfax St., Kensington, Md.
Carlson (Kans.)	George Stafford, 5704 Newington Rd., 20016.	Mattie Gingrich, 1 Washington Circle, 20037.
Case (N.J.)	Samuel Zagoria, 3537 Marlbrough Way, College Park, Md., 20741.	Frances Henderson, 5951 Suitland Rd. SE., 20023.
Church (Idaho)	Verda Barnes, 2500 Q St	Jennie-Marie Ward, 12507 Kembridge Dr., Bowie, Md.
Clark (Pa.)	Bernard E. Norwitch, 645 A St. SE.	Marie E. Conlow, 2512 Q St.
Cooper (Ky.)	Bailey Guard, 5112 Wessling Lane, Bethesda, Md.	Ruth Midthun, 1600 16th St.
Cotton (N.H.)	Chester M. Wiggin, Jr., 4201 Massachusetts Ave., 20016.	Dolores Drayer, Hunting Towers, Alexandria, Va.
Curtis (Nebr.)	Doris M. Rook, 103 Granville Dr., Silver Spring, Md.	Don Shearon, 4527 Q St.

LIST OF SENATORS, ADMINISTRATIVE ASSISTANTS, AND
SECRETARIES—Continued

Senator	Administrative Assistant	Secretary
Dirksen (Ill.)	John R. Gomien, 5509 Cromwell Dr., 20016.	Glee D. Gomien, 5509 Cromwell Dr., 20016.
Dodd (Conn.)	James F. Gartland, 6014 Berkshire Dr. SE.	Doreen F. Moloney, 1502 31st St.
Dominick (Colo.)	Walter L. Morgan, Jr., 9819 Newhall Rd., Potomac, Md., 20850.	Maxine Hyde, 305 C St. NE., 20002.
Douglas (Ill.)	Howard E. Shuman, 2433 North Kenmore St., Arlington, Va.	Jane C. Enger, 3361 Runnymede Pl.
Eastland (Miss.)	Courtney C. Pace, 4826 17th St. North, Arlington, Va.	Jean H. Allen, 1811 Nealon Dr., Falls Church, Va.
Ellender (La.)	James W. Finley, 3958 Suitland Rd. SE., 20023.	Florence Le Compte, 1954 Columbia St., 20009.
Ervin (N.C.)	Jack Spain, 2127 Suitland Ter. SE.	John Giles, 4253 35th St. South, Arlington, Va.
Fannin (Ariz.)	Gordon D. Murphy, 6223 85th Pl., Hyattsville, Md.	Alice M. Flickinger, 1733 N St.
Fong (Hawaii)	Robert T. Carson, 730 24th St.	Rita K. Peine, 3711 Donnell Dr. SE., 20028.
Fulbright (Ark.)	Lee Williams, 253 Fort Williams Pkwy., Alexandria, Va., 22304.	Joe W. (Pat) Fleming, 6241 30th St.
Gore (Tenn.)	William G. Allen, 1331 Kingston Ave., Alexandria, Va., 22302.	------------------------
Gruening (Alaska)	George Sundborg, 2361 49th St., 20007.	Frances Abelitis, 6101 Lamont Dr., Carrollton, Hyattsville, Md., 20784.
Harris (Okla.)	Burl Hays, 333 2d St. NE., 20002.	Marjorie Banner, 101 G St. SW., 20024.
Hart (Mich.)	William B. Welsh, 6801 Galax Ct., Springfield, Va.	Florence Roth, 2800 Quebec St.
Hartke (Ind.)	Mace Broide, 4515 Burlington Pl.	Rosemary Rorick, 8600 16th St., Silver Spring, Md.
Hayden (Ariz.)	Roy L. Elson, 8 Edgehill Dr., Alexandria, Va.	Edward E. Davis, 7853 Patriot Dr., Annandale, Va.
Hickenlooper (Iowa)	Dan O'Brien, 2480 16th St.	Marjorie Bolger, 2408 32d St. SE., 20020.
Hill (Ala.)	Donald J. Cronin, 5406 Blackistone Rd., Westmoreland Hills, Md.	------------------------
Holland (Fla.)	Merrill Winslett, 3503 Carpenter St. SE.	William M. Christie, 915 South Washington St., Alexandria, Va.
Hruska (Nebr.)	Dean Pohlenz, 5303 Marlyn Dr., 20016.	Libbye A. Fauver, 6605 Newport Rd., Hyattsville, Md.
Inouye (Hawaii)	Dr. Ralph M. Miwa, 1102 South Oakcrest Rd., Arlington, Va., 22202.	Kimie Ishibashi, 305 C St. NE., 20002.
Jackson (Wash.)	S. Sterling Munro, Jr., 711 Lamberton Dr., Silver Spring, Md.	Doris Whitmus, 2500 Wisconsin Ave., 20007.
Javits (N.Y.)	Richard R. Aurelio, 336 N St. SW.	Shari Gebhardt, 539 7th St. SE.

LIST OF SENATORS, ADMINISTRATIVE ASSISTANTS, AND
SECRETARIES—Continued

Senator	Administrative Assistant	Secretary
Johnston (S.C.)	J. Baxter Funderburk, 8108 West Beach Dr., 20012.	Robert L. Alexander, 3203 Wintergreen St., District Heights.
Jordan (Idaho)	John E. Martin, 4203 Senate Office Bldg.	Gwenn Lewis, 4203 Senate Office Bldg.
Jordan (N.C.)	William M. Cochrane, 227 A St. NE., 20002.	William B. Whitley, 12824 Jingle Lane, Silver Spring, Md.
Kennedy (Mass.)	Joseph W. McIntyre, 9701 Cable Dr., Kensington, Md.	Angelique Voutselas, 1400 20th St.
Kennedy (N.Y.)	Joseph Dolan, 4316 Woodley Rd., McLean, Va.	Angela Novello, 2500 Q St., 20007.
Kuchel (Calif.)	Ewing Hass, 4201 Cathedral Ave.	Stephen Horn, 3207 Foxhall Dr.
Lausche (Ohio)	Ray M. White, 4301 Columbia Pike, Arlington, Va.	Celie M. Jirsa, 2500 Wisconsin Ave., 20007.
Long (La.)	Robert E. Hunter, 2400 36th St. SE.	Will E. Leonard, 3634 Camden St. SE.
Long (Mo.)	Daniel B. Miles, 4128 West Leland St., Chevy Chase, Md.	Helen Dunlop, 4201 Cathedral Ave., 20016.
McCarthy (Minn.)	Jerome N. Eller, 3445 North Edison, Arlington, Va., 22207	Jean Stack, 151 D St. SE., 20003.
McClellan (Ark.)	Ralph Matthews, 317 Skyhill Rd., Alexandria, Va.	Margie Nicholson, 1111 Army-Navy Dr., Arlington, Va.
McGee (Wyo.)	K. Richard Cook, 5316 Landgrave Lane, Springfield, Va.	Elizabeth Strannigan, 3201 Wisconsin Ave., 20016.
McGovern (S. Dak.)	Owen J. Donley, 1400 Kingston Ave., Alexandria, Va., 22300.	Patricia J. Donovan, 2352 Jameson St., Hillcrest Heights, Md., 20031.
McIntyre (N.H.)	James T. Keefe	Betty M. McQueen.
McNamara (Mich.)	Robert Perrin, 1433 Highland Dr., Silver Spring, Md.	Edwin N. Winge, 9103 Wire Ave., Silver Spring, Md.
Magnuson (Wash.)	Frederick J. Lordan, 2500 Q St.	Jessie V. Robertson, 2122 California St.
Mansfield (Mont.)	Margaret C. DeMichele, RFD 4287, Upper Marlboro, Md.	Mary Jane Del Balzo, 11708 Hatcher Pl., Wheaton, Md., 20902.
Metcalf (Mont.)	Merrill W. Englund, 11703 College View Dr., Silver Spring, Md., 20902.	Victor Reinemer, 1907 St. James Pl., Falls Church, Va., 22042.
Miller (Iowa)	Stanley R. Browne, 1400 South Joyce St., Arlington, Va., 22202.	Barbara Bengston, 3000 Spout Run Pkwy., Arlington, Va., 22201.
Mondale (Minn.)	Jerome D. Schaller, 5020 37th Pl., 20023.	Doris Fleischer, 2829 Connecticut Ave., 20008.
Monroney (Okla.)	Carter W. Bradley, 4206 35th St. North, Arlington, Va.	Betty Lund, 1000 6th St. SW.
Montoya (N. Mex.)	Paul T. Demos, 3603 Inverness Dr., Chevy Chase, Md.	Rose Marie West, 2424 Pennsylvania Ave.

LIST OF SENATORS, ADMINISTRATIVE ASSISTANTS, AND
SECRETARIES—Continued

Senator	Administrative Assistant	Secretary
Morse (Oreg.)	William Berg, Jr., 5906 Onondaga Rd., 20016.	Mildred McCullough, 316 Highview Pl., Silver Spring, Md.
Morton (Ky.)	A. B. Brooke, Jr., 821 Fairway Dr., Towson 4, Md.	Rose Blakely, 1410 33d St.
Moss (Utah)	Grant W. Midgley, 6212 31st St., 20015.	Beverly Fisher, 3535 North Ohio St., Arlington, Va., 22207.
Mundt (S. Dak.)	R. L. McCaughey, 2405 Gaither St. SE., 20031.	Roberta Van Beek, 103 G St. SW., 20024.
Murphy (Calif.)	John Ahlers, 6211 Pioneer Drive, Baltimore, Md.	Jane Dannenhauer, 1414 17th St., 20006.
Muskie (Maine)	Donald E. Nicoll, 3914 Livingston St.	Joanne E. Amnott, 4201 Massachusetts Ave.
Nelson (Wis.)	William R. Bechtel, 3110 Aberfoyle Pl.	Warren Sawall, 4835 8th Rd. South, Arlington, Va.
Neuberger (Oreg.)	W. Lloyd Tupling, 3619 Tilden St., 20008.	Mary Jane Christgau, 1920 35th Pl., 20007.
Pastore (R.I.)	C. J. Maisano, 3880 Rodman St.	James A. McKenna, 1821 Brisbane St., Silver Spring, Md.
Pearson (Kans.)	Allen E. Pritchard, Jr., 7300 Marbury Rd., Bethesda, Md.	Dorothy L. Silcott, 1648 Mount Eagle Pl., Alexandria, Va., 22302.
Pell (R.I.)	Ray Nelson, 6118 Wilson Lane, Bethesda, Md.	Miss Lee Szilagyi, 2800 Woodley Rd., 20008.
Prouty (Vt.)	Thomas L. Hayes, 5300 Everest Dr. SE.	Betty J. Collins, 5306 Everest Dr. SE.
Proxmire (Wis.)	Roy Moor, 5452 Mohican Rd., Bethesda, Md.	Nancy Murry Barkla, 510 A St. SE.
Randolph (W. Va.)	Marie Lantz, 3900 Tunlaw Rd., 20007.	James W. Harris, 2744 North Wyoming St., Arlington, Va., 22213.
Ribicoff (Conn.)	Wayne Granquist, 4516 Davenport St., 20016.	Vergie L. Cass, 301 G St. SW., 20024.
Robertson (Va.)	William B. Foster, Jr., 4410 Forest Glen Ct., Annandale, Va., 22003.	Robert B. McNeil, 3748 Orange Ct., Alexandria, Va., 22309.
Russell (Ga.)	Leeman Anderson, 1628 Mount Eagle Pl., Alexandria, Va., 22302.	William H. Jordan, Jr., 410 Wake Forest Dr., Alexandria, Va., 22307.
Saltonstall (Mass.)	William L. Saltonstall, 1727 Hoban Rd., 20007.	John A. Jackson, 920 South Carolina Ave. SE., 20003.
Scott (Pa.)	Robert L. Kunzig, 6827 Wilson Lane, Bethesda, Md.	Edith V. Skinner, 2601 Woodley Pl., 20008.
Simpson (Wyo.)		Louise H. Dagney, 5415 MacBeth St., Cheverly, Md., 20780.
Smathers (Fla.)		Warren Buck, 4217 4th St. SE.
Smith (Maine)	William C. Lewis, Jr., 2121 Senate Office Bldg.	Joseph A. Bernier, 4311 Thornapple St., Chevy Chase, Md.
Sparkman (Ala.)		Wiley S. Messick, 309 Stoneleigh Ct., Fairfax, Va.

LIST OF SENATORS, ADMINISTRATIVE ASSISTANTS, AND
SECRETARIES—Continued

Senator	Administrative Assistant	Secretary
Stennis (Miss.)	W. E. Cresswell, 407 Westgrove Blvd., Alexandria, Va.	Lorane Lowry Robinson, 305 C St. NE., 20002.
Symington (Mo.)	Stanley R. Fike, 511 Boston Ave., Takoma Park, Md., 20012.	Virginia T. Laird, Falls Church, Va., 22044.
Talmadge (Ga.)	Kenneth H. Turner, 4401 Holly Hill Rd., Hyattsville, Md.	--------------------
Thurmond (S.C.)	Harry S. Dent, 320 Westmoreland Rd., Alexandria, Va.	J. Fred Buzhardt, Jr., 1803 Christopher St., Fairfax, Va.
Tower (Tex.)	Ed Munden, 9500 Edgeley Rd., Bethesda, Md., 20014.	Earline Shelton, 5539 Columbia Pike, Arlington, Va., 22204.
Tydings (Md.)	J. Hardin Marion, 7217 Lanark Rd., Baltimore, Md., 21212.	Charlotte K. Reynolds, 3113 Gibbons Ave., Baltimore, Md., 21214.
Williams (Del.)	Ralph R. Peters, 127 C St. NE.	Eleanor R. Lenhart, 2117 E St.
Williams (N.J.)	--------------------	Mary Jane Cox, 607 Massachusetts Ave. NE.
Yarborough (Tex.)	Alex Dickie, Jr., 4013 North Chesterbrook Rd., Arlington, Va., 22207.	Frances Ronshausen, 320 East Capitol St., 20003.
Young (N. Dak.)	Christopher U. Sylvester, 3009 Daniel Lane, 20015.	Patricia M. Byrne, 6101 16th St., 20011.
Young (Ohio)	Herbert A. Jolovitz, 3900 Tunlaw Rd.	Jeannine M. Anderson, R.R. 1, Box 297, Fairfax, Va.

LIST OF REPRESENTATIVES AND SECRETARIES

Representative	Secretary
Abbitt (Va.)	W. Fred Fletcher, 3701 Lyons Lane, Alexandria, Va.
Abernethy (Miss.)	Mrs. Clair Stevens, 2610 Fordham Rd., Alexandria, Va.
Adair (Ind.)	Richard C. Prickett, 1511 House Office Bldg.
Adams (Wash.)	Henry R. Seidel, 3605 Livingston St., 20015.
Addabbo (N.Y.)	Louise W. Snowden, 5615 Paul St., Alexandria, Va., 22311.
Albert (Okla.)	Verneil G. English, 6542 Abbington Dr., Oxon Hill, Md., 21654.
Anderson (Ill.)	Rita Machakos, 1418 House Office Bldg.
Anderson (Tenn.)	James A. Wise, 130 4th St., Woodbridge, Va., 22191.
Andrews, George (Ala.)	Eva Hammond, 2731 North George Mason Dr., Arlington, Va. 22207.
Andrews, Glenn (Ala.)	Nicholas Nonnenmacher, 5408 Wehawken Rd.
Andrews (N. Dak.)	Irene Martin Edwards, 3520 Woodbine St., Chevy Chase, Md., 20015.
Annunzio (Ill.)	Miss Vince Bellucci, 117 School St., Alexandria, Va., 22303.
Arends (Ill.)	William R. Pitts, 1725 38th St. SE.
Ashbrook (Ohio)	Pat Hennessey, 1600 South Joyce St., Arlington, Va.
Ashley (Ohio)	June G. Clendening, 4898 Forestville Rd., SE., 20028.
Ashmore (S.C.)	Rhoda McCarrell, 4707 Connecticut Ave., 20008.
Aspinall (Colo.)	Harriet Sheridan, 2500 Wisconsin Ave.
Ayres (Ohio)	Rita W. Baker, 1900 South Eads St., Arlington, Va.
Baldwin (Calif.)	Ann Schreiber, 174 North Carolina Ave. SE., 20003.
Bandstra (Iowa)	Una M. McLean, 2214 Gaylord Dr., Bradbury Park, Md., 20023.
Baring (Nev.)	George H. Seward, 8202 Oxman Rd., Palmer Park, Hyattsville, Md.
Barrett (Pa.)	Robert R. Miller, House Office Bldg.
Bates (Mass.)	Carleton B. Hovey, 101 G St. SW., 20024.
Battin (Mont.)	J. N. McKean, 3206 Morrison St., 20015.
Beckworth (Tex.)	--
Belcher (Okla.)	Mary C. Higgins, 1427 North Nash St., Arlington, Va.
Bell (Calif.)	Leah C. Crees, 1225 North Pierce St., Arlington, Va., 22209.
Bennett (Fla.)	J. Richard Sewell, 201 I St. SW.
Berry (S. Dak.)	Mavis G. Daly, 7207 Hawthorne Ter., Hyattsville, Md.
Betts (Ohio)	Donald Zahn, 6014 85th Pl., Carrollton Manor, Hyattsville, Md.
Bingham, (N.Y.)	Edmond F. Rovner, 6308 Owen Pl., Bethesda, Md., 20034.
Blatnik (Minn.)	James L. Oberstar, 2727 29th St.
Boggs (La.)	Barbara A. Rathe, 3410 Dent Pl., 20007.
Boland (Mass.)	P. Joseph Donoghue, 215 C St. SE.
Bolling (Mo.)	James H. Toughill, 3715 S St., 20013.
Bolton (Ohio)	Irene Lewis, 503 East Capitol St., 20003.

LIST OF REPRESENTATIVES AND SECRETARIES—Continued

Representative	Secretary
Bonner (N.C.)	Henry C. Oglesby, 4425 34th St. South, Arlington, Va.
Bow (Ohio)	Gilbert LeKander, RD3, Box 299, Manassas, Va., 22110.
Brademas (Ind.)	Fred W. Wegner, Jr., 53A G St. SW., 20024.
Bray (Ind.)	Don R. Kendall, 4417 Ridge St., Chevy Chase, Md., 20015.
Brock (Tenn.)	William E. Timmons, 5308 Westport Rd., Chevy Chase, Md., 20015.
Brooks (Tex.)	Eugene F. Peters, 4406 Edgefield Rd., Kensington, Md.
Broomfield (Mich.)	Roy A. Gast, 3611 Spruell Dr., Silver Spring, Md.
Brown (Calif.)	Ray Sebens, 3418 Terrace Dr., Alexandria, Va., 22300.
Brown (Ohio)	Margaret Harpster, 3033 New Mexico Ave., 20016.
Broyhill (N.C.)	L. Vincent Monzel, 7501 Democracy Blvd., Bethesda, Md.
Broyhill (Va.)	Homer Lee Krout, 1605 North Johnson St., Arlington, Va., 22201.
Buchanan (Ala.)	Sylvia H. Comfort, 216 Maryland Ave. NE., 20002.
Burke (Mass.)	Frederic L. Driscoll, 215 C St. SE.
Burleson (Tex.)	Zeno Phillips, 1531 House Office Bldg.
Burton (Calif.)	Joe Beeman, 634 North Carolina Ave. SE.
Burton (Utah)	Florence T. Davis, 815 18th St. South, Arlington, Va.
Byrne (Pa.)	Christine V. Ball, 1937 Elkridge Heights Ave., Elkridge, Md., 21227.
Byrnes (Wis.)	William M. Gage, 4001 Garrison St., 20016.
Cabell (Tex.)	Harry Crutcher III, 1213 33d St.
Cahill (N.J.)	Eugenia M. Daugherty, 1440 House Office Bldg.
Callan (Nebr.)	Carolyn M. Andrade, 1241 28th St.
Callaway (Ga.)	William G. Amos, 1541 House Office Bldg.
Cameron (Calif.)	Alexander A. Silva, 3829 Taft Ave., Alexandria, Va.
Carey (N.Y.)	Mildred Akins, 2100 Connecticut Ave.
Carter (Ky.)	Roy Woolum, 2313 25th St. SE.
Casey (Tex.)	Charles A. Frandolig, 3201 Wisconsin Ave., 20016.
Cederberg (Mich.)	William H. Hackett, 907 Brantford Ave., Silver Spring, Md.
Celler (N.Y.)	Minnie White, 2800 Quebec St., 20008.
Chamberlain (Mich.)	Donald H. Ackerman, 4800 Chevy Chase Blvd., Chevy Chase, Md., 20015.
Chelf (Ky.)	Mary Prudence Kelly, 1 Scott Circle, 20036.
Clancy (Ohio)	Marjorie R. Hein, 4805 Tallahassee Ave., Rockville, Md., 20853.
Clark (Pa.)	Diane Taylor, 4117 Arkansas Ave.
Clausen, Don H. (Calif.)	Nan Delagnes, 6312 31st St., 20015.
Clawson, Del (Calif.)	Anita S. Charles, 4201 Cathedral Ave.
Cleveland (N.H.)	Madeleine M. Marceau, 6045 27th St. North, Arlington, Va.
Clevenger (Mich.)	Raymond L. Courage, 4507 Traymore St., Bethesda, Md., 20014.
Cohelan (Calif.)	Marie K. Wernick, 221 Springvale Ave., McLean, Va., 22101.
Collier (Ill.)	Marie Hershey, 628 C St. NE.
Colmer (Miss.)	Waller Batson, 2506 North Quincy St., Arlington, Va., 22207.
Conable (N.Y.)	Jane Borth, 436 House Office Bldg.
Conte (Mass.)	Carole Ann Long, 1301 South Arlington Ridge Rd., Arlington, Va.

LIST OF REPRESENTATIVES AND SECRETARIES—Continued

Representative	Secretary
Conyers (Mich.)	Kay Shannon, 304 Independence Ave. SE., 20003.
Cooley (N.C.)	
Corbett (Pa.)	Harold F. Eberle, 3636 16th St., 20010.
Corman (Calif.)	Jacqueline A. Gerachis, 5155 Oakcrest Dr., Oxon Hill, Md.
Craley (Pa.)	Margaret A. Matus, 1620 House Office Bldg.
Cramer (Fla.)	Hazel H. Kennedy, 5607 7th Pl. South, Arlington, Va.
Culver (Iowa)	Richard C. Clark, 12120 New Hampshire Ave., Springbrook, Md.
Cunningham (Nebr.)	James Roberts, 2107 Villanova Dr., Vienna, Va.
Curtin (Pa.)	
Curtis (Mo.)	Eugene F. Jordan, 3915 Havard, Silver Spring, Md.
Daddario (Conn.)	Thomas E. J. Keena, 4019 Veazey St., 20016.
Dague (Pa.)	Katharine R. Shunk, 3625 South Taylor St., Arlington, Va., 22206.
Daniels (N.J.)	Frank A. Madden, 11431 Schuylkill Rd., Rockville, Md.
Davis (Ga.)	Mrs. John D. Penn, 7504 Highland Ave., Springfield, Va., 22150.
Davis (Wis.)	James C. Bolton.
Dawson (Ill.)	Norma O. Williams, 1632 S St., 20009.
de la Garza (Tex.)	Celia Hare Martin, 2500 Q St., 20007.
Delaney (N.Y.)	Dolores Cook, 1727 Massachusetts Ave., 20036.
Dent (Pa.)	
Denton (Ind.)	Mary Verkouteren, 8210 West Beach Drive, 20012.
Derwinski (Ill.)	James Bolton, 6031 22d Rd. North, Arlington, Va.
Devine (Ohio)	John Sidney Hoyt, North Springfield, Va.
Dickinson (Ala.)	Elizabeth G. Melvin, 2753 Iverson St. SE., 20031.
Diggs (Mich.)	Dorothy E. Quarker, 301 G St. SW., 20024.
Dingell (Mich.)	Jeannette H. Cantwell, 5507 21st Pl., Hillcrest Heights, Md., 20031.
Dole (Kans.)	William A. Kats, 4918 28th Parkway SE., 20031.
Donohue (Mass.)	William A. Rourke, 3921 Langley Ct., 20016.
Dorn (S.C.)	Sam J. McDowell, 330 House Office Bldg.
Dow (N.Y.)	Elizabeth Murray, 206 G St. SW., 20024.
Dowdy (Tex.)	Eunice D. McDonnell, 3819 Woodbine St., Chevy Chase, Md.
Downing (Va.)	Norman L. Dobyns, 8022 Harwood Pl., Springfield, Va.
Dulski (N.Y.)	Irene Neese, 5204 26th Ave. SE.
Duncan (Oreg.)	Richard H. Martin, 330 A St. SE.
Duncan (Tenn.)	Robert Rule, 236 G St. SW.
Dwyer (N.J.)	Francis J. Keenan, 115 6th St. SE., 20003.
Dyal (Calif.)	Mrs. Jo Hughes, 2405 32d St. SE., 20020.
Edmondson (Okla.)	
Edwards (Ala.)	David C. Pruitt III, 16 3d St. NE.
Edwards (Calif.)	Lu Verne Conway, 3606 35th St.
Ellsworth (Kans.)	Venita Rita Clair, 4620 22d St. North, Arlington, Va.
Erlenborn (Ill.)	
Evans (Colo.)	Mrs. Pat Bergman, 1405 Alger Rd., Falls Church, Va., 22046.
Everett (Tenn.)	Hope Hart, 2475 Virginia Ave.
Evins (Tenn.)	Rebecca Johnson, 2800 Quebec St., 20008.
Fallon (Md.)	Frances Burns Hoyland, The Westchester.
Farbstein (N.Y.)	Ethel Maness, 7316 Durbin Ter., Bethesda, Md.
Farnsley (Ky.)	Jean Armistead, 4000 Massachusetts Ave., 20016.

LIST OF REPRESENTATIVES AND SECRETARIES—Continued

Representative	Secretary
Farnum (Mich.)	William J. Coughlin, 511 Thayer Ave., Silver Spring, Md.
Fascell (Fla.)	John R. Buckley, 5483 30th St.
Feighan (Ohio)	Irene M. Hopkins, 2000 F St., 20006.
Findley (Ill.)	Ray McRae, 119 2d St.
Fino (N.Y.)	Helen T. MacDonald, 3130 Wisconsin Ave.
Fisher (Tex.)	Helen Pauly, 439 New Jersey Ave. SE., 20003.
Flood (Pa.)	Eugene D. Hegarty, 6936 Alpine Dr., Annandale, Va.
Flynt (Ga.)	John H. Harper, 123 6th St. NE.
Fogarty (R.I.)	George J. Kelley, 1235 House Office Bldg.
Foley (Wash.)	Amy C. Lee, 610 G St. SE., 20003.
Ford, Gerald R. (Mich.)	Mildred Leonard, 4545 Connecticut Ave., 20008.
Ford, William D. (Mich.)	Frank Rathbun, 200 C St. SE.
Fountain (N.C.)	Walter J. Pittman, 2408 Sanford Ct., Annandale, Va., 22003.
Fraser (Minn.)	Dale MacIver, 1001 3d St. SW., 20024.
Frelinghuysen (N.J.)	William T. Kendall, 7606 Geranium St., Bethesda, Md., 20034.
Friedel (Md.)	Hazel R. Justice, 3636 16th St., 20010.
Fulton (Pa.)	---
Fulton (Tenn.)	
Fuqua (Fla.)	Herbert Wadsworth, Jr., 1223 House Office Bldg.
Gallagher (N.J.)	Elizabeth May, 301 G St. SW., 20024.
Garmatz (Md.)	Elizabeth Garmatz, 1805 23d St. SE., 20020.
Gathings (Ark.)	Mary Williams, 101 North Carolina Ave. SE.
Gettys (S.C.)	B. Bayles Mack, 504 Roberta Ct., McLean, Va.
Giaimo (Conn.)	D. Eileen Nixon, 3143 Lyndale Pl. SE.
Gibbons (Fla.)	Hector Alcalde, 8422 Stonewall Dr., Vienna, Va.
Gilbert (N.Y.)	Florence Palmer, 1932 North Kenilworth St., Arlington, Va., 22205.
Gilligan (Ohio)	Margaret H. Moorhous, 925 25th St., 20037.
Gonzalez (Tex.)	Gail Beagle, 35 E St., 20001.
Goodell (N.Y.)	Mary E. Nichols, 2312 Huidekoper Pl., 20007.
Grabowski (Conn.)	William J. Scully, 5009 Weber St., Annandale, Va., 22003.
Gray (Ill.)	Margaret J. Bergin, 3355 16th St.
Green (Oreg.)	Wes Barthelmes, 6006 Welborn Dr., 20016.
Green (Pa.)	Estelle M. Tyler.
Greigg (Iowa)	John T. O'Brien, 2802 Washington Ave., Chevy Chase, Md.
Grider (Tenn.)	Sidney Genette, 443 House Office Bldg.
Griffin (Mich.)	John J. Crowley, 1400 Stratton Dr., Rockville, Md., 20850.
Griffiths (Mich.)	Marilynne Mikulich, House Office Bldg.
Gross (Iowa)	Robert E. Case, 5428 Roanoke Ave., Alexandria, Va.
Grover (N.Y.)	Mary J. Papworth, 1111 Army-Navy Dr., Arlington, Va.
Gubser (Calif.)	Jean E. Gordon, 2929 Connecticut Ave.
Gurney (Fla.)	Mrs. John P. Elliott, 1117 Prince St., Alexandria, Va.
Hagan (Ga.)	Ronald B. Ginn, 5322 Charlottesville Rd., Springfield, Va.
Hagen (Calif.)	George C. Baker, 5128 Crisfield Dr., 20021.
Haley (Fla.)	Alice V. Myers, 412 1st St. SE., 20003.
Hall (Mo.)	Helen Zander, 4016 Nicholson St., Hyattsville, Md., 20782.
Halleck (Ind.)	Robert G. Allett, 201 Panorama Dr., 20021.
Halpern (N.Y.)	Ruby Moy, 405 Seward Sq.

39–650°—65——23

LIST OF REPRESENTATIVES AND SECRETARIES—Continued

Representative	Secretary
Hamilton (Ind.)	David M. McFall, 7106 Jayhawk St., Annandale, Va.
Hanley (N.Y.)	John F. Mahoney, 216 3d St. SE., 20003.
Hanna (Calif.)	William A. Butcher, 9314 Piney Branch Rd., Silver Spring, Md.
Hansen (Idaho)	J. B. Thayn, 2708 Cheverly Ave., Cheverly, Md.
Hansen (Iowa)	Lester L. Moore, House Office Bldg.
Hansen (Wash.)	Donald M. Brown, 5714 Rhode Island Ave., Falls Church, Va., 22043.
Hardy (Va.)	Thad S. Murray, 203 Farmington Dr., Fairfax, Va.
Harris (Ark.)	Willie Harris, 2057 38th St. SE., 20020.
Harsha (Ohio)	Joan L. Ferguson, 4000 Tunlaw Rd.
Harvey (Ind.)	Jack Carmichael, 11 2d St. NE., 20002.
Harvey (Mich.)	James M. Sparling, Jr., 4310 Merton Rd., Rockville, Md., 20850.
Hathaway (Maine)	Albert Gamache, 15 E St.
Hawkins (Calif.)	Juanita Barbee, 1830 16th St., 20009.
Hays (Ohio)	H. Elaine Heslin, Arlington Towers, Arlington, Va.
Hébert (La.)	Mary Swann, 513 D St. SE., 20003.
Hechler (W. Va.)	Robert R. Nelson.
Helstoski (N.J.)	Joseph S. Brzostowski, 209 Patterson St., Falls Church, Va., 22046.
Henderson (N.C.)	Charles O. Whitley, 127 C St. NE.
Herlong (Fla.)	A. W. Gilliam, Burke, Va.
Hicks (Wash.)	--
Holifield (Calif.)	Dorothy Dunn Morrison, 1303 4th St. SW., 20024.
Holland (Pa.)	Veronica M. Conlon, House Office Bldg.
Horton (N.Y.)	William F. Dwyer, 8111 Hatteras La., Springfield, Va., 22151.
Hosmer (Calif.)	Eilleen Case, 2828 Connecticut Ave.
Howard (N.J.)	Marjorie Morgan, 9819 Newhall Rd., Potomac, Md., 20854.
Hull (Mo.)	Kimball Clark, 3807 North Abingdon St., Arlington, Va., 22207.
Hungate (Mo.)	Nathan A. Ricks.
Huot (N.H.)	Andrew Nighswander, 745 Delaware Ave. SW.
Hutchinson (Mich.)	Helen M. Boyer, 2725 39th St., 20007.
Ichord (Mo.)	Virginia Wekenborg, 6626 Hopewell, Springfield, Va.
Irwin (Conn.)	Robert Bryan, 904 Twinbrook Pkwy., Rockville, Md.
Jacobs (Ind.)	Paul F. Cantwell, 2608 North Potomac, Arlington, Va., 22207.
Jarman (Okla.)	Juanita B. Mosher, 1304 North Meade St., Arlington, Va.
Jennings (Va.)	W. Raymond Colley, 205 Dalebrook Dr., Alexandria, Va., 22308.
Joelson (N.J.)	James Gavin.
Johnson (Calif.)	Dwight H. Barnes, 1204 Highland Dr., Silver Spring, Md.
Johnson (Okla.)	Martin W. Cunningham, 111 4th St. NE., 20002.
Johnson (Pa.)	Betty L. Lantz, 1415 House Office Bldg.
Jonas (N.C.)	Richard N. Rigby, Jr., 638 G St. SE., 20003.
Jones (Ala.)	George L. Milstead, 508 Linden St., Fairfax, Va.
Jones (Mo.)	Blanche J. Middleton, 5841 Nebraska Ave., 20015.
Karsten (Mo.)	Martha Rebori, 103 G St. SW., 20024.
Karth (Minn.)	Gerald Christenson, 1033 House Office Bldg.

LIST OF REPRESENTATIVES AND SECRETARIES—Continued

Representative	Secretary
Kastenmeier (Wis.)	Kaz Oshiki, 312 North Carolina Ave. SE., 20003.
Kee (W. Va)	Frank G. Tsutras, 427 House Office Bldg.
Keith (Mass.)	
Kelly (N.Y.)	Shirley M. Albert, 7404 Lansdale St., District Heights, Md., 20028.
Keogh (N.Y.)	Agnes L. Mathisen, 3817 Military Rd., 20015.
King (Calif.)	Erwin L. Pummer, 2720 Wisconsin Ave., 20007.
King (N.Y.)	George L. Berg, Jr., 212 G St. SW., 20024.
King (Utah)	R. Frank Mensel, 131 House Office Bldg.
Kirwan (Ohio)	Roberta G. Messerly, 4943 Eskridge Ter.
Kluczynski (Ill.)	James J. Guinea, 1650 Harvard St.
Kornegay (N.C.)	Margaret W. Graves, 110 D St. SE., 20003.
Krebs (N.J.)	Robert A. Reveles, 414 Jackson Rd., Alexandria, Va.
Kunkel (Pa.)	June H. Burke, 10219 Big Rock Rd., Silver Spring, Md.
Laird (Wis.)	Carl S. Wallace, 1903 Ashwood Dr., Alexandria, Va.
Landrum (Ga.)	
Langen (Minn.)	Audrey Hagen, 4000 Cathedral Ave., 20016.
Latta (Ohio)	Kaye Burchell.
Leggett (Calif.)	Lee Wilber, 728 Lakeview Dr., Falls Church, Va.
Lennon (N.C.)	John K. Slear, 100 Maryland Ave. NE., 20002.
Lindsay (N.Y.)	Marian G. Clow, 4810 20th Pl. North, Arlington, Va., 22207.
Lipscomb (Calif.)	Melvin M. Miller, 4720 Kellogg Dr., McLean, Va.
Long (La.)	Ted L. Jones, River House Apts., Arlington, Va.
Long (Md.)	David T. Parry, 1882 Columbia Rd., 20009.
Love (Ohio)	Shirley H. Freeman, 117 White Oaks Dr., Alexandria, Va., 22306.
McCarthy (N.Y.)	Betty White, 5010 8th Rd. South, Arlington, Va., 22204.
McClory (Ill.)	Donald E. Deuster, 737 3d St. SW., 20024.
McCormack (Mass.)	Eugene T. Kinnaly, 5410 Connecticut Ave., 20015.
McCulloch (Ohio)	Vera W. Page, Box 11–A, Nanjemoy, Md.
McDade (Pa.)	Gertrude L. Moser, 3016 North Stuart St., Arlington, Va., 22207.
McDowell (Del.)	Nellie W. Norbet, 200 C St. SE., 20003.
McEwen (N.Y.)	George T. Caffrey, 926 17th St. South, Arlington, Va.
McFall (Calif.)	Raymond F. Barnes, 3002 Teak La., Bowie, Md.
McGrath (N.J.)	Josef Grossman, 4332 Livingston Rd. SE.
McMillan (S.C.)	Major McGee.
McVicker (Colo.)	Robert R. Stapp, 1900 South Eads, Arlington, Va.
Macdonald (Mass.)	Edna Sanders, 1209 House Office Bldg.
MacGregor (Minn.)	David N. Krogseng, 4507 Saul Rd., Kensington, Md.
Machen (Md.)	Miss Gene Miller, 73 Maryland Ave., Annapolis, Md., 21401.
Mackay (Ga.)	John Maull Heritage, 5330 Sanger Ave., Alexandria, Va., 22311.
Mackie (Mich.)	Tom Farrell, 1705 Byrnes Dr., McLean, Va., 22101.
Madden (Ind.)	
Mahon (Tex.)	Helen Boyle, 1510 Buchanan St., 20011.
Mailliard (Calif.)	Richard L. Harcourt, 1400 20th St., 20036.
Marsh (Va.)	Chris Mathisen, 231 House Office Bldg.
Martin (Ala.)	Ralph H. Marlatt, 3450 Toledo Ter., West Hyattsville, Md., 20782.

LIST OF REPRESENTATIVES AND SECRETARIES—Continued

Representative	Secretary
Martin (Mass.)	Helen E. Morris, 1815 Randolph St., 20011.
Martin (Nebr.)	Nancy S. Gilbert, 1400 Ivanhoe St., Alexandria, Va.
Mathias (Md.)	Evelyn F. Slater, House Office Bldg.
Matsunaga (Hawaii)	Margaret Makino, 1600 16th St., 20009.
Matthews (Fla.)	Wm. D. Ladd, 2400 41st St., 20007.
May (Wash.)	John Knievel, 1118 House Office Bldg.
Meeds (Wash.)	Al Swift, 8622 Trafalgar, Fairfax, Va.
Michel (Ill.)	James Cromwell, 797 West Boulevard Dr., Alexandria, Va.
Miller (Calif.)	John T. Kehoe, 5361 Sanger Ave., Alexandria, Va.
Mills (Ark.)	Gene Goss, 5831 Quantrell Ave., Alexandria, Va.
Minish (N.J.)	Margaret M. Sullivan, 136 North Carolina Ave. SE., 20003.
Mink (Hawaii)	Alan L. Goodfader, 1016 House Office Bldg.
Minshall (Ohio)	
Mize (Kans.)	Charles R. Freburg, 2000 Stirrup La., Alexandria, Va.
Moeller (Ohio)	Christopher R. Brady, 12330 Riverview Rd., 20022.
Monagan (Conn.)	Joseph P. Donahue, 1528 House Office Bldg.
Moore (W. Va.)	Clara D. Macrae, 714 North Lincoln St., Arlington, Va.
Moorhead (Pa.)	Mollie D. Cohen, 555 Thayer Ave., Silver Spring, Md., 20910.
Morgan (Pa.)	John H. Weiner, 3501 Carpenter St. SE.
Morris (N. Mex.)	Ella Marice Ryan, 221 Constitution Ave. NE., 20002.
Morrison (La.)	Florence H. Cooley, 2117 E St., 20007.
Morse (Mass.)	Linda K. Lee, 2713 P St., 20007.
Morton (Md.)	Opal Van Horn, 2480 16th St., 20009.
Mosher (Ohio)	Bette B. Welch, 2718 Bryan Pl., Alexandria, Va., 22302.
Moss (Calif.)	Ernest Y. Cox, 9531 Lawnsberry Ter., Silver Spring, Md.
Multer (N.Y.)	Jeanne Stratton, 307 A St. NE.
Murphy (Ill.)	Clara L. Lambert, 3159 Martha Custis Dr., Alexandria, Va., 22302.
Murphy (N.Y.)	Helen R. Smith, 2700 Q St., 20007.
Murray (Tenn.)	Sara L. Ward, 2745 29th St., 20008.
Natcher (Ky.)	Yvonne Ellis, 2313 North Trenton, Arlington, Va., 22207.
Nedzi (Mich.)	James G. Pyrros, 1000 6th St. SW.
Nelsen (Minn.)	Donald W. Olson, 407 Colmac Dr., Falls Church, Va., 22044.
Nix (Pa.)	Cyrill O. Sledd, 4830 Ft. Totten Dr. NE.
O'Brien (N.Y.)	Francis X. Kilroy, 403 Russell Rd., Alexandria, Va., 22301.
O'Hara (Ill.)	Marie Crowe, The Congressional.
O'Hara (Mich.)	Richard D. Warden, 500 North Naylor, Alexandria, Va.
O'Konski (Wis.)	Robert Shafer, 920 North Carolina Ave. SE.
Olsen (Mont.)	Max Lloyd, Route 109, Sellman, Md.
Olson (Minn.)	Ed O'Brien, 1017 Plantation Pkwy., Fairfax, Va.
O'Neal (Ga.)	John W. Elllis, 408 Wellington Rd., Alexandria, Va.
O'Neill (Mass.)	Harryette M. Smith, 4906 47th St., 20016.
Ottinger (N.Y.)	Paul Schosberg, 4433 31st St. South, Arlington, Va.
Passman (La.)	Martha K. Williams, 1111 Army-Navy Dr., Arlington, Va.

LIST OF REPRESENTATIVES AND SECRETARIES—Continued

Representative	Secretary
Patman (Tex.)_____	_____
Patten (N.J.)_____	Olga Jamison Brown, 2129 Suitland Ter. SE., 20020.
Pelly (Wash.)_____	Charles Odell, 1125 Spotswood Dr., Silver Spring, Md., 20904.
Pepper (Fla.)_____	Mildred Waller, 352 House Office Bldg.
Perkins (Ky.)_____	Lucille H. Blake, 110 D St. SE.
Philbin (Mass.)_____	Clifford O. Gaucher, 2411 32d St. SE., 20020.
Pickle (Tex.)_____	John Goldsum.
Pike (N.Y.)_____	Mrs. Robert Gale Woolbert, 6628 Rannoch Rd., Bethesda, Md., 20034.
Pirnie (N.Y.)_____	Sherwood L. Boehlert, 8109 Bullock La., Springfield, Va., 22150.
Poage (Tex.)_____	_____
Poff (Va.)_____	Robert E. Bradford, 6 Densmore Ct., Alexandria, Va., 22309.
Pool (Tex.)_____	Jean Jones, 3610 Greenway Pl., Alexandria, Va.
Powell (N.Y.)_____	Hattie Dodson, 132 West 138th St., New York City, 10030.
Price (Ill.)_____	Goldie Hallas, 8506 Leonard Dr., Silver Spring, Md.
Pucinski (Ill.)_____	Cynthia A. Crites, 1423–C North Van Dorn St., Alexandria, Va.
Purcell (Tex.)_____	Norman Duncan, 3910 Wagon Wheel Rd., Alexandria, Va., 22309.
Quie (Minn.)_____	Reynold T. Bergquist, 5708 Huntington Pkwy., Bethesda, Md., 21811.
Quillen (Tenn.)_____	Helen W. Kirkman, 307 Stoneleigh Ct., Fairfax, Va.
Race (Wis.)_____	Russell Meerdink, 101 G St. SW.
Randall (Mo.)_____	Mrs. Irah E. Hocker, 3000 Arizona Ave., 20016.
Redlin (N. Dak.)_____	William Scouton, 103 G St. SW.
Reid (Ill.)_____	Alice V. Isley, 623 Woodland Circle, Falls Church, Va., 22040.
Reid (N.Y.)_____	_____
Reifel (S. Dak.)_____	Vernon C. Loen, 5201 Bangor Dr., Kensington, Md.
Reinecke (Calif.)_____	Elizabeth A. Seeley, 1310 Telegraph Rd., Alexandria, Va.
Resnick (N.Y.)_____	Ruth Singer, 2070 Belmont Rd., 20011.
Reuss (Wis.)_____	Sara M. Robinson, 1707 Columbia Rd., 20009.
Rhodes (Ariz.)_____	Alma Alkire, 4201 Massachusetts Ave., 20016.
Rhodes (Pa.)_____	Mary B. Robertson, 2908 Richmond Lane, Alexandria, Va., 22305.
Rivers (Alaska)_____	Martha M. Rivers, 2305 Wemberly Way, McLean, Va., 22101.
Rivers (S.C.)_____	Coyte W. White, House Office Bldg.
Roberts (Tex.)_____	Lorraine M. Kimbrough, 5305 7th St. South, Arlington, Va., 22204.
Robison (N.Y.)_____	John T. Calkins, 2916 Upton St., 20008.
Rodino (N.J.)_____	John J. Sullivan, Jr., 2121 Virginia Ave.
Rogers (Colo.)_____	Nina N. Kelly.
Rogers (Fla.)_____	Robert B. Lochrie, Jr., 301 G St. SW.
Rogers (Tex.)_____	John S. Masterman, 516 Patrick Henry Dr., Falls Church, Va.
Ronan (Ill.)_____	James A. Dupree, 127 C St. SE., 20003.
Roncalio (Wyo.)_____	William D. Bagley, 1400 South Joyce Ave., Arlington, Va.
Rooney (N.Y.)_____	Jenalee D. Nivens, 5244 5th St. North, Arlington, Va., 22203.

LIST OF REPRESENTATIVES AND SECRETARIES—Continued

Representative	Secretary
Rooney (Pa.)	Leonard W. Randolph, 407 Waynewood Blvd., Alexandria, Va., 22308.
Roosevelt (Calif.)	Gloria V. Caruthers, 800 4th St. SW., 20024.
Rosenthal (N.Y.)	Mary W. Davis, 3505 Inverness Dr., Chevy Chase, Md., 20015.
Rostenkowski (Ill.)	Clary Sochowski, 1721 House Office Bldg.
Roudebush (Ind.)	Max L. Friedersdorf, 3125 Elba Rd., Alexandria, Va.
Roush (Ind.)	William Stanton, 3830 Columbia Pike, Arlington, Va.
Roybal (Calif.)	Clara Ignatius, 140 House Office Bldg.
Rumsfeld (Ill.)	Barbara A. Ludden, 21 Dakota Ct., Alexandria, Va., 22312.
Ryan (N.Y.)	Erika Teutsch, 1517 House Office Bldg.
St Germain (R.I.)	Ruth H. Bamber, 3714 Camden St. SE., 20020.
St. Onge (Conn.)	Murray Frank, 7810 16th St., 20012.
Satterfield (Va.)	Andrew H. McCutcheon, 18 West Grove Dr., Alexandria, Va., 22307.
Saylor (Pa.)	O. Ann Dunbar, 132 Duddington Pl. SE., 20003.
Scheuer (N.Y.)	Richard Brown, 1924 Belmont Rd.
Schisler (Ill.)	Craig E. Lovitt.
Schmidhauser (Iowa)	Janet Peters, 2801 Quebec St., 20008.
Schneebeli (Pa.)	Virginia Ford, 2817 24th St. North, Arlington, Va.
Schweiker (Pa.)	David Newhall III, 521 7th St. SE., 20003.
Scott (N.C.)	Harold W. Thomerson, 3729 Carpenter St. SE.
Secrest (Ohio)	---
Selden (Ala.)	Thomas M. Gilbert, 220 C St. SE.
Senner (Ariz.)	Larry B. Marton, 1019 Byrd Dr., Fairfax, Va.
Shipley (Ill.)	Goldie Mae Patterson, 510 Adelman Circle, Vienna, Va.
Shriver (Kans.)	Lester Rosen, 7 Fulham Ct., Silver Spring, Md.
Sickles (Md.)	Ted Venetoulis, 4201 Cathedral Ave.
Sikes (Fla.)	Alma D. Butler, 2802 Devonshire Pl., 20008.
Sisk (Calif.)	Jackson T. Carle, 129 E St. SE., 20003.
Skubitz (Kans.)	Garnette Jones, 2033 38th St. SE.
Slack (W. Va.)	Paul H. Becker, 1001 3d St. SW.
Smith (Calif.)	Irene Finnerty, 1406 House Office Bldg.
Smith (Iowa)	Clifton Larson.
Smith (N.Y.)	Russell A. Rourke, RFD 2, Amberley, Annapolis, Md.
Smith (Va.)	Calvin Haley, 2409 Fort Scott Dr., Arlington, Va.
Springer (Ill.)	Helen M. Dubino, 803 Independence Ave. SE.
Stafford (Vt.)	Neal J. Houston, 312 Cameron Rd., Alexandria, Va.
Staggers (W. Va.)	Marguerite Furfari, 1421 Massachusetts Ave.
Stalbaum (Wis.)	Joseph J. Jacoby, 2309 Ross Rd., Silver Spring, Md.
Stanton (Ohio)	Shirlee Enders McGloon, 4510 Amherst La., Bethesda, Md., 20014.
Steed (Okla.)	Truman Richardson, 2037 North Kensington, Arlington, Va.
Stephens (Ga.)	David Mayne Elder, 1201 South Courthouse Rd., Arlington, Va.
Stratton (N.Y.)	Virginia Gunther, 5028 25th Pl., Hillcrest Heights, Md., 20031.
Stubblefield (Ky.)	Morton Langstaff, 400 North View Ter., Alexandria, Va.
Sullivan (Mo.)	Roselyn Kenny, 1914 Connecticut Ave., 20009.
Sweeney (Ohio)	Robert J. O'Malley.

LIST OF REPRESENTATIVES AND SECRETARIES—Continued

Representative	Secretary
Talcott (Calif.)	Bernice Donahue, 110 D St. SE., 20003.
Taylor (N.C.)	Luther Shaw, 3513 North Delaware St., Arlington, Va.
Teague (Calif.)	Montgomery K. Winkler, 3220 44th St., 20016.
Teague (Tex.)	George W. Fisher, 10403 Royalton Ter., Silver Spring, Md.
Tenzer (N.Y.)	Michael D. Bromberg, 1812 Metzerott Rd., Adelphi, Md.
Thomas (Tex.)	Rose Zamaria, 7724 Backlick Rd., Springfield, Va., 22150.
Thompson (La.)	Frances A. Forgy, 4165 Southern Ave. SE., 20020.
Thompson (N.J.)	Charlotte Eldredge Bouton, 2857 Monroe St. NE.
Thompson (Tex.)	Robert H. Miller, 6607 Northan Rd., 20031.
Thomson (Wis.)	---
Todd (Mich.)	Philip H. Power, 1611 21st St., 20009.
Toll (Pa.)	Nancy Nelson, 1428 House Office Bldg.
Trimble (Ark.)	Mary McGill, 5413 Border Dr. SE., 20022.
Tuck (Va.)	V. C. Pat Jones, Centreville, Va., 22020.
Tunney (Calif.)	David A. Tunno, 1910 Brad St., Falls Church, Va.
Tupper (Maine)	Henry R. Albert, 2511 Keating St. SE., 20031.
Tuten (Ga.)	Louise W. Tate, 3423 Valley Dr., Alexandria, Va., 22302.
Udall (Ariz.)	Richard C. Olson, 4205 Mt. Pleasant Dr., McLean, Va.
Ullman (Oreg.)	Ron Ahern, 20 Maryland Ave. SE., 20028.
Utt (Calif.)	Marie E. Adams, 2712 Wisconsin Ave., 20007.
Van Deerlin (Calif.)	Margaret W. Moore, 800 4th St. SW., 20024.
Vanik (Ohio)	Mark E. Talisman, 408 A St. NE., 20003.
Vigorito (Pa.)	Dolores C. McCartney, 5700 Mohican Pl., 20016.
Vivian (Mich.)	Michael J. Berla, 44 G St. SW., 20024.
Waggonner (La.)	David Kent, 1126 Ft. Hunt Rd., Alexandria, Va.
Walker (Miss.)	Patricia Hutchinson, 3937 Davis Pl., 20007.
Walker (N. Mex.)	Mary B. Boulware, 110 D St. SE., 20003.
Watkins (Pa.)	Sallie K. Weaver, 110 D St. SE., 20003.
Watts (Ky.)	Cora P. Bane.
Weltner (Ga.)	Wyche Fowler, Jr., 2823 Q St.
Whalley (Pa.)	Julia W. Kogut, 156 North Carolina Ave. SE., 20003.
White (Idaho)	John B. Tacke, 504 Mangum Pl., Alexandria, Va.
White (Tex.)	Conrey Bryson, 3207 Toledo Ter., Hyattsville, Md., 20782.
Whitener (N.C.)	Herbert M. Lineberger, 215 C St. SE.
Whitten (Miss.)	Ann T. Watson, 2707 North Nelson St., Arlington, Va., 22207.
Widnall (N.J.)	Martha Schubmehl, 3307 North Frederick St., Arlington, Va., 22200.
Williams (Miss.)	Charles H. Griffin, 3015 South Grant St., Arlington, Va., 22202.
Willis (La.)	James E. Guirard, Jr., 3725 Donnell Dr. SE., 20028.
Wilson, Bob (Calif.)	Edgar M. Gillenwaters, 2335 49th St.
Wilson, Charles H. (Calif.)	Norma Murphy, 2800 Quebec St., 20008.
Wolff (N.Y.)	Evelyn K. Carson, 9511 Pin Oak Dr., Silver Spring, Md., 20910.
Wright (Tex.)	Marshall Lynam, 909 North Ivy St., Arlington, Va.
Wyatt (Oreg.)	L. Stanley Kemp, 1030 House Office Bldg.
Wydler (N.Y.)	Elizabeth D. Hoppel, 3620 16th St.
Yates (Ill.)	Janet Schnitz, 2480 16th St., 20009.

LIST OF REPRESENTATIVES AND SECRETARIES—Continued

Representative	Secretary
Young (Tex.) _____	Harry McAdams, 4012 Whispering La., Sleepy Hollow Run, Annandale, Va.
Younger (Calif.) _____	Shirley Jones, 3725 Macomb St., 20016.
Zablocki (Wis.) _____	John H. Sullivan, 1850 Columbia Pike, Arlington, Va.

RESIDENT COMMISSIONER

Polanco-Abreu (P.R.) _____	Orville Watkins, House Office Bldg.

STATISTICAL INFORMATION

STATISTICAL

SESSIONS OF CONGRESS

Congress	Session	Date of beginning	Date of adjournment	Length in days	President pro tempore of the Senate [1]	Speaker of the House of Representatives
1st	1	Mar. 4, 1789 [2]	Sept. 29, 1789	210	John Langdon,[3] of New Hampshire.	Frederick A. C. Muhlenberg, of Pennsylvania.
	2	Jan. 4, 1790	Aug. 12, 1790	221		
	3	Dec. 6, 1790	Mar. 3, 1791	88		
2d	1	Oct. 24, 1791	May 8, 1792	197	Richard Henry Lee, of Virginia.	Jonathan Trumbull, of Connecticut.
	2	Nov. 5, 1792	Mar. 2, 1793	119	John Langdon, of New Hampshire.	
3d	1	Dec. 2, 1793	June 9, 1794	190	...do...	Frederick A. C. Muhlenberg, of Pennsylvania.
	2	Nov. 3, 1794	Mar. 3, 1795	121	Ralph Izard, of South Carolina. Henry Tazewell, of Virginia.	
4th	1	Dec. 7, 1795	June 1, 1796	177	...do...	Jonathan Dayton, of New Jersey.
	2	Dec. 5, 1796	Mar. 3, 1797	89	Samuel Livermore, of New Hampshire. William Bingham, of Pennsylvania.	
5th	1	May 15, 1797	July 10, 1797	57	William Bradford, of Rhode Island.	Do.
	2	Nov. 13, 1797	July 16, 1798	246	Jacob Read, of South Carolina.	George Dent, of Maryland.[4]
	3	Dec. 3, 1798	Mar. 3, 1799	91	Theodore Sedgwick, of Massachusetts. John Laurence, of New York. James Ross, of Pennsylvania.	
6th	1	Dec. 2, 1799	May 14, 1800	164	Samuel Livermore, of New Hampshire. Uriah Tracy, of Connecticut.	Theodore Sedgwick, of Massachusetts.
	2	Nov. 17, 1800	Mar. 3, 1801	107	John E. Howard, of Maryland. James Hillhouse, of Connecticut.	
7th	1	Dec. 7, 1801	May 3, 1802	148	Abraham Baldwin, of Georgia.	Nathaniel Macon, of North Carolina.
	2	Dec. 6, 1802	Mar. 3, 1803	88	Stephen R. Bradley, of Vermont.	
8th	1	Oct. 17, 1803	Mar. 27, 1804	163	John Brown, of Kentucky. Jesse Franklin, of North Carolina.	Do.
	2	Nov. 5, 1804	Mar. 3, 1805	119	Joseph Anderson, of Tennessee.	
9th	1	Dec. 2, 1805	Apr. 21, 1806	141	Samuel Smith, of Maryland.	Do.
	2	Dec. 1, 1806	Mar. 3, 1807	93	...do...	

[1] Until within recent years the appointment or election of a President pro tempore was held by the Senate to be for the occasion only, so that more than one appears in several sessions and in others none was chosen. Since Mar. 12, 1890, they have served until "the Senate otherwise ordered."

[2] The Constitution (art. I, sec. 4) provided that "The Congress shall assemble at least once in every year * * * on the first Monday in December, unless they shall by law appoint a different day." Pursuant to a resolution of the Continental Congress, the first session of the First Congress convened Mar. 4, 1789. Up to and including May 20, 1820, 18 acts were passed providing for the meeting of Congress on other days in the year. Since that year Congress met regularly on the first Monday in December until 1934, when the twentieth amendment to the Constitution became effective, changing the meeting of Congress to Jan. 3. The first and second sessions of the First Congress were held in New York City; subsequently, including the first session of the Sixth Congress, Philadelphia was the meeting place; since then Congress has convened in Washington.

[3] Elected to count the vote for President and Vice President, which was done Apr. 6, 1789, a quorum of the Senate then appearing for the first time. John Adams, Vice President, appeared Apr. 21, 1789, and took his seat as President of the Senate.

[4] Elected Speaker pro tempore for Apr. 20, 1798, and again for May 28, 1798.

SESSIONS OF CONGRESS—Continued

Congress	Session	Date of beginning	Date of adjournment	Length in days	President pro tempore of the Senate	Speaker of the House of Representatives
10th	1	Oct. 26, 1807	Apr. 25, 1808	182	Samuel Smith, of Maryland.	Joseph B. Varnum, of Massachusetts.
	2	Nov. 7, 1808	Mar. 3, 1809	117	Stephen R. Bradley, of Vermont. John Milledge, of Georgia.	
11th	1	May 22, 1809	June 28, 1809	38	Andrew Gregg, of Pennsylvania.	Do.
	2	Nov. 27, 1809	May 1, 1810	156	John Gaillard, of South Carolina.	
	3	Dec. 3, 1810	Mar. 3, 1811	91	John Pope, of Kentucky.	
12th	1	Nov. 4, 1811	July 6, 1812	245	William H. Crawford, of Georgia.	Henry Clay, of Kentucky.
	2	Nov. 2, 1812	Mar. 3, 1813	122	----do-----------------	
13th	1	May 24, 1813	Aug. 2, 1813	71	----do-----------------	Do.
	2	Dec. 6, 1813	Apr. 18, 1814	134	Joseph B. Varnum, of Massachusetts.	
	3	Sept. 19, 1814	Mar. 3, 1815	166	John Gaillard, of South Carolina.	Langdon Cheves,[5] of South Carolina.
14th	1	Dec. 4, 1815	Apr. 29, 1816	148	----do-----------------	Henry Clay, of Kentucky.
	2	Dec. 2, 1816	Mar. 3, 1817	92	----do-----------------	
15th	1	Dec. 1, 1817	Apr. 20, 1818	141	----do-----------------	Do.
	2	Nov. 16, 1818	Mar. 3, 1819	108	James Barbour, of Virginia.	
16th	1	Dec. 6, 1819	May 15, 1820	162	John Gaillard, of South Carolina.	Do.
	2	Nov. 13, 1820	Mar. 3, 1821	111	----do-----------------	John W. Taylor,[6] of New York.
17th	1	Dec. 3, 1821	May 8, 1822	157	----do-----------------	Philip P. Barbour, of Virginia.
	2	Dec. 2, 1822	Mar. 3, 1823	92	----do-----------------	
18th	1	Dec. 1, 1823	May 27, 1824	178	----do-----------------	Henry Clay, of Kentucky.
	2	Dec. 6, 1824	Mar. 3, 1825	88	----do-----------------	
19th	1	Dec. 5, 1825	May 22, 1826	169	Nathaniel Macon, of North Carolina.	John W. Taylor, of New York.
	2	Dec. 4, 1826	Mar. 3, 1827	90	----do-----------------	
20th	1	Dec. 3, 1827	May 26, 1828	175	Samuel Smith, of Maryland.	Andrew Stevenson, of Virginia.
	2	Dec. 1, 1828	Mar. 3, 1829	93	----do-----------------	
21st	1	Dec. 7, 1829	May 31, 1830	176	----do-----------------	Do.
	2	Dec. 6, 1830	Mar. 3, 1831	88	Littleton Waller Tazewell, of Virginia.	
22d	1	Dec. 5, 1831	July 16, 1832	225	----do-----------------	Do.
	2	Dec. 3, 1832	Mar. 2, 1833	91	Hugh Lawson White, of Tennessee.	
23d	1	Dec. 2, 1833	June 30, 1834	211	George Poindexter, of Mississippi.	Do.
	2	Dec. 1, 1834	Mar. 3, 1835	93	John Tyler, of Virginia.	John Bell,[7] of Tennessee.
24th	1	Dec. 7, 1835	July 4, 1836	211	William R. King, of Alabama.	James K. Polk, of Tennessee.
	2	Dec. 5, 1836	Mar. 3, 1837	89	----do-----------------	
25th	1	Sept. 4, 1837	Oct. 16, 1837	43	----do-----------------	Do.
	2	Dec. 4, 1837	July 9, 1838	218	----do-----------------	
	3	Dec. 3, 1838	Mar. 3, 1839	91	----do-----------------	
26th	1	Dec. 2, 1839	July 21, 1840	233	----do-----------------	Robert M. T. Hunter, of Virginia.
	2	Dec. 7, 1840	Mar. 3, 1841	87		
27th	1	May 31, 1841	Sept. 13, 1841	106	Samuel L. Southard, of New Jersey.	John White, of Kentucky.
	2	Dec. 6, 1841	Aug. 31, 1842	269	Willie P. Mangum, of North Carolina.	
	3	Dec. 5, 1842	Mar. 3, 1843	89	----do-----------------	
28th	1	Dec. 4, 1843	June 17, 1844	196	----do-----------------	John W. Jones, of Virginia.
	2	Dec. 2, 1844	Mar. 3, 1845	92	----do-----------------	
29th	1	Dec. 1, 1845	Aug. 10, 1846	253	David R. Atchison, of Missouri.	John W. Davis, of Indiana.
	2	Dec. 7, 1846	Mar. 3, 1847	87	----do-----------------	
30th	1	Dec. 6, 1847	Aug. 14, 1848	254	----do-----------------	Robert C. Winthrop, of Massachusetts.
	2	Dec. 4, 1848	Mar. 3, 1849	90	----do-----------------	
31st	1	Dec. 3, 1849	Sept. 30, 1850	302	William R. King, of Alabama.	Howell Cobb, of Georgia.
	2	Dec. 2, 1850	Mar. 3, 1851	92	----do-----------------	

[5] Elected Speaker Jan. 19, 1814, vice Henry Clay, who resigned Jan. 19, 1814.
[6] Elected Speaker Nov. 15, 1820, vice Henry Clay, who resigned Oct. 28, 1820.
[7] Elected Speaker June 2, 1834, vice Andrew Stevenson, of Virginia, resigned.

SESSIONS OF CONGRESS—Continued

Congress	Session	Date of beginning	Date of adjournment	Length in days	President pro tempore of the Senate	Speaker of the House of Representatives
32d	1	Dec. 1, 1851	Aug. 31, 1852	275	William R. King, of Alabama.	Linn Boyd, of Kentucky.
	2	Dec. 6, 1852	Mar. 3, 1853	88	David R. Atchison, of Missouri.	Do.
33d	1	Dec. 5, 1853	Aug. 7, 1854	246	----do----	
	2	Dec. 4, 1854	Mar. 3, 1855	90	Jesse D. Bright, of Indiana. Lewis Cass, of Michigan.	
34th	1	Dec. 3, 1855	Aug. 18, 1856	260	Jesse D. Bright, of Indiana.	Nathaniel P. Banks, of Massachusetts.
	2	Aug. 21, 1856	Aug. 30, 1856	10	----do----	
	3	Dec. 1, 1856	Mar. 3, 1857	93	James M. Mason, of Virginia. Thomas J. Rusk, of Texas.	
35th	1	Dec. 7, 1857	June 14, 1858	189	Benjamin Fitzpatrick, of Alabama.	James L. Orr, of South Carolina.
	2	Dec. 6, 1858	Mar. 3, 1859	88	----do----	
36th	1	Dec. 5, 1859	June 25, 1860	202	(blank) Jesse D. Bright, of Indiana.	William Pennington, of New Jersey.
	2	Dec. 3, 1860	Mar. 3, 1861	93	Solomon Foot, of Vermont.	
37th	1	July 4, 1861	Aug. 6, 1861	34	----do----	Galusha A. Grow, of Pennsylvania.
	2	Dec. 2, 1861	July 17, 1862	228	----do----	
	3	Dec. 1, 1862	Mar. 3, 1863	93	----do----	
38th	1	Dec. 7, 1863	July 4, 1864	209	----do---- Daniel Clark, of New Hampshire.	Schuyler Colfax, of Indiana.
	2	Dec. 5, 1864	Mar. 3, 1865	89	----do----	
39th	1	Dec. 4, 1865	July 28, 1866	237	Lafayette S. Foster, of Connecticut.	Do.
	2	Dec. 3, 1866	Mar. 3, 1867	91	Benjamin F. Wade, of Ohio.	Do.
40th	1	Mar. 4, 1867[8]	Dec. 2, 1867	274	----do----	Do.
	2	Dec. 2, 1867[9]	Nov. 10, 1868	345	----do----	
	3	Dec. 7, 1868	Mar. 3, 1869	87	----do----	Theodore M. Pomeroy,[10] of New York.
41st	1	Mar. 4, 1869	Apr. 10, 1869	38	Henry B. Anthony, of Rhode Island.	James G. Blaine, of Maine.
	2	Dec. 6, 1869	July 15, 1870	222	----do----	
	3	Dec. 5, 1870	Mar. 3, 1871	89	----do----	
42d	1	Mar. 4, 1871	Apr. 20, 1871	48	----do----	Do.
	2	Dec. 4, 1871	June 10, 1872	190	----do----	
	3	Dec. 2, 1872	Mar. 3, 1873	92	----do----	
43d	1	Dec. 1, 1873	June 23, 1874	204	Matthew H. Carpenter, of Wisconsin.	Do.
	2	Dec. 7, 1874	Mar. 3, 1875	87	----do---- Henry B. Anthony, of Rhode Island.	
44th	1	Dec. 6, 1875	Aug. 15, 1876	254	Thomas W. Ferry, of Michigan.	Michael C. Kerr,[11] of Indiana. Samuel S. Cox,[12] of New York, pro tempore. Milton Sayler,[13] of Ohio, pro tempore.
	2	Dec. 4, 1876	Mar. 3, 1877	90	----do----	Samuel J. Randall, of Pennsylvania.
45th	1	Oct. 15, 1877	Dec. 3, 1877	50	----do----	Do.
	2	Dec. 3, 1877	June 20, 1878	200	----do----	
	3	Dec. 2, 1878	Mar. 3, 1879	92	----do----	
46th	1	Mar. 18, 1879	July 1, 1879	106	Allen G. Thurman, of Ohio.	Do.
	2	Dec. 1, 1879	June 16, 1880	199	----do----	
	3	Dec. 6, 1880	Mar. 3, 1881	88	----do----	

[8] There were recesses in this session from Saturday, Mar. 30, to Wednesday, July 1, and from Saturday, July 20, to Thursday, Nov. 21.

[9] There were recesses in this session from Monday, July 27, to Monday, Sept. 21, to Friday, Oct. 6, and to Tuesday, Nov. 10. No business was transacted subsequent to July 27.

[10] Elected Speaker Mar. 3, 1869, and served 1 day.

[11] Died Aug. 19, 1876.

[12] Appointed Speaker pro tempore Feb. 17, May 12, June 19.

[13] Appointed Speaker pro tempore June 4.

SESSIONS OF CONGRESS—Continued

Congress	Session	Date of beginning	Date of adjournment	Length in days	President pro tempore of the Senate	Speaker of the House of Representatives
47th	1	Dec. 5, 1881	Aug. 8, 1882	247	Thomas F. Bayard, of Delaware. David Davis, of Illinois.	J. Warren Keifer, of Ohio.
	2	Dec. 4, 1882	Mar. 3, 1883	90	George F. Edmunds, of Vermont.	
48th	1	Dec. 3, 1883	July 7, 1884	218	----do----	John G. Carlisle, of Kentucky.
	2	Dec. 1, 1884	Mar. 3, 1885	93	----do----	
49th	1	Dec. 7, 1885	Aug. 5, 1886	242	John Sherman, of Ohio	Do.
	2	Dec. 6, 1886	Mar. 3, 1887	88	John J. Ingalls, of Kansas.	
50th	1	Dec. 5, 1887	Oct. 20, 1888	321	----do----	Do.
	2	Dec. 3, 1888	Mar. 3, 1889	91	----do----	
51st	1	Dec. 2, 1889	Oct. 1, 1890	304	----do----	Thomas B. Reed, of Maine.
	2	Dec. 1, 1890	Mar. 3, 1891	93	Charles F. Manderson, of Nebraska.	
52d	1	Dec. 7, 1891	Aug. 5, 1892	251	----do----	Charles F. Crisp, of Georgia.
	2	Dec. 5, 1892	Mar. 3, 1893	89	Isham G. Harris, of Tennessee.	
53d	1	Aug. 7, 1893	Nov. 3, 1893	89	----do----	Do.
	2	Dec. 4, 1893	Aug. 28, 1894	268	----do----	
	3	Dec. 3, 1894	Mar. 3, 1895	97	Matt W. Ransom, of North Carolina. Isham G. Harris, of Tennessee.	
54th	1	Dec. 2, 1895	June 11, 1896	193	William P. Frye, of Maine.	Thomas B. Reed, of Maine.
	2	Dec. 7, 1896	Mar. 3, 1897	87	----do----	
55th	1	Mar. 15, 1897	July 24, 1897	131	----do----	Do.
	2	Dec. 6, 1897	July 8, 1898	215	----do----	
	3	Dec. 5, 1898	Mar. 3, 1899	89	----do----	
56th	1	Dec. 4, 1899	June 7, 1900	186	----do----	David B. Henderson, of Iowa.
	2	Dec. 3, 1900	Mar. 3, 1901	91	----do----	
57th	1	Dec. 2, 1901	July 1, 1902	212	----do----	Do.
	2	Dec. 1, 1902	Mar. 3, 1903	93	----do----	
58th	1	Nov. 9, 1903	Dec. 7, 1903	29	----do----	Joseph G. Cannon, of Illinois.
	2	Dec. 7, 1903	Apr. 28, 1904	144	----do----	
	3	Dec. 5, 1904	Mar. 3, 1905	89	----do----	
59th	1	Dec. 4, 1905	June 30, 1906	209	----do----	Do.
	2	Dec. 3, 1906	Mar. 3, 1907	91	----do----	
60th	1	Dec. 2, 1907	May 30, 1908	181	----do----	Do.
	2	Dec. 7, 1908	Mar. 3, 1909	87	----do----	
61st	1	Mar. 15, 1909	Aug. 5, 1909	144	----do----	Do.
	2	Dec. 6, 1909	June 25, 1910	202	----do----	
	3	Dec. 5, 1910	Mar. 3, 1911	89	----do----	
62d	1	Apr. 4, 1911	Aug. 22, 1911	141	----do.[14]----	Champ Clark, of Missouri.
	2	Dec. 4, 1911	Aug. 26, 1912	267	Bacon,[15] Brandegee,[16] Curtis,[17] Gallinger,[18] Lodge.[19]	
	3	Dec. 2, 1912	Mar. 3, 1913	92	Bacon,[20] Gallinger,[21]	
63d	1	Apr. 7, 1913	Dec. 1, 1913	239	James P. Clarke, of Arkansas.	Do.
	2	Dec. 1, 1913	Oct. 24, 1914	328	----do----	
	3	Dec. 7, 1914	Mar. 3, 1915	87	----do----	
64th	1	Dec. 6, 1915	Sept. 8, 1916	278	----do.[22]----	Do.
	2	Dec. 4, 1916	Mar. 3, 1917	90	Willard Saulsbury, of Delaware.	
65th	1	Apr. 2, 1917	Oct. 6, 1917	188	----do----	Do.
	2	Dec. 3, 1917	Nov. 21, 1918	354	----do----	
	3	Dec. 2, 1918	Mar. 3, 1919	92	----do----	
66th	1	May 19, 1919	Nov. 19, 1919	185	Albert B. Cummins, of Iowa.	Frederick H. Gillett, of Massachusetts.
	2	Dec. 1, 1919	June 5, 1920	188	----do----	
	3	Dec. 6, 1920	Mar. 3, 1921	88	----do----	
67th	1	Apr. 11, 1921	Nov. 23, 1921	227	----do----	Do.
	2	Dec. 5, 1921	Sept. 22, 1922	292	----do----	
	3	Nov. 20, 1922	Dec. 4, 1922	15	----do----	
	4	Dec. 4, 1922	Mar. 3, 1923	90	----do----	

[14] Resigned as President pro tempore Apr. 27, 1911.
[15] Elected to serve Jan. 11-17, Mar. 11-12, Apr. 8, May 10, May 30 to June 1 and 3, June 13 to July 5, Aug. 1-10, and Aug. 27 to Dec. 15, 1912.
[16] Elected to serve May 25, 1912.
[17] Elected to serve Dec. 4-12, 1911.
[18] Elected to serve Feb. 12-14, Apr. 26-27, May 7, July 6-31, Aug. 12-26, 1912.
[19] Elected to serve Mar. 25-26, 1912.
[20] Elected to serve Aug. 27 to Dec. 15, 1912, Jan. 5-18, and Feb. 2-15, 1913.
[21] Elected to serve Dec. 16, 1912, to Jan. 4, 1913, Jan. 19 to Feb. 1, and Feb. 16 to Mar. 3, 1913.
[22] Died Oct. 1, 1916.

SESSIONS OF CONGRESS—Continued

Congress	Session	Date of beginning	Date of adjournment	Length in days	President pro tempore of the Senate	Speaker of the House of Representatives
68th	1	Dec. 3, 1923	June 7, 1924	188	Albert B. Cummins, of Iowa.	Frederick H. Gillett, of Massachusetts.
	2	Dec. 1, 1924	Mar. 3, 1925	93	_____do_____	
69th	1	Dec. 7, 1925	July 3, 1926	209	George H. Moses, of New Hampshire.	Nicholas Longworth, of Ohio.
	2	Dec. 6, 1926	Mar. 3, 1927	88	_____do_____	
70th	1	Dec. 5, 1927	May 29, 1928	177	_____do_____	Do.
	2	Dec. 3, 1928	Mar. 3, 1929	91	_____do_____	
71st	1	Apr. 15, 1929	Nov. 22, 1929	222	_____do_____	Do.
	2	Dec. 2, 1929	July 3, 1930	214	_____do_____	
	3	Dec. 1, 1930	Mar. 3, 1931	93	_____do_____	
72d	1	Dec. 7, 1931	July 16, 1932	223	_____do_____	John N. Garner, of Texas.
	2	Dec. 5, 1932	Mar. 3, 1933	89	_____do_____	
73d	1	Mar. 9, 1933	June 15, 1933	99	Key Pittman, of Nevada.	Henry T. Rainey,[23] of Illinois.
	2	Jan. 3, 1934	June 18, 1934	167	_____do_____	
74th	1	Jan. 3, 1935	Aug. 26, 1935	236	_____do_____	Joseph W. Byrns,[24] of Tennessee.
	2	Jan. 3, 1936	June 20, 1936	170	_____do_____	William B. Bankhead,[25] of Alabama.
75th	1	Jan. 5, 1937	Aug. 21, 1937	229	_____do_____	Do.
	2	Nov. 15, 1937	Dec. 21, 1937	37	_____do_____	
	3	Jan. 3, 1938	June 16, 1938	165	_____do_____	
76th	1	Jan. 3, 1939	Aug. 5, 1939	215	_____do_____	Do.[26]
	2	Sept. 21, 1939	Nov. 3, 1939	44	_____do_____	
	3	Jan. 3, 1940	Jan. 3, 1941	366	_____do.[27]	Sam Rayburn,[28] of Texas.
77th	1	Jan. 3, 1941	Jan. 2, 1942	365	William H. King,[29] of Utah. Pat Harrison,[30] of Mississippi; Carter Glass,[31] of Virginia.	Do.
	2	Jan. 5, 1942	Dec. 16, 1942	346	Carter Glass, of Virginia.	
78th	1	Jan. 6, 1943[32]	Dec. 21, 1943	350	_____do_____	Do.
	2	Jan. 10, 1944[33]	Dec. 19, 1944	345	_____do_____	
79th	1	Jan. 3, 1945[34]	Dec. 21, 1945	353	Kenneth McKellar, of Tennessee.	Do.
	2	Jan. 14, 1946[35]	Aug. 2, 1946	201	_____do_____	
80th	1	Jan. 3, 1947[36]	Dec. 19, 1947	351	Arthur H. Vandenberg, of Michigan.	Joseph W. Martin, Jr., of Massachusetts.
	2	Jan. 6, 1948[37]	Dec. 31, 1948	361	_____do_____	
81st	1	Jan. 3, 1949	Oct. 19, 1949	290	Kenneth McKellar, of Tennessee.	Sam Rayburn, of Texas.
	2	Jan. 3, 1950[38]	Jan. 2, 1951	365	_____do_____	
82d	1	Jan. 3, 1951[39]	Oct. 20, 1951	291	_____do_____	Do.
	2	Jan. 8, 1952[40]	July 7, 1952	182	_____do_____	

[23] Died Aug. 19, 1934.
[24] Died June 4, 1936.
[25] Elected June 4, 1936.
[26] Died Sept. 15, 1940.
[27] Died Nov. 10, 1940.
[28] Elected Sept. 16, 1940.
[29] Elected Nov. 19, 1940.
[30] Elected Jan. 6, 1941; died June 22, 1941.
[31] Elected July 10, 1941.
[32] There was a recess in this session from Thursday, July 8, to Tuesday, Sept. 14.
[33] There were recesses in this session from Saturday, Apr. 1, to Wednesday, Apr. 12; from Friday, June 23, to Tuesday, Aug. 1; and from Thursday, Sept. 21, to Tuesday, Nov. 14.
[34] The House was in recess in this session from Saturday, July 21, 1945, to Wednesday, Sept. 5, 1945, and the Senate from Wednesday, Aug. 1, 1945, to Wednesday, Sept. 5, 1945.
[35] The House was in recess in this session from Thursday, Apr. 18, 1946, to Tuesday, Apr. 30, 1946.
[36] There was a recess in this session from Sunday, July 27, 1947, to Monday, Nov. 17, 1947.
[37] There were recesses in this session from Sunday, June 20, 1948, to Monday, July 26, 1948, and from Saturday, Aug. 7, 1948, to Friday, Dec. 31, 1948.
[38] The House was in recess in this session from Thursday, Apr. 6, 1950, to Tuesday, Apr. 18, 1950, and both the Senate and the House were in recess from Saturday, Sept. 23, 1950, to Monday, Nov. 27, 1950.
[39] The House was in recess in this session from Thursday, Mar. 22, 1951, to Monday, Apr. 2, 1951, and from Thursday, Aug. 23, 1951, to Wednesday, Sept. 12, 1951.
[40] The House was in recess in this session from Thursday, Apr. 10, 1952, to Tuesday, Apr. 22, 1952.

SESSIONS OF CONGRESS—Continued

Congress	Session	Date of beginning	Date of adjournment	Length in days	President pro tempore of the Senate	Speaker of the House of Representatives
83d_____	1	Jan. 3, 1953[41]	Aug. 3, 1953	213	Styles Bridges, of New Hampshire.	Joseph W. Martin, Jr., of Massachusetts.
	2	Jan. 6, 1954[42]	Dec. 2, 1954	331	_____do_____	
84th_____	1	Jan. 5, 1955[43]	Aug. 2, 1955	210	Walter F. George, of Georgia.	Sam Rayburn, of Texas.
	2	Jan. 3, 1956[44]	July 27, 1956	207	_____do_____	
85th_____	1	Jan. 3, 1957[45]	Aug. 30, 1957	239	Carl Hayden, of Arizona.	Do.
	2	Jan. 7, 1958[46]	Aug. 24, 1958	230	_____do_____	
86th_____	1	Jan. 7, 1959[47]	Sept. 15, 1959	252	_____do_____	Do.
	2	Jan. 6, 1960[48]	Sept. 1, 1960	240	_____do_____	
87th_____	1	Jan. 3, 1961[49]	Sept. 27, 1961	268	_____do_____	Do. [50]
	2	Jan. 10, 1962[51]	Oct. 13, 1962	277	_____do_____	John W. McCormack,[52] of Massachusetts.
88th_____	1	Jan. 9, 1963[53]	Dec. 30, 1963	356	_____do_____	Do.
	2	Jan. 7, 1964[54]	Oct. 3, 1964	270	_____do_____	Do.
89th_____	1	Jan. 4, 1965	_____	_____	_____do_____	Do.

[41] The House was in recess in this session from Thursday, Apr. 2, 1953, to Monday, Apr. 13, 1953.

[42] The House was in recess in this session from Thursday, Apr. 15, 1954, to Monday, Apr. 26, 1954, and adjourned sine die Aug. 20, 1954. The Senate was in recess in this session from Friday, Aug. 20, 1954, to Monday, Nov. 8, 1954; from Thursday, Nov. 18, 1954, to Monday, Nov. 29, 1954, and adjourned sine die December 2, 1954.

[43] There was a recess in this session from Monday, Apr. 4, 1955, to Wednesday, Apr. 13, 1955.

[44] There was a recess in this session from Thursday, Mar. 29, 1956, to Monday, April 9, 1956.

[45] There was a recess in this session from Thursday, Apr. 18, 1957, to Monday, Apr. 29, 1957.

[46] There was a recess in this session from Thursday, Apr. 3, 1958, to Monday, Apr. 14, 1958.

[47] There was a recess in this session from Thursday, Mar. 26, 1959, to Tuesday, Apr. 7, 1959.

[48] The Senate was in recess in this session from Thursday, Apr. 14, 1960, to Monday, Apr. 18, 1960; from Friday, May 27, 1960, to Tuesday, May 31, 1960, and from Sunday, July 3, 1960, to Monday, Aug. 8, 1960. The House was in recess in this session from Thursday, Apr. 14, 1960, to Monday, Apr. 18, 1960; from Friday, May 27, 1960, to Tuesday, May 31, 1960, and from Sunday July 3, 1960, to Monday, Aug. 15, 1960.

[49] The House was in recess in this session from Thursday, Mar. 30, 1961, to Monday, Apr. 10, 1961.

[50] Died November 16, 1961.

[51] The House was in recess in this session from Thursday, Apr. 19, 1962, to Monday, Apr. 30, 1962.

[52] Elected Jan. 10, 1962.

[53] The House was in recess in this session from Thursday, Apr. 11, 1963, to Monday, Apr. 22, 1963.

[54] The House was in recess in this session from Thursday, Mar. 26, 1964, to Monday, Apr. 6, 1964; from Thursday, July 2, 1964, to Monday, July 20, 1964; from Friday, Aug. 21, 1964, to Monday, Aug. 31, 1964. The Senate was in recess in this session from Friday, July 10, 1964, to Monday, July 20, 1964; from Friday Aug. 1, 1964, to Monday, Aug. 31, 1964.

SPECIAL SESSIONS OF THE SENATE

Year	Date of beginning	Date of adjournment
1791	Friday, Mar. 4	Friday, Mar. 4.
1793	Monday, Mar. 4	Monday, Mar. 4.
1795	Monday, June 8	Friday, June 26.
1797	Saturday, Mar. 4	Saturday, Mar. 4.
1798	Tuesday, July 17	Thursday, July 19.
1801	Wednesday, Mar. 4	Thursday, Mar. 5.
1805	Tuesday, Mar. 4	Thursday, Mar. 6.
1809	Saturday, Mar. 4	Tuesday, Mar. 7.
1817	Monday, Mar. 4	Monday, Mar. 4.
1825	Friday, Mar. 4	Wednesday, Mar. 9.
1829	Wednesday, Mar. 4	Tuesday, Mar. 17.
1837	Saturday, Mar. 4	Friday, Mar. 10.
1841	Thursday, Mar. 4	Monday, Mar. 15.
1845	Tuesday, Mar. 4	Thursday, Mar. 20.
1849	Monday, Mar. 5	Friday, Mar. 23.
1851	Tuesday, Mar. 4	Thursday, Mar. 13.
1853	Friday, Mar. 4	Monday, Apr. 11.
1857	Wednesday, Mar. 4	Saturday, Mar. 14.
1858	Tuesday, June 15	Wednesday, June 16.
1859	Friday, Mar. 4	Thursday, Mar. 10.
1860	Tuesday, June 26	Thursday, June 28.
1861	Monday, Mar. 4	Thursday, Mar. 28.
1863	Wednesday, Mar. 4	Saturday, Mar. 14.
1865	Saturday, Mar. 4	Saturday, Mar. 11.
1867	Monday, Apr. 1	Saturday, Apr. 20.
1869	Monday, Apr. 12	Thursday, Apr. 22.
1871	Wednesday, May 10	Saturday, May 27.
1873	Tuesday, Mar. 4	Wednesday, Mar. 26.
1875	Friday, Mar. 5	Wednesday, Mar. 24.
1877	Monday, Mar. 5	Saturday, Mar. 17.
1881	{ Friday, Mar. 4 Monday, Oct. 10	Friday, May 20. Saturday, Oct. 29.
1885	Wednesday, Mar. 4	Thursday, Apr. 2.
1889	Monday, Mar. 4	Tuesday, Apr. 2.
1893	Saturday, Mar. 4	Friday, Apr. 15.
1897	Thursday, Mar. 4	Wednesday, Mar. 10.
1901	Monday, Mar. 4	Saturday, Mar. 9.
1903	Thursday, Mar. 5	Thursday, Mar. 19.
1905	Saturday, Mar. 4	Saturday, Mar. 18.
1909	Thursday, Mar. 4	Saturday, Mar. 6.
1913	Tuesday, Mar. 4	Monday, Mar. 17.
1917	Monday, Mar. 5	Friday, Mar. 16.
1921	Friday, Mar. 4	Tuesday, Mar. 15.
1925	Wednesday, Mar. 4	Wednesday, Mar. 18.
1929	Monday, Mar. 4	Tuesday, Mar. 5.
1930	Monday, July 7	Monday, July 21.
1933	Saturday, Mar. 4	Monday, Mar. 6.

COURT OF IMPEACHMENT

The Senate has sat as a Court of Impeachment in the cases of the following accused officials, with the result stated, for the periods named:

WILLIAM BLOUNT, a Senator of the United States from Tennessee; charges dismissed for want of jurisdiction: Monday, December 17, 1798, to Monday, January 14, 1799.

JOHN PICKERING, judge of the United States district court for the district of New Hampshire; removed from office; Thursday, March 3, 1803, to Monday, March 12, 1804.

SAMUEL CHASE, Associate Justice of the Supreme Court of the United States; acquitted; Friday, November 30, 1804, to March 1, 1805.

JAMES H. PECK, judge of the United States district court for the district of Missouri; acquitted; Monday, April 26, 1830, to Monday, January 31, 1831.

WEST H. HUMPHREYS, judge of the United States district court for the middle, eastern, and western districts of Tennessee; removed from office; Wednesday, May 7, 1862, to Thursday, June 26, 1862.

ANDREW JOHNSON, President of the United States; acquitted; Tuesday, February 25, 1868, to Tuesday, May 26, 1868.

WILLIAM W. BELKNAP, Secretary of War; acquitted; Friday, March 3, 1876, to Tuesday, August 1, 1876.

CHARLES SWAYNE, judge of the United States district court for the northern district of Florida; acquitted; Wednesday, December 14, 1904, to Monday, February 27, 1905.

ROBERT W. ARCHBALD, associate judge, United States Commerce Court; removed from office; Saturday, July 13, 1912, to Monday, January 13, 1913.

GEORGE W. ENGLISH, judge of the United States district court for the eastern district of Illinois; resigned office November 4, 1926; Court of Impeachment adjourned to December 13, 1926, when, on request of House managers, impeachment proceedings were dismissed.

HAROLD LOUDERBACK, judge of the United States district court for the northern district of California; acquitted; Monday, May 15, 1933, to Wednesday, May 24, 1933.

HALSTED L. RITTER, judge of the United States district court for the southern district of Florida; removed from office; Monday, April 6, 1936, to Friday, April 17, 1936.

VOTES CAST FOR SENATORS IN 1960, 1962, AND 1964

[The figures show the vote for the Democratic and Republican nominees, except as otherwise indicated. Compiled from official statistics]

State	1960 Democrat	1960 Republican	1962 Democrat	1962 Republican	1964 Democrat	1964 Republican	Total vote cast in 1964
Alabama	389,196	164,868	201,937	195,134			
Alaska	38,041	21,937	33,827	24,354			
Arizona			199,217	163,388	227,712	241,089	468,801
Arkansas	377,036		214,867	98,013			
California			2,452,839	3,180,483	3,411,912	3,628,555	[1] 7,041,821
Colorado	331,752	389,428	279,586	328,655			
Connecticut			527,522	501,694	781,008	426,939	[1] 1,208,163
Delaware	96,090	98,847			96,850	103,782	[1] 200,703
Florida			657,633	329,381	997,585	562,212	[1] 1,560,337
Georgia	576,140		306,250				
Hawaii			136,294	60,067	96,789	110,747	[1] 208,814
Idaho	139,448	152,648	{ [2] 126,398 / 141,657	{ [2] 131,279 / 117,129			
Illinois	2,530,943	2,093,846	1,748,007	1,961,202			
Indiana			905,491	894,547	1,128,505	941,519	[1] 2,076,963
Iowa	595,119	642,463	376,602	431,364			
Kansas	388,895	485,499	{ [2] 260,756 / 223,630	{ [2] 344,689 / 388,500			
Kentucky	444,830	644,087	387,440	432,648			
Louisiana	432,228	109,698	318,838	103,066			
Maine	159,809	256,890			253,511	127,040	380,551
Maryland			439,723	269,131	678,649	402,393	[1] 1,081,049
Massachusetts	1,050,725	1,358,556	1,162,611	787,669	1,716,907	587,663	[1] 2,312,028
Michigan	1,669,179	1,548,873			1,996,912	1,096,272	[1] 3,101,667
Minnesota	884,168	648,586			931,353	605,933	[1] 1,543,590
Mississippi	244,341	21,807			343,364		343,364
Missouri	999,656	880,576	666,929	555,330	1,186,666	596,377	1,783,043
Montana	140,331	136,281			180,643	99,367	280,010
Nebraska	245,807	352,748			217,605	345,772	[1] 563,401
Nevada			63,443	33,749	66,907	66,823	133,730
New Hampshire	114,024	173,521	{ [2] 117,612 / 90,444	{ [2] 107,199 / 134,035			
New Jersey					1,677,515	1,011,280	[1] 2,709,575
New Mexico	190,654	109,897			178,209	147,562	325,771
New York			2,289,323	3,272,417	[3] 3,823,749	3,104,056	[a] [1] 7,151,581
North Carolina	792,491	497,964	491,520	321,635			
North Dakota			88,032	135,705	149,264	109,681	258,945
Ohio			1,843,813	1,151,173	1,923,608	1,906,781	3,830,389
Oklahoma	474,116	385,646	353,890	307,966	466,782	445,392	912,174
Oregon	{ [4] 422,024 / 412,757	{ [4] 345,464 / 343,009	{ 344,716	291,587			
Pennsylvania			2,238,383	2,134,649	2,359,026	2,429,448	[1] 4,803,145
Rhode Island	275,575	124,408			319,607	66,715	386,322
South Carolina	330,167		178,712	133,930			
South Dakota	145,261	160,181	127,458	126,861			
Tennessee	594,460	234,053			{ [2] 568,905 / 570,542	{ [2] 517,330 / 493,475	{ [1] 1,091,088 / 1,064,017
Texas	1,306,625	926,653			1,463,958	1,134,337	[1] 2,603,837
Utah			151,656	166,755	227,822	169,562	397,384
Vermont			40,134	81,242	76,457	[4] 87,879	[1] 164,350
Virginia	506,169				592,270	176,624	[1] 928,373
Washington	458,355	369,935	491,365	446,204	875,950	337,138	1,213,088
West Virginia					515,015	246,072	761,087
Wisconsin			662,342	594,846	892,013	780,116	[1] 1,673,776
Wyoming	60,447	78,103	[2] 50,329	[2] 69,043	76,485	65,185	141,670

[a] Blank, void, and scattering votes not included.
[1] Includes the vote for various other candidates.
[2] For unexpired term ending Jan. 3, 1967.
[3] Total vote received, as candidate had one or more other party endorsements.
[4] For unexpired term ending Jan. 3, 1961.

VOTES CAST FOR REPRESENTATIVES AND RESIDENT COMMISSIONER IN 1960, 1962, AND 1964

[The figures show the votes for the Democratic and Republican nominees, except as otherwise indicated. Compiled from official statistics]

State and district, old apportionment	Vote cast in 1960 Democrat	Republican	State and district, new apportionment	Vote cast in 1962 Democrat	Republican	State and district, new apportionment	Vote cast in 1964 Democrat	Republican	Total vote cast in 1964
Ala.:			Ala.:			Ala.:			
1st	45,225	---------	At large	304,210	141,202	1st	36,482	54,522	91,004
2d	44,487	---------	At large	295,882	138,963	2d	29,628	49,936	[1] 80,980
3d	33,881	---------	At large	293,182	136,339	3d	27,939	---------	27,939
4th	34,855	---------	At large	288,074	---------	4th	27,800	40,143	[1] 68,545
5th	48,772	---------	At large	271,075	---------	5th	42,784	37,960	80,744
6th	23,245	---------	At large	269,410	---------	6th	45,090	69,246	114,336
7th	36,124	---------	At large	258,674	---------	7th	44,386	65,353	109,739
8th	52,411	13,800	At large	257,299	---------	8th	43,842	---------	43,842
9th	70,567	34,317							
Alaska:			Alaska:			Alaska:			
At large	33,546	25,517	At large	31,953	26,638	At large	34,590	32,556	67,146
Ariz.:			Ariz.:			Ariz.:			
1st	83,676	121,563	1st	79,763	113,240	1st	113,669	140,507	254,176
2d	95,512	75,811	2d	64,510	46,219	2d	86,499	60,782	147,281
			3d	25,359	19,933	3d	30,565	28,802	59,367
Ark.:			Ark.:			Ark.:			
1st	---------	---------	1st	---------	---------	1st	---------	---------	(a)
2d	---------	---------	2d	---------	---------	2d	---------	---------	(a)
3d	---------	---------	3d	58,786	25,987	3d	71,228	58,884	130,112
4th	---------	---------	4th	74,972	21,818	4th	---------	---------	(a)
5th	57,617	12,054							
6th	---------	---------							
Calif.:			Calif.:			Calif.:			
1st	115,829	108,505	1st	100,962	97,949	1st	97,651	141,048	[1] 238,710
2d	109,565	65,198	2d	106,239	58,150	2d	125,774	68,835	[1] 194,620
3d	200,000	---------	3d	138,257	46,510	3d	166,688	57,630	[1] 224,332
4th	62,814	118,249	4th	55,563	42,762	4th	84,949	33,160	[1] 118,122
5th	104,507	20,305	5th	64,493	15,670	5th	71,638	---------	[1] 71,639
6th	90,260	128,418	6th	74,429	105,762	6th	71,894	125,869	197,763
7th	79,776	60,065	7th	86,215	47,409	7th	100,901	51,675	[1] 152,592
8th	152,476	93,403	8th	97,014	36,810	8th	108,771	46,063	[1] 154,842
9th	80,227	116,589	9th	79,616	41,104	9th	115,954	50,261	[1] 166,229
10th	118,520	170,063	10th	68,885	106,419	10th	88,240	151,027	[1] 239,277
11th	97,368	51,473	11th	61,623	101,963	11th	95,747	116,022	[1] 211,774
12th	[2] 141,974	---------	12th	47,576	75,424	12th	57,243	93,112	[1] 150,374
13th	78,597	146,072	13th	45,746	84,743	13th	77,763	104,744	[1] 182,511
14th	97,026	74,800	14th	58,369	99,040	14th	63,469	117,272	[1] 180,759
15th	84,650	89,234	15th	97,322	41,726	15th	109,560	44,977	[1] 154,552
16th	67,318	83,601	16th	108,339	42,401	16th	117,727	58,604	[1] 176,340
17th	206,620	98,510	17th	74,964	36,663	17th	95,640	45,688	[1] 141,348
18th	55,735	129,851	18th	91,684	64,037	18th	121,304	60,523	[1] 181,389
19th	145,479	40,491	19th	78,436	48,976	19th	97,934	51,747	[1] 149,693
20th	38,497	90,214	20th	49,850	119,938	20th	62,645	132,402	[1] 195,054
21st	127,591	179,376	21st	73,465	13,371	21st	106,231	11,374	[1] 117,677
22d	104,919	100,321	22d	75,294	65,087	22d	94,141	92,133	[1] 186,294
23d	148,415	51,548	23d	83,269	46,488	23d	72,903	90,721	[1] 163,664
24th	55,613	82,497	24th	50,970	120,884	24th	65,967	139,784	[1] 205,758
25th	158,293	182,545	25th	62,371	53,961	25th	81,320	65,344	[1] 146,672
26th	150,318	54,540	26th	112,162	52,063	26th	136,026	57,219	[1] 193,247
27th	123,645	61,484	27th	66,979	61,538	27th	77,587	83,141	[1] 160,743
28th	155,221	241,765	28th	91,305	162,233	28th	107,852	205,473	[1] 313,366
29th	76,139	57,319	29th	73,740	58,760	29th	90,208	63,836	[1] 154,049
30th	108,882	158,679	30th	69,008	53,104	30th	90,329	45,912	[1] 136,248
			31st	76,631	70,154	31st	114,246	64,256	[1] 178,529
			32d	47,917	115,915	32d	59,765	132,603	[1] 192,385
			33d	96,192	66,764	33d	109,047	101,742	[1] 210,830
			34th	90,758	71,478	34th	137,588	98,606	[1] 236,206
			35th	61,395	133,737	35th	90,295	167,791	[1] 258,101
			36th	56,637	91,626	36th	73,034	105,346	[1] 178,395
			37th	63,821	60,460	37th	85,624	61,373	[1] 147,008
			38th	54,022	68,583	38th	85,661	76,525	[1] 162,187
Colo.:			Colo.:			Colo.:			
1st	121,610	81,042	1st	94,680	74,392	1st	139,475	65,423	[1] 206,081
2d	111,077	150,964	2d	83,235	134,939	2d	109,526	106,738	216,264
3d	79,069	85,825	3d	62,097	74,848	3d	85,404	81,544	166,948
4th	58,731	26,960	4th	42,462	29,943	4th	106,685	62,617	169,302
Conn.:			Conn.:			Conn.:			
1st	193,330	137,386	1st	162,844	118,767	1st	141,310	60,654	[1] 201,969
2d	93,515	93,971	2d	83,652	81,010	2d	119,530	69,403	[1] 188,990
3d	124,547	102,271	3d	104,728	82,215	3d	126,353	71,393	[1] 197,749
4th	150,205	160,654	4th	122,362	132,590	4th	117,220	109,027	[1] 226,264
5th	88,310	71,964	5th	83,321	59,072	5th	133,072	64,651	[1] 197,724
At large	657,680	560,803	At large	543,424	487,575	6th	115,498	81,105	[1] 196,683

See footnotes at end of table.

VOTES CAST FOR REPRESENTATIVES AND RESIDENT COMMISSIONER IN 1960, 1962, AND 1964—Continued

State and district, old apportionment	Vote cast in 1960 Democrat	Vote cast in 1960 Republican	State and district, new apportionment	Vote cast in 1962 Democrat	Vote cast in 1962 Republican	State and district, new apportionment	Vote cast in 1964 Democrat	Vote cast in 1964 Republican	Total vote cast in 1964
Del.:			Del.:			Del.:			
At large	98,227	96,337	At large	81,166	71,934	At large	112,361	86,254	[1] 198,691
Fla.:			Fla.:			Fla.:			
1st	113,504	159,515	1st	35,781	7,902	1st	74,615	--------	[1] 76,178
2d	94,570	20,090	2d	41,378	--------	2d	99,191	37,283	136,474
3d	95,062	--------	3d	59,985	44,164	3d	101,162	52,758	[1] 153,973
4th	194,023	81,209	4th	67,136	36,981	4th	94,726	53,468	[1] 148,247
5th	113,938	--------	5th	54,383	29,008	5th	85,851	--------	[1] 85,879
6th	138,226	84,776	6th	102,396	57,112	6th	168,573	86,657	[1] 255,236
7th	65,144	40,923	7th	52,417	26,042	7th	79,504	--------	[1] 79,515
8th	46,794	--------	8th	23,387	--------	8th	49,374	--------	[1] 49,409
			9th	23,651	7,735	9th	44,917	--------	[1] 45,452
			10th	41,426	17,214	10th	69,860	--------	[1] 70,165
			11th	43,348	46,814	11th	59,746	91,731	[1] 151,480
			12th	43,431	78,982	12th	64,378	98,959	[1] 163,345
Ga.:			Ga.:			Ga.:			
1st	53,749	--------	1st	25,229	--------	1st	65,146	--------	[1] 90,155
2d	43,596	--------	2d	18,967	--------	2d	37,634	--------	[1] 37,656
3d	55,005	182	3d	25,001	--------	3d	33,733	45,145	[1] 78,893
4th	53,394	--------	4th	21,214	--------	4th	66,488	50,326	[1] 116,818
5th	80,023	--------	5th	60,583	48,466	5th	65,803	55,983	121,786
6th	44,237	--------	6th	19,701	--------	6th	69,712	--------	[1] 69,713
7th	69,717	24,285	7th	28,994	11,048	7th	69,575	57,562	127,137
8th	50,456	84	8th	19,694	10	8th	49,727	--------	[1] 49,746
9th	57,549	--------	9th	25,942	--------	9th	59,186	38,608	[1] 97,801
10th	41,679	--------	10th	27,169	--------	10th	45,418	--------	[1] 45,419
Hawaii:			Hawaii:			Hawaii:			
At large	135,827	46,812	At large	123,649	70,880	At large	140,224	89,425	229,649
			At large	123,599	46,292	At large	106,909	56,147	163,056
Idaho:			Idaho:			Idaho:			
1st	68,863	45,166	1st	51,422	45,552	1st	56,203	52,468	108,671
2d	90,161	86,100	2d	83,152	74,203	2d	84,022	91,838	175,860
Ill.:			Ill.:			Ill.:			
1st	75,938	21,660	1st	98,305	34,379	1st	150,953	26,823	177,776
2d	103,535	52,028	2d	78,119	47,336	2d	107,795	52,416	160,211
3d	114,523	79,307	3d	82,866	77,814	3d	120,711	83,404	204,115
4th	142,772	179,480	4th	62,189	114,954	4th	100,895	144,762	245,657
5th	121,240	49,030	5th	84,455	48,825	5th	101,626	57,871	159,497
6th	107,474	42,361	6th	72,183	20,690	6th	89,850	17,918	107,768
7th	98,494	23,840	7th	86,677	23,285	7th	106,708	17,471	124,179
8th	81,092	39,651	8th	112,778	72,726	8th	137,715	70,624	208,339
9th	80,681	53,686	9th	80,378	66,196	9th	113,851	64,428	178,279
10th	95,214	126,671	10th	74,986	149,761	10th	111,029	172,499	283,528
11th	101,224	86,305	11th	103,677	92,910	11th	129,337	98,132	227,469
12th	94,907	91,978	12th	43,200	76,335	12th	68,555	97,003	[1] 165,559
13th	138,348	268,647	13th	79,419	139,230	13th	120,449	165,129	285,578
14th	94,945	167,128	14th	72,390	107,285	14th	101,432	145,830	247,262
15th	92,301	93,986	15th	49,444	77,718	15th	73,741	103,709	177,450
16th	69,944	115,693	16th	38,853	78,594	16th	71,992	93,051	165,043
17th	68,020	107,896	17th	52,592	87,612	17th	74,261	96,209	170,470
18th	64,885	94,388	18th	48,177	75,957	18th	77,711	91,173	168,884
19th	80,700	82,622	19th	52,482	66,547	19th	81,800	74,290	156,090
20th	61,790	77,286	20th	89,522	100,558	20th	98,256	119,184	[1] 217,446
21st	102,154	84,471	21st	96,971	64,687	21st	117,701	63,431	181,132
22d	61,837	98,438	22d	47,745	70,870	22d	71,875	80,895	152,770
23d	80,718	75,809	23d	99,133	92,562	23d	119,447	99,496	218,943
24th	144,560	55,620	24th	95,522	33,993	24th	144,743	46,419	191,162
25th	92,227	67,067							
Ind.:			Ind.:			Ind.:			
1st	136,433	73,984	1st	104,212	67,230	1st	133,089	75,226	[1] 209,049
2d	70,464	95,920	2d	61,076	82,971	2d	78,566	88,204	166,770
3d	115,070	104,430	3d	92,609	85,845	3d	121,209	78,642	199,851
4th	72,251	100,419	4th	64,553	80,693	4th	82,284	89,437	171,721
5th	(a)	(a)	5th	92,264	86,403	5th	114,252	92,802	207,054
6th	78,247	84,662	6th	68,777	76,506	6th	73,002	86,168	159,176
7th	63,646	95,998	7th	59,953	82,160	7th	71,461	84,427	155,888
8th	108,058	94,694	8th	95,126	75,731	8th	109,134	84,135	193,269
9th	69,761	71,402	9th	59,985	65,287	9th	74,939	62,780	137,719
10th	78,716	104,885	10th	72,009	81,007	10th	87,721	89,303	177,024
11th	133,153	154,676	11th	107,747	127,763	11th	149,342	146,424	295,766

See footnotes at end of table.

VOTES CAST FOR REPRESENTATIVES AND RESIDENT COMMISSIONER IN 1960, 1962, AND 1964—Continued

State and district, old apportionment	Vote cast in 1960 Democrat	Vote cast in 1960 Republican	State and district, new apportionment	Vote cast in 1962 Democrat	Vote cast in 1962 Republican	State and district, new apportionment	Vote cast in 1964 Democrat	Vote cast in 1964 Republican	Total vote cast in 1964
Iowa:			**Iowa:**			**Iowa:**			
1st	67,287	104,737	1st	42,000	65,975	1st	84,042	80,697	[1] 164,896
2d	97,608	108,137	2d	60,296	67,475	2d	97,470	89,299	[1] 186,772
3d	76,837	99,046	3d	50,580	66,337	3d	83,036	83,455	166,491
4th	49,918	65,016	4th	51,810	65,538	4th	85,518	73,898	159,416
5th	91,808	81,474	5th	73,963	43,877	5th	108,212	46,160	[1] 155,447
6th	70,353	60,834	6th	47,542	66,940	6th	86,323	75,478	[1] 162,360
7th	52,214	66,037	7th	44,171	56,341	7th	78,243	67,942	[1] 146,189
8th	57,333	77,583							
Kans.:			**Kans.:**			**Kans.:**			
1st	49,598	84,816	1st	81,092	102,499	1st	108,086	113,212	221,298
2d	86,905	95,346	2d	38,923	72,945	2d	77,189	80,806	157,995
3d	47,127	49,429	3d	35,166	60,865	3d	54,522	89,588	144,110
4th	96,706	119,275	4th	35,922	72,712	4th	58,057	84,800	142,857
5th	75,687	60,794	5th	58,453	66,705	5th	64,308	83,120	147,428
6th	42,869	62,335							
Ky.:			**Ky.:**			**Ky.:**			
1st	66,248		1st	53,240		1st	84,574		84,574
2d	55,877		2d	45,999		2d	79,519	36,664	116,183
3d	115,421	114,263	3d	91,544	94,579	3d	117,892	101,168	219,060
4th	48,473		4th	57,956	51,637	4th	88,337	54,937	143,274
5th	63,555	51,126	5th		59,326	5th	53,916	61,137	115,053
6th	74,500	61,795	6th	53,454		6th	92,322	38,869	131,191
7th	82,746	64,687	7th	70,185	52,640	7th	100,929	43,921	144,850
8th	32,163	81,963							
La.:			**La.:**			**La.:**			
1st	70,465	15,314	1st	57,326		1st	76,455		76,455
2d	81,034	22,818	2d	57,395	27,971	2d	77,009	62,881	139,890
3d	52,428	10,286	3d	26,170		3d	52,532	31,806	84,338
4th	48,286	16,287	4th	29,754		4th	44,599		44,599
5th	22,181		5th	24,609		5th	24,544		24,544
6th	78,640	13,233	6th	48,894		6th	82,686	48,715	131,401
7th	60,007		7th	33,983		7th	38,492		38,492
8th	28,492		8th	25,682	14,448	8th	33,250	27,735	60,985
Maine:			**Maine:**			**Maine:**			
1st	73,826	85,821	1st	58,129	85,864	1st	95,195	95,398	190,593
2d	62,309	71,271	2d	69,159	72,349	2d	110,931	67,978	178,909
3d	41,307	73,742							
Md.:			**Md.:**			**Md.:**			
1st	42,219	36,508	1st	29,653	33,664	1st	36,013	40,762	76,775
2d	126,452	89,262	2d	85,383	79,075	2d	143,132	74,067	[1] 217,200
3d	37,154	14,626	3d	41,446		3d	56,295		56,295
4th	48,145	25,394	4th	35,077	13,425	4th	57,229	16,372	73,601
5th	20,773	73,433	5th	85,606	58,332	5th	131,712	84,318	216,030
6th	106,098	115,088	6th	68,116	106,212	6th	112,410	134,521	246,931
7th	81,474	44,779	7th	57,958	24,825	7th	99,654	25,706	125,360
			At large	388,107	308,801	At large	683,143	301,250	[1] 984,418
Mass.:			**Mass.:**			**Mass.:**			
1st	46,863	102,921	1st	36,711	106,498	1st		139,503	[1] 139,536
2d	135,815		2d	92,340	43,873	2d	125,894		[1] 125,907
3d	145,287		3d	129,326	49,418	3d	177,917		[1] 177,956
4th	122,364	67,270	4th	145,166		4th	142,339	56,034	198,373
5th	102,765	123,161	5th	83,504	112,455	5th	74,133	137,735	[1] 211,869
6th	58,312	112,835	6th	88,187	113,104	6th	77,646	141,733	219,379
7th	117,239		7th	119,117	47,289	7th	139,095	41,671	180,790
8th	114,333	59,550	8th	100,814	37,374	8th	122,050		[1] 122,063
9th	88,222	110,955	9th	105,565		9th	118,385	21,557	[1] 147,382
10th	70,150	98,257	10th	65,443	124,091	10th	78,415	133,403	[1] 211,820
11th	87,866		11th	121,030	67,138	11th	179,261		[1] 179,303
12th	86,057		12th	59,681	107,000	12th	78,313	115,656	[1] 193,980
13th	126,936	89,921							
14th	75,815	115,209							
Mich.:			**Mich.:**			**Mich.:**			
1st	102,948	13,157	1st	82,321	9,916	1st	138,589	25,735	[1] 165,828
2d	74,276	110,124	2d	63,036	88,427	2d	77,806	76,280	[1] 154,306
3d	65,402	100,918	3d	52,667	77,316	3d	85,001	76,350	161,351
4th	54,655	90,831	4th	41,620	73,308	4th	70,212	83,391	[1] 153,607
5th	65,064	131,461	5th	54,112	110,043	5th	64,488	101,810	166,298
6th	165,864	138,355	6th	94,157	112,861	6th	68,265	88,882	[1] 157,148
7th	142,795	124,750	7th	127,067	98,742	7th	104,115	54,307	158,422
8th	57,126	94,405	8th	50,376	77,022	8th	69,931	84,588	154,519
9th	52,375	77,541	9th	45,536	66,645	9th	70,693	95,376	[1] 166,070
10th	46,140	75,846	10th	39,771	63,452	10th	66,835	87,232	[1] 154,068

See footnotes at end of table.

VOTES CAST FOR REPRESENTATIVES AND RESIDENT COMMISSIONER IN 1960, 1962, AND 1964—Continued

State and district, old apportionment	Vote cast in 1960 Democrat	Vote cast in 1960 Republican	State and district, new apportionment	Vote cast in 1962 Democrat	Vote cast in 1962 Republican	State and district, new apportionment	Vote cast in 1964 Democrat	Vote cast in 1964 Republican	Total vote cast in 1964
Mich.—Con.			**Mich.—Con.**			**Mich.—Con.**			
11th	44,650	54,300	11th	36,886	48,244	11th	86,557	75,955	162,512
12th	31,137	48,422	12th	24,240	41,784	12th	126,769	42,615	1 169,386
13th	76,812	30,369	13th	59,688	24,134	13th	102,413	16,585	1 119,343
14th	132,602	78,548	14th	108,025	66,889	14th	120,308	59,487	179,795
15th	111,671	28,532	15th	94,197	19,258	15th	103,724	42,464	146,188
16th	211,733	108,332	16th	180,626	85,485	16th	112,763	40,673	1 153,625
17th	134,660	98,721	17th	122,021	83,870	17th	136,230	50,580	1 187,041
18th	128,678	163,233	18th	101,468	149,863	18th	74,576	109,777	1 184,498
			At large	1,392,221	1,282,082	19th	88,441	77,204	165,645
Minn.:			**Minn.:**			**Minn.:**			
1st	65,422	100,381	1st	66,956	90,632	1st	87,789	108,639	196,428
2d	72,239	96,471	2d	49,543	81,557	2d	69,801	97,804	167,605
3d	139,908	154,847	3d	58,066	87,730	3d	94,682	125,464	220,146
4th	108,738	69,635	4th	93,519	63,766	4th	144,801	54,221	1 200,333
5th	55,377	86,223	5th	87,002	80,865	5th	127,963	78,767	206,730
6th	87,332	59,305	6th	77,310	76,962	6th	95,848	89,228	185,076
7th	66,609	73,487	7th	65,161	70,546	7th	81,718	84,304	166,022
8th	107,154	47,099	8th	101,567	52,996	8th	124,277	54,691	178,968
9th	57,114	62,322							
Miss.:			**Miss.:**			**Miss.:**			
1st	44,381	3,018	1st	26,251	----------	1st	60,052	----------	60,052
2d	23,942	----------	2d	31,345	----------	2d	70,218	----------	70,218
3d	25,592	2,018	3d	38,093	----------	3d	84,503	----------	84,503
4th	58,974	----------	4th	21,730	----------	4th	28,057	35,277	63,334
5th	40,480	----------	5th	39,735	----------	5th	83,120	----------	83,120
6th	59,372	----------							
Mo.:			**Mo.:**			**Mo.:**			
1st	161,394	66,640	1st	82,216	34,089	1st	140,848	42,351	183,199
2d	114,803	15,327	2d	79,732	102,861	2d	115,446	130,894	246,340
3d	87,637	31,902	3d	81,346	34,031	3d	123,193	48,709	171,902
4th	111,557	95,070	4th	59,599	50,945	4th	109,375	61,854	171,229
5th	74,834	47,810	5th	54,166	37,835	5th	91,721	43,314	135,035
6th	93,285	77,638	6th	62,366	50,339	6th	110,532	60,356	170,888
7th	88,162	107,208	7th	62,082	84,631	7th	96,120	102,924	199,044
8th	79,020	57,234	8th	77,535	53,862	8th	117,672	62,823	180,495
9th	107,384	72,098	9th	74,254	47,026	9th	112,907	68,032	1 181,140
10th	69,997	----------	10th	50,581	32,828	10th	89,698	43,304	133,002
11th	74,866	74,505							
Mont.:			**Mont.:**			**Mont.:**			
1st	63,081	55,347	1st	55,611	49,760	1st	64,847	55,417	1 120,908
2d	75,507	78,277	2d	63,755	79,315	2d	71,461	84,241	155,702
Nebr.:			**Nebr.:**			**Nebr.:**			
1st	71,626	89,376	1st	73,768	85,559	1st	107,683	102,113	1 209,804
2d	50,768	101,347	2d	36,577	83,139	2d	72,003	81,660	153,667
3d	63,838	67,129	3d	54,058	103,079	3d	93,236	104,380	197,617
4th	66,699	69,754							
Nev.:			**Nev.:**			**Nev.:**			
At large	59,616	43,986	At large	66,866	26,458	At large	82,748	47,989	130,737
N.H.:			**N.H.:**			**N.H.:**			
1st	67,717	88,118	1st	57,910	65,651	1st	79,097	74,939	154,636
2d	51,145	77,701	2d	41,539	56,152	2d	62,185	63,077	125,262
N.J.:			**N.J.:**			**N.J.:**			
1st	112,802	153,817	1st	83,405	119,633	1st	117,227	150,805	1 268,419
2d	59,520	77,894	2d	54,317	61,285	2d	73,264	70,997	144,261
3d	123,280	139,590	3d	62,258	82,220	3d	105,803	104,063	209,866
4th	115,761	76,067	4th	88,668	49,952	4th	134,747	64,447	1 199,545
5th	120,302	170,859	5th	43,347	86,133	5th	70,001	122,168	192,169
6th	98,043	136,723	6th	73,436	110,143	6th	95,021	140,999	236,020
7th	88,649	156,758	7th	68,330	110,926	7th	110,328	144,585	1 255,930
8th	88,100	74,165	8th	75,820	39,903	8th	112,483	53,732	1 166,601
9th	91,065	127,088	9th	66,140	89,345	9th	111,741	109,313	1 222,908
10th	84,859	43,238	10th	62,616	22,819	10th	92,488	31,306	1 124,923
11th	75,533	44,580	11th	48,102	30,244	11th	82,457	35,956	118,413
12th	73,119	76,945	12th	50,783	57,169	12th	82,726	72,601	157,967
13th	80,490	37,350	13th	62,636	17,063	13th	89,360	24,874	1 115,868
14th	64,359	46,770	14th	54,000	21,303	14th	73,635	25,068	98,703
			15th	86,651	66,142	15th	131,393	76,686	208,079
N. Mex.:			**N. Mex.:**			**N. Mex.:**			
At large	176,514	123,683	At large	128,651	116,262	At large	194,407	120,349	314,756
At large	172,577	124,101	At large	152,684	84,457	At large	164,863	154,780	319,643

See footnotes at end of table.

VOTES CAST FOR REPRESENTATIVES AND RESIDENT COMMISSIONER IN 1960, 1962, AND 1964—Continued

State and district, old apportionment	Vote cast in 1960 Democrat	Republican	State and district, new apportionment	Vote cast in 1962 Democrat	Republican	State and district, new apportionment	Vote cast in 1964 Democrat	Republican	Total vote cast in 1964
N.Y.:			N.Y.:			N.Y.:			
1st	²187,286	184,549	1st	²85,619	53,133	1st	²126,529	68,362	194,891
2d	²89,176	139,423	2d	²55,963	70,352	2d	²82,757	88,390	171,147
3d	²113,143	133,416	3d	²59,635	86,430	3d	²96,503	93,883	190,389
4th	²94,390	115,736	4th	²56,438	74,508	4th	73,149	89,971	¹169,276
5th	²60,453	51,129	5th	²66,502	89,964	5th	²112,899	89,455	202,354
6th	²155,904	81,694	6th	²55,883	96,475	6th	75,327	100,069	175,396
7th	²92,424	59,882	7th	²80,983	55,654	7th	121,091	49,151	¹173,482
8th	²60,030	22,318	8th	²104,895	53,122	8th	²148,696	44,398	¹198,165
9th	²84,941	32,538	9th	85,987	51,325	9th	109,973	48,878	¹166,974
10th	²98,938	30,243	10th	²90,216	21,210	10th	²118,941	16,941	135,582
11th	²139,397	31,378	11th	²60,082	23,844	11th	²75,073	17,732	¹95,234
12th	²65,996	64,899	12th	²106,375	45,492	12th	²141,570	31,737	173,307
13th	²117,078	38,189	13th	²116,753	39,765	13th	129,414	34,809	¹187,371
14th	²80,972	33,769	14th	²54,298	22,287	14th	²68,165	19,861	88,026
15th	77,812	80,218	15th	²55,602	55,219	15th	²66,567	53,689	¹124,193
16th	59,957	14,706	16th	57,666	55,821	16th	²89,438	49,309	¹145,676
17th	²53,574	81,006	17th	²44,728	98,024	17th	²44,533	135,807	¹189,831
18th	47,749	27,419	18th	59,125	18,313	18th	94,222	11,621	¹111,331
19th	²68,445	26,054	19th	59,880	31,244	19th	84,781	24,829	¹123,102
20th	55,272	30,046	20th	²94,425	35,664	20th	²124,128	23,409	¹150,531
21st	²87,775	29,835	21st	65,242	20,354	21st	²91,898	15,380	¹108,994
22d	78,717	24,958	22d	51,241	14,901	22d	70,147	10,134	¹86,003
23d	61,474	15,208	23d	69,836	39,692	23d	108,205	30,476	¹151,744
24th	89,140	43,110	24th	46,455	77,785	24th	51,740	89,814	¹146,774
25th	66,539	112,187	25th	²68,859	109,989	25th	²122,260	95,214	217,474
26th	²88,879	98,506	26th	²59,725	93,064	26th	²78,546	102,064	¹185,949
27th	86,997	121,533	27th	²63,306	86,958	27th	²97,337	91,172	188,509
28th	²75,448	107,179	28th	²52,994	44,531	28th	²84,008		¹185,316
29th	²79,252	103,966	29th	²126,313	83,719	29th	²158,797	²70,518	229,315
30th	²117,692	69,549	30th	57,822	108,860	30th	²99,841	100,950	200,791
31st	²65,305	59,882	31st	²44,171	66,283	31st	²61,726	²74,380	136,106
32d	²98,990	59,890	32d	²57,414	77,875	32d	75,660	86,717	162,377
33d	53,130	91,710	33d	41,412	92,440	33d	²69,277	97,213	166,490
34th	²79,153	98,063	34th	67,149	84,780	34th	²96,219	²91,697	187,916
35th	87,347	105,241	35th	²78,560	65,697	35th	110,948	²62,463	173,411
36th	²76,120	84,441	36th	²66,371	96,581	36th	81,509	107,406	¹191,749
37th	²71,354	123,782	37th	²56,428	101,821	37th	80,411	98,923	¹182,630
38th	²84,716	114,871	38th	36,992	83,361	38th	²64,179	90,201	154,380
39th	²69,704	103,162	39th	55,774	99,527	39th	²108,235	96,934	205,169
40th	85,005	104,752	40th	²67,004	72,706	40th	81,531	90,745	¹176,073
41st	²82,114	63,889	41st	²93,982	37,544	41st	²130,961	28,578	159,539
42d	93,492	122,073							
43d	48,423	87,585							
N.C.:			N.C.:			N.C.:			
1st	48,809	7,587	1st	17,898		1st	52,567	11,108	63,675
2d	51,156	7,135	2d	21,050		2d	62,406		62,406
3d	51,193	20,674	3d	34,056		3d	63,235	30,557	93,792
4th	75,464	37,821	4th	45,249	32,593	4th	73,470	68,387	141,857
5th	66,079	48,572	5th	47,009	32,427	5th	72,254	67,781	140,035
6th	79,809	54,028	6th	43,021	28,827	6th	84,151	52,964	137,115
7th	71,726	21,997	7th	33,173	9,895	7th	71,357		71,357
8th	71,429	55,372	8th	50,926	64,703	8th	72,269	85,869	158,138
9th	75,909	67,033	9th	66,332	67,608	9th	71,629	88,195	159,824
10th	68,761	97,138	10th	52,641	42,908	10th	78,684	55,483	134,167
11th	65,478	41,763	11th	70,791	57,422	11th	85,880	55,996	141,876
12th	61,170	56,368							
N. Dak.:			N. Dak.:			N. Dak.:			
At large	120,773	135,579	1st	50,924	61,330	1st	63,208	69,575	¹133,442
At large	109,207	127,118	2d	47,825	56,203	2d	60,751	54,878	115,629
Ohio:			Ohio:			Ohio:			
1st	62,043	88,899	1st	44,264	74,324	1st	74,525	69,114	143,639
2d	87,531	118,046	2d	62,733	105,750	2d	79,824	122,487	202,311
3d	102,237	167,117	3d	85,573	113,584	3d	129,469	119,400	248,869
4th	52,797	99,683	4th	32,866	77,790	4th	64,667	81,204	145,871
5th	41,375	85,175	5th	29,114	69,272	5th	41,621	80,394	122,015
6th	65,045	80,124	6th	47,737	72,743	6th	57,223	86,015	143,238
7th	55,451	105,026	7th	39,908	83,680	7th	70,857	93,022	163,879
8th	38,871	81,373	8th	28,400	66,458	8th	45,445	73,395	118,840
9th	108,688	82,433	9th	86,443	64,279	9th	109,167	64,401	173,568
10th	58,085	52,479	10th	42,131	46,158	10th	54,729	49,744	104,473

See footnotes at end of table.

VOTES CAST FOR REPRESENTATIVES AND RESIDENT COMMISSIONER IN 1960, 1962, AND 1964—Continued

State and district, old apportionment	Vote cast in 1960		State and district, new apportionment	Vote cast in 1962		State and district, new apportionment	Vote cast in 1964		Total vote cast in 1964
	Democrat	Republican		Democrat	Republican		Democrat	Republican	
Ohio— Con.			Ohio— Con.			Ohio— Con.			
11th	104,183	99,991	11th	72,936	74,573	11th	82,728	102,619	185,347
12th	90,894	140,236	12th	60,563	130,316	12th	118,299	146,971	265,270
13th	69,023	73,100	13th	52,030	63,858	13th	62,780	75,945	138,725
14th	91,103	145,526	14th	86,947	100,909	14th	104,547	126,088	230,635
15th	47,366	49,742	15th	41,856	38,095	15th	62,438	31,803	94,241
16th	78,257	130,542	16th	64,213	96,512	16th	93,255	10,808	195,063
17th	70,470	79,609	17th	49,415	69,976	17th	71,291	75,674	146,965
18th	96,474	50,698	18th	66,327	42,336	18th	94,768	42,960	137,728
19th	102,874	46,537	19th	90,719	55,171	19th	111,682	34,654	146,336
20th	113,302	53,845	20th	91,544	37,325	20th	115,675	39,747	155,422
21st	103,460	38,326	21st	79,514	20,027	21st	113,157	12,416	125,573
22d	66,930	88,389	22d	35,353	74,603	22d	64,454	84,183	148,637
23d	59,893	123,364	23d	42,907	107,510	23d	64,162	131,554	195,716
			At large	1,164,628	1,786,018	At large	1,872,351	1,716,480	3,588,831
Okla.:			Okla.:			Okla.:			
1st	75,934	133,964	1st	46,949	102,585	1st	71,998	125,377	197,375
2d	79,732	60,253	2d	65,968	50,481	2d	90,466	56,843	147,309
3d	56,138	18,799	3d	56,010	--------	3d	62,952	16,706	79,658
4th	54,171	35,028	4th	66,000	--------	4th	98,419	--------	98,419
5th	125,286	62,971	5th	90,392	40,825	5th	130,014	53,596	183,610
6th	68,192	68,116	6th	56,418	48,985	6th	75,879	58,041	133,920
Oreg.:			Oreg.:			Oreg.:			
1st	77,689	144,743	1st	73,641	119,263	1st	107,920	122,010	[1] 229,971
2d	62,690	42,516	2d	53,335	29,995	2d	70,136	32,916	[1] 103,055
3d	157,243	88,906	3d	131,573	67,830	3d	157,882	82,468	[1] 240,682
4th	91,947	96,022	4th	83,660	71,483	4th	125,752	68,288	[1] 194,049
Pa.:			Pa.:			Pa.:			
1st	88,805	26,601	1st	102,722	58,953	1st	129,471	50,780	180,251
2d	109,452	42,019	2d	86,812	42,607	2d	125,100	30,801	155,901
3d	80,258	34,956	3d	81,405	55,827	3d	111,885	43,471	155,356
4th	84,053	23,146	4th	104,300	82,014	4th	135,681	75,901	211,582
5th	140,658	90,087	5th	94,501	74,557	5th	117,049	62,446	179,495
6th	109,275	74,132	6th	112,959	107,724	6th	--------	--------	(a)
7th	120,839	136,021	7th	88,482	136,955	7th	123,750	129,572	253,322
8th	95,140	121,564	8th	84,043	101,853	8th	107,670	112,472	220,142
9th	64,659	128,917	9th	55,565	113,880	9th	81,823	111,545	193,368
10th	80,097	97,012	10th	86,680	95,754	10th	88,082	90,903	178,985
11th	115,042	56,428	11th	101,754	51,263	11th	116,875	34,057	150,932
12th	65,585	72,061	12th	64,227	98,190	12th	68,703	97,114	165,817
13th	88,486	142,966	13th	68,234	135,847	13th	96,849	139,817	236,666
14th	60,211	51,746	14th	93,130	48,726	14th	117,525	39,513	157,038
15th	67,830	55,125	15th	63,574	46,928	15th	81,062	41,656	122,718
16th	56,267	93,831	16th	44,932	90,113	16th	50,509	90,331	140,840
17th	62,695	82,040	17th	56,692	96,088	17th	66,266	91,504	157,770
18th	53,453	88,397	18th	60,260	108,433	18th	71,621	119,938	191,559
19th	78,043	88,776	19th	62,995	82,924	19th	82,498	79,809	162,307
20th	36,997	77,776	20th	106,971	51,688	20th	126,846	43,591	170,437
21st	85,853	65,551	21st	80,410	54,543	21st	97,379	50,513	147,892
22d	66,383	89,261	22d	61,054	82,584	22d	61,482	81,400	142,882
23d	43,927	74,542	23d	54,798	79,158	23d	62,932	76,575	139,507
24th	91,498	95,149	24th	77,749	82,213	24th	92,612	89,828	182,440
25th	102,750	74,217	25th	87,552	67,630	25th	121,140	51,071	172,211
26th	111,362	63,702	26th	94,932	58,945	26th	109,532	51,219	160,751
27th	88,660	127,995	27th	58,984	112,034	27th	71,519	[1]20,395	191,914
28th	99,491	47,232							
29th	80,497	117,009							
30th	126,619	58,063							
R.I.:			R.I.:			R.I.:			
1st	117,162	59,737	1st	80,333	61,184	1st	110,056	56,056	166,112
2d	151,544	63,795	2d	127,182	49,955	2d	168,374	38,601	206,975
S.C.:			S.C.:			S.C.:			
1st	47,153	--------	1st	39,176	--------	1st	56,152	--------	[1] 56,396
2d	63,207	--------	2d	39,149	34,947	2d	88,682	--------	[1] 90,891
3d	52,398	--------	3d	34,545	--------	3d	65,920	--------	[1] 65,967
4th	68,973	--------	4th	47,044	--------	4th	81,727	--------	81,727
5th	46,815	--------	5th	28,989	1,861	5th	44,859	22,384	67,243
6th	49,780	--------	6th	36,811	--------	6th	49,398	26,586	[1] 75,985
S. Dak.:			S. Dak.:			S. Dak.:			
1st	103,755	126,033	1st	78,421	113,975	1st	92,057	124,791	216,848
2d	28,666	42,550	2d	23,243	37,092	2d	31,208	39,657	70,865

See footnotes at end of table.

VOTES CAST FOR REPRESENTATIVES AND RESIDENT COMMISSIONER IN 1960, 1962, AND 1964—Continued

State and district, old apportionment	Vote cast in 1960 Democrat	Republican	State and district, new apportionment	Vote cast in 1962 Democrat	Republican	State and district, new apportionment	Vote cast in 1964 Democrat	Republican	Total vote cast in 1964
Tenn.:			Tenn.:			Tenn.:			
1st	33,873	103,872	1st	40,113	49,320	1st	37,252	94,535	131,787
2d	----	98,839	2d	25,579	61,306	2d	70,119	84,868	1 157,684
3d	62,827	----	3d	45,597	47,604	3d	59,027	71,005	130,032
4th	60,738	----	4th	46,005	----	4th	85,286	----	85,286
5th	42,524	----	5th	4 47,756	----	5th	74,597	50,210	124,807
6th	55,736	----	6th	36,404	----	6th	66,817	18,595	85,412
7th	34,130	----	7th	24,746	----	7th	35,612	----	1 66,544
8th	30,124	----	8th	23,521	----	8th	43,876	----	1 46,741
9th	120,159	----	9th	55,345	54,132	9th	108,425	97,537	1 206,505
Tex.:			Tex.:			Tex.:			
1st	58,674	----	1st	26,669	12,938	1st	52,698	17,967	70,665
2d	75,657	32,473	2d	47,037	21,385	2d	75,226	44,772	119,998
3d	59,386	----	3d	26,915	24,803	3d	53,331	36,566	89,897
4th	44,902	----	4th	23,573	9,165	4th	46,782	10,707	57,489
5th	96,709	129,886	5th	69,813	89,938	5th	172,287	127,568	299,855
6th	56,603	----	6th	33,617	----	6th	55,155	11,967	67,122
7th	61,586	----	7th	37,756	5,045	7th	64,456	12,606	77,062
8th	76,767	24,486	8th	51,285	20,475	8th	103,595	31,351	134,946
9th	98,586	----	9th	56,179	28,594	9th	105,631	34,692	140,323
10th	75,165	----	10th	43,396	25,165	10th	80,045	25,594	105,639
11th	64,351	----	11th	41,698	----	11th	62,175	14,094	76,269
12th	115,797	----	12th	53,705	34,879	12th	107,896	49,633	157,529
13th	75,972	----	13th	37,941	18,578	13th	67,947	22,429	90,376
14th	105,792	----	14th	60,803	25,623	14th	105,352	30,522	135,874
15th	76,421	----	15th	53,552	----	15th	68,897	29,551	96,448
16th	63,634	19,482	16th	37,821	44,095	16th	70,262	55,951	126,213
17th	61,031	17,400	17th	46,895	----	17th	59,769	18,440	78,209
18th	79,675	----	18th	43,389	30,393	18th	58,701	48,054	106,755
19th	77,415	----	19th	46,925	23,022	19th	87,555	25,243	112,798
20th	84,487	----	20th	62,776	----	20th	103,464	56,601	160,065
21st	63,277	----	21st	39,261	12,310	21st	61,785	17,295	79,080
22d	109,418	73,503	22d	73,141	63,452	22d	136,289	98,287	234,576
			At large	870,860	680,839	At large	1,690,674	826,991	1 2,526,855
Utah:			Utah:			Utah:			
1st	65,939	65,871	1st	56,989	59,032	1st	59,768	75,986	135,754
2d	120,771	116,881	2d	92,631	108,358	2d	149,754	110,512	260,266
Vt.:			Vt.:			Vt.:			
At large	71,111	94,905	At large	52,535	68,822	At large	68,987	2 94,458	1 163,452
Va.:			Va.:			Va.:			
1st	53,768	11,329	1st	21,664	----	1st	72,819	19,698	92,517
2d	49,750	15,758	2d	30,306	10,121	2d	54,315	17,082	1 79,032
3d	52,908	----	3d	28,914	28,566	3d	43,880	43,226	1 127,270
4th	39,408	----	4th	30,642	----	4th	53,857	----	1 77,548
5th	30,154	----	5th	13,827	----	5th	39,867	22,946	1 62,814
6th	----	60,371	6th	23,280	44,060	6th	45,113	57,987	1 103,104
7th	42,199	----	7th	26,302	25,704	7th	47,888	20,911	1 68,863
8th	42,809	13,410	8th	20,931	----	8th	49,440	----	1 71,257
9th	47,372	34,280	9th	32,893	20,851	9th	51,106	36,668	1 87,775
10th	52,647	64,408	10th	39,940	49,611	10th	78,242	80,370	158,612
Wash.:			Wash.:			Wash.:			
1st	53,009	124,721	1st	38,669	108,561	1st	78,876	117,851	196,727
2d	58,154	87,802	2d	47,333	70,498	2d	88,551	72,830	161,381
3d	76,930	67,060	3d	69,045	36,629	3d	102,080	43,415	145,495
4th	65,964	94,210	4th	40,887	83,182	4th	54,819	102,964	157,783
5th	64,321	94,042	5th	43,333	78,504	5th	84,830	73,884	158,714
6th	64,167	83,158	6th	32,513	79,838	6th	79,042	72,702	151,744
7th	95,663	95,524	7th	66,052	86,106	7th	125,223	100,119	1 225,679
W.Va.:			W.Va.:			W.Va.:			
1st	53,318	81,018	1st	65,328	97,556	1st	72,714	115,799	188,513
2d	74,184	48,903	2d	62,291	43,769	2d	87,928	47,457	135,385
3d	71,719	48,258	3d	74,743	46,344	3d	103,117	54,566	157,683
4th	82,931	73,052	4th	83,507	60,931	4th	109,287	69,253	178,540
5th	77,524	34,052	5th	57,405	21,144	5th	77,156	33,108	110,264
6th	108,452	67,070							

See footnotes at end of table.

VOTES CAST FOR REPRESENTATIVES AND RESIDENT COMMISSIONER IN 1960, 1962, AND 1964—Continued

State and district, old apportionment	Vote cast in 1960		State and district, new apportionment	Vote cast in 1962		State and district, new apportionment	Vote cast in 1964		Total vote cast in 1964
	Democrat	Republican		Democrat	Republican		Democrat	Republican	
Wis.:			Wis.:			Wis.:			
1st____	87,646	97,662	1st____	62,800	71,657	1st____	90,450	85,117	[1] 175,622
2d____	119,885	104,744	2d____	89,740	81,274	2d____	108,148	61,865	170,013
3d____	59,527	71,677	3d____	34,240	54,237	3d____	59,173	91,092	[1] 150,266
4th____	155,789	61,468	4th____	117,029	44,368	4th____	125,683	43,773	[1] 169,466
5th____	126,314	92,526	5th____	103,705	59,441	5th____	107,610	34,059	[1] 141,712
6th____	72,442	91,450	6th____	49,238	71,298	6th____	84,690	82,103	[1] 166,798
7th____	46,606	95,152	7th____	35,151	68,418	7th____	60,758	98,110	[1] 158,869
8th____	70,740	101,132	8th____	47,833	80,808	8th____	65,292	96,160	161,452
9th____	74,268	57,069	9th____	50,025	39,955	9th____	85,071	105,332	[1] 190,426
10th____	_____	73,114	10th____	30,556	52,451	10th____	71,983	92,198	[1] 164,207
Wyo.:			Wyo.:			Wyo.:			
At large_	64,090	70,241	At large_	44,985	71,489	At large_	70,693	68,482	139,175

Commonwealth	Vote						Total vote cast in 1964
	1960		1962		1964		
	Democrat	Republican	Democrat	Republican	Democrat	Republican	
Puerto Rico: Resident Commissioner (4-year term)__	[5] 458,535	[6] 252,737	_____	_____	[5] 492,095	[6] 287,309	[1] 829,901

[a] Figures not available.
[1] Includes the vote for various other candidates.
[2] Total vote received, as candidate had one or more other party endorsements.
[3] Republican vote cast for Democratic candidate.
[4] Independent Democrat.
[5] Popular Democrat.
[6] Statehood Republican.

REPRESENTATIVES UNDER EACH APPORTIONMENT

State	Constitutional apportionment	First Census, 1790	Second Census, 1800	Third Census, 1810	Fourth Census, 1820	Fifth Census, 1830	Sixth Census, 1840	Seventh Census, 1850	Eighth Census, 1860	Ninth Census, 1870	Tenth Census, 1880	Eleventh Census, 1890	Twelfth Census, 1900	Thirteenth Census, 1910[1]	Fifteenth Census, 1930	Sixteenth Census, 1940	Seventeenth Census, 1950	Eighteenth Census, 1960
Alabama				[2]1	3	5	7	7	6	8	8	9	9	10	9	9	9	8
Alaska																	[2]1	1
Arizona														[2]1	1	2	2	3
Arkansas						[2]1	1	2	3	4	5	6	7	7	7	7	6	4
California							[2]2	2	3	4	6	7	8	11	20	23	30	38
Colorado										[2]1	1	2	3	4	4	4	4	4
Connecticut	5	7	7	7	6	6	4	4	4	4	4	4	5	5	6	6	6	6
Delaware	1	1	1	2	1	1	1	1	1	1	1	1	1	1	1	1	1	1
Florida							[2]1	1	1	2	2	2	3	4	5	6	8	12
Georgia	3	2	4	6	7	9	8	8	7	9	10	11	11	12	10	10	10	10
Hawaii																	[2]1	2
Idaho											[2]1	1	1	2	2	2	2	2
Illinois				[2]1	1	3	7	9	14	19	20	22	25	27	27	26	25	24
Indiana				[2]1	3	7	10	11	11	13	13	13	13	13	12	11	11	11
Iowa							[2]2	2	6	9	11	11	11	11	9	8	8	7
Kansas									1	3	7	8	8	8	7	6	6	5
Kentucky		2	6	10	12	13	10	10	9	10	11	11	11	11	9	9	8	7
Louisiana				[2]1	3	3	4	4	5	6	6	6	7	8	8	8	8	8
Maine				[3]7	7	8	7	6	5	5	4	4	4	4	3	3	3	2
Maryland	6	8	9	9	9	8	6	6	5	6	6	6	6	6	6	6	7	8
Massachusetts	8	14	17	[3]13	13	12	10	11	10	11	12	13	14	16	15	14	14	12
Michigan						[2]1	3	4	6	9	11	12	12	13	17	17	18	19
Minnesota								[2]2	2	3	5	7	9	10	9	9	9	8
Mississippi				[2]1	1	2	4	5	5	6	7	7	8	8	7	7	6	5
Missouri					1	2	5	7	9	13	14	15	16	16	13	13	11	10
Montana											[2]1	1	1	2	2	2	2	2
Nebraska									[2]1	1	3	6	6	6	5	4	4	3
Nevada									[2]1	1	1	1	1	1	1	1	1	1
New Hampshire	3	4	5	6	6	5	4	3	3	3	2	2	2	2	2	2	2	2
New Jersey	4	5	6	6	6	6	5	5	5	7	7	8	10	12	14	14	14	15
New Mexico														[2]1	1	2	2	2
New York	6	10	17	27	34	40	34	33	31	33	34	34	37	43	45	45	43	41
North Carolina	5	10	12	13	13	13	9	8	7	8	9	9	10	10	11	12	12	11
North Dakota											[2]1	1	2	3	2	2	2	2
Ohio			[2]1	6	14	19	21	21	19	20	21	21	21	22	24	23	23	24
Oklahoma													[2]5	8	9	8	6	6
Oregon								[2]1	1	1	1	2	2	3	3	4	4	4
Pennsylvania	8	13	18	23	26	28	24	25	24	27	28	30	32	36	34	33	30	27
Rhode Island	1	2	2	2	2	2	2	2	2	2	2	3	3	2	2	2	2	2
South Carolina	5	6	8	9	9	9	7	6	4	5	7	7	7	6	6	6	6	6
South Dakota											[2]2	2	2	3	2	2	2	2
Tennessee		[2]1	3	6	9	13	11	10	8	10	10	10	10	10	9	10	9	9
Texas							[2]2	2	4	6	11	13	16	18	21	21	22	23
Utah												[2]1	1	2	2	2	2	2
Vermont		2	4	6	5	5	4	3	3	3	2	2	2	2	1	1	1	1
Virginia	10	19	22	23	22	21	15	13	11	9	10	10	10	10	9	10	10	10
Washington											[2]1	2	3	5	6	6	7	7
West Virginia									3	3	4	4	5	6	6	6	6	5
Wisconsin							[2]2	3	6	8	9	10	11	11	10	10	10	10
Wyoming											[2]1	1	1	1	1	1	1	1
Total	65	106	142	186	213	242	232	237	243	293	332	357	391	435	435	435	437	435

[1] No apportionment was made in 1920.

[2] The following representation was added after the several census apportionments indicated when new States were admitted and is included in the above table:

First. Tennessee, 1.
Second. Ohio, 1.
Third. Alabama, 1; Illinois, 1; Indiana, 1; Louisiana, 1; Mississippi, 1.
Fifth. Arkansas, 1; Michigan, 1.
Sixth. California, 2; Florida, 1; Iowa, 2; Texas, 2; Wisconsin, 2.
Seventh. Minnesota, 2; Oregon, 1.
Eighth. Nebraska, 1; Nevada, 1.
Ninth. Colorado, 1.
Tenth. Idaho, 1; Montana, 1; North Dakota, 1; South Dakota, 2; Washington, 1; Wyoming, 1.
Eleventh. Utah, 1.
Twelfth. Oklahoma, 5.
Thirteenth. Arizona, 1; New Mexico, 1.
Seventeenth. Alaska, 1; Hawaii, 1.

[3] Twenty Members were assigned to Massachusetts, but 7 of these were credited to Maine when that area became a State.

GOVERNORS OF THE STATES AND TERRITORIES

State or territory	Capital	Governor	Politics	Term of service	Expiration of term	Salary
STATE				*Years*		
Alabama	Montgomery	George C. Wallace	D.	a 4	Jan. 1967	1 $25,000
Alaska	Juneau	William A. Egan	D.	c 4	Dec. 1966	1 25,000
Arizona	Phoenix	Sam Goddard	D.	b 2	Jan. 1967	22,500
Arkansas	Little Rock	Orval Faubus	D.	b 2	Jan. 1967	1 10,000
California	Sacramento	Edmund G. (Pat) Brown	D.	b 4	Jan. 1967	1 44,100
Colorado	Denver	John A. Love	R.	b 4	Jan. 1967	2 20,000
Connecticut	Hartford	John N. Dempsey	D.	b 4	Jan. 1967	2 15,000
Delaware	Dover	Charles L. Terry, Jr	D.	c 4	Jan. 1969	1 25,000
Florida	Tallahassee	Haydon Burns	D.	c 2	Jan. 1967	2 25,999
Georgia	Atlanta	Carl Sanders	D.	a 4	Jan. 1967	1 12,000
Hawaii	Honolulu	John A. Burns	D.	b 4	Dec. 1966	1 27,500
Idaho	Boise	Robert E. Smylie	R.	b 4	Jan. 1967	1 15,000
Illinois	Springfield	Otto Kerner	D.	b 4	Jan. 1969	1 30,000
Indiana	Indianapolis	Roger D. Branigin	D.	a 4	Jan. 1969	1 25,000
Iowa	Des Moines	Harold E. Hughes	D.	b 2	Jan. 1967	1 18,500
Kansas	Topeka	William H. Avery	R.	b 2	Jan. 1967	1 20,000
Kentucky	Frankfort	Edward T. Breathitt, Jr	D.	a 4	Dec. 1967	1 18,000
Louisiana	Baton Rouge	John J. McKeithen	D.	a 4	May 1968	1 20,000
Maine	Augusta	John H. Reed	R.	c 4	Jan. 1967	1 15,000
Maryland	Annapolis	J. Millard Tawes	D.	c 4	Jan. 1967	1 15,000
Massachusetts	Boston	John A. Volpe	R.	b 2	Jan. 1967	35,000
Michigan	Lansing	George Romney	R.	b 2	Jan. 1967	3 30,000
Minnesota	St. Paul	Karl F. Rolvaag	D.F.L.	b 4	Jan. 1967	3 22,500
Mississippi	Jackson	Paul B. Johnson	D.	a 4	Jan. 1968	1 25,000
Missouri	Jefferson City	Warren E. Hearnes	D.	a 4	Jan. 1969	1 25,000
Montana	Helena	Tim M. Babcock	R.	b 4	Jan. 1969	1 22,000
Nebraska	Lincoln	Frank B. Morrison	D.	b 2	Jan. 1967	1 18,000
Nevada	Carson City	Grant Sawyer	D.	b 4	Jan. 1967	1 20,000
New Hampshire	Concord	John W. King	D.	b 2	Jan. 1967	16,587
New Jersey	Trenton	Richard J. Hughes	D.	c 4	Jan. 1966	1 35,000
New Mexico	Santa Fe	Jack M. Campbell	D.	c 2	Jan. 1967	1 17,500
New York	Albany	Nelson A. Rockefeller	R.	b 4	Jan. 1967	2 50,000
North Carolina	Raleigh	Dan K. Moore	D.	a 4	Jan. 1969	1 25,000
North Dakota	Bismarck	William L. Guy	D.	b 4	Jan. 1969	2 10,000
Ohio	Columbus	James A. Rhodes	R.	c 4	Jan. 1967	1 25,000
Oklahoma	Oklahoma City	Henry Bellmon	R.	a 4	Jan. 1967	1 25,000
Oregon	Salem	Mark O. Hatfield	R.	c 4	Jan. 1967	3 21,500
Pennsylvania	Harrisburg	William W. Scranton	R.	a 4	Jan. 1967	1 35,000
Rhode Island	Providence	John H. Chafee	R.	b 2	Jan. 1967	25,000
South Carolina	Columbia	Donald Russell	D.	a 4	Jan. 1967	1 20,000
South Dakota	Pierre	Nils A. Boe	R.	c 2	Jan. 1967	1 15,500
Tennessee	Nashville	Frank G. Clement	D.	a 4	Jan. 1967	1 18,500
Texas	Austin	John Connally	D.	b 2	Jan. 1967	2 25,000
Utah	Salt Lake City	Calvin L. Rampton	D.	c 4	Jan. 1969	1 15,000
Vermont	Montpelier	Philip H. Hoff	D.	b 2	Jan. 1967	3 13,750
Virginia	Richmond	Albertis S. Harrison, Jr	D.	a 4	Jan. 1966	1 25,000
Washington	Olympia	Daniel J. Evans	R.	b 4	Jan. 1969	1 22,500
West Virginia	Charleston	Hulett Smith	D.	a 4	Jan. 1969	1 25,000
Wisconsin	Madison	Warren P. Knowles	R.	b 2	Jan. 1967	1 25,000
Wyoming	Cheyenne	Cliff Hansen	R.	b 4	Jan. 1967	1 20,000
COMMONWEALTH OF PUERTO RICO						
Puerto Rico	San Juan	Roberto Sánchez-Vilella	P.D. 4	b 4	Jan. 1969	1 25,000
TERRITORIES						
Guam 5	Agana	Manuel F. L. Guerrero	D.			
Virgin Islands 5	Charlotte Amalie	Ralph M. Paiewonsky	D.	(d)		1 24,500
ISLAND POSSESSION						
American Samoa 6	Pago Pago	H. Rex Lee	D.	(d)		1 24,500

a Cannot succeed himself.
b No limit.
c Can serve two consecutive terms.
d Indefinite term.
1 Use of executive mansion and fund for maintenance and expenses.
2 Executive mansion furnished.
3 No executive mansion; nominal appropriation for expenses.
4 Popular Democrat Party.
5 Governors nominated by the President and confirmed by the Senate.
6 Appointed by Secretary of Interior.

PRESIDENTS AND VICE PRESIDENTS AND THE CONGRESSES COINCIDENT WITH THEIR TERMS

President	Vice President	Service	Congress
George Washington	John Adams	Apr. 30, 1789–Mar. 3, 1797	1, 2, 3, 4.
John Adams	Thomas Jefferson	Mar. 4, 1797–Mar. 3, 1801	5, 6.
Thomas Jefferson	Aaron Burr	Mar. 4, 1801–Mar. 3, 1805	7, 8.
Do	George Clinton	Mar. 4, 1805–Mar. 3, 1809	9, 10.
James Madison	do.[1]	Mar. 4, 1809–Mar. 3, 1813	11, 12.
Do	Elbridge Gerry [2]	Mar. 4, 1813–Mar. 3, 1817	13, 14.
James Monroe	Daniel D. Tompkins	Mar. 4, 1817–Mar. 3, 1825	15, 16, 17, 18.
John Quincy Adams	John C. Calhoun	Mar. 4, 1825–Mar. 3, 1829	19, 20.
Andrew Jackson	do.[3]	Mar. 4, 1829–Mar. 3, 1833	21, 22.
Do	Martin Van Buren	Mar. 4, 1833–Mar. 3, 1837	23, 24.
Martin Van Buren	Richard M. Johnson	Mar. 4, 1837–Mar. 3, 1841	25, 26.
William Henry Harrison [4]	John Tyler	Mar. 4, 1841–Apr. 4, 1841	27.
John Tyler		Apr. 6, 1841–Mar. 3, 1845	27, 28.
James K. Polk	George M. Dallas	Mar. 5, 1845–Mar. 3, 1849	29, 30.
Zachary Taylor [4]	Millard Fillmore	Mar. 5, 1849–July 9, 1850	31.
Millard Fillmore		July 10, 1850–Mar. 3, 1853	31, 32.
Franklin Pierce	William R. King [5]	Mar. 4, 1853–Mar. 3, 1857	33, 34.
James Buchanan	John C. Breckinridge	Mar. 4, 1857–Mar. 3, 1861	35, 36.
Abraham Lincoln	Hannibal Hamlin	Mar. 4, 1861–Mar. 3, 1865	37, 38.
Do.[4]	Andrew Johnson	Mar. 4, 1865–Apr. 15, 1865	39.
Andrew Johnson		Apr. 15, 1865–Mar. 3, 1869	39, 40.
Ulysses S. Grant	Schuyler Colfax	Mar. 4, 1869–Mar. 3, 1873	41, 42.
Do	Henry Wilson [6]	Mar. 4, 1873–Mar. 3, 1877	43, 44.
Rutherford B. Hayes	William A. Wheeler	Mar. 4, 1877–Mar. 3, 1881	45, 46.
James A. Garfield [4]	Chester A. Arthur	Mar. 4, 1881–Sept. 19, 1881	47.
Chester A. Arthur		Sept. 20, 1881–Mar. 3, 1885	47, 48.
Grover Cleveland [7]	Thomas A. Hendricks [8]	Mar. 4, 1885–Mar. 3, 1889	49, 50.
Benjamin Harrison	Levi P. Morton	Mar. 4, 1889–Mar. 3, 1893	51, 52.
Grover Cleveland [7]	Adlai E. Stevenson	Mar. 4, 1893–Mar. 3, 1897	53, 54.
William McKinley	Garret A. Hobart [9]	Mar. 4, 1897–Mar. 3, 1901	55, 56.
Do.[4]	Theodore Roosevelt	Mar. 4, 1901–Sept. 14, 1901	57.
Theodore Roosevelt		Sept. 14, 1901–Mar. 3, 1905	57, 58.
Do	Charles W. Fairbanks	Mar. 4, 1905–Mar. 3, 1909	59, 60
William H. Taft	James S. Sherman [10]	Mar. 4, 1909–Mar. 3, 1913	61, 62.
Woodrow Wilson	Thomas R. Marshall	Mar. 4, 1913–Mar. 3, 1921	63, 64, 65, 66.
Warren G. Harding [4]	Calvin Coolidge	Mar. 4, 1921–Aug. 2, 1923	67.
Calvin Coolidge		Aug. 3, 1923–Mar. 3, 1925	68.
Do	Charles G. Dawes	Mar. 4, 1925–Mar. 3, 1929	69, 70.
Herbert C. Hoover	Charles Curtis	Mar. 4, 1929–Mar. 3, 1933	71, 72.
Franklin D. Roosevelt	John N. Garner	Mar. 4, 1933–Jan. 20, 1941	73, 74, 75, 76.
Do	Henry A. Wallace	Jan. 20, 1941–Jan. 20, 1945	77, 78.
Do.[4]	Harry S. Truman	Jan. 20, 1945–Apr. 12, 1945	79.
Harry S. Truman		Apr. 12, 1945–Jan. 20, 1949	79, 80.
Do	Alben W. Barkley	Jan. 20, 1949–Jan. 20, 1953	81, 82.
Dwight D. Eisenhower	Richard M. Nixon	Jan. 20, 1953–Jan. 20, 1961	83, 84, 85, 86.
John F. Kennedy [4]	Lyndon B. Johnson	Jan. 20, 1961–Nov. 22, 1963	87, 88.
Lyndon B. Johnson		Nov. 22, 1963–Jan. 20, 1965	88.
Do	Hubert H. Humphrey	Jan. 20, 1965–	89.

[1] Died Apr. 20, 1812.
[2] Died Nov. 23, 1814.
[3] Resigned Dec. 28, 1832, to become United States Senator.
[4] Died in office.
[5] Died Apr. 18, 1853.
[6] Died Nov. 22, 1875.
[7] Terms not consecutive.
[8] Died Nov. 25, 1885.
[9] Died Nov. 21, 1899.
[10] Died Oct. 30, 1912.

THE CAPITOL

THE CAPITOL

OFFICERS OF THE SENATE

Phone, 224-3121 (Code 180)

PRESIDENT

Room 5117, Senate Office Building. Phone, 225-2424

Vice President of the United States and President of the Senate.—Hubert H. Humphrey, 3216 Coquelin Terrace, Chevy Chase, Md., 20015.
Administrative Assistant to the Vice President and Assistant to the Vice President for National Security Affairs.—William Connell, 4809 Morgan Drive, Chevy Chase, Md.
Legislative Assistant to the Vice President.—John Stewart, 208 Ninth Street SE.
Executive Secretary to the Vice President.—Julius Cahn, 9211 Harrington Drive, Bethesda, Md.
Aide to the Vice President.—David Gartner, 1301 Delaware Avenue SW.
Private Secretary to the Vice President.—Violet Williams, 1825 South George Mason Drive, Arlington, Va.
Appointment Secretary to the Vice President.—Mrs. Patricia Gray, 3359 South Stafford Street, Arlington, Va.
Assistant to the Vice President.—Norman Sherman, 6825 Riverdale Road, Apt. D-201, Riverdale, Md.

PRESIDENT PRO TEMPORE

President pro Tempore of the Senate.—Carl Hayden.

CHAPLAIN

Chaplain of the Senate.—Rev. Frederick Brown Harris, D. D., Litt. D., LL. D., 4000 Cathedral Avenue.

MAJORITY LEADER

Majority Floor Leader.—Mike Mansfield.
Secretary to the Majority Leader.—Mary Jane Del Balzo, 11708 Hatcher Place, Wheaton, Md.

MAJORITY WHIP

Majority Whip.—Russell B. Long.

MINORITY FLOOR LEADER

Minority Floor Leader.—Everett McKinley Dirksen.
Administrative Assistant.—John R. Gomien, 5509 Cromwell Drive, 20016.
Research Assistant.—Oliver J. Dompierre, 6816 32d Street, 20015.
Executive Secretary.—Glee D. Gomien, 5509 Cromwell Drive, 20016.

MINORITY WHIP

Minority Whip.—Thomas H. Kuchel, 3118 Arizona Avenue.
Administrative Assistant.—Ewing Hass.

OFFICE OF THE SECRETARY

FELTON McLELLAN JOHNSTON, Secretary of the Senate (2010 48th Street, 20007, phone 333–0323); born March 10, 1909, in Tallulah, La.; educated in public schools of Clarksdale, Miss.; graduated from University of Mississippi in 1929 with B.S.C. degree; began Senate service in August 1929, as a stenographer in the office of the late Senator Pat Harrison of Mississippi; assistant clerk, Committee on Finance, 1933, and clerk, Committee on Finance, from 1934 through 1941; served in the Department of State in 1942, 1943, and part of 1945; enlisted man, U.S. Army, 1944; elected Secretary for the Senate Majority on October 15, 1945, and served in the capacities of Secretary for the Senate Majority and Minority until elected Secretary of the Senate on January 5, 1955: served as secretary, Committee on Platform and Resolutions, Democratic National Conventions, Philadelphia, Pa., 1948, and Chicago, Ill., 1952; married Wanda Stippich of Norfolk, Nebr.; two children, Mrs. A. B. Chatfield, Jr., and Lieutenant Felton McLellan Johnston, Jr., USAFR; member of Sigma Alpha Epsilon Fraternity, Alfalfa Club, Burning Tree Club, Jefferson Islands Club, Metropolitan Club, National Capital Democratic Club, and the National Press Club.

Administrative Assistant to the Secretary.—Dorothye G. Scott, 430 Pershing Drive, Silver Spring, Md., 20910.

Secretaries to the Secretary.—Christine Johnson, 1711 Rhode Island Avenue, 20036; Rose Ann Johnson, 6212 19th Street North, Arlington, Va., 22205.

Chief Clerk.—Emery L. Frazier, 4611 Verplanck Place, 20016.

Parliamentarian.—Floyd M. Riddick, Manassas, Va., R.F.D. 1.

Assistant Parliamentarian.—Murray Zweben, 3205 McKinley Street, 20015.

Secretary to the Parliamentarian.—Dale R. Thomas, 1232 31st Street, 20007.

Journal Clerk.—Bernard V. Somers, 5210 Colony Road, 20021.

Assistant Journal Clerk.—James E. Thorndike, 1301 Delaware Avenue SW., Apt. N–308, 20024.

Legislative Clerk.—Edward E. Mansur, Jr., 5431 Neptune Drive, Alexandria, Va., 22309.

Financial Clerk.—Robert A. Brenkworth, 11009 Babington Drive, Silver Spring, Md, 20900.

Assistant Financial Clerk.—William A. Ridgely, 6850 Lamont Drive, Kingswood, Lanham, Md., 20801.

Chief Bookkeeper.—Robert A. Malstrom, 8806 Lowell Place, Bethesda, Md., 20034.

Enrolling Clerk.—Emory S. Arrington, 107 Washington Street, Savage, Md., 20863

Enrolling Technical Assistant.—Thomas F. Bradley, 2901 Traymore Lane, Bowie, Md., 20715.

Executive Clerk.—Larry M. Wheeler, 407 Wake Forest Drive, Alexandria, Va., 22307.

Assistant Executive Clerk.—Gerald A. Hackett, 602 East Capitol Street, 20003.

Clerk of Enrolled Bills.—Harry C. Burke, 2435 33d Street SE., 20020.

Bill Clerk.—Harold G. Ast, 6127 Lee Highway, Arlington, Va., 22205.

Assistant Bill Clerk.—David P. Lambert, 912 East Capitol Street, 20003.

Printing Clerk.—William H. Wannall, 300 Quaint Acres Drive, Silver Spring, Md., 20904.

Assistant Printing Clerk.—Thomas N. Gay, 3017 Laurel Avenue, Cheverly, Md., 20785.

Registration Clerk.—James L. Johnson, 4223 36th Street South, Arlington, Va., 22006.

Assistant Registration Clerk.—William F. Farmer, Jr., 2884 South Buchanan Street, Arlington, Va., 22206.

Superintendent of Document Room.—Theron W. Marshall, 1401 North Nicholas Street, Arlington, Va., 22205.

Assistant Superintendent of Document Room.—Copher Howell, 5431 16th Avenue, Hyattsville, Md., 20782.

Keeper of Stationery.—Harry F. Sonnenberg, 6011 Wise Street, McLean Manor, McLean, Va., 22101.

Assistant Keeper of Stationery.—Lloyd L. Hysell, 4208 74th Avenue, Hyattsville, Md., 20784.

Custodian of Records.—William W. Vaughan, 13 West Caton Avenue, Alexandria Va., 22301.

Librarian.—Richard D. Hupman, 3104 V Place SE., 20020.

Assistant Librarian.—Eiler C. Ravnholt, 7123 Fairfax Road, Bethesda, Md., 20014.

Chief Messenger.—Ellsworth B. Dozier, 1443 Chapin Street, 20009.

OFFICE OF THE SERGEANT AT ARMS

JOSEPH C. DUKE, Sergeant at Arms, United States Senate; married 1931 to Miss Dorothea E. Hart, of Denver, Colo.; elected as Sergeant at Arms of the United States Senate on January 3, 1949, and served in that capacity until January 2, 1953; reelected January 5, 1955.

Administrative Assistant.—William S. Cheatham, 8404 Farrell Drive, Chevy Chase, Md., 20015.

Secretaries.—Emily A. Kennedy, 4101 Cathedral Avenue; Evelyn L. Raper, 1710 Black Oak Lane, Silver Spring, Md.; Patricia Enright, 2000 F Street.

Deputy Sergeant at Arms, Auditor, and Procurement Officer.—Robert G. Dunphy, 3509 Farthing Drive, Silver Spring, Md., 20906.

Chief Clerk.—Dorothy G. McCarty, 128 Duddington Place SE., 20003.

Assistant Chief Clerk.—Edna G. Cook, 314 East Capitol Street.

Clerk.—Hilda B. Glesner, 4545 Connecticut Avenue.

Clerk.—Angioletta Landon, 1705 Dublin Drive, Silver Spring, Md.

Clerk.—Mildred C. Townshend, 215 Constitution Avenue NE.

Clerk.—Ena B. Trezise, 2824 27th Street.

Clerk.—Ruth L. Parris, 5309 Shadyside Avenue SE.

Assistant Doorkeeper.—Charlie W. Jones, 1010 Croton Drive, Alexandria, Va.

Messenger at Card Door.—Philip H. Weymouth, 219 Third Street SE.

Press Liaison.—Richard Langham Riedel, Horizons West, R. F. D. No. 1, Centreville, Va.

Director, Recording Studio.—Robert J. Coar, Box 119, Annandale, Va.

Director of Photography.—Henry M. Esper, 1909 North Rhodes Street, Arlington, Va.

Administrative Officer, Recording Studio.—Nicholas J. Lacovara, 14201 Dav Road, Rockville, Md.

Superintendent of Service Department.—John T. Chambers, 6097 Davis Court McLean, Va.

Assistant Superintendent.—Charles David Ebert, 149 Kentucky Avenue SE.

Secretary.—Rosemary M. Graham, 2510 Marlboro Avenue, Hyattsville, Md.

Night Supervisor.—Wilbur E. Turner, 5909 15th Avenue, West Hyattsville, Md.

Foreman of Automatic Typing Section.—Lewis E. Payne, Jr., 2614 Afton Street Hillcrest Heights, Md.

Foreman of Duplicating Section.—William R. Baxter, 5006 54th Place, Hyattsville, Md.

Supervisor of Typewriters and Supplies.—Edward L. Kettler, 317 West Boulevard Drive, Alexandria, Va.

Foreman of Speech Room.—Joseph J. Fahey, 5024 Silver Hill Court, Suitland, Md.

Foreman of Document Warehouse.—Walter Watt, 11010 Burnley Terrace, Silver Spring, Md.

Foreman in Cabinet Shop.—Michael J. Vanni, Bryantown, Md.

Assistant Cabinetmakers.—Domenick Bellia, 1227 Dale Drive, Silver Spring, Md.; Angelo Cevrain, 1813 Brisbane Street, Silver Spring, Md.; Renzo Vanni, Bryantown, Md.

Upholsterer.—Elmer Cheseldine, 2921 M Street SE.

Finisher.—Clifford C. Chronstrom, 10302 Brookmoor Drive, Silver Spring, Md.

Foreman-Automotive.—Charles G. Loudermilk, 6408 Broad Street, Brookmont, Md.

Superintendent of Janitors' Department.—Robert S. Collins, 1365 A Street NE.

Captain of Guides.—Floyd Kirby, 3825 North Westmoreland Street, Falls Church, Va.

Assistant Captain of Guides.—Calvin Kimbrough, 5305 Seventh Street South, Arlington, Va.

Postmaster.—David D. Jennings, 107 Tedrich Boulevard, Fairfax, Va.

Assistant Postmaster.—Gordon R. Olson, 332 Onondaga Drive, Forest Heights, Md.

Superintendent of Mails.—David C. Longinotti, 2357 South Arlington Ridge Road, Arlington, Va.

Chief Clerk.—Nolan P. Rasnick, 4105 Weller Road, Wheaton, Md.

Registry Clerk.—Morgan D. Roderick, 127 C Street NE.

Forwarding Clerk.—Bolling Flood, 2740 34th Street.

OFFICE OF THE MAJORITY SECRETARY

Room S-148, Capitol. Phone, 225-3735 (Code 180)

Secretary for the Majority.—Francis R. Valeo, 3420 17th Street (phone, ADams 4-1777).
Assistant Secretary for the Majority.—John L. Graves, 616 G Street SE. (phone, LIncoln 4-0943).
Administrative Assistant to the Secretary.—Elizabeth O. Shotwell, 112 Fourth Street SE. (phone, 547-3867).
Assistants, Democratic Cloakroom:
  Gary Fernandez, Shirlington House, 4201 31st Street South, Arlington, Va. (phone, 578-3913).
  Patrick Hynes, 3217 North Pershing Drive, Arlington, Va. (phone, JAckson, 4-4813).
  Don Robinson, 148 G Street SW. (phone, 638-1747).

OFFICE OF THE MINORITY SECRETARY

Room S-337, Capitol. Phone, 225-3835 (Code 180)

Secretary for the Minority.—J. Mark Trice, 5017 Worthington Drive, Westmoreland Hills, Md., 20016 (phone, OLiver 2-2777).
Assistant Secretary for the Minority.—William Brownrigg III, 9603 Parkwood Drive, Bethesda, Md. (phone, WHitehall 2-2940).
Assistant to Minority.—Irving W. Swanson, 1501 South Edgewood Street, Arlington, Va. (phone, JAckson 5-1094).
Clerk.—Dorothy M. Burns, 4201 Cathedral Avenue, 20016 (phone, EMerson 2-0573).
Assistants, Republican Cloakroom:
  Donn L. Larson, 4410 Oglethorpe Street, Hyattsville, Md. (phone, 864-7238).
  F. C. Duke Zeller, 1311 Delaware Avenue SW. (phone, 543-9011).
  Lawrence J. Brady, 7717 Walters Lane, Forestville, Md. (phone, 735-4459).

OFFICIAL REPORTERS OF DEBATES

Room S-219, Capitol. Phone, 225-3152 (Code 180)

Gregor Macpherson, 1100 Sixth Street SW., Apt. 115, 20024.
Herbert N. Budlong, 5007 Waggaman Circle, McLean, Va., 22101.
Charles J. Drescher, 3738 Fourth Street North, Arlington, Va., 22203.
Francis J. Attig, 3919 Livingston Street, 20015.
Nicholas J. Cinciotta, 216 Normandie Drive, Silver Spring, Md.
Joseph J. Sweeney, 101 G Street SW., 20024.
Jack Romagna, 9908 Indian Lane, Silver Spring, Md.
Francis J. McSwiggen, 200 River Tower Drive, Alexandria, Va.
Assistant.—Elmer L. Koons, 826 Aspen Street.
Clerks:
  Willard W. Pruett, 701 North Harrison Street, Arlington, Va.
  Placidino Zagami, 5805 10th Place, Chillum, Md.
Expert Transcribers:
  Joseph A. Koons, 5122 26th Avenue SE.
  Wilbur T. Smith, 505 Southwick Street, Fairfax, Va.
  R. Thomas Loftus, 2512 Riviera Street.
  Perry B. Smith, 2022 Add Drive, Falls Church, Va.
  Hilda G. Clardy, 5510 North 33d Street, Arlington, Va., 22207.
  Lee H. Timberlake, 2510 Kinderbrook, Bowie, Md.

OFFICE OF THE LEGISLATIVE COUNSEL

Room 6123, Senate Office Building. Phone, 225-6461 (Code 180)

Legislative Counsel.—John H. Simms, 3019 Arizona Avenue.
Assistant Counsel.—Dwight J. Pinion, 311 Bright Avenue, McLean, Va.; John C. Herberg, 404 Hamilton Avenue, Silver Spring, Md.; John M. Reynolds, 4107 Pine Tree Road, McLean, Va.; Harry B. Littell, 937 North Potomac Street, Arlington, Va.; Peter W. LeRoux, 5720 Barbee Street, McLean, Va.; Douglas B. Hester, 408 Constitution Avenue NE.; Hugh C. Evans, 108 Fifth Street NE.; Robert C. Louthian, Jr., 1 North Flaxton Place, Alexandria, Va.; J. Terry Emerson, 1101 Third Street SW.; Blair Crownover, 1507 Foxhall Road.
Clerk.—Dale E. Isley, 623 Woodland Circle, Falls Church, Va.
Assistant Clerks.—S. Michael Derato, 413 Lincoln Avenue, Takoma Park, Md.; Mary F. Ford, 3133 Connecticut Avenue; Ruth W. Warner, 1318 Stoneybrae Drive, Falls Church, Va.

OFFICERS OF THE HOUSE

Phone, 224-3121 (Code 180)

OFFICE OF THE SPEAKER

The Speaker.—John W. McCormack, Hotel Washington.
Administrative Assistant to the Speaker.—Eugene T. Kinnaly, 5410 Connecticut
Avenue, 20015.
Legislative Assistant and Secretary, Washington Office.—Dr. Martin Sweig, 115 E
Street SE., 20003.
Secretary, Boston Office.—James V. Hartrey.
Clerks to the Speaker.—William E. Brennan, Bertha D. Drotos, Kathleen Forry,
George F. Edwards, John L. Monahan, James Q. McDonough, Raymond
V. O'Brien, Bernard A. O'Sullivan, Edythe A. Pargament, Edward F.
Ronan, Charles S. Sullivan, Jr.

OFFICE OF THE PARLIAMENTARIAN

Parliamentarian.—Lewis Deschler, 101 Lucas Lane, Bethesda, Md., 20014.
Assistant Parliamentarians.—William P. Cochrane, 9 Ninth Street NE., 20002;
William H. Brown, 16 Third Street NE., 20002.
Legal Assistant to the Parliamentarian.—Charles W. Johnson, 3252 Valley Drive,
Alexandria, Va.
Clerk.—Joseph F. Metzger, 401 East Alexandria Avenue, Alexandria, Va.

CHAPLAIN

Chaplain of the House.—Rev. Bernard Braskamp, D.D., 1421 Montague Street
(phone, RAndolph 3-6541).

OFFICE OF THE MAJORITY LEADER

Floor Leader.—Carl Albert, 4614 Reno Road, 20008.
Administrative Assistant.—Charles L. Ward, 1417 Key Boulevard, Arlington, Va.,
22209.

OFFICE OF THE MAJORITY WHIP

Majority Whip.—Hale Boggs, 5315 Bradley Boulevard, Bethesda, Md., 20014.
Administrative Assistant.—D. B. Hardeman, 2500 Q Street.
Officer Manager.—Margaret M. Broome, 325 C Street SE.

OFFICE OF THE MINORITY LEADER

Floor Leader.—Gerald R. Ford, 514 Crown View Drive, Alexandria, Va.
Administrative Assistant.—Frank Meyer, 5203 Fenwood Avenue SE., 20021.
Executive Secretary.—Mildred Leonard, 4545 Connecticut Avenue, 20008.
Legislative Clerk.—Josephine E. Wilson, 3816 Van Ness Street, 20016.
Press Secretary.—James M. Mudge, 525 Thayer Avenue, Apt. 102, Silver Spring,
Md.
Secretaries.—James H. Bersie, 800 Fourth Street SW., 20024; Anne Kamstra,
6601 Fourteenth Street, 20012; Ruth Mahder, 2000 North Adams Street,
Arlington, Va.; George Willis, 1818 Kalorama Road, 20009; Esther Dukov,
808 A Street SE., 20003.

OFFICE OF THE MINORITY WHIP

Minority Whip.—Leslie C. Arends, 4815 Dexter Street.
Administrative Assistant.—William R. Pitts, 1725 38th Street SE.

OFFICE OF THE CLERK

RALPH R. ROBERTS, Clerk of the House of Representatives, of Rockport, Ind.; education at Indiana University, United States Naval Academy, United States Military Academy, and National University Law School; enlisted and served overseas with United States Marines in the First World War; secretary to Member of Congress from Indiana 1923 to 1925; secretary, Democratic National Congressional Committee 1925 to 1930; served with Speaker's Bureau, Democratic National Committee, during the campaign of 1928; County chairman, Spencer County, Ind.; practiced law in Rockport, Ind.; special officer of the House; elected Doorkeeper for 78th and 79th Congresses; elected officer of Democratic National Convention at Chicago in 1944; elected Minority Clerk in 1947; elected Clerk of the House for the 81st, 82d, 84th, 85th, 86th, 87th, 88th, and 89th Congresses.

Administrative Assistant.—Ray M. Young, 11809 Hickory Drive, 20022.
Secretary.—Michael Dee Vandeveer, 433 New Jersey Avenue SE.
Journal Clerk.—Francis P. Hoye, 1737 Highwood Place SE.
  Assistants.—Francis A. Del Balzo, 11708 Hatcher Place, Wheaton, Md.; W. H. Fountain, Jr.; Lee Thomas, 5120 Van Ness Street; Robert F. Hardgrove, 1310 North Oak Street, Arlington, Va.; Margaret Marsh.
Reading Clerks.—Charles W. Hackney, Jr., 110 D Street SE.; Joe Bartlett, 6646 Barnaby Street.
Legal Adviser.—William E. Brady.
Tally Clerk.—Thomas V. Cooke.
  Assistants.—William H. Hickson, 3800 39th Street; Curtis Christianson, 893 North Kentucky Street, Arlington, Va.
Enrolling Clerk.—James E. Kent, 6808 Kerby Drive, Oxon Hill, Md.
  Assistants.—Louis Breskin, Continental Hotel; H. Robert Ferneau, 4520 Jamestown Road, Westmoreland Hills, Md.
Administrative Assistant for Budget and Finance.—H. Newlin Megill, 4405 35th Street; Chief Auditor, Arlen V. Mitchell, Disbursing Clerks: Harry M. Livingston, 5401 Christy Drive, Springfield, Md., Frederick M. Kissinger, Brandywine, Md., Robert Crosser, Caroline Schaefle, Ralph J. Devlin, Josephine B. Neuman, Madeline Jones, Eleanor Williamson, Dora-Ann Purtell, Juanita L. Entrekin, Don C. Gibson, Asselia S. Lichliter, Margaret Brennan, David G. Phillips, Evelyn Creel Brady, Lucy Gossett, Nancy Calender, Betty Jane Burkholder, Janeen Arguelles, Anne L. Wanamaker, Sophie A. Siamis, Marvin R. Evans.
File Clerk.—Peter Lektrich, 110 D Street SE.
  Assistants.—Victor Kennamer; Julia Virginia Whitamore, 200 C Street SE.; Lucye Summers.
Bill Clerk.—Madison F. Boyce, 812 Massachusetts Avenue NE., and Leesburg, Va.
  Assistants.—Byron C. Anglin, 509 Tennessee Avenue, Alexandria, Va.; T. Howard Dolan; Gregory S. Reising, Marcel L. Beitel.
Stationery Clerk.—John D. Penn, 7504 Highland Avenue, Springfield, Va.
  Assistant Stationery Clerk.—David R. Ramage, 4836 Red Fox Drive, Annandale, Va.
    Assistants.—Willard Stevens, Lonas M. Hinton, Lelia Parker, Christopher Cooney, Simon Halle, Albert M. Smith, Harry Hall, Catherine Miles, Marianne Lemucchi, Jo Anne Pate, G. G. Garcia.
    Laborers.—Dennis Mosby, Stanley Smith, Charles Jones, Thomas Richmond.
House Library.—Librarian, Sally Morgan, 1530 16th Street; Assistants, James C. Healey, Jr., John P. Jenkins, Edward Shaw.
Capitol Law Library.—Library Assistants: Imogene Ward, George Treasurer.
Daily Digest.—Editor, Jerry E. Allen, 5906 Forest Road, Cheverly, Md.; Assistant Editor, John A. Roberts, 9301 Ogden Place, Greenwood Forest, Md.; Secretary, Barbara Hunter.
Property Custodian.—Edward B. Carney, 3701 Massachusetts Avenue.
  Assistant Property Custodians.—Dillard C. Rogers; Edward T. Kellaher; Earnest J. Hirschfeld; James V. Maraney; George Wright; William A. Grant.

Electrical and Mechanical Equipment.—Administrative Assistant, Gladys
Gordon; Bookkeeper, Patricia Apcar; Technicians: Jerome J. Cantrell,
August Drive, Springfield, Va.; Richard Seward; Laborers: Nathaniel Moody,
James L. Carter; Messengers: David Jones, Austin McFadden.
Furniture Shops.—Upholsterers: James W. Stephenson, Howard B. Stephenson,
Wilbur A. Shipley, Edward P. Polen, William W. Willett; Cabinetmakers:
Richard Sepesy, Guy Tasciotti, Jr.; Finishers: Orlie V. Barker, Lionel B.
Ridgell; Helpers: Harry M. Battle, Thomas Battle, Levy Ernest Dunn,
John Ingraham, James Toliver, Roosevelt Taylor, Henry Price, William
Cherry, George Taylor, Herman Richardson, Ralph Stewart.
Clerk's Document Room.—Superintendent, Anthony A. McNulty, 329 East
Capitol Street; Helpers: Winant S. Ellmore, 909 Quaker Lane, Alexandria,
Va., Seymour Weil; Laborer: Edward G. Bell.
House Recording Studios.—Director, James B. Perry; Bookkeeper, Fred Lopez;
Chief Cameraman, Leonard Hughes; Chief Radio Engineer, Paul Clark;
Cameraman, Ralph Grubbs; Motion Picture Soundman, Joseph Pettis,
Laboratory Technicians, Charles Grandmaison, Arthur N. Bienacker, Paul
V. Baisch, Fred Pettis, Ronald Mayer; Radio Technicians, William Clarke,
Carl R. Ruble; General Clerk, Eileen Goldbeck; Receptionist, Mary
Jennings; Stock Clerk, Peter Allen.
Assistant Chief Telephone Operator.—Adele M. Mallon, 2445 15th Street.
Messengers.—Richard E. Jenkins, Rex Harold Wellman.

OFFICE OF THE SERGEANT AT ARMS

ZEAKE W. JOHNSON, JR., Sergeant at Arms, Democrat, of Jackson, Tenn.;
born in Dyersburg, Tenn., on April 2, 1910; Assistant Sergeant at Arms, 1937 to
1942; enlisted in United States Coast Guard, October 1, 1942, honorably discharged September 8, 1945; elected Sergeant at Arms of the United States House
of Representatives on January 5, 1955; address: 100 Maryland Avenue NE.,
20002.

Secretary.—Eleanor A. Sharkey, 3211 Pickwick Lane, Chevy Chase, Md.
Bank Manager.—Elwyn G. Riaden, 6108 Foxhill Street, Springfield, Va.
Assistant Cashiers.—H. Eldred Wilson, 3968 Second Street SW.; Stockton M.
Hotze, 409 North George Mason Drive, Arlington, Va.
Payroll and Reports Clerk.—Margaret L. Fela, 1111 Army and Navy Drive,
Arlington, Va.
Bookkeepers.—Walter J. Behrens, 7869 Pennsylvania Avenue SE.; Charles A.
Mallon, Riverdale Towers, 5600 54th Avenue, Riverdale, Md.
Retirement Officer.—William Johnson, 415 Juniper Lane, Falls Church, Va.
Clerk.—Eleanor Ann Tydings, 3340 Prospect Street
Deputy Sergeant at Arms in Charge of Mace.—Kenneth R. Harding, 6936 Greentree
Drive, Lake Barcroft, Falls Church, Va.
Deputy Sergeant at Arms in Charge of Pairs.—D. Thomas Iorio, 9107 Waldon
Road, Silver Spring, Md.
Special Assistant to Sergeant at Arms.—John L. Sullivan, 120 C Street NE.
Clerk-Messenger.—Leo Glascoe, 4243 Blaine Street NE.

OFFICE OF THE DOORKEEPER

WILLIAM M. MILLER, Doorkeeper, 3119 North Harrison Street, Arlington, Va.,
22207; phone, KEnmore 8–2532; born at Pascagoula, Miss., July 20, 1909; graduated Pascagoula High School; Harrison-Stone-Jackson Junior College, Perkinston,
Miss.; and attended George Washington Law School; Doctor of Laws, Atlanta
Law School, Atlanta, Ga.; married his nurse, the former Mable Breeland, of
Tylertown, Miss., and they have one daughter, Sarah Patsy; has worked in the
House Post Office; as messenger to the Doorkeeper; Assistant Sergeant at Arms;
Minority (Democratic) Doorkeeper in the 80th and 83d Congresses; and elected
Doorkeeper of the House for the 81st, 82d, 84th, 85th, 86th, 87th, 88th, and 89th
Congresses; served as Assistant Sergeant at Arms for the 1944 Democratic

National Convention, and as Chief Doorkeeper at the 1948, 1952, 1956, and 1964 Democratic National Conventions; Mason (Thirty-second Degree) and Shriner; member of the Memorial Baptist Church.

Secretary to the Doorkeeper.—Mildred Basinger, 3800 V Street SE., 20020.
Janitor-Messenger.—Carl E. Sommers, 2927 Stanton Road SE.
Majority Manager of Telephones.—C. H. Emerson, Continental Hotel.
Assistant Majority Manager of Telephones.—Arthur E. Cameron, 3926 Suitland Road.
Majority Chief Page.—Turner N. Robertson, 6202 Crestwood Drive, Alexandria, Va.
Special Employee.—Landon Mitchell, 9008 Waldon Road, Silver Spring, Md.
Chief Doorman—House Floor.—Warren Jernigan, 326 Independence Avenue SE.
Chief Doorman—House Gallery.—Albert D. Bryson, 9 Fourth Street NE.
House Custodian.—Daniel J. Moley, 4320 Nichols Avenue SE.
Assistant Custodian (Minority).—Herman T. Coiner, 3127-11 University Boulevard, Kensington, Md.
Minority Manager of Telephones.—Allan M. Ames, North Beach Park, Md.
Assistant Minority Manager of Telephones.—Robert Bauman, 819 Independence Avenue SE.
Minority Chief Page.—Thomas H. Tear, Viewtown, Va.
Supervisor Pages' Cloakroom.—Frank Cubero, 1511 S Street SE.
Prayer Room Attendant.—Fridge L. Jester, 1137 Wayne Road, Falls Church, Va.
Office of the Gallery Doormen, Chief.—Albert D. Bryson, 9 Fourth Street NE.
Doormen (Gallery):
   Charles G. Drago, 6604 Belcrest Road, Apt. K, Hyattsville, Md.
   John W. Truslow, 515 Seward Square SE.
   Homer Hall, 5601 35th Street North, Arlington, Va.
   William L. Lee, 3211 19th Street.
   William W. Belcher, 2021 South Fillmore Street, Arlington, Va.
   Richard L. Overgaard, 2004 G Street.
   John Miklos, 1810 Kenyon Street.
   Henry R. Hendley, 4804 30th Street South, Arlington, Va.
   Charles Cipriotti, 1708 Hartsdale Road, Baltimore, Md.
   A. J. Harty, 1731 New Hampshire Avenue.
   Thomas J. Duffley, Dodge House, 20 E Street.
   Lou Randall, 1626 28th Street SE.
   George L. Robinson, 5201 Addison Chapel Road, Beaver Heights, Md.
   James L. Whitten, 5804 Nebraska Avenue.
   Otis T. Bradley, 117 C Street SE.
   Donnie R. Patman, 2385 North Danville Street, Arlington, Va.
   Thomas Hart, 3731 39th Street.
   Robert Gaucher, 2411 32d Street SE.
   Robert J. Kelly, 3812 W Street.
   Irvin Oberman, 5615 Wesley Avenue, Baltimore, Md.
   William A. Maguire, 1618 Cliftview, Baltimore, Md.
   Richard Blackwell, 122 Falster Road, Alexandria, Va.
   John Gornik, 1022 Wahler Place SE.
   Roy W. Bickford, 1422 V Street SE.
Check Room Attendant.—J. Ralph Granara, Hotel Plaza.
Chief Floor Doorman.—Warren Jernigan, 326 Independence Avenue SE.
Doormen (Floor):
   Charles N. Baine, 23 Second Street NE.
   Charles Larry May, 320 G Street SW.
   Thomas J. Purdom, 1201 Courthouse Road, Arlington, Va.
   Fowler C. West.
   Etson D. White, 414 Seward Square SE.
   Thomas O. Sheffield, 101 Fifth Street NE.
   Francis P. McGrath, 6380 Jarrett Avenue.
   Jack F. Brown, 219 Buena Vista, McLean, Va.
   William G. Weissert, 1230 13th Street.
   James J. Montelaro, 220 C Street, Apt. 108.
   Robert Williamson, 13 Third Street NE.
   Richard L. Fagert, 3426 Tulane Drive, West Hyattsville, Md.

DOCUMENT ROOM

Superintendent.—Gilman G. Udell, 5907 Kimble Court, Falls Church, Va.
Assistant Superintendent.—Al T. Griffith, 3207 Old Dominion Boulevard, Alexandria, Va.
Special Searcher.—William Graf, Jr., 20 Randall Circle SE.
Counter Assistants:
   C. B. Slemp, II–2442 Lexington Street, Arlington, Va.
   Harold Hohnadel, 2480 16th Street.
   William J. MacInnis, 218 East Greenway, Falls Church, Va.
   Prentice Maxwell.
   Ernest Joynes, 3504 43d Avenue, Brentwood, Md.
   Drayne Conyers, 1404 Perry Place.
   Paul J. Connolly, 2774 Tivoly Avenue, Baltimore, Md.
File Clerks:
   Fred E. Claunts, Park Adams Apartments, Arlington, Va.
   Miles D. Simmons, 2405 Hannon Street, Hyattsville, Md.
   Eduardo Rodriquez, 116 North Carolina Avenue, SE.
Messenger–Counter Clerk.—Lindsay E. Patrick, 843 Crittenden Street NE.

PUBLICATIONS DISTRIBUTION SERVICE

Chief.—Eli S. Bjellos, 8804 Lanier Drive, Silver Spring, Md.
Assistant Chief.—Frank A. Bechtel, Hunting Towers, Arlington, Va.
Secretary.—Doris L. Gowen, 4806 Clark Street SE.
Operations Section Chief.—Garland Osborne, 412 North Garfield Street, Arlington, Va.
Operations Section, Assistant Chief.—W. S. Elgin, Clifton, Va.
Ledger Clerks.—Leo Bryan Mosley, 500 A Street SE.
   Virginia N. Kidd, 502 A Street SE.
   Stanley M. Billingsley, 3645 Sixth Street SE.

OFFICE OF THE POSTMASTER

POST OFFICE IN LONGWORTH HOUSE OFFICE BUILDING

H. H. MORRIS, Postmaster, New Castle, Ky.; born in Carrollton, Ky., September 23, 1911; son of former Representative Joseph W. and Mildred (Guillion) Morris; came to Washington January 4, 1932, on patronage of the late Virgil M. Chapman, Representative and Senator from Kentucky; married Lyda Secrest of Shelbyville, Ky., November 2, 1935; elected Postmaster on January 5, 1955; member of Baptist Church, Kappa Sigma and Phi Beta Gamma legal fraternity.

Assistant Postmaster.—C. Elmo Boydston.
Secretary.—Mary C. Bowman.
Superintendent of Mails.—Day: Charles Donelson; Night: Robert P. Gibson.
Clerk in Charge.—[Vacant.]
Counter Clerks.—Peter Benedict, Harold Grow, Jerry C. Pritchett, Helen D. Whitaker.
Foreman of Mail Platform.—Franklin S. Walker.
Foreman of Evening Shift.—Richard A. Jones.
Primary Sorters.—James H. Alston, Ernest Bowie, Walter R. Fatzinger, Thomas Flood, Danny Glenn, Nicholas Karas, Charles LeGrand, Samuel Miller, Edd C. Nolen, Garth Pincock, Thomas K. Rogers, Robert E. Sharkey, James C. Smith, Jethro Switzer, Matthew P. Ward, Jr., Robert G. Wedemeier.
Delivery Clerks.—Timothy Arbogast, Walter G. Brandt, Joseph A. Braun, Carl Brygger, Robert Contois, Jr., Allen W. Counts, Robert Curran, Thomas K. Dunn, Myron Fleming, Wilbur Glascoe, Robert Gutierrez, Benjamin B. Kessler, James P. McNeely, Roy W. Perry, John J. Skiffington, Jr., Keith A. Stubblefield, Alfred Treder, Harry Tweed, William Warren, John Wine, Jann L. Yuen.
Mail Collectors.—Parle Thomas Blake, Harry Korsover, Michael Levock, Don Preslik, Charles A. Puryear, Michael Sprague.
Custodial.—Thomas Lastrape, Mose McCoy, Robert Patterson.

BRANCH OFFICE IN CANNON HOUSE OFFICE BUILDING

Clerk in Charge.—Richard F. Nash.
Counter Clerks.—James C. Butts, Lee Leonard Garling, Jr., William G. Yates, Jr.

BRANCH OFFICE IN CAPITOL

Clerk in Charge.—Reatha Perkins.
Counter Clerk.—Clarence Parker.

MINORITY EMPLOYEES

House of Representatives

Room HB–13, Capitol. Phone, 225–2139, 225–3479, or 225–3991 (Code 180)

Clerk to the Minority.—Harry L. Brookshire, 5017 Allan Road, Bethesda, Md. (Washington, D.C., 20016) (phone, OLiver 2–8706).
Minority Sergeant-at-Arms.—William B. Prendergast, 3 Barry Avenue, Bay Ridge, Annapolis, Md. (phone, 301 892–4181).
Minority Doorkeeper.—William R. Bonsell, 3212 12th Street South, Arlington, Va. (phone, 671–4937).
Minority Postmaster.—Tommy L. Winebrenner, 112 Croton Drive, Alexandria, Va. (phone, SOuth 5–0956).
Minority Pair Clerk.—Walter P. Kennedy, 9804 Parkwood Drive, Bethesda, Md. (phone, WHitehall 2–2345).

MAJORITY AND MINORITY ROOMS

B–99 and B–98, Cannon House Office Building

Majority Clerk.—Truman Ward, 3901 Illinois Avenue (phone, TAylor 9–3901).
Minority Clerk.—Thomas J. Lankford, 9209 Farnsworth Drive, Potomac, Md. (phone, 365–1633).

OFFICIAL REPORTERS OF DEBATES

Room H–132, Capitol. Phone, extension 5621

F. S. Milberg, 3 Pooks Hill Road, Bethesda, Md.
Elmer B. Clark, 604 Bennington Drive, Silver Spring, Md.
Frank E. Battaglia, 957 East-West Highway.
Albert Schneider, 2737 Devonshire Place.
Cleveland Tucker, Route 1, Athens Road, Burke, Va.
Jack Rund, 2389 North Quincy Street, Arlington, Va.
Julian R. Serles, Jr., 4225 31st Street North, Arlington, Va.
Clerk.—Sidney W. Williston. 1830 Longford Drive, Hyattsville, Md.
Assistant Clerks.—Bjarne J. Sigurdsen, 1921 U Place SE.; James W. Lea, Box 179, Prince Frederick, Calvert County, Md.
Expert Transcribers:
  Dorothy E. Bedell, 7225 Western Avenue.
  Andrew F. Gallagher, Jr., 8306 15th Avenue, Hyattsville, Md.
  Mary B. Murray, Shady Side, Md.
  Virginia C. Hammer, 5726 Clarence Avenue, Alexandria, Va.
  Walton H. Grubbs, 6706 Westmoreland Avenue, Takoma Park, Md.
  Darrell L. Montgomery, 4522 31st Street South, Arlington, Va.
  Faye G. Neil, 2110 North Monroe Street, Apt. 3, Arlington, Va.
Government Printing Office Clerk.—James L. Miner, 3800 38th Avenue, Cottage City, Md. (phone, APpleton 7–3694).

OFFICIAL REPORTERS TO HOUSE COMMITTEES

Room 156–A, Cannon House Office Building. Phone, 225-2627

Lanham Connor, 1712 North Jefferson Street, Arlington, Va., 22205.
Althea Arceneaux Eccles, 4808 Morgan Drive, Chevy Chase, Md., 20015.
Joseph J. Gimelli, 811 West Boulevard Drive, Alexandria, Va., 22308.
Raymond H. Lushin, 3900 Tunlaw Road., 20007.
Charles C. Dudley, 2720 North Kensington, Arlington, Va., 22207.
Robert C. Cochran, Route 1, Box 110, Vienna, Va., 22180.
Anton Papich, Jr., 7200 Masonville Drive, Annandale, Va., 22003.
Karl F. Veley, 18 Sixth Street, SE., 20003.
Clerk.—E. Homer McMurray, 8502 Irvington Avenue, Bethesda, Md., 20014.
Expert Transcribers:
  Phyllis V. Morgan, 1912 Neal Drive, Alexandria, Va., 22308.
  Gentle M. Bowers, 2150 Pennsylvania Avenue, 20037.
  Allene G. Johnson, 5709 Chevy Chase Parkway, 20015.
  Alexander S. Ornstein, 8101 Eastern Avenue, Silver Spring, Md., 20910.
  Mary J. Donock, 4151 Southern Avenue SE., 20020.
  Francis G. Shirley, 5413 Weymouth Drive, Springfield, Va., 22151.
  Ruth W. Hardin, 5167 Oakcrest Drive, Oxon Hill, Md., 20021.
  Mary M. Cochran, 4901 Seminary Road, Alexandria, Va., 22311.

OFFICE OF THE LEGISLATIVE COUNSEL

Room 159, Cannon House Office Building. Phone, 225-4951 (Code 180)

Legislative Counsel.—Edward O. Craft, 4826 Drummond Avenue, Chevy Chase,
  Md., 20015.
Assistant Counsel.—Ward M. Hussey, 312 Princeton Boulevard, Alexandria,
  Va.; David B. Carper, 1464 Rhode Island Avenue; George S. Skinner, 1047
  26th Road South, Arlington, Va.; Lawrence E. Filson, 11021 Brent Road
  Potomac, Md.; Robert L. Mowson, 2307 Executive Avenue, Falls Church,
  Va.; William P. Adams, 7311 Hallmark Place, Springfield, Va.; Robert F.
  Guthrie, 1816 North Lexington Street, Arlington, Va.; Grasty Crews II,
  4762 26th Street North, Arlington, Va.
Law Assistant.—David E. Meade, 2601 36th Street; Robert Riggs Nordhaus,
  120 Rumsey Court SE., 20003.
Clerk.—John L. Pestell, 2313 Chester Drive, Annandale, Va.
Assistant Clerks.—William S. Wilson, 7026 Nashville Road, Lanham, Md.; Cleo
  A. Garrett, 109 Fourth Street NE., 20002; Mary Elizabeth Jackson; Marianne
  J. Gscheidle, 7102 Country Club Court, Hyattsville, Md.; Sandra Smith
  7822 Lakecrest Drive, Greenbelt, Md.

OFFICE OF COORDINATOR OF INFORMATION

Room 546, Cannon House Office Building. Phone, 225-4446 (Code 180)

Coordinator.—Lawrence Sullivan, 6908 Oakridge Avenue, Chevy Chase, Md.,
  20015.
Executive Assistant.—Jesse Laventhol, 4892 Chevy Chase Boulevard, Chevy
  Chase, Md., 20015.
Research Specialist.—Jack B. Neathery, 10915 Montrose Avenue, Garrett Park,
  Md., 20766.
Editors.—Samuel R. Davenport, 407 South Cherry Street, Falls Church, Va.;
  Oscar L. Hume, 5136 Newport Avenue, 20016; E. A. Wilkins, 5804 Mada-
  waska Road, 20016.
Secretary to Coordinator.—Dora Lopez James, 3602 Third Street North, Arling-
  ton, Va.
Librarian.—Helen Roberts, 200 C Street SE., 20003.
Stenographer.—Nancy Laws Reifsnyder, 4201 Massachusetts Avenue, 20016.

MISCELLANEOUS OFFICIALS

ARCHITECT OF THE CAPITOL

ARCHITECT'S OFFICE

Room SB-15, Capitol Building.   Phone, 224-3121, extensions 2334, 2335, 2336

Architect.—J. George Stewart, 3701 Connecticut Avenue, 20008.
Assistant Architect.—Mario E. Campioli, 3810 Basil Road, McLean, Va., 22101.
Second Assistant Architect.—James H. Banks, 7921 Columbia Pike, Falls Church, Va., 22041.
Administrative Officer.—Charles A. Henlock, 3860 Columbia Pike, Arlington, Va., 22204.
Executive Assistant.—Philip L. Roof, 7717 Emerson Road, Hyattsville, Md., 20784.
Supervising Engineer.—Thomas F. Clancy, 2101 34th Street SE., 20020.
Coordinating Engineer.—Walter L. Rubel, 4502 Wetherill Road, Westmoreland Hills, Md., 20016.
Head, Contracts and Specifications Division.—Arthur L. Jenkins, 4611 North 37th Street, Arlington, Va., 22207.
Landscape Architect and Horticulturist.—Paul Pincus, 10823 Margate Road, Silver Spring, Md., 20901.
Chief Engineer (Power Plant).—William C. Justice, 9909 Edgehill Lane, Silver Spring, Md., 20901.
Electrical Engineer.—William M. Lanier, 1317 Seaton Lane, Falls Church, Va., 22046.
Air Conditioning Engineer.—Miles A. Bonnar, 6408 Queens Chapel Road, University Park, Md., 20781.
Elevator Engineer.—Elmer L. White, 719 Chesapeake Avenue, Silver Spring, Md., 20910.

SENATE OFFICE BUILDINGS

Room G-245, New Building, Phone, extension 3141

Superintendent.—J. Lewey Caraway, 2105 Old Georgetown Pike, McLean, Va., 22101.
Assistant Superintendent.—William R. Lewis, 7310 23d Avenue, Lewisdale, Md., 20783.

HOUSE OFFICE BUILDINGS

Office on second floor, northwest corner, Cannon House Office Building. Phone, extension 4141

Superintendent.—A. Emmanuel Ridgell, 113 South Utah Street, Arlington, Va., 22004.
Assistant Superintendent.—Can M. Bates, Jr., 1409 Carol Lane, Falls Church, Va., 22042.

CAPITOL POLICE BOARD

Joseph C. Duke, Sergeant at Arms, United States Senate.
Zeake W. Johnson, Jr., Sergeant at Arms, House of Representatives.
J. George Stewart, Architect of the Capitol.

U.S. CAPITOL POLICE

Office in lower west terrace, room ST-3, Capitol. Phone, 225-5151 (Code 180)

Chief.—Carl D. Schamp, Deputy Chief, District of Columbia Metropolitan Police.
Captains:
   Leonard H. Ballard, 5818 Hanover Avenue, Springfield, Va.
   James M. Powell, District of Columbia Metropolitan Police.
   Howard B. Quantrille, District of Columbia Metropolitan Police.
   Herman W. Xander, District of Columbia Metropolitan Police.

369

Administrative Clerk.—John F. Hudak, 4700 30th Street, Mt. Rainier, Md.
Traffic Clerk.—Michael A. Searcey, 4207 58th Avenue, Bladensburg, Md.
Communications Clerk.—Harry B. Grevey, 2107 Ft. Davis Street SE.
Property Clerk.—George B. Carver, 1021 Arlington Boulevard, Arlington, Va.
Lieutenants:
  James H. Boyer, 2318 High Street SE.
  Lewis F. Disney, 6304 Allentown Road, Camp Springs, Md.
  Wilbert McDonald, 2224 Jameson Street SE.
  Thomas Onofrio, 3425 Carpenter Street SE.
  William W. Kirby, 5812 Hanover Avenue, Springfield, Va.
  James T. Trollinger, 3107 Belleview Avenue, Cheverly Manor, Md.
  Robert W. Young, 6908 Quincy Street, Hyattsville, Md.
Special Officer:
  James M. Mills, 4522 South 31st Street, Arlington, Va.
Sergeants:
  James V. Blakney, 332 2d Street NE.
  Thomas C. Buckley, 2714 Minnesota Avenue SE.
  Terrence J. Collette, 331 First Street NE.
  James L. Goodall, Route 4, Box 456, Fairfax, Va.
  Willie C. Hall, Jr., 4109 55th Avenue, Bladensburg, Md.
  Howard H. Hastings, 7415 Keystone Lane, Forrestville, Md.
  Joseph H. Reed, 6835 Riverdale Road, Riverdale, Md.
  W. George Reid, 2414 Colebrooke Drive, Hillcrest Heights, Md.
  Robert R. Reuss, 5319 Birchwood Road, Oxon Hill, Md.
  Eugene J. Rucchio, 4201 31st Street South, Arlington, Va.
  Joseph R. Schaap, 11914 Centerhill Street, Wheaton, Md.

CAPITOL PAGE SCHOOL

Library of Congress, third floor, 20043. Phone, 225–2021 (Code 180)

Principal.—Henry L. De Keyser, 1424 Claremont Drive, Falls Church, Va.
Secretary.—Lucile F. Bungor, 5309 First Street.
Chairman, Department of Business Education.—Ruth H. Harper, 4801 Connecticut
  Avenue.
Chairman, Department of English.—Jessie L. Williams, 1902 North Rhodes Street,
  Arlington, Va.
Chairman, Department of Foreign Languages.—Florence C. Block, 6308 31st Place.
Chairman, Department of Mathematics.—Lewis R. Steely, 301 Waterford Road,
  Silver Spring, Md.
Chairman, Department of Science.—Naomi Z. Ulmer, 6605 Little Falls Road,
  Arlington, Va.
Chairman, Department of Social Studies.—Fred H. Hilton, Jr., 2500 Q Street.

OFFICE OF THE ATTENDING PHYSICIAN

Office in Capitol, Room H–166. Phone, 225–5421 (Code 180)

Medical Officer.—Dr. George W. Calver, 3135 Ellicott Street, phone, EMerson
  3–0444.

CONGRESSIONAL DAILY DIGEST

SENATE SECTION

Room H–113, The Capitol. Phone, 225–2658 (Code 180)

Senate Editor.—Frederick H. Green, 220 Cedar Lane, Fairfax, Va.
Senate Assistant Editor.—Dwight B. Galt, Jr., Box 164DX, R.F.D. 2, Edgewater,
  Md.
Senate Secretary.—Frances Harris Farmer, 2480 16th Street.

HOUSE SECTION

Room H–111, The Capitol. Phone, 225–2868 (Code 180)

House Editor.—Jerry E. Allen, 5906 Forest Road, Cheverly, Md.
House Assistant Editor.—John A. Roberts, 9301 Ogden Place, Seabrook, Md.
House Secretary.—Barbara J. Hunter, 4204 13th Street South, Arlington, Va.

CONGRESSIONAL RECORD
Office in Capitol, Room H–112. Phone, 225–2100 (Code 180)

Clerk in Charge at the Capital.—Raymond F. Noyes, 440 Orange Street SE., 20032, phone, 562–4832.

COMBINED AIRLINES TICKET OFFICE
Office in Capitol, Room H–101. Phone, 225–6653 (Code 180)

General Manager.—Randall J. Richardson, 1918 North Quantico Street, Arlington, Va.
Supervisor.—Edward J. Ryan, 734 10th Street SE., 20003.
Chief Agent.—Roberta Adams, 6820 Columbia Pike, Falls Church, Va., 22040.
Ticket Agent.—Gwen K. Ludwig, 4427 Arnold Road, Suitland, Md., 20023.

RAILROAD TICKET OFFICE
Office in Capitol, Room S–101. Phone, 225–5948 (Code 180)

Ticket Agent.—A. J. Klein, 4322 Monroe Street, Colmar Manor, Md.
In Charge Capitol Ticket Office.—A. E. Baker, 157 Upsal Street SE.

TELEPHONE EXCHANGE
Office, New Senate Office Building

Chief Operator in Charge.—Elizabeth Cole, 2900 O Street SE.
Assistants.—Adele M. Mallon, 2445 15th Street; Lucille Thomas, 2515 K Street; Mary L. Waters, 4201 12th Street NE.; Anna E. Rowe, 1913 21st Place SE.

WESTERN UNION TELEGRAPH CO.
Phones; Senate Office Building, extension 2181; Cannon House Office Building, extension 4181; Longworth House Office Building, extension 5181; House Press Gallery, extension 6530; Senate Press Gallery, extension 4330

House and Senate Legislative Representative.—Joseph G. Corona, 3564 Alton Place, 20808.
Manager Senate Office Building.—Lee Helbig, 4403 Warner Avenue, McLean, Va., 22101.
Manager New Senate Office Building.—C. A. Penkert, 401 Addison Road, Seat Pleasant, Md., 20027.
Manager Old House Office Building.—Charles E. Payne, 444 North Thomas Street, Arlington, Va., 22203.
Manager New House Office Building.—Alma T. Patton, 1413 Downing Street NE.
Offices in the Press Galleries:
  Senate Gallery.—James O. Mathis, 2901 18th Street.
  House Gallery.—Eleanor B. Lemmon, 3513 Minnesota Avenue SE.

GENERAL ACCOUNTING OFFICE LIAISON OFFICE
441 G Street, Room 7014. Phone, 386–4162 (Code 129, extension 4162)

Charles E. Eckert, 5700 Forest Road, Cheverly, Md., 20901.
Owen A. Kane, 202 Baden Street, Silver Spring, Md., 20785.
Lucius F. Thompson, 634 A Street SE., 20003.

UNITED STATES CIVIL SERVICE COMMISSION LIAISON OFFICE
Cannon House Office Building, Room 248. 225–4955 or 225–4956

Mary E. Conroy, 616 South Fairfax Street, Alexandria, Va., 22314.
Juliette Guidry, 2000 South Eads Street, Arlington, Va., 22202.
Ernest W. Huggs, 83 54th Street SE., 20019.

VETERANS ADMINISTRATION CONGRESSIONAL LIAISON SERVICE

Cannon House Office Building, Room 525; Capitol phone, extensions 2281-2282; Senate service, extensions 5351 and 5352

Director.—William C. Welch, 305 Cameron Street, Alexandria, Va.
Secretary.—Sandra J. Hinkson, 216 Maryland Avenue NE., Apt. 401.
House Staff:
    Chief.—David Pogoloff, 1523 Jasper Street, Silver Spring, Md.
    Dorothy K. Ham, 1109 Westley Road, Falls Church, Va.
    Mary R. Palmer, 3666 North Military Road, Arlington, Va.
    Frederick P. McAvey, 2519 39th Street.
    Robert F. Dove, 3410 Notre Dame Street, Hyattsville, Md.
Senate Staff:
    Chief.—Salvatore J. DePrenda, 1017 Baltimore Road, Rockville, Md.
    Arthur M. Gottschalk, 10545 Wheatley Street, Kensington, Md.
    Edward J. Kelleher, 2112 Lanier Drive, Silver Spring, Md.

ARMY LIAISON OFFICE

Rayburn House Office Building, Room B-325. Phone, 225-3853 (Code 180)

Col. Robert E. Lanigan, U.S. Army, 507 Eden Court, Waynewood, Alexandria, Va., 22308.
Lt. Col. James R. Koenig, U.S. Army, BOQ Maryland Hall, Fort Myer, South Area, Va., 22208.
Lt. Col. Richard T. McCrady, U.S. Army, 601 Pike Court, Alexandria, Va., 22310.
Maj. William W. Palmer, U.S. Army, 5105 First Street, Arlington, Va., 22203.
Maj. Zetta W. H. Jones, U.S. Army, 1200 North Nash Street, Arlington, Va., 22209.
Clara S. Deaton, 800 Fourth Street SW., 20024.
Lorena P. Dickerson, 826 North Iverson Street, Alexandria, Va., 22304.
Virginia Johnson, 2217 South Buchanan Street, Arlington, Va., 22311.

Senate Office Building, Room 152. Phone, 225-2881 (Code 180)

Col. Joseph S. Kimmitt, U S. Army, 1712 Beverly Avenue, McLean, Va., 22101.
Lt. Col. Guy G. McConnell, 801 Moss Drive, Annandale, Va., 22003.
Maj. Edward C. Peter, II, 4908 Ravensworth Road, Annandale, Va., 22003.
Maj. Dorothy R. Manning, 201 Massachusetts Avenue, NE., 20002.
Lee Amos, 301 G. Street SW., 20024.
Bette Cudworth, 2000 F Street, 20006.

Chief, Located in Pentagon— Extension 77271

Col. Ben. L. Anderson, U.S. Army, 3166 North 20th Street, Arlington, Va., 22201.

NAVAL LIAISON OFFICE

Room 326, Cannon House Office Building. Phone, extensions 5978, 5979 (Code 180)

Capt. Stephen S. Mann, Jr., USN, 315 Beverly Drive, Alexandria, Va.
Col. Richard M. Hunt, USMC, 1111 Army-Navy Drive, River House Apt. A-611, Arlington, Va.
Comdr. "H" R. Hunter, USN, 3732 Wagon Wheel Road, Alexandria, Va.
Comdr. Alma G. Ellis, USN, 817 E Street SE.
Janet L. Kulick, Corporal, USMC.
Cynthia L. Nelson, YN3, USN.

Room 152, Senate Office Building. Phone, extensions 4681, 4682 (Code 180)

Capt. Hoke M. Sisk, USN, 1810 24th Street.
Comdr. Jack A. Davenport, USN, 5104 25th Avenue, Hillcrest Heights, Md.
Judith Ann Bridges, SN, USN.

AIR FORCE LIAISON OFFICE

Cannon House Office Building, Room 538. Phone, extension 6656

Col. John M. Chapman, USAF, River House, 1600 South Joyce Street, Arlington, Va., 22202.
Lt. Col. John P. Moore, 504 Peace Valley, Falls Church, Va., 22044.
Maj. Harry M. Funk, USAF, Crystal House, 1900 South Eads Street, Arlington, Va., 22202.
Edith I. Johnson, Executive Central, 1201 South Scott Street, Arlington, Va., 22204.
Margaret J. DeCamp, Arlington Towers, M–413, 1111 Arlington Boulevard, Arlington, Va., 22209.
Warrie Cotton, 2825 Ninth Street South, Arlington, Va., 22204.
A/2C Ann Johnson, USAF, WAF Barracks, Bolling Air Force Base., D.C., 20332.

Old Senate Building, Room 152. Phone, extension 2481

Col. William F. Pitts, USAF, 2500 North Randolph Street, Arlington, Va., 22207.
Maj. Robert Q. Old, USAF, 607 Governors Court, Alexandria, Va., 22308.
Elizabeth A. Nelson, 6500 Cabin John Road, Springfield, Va., 22150.
Helen M. Jeffrey, 401 South George Mason Drive, Arlington, Va., 22204.

GENERAL ACCOUNTING OFFICE

General Accounting Office Building, 441 G Street, 20548.   Phone, 393-4621 (Code 129)

Comptroller General of the United States.—Joseph Campbell, 3111 Woodland Drive, 20008.
The Assistant to the Comptroller General.—Lawrence J. Powers, 6001 Ramsgate Road, Wood Acres, 20016.
Administrative Assistant.—Maude La Monte, 2500 Wisconsin Avenue, 20007.
Assistant Comptroller General of the United States.—Frank H. Weitzel, 6294 29th Street, 20015.
Administrative Assistant.—Margaret R. Bundick, 919 Frederick Street SW., Vienna, Va., 22180.

DIVISIONS

General Counsel, Office of.—General Counsel, Robert F. Keller, 5604 Namakagan Road, 20016; Deputy General Counsel, James E. Welch, 3034 Chestnut Street, 20015; Associate General Counsels: John T. Burns, 2014 Amherst Road, Lewisdale, Md., 20783; Ralph E. Ramsey, 811 Forest Glen Road, Silver Spring, Md., 20901.
Accounting and Auditing Policy Staff.—Director, Ellsworth H. Morse, Jr., 411 Huntly Place, Alexandria, Va., 22307; Deputy Director, Frederic H. Smith, 2800 Quebec Street, 20008; Associate Directors: Edward J. Mahoney, 1410 Oak Ridge Road, Falls Church, Va., 22042; Robert L. Rasor, 497 North Owen Street, Alexandria, Va., 22304.
Civil Accounting and Auditing Division.—Director, Adolph T. Samuelson, 2000 F Street, 20006; Deputy Director, Arthur Schoenhaut, 600 Bromley Street, Silver Spring, Md., 20902; Associate Directors: Philip Charam, 1801 Clydesdale Place, 20009; L. Kermit Gerhardt, 2800 Quebec Street, 20008; Lloyd A. Nelson, 12200 Brookhaven Drive, Silver Spring, Md., 20902; George H. Staples, 1809 Randolph Street NE., 20018.
Defense Accounting and Auditing Division.—Director, William A. Newman, Jr., 3745 30th Road North, Arlington, Va., 22207; Deputy Director, Charles M. Bailey, 11817 Kim Place, Potomac, Md., 20854; Associate Directors: Hassell B. Bell, 8410 Cathedral Avenue, Carrollton, Hyattsville, Md., 20784; J. Kenneth Fasick, 17 Renault Place, Sulgrove Manor, Alexandria, Va., 22309; Richard W. Gutmann, 2303 Surrey Lane, Falls Church, Va., 22042; James H. Hammond, 6206 Maiden Lane, Bethesda, Md., 20034; Harold H. Rubin, 1616 Belvedere Boulevard, Silver Spring, Md., 20902; Simmons B. Savage, Jr., 409 Jeffersond Street, Alexandria, Va., 22314.
International Operations Division.—Director, Oye V. Stovall, 4113 North Randolph Street, Arlington, Va., 22207.
Field Operations Division.—Director, John E. Thornton, 3801 Connecticut Avenue, 20008; Deputy Director, Hyman L. Krieger, 4811 Colleen Lane, McLean, Va., 22101.
Staff Management, Office of.—Director, Leo Herbert, 5228 32d Street North, Arlington, Va., 22207; Assistant Directors: H. Edward Breen, 4818 Kenmore Avenue, Alexandria, Va., 22304; Lawrence R. Kirvan, 4010 25th Road North, Arlington, Va., 22207.
Transportation Division.—Director, Thomas E. Sullivan, 4629 Tompkins Drive, McLean, Va., 22101; Associate Director, Joseph P. Normile, 4906 Brookway Drive, Sumner, Md., 20016; Assistant Directors: Angus K. McKinnon, 2819 Hardy Avenue, Silver Spring, Md., 20902; Fred J. Shafer, 7600 Wellesley Drive, College Park, Md., 20740.
Claims Division.—Director, Lawrence V. Denney, 4535 48th Street, 20016; Deputy Director, Charles M. Howard, 633 North Buchanan Street, Arlington, Va., 22203.
Administrative Services, Office of.—Administrative Officer, John F. Feeney, 1425 Rhode Island Avenue, 20005; Assistant Administrative Officer, Herschel J. Simmons, 1506 East-West Highway, Silver Spring, Md., 20910.

Personnel, Division of.—Director, T. A. Flynn, 5308 Briley Place, 20016; Assistant Director, V. J. Kirby, 2009 Lanier Drive, Silver Spring, Md., 20910.

Report Department.—Manager, George M. Sullivan, 1307 Woodland Terrace, Laurel, Md., 20810.

FOREIGN BRANCHES

European Branch.—Director, Edward T. Johnson, c/o American Consulate General, Platenstrasse 7, Frankfurt/Main, Germany.

Far East Branch.—Director, Charles H. Roman, Kikai Boeki Kaikan Bldg., No. 3—Tamachi 7—Chome, Akasaka, Minato-Ku, Tokyo, Japan.

REGIONAL OFFICES

Atlanta.—Regional Manager, Richard J. Madison, 734 Woodley Drive NW., Atlanta, Ga., 30318.

Boston.—Regional Manager, Joseph Eder, 224 Marlborough Street, Boston, Mass., 02116.

Chicago.—Regional Manager, Myer R. Wolfson, 6444 North Rockwell, Chicago, Ill., 60645.

Cincinnati.—Regional Manager, Kenneth L. Weary, Jr., 11029 Corona Road, Cincinnati, Ohio, 45240.

Dallas.—Regional Manager, Walton H. Sheley, Jr., 11032 Fernald, Dallas, Tex., 75218.

Denver.—Regional Manager, Stewart D. McElyea, 2447 South Colorado Boulevard, Apt. 431, Denver, Colo., 80222.

Detroit.—Regional Manager, Charles H. Moore, 354 Tannahill Street, Dearborn, Mich., 48124.

Kansas City.—Regional Manager, Forrest R. Browne, 6205 Elm Street, Kansas City, Mo., 64133.

Los Angeles.—Regional Manager, Harold L. Ryder, 14576 Greenleaf Street, Sherman Oaks, Calif., 91403.

New Orleans.—Regional Manager, Walter H. Henson, 4100 Davey Street, Apt. 20, New Orleans, La., 70122.

New York.—Regional Manager, Robert H. Drakert, 55 East End Avenue, New York, N.Y., 10028.

Norfolk.—Regional Manager, Clyde E. Merrill, 5645 Lawson Hall Road, Virginia Beach, Va., 23455.

Philadelphia.—Regional Manager, James H. Rogers, Jr., 104 Granville Drive, Haddonfield, N.J., 08034.

San Francisco.—Regional Manager, Alfred M. Clavelli, 12 Sunset Court, Menlo Park, Calif., 94026.

Seattle.—Regional Manager, William N. Conrardy, General Delivery, 128 Mt. Jupiter Drive, Issaquah, Wash., 98027.

Washington.—Regional Manager, Donald L. Scantlebury, 3503 Charleson Street, Annandale, Va., 22003.

LIBRARY OF CONGRESS

10 First Street SE.   Phone, STerling 3-0400 (Code 173)

Librarian of Congress.—L. Quincy Mumford, 3721 49th Street, 20016.
  Executive Assistant to the Librarian.—Mrs. Marlene D. Morrisey, 5023 North Washington Boulevard, Arlington, Va., 22205.

Deputy Librarian of Congress.—[Vacant.]

Assistant Librarian.—Mrs. Elizabeth E. Hamer, 6620 River Road, Bethesda, Md., 20034.
  Exhibits Officer.—Herbert J. Sanborn, 3541 Forest Drive, Alexandria, Va., 22302.
  Information Officer.—Helen-Anne Hilker, 4201 Cathedral Avenue, 20016.
  Publications Officer.—Sarah L. Wallace, 8705 Jones Mill Road, 20015.
  Information Systems Specialist.—Samuel S. Snyder, 10726 Saint Margarets Way, Silver Spring, Md., 20902.

Director of Personnel.—[Vacant.]
  Acting Director of Personnel.—Eugene C. Powell, Jr., 2222 Westminster Court, Falls Church, Va.

Chief Internal Auditor.—Ernest C. Barker, 314 A Street SE., 2003.

ADMINISTRATIVE DEPARTMENT

Director.—Robert C. Gooch, 4826 Langdrum Lane, Chevy Chase, Md., 20015; Paul L. Berry, associate director, 2104 Cascade Road, Silver Spring, Md.; 20902; Duard M. Eddins, executive officer, 3315 Brothers Place SE., 20032; Julius Davidson, assistant director for financial management, 4201 Cathedral Avenue, 20016.

Buildings and Grounds Division.—Merton J. Foley, chief, 2811 63d Avenue, Cheverly, Md., 20027; Edward L. Ay, Engineer-in-charge, 322 Scott Drive, Silver Spring, Md., 20904.

Guard Division.—John W. Cormier, captain of the guard, 220 C Street SE., 20003.

Collections Maintenance and Preservation Officer.—[Vacant.]

Office of Fiscal Services.—Arthur Yabroff, chief, 1850 Columbia Pike, Arlington, Va., 22204; William W. Rossiter, deputy chief and budget officer, 6511 Adelphi Road, University Park, Md., 20782.

Accounting Office.—William C. Myers, accounting officer. 318 Amherst Road, Bryans Road, Md.

Disbursing Office.—James A. Severn, Jr., disbursing officer, 2336 Skyland Place SE., 20020.

Office of the Secretary.—Mildred C. Portner, secretary of the Library, 1621 21st Street, 20009.

Photoduplication Service.—Donald C. Holmes, chief, 213 Shaw Avenue, Silver Spring, Md., 20904.

COPYRIGHT OFFICE

Library of Congress, 10 First Street SE., 20540

Register of Copyrights.—Abraham L. Kaminstein, 5407 Mohican Road, 20016; George D. Cary, Deputy Register of Copyrights, 6323 Western Avenue, 20015; Abe A. Goldman, General Counsel, 2834 28th Street, 20008; William P. Siegfried, Assistant Register of Copyrights, 7826 Lakecrest Drive, Greenbelt, Md., 20770. Barbara Ringer, Assistant Register of Copyrights for Examining, 5102 Fairglen Lane, Chevy Chase, Md., 20015.

LAW LIBRARY

Law Librarian and General Counsel.—Lewis C. Coffin, 6432 Barnaby Street, 20015. Francis X. Dwyer, associate law librarian, 4217 Oakridge Lane, Chevy Chase Md., 20015; deputy general counsel, William H. Crouch, 7522 Sebago Road, Bethesda, Md., 20034; assistant general counsel, William S. Strauss, 301 South Oak Street, Falls Church, Va.

American-British Law Division.—William H. Crouch, chief, 7522 Sebago Road, Bethesda, Md., 20034.

European Law Division.—Edmund C. Jann, chief, 802 South Royal Street, Alexandria, Va., 22314.

Far Eastern Law Division.—Tao-tai Hsia, chief, 7522 Sweetbriar Drive, College Park, Md., 20741.

Hispanic Law Division.—Mrs. Helen L. Clagett, chief, 2801 Quebec Street, 20008.

Law Library Reading Room.—James G. McEwan, librarian in charge, 320 Park Street NE., Vienna, Va., 22180.

Law Library in the Capitol.—Robert V. Shirley, attorney in charge, Senate Courts, 120 C Street NE., 20002.

Near Eastern and African Law Division.—Zuhair Elias Jwaideh, chief, 2828 Connecticut Avenue, 20008.

LEGISLATIVE REFERENCE SERVICE

Director.—Hugh L. Elsbree, 7203 Clarendon Road, Bethesda, Md., 20014; Lester S. Jayson, deputy director, 7512 New Market Drive, Bethesda, Md.; Charles A. Goodrum, coordinator of research, 2808 Pierpont Street, Alexandria, Va.; Burnis Walker, executive officer, 7344 Spring Road, Clinton, Md.

American Law Division.—Harry N. Stein, chief, 7520 Maple Avenue, Takoma Park, Md., 20012.

Economics Division.—Julius W. Allen, chief, 9901 Connecticut Avenue, Kensington, Md., 20015.

Education and Public Welfare Division.—Frederick B. Arner, chief, 427 Whittier Street, 20012.
Foreign Affairs Division.—William C. Olson, chief, 6713 Loring Court, Bethesda, Md., 20034.
Government and General Research Division.—Merlin H. Nipe, chief, 3009 30th Street SE., 20020; Harvey F. Baugh III, librarian, Congressional Reading Room, and supervisor, Saturday and evening services, 1717 20th Street, 20009.
Library Services Division.—Norman A. Pierce, chief, 5808 Carlyle Street, Cheverly, Md.
Natural Resources Division.—Tom V. Wilder, chief, 3100 Bel Pre Road, R.F.D. 1, Silver Spring, Md., 20906.
Science Policy Research Division.—Edward Wenk, Jr., chief, 4600 Oxford Street, Garrett Park, Md.
Specialists.—Asher Achinstein (senior specialist, price economics), 8504 Meadowlark Lane, Bradley Hills Grove, Bethesda, Md.; Richard A. Carpenter (senior specialist, science and technology), 9606 Wadsworth Drive, Bethesda, Md.; William A. Coblenz (specialist, social science), 1855 Taylor Street, 20011; Charles H. Donnelly (senior specialist, national defense), 401 Sixth Street SE.; Vincent A. Doyle (legislative attorney), 5138 Nebraska Avenue; Hermann Ficker (specialist, international finance and trade), 9008 Flower Avenue, Silver Spring, Md.; Eilene M. Galloway (specialist, national defense), 4612 29th Place, 20008; George B. Galloway (senior specialist, American government and public administration), 4612 29th Place, 20008; W. Brooke Graves (specialist, American government and public administration), 2940 Newark Street, 20008; Rieck Bennett Hannifin (specialist, Latin American affairs), 1378 Fourth Street SW.; Lawton M. Hartman III (senior specialist, science and technology), 2500 Q Street; Leon M. Herman (analyst, Soviet economics), 10027 Brunett Avenue, Silver Spring, Md.; John C. Jackson (assistant chief, economics division and specialist, fiscal and financial economics), 634 North Carolina Avenue SE., 20003; James W. Kelley (specialist, social legislation), 8602 Fremont Street, Hyattsville, Md.; Harold A. Kohnen (analyst in taxation and fiscal policy), 5435 Rosecroft Boulevard, 20022; Israel M. Labovitz (senior specialist, social welfare), 1370 Fourth Street SW., 20024; Ernest S. Lent (analyst U. S. foreign policy and western European affairs), 3405 Stanford Street, Hyattsville, Md., 20783; Helen E. Livingston (specialist, social legislation and assistant chief, education and public welfare division), 1520 32d Street, 20007; Allan S. Nanes (analyst in U.S. foreign policy), 1313 Ridgecrest Drive, Alexandria, Va.; Gustav Peck (senior specialist, labor), 4501 Connecticut Avenue; Howard S. Piquet (senior specialist, international economics), 2209 Yorktown Road, 20012; Charles A. Quattlebaum (specialist, education), 1022 South 26th Road, Arlington, Va.; James P. Radigan, Jr. (senior specialist, American public law), 1200 North Nash Street, Arlington, Va.; Mary Louise Ramsey (legislative attorney), 2022 Columbia Road, 20008; John Kerr Rose (senior specialist, conservation), 117 E Street SE 20002; Theodore M. Schad (senior specialist, engineering and public works), 4138 26th Road, Arlington, Va.; Freeman W. Sharp (legislative attorney), 6100 43d Street, Hyattsville, Md.; Norman J. Small (legislative attorney), 215 Constitution Avenue NE., 20002; William R. Tansill (specialist, American national government), 4302 Clagett Road, University Park, Md.; James R. Wason (specialist, labor economics and relations and industrial development), 2423 Foster Place, Hillcrest Heights, Md., 20031; Joseph G. Whelan (analyst, Soviet and East European affairs), 308 Fairchester Drive, Fairfax, Va.; Walter W. Wilcox (senior specialist, agriculture), 4810 Essex Avenue, Chevy Chase, Md., 20015; Sergius Yakobson (senior specialist, Russian affairs), 3518 Porter Street, 20016.

PROCESSING DEPARTMENT

Director.—John W. Cronin, 2129 32d Place SE., 20020; William J. Welsh, associate director, 4805 Edgefield Road, Bethesda, Md.; Edmond L. Applebaum, executive officer, 7322 Edmondston Avenue, College Park, Md.; Donald F. Jay, coordinator, P. L. 480 Programs, 60–A G Street SW., 20024; Jean B. Metz, selection officer, 2475 Virginia Avenue, 20027.
Binding Division.—George E. Smith, chief, 701 Venice Drive, Silver Spring, Md.

378 Congressional Directory

Card Division.—Alpheus L. Walter, chief, 4719 24th Street North, Arlington, Va., 22207.
Catalog Maintenance Division.—Alice F. Toomey, chief, 4200 Cathedral Avenue, 20016.
Decimal Classification Office.—Benjamin A. Custer, editor, 9305 20th Avenue, Adelphi, Md.
Descriptive Cataloging Division.—Lucile M. Morsch, 1579 Mount Eagle Place, Alexandria, Va.
Exchange and Gift Division.—Jennings Wood, chief, 6415 Park Street, Alexandria, Va.
Order Division.—Francis H. Henshaw, chief, 4802 R Street SE., 20027.
Serial Record Division.—Mary E. Kahler, chief, 712 Lakeview Drive, Falls Church, Va.
Subject Cataloging Division.—Richard S. Angell, chief, 4913 Flint Drive, 20016.
Union Catalog Division.—George A. Schwegmann, Jr., chief, 3534 Porter Street, 20016.

REFERENCE DEPARTMENT

Director.—Roy P. Basler, director, 3030 Lake Avenue, Cheverly, Md., 20785; John Lester Nolan, associate director, 4007 Dresden Street, Kensington, Md., 20795; John Charles Finzi, coordinator for the development and organization of the collections, 301 G Street SW., 20024.
Aerospace Information Division.—George A. Pughe, Jr., chief, 213 Grove Avenue, Washington Grove, Md., 20040.
Defense Research Division.—William T. Walsh, Jr., chief, 114 Eldrid Drive, Silver Spring, Md., 20904.
Division for the Blind.—Robert S. Bray, chief, Route 2, Herndon, Va., 22070.
General Reference and Bibliography Division.—Robert H. Land, chief, 220 Virginia Avenue, Alexandria, Va., 22302.
Hispanic Foundation.—Howard F. Cline, director, 1701 North Patrick Henry Drive, Arlington, Va., 22205.
Loan Division.—Legare H. B. Obear, chief, 2 Terrace Court NE., 20002; Library Station at the Capitol, Charles H. Stephenson, Jr., custodian, 1912 R Street SE., 20020.
Manuscript Division.—David C. Mearns, chief and assistant librarian for the American collections, 4740 Connecticut Avenue, 20008.
Map Division.—Arch C. Gerlach, chief, 5615 Newington Road, 20016.
Music Division.—Harold Spivacke, chief, 3201 Rowland Place, 20008.
National Referral Center for Science and Technology.—John F. Stearns, chief, 116 North Carolina Avenue SE., 20003.
Orientalia Division.—Horace I. Poleman, chief, 5 Bolling Road, Alexandria, Va., 22308.
Prints and Photographs Division.—Edgar Breitenbach, chief, 3223 Coquelin Terrace, Chevy Chase, Md., 20015.
Rare Book Division.—Frederick R. Goff, chief, 5034 Sherrier Place, 20016.
Science and Technology Division.—Dwight E. Gray, chief, 117 Fourth Street NE., 20002.
Serial Division.—Charles G. LaHood, Jr., chief, 10102 East Bexhill Drive, Kensington, Md., 20795.
Slavic and Central European Division.—Sergius Yakobson, chief, 3518 Porter Street, 20016.
Stack and Reader Division.—Edward N. MacConomy, Jr., chief, 3330–A South Wakefield Street, Arlington, Va., 22206.

THE LIBRARY OF CONGRESS TRUST FUND BOARD

[A quasi corporation, created by an act of Congress approved March 3, 1925, with perpetual succession and "all the usual powers of a trustee," including the power to "invest, reinvest, and retain investments," and, specifically, the authority to "accept, receive, hold, and administer such gifts, bequests, or devises of property for the benefit of, or in connection with, the Library, its collections .or its service, as may be approved by the board by the Joint Committee on the Library."]

Chairman.—Henry H. Fowler, Secretary of the Treasury.
Secretary.—L. Quincy Mumford, Librarian of Congress.
  Representative Omar Burleson, Chairman of the Joint Committee on the Library.
  Mrs. Eugene Meyer, 1624 Crescent Place, 20009.
  Benjamin M. McKelway, 4920 Palisade Lane, 20016.

GOVERNMENT PRINTING OFFICE

Corner North Capitol and H Streets, 20401. Phone, STerling 3–6840 (Code 149)

Public Printer.—James L. Harrison, 4000 Massachusetts Avenue, 20016.

Deputy Public Printer.—Harry D. Merold, 146 South Columbus Street, Arlington, Va., 22204.

Administrative Assistant to the Public Printer.—Felix E. Cristofane, 3901 48th Street, Bladensburg, Md., 20710.

Special Assistant to the Public Printer.—Robert E. Kling, Jr., 6105 43d Avenue, Hyattsville, Md., 20781.

Director of Personnel.—John H. Gruver, 6002 Welborn Drive, Wood Acres, Md., 20016.

Comptroller.—Frank Higginbotham, 6603 44th Avenue, University Park, Hyattsville, Md., 20782.

Director of Purchases.—Daniel H. Campbell, 4209 Van Buren Street, University Park, Md., 20782.

Plant Engineer.—Louis J. Naecker, Clarksville, Md., 21029.

Superintendent of Documents.—Carper W. Buckley, 2001 North Adams Street, Arlington, Va., 22201.

Technical Director.—Morris S. Kantrowitz, 2220 Westview Drive, Silver Spring, Md., 20910.

Disbursing Officer.—Walter Spauls, Jr., 1414 North Johnson Street, Arlington, Va., 22201.

Medical Officer.—Dr. Lester J. Dugan, 4760 Reservoir Road, 20007.

Production Manager.—Albert O. Luther, 147 North Park Drive, Arlington, Va., 22203.

Planning Manager.—James W. Tew, 9922 Markham Street, Silver Spring, Md., 20901.

Typography and Design Manager.—Frank H. Mortimer, 6029 Avon Drive, Bethesda, Md., 20014.

Assistant Production Manager.—Wallace L. Burton, 5010 Hollywood Road, College Park, Md., 20740.

Night Production Manager.—Joseph D. Mudd, 9303 Van Buren Street, P.O. Box 89, Lanham, Md., 20801.

Superintendent of Offset.—Herbert C. Much, 2719 Arvin Street, Wheaton, Md., 20902.

Superintendent of Letterpress.—Howard W. Amos, 4112 Beall Street, Landover Hills, Md., 20784.

Superintendent of Platemaking.—Donald G. DeGraw, 4610 Cedar Ridge Drive, Washington, D.C., 20021.

Superintendent of Binding.—Harold C. Leonard, 4513 Sangamore Road, 20016.

Superintendent of Composition.—Robert B. Willhide, Jr., 3513 Madison Street, Hyattsville, Md., 20782.

Superintendent of Field Service Division.—Mathew S. Stepienski, 4607 25th Street, Mount Rainier, Md., 20822.

Superintendent of Planning Service.—Russel L. Weaver, 20 Wessex Road, Silver Spring, Md., 20910.

Superintendent of Plant Planning.—William T. Meany, 4302 Russell Avenue, Mount Rainier, Md., 20822.

Superintendent of Typography and Design.—Clifford W. Shankland, 1410 Wade Place, Falls Church, Va., 22042.

Chief, Congressional Information Section.—Donald W. Casey, 3204 Toledo Place, Hyattsville, Md., 20782.

Congressional Record Clerk at the Capitol.—Raymond F. Noyes, 440 Orange Street SE., 20032.

BOTANIC GARDEN

West of the Capitol Grounds

Acting Director.—J. George Stewart, Architect of the Capitol, 3701 Connecticut Avenue, 20008 (phone, office, 224–3121, extension 2334).

Assistant Director.—Edmund E. H. Sauerbrey, 1911 17th Street SE., 20020 (phone, office, 224–3121, extension 6520).

Administrative Assistant.—James I. Jones, 7104 Alpine Street SE., 20028 (phones, office, 224–3121, extension 6520; home REdwood 5–5570).

Horticulturist.—Albert T. De Pilla, 636 Massachusetts Avenue NE., 20002 (phones, office, 224–3121, extension 6646; home, LIncoln 4–2658).

Clerk.—Eleanor K. Delhomme, 7101 Alpine Street SE., 20028 (phones, office, 224–3121, extension 6520; home, REdwood 6–6006).

CAPITOL BUILDINGS AND GROUNDS

THE CAPITOL

This building is situated on a plateau 88 feet above the level of the Potomac River and covers an area of 175,170 square feet, or approximately 4 acres. Its length, from north to south, is 751 feet 4 inches; its greatest width, including approaches, is 350 feet; and the geographic position of the head of the Statue of Freedom surmounting the dome is described by the U.S. Coast and Geodetic Survey as latitude 38°53'22.909" north and longitude 77°00'33.706" west from Greenwich.

Its height above the base line on the east front to the top of the Statue of Freedom is 287 feet 5½ inches. The dome is built of iron, and the aggregate weight of material used in its construction is 8,909,200 pounds.

The Statue of Freedom, 19 feet 6 inches in height, surmounting the dome is entirely of bronze and weighs 14,985 pounds. It was modeled by Thomas Crawford, father of Francis Marion Crawford, the novelist, in Rome, Italy, and the plaster model shipped to this country. It was cast in bronze at the shops of Clark Mills, near the Bladensburg Road in Northeast Washington. The cost of the bronze casting and the expenses in connection therewith were $20,796.82, and, as the sculptor Crawford was paid $3,000 for the plaster model, the entire cost of the statue, exclusive of erection, was $23,796.82. It was erected and placed in its present position December 2, 1863.

SELECTION OF A SITE FOR THE NATIONAL CAPITAL

When this Nation emerged victorious from its struggle for liberty, it had no site for its Federal Government. The Continental Congress, either through necessity or voluntarily, met in eight different cities: Philadelphia, Baltimore, Lancaster, York, Princeton, Annapolis, Trenton, and New York City.

The subject of a permanent Capital for the General Government of the United States was first approached in Congress on the 30th day of April 1783.

The Constitution of the United States, provided in Article I, Section 8, the following:

> "To exercise exclusive legislation in all cases whatsoever over such district (not exceeding ten miles square) as may, by cession of particular States, and the acceptance of Congress, become the seat of the Government of the United States, ..."

The State of Maryland, by Act approved December 23, 1788, did cede to Congress "any district in this State, not exceeding ten miles square, ..."

The State of Virginia, by Act approved December 3, 1789, also ceded "not exceeding ten miles square, or any lesser quantity . . . ."

These cessions of territory were accepted by Act of Congress approved July 16, 1790. "That a district or territory not exceeding ten miles square to be located as hereafter directed on the river Potomac, at some space between the mouths of the Eastern branch and Conogocheague, be, and the same is hereby, accepted for the permanent seat of the Government of the United States: . . . ."

President Washington, by Proclamation dated January 24, 1791, designated the experimental boundary lines of the District, as beginning at a point on Hunting Creek (in Virginia where it enters the Potomac River) and ordered the Commissioners appointed by him on January 22, 1791, "to survey, and by proper metes and bounds to define and limit the part within the same which is hereinbefore directed for immediate location and acceptance; . . . "

The lines designated in the proclamation of January 24, 1791, were approved by Congress but as the original act of July 16, 1790, required the location of the District "above the mouth of the Eastern Branch or Anacostia river," the act was amended March 3, 1791, as follows: "and that it shall be lawful for the President to make any part of the said territory, below the said limit, and above the mouth of Huntington (sic) Creek, a part of the said district," and also provided "That nothing herein contained shall authorize the erection of the public buildings otherwise than on the Maryland side of the river Potomac, as required by the aforesaid act."

After an agreement with the landowners of the area within the city proper on March 30, 1791, President Washington by proclamation on the same day, fixed the boundary as "Beginning at Jones's Point, being the upper Cape of Hunting Creek, in Virginia, and at an angle in the outset of forty-five degrees west of the north and running in a direct line ten miles, for the first line; then beginning again at the same Jones's Point, and running another direct line, at a right angle with the first, across the Potomac ten miles, for the second line; thence from the termination of the said first and second lines, running two other lines of ten miles each, the one crossing the Eastern Branch aforesaid and the other the Potomac, and meeting each other in a point."

On April 15, 1791, the cornerstone of the lines of the Federal territory was laid at Jones's Point "with great solemnity" in the presence of the Commissioners and a large number of persons.

Major Pierre Charles L'Enfant was entrusted to prepare plans for laying out the city into streets, avenues, squares, lots, etc., and the plan was carried out under the direction of Andrew Ellicott.

On March 2, 1797, President Washington, by proclamation, directed the trustees, Thomas Beall of George, and John M. Gantt, to "convey all the streets in the city of Washington as they are laid out and delineated in the plan of the said city . . . to the use of the United States forever, . . ."

The proclamation also described the public appropriations (later called reservations) as areas for public domain of which number two, including the Mall, East of 15th Street, was to be Capitol Square.

The area selected for "the Congress House" was on Jenkins' Hill, a part of Cerne Abbey Manor, owned by Daniel Carroll of Duddington, who was one of the original proprietors and a signer of the agreement of March 30, 1791, wherein it recites, "For the streets, the proprietors shall receive no compensation, but for the squares or lands in any form which shall be taken for public buildings or any kind of public improvements or uses, the proprietors whose land shall be so taken shall receive at the rate of £25 per acre, to be paid by the public." (Note: a pound of currency at that time was equal to $2.66+ or $66.66 per acre.)

Daniel Carroll of Duddington was a cousin of Daniel Carroll of Maryland, one of the original Commissioners of the city appointed by President Washington on January 22, 1791.

By Act of Congress approved July 9, 1846 (9 Stat. 35), the entire area previously ceded by the State of Virginia on December 3, 1789, was returned to that State as not being required or necessary for the use of the District.

PLANS FOR THE CAPITOL BUILDING

Following the selection of a site for the Capital, some little time elapsed before advertisements appeared offering a prize of $500, or a medal of the same value, to be awarded for the "most approved plan" for a Capitol Building. Some 14 plans were submitted—some writers claim 16—but of these plans none was wholly satisfactory. In October 1792, Dr. William Thornton, a versatile physician of Tortola, West Indies, requested by letter an opportunity to present a plan as within the terms of the original advertisement. The request was granted and his plan accepted by the Commissioners on April 5, 1793.

Affairs seemed to move rapidly in those days, for on September 18, 1793, the cornerstone was laid with Masonic ceremonies in the southeast corner of the north section of the building. Thornton's plan provided for a central section nearly square in area, surmounted by a low dome, this central section to be flanked on the north and south by rectangular buildings, with a length of 126 feet and a width of 120 feet. The northern wing was the first completed, and in this small building the legislative and judicial branches of the Government, as well as the courts of the District of Columbia, were accommodated at the time of the removal of the Government from Philadelphia, the legislative in 1800 and the judicial in 1801.

BUILDING OF THE CAPITOL

Development of the Thornton plan began with the construction of the first unit of the building, now known as the northern, or Supreme Court section. Three architects were employed on this work—Stephen H. Hallet, George Hadfield and James Hoban, architect of the White House. The construction of the southern section of the Capitol, now occupied by Statuary Hall, was carried out by

Benjamin H. Latrobe, and in 1807 the House of Representatives occupied this new legislative chamber. Previously, the House had met in the Supreme Court section of the Capitol and later in a temporary brick structure within the walls of the southern portion of the building, known as the Oven. The north wing was completed in 1800 and the south wing in 1811. A wooden passageway connected the two wings of the original building, and was still in use when the building was burned by the British on August 24. 1814.

The work of reconstructing the damaged interiors was begun by Latrobe, who continued the restoration until November 1817, when he resigned, and Charles Bulfinch, a prominent architect of Boston, Massachusetts, was appointed architect to continue the restoration and complete the central portion of the building. Bulfinch was occupied with this work from 1818 until its completion in 1829.

During the period of restoration and the completion of the central portion, Congress met for the first session after the fire, in Blodget's Hotel at Seventh and E Streets NW., and soon thereafter in a building erected for that purpose on First Street NE., on part of the site now occupied by the Supreme Court Building. Congress remained here until 1819 when the Capitol was once again ready for occupancy.

The original Capitol as completed in 1829 was built of Aquia Creek sandstone from Virginia. The structure was 351 feet 7½ inches in length at ground level and 282 feet 10½ inches in depth at ground level, including the East Portico and steps. The central element of the building was surmounted by a low dome, which was to be a dominant feature of the Capitol for more than a quarter of a century.

Following the completion of the original Capitol in 1829, and the termination of the services of Charles Bulfinch the same year, such architectural services as were needed were performed by different architects until 1851. By this date the expanding needs of Congress had made additions to the building necessary and plans for the present Senate and House wings drawn by Thomas U. Walter, an architect of Philadelphia, Pennsylvania, were selected in preference to others submitted.

On July 4, 1851, the cornerstone of the extensions was laid in the northeast corner of the House wing. Daniel Webster delivered an address at the ceremony, and portions of this oration have been quoted frequently through the years. The exterior marble for the Senate and House wings came from quarries at Lee, Massachusetts, and the marble for the columns from quarries at Cockeysville, Maryland.

The work of constructing the Senate and House wings was carried out under the architectural direction of Thomas U. Walter from 1851 until 1865, during his tenure as Architect of the Capitol, and thereafter certain uncompleted details were supervised by his successor, Edward Clark, whose service as Architect of the Capitol began in 1865 and continued until 1902. The present House Chamber was occupied for legislative purposes December 16, 1857, and the Senate Chamber January 4, 1859.

The addition of the Senate and House wings made the construction of a new dome necessary for the preservation of good architectural proportions. The dome of the original central portion of the Capitol was built of wood and covered with copper. This low dome, designed by Bulfinch, was replaced with the present cast iron structure, the work beginning in 1856 and being completed in 1865. The overall width of the dome at the base is 135 feet 5 inches. The rotunda, or interior of the dome, is 96 feet in diameter and its height from the floor to the apex of the fresco in the canopy is 180 feet 3 inches.

The Capitol has a floor area of 16½ acres, with approximately 540 rooms devoted to office, committee, storage, restaurant and other purposes. There are 658 windows and approximately 850 doorways. The dome receives light through 108 windows, and from the Architect's office on the basement floor to the top of the dome there is a winding stairway with 365 steps.

During the period from July 1949 to January 1951, under appropriations totaling $5,102,000, the roofs and skylights of the Senate and House wings and the connecting corridors were replaced with new roofs of concrete and steel, covered with copper.

The cast-iron and glass ceilings of the Senate and House Chambers were replaced with new ceilings of stainless steel and plaster, and a laylight of carved glass and bronze was placed in the center of each ceiling. Alterations and improvements were made to the interior of each Chamber, the cloakrooms and adjacent areas, and included improvements in air conditioning, lighting and acoustics. These alterations were the first major changes in the Senate and House roofs and Chambers in the 90 years since their initial occupancy. The roof of the central portion, however, had been reconstructed and fireproofed in 1902.

Plans for remodeling the Senate and House Chambers incorporated design elements from sources of Federal architecture used by Thornton and Latrobe in the Supreme Court and Statuary Hall sections of the Capitol, and from other buildings of the early Republic.

During the renovation program the Senate vacated the Chamber on three occasions to allow the work to progress. The first time was in 1940 when the temporary supports were installed under the old ceiling of the Senate Chamber. On this occasion, the Senate vacated its Chamber November 22, 1940, and returned to its Chamber January 3, 1941. The second time was in 1949 when the first-stage construction work was performed. On this occasion, the Senate vacated its Chamber July 1, 1949, and returned to its Chamber January 3, 1950. The third time was in 1950 when the second- or final-stage construction work was performed. On this occasion, the Senate vacated its Chamber August 11, 1950, and returned to its refurbished Chamber January 3, 1951.

In order that the House roof and Chamber improvements might be accomplished, it was necessary for the House to vacate its Chamber and meet in the caucus room in the Longworth House Office Building on three different occasions. The first time was in 1940 when the temporary supports were installed under the old skylight ceiling of the House Chamber. On this occasion, the House vacated its Chamber November 22, 1940, and returned to its Chamber January 3. 1941. The second time was in 1949 when the first-stage construction work was performed. On this occasion, the House vacated its Chamber July 1, 1949, and returned to its Chamber January 3, 1950. The third time was in 1950 when the second- or final-stage construction work was performed. On this occasion, the House vacated its Chamber September 1, 1950, and returned to its refurbished Chamber January 1, 1951.

EXTENSION OF THE CAPITOL

Under legislation contained in the Legislative Appropriation Act, 1956, as amended by Public Law 406, 84th Congress, provision is made for extension, reconstruction, and replacement of the east central portion of the United States Capitol and other related improvements.

Under the approved plans, a new front in marble, faithfully reproducing the design of the old sandstone front, has been constructed 32½ feet east of the old front. The east walls of the connections between the central front and the Senate and House wings have also been reproduced to the east. The old sandstone walls have remained in place and become a part of the interior wall construction.

This work was begun in 1958 and completed in 1962. The project was carried forward by the Architect of the Capitol under the direction of the Commission for Extension of the United States Capitol created by Public Law 406.

Authorized cost for this work, including repairs to and rehabilitation of the dome, construction of a subway terminal under the Senate wing steps and reconstruction of such steps, cleaning of the Senate and House wings, birdproofing the building, furniture and furnishings for the new areas, and providing improved lighting throughout the building, totals $24 million.

CAPITOL GROUNDS

The original Capitol Grounds, at one time a part of Cerne Abbey Manor, were, at an early date occupied by a subtribe of the Algonquin Indians known as the Powhatans, whose council house was then located at the foot of the hill.

These grounds, part of original reservation 2, were acquired under President Washington's proclamations of 1790 and 1797, for use as a site for the United States Capitol Building. These proclamations authorized the appropriation of all of reservation 2 which, in its entirety, included the "Capitol Square and the Mall east of Fifteenth Street West."

Additional ground (squares 687–688) was acquired under appropriations provided by Congress in 1872 and 1873 in order to obtain a better landscape surrounding in keeping with the Senate and House wings which had been added to the building since the acquisition of the original site. The purchase of this additional property completed the acquisition of the area known as the old section of the Capitol Grounds, totaling, in all 58.8 acres.

In the immediately ensuing years, under a plan developed by Frederick Law Olmsted of New York, the terraces were built on the north, west, and south sides of the building from 1884 to 1892; the entire grounds were developed and improved from 1874 to 1892.

During the period 1910–35 the Capitol Grounds were further enlarged and improved by the purchase, annexation, and development of 61.4 additional acres located north of Constitution Avenue.

During the period 1955 to 1957 part of the new area, located over and in the vicinity of the Legislative Garage, was reconstructed from funds provided in the Second Supplemental Appropriation Act, 1955.

Public Law 570, Seventy-ninth Congress, approved July 31, 1946, redefined the boundaries of the Capitol Grounds to include as a part of the Capitol Grounds the areas immediately surrounding the Senate and House Office Buildings and certain border streets and sidewalks, with the result that the area of the Capitol Grounds, developed as a park area, now totals 131.1 acres.

HOUSE OFFICE BUILDINGS

CANNON HOUSE OFFICE BUILDING (OLD BUILDING)

An increased membership of the Senate and House resulted in a demand for additional rooms for the accommodation of the Senators and Representatives, and on March 3, 1903, the Congress authorized the erection of a fireproof office building for the use of the House Members as office and committee rooms. The first brick was laid July 5, 1905, in square No. 690, and formal exercises were held at the laying of the cornerstone on April 14, 1906, in which President Theodore Roosevelt participated. The building was completed and occupied January 10, 1908. A subsequent change in the basis of congressional representation made necessary the building of an additional story in 1913–14. The total cost of the building, including site, furnishings, equipment, and the subway connecting the House Office Building with the United States Capitol, amounted to $4,860,155. This office building contains about 500 rooms, and was considered at the time of its completion fully equipped for all the needs of a modern building for office purposes.

LONGWORTH HOUSE OFFICE BUILDING (NEW BUILDING)

Under legislation contained in authorization act of January 10, 1929, and in the urgent deficiency bill of March 4, 1929, provisions were made for an additional House Office Building, to be located on the west side of New Jersey Avenue (opposite the first House Office Building).

The cornerstone was laid June 24, 1932, and the building was completed and ready for beneficial occupancy April 20, 1933. It contains 251 two-room suites, 16 committee rooms, each suite and committee room being provided with a storeroom. Eight floors are occupied by Members; the basement and subbasement by shops and mechanics needed for the proper maintenance of the building. The cost of this building, including site, furnishings, and equipment, was $7,805,705.

RAYBURN HOUSE OFFICE BUILDING (ADDITIONAL HOUSE OFFICE BUILDING)

AND OTHER RELATED CHANGES AND IMPROVEMENTS

Under legislation contained in the Second Supplemental Appropriation Act, 1955, provision was made for construction of an additional fireproof office building and other appurtenant and necessary facilities for the use of the House of Representatives; for acquisition of real property located south of Independence Avenue in the vicinity of the Capitol Grounds for purposes of construction of such building and facilities and as additions to the Capitol Grounds; for changes to the present House Office Buildings and changes or additions to the present subway systems.

All work is being carried forward by the Architect of the Capitol under the direction of the House Office Building Commission at an authorized limit of cost to be fixed by such Commission. Appropriations totaling $122 million have been provided to date for carrying forward work under this project through the fiscal year 1965.

Under this program, property consisting of seven city squares has been acquired. Contracts have been let for necessary architectural and engineering services for the project; for reconstruction of a section of Tiber Creek sewer running through the site of the new building; for excavations and foundations, structural steel, superstructure, furniture and furnishings for the new building; for a cafeteria in the courtyard of the existing Longworth House Office Building; and for an underground garage in the courtyard of the Cannon House Office Building and two underground garages in Squares 637 and 691, south of the Rayburn and Longworth Buildings.

The Rayburn Building is connected to the Capitol by a subway from the center of the Independence Avenue upper garage level to the southwest corner of the Capitol.

The building contains 169 congressional suites; nine full-committee hearing rooms for nine standing committees, 16 subcommittee hearing rooms, committee staff rooms and other committee facilities; a large cafeteria and other restaurant facilities; an underground garage accommodating 1,600 automobiles; and a variety of liaison offices, press and television facilities, maintenance and equipment shops or rooms, and storage areas.

The cornerstone was laid May 24, 1962, by Hon. John W. McCormack, Speaker of the House of Representatives. President John F. Kennedy participated in the cornerstone laying and delivered the address.

The building is being occupied early in 1965.

SENATE OFFICE BUILDINGS

OLD BUILDING

The demand for a building to be used for offices was greater for the Representatives, on account of the large number forming the membership of that body, and because the Members of the Senate were supplied with additional office space by the purchase of the Maltby Building, located on the northwest corner of B Street and New Jersey Avenue NW. However, the acquisition of this building supplied but a temporary purpose, and its condemnation as an unsafe structure created on the part of the Senators a desire for safer and more commodious quarters. Accordingly, under authorization of act of April 28, 1904, square 686, on the northeast corner of Delaware Avenue and B Street NE., was purchased as a site for the Senate Office Building, and the plans for the House Office Building were adapted for the Senate Office Building, the only change being the omission of the fourth side of the building fronting on First Street NE., this being planned for but not completed. The cornerstone of this building was laid without special exercises on July 31, 1906, and the building was occupied March 5, 1909. In June 1933 the building was completed by the erection of the First Street wing, construction of which was commenced in 1931, together with alterations to the C Street facade, and construction of terraces, balustrades, and approaches. The cost of the completed building, including site, furnishings, equipment, and the subway connecting the Senate Office Building with the United States Capitol, was $8,390,892.

NEW BUILDING

Under legislation contained in the Second Deficiency Appropriation Act, 1948, Public Law 785, 80th Congress, provision was made for an additional office building for the United States Senate with limits of cost of $1,100,000 for acquisition of the site and $20,600,000 for constructing and equipping the building.

The authorized limit of cost for construction and equipment of the building was increased to $23,446,000 by the Legislative Branch Appropriation Act, 1958, and Public Law 85–85, 85th Congress and to $24,196,000 by the Second Supplemental Appropriation Act, 1959, Public Law 86–30, 86th Congress. All work was carried forward by the Architect of the Capitol under the direction of the Senate Office Building Commission.

The site was acquired and cleared in 1948–49 at a total cost of $1,011,492.

A contract for excavation, concrete footings and mats for the new building was awarded in January 1955, in the amount of $747,200. Ground breaking ceremonies were held January 26, 1955.

A contract for the superstructure of the new building was awarded September 9, 1955, in the amount of $17,200,000 and the building is now completed. The cornerstone was laid July 13, 1956.

As a part of this project, a new underground subway system has been installed from the Capitol to both the Old and New Senate Office Buildings.

An appropriation of $1,000,000 for furniture and furnishings for the new building was provided in the Supplemental Appropriation Act, 1958, Public Law 85–170, 85th Congress. An additional appropriation of $283,550 was provided in the Second Supplemental Appropriation Act, 1959, Public Law 86–30, 86th Congress. The building was accepted for beneficial occupancy October 15, 1958.

CAPITOL POWER PLANT

During the development of the plans for fireproof office buildings for occupancy by the Senators and Representatives, the question of heat, light, and power was considered. The Senate and House wings of the Capitol were heated by separate heating plants. The Library of Congress also had in use a heating plant for that building, and it was finally determined that the solution of the heating and lighting, with power for elevators, could be adequately met by the construction of a central power plant to furnish all heat and power, as well as light, for the Capitol group of buildings.

Having determined the need of a central power plant, a site was selected in Garfield Park, bounded by New Jersey Avenue, South Capitol Street, Virginia Avenue, and E Street SE. This park being a Government reservation, an appropriation of money was not required to secure title. The determining factors leading to the selection of this site were its nearness to the tracks of the Pennsylvania Railroad and its convenient distance to the river and the buildings to be cared for by the plant.

The dimensions of the Capitol Power Plant, which was constructed under authorization of act of April 28, 1904, and completed and placed in operation in 1910, are 244 feet 8 inches by 117 feet, with a maximum height of 85 feet. A later additional building, for accommodation of shops and storerooms, is located near the power plant and is built of selected red brick, it being 90 feet long, 50 feet wide, and 2 stories high. The building is located upon concrete foundations resting upon 923 simplex reinforced concrete piles (originally 790; 133 added in 1951–52); the superstructure is of red brick. There are 2 Alphons Custodis radial brick chimneys 174 feet in height (reduced from 212 feet to 174 feet in 1951–52) and 11 feet in diameter at the top.

The buildings served by the power plant are connected by a reinforced-concrete steam tunnel 7 feet high by 4½ feet wide, with walls approximately 12 inches thick. This tunnel originally ran from the power plant to the Senate Office Building, with connecting tunnels for the House Office Building, the Capitol, and the Library of Congress, and has since been extended to the Government Printing Office and the Washington City Post Office, with steam lines extended to serve the new House Office Building, the Supreme Court Building, the Annex to the Library of Congress, and the relocated Botanic Garden.

Under authority of Public Law 413, 81st Congress, a new reinforced concrete walk-through tunnel, 10 feet 6 inches wide by 11 feet high, with walls of a minimum thickness of 14 inches, containing steam lines, condensate return lines, and chilled water lines, was constructed during the period 1952–54 from the Capitol Power Plant to the Senate Office Building. This tunnel was placed in service during the calendar year 1954, at which time the use of the section of the old tunnel under First Street between Independence Avenue and Constitution Avenue was discontinued. The new tunnel also serves the new Senate Office Building.

Three new steam generators, with a total steam generating capacity of 330,000 pounds per hour, were installed at the plant during the period 1951–53 and were placed in service in the calendar year 1954, at which time the old boilers in use for 30 years were abandoned.

In September 1951 when the demand for electrical energy was approaching the maximum capability of the obsolescent equipment at the Capitol Power Plant, arrangements were made under the authority of Public Law 413, 81st Congress, to purchase all electric service from the local public utility company and, simultaneously, to discontinue the generation of electrical energy at the Capitol Power Plant. The soundness of the judgment and engineering analysis which prompted these actions has since been confirmed by the actual increased demand for electrical energy during the past 11 years. Since September 1951 the simultaneous demand resulting from the increasing needs of the Legislative Buildings, the Library of Congress Buildings, the Supreme Court Building and the Capitol Power Plant has increased from 13,000 kw. in 1951 to over 22,000 kw. in 1963 and, during the same period, the energy consumption has increased from approximately 41,000,000 kw. hours to approximately 75,000,000 kw. hours annually. Furthermore, the imminent future coincidental demand for electric power is in the order of 32,000 kw. with a corresponding annual energy consumption of 110,000,000 kw. hours.

Under authority of Public Law 413 the electrical distribution systems in all buildings and facilities under the Architect of the Capitol have been converted from 25-cycle alternating current and direct-current to 60-cycle alternating current. On January 11, 1963, the last of the five AC/DC motor-generator sets in the Dynamo Room in the Capitol Building was permanently shut down and the old equipment in this room has been dismantled and removed from the Building

In 1935 the Congress authorized the air-conditioning of the Capitol, Senate and House Office Buildings and provided therefor an appropriation of $2,550,000 and, in 1937, an additional amount of $1,672,000, including authorization for construction of a central refrigeration plant to serve the systems. An addition to the Power Plant Building, 123 feet 2 inches long, 79 feet 6 inches wide, with a height of 37 feet 10 inches, was constructed to house six 800-ton reciprocating-type refrigeration machines, auxiliary apparatus and piping. This plant was placed in operation May 16, 1938, and was, at that time, the largest central chilled-water plant ever constructed. Under authority of Public Law 413, 81st Congress, the obsolete reciprocating-type refrigeration machines installed in 1938 were replaced by four 2,200-ton centrifugal-type refrigeration machines thereby increasing the capacity of the plant from 4,800 to 8,800 tons. Also a new cooling tower was installed on the Capitol Power Plant Grounds to replace the old River Pump House which, until that time, supplied condensing water from the Anacostia River for the old steam-electric generating equipment and the reciprocating-type refrigeration machines. The River Pump House has since been transferred to the custody of the Government of the District of Columbia. The four new centrifugal-type refrigeration compressors were installed during the period 1955–57. In addition to the Capitol, the two Senate Office Buildings and the two House Office Buildings, this refrigeration plant now serves the Library of Congress Annex and the United States Supreme Court Building which were originally supplied with refrigeration for air-conditioning by separate isolated plants in each building. New air-conditioning facilities for the Main Building of the Library of Congress, authorized under Public Law 87–130, 87th Congress, will be served by the central refrigeration plant and its chilled-water distribution system in the summer of 1964.

Under authority of Public Law 85–895, 85th Congress, a program for further expansion of the Capitol Power Plant has been authorized, to be carried forward by the Architect of the Capitol at a total cost of $6.5 million. This program is to effect the necessary enlargement of the capacity of the plant and its distribution systems to provide heat and refrigeration for the Rayburn House Office Building and other authorized improvements. Under this program two additional 1,100-ton refrigeration machines and a 6,600-ton cooling tower have been installed and placed in operation. Other work under this program now in progress includes the installation of two more 2,200-ton refrigeration machines, piping and auxiliary equipment. The construction of a buried chilled-water pipe line from the southeast corner of the Old Senate Office Building to the west side of the central portion of the Capitol Building was completed in March 1963. The construction of this pipe line provides an interconnection between the existing east and west chilled-water distribution systems to provide adequate and proper pressure differentials at all buildings when the Rayburn House Office Building is served by the central refrigeration plant. In anticipation of the installation of four additional steam boilers and two additional 2,200-ton centrifugal-type refrigeration machines, eight obsolete, disused boilers and four disused steam-turbine driven electric generators have been removed from the Capitol Power Plant under the authority of Public Law 85–895. During the calendar year 1964 the installation of the two new aforementioned 2200-ton refrigeration machines was completed and preliminary operating tests were performed successfully at the end of the 1964 cooling season. At the beginning of the 1965 cooling season operational tests will be completed when sufficient cooling load is available. Also during the calendar year 1964 the four new oil-fired steam generators were installed and these units will be ready for operation in the summer of 1965. A new railroad siding was completed in 1964 and is in operation. This installation accommodates 8 loaded coal cars of 70 tons capacity each, and 8 empty cars. The redesign of the track system on the Capitol Power Plant Grounds has not only provided the coal delivery capacity needed for the increased heating load but it also has released for future expansion of the plant facilities about 3½ acres of plant property not previously available for such purpose. The new railroad siding also makes possible more expeditious handling of coal cars and has eliminated the hazards associated with car derailments experienced with the old system of tracks.

CAPITOL DIAGRAMS

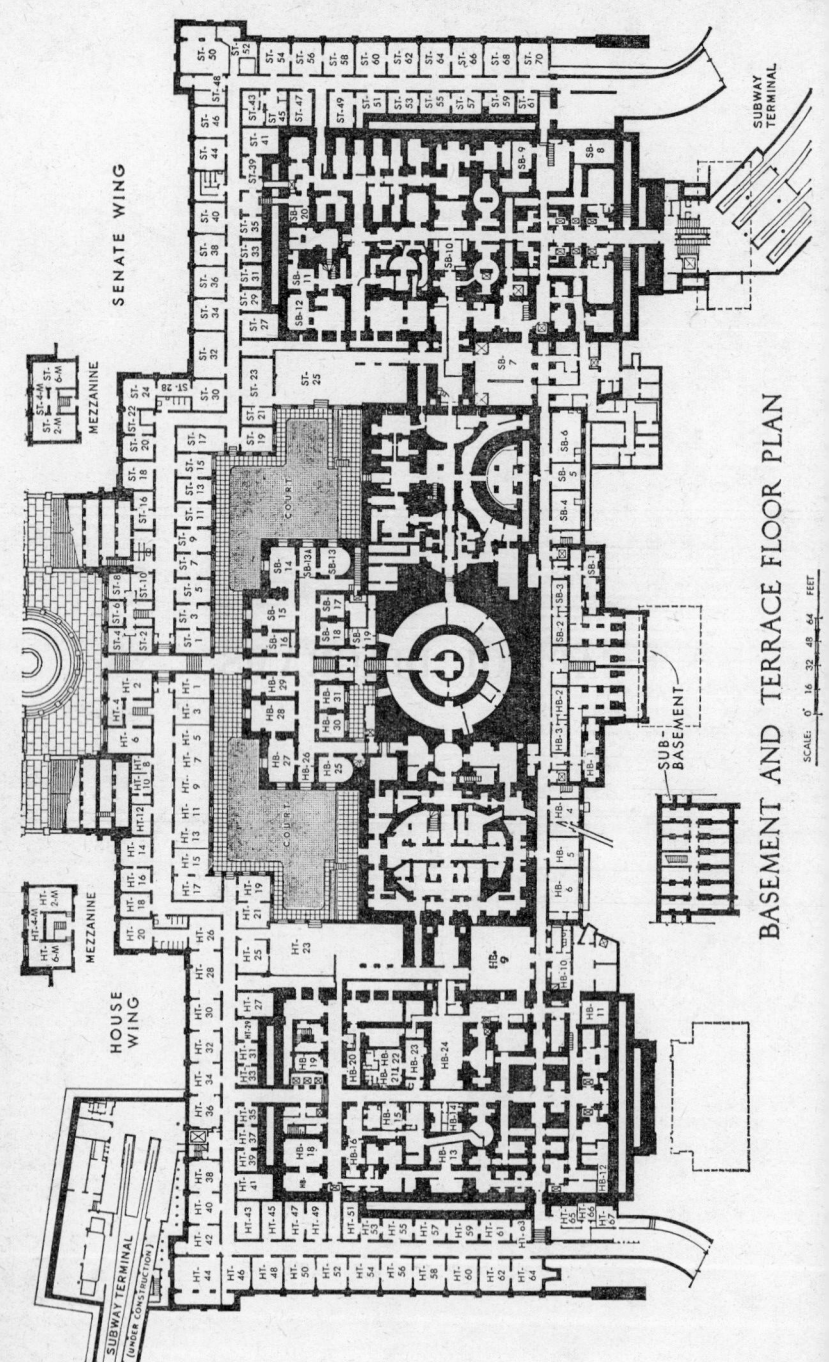

BASEMENT AND TERRACE FLOOR PLAN

SCALE: 0' 16 32 48 64 FEET

ROOMS IN BASEMENT AND TERRACE OF THE CAPITOL

HOUSE SIDE

TERRACE

HT-2, 4, 6. Architect's Office.
HT-8, 10. Room for page boys.
HT-12. Char force.
HT-14. Architect of Capitol, contracts division.
HT-16. Architect of Capitol, flag department.
HT-18. Repair shop, dynamo room.
HT-19, 21. Sheetmetal shop.
HT-28, 30, 32, 34, 36. Carpenter shop.
HT-40. Machine shop.
HT-42. Electrical shop.
HT-44. Storeroom.
HT-46. Plumber's shop.

BASEMENT

HB-4. Library of Congress station.
HB-6. House restaurant accounting office.
HB-9. House cafeteria.
HB-11. House restaurant storeroom.
HB-24. Kitchen.
HB-25. Coordinator of Information.
HB-26, 27, 28. Architect's Office.
HB-30. Office of Congressional Directory.
HB-31. House Foreign Affairs Committee.

SENATE SIDE

TERRACE

ST-1, 3, 5, 7, 9. Chief of Police.
ST-17. Sergeant at Arms.
ST-19. Electrical engineer.
ST-43, 45, 47, 48, 50, 54, 56. Recording studio.
ST-46. Printing Clerk.
ST-60. Janitor's office.

BASEMENT

SB-8. Democratic Senatorial Campaign photo room.
SB-10. Senate snack bar.
SB-11. Senate engineers.
SB-13, 13A, 14, 15, 16, 17, 18, 19. Architect's Office.

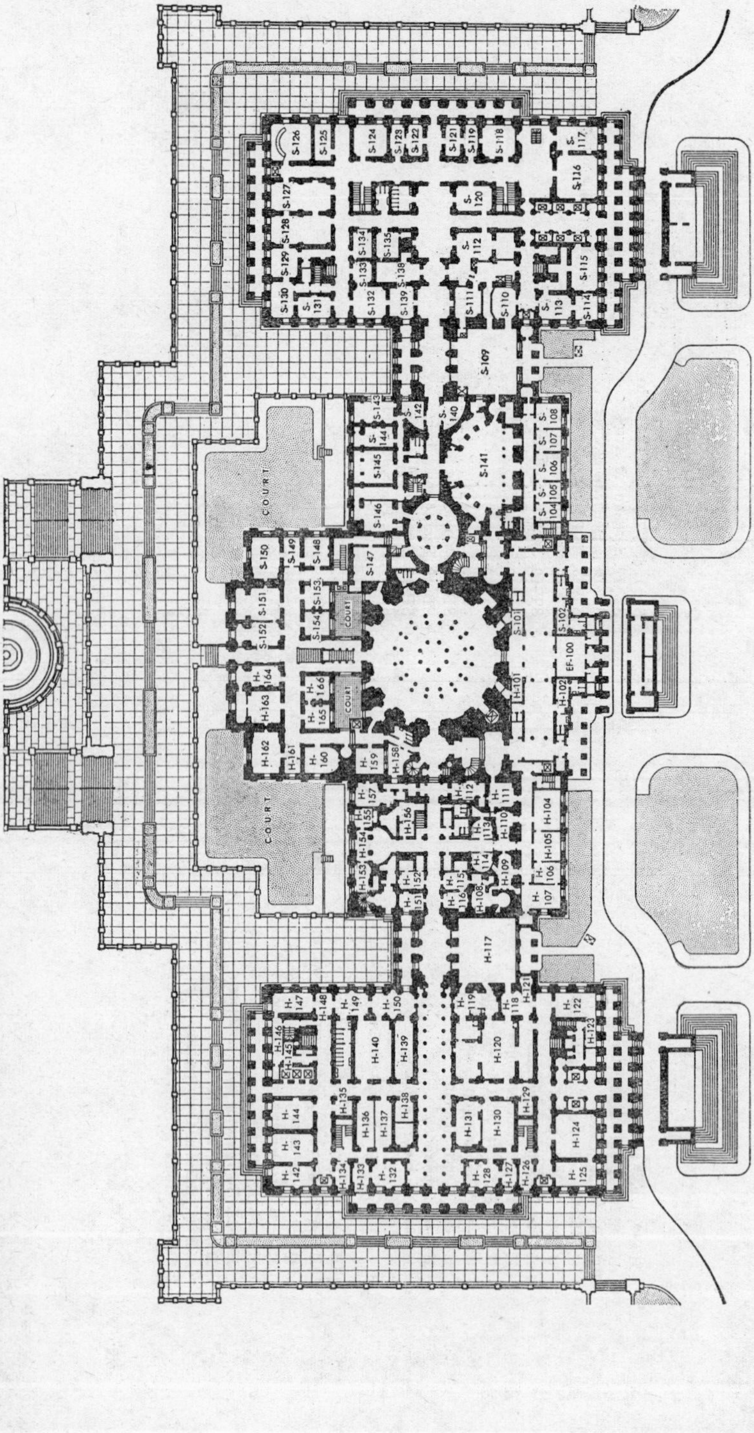

FIRST FLOOR PLAN

ROOMS ON FIRST FLOOR OF THE CAPITOL

HOUSE SIDE

H-101. Airline Ticket Office.
H-104, 105, 106. Clerk of the House.
H-107, 108, 109. House Democratic Whip.
H-110. House Chaplain.
H-111, 113. Daily Digest.
H-112. Congressional Record Office.
H-117, 118, 119, 120, 131. Restaurant.
H-122. Private dining room (Speaker).
H-124, 125. Office of Sergeant at Arms.
H-126. Parliamentarian.
H-129. Office, House Restaurant.
H-130. Members' private dining room
H-132, 133, 134. Official Reporters of Debates.
H-136. Barber shop.
H-140. Committee on Appropriations.
H-142, 143, 144. Subcommittee on Appropriations.
H-147, 148, 149, 150. Majority Leader.
H-151. Annex office, post office.
H-152. Clerk's storeroom.
H-153, 154, 155, 156. Office of Doorkeeper of the House.
H-157. Enrolling Clerk.
H-159, 160, 161, 162, 165, 166. Capitol Physician.
H-163, 164. House Subcommittee on Appropriations.
EF-100. Reception room.

SENATE SIDE

S-101. Railroad Ticket Office.
S-109, 110, 111, 112, 113, 114, 115, 120, 138. Restaurant.
S-116, 117. Committee on Foreign Relations.
S-118. Democratic Policy.
S-124. Republican Conference Committee.
S-125, 126, 127, 128, 129, 130, 131. Committee on Appropriations.
S-132. Parliamentarian.
S-139. Engrossing and enrolling clerks.
S-141. Old Supreme Court Chamber.
S-145. Senators' barber shop.
S-146. Appropriations Hearing Room.
S-148, 149, 150. Secretary to Majority.
S-151, 152. Joint Committee on Printing.
EF-100. Reception room.

Note: For Joint Committee on Atomic Energy—Use express elevator at southeast wall of Crypt, First Floor, to Committee Reception Room (H-403) on Fourth Floor of Capitol.

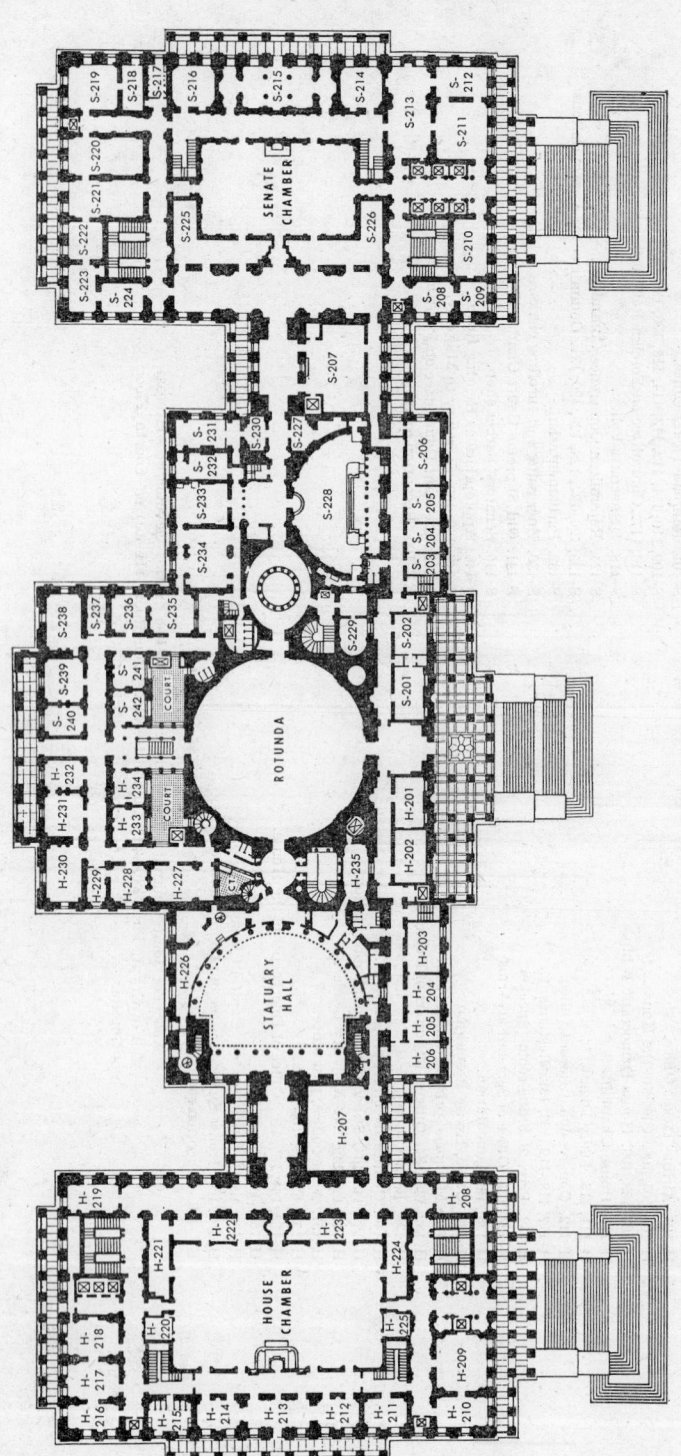

SECOND (PRINCIPAL) FLOOR PLAN

SCALE: 0 16 32 48 64 FEET

ROOMS ON SECOND FLOOR OF THE CAPITOL

HOUSE SIDE

H-201. House majority conference room.
H-202. House minority conference room.
H-203, 204, 205, 206. Speaker.
H-207. House reception room.
H-208. Committee on Ways and Means.
H-209, 210. Speaker.
H-211. Parliamentarian.
H-212, 213, 214. Members' retiring rooms.
H-216, 217, 218. Committee on Appropriations.
H-219. Republican Whip.
H-221, 222, 223, 224. Cloakrooms.
H-225. Library.
H-226. House document room.
H-227. House Subcommittee on Foreign Affairs.
H-230, 231, 232. House Minority Leader.
H-234. Prayer room.
H-235. Congressional ladies' retiring room.

SENATE SIDE

S-207. Senators' conference room.
S-208. Majority Leader.
S-212. The Vice President.
S-213. The Senators' reception room.
S-214. Formal Office of the Vice President.
S-216. Room of the President.
S-218, 219. Official Reporters of Debates.
S-220. Bill Clerk and Journal Clerk.
S-221. Chief Clerk.
S-222, 224. Office of the Secretary.
S-223. Secretary.
S-225, 226. Cloakrooms.
S-227. Executive Clerk.
S-228. Formerly the Old Senate Chamber and later the Supreme Court Chamber.
S-230. Senate Minority Leader.
S-233, 234, 235. Senate disbursing office.

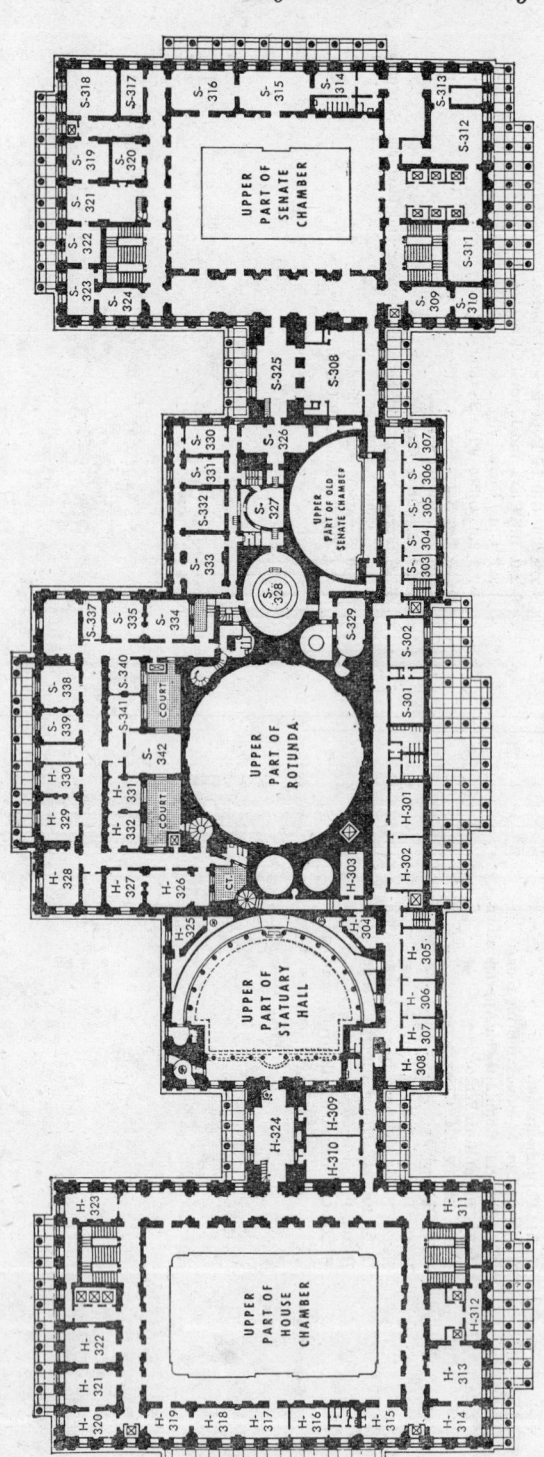

THIRD (GALLERY) FLOOR PLAN

SCALE: 0 16 32 48 64 FEET

ROOMS ON THIRD FLOOR OF THE CAPITOL

HOUSE SIDE

H-301, 302, 303, 304, 305, 306, 307, 308, 309, 310. House Appropriations Committee.
H-311. Ladies' retiring room.
H-312. Periodical Press Gallery.
H-313, 314. Committee on Rules.
H-315, 316, 317, 318, 319. Press Gallery.
H-320, 321, 322. Committee on Foreign Affairs.
H-323. Radio Correspondents' Gallery.
H-324. House Journal, tally, and bill clerks.
H-325. House document rooms.
H-326, 327. Representative Joseph W. Martin, Jr.
H-328, 329, 330. House Administration Committee.

SENATE SIDE

S-308. Senate document room.
S-309. Majority Whip.
S-311. Ladies' retiring room.
S-312. Radio-TV Correspondents' Gallery.
S-313, 314, 315, 316. Press Gallery.
S-317. Press Photographers Gallery.
S-318. Democratic Policy Committee.
S-320. Periodical Press.
S-321, 322, 323, 324, 319. Sergeant at Arms.
S-325. Superintendent of the Senate document room.
S-326, 327, 328. Senate document rooms.
S-332, 333. Senate Library.
S-337. Secretary to Senate Minority.

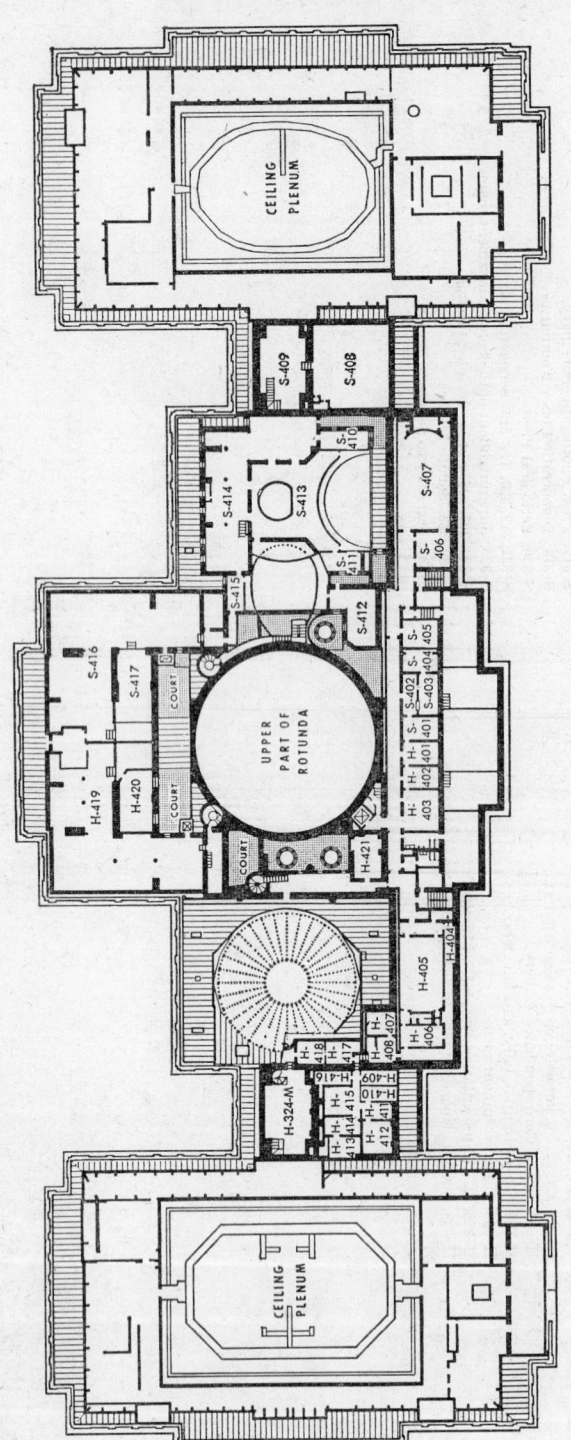

FOURTH (ATTIC) FLOOR PLAN

SCALE: 0   16   32   48   64   FEET

ROOMS ON FOURTH FLOOR OF THE CAPITOL

HOUSE SIDE

H-419. House document room (storage).
H-403. Joint Committee on Atomic Energy (reception room).

SENATE SIDE

S-413, 414. Senate Library.
S-416. Senate Law Library.

Note: For Joint Committee on Atomic Energy—Use express elevator at southeast wall of Crypt, First Floor, to Committee Reception Room (H-403) on Fourth Floor of Capitol.

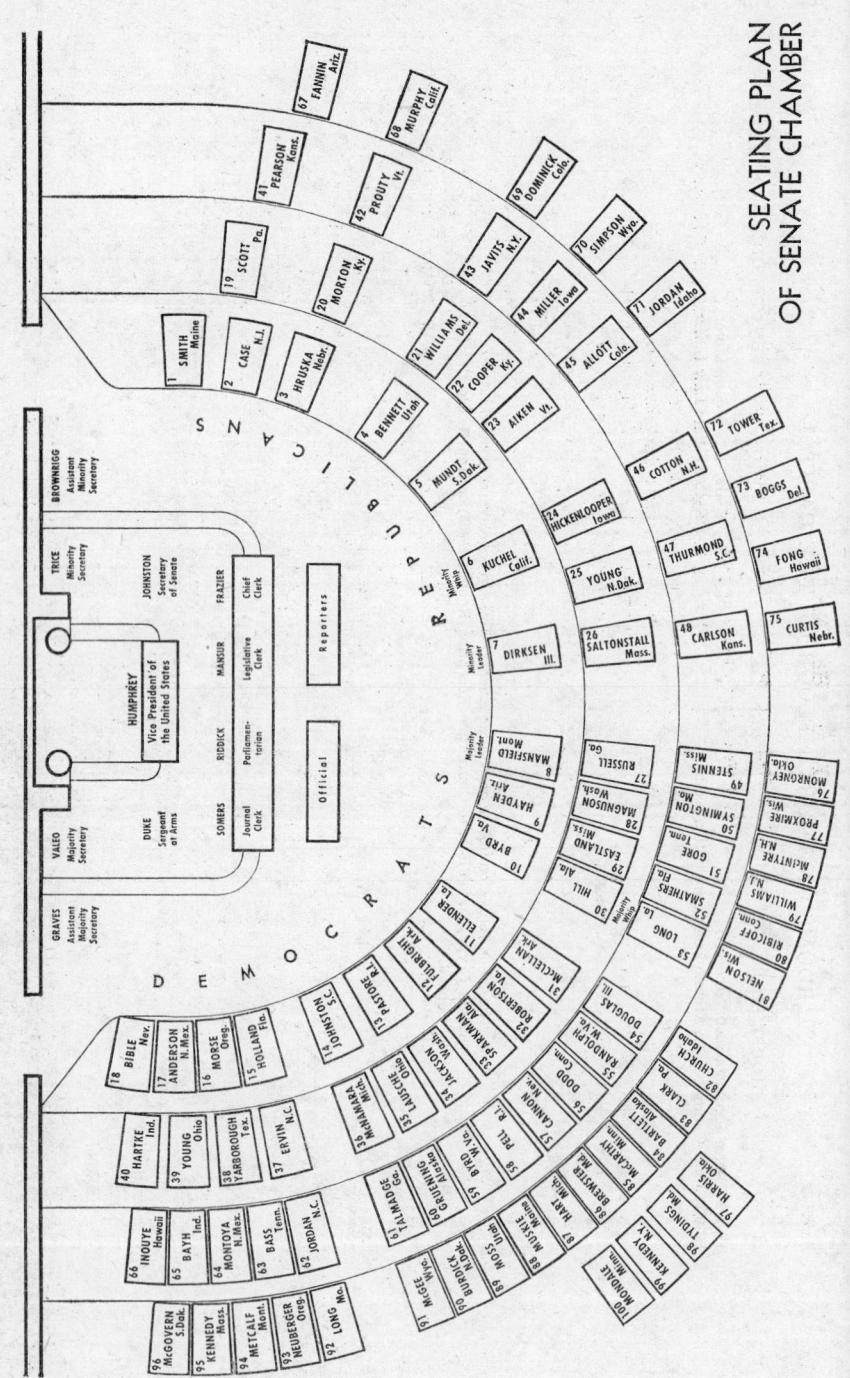

SEATING PLAN
OF SENATE CHAMBER

DIRECTORY OF THE SENATE

HUBERT H. HUMPHREY, *Vice President of the United States and President of the Senate*

CARL HAYDEN, *President pro tempore of the Senate*

FELTON M. JOHNSTON, *Secretary*
JOSEPH C. DUKE, *Sergeant at Arms*
FRANCIS R. VALEO, *Secretary for the Majority*
J. MARK TRICE, *Secretary for the Minority*
JOHN L. GRAVES, *Assistant Secretary for the Majority*

WILLIAM BROWNRIGG III, *Assistant Secretary for the Minority*
EMERY L. FRAZIER, *Chief Clerk*
FLOYD M. RIDDICK, *Parliamentarian*
EDWARD E. MANSUR, JR., *Legislative Clerk*
BERNARD V. SOMERS, *Journal Clerk*

REV. FREDERICK BROWN HARRIS, D.D., LITT. D., LL.D., *Chaplain*

23. Aiken, George D., Vermont
45. Allott, Gordon, Colorado
17. Anderson, Clinton P., New Mexico
84. Bartlett, E. L., Alaska
63. Bass, Ross, Tennessee
65. Bayh, Birch, Indiana
4. Bennett, Wallace F., Utah
18. Bible, Alan, Nevada
73. Boggs, J. Caleb, Delaware
86. Brewster, Daniel B., Maryland
90. Burdick, Quentin N., North Dakota
10. Byrd, Harry Flood, Virginia
59. Byrd, Robert C., West Virginia
57. Cannon, Howard W., Nevada
48. Carlson, Frank, Kansas
2. Case, Clifford P., New Jersey
82. Church, Frank, Idaho
83. Clark, Joseph S., Pennsylvania
22. Cooper, John Sherman, Kentucky
46. Cotton, Norris, New Hampshire
75. Curtis, Carl T., Nebraska
7. Dirksen, Everett McKinley, Illinois
56. Dodd, Thomas J., Connecticut
69. Dominick, Peter H., Colorado
54. Douglas, Paul H., Illinois

29. Eastland, James O., Mississippi
11. Ellender, Allen J., Louisiana
37. Ervin, Sam J., Jr., North Carolina
67. Fannin, Paul J., Arizona
74. Fong, Hiram L., Hawaii
12. Fulbright, J. W., Arkansas
51. Gore, Albert, Tennessee
60. Gruening, Ernest, Alaska
97. Harris, Fred R., Oklahoma
87. Hart, Philip A., Michigan
40. Hartke, Vance, Indiana
9. Hayden, Carl, Arizona
24. Hickenlooper, Bourke B., Iowa
30. Hill, Lister, Alabama
15. Holland, Spessard L., Florida
3. Hruska, Roman L., Nebraska
66. Inouye, Daniel K., Hawaii
34. Jackson, Henry M., Washington
43. Javits, Jacob K., New York
14. Johnston, Olin D., South Carolina
62. Jordon, B. Everett, North Carolina
71. Jordan, Len B., Idaho
95. Kennedy, Edward M., Massachusetts
99. Kennedy, Robert F., New York
6. Kuchel, Thomas H., California

35. Lausche, Frank J., Ohio
92. Long, Edward V., Missouri
53. Long, Russell B., Louisiana
85. McCarthy, Eugene J., Minnesota
31. McClellan, John L., Arkansas
91. McGee, Gale W., Wyoming
96. McGovern, George, South Dakota
78. McIntyre, Thomas J., New Hampshire
36. McNamara, Pat, Michigan
8. Magnuson, Warren G., Washington
94. Mansfield, Mike, Montana
44. Metcalf, Lee, Montana
100. Miller, Jack, Iowa
100. Mondale, Walter F., Minnesota
76. Monroney, A. S. Mike, Oklahoma
64. Montoya, Joseph M., New Mexico
16. Morse, Wayne, Oregon
20. Morton, Thruston B., Kentucky
89. Moss, Frank E., Utah
5. Mundt, Karl E., South Dakota
68. Murphy, George, California
88. Muskie, Edmund S., Maine
81. Nelson, Gaylord, Wisconsin
93. Neuberger, Maurine B., Oregon
13. Pastore, John O., Rhode Island

41. Pearson, James B., Kansas
58. Pell, Claiborne, Rhode Island
42. Prouty, Winston L., Vermont
77. Proxmire, William, Wisconsin
55. Randolph, Jennings, West Virginia
80. Ribicoff, Abraham A., Connecticut
32. Robertson, A. Willis, Virginia
27. Russell, Richard B., Georgia
26. Saltonstall, Leverett, Massachusetts
19. Scott, Hugh, Pennsylvania
70. Simpson, Milward L., Wyoming
52. Smathers, George A., Florida
1. Smith, Margaret Chase, Maine
33. Sparkman, John J., Alabama
49. Stennis, John, Mississippi
50. Symington, Stuart, Missouri
61. Talmadge, Herman E., Georgia
47. Thurmond, Strom, South Carolina
72. Tower, John G., Texas
98. Tydings, Joseph D., Maryland
79. Williams, Harrison A., Jr., New Jersey
21. Williams, John J., Delaware
38. Yarborough, Ralph W., Texas
25. Young, Milton R., North Dakota
39. Young, Stephen M., Ohio

DIAGRAM OF HOUSE CHAMBER

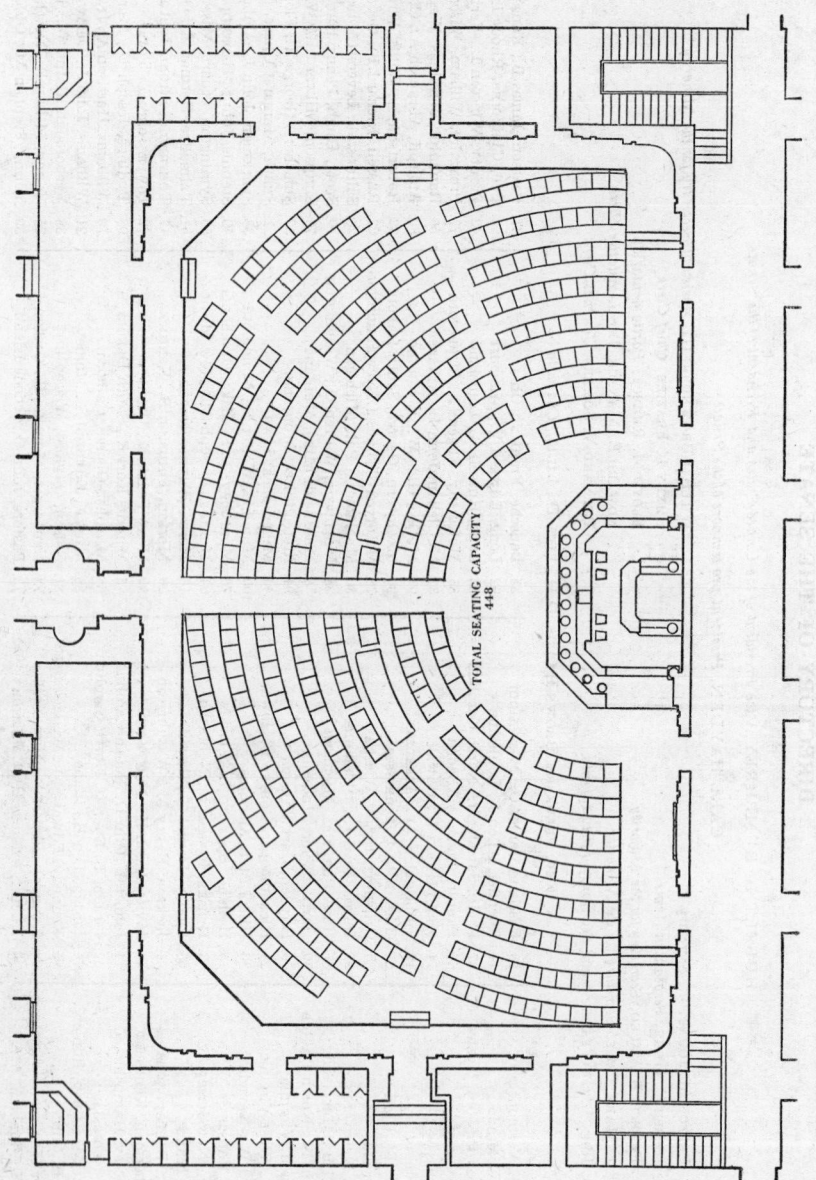

TOTAL SEATING CAPACITY
448

ROOMS AND TELEPHONES

ROOMS AND TELEPHONES

SENATORS

Telephone numbers are branches of Capitol exchange—224-3121 (Code 180)

[Room numbers with 3 digits are in Old Building and 4 digits are in New Building]

Name	Office building		Chairmanship	Capitol	
	Room	Phone		Location	Phone
Aiken, George D. (Vt.)	358	4242			
Allott, Gordon (Colo.)	5229	5941			
Anderson, Clinton P. (N. Mex.).	4215	6621	Aeronautical and Space Sciences.		
Bartlett, E. L. (Alaska)	248	6665			
Bass, Ross (Tenn.)	232	4944			
Bayh, Birch E. (Ind.)	304	5623			
Bennett, Wallace F. (Utah)	2311	5444			
Bible, Alan (Nev.)	145	3542	District of Columbia.		
Boggs, J. Caleb (Del.)	2106	5042			
Brewster, Daniel B. (Md.)	240	4654			
Burdick, Quentin N. (N. Dak.)	110	2551			
Byrd, Harry Flood (Va.)	209	4024	Finance		
Byrd, Robert C. (W. Va.)	342	3954			
Cannon, Howard W. (Nev.)	259	6244			
Carlson, Frank (Kans.)	3227	6521			
Case, Clifford P. (N.J.)	463	3224			
Church, Frank (Idaho)	405	6142			
Clark, Joseph S. (Pa.)	361	4254			
Cooper, John Sherman (Ky.)	125	2542			
Cotton, Norris (N.H.)	5109	3324			
Curtis, Carl T. (Nebr.)	5311	4224			
Dirksen, Everett McKinley (Ill.).	204	2854	Minority Leader.		
Dodd, Thomas J. (Conn.)	105	4041			
Dominick, Peter H. (Colo.)	140	5852			
Douglas, Paul H. (Ill.)	109	2152			
Eastland, James O. (Miss.)	2241	5054	Judiciary		
Ellender, Allen J. (La.)	245	5824	Agriculture and Forestry.		
Ervin, Sam J., Jr. (N.C.)	337	3154			
Fannin, Paul J. (Ariz.)	1251	4521			
Fong, Hiram L. (Hawaii)	1107	6361			
Fulbright, J. W. (Ark.)	1215	4843	Foreign Relations.		
Gore, Albert (Tenn.)	1311	3344			
Gruening, Ernest (Alaska)	4106	3004			
Harris, Fred R. (Okla.)	254	4721			
Hart, Philip A. (Mich.)	362	4822			
Hartke, Vance (Ind.)	451	4814			
Hayden, Carl (Ariz.)	133	2235	Appropriations		
Hickenlooper, Bourke B. (Iowa).	5205	3744			
Hill, Lister (Ala.)	4241	5744	Labor and Public Welfare.		

SENATORS—Continued

Name	Office building		Chairmanship	Capitol	
	Room	Phone		Location	Phone
Holland, Spessard L. (Fla.)____	421	5274			
Hruska, Roman L. (Nebr.)____	313	6551			
Inouye, Daniel K. (Hawaii)____	442	3934			
Jackson, Henry M. (Wash.)___	137	3441	Interior and In- sular Affairs.		
Javits, Jacob K. (N.Y.)_____	326	6542			
Johnston, Olin D. (S.C.)_____	3203	6121	Post Office and Civil Service.		
Jordan, B. Everett (N.C.)_____	6225	6342	Rules and Ad- ministration.		
Jordan, Len B. (Idaho)_____	4203	2752			
Kennedy, Edward M. (Mass.)__	432	4543			
Kennedy, Robert F. (N.Y.)____	1205	4451			
Kuchel, Thomas H. (Calif.)____	315	3553	Minority Whip__		
Lausche, Frank J. (Ohio)_____	1327	3353			
Long, Edward V. (Mo.)_____	3107	5721			
Long, Russell B. (La.)_____	217	4623	Majority Whip__		
McCarthy, Eugene J. (Minn.)__	411	3244			
McClellan, John L. (Ark.)_____	3241	2353	Government Operations.		
McGee, Gale W. (Wyo.)_____	344	6441			
McGovern, George S. (S. Dak.)_	353	2321			
McIntyre, Thomas J. (N.H.)___	5327	2841			
McNamara, Pat (Mich.)_____	255	6221	Public Works___		
Magnuson, Warren G. (Wash.)_	127	2621	Commerce_____		
Mansfield, Mike (Mont.)_____	113	2644	Majority Leader.		
Metcalf, Lee (Mont.)_____	427	2651			
Miller, Jack (Iowa)_____	2327	3254			
Mondale, Walter F. (Minn.)___	443	5641			
Monroney, A. S. Mike (Okla.)_	6205	5754			
Montoya, Joseph M. (N. Mex.).	2203	5521			
Morse, Wayne (Oreg.)_____	417	5244			
Morton, Thruston B. (Ky.)____	437	4343			
Moss, Frank E. (Utah)_____	6241	5251			
Mundt, Karl E. (S. Dak.)_____	4121	5842			
Murphy, George (Calif.)_____	452	3841			
Muskie, Edmund S. (Maine)___	221	5344			
Nelson, Gaylord (Wis.)_____	404	5323			
Neuberger, Maurine B. (Oreg.)_	431	3753			
Pastore, John O. (R.I.)_____	4107	2921			
Pearson, James B. (Kans.)____	6317	4774			
Pell, Claiborne (R.I.)_____	325	4642			
Prouty, Winston L. (Vt.)_____	444	2051			
Proxmire, William (Wis.)_____	4327	5653			
Randolph, Jennings (W. Va.)__	2109	6472			
Ribicoff, Abraham A. (Conn.)_	321	2823			
Robertson, A. Willis (Va.)_____	5241	2023	Banking and Currency.		
Russell, Richard B. (Ga.)_____	205	3521	Armed Services_		
Saltonstall, Leverett (Mass.)___	1123	2742			
Scott, Hugh (Pa.)_____	260	6324			
Simpson, Milward L. (Wyo.)___	3327	3424			
Smathers, George A. (Fla.)____	4313	3041			
Smith, Margaret Chase (Maine).	2121	2523			
Sparkman, John J. (Ala.)_____	3213	4124			
Stennis, John (Miss.)_____	5213	6253			
Symington, Stuart (Mo.)_____	229	6154			

SENATORS—Continued

Name	Office building		Chairmanship	Capitol	
	Room	Phone		Location	Phone
Talmadge, Herman E. (Ga.)___	347	3643			
Thurmond, Strom (S.C.)_____	3311	5972			
Tower, John G. (Tex.)_____	142	2934			
Tydings, Joseph D. (Md.)_____	6325	4524			
Williams, Harrison A., Jr. (N.J.).	352	4744			
Williams, John J. (Del.)_____	2213	2441			
Yarborough, Ralph W. (Tex.)_	460	5922			
Young, Milton R. (N. Dak.)___	3121	2043			
Young, Stephen M. (Ohio)____	458	2315			

REPRESENTATIVES

[Room numbers with 3 digits are in Cannon House Office Building, 4 digits beginning with 1 are in Longworth House Office Building, and 4 digits beginning with 2 are in Rayburn House Office Building]

Name	Office building		Chairmanship	Capitol	
	Room	Phone		Location	Phone
Abbitt, Watkins M. (Va.)	2209	6365			
Abernethy, Thomas G. (Miss.)	2371	5876			
Adair, E. Ross (Ind.)	2263	4436			
Adams, Brock (Wash.)	413	3106			
Addabbo, Joseph P. (N.Y.)	1727	3461			
Albert, Carl (Okla.)			Democratic Leader.	H-150	4565
Anderson, John B. (Ill.)	1418	5676			
Anderson, William R. (Tenn.)	127	2811			
Andrews, George (Ala.)	2466	4422			
Andrews, Glenn (Ala.)	107	3261			
Andrews, Mark (N. Dak.)	1707	2611			
Annunzio, Frank (Ill.)	1429	6661			
Arends, Leslie C. (Ill.)	2306	2976			
Ashbrook, John M. (Ohio)	424	6431			
Ashley, Thomas L. (Ohio)	2423	4146			
Ashmore, Robert T. (S.C.)	2232	3126			
Aspinall, Wayne, N. (Colo.)	2313	4431	Interior and Insular Affairs.		
Ayres, William H. (Ohio)	2367	5231			
Baldwin, John F. (Calif.)	2240	5511			
Bandstra, Bert (Iowa)	108	3906			
Baring, Walter S. (Nev.)	2434	5965			
Barrett, William A. (Pa.)	2304	4731			
Bates, William H. (Mass.)	2227	4265			
Battin, James F. (Mont.)	1110	4415			
Beckworth, Lindley (Tex.)	2418	2571			
Belcher, Page (Okla.)	2230	2211			
Bell, Alphonzo (Calif.)	1504	6451			
Bennett, Charles E. (Fla.)	2113	2501			
Berry, E. Y. (S. Dak.)	2428	5165			
Betts, Jackson E. (Ohio)	2330	3865			
Bingham, Jonathan B. (N.Y.)	305	4411			
Blatnik, John A. (Minn.)	2449	6211			
Boggs, Hale (La.)	2207	6636	Majority Whip		
Boland, Edward P. (Mass.)	2350	5601			
Bolling, Richard (Mo.)	2465	4535			
Bolton, Frances P. (Ohio)	2373	3565			
Bonner, Herbert C. (N.C.)	2308	3101	Merchant Marine and Fisheries.		
Bow, Frank T. (Ohio)	2182	3876			
Brademas, John (Ind.)	1329	3915			
Bray, William G. (Ind.)	2305	2276			
Brock, William E., 3d (Tenn.)	1441	3271			
Brooks, Jack (Tex.)	2239	6565			
Broomfield, William S. (Mich.)	2435	6135			
Brown, Clarence J. (Ohio)	1401	4324			
Brown, George E., Jr. (Calif.)	141	5464			
Broyhill, James T. (N.C.)	1020	2576			
Broyhill, Joel T. (Va.)	2229	5136			
Buchanan, John (Ala.)	1720	4921			
Burke, James A. (Mass.)	258	3215			
Burleson, Omar (Tex.)	2369	6605			
Burton, Laurence J. (Utah)	1605	3171			
Burton, Phillip (Calif.)	1622	4965			
Byrne, James A. (Pa.)	2412	2431			
Byrnes, John W. (Wis.)	2206	5665			

Name	Office building		Chairmanship	Capitol	
	Room	Phone		Location	Phone
Cabell, Earle (Tex.)	145	2231			
Cahill, William T. (N.J.)	1440	4765			
Callan, Clair A. (Nebr.)	1608	4806			
Callaway, Howard H. (Ga.)	1541	5901			
Cameron, Ronald Brooks (Calif.).	139	4111			
Carey, Hugh L. (N.Y.)	1706	4105			
Carter, Tim Lee (Ky.)	439	4601			
Casey, Bob (Tex.)	1331	5951			
Cederberg, Elford A. (Mich.)	2303	3561			
Celler, Emanuel (N.Y.)	2136	3531	Judiciary		
Chamberlain, Charles E. (Mich.).	2444	4872			
Chelf, Frank (Ky.)	2462	3465			
Clancy, Donald D. (Ohio)	1432	2216			
Clark, Frank M. (Pa.)	2238	2565			
Clausen, Don H. (Calif.)	229	3311			
Clawson, Del (Calif.)	1430	3576			
Cleveland, James C. (N.H.)	1506	5206			
Clevenger, Raymond F. (Mich.).	1319	4735			
Cohelan, Jeffery (Calif.)	1028	2661			
Collier, Harold R. (Ill.)	2438	4561			
Colmer, William M. (Miss.)	2307	5772			
Conable, Barber B., Jr. (N.Y.)	436	3615			
Conte, Silvio O. (Mass.)	257	5335			
Conyers, John, Jr. (Mich.)	426	5126			
Cooley, Harold D. (N.C.)	2409	3715	Agriculture		
Corbett, Robert J. (Pa.)	2467	2135			
Corman, James C. (Calif.)	238	5811			
Craley, N. Neiman, Jr. (Pa.)	1620	5836			
Cramer, William C. (Fla.)	2458	5961			
Culver, John C. (Iowa)	130	2911			
Cunningham, Glenn (Nebr.)	2447	4156			
Curtin, Willard S. (Pa.)	2432	4276			
Curtis, Thomas B. (Mo.)	1336	2311			
Daddario, Emilio Q. (Conn.)	1006	2265			
Dague, Paul B. (Pa.)	2211	2011			
Daniels, Dominick V. (N.J.)	237	2765			
Davis, Glenn R. (Wis.)	201	5101			
Davis, John W. (Ga.)	1728	2931			
Dawson, William L. (Ill.)	2111	4372	Government Operations.		
de la Garza, Eligio (Tex.)	303	2531			
Delaney, James J. (N.Y.)	2267	3965			
Dent, John H. (Pa.)	453	5631			
Denton, Winfield K. (Ind.)	2347	4636			
Derwinski, Edward J. (Ill.)	1535	3961			
Devine, Samuel L. (Ohio)	1113	5355			
Dickinson, William L. (Ala.)	110	2901			
Diggs, Charles C., Jr. (Mich.)	2464	2261			
Dingell, John D. (Mich.)	2452	4071			
Dole, Bob (Kans.)	244	2715			
Donohue, Harold D. (Mass.)	2265	6101			
Dorn, W. J. Bryan (S.C.)	2256	5301			
Dow, John G. (N.Y.)	415	6231			
Dowdy, John (Tex.)	2301	2401			
Downing, Thomas N. (Va.)	528	4261			
Dulski, Thaddeus J. (N.Y.)	1719	3306			
Duncan, John J. (Tenn.)	410	5435			

REPRESENTATIVES—Continued

Name	Office building		Chairmanship	Capitol	
	Room	Phone		Location	Phone
Duncan, Robert B. (Oreg.)	125	6416			
Dwyer, Florence P. (N.J.)	2421	5361			
Dyal, Ken W. (Calif.)	339	5861			
Edmondson, Ed (Okla.)	2402	2701			
Edwards, Don (Calif.)	136	3072			
Edwards, Jack (Ala.)	408	4931			
Ellsworth, Robert F. (Kans.)	1709	2865			
Erlenborn, John N. (Ill.)	340	3515			
Evans, Frank E. (Colo.)	121	4761			
Everett, Robert A. (Tenn.)	211	4715			
Evins, Joe L. (Tenn.)	2300	4231			
Fallon, George H. (Md.)	2188	4016	Public Works		
Farbstein, Leonard (N.Y.)	2455	5635			
Farnsley, Charles P. (Ky.)	209	5401			
Farnum, Billie S. (Mich.)	122	2101			
Fascell, Dante B. (Fla.)	2160	4506			
Feighan, Michael A. (Ohio)	2112	5871			
Findley, Paul (Ill.)	1032	5271			
Fino, Paul A. (N.Y.)	2331	2465			
Fisher, O. C. (Tex.)	2407	4236			
Flood, Daniel J. (Pa.)	449	6511			
Flynt, John J., Jr. (Ga.)	2335	4501			
Fogarty, John E. (R.I.)	1235	2735			
Foley, Thomas S. (Wash.)	1521	2006			
Ford, Gerald R. (Mich.)			Minority Leader	H–230	3831
Ford, William D. (Mich.)	432	6261			
Fountain, L. H. (N.C.)	2400	4531			
Fraser, Donald M. (Minn.)	460	4756			
Frelinghuysen, Peter, H. B. (N.J.).	2162	3131			
Friedel, Samuel N. (Md.)	2233	4741			
Fulton, James G. (Pa.)	2134	2915			
Fulton, Richard H. (Tenn.)	216	4313			
Fuqua, Don (Fla.)	1223	5235			
Gallagher, Cornelius E. (N.J.)	233	5801			
Garmatz, Edward A. (Md.)	2187	6161			
Gathings, E. C. (Ark.)	2405	4076			
Gettys, Tom S. (S.C.)	1505	5501			
Giaimo, Robert N. (Conn.)	1715	3661			
Gibbons, Sam M. (Fla.)	1232	3376			
Gilbert, Jacob H. (N.Y.)	1723	4361			
Gilligan, John J. (Ohio)	442	3165			
Gonzalez, Henry B. (Tex.)	1741	3236			
Goodell, Charles E. (N.Y.)	1017	3161			
Grabowski, Bernard F. (Conn.).	1740	4476			
Gray, Kenneth J. (Ill.)	2457	5201			
Green, Edith (Oreg.)	2441	4811			
Green, William J. (Pa.)	124	6271			
Greigg, Stanley L. (Iowa)	1520	5476			
Grider, George W. (Tenn.)	443	3265			
Griffin, Robert P. (Mich.)	2453	3511			
Griffiths, Martha W. (Mich.)	1536	4961			
Gross, H. R. (Iowa)	2368	3301			
Grover, James R., Jr. (N.Y.)	1606	3335			
Gubser, Charles S. (Calif.)	2338	2631			
Gurney, Edward J. (Fla.)	137	3671			
Hagan, G. Elliott (Ga.)	419	5831			
Hagen, Harlan (Calif.)	2404	3341			
Haley, James A. (Fla.)	1236	5015			

REPRESENTATIVES—Continued

Name	Office building		Chairmanship	Capitol	
	Room	Phone		Location	Phone
Hall, Durward G. (Mo.)_____	1037	6536	_____	_____	_____
Halleck, Charles A. (Ind.)_____	2204	5777	_____	_____	_____
Halpern, Seymour (N.Y.)_____	1714	2536	_____	_____	_____
Hamilton, Lee H. (Ind.)_____	1421	5315	_____	_____	_____
Hanley, James M. (N.Y.)_____	1416	3701	_____	_____	_____
Hanna, Richard T. (Calif.)____	1516	2965	_____	_____	_____
Hansen, George V. (Idaho)____	204	4131	_____	_____	_____
Hansen, John R. (Iowa)_____	1609	3806	_____	_____	_____
Hansen, Julia Butler (Wash.)__	1132	3536	_____	_____	_____
Hardy, Porter, Jr. (Va.)_____	2109	4215	_____	_____	_____
Harris, Oren (Ark.)_____	2328	3772	Interstate and Foreign Commerce.	_____	_____
Harsha, William H. (Ohio)____	1338	5705	_____	_____	_____
Harvey, James (Mich.)_____	1107	2806	_____	_____	_____
Harvey, Ralph (Ind.)_____	1431	5805	_____	_____	_____
Hathaway, William D. (Maine)_	221	6306	_____	_____	_____
Hawkins, Augustus F. (Calif.)__	1124	2201	_____	_____	_____
Hays, Wayne L. (Ohio)_____	2264	6265	_____	_____	_____
Hébert, F. Edward (La.)_____	2340	3015	_____	_____	_____
Hechler, Ken (W. Va.)_____	1008	3452	_____	_____	_____
Helstoski, Henry (N.J.)_____	437	5061	_____	_____	_____
Henderson, David N. (N.C.)__	324	3415	_____	_____	_____
Herlong, A. Sydney, Jr. (Fla.)_	2221	4035	_____	_____	_____
Hicks, Floyd V. (Wash.)_____	322	5916	_____	_____	_____
Holifield, Chet (Calif.)_____	2469	3976	_____	_____	_____
Holland, Elmer J. (Pa.)_____	2104	4631	_____	_____	_____
Horton, Frank J. (N.Y.)_____	1220	4916	_____	_____	_____
Hosmer, Craig (Calif.)_____	2348	2415	_____	_____	_____
Howard, James J. (N.J.)_____	235	4671	_____	_____	_____
Hull, W. R., Jr. (Mo.)_____	2349	7041	_____	_____	_____
Hungate, William L. (Mo.)____	1712	2956	_____	_____	_____
Huot, L. Oliva (N.H.)_____	1632	5456	_____	_____	_____
Hutchinson, Edward (Mich.)__	1420	3761	_____	_____	_____
Ichord, Richard H. (Mo.)_____	1518	5155	_____	_____	_____
Irwin, Donald J. (Conn.)_____	1023	5541	_____	_____	_____
Jacobs, Andrew, Jr. (Ind.)_____	234	4011	_____	_____	_____
Jarman, John (Okla.)_____	2416	2131	_____	_____	_____
Jennings, W. Pat (Va.)_____	2241	3861	_____	_____	_____
Joelson, Charles S. (N.J.)_____	433	5751	_____	_____	_____
Johnson, Albert W. (Pa.)_____	1415	5121	_____	_____	_____
Johnson, Harold T. (Calif.)____	1031	3076	_____	_____	_____
Johnson, Jed, Jr. (Okla.)_____	422	5565	_____	_____	_____
Jonas, Charles R. (N.C.)_____	2133	3476	_____	_____	_____
Jones, Paul C. (Mo.)_____	2302	4405	_____	_____	_____
Jones, Robert E. (Ala.)_____	2426	4801	_____	_____	_____
Karsten, Frank M. (Mo.)_____	2110	2406	_____	_____	_____
Karth, Joseph E. (Minn.)_____	1033	6631	_____	_____	_____
Kastenmeier, Robert W. (Wis.)_	1725	2906	_____	_____	_____
Kee, James (W. Va.)_____	427	2176	_____	_____	_____
Keith, Hastings (Mass.)_____	1317	3111	_____	_____	_____
Kelly, Edna F. (N.Y.)_____	2262	3776	_____	_____	_____
Keogh, Eugene J. (N.Y.)_____	2310	5471	_____	_____	_____
King Carleton J. (N.Y.)_____	1116	5615	_____	_____	_____
King, Cecil R. (Calif.)_____	2309	6676	_____	_____	_____
King, David S. (Utah)_____	131	3011	_____	_____	_____
Kirwan, Michael J. (Ohio)_____	2470	5261	_____	_____	_____
Kluczynski, John C. (Ill.)_____	2244	5701	_____	_____	_____

REPRESENTATIVES—Continued

Name	Office building		Chairmanship	Capitol	
	Room	Phone		Location	Phone
Kornegay, Horace R. (N.C.)___	441	3065			
Krebs, Paul J. (N.J.)_____	239	6501			
Kunkel, John C. (Pa.)_____	123	2411			
Laird, Melvin R. (Wis)._____	2246	3365			
Landrum, Phil M. (Ga.)_____	2334	5211			
Langen, Odin (Minn.)_____	1519	2165			
Latta, Delbert L. (Ohio)_____	1529	6405			
Leggett, Robert L. (Calif.)____	1038	5716			
Lennon, Alton (N.C.)_____	2437	2731			
Lindsay, John V. (N.Y.)_____	1207	2436			
Lipscomb, Glenard P. (Calif.)__	2245	4206			
Long, Clarence D. (Md.)_____	1522	3061			
Long, Speedy O. (La.)_____	1627	4926			
Love, Rodney M. (Ohio)_____	1009	6465			
McCarthy, Richard D. (N.Y.)_	418	5265			
McClory, Robert (Ill.)_____	1630	5221			
McCormack, John W. (Mass.)_			Speaker_____	H-206	5415
McCulloch, William M. (Ohio)_	2186	2676			
McDade, Joseph M. (Pa.)_____	335	3731			
McDowell, Harris B., Jr. (Del.)_	457	4165			
McEwen, Robert C. (N.Y.)____	309	4611			
McFall, John J. (Calif.)_____	2445	2511			
McGrath, Thomas C., Jr. (N.J.).	1710	6752			
McMillan, John L. (S.C.)_____	2208	3315	District of Columbia.		
McVicker, Roy H. (Colo.)_____	1238	2161			
Macdonald, Torbert H. (Mass.)	2448	2836			
MacGregor, Clark (Minn.)____	336	2871			
Machen, Hervey G. (Md.)_____	438	5531			
Mackay, James A. (Ga.)_____	1509	4272			
Mackie, John C. (Mich.)_____	1022	3611			
Madden, Ray J. (Ind.)_____	1436	2461			
Mahon, George H. (Tex.)_____	2314	4005			
Mailliard, William S. (Calif.)__	2336	5161			
Marsh, John O., Jr. (Va.)_____	231	6561			
Martin, David T. (Nebr.)_____	1409	6435			
Martin, James D. (Ala.)_____	1515	4876			
Martin, Joseph W., Jr. (Mass.)_				H-326	4335
Mathias, Charles McC., Jr. (Md.)	333	2721			
Matsunaga, Spark M. (Hawaii)_	1321	2726			
Matthews, D. R. (Billy) (Fla.)_	2236	3026			
May, Catherine (Wash.)_____	1118	5816			
Meeds, Lloyd (Wash.)_____	1018	2605			
Michel, Robert H. (Ill.)_____	2431	6201			
Miller, George P. (Calif.)_____	2365	5065	Science and Astronautics.		
Mills, Wilbur D. (Ark.)_____	1134	2506	Ways and Means.		
Minish, Joseph G. (N.J.)_____	302	5035			
Mink, Patsy T. (Hawaii)_____	1016	4906			
Minshall, William E. (Ohio)___	2243	5731			
Mize, Chester L. (Kans.)_____	240	6601			
Moeller, Walter H. (Ohio)_____	116	5131			
Monagan, John S. (Conn.)_____	1528	3822			
Moore, Arch A., Jr. (W. Va.)__	2440	4172			
Moorhead, William S. (Pa.)____	1126	2301			
Morgan, Thomas E. (Pa.)_____	2183	4665	Foreign Affairs__		

REPRESENTATIVES—Continued

Name	Office building		Chairmanship	Capitol	
	Room	Phone		Location	Phone
Morris, Thomas G. (N. Mex.)	1021	6316			
Morrison, James H. (La.)	2354	3901			
Morse, F. Bradford (Mass.)	250	3411			
Morton, Rogers C. B. (Md.)	319	5311			
Mosher, Charles A. (Ohio)	1227	3401			
Moss, John E. (Calif.)	2353	7163			
Multer, Abraham J. (N.Y.)	2185	2361			
Murphy, John M. (N.Y.)	1716	3371			
Murphy, William T. (Ill.)	1628	3406			
Murray, Tom (Tenn.)	347	4701	Post Office and Civil Service.		
Natcher, William H. (Ky.)	2333	3501			
Nedzi, Lucien N. (Mich.)	1523	6276			
Nelsen, Ancher (Minn.)	1533	2472			
Nix, Robert N. C. (Pa.)	104	4001			
O'Brien, Leo W. (N.Y.)	2446	4861			
O'Hara, Barratt (Ill.)	2427	4835			
O'Hara, James G. (Mich.)	1109	2106			
O'Konski, Alvin E. (Wis.)	2406	3361			
Olsen, Arnold (Mont.)	1423	3211			
Olson, Alec G. (Minn.)	1228	2331			
O'Neal, Maston (Ga.)	109	3631			
O'Neill, Thomas P., Jr. (Mass.).	2231	5111			
Ottinger, Richard L. (N.Y.)	1215	5536			
Passman, Otto E. (La.)	2108	2376			
Patman, Wright (Tex.)	1136	3035	Banking and Currency.		
Patten, Edward J. (N.J.)	440	6301			
Pelly, Thomas M. (Wash.)	2342	6311			
Pepper, Claude (Fla.)	352	3931			
Perkins, Carl D. (Ky.)	2252	4935			
Philbin, Philip J. (Mass.)	2372	5931			
Pickle, J. J. (Jake) (Tex.)	318	4865			
Pike, Otis G. (N.Y.)	1417	3826			
Pirnie, Alexander (N.Y.)	1434	3665			
Poage, W. R. (Tex.)	2107	6105			
Poff, Richard H. (Va.)	2228	5431			
Polanco-Abreu, Santiago (P.R.).	243	2615			
Pool, Joe (Tex.)	142	4201			
Powell, Adam C. (N.Y.)	2161	4365	Education and Labor.		
Price, Melvin (Ill.)	2468	5661			
Pucinski, Roman C. (Ill.)	1027	4211			
Purcell, Graham (Tex.)	1219	3605			
Quie, Albert H. (Minn.)	1212	2271			
Quillen, James H. (Tenn.)	1318	6356			
Race, John A. (Wis.)	1019	2476			
Randall, Wm. J. (Mo.)	1029	2876			
Redlin, Rolland (N. Dak.)	1419	5736			
Reid, Charlotte T. (Ill.)	1315	3635			
Reid, Ogden R. (N.Y.)	1216	6506			
Reifel, Ben (S. Dak.)	348	2801			
Reinecke, Ed (Calif.)	1239	4461			
Resnick, Joseph Y. (N.Y.)	135	5441			
Reuss, Henry S. (Wis.)	2159	3571			
Rhodes, George M. (Pa.)	2210	5546			
Rhodes, John J. (Ariz.)	2332	2635			
Rivers, L. Mendel (S.C.)	2205	3176	Armed Services		

REPRESENTATIVES—Continued

Name	Office building		Chairmanship	Capitol	
	Room	Phone		Location	Phone
Rivers, Ralph J. (Alaska)	1540	5765			
Roberts, Ray (Tex.)	323	6673			
Robison, Howard W. (N.Y.)	2436	6335			
Rodino, Peter W., Jr. (N.J.)	2266	3436			
Rogers, Byron G. (Colo.)	2201	3331			
Rogers, Paul G. (Fla.)	2417	3001			
Rogers, Walter (Tex.)	2312	3706			
Ronan, Daniel J. (Ill.)	310	5006			
Roncalio, Teno (Wyo.)	1323	2561			
Rooney, Fred B. (Pa.)	1119	6411			
Rooney, John J. (N.Y.)	2268	5936			
Roosevelt, James (Calif.)	2454	5911			
Rosenthal, Benjamin S. (N.Y.)	1530	2601			
Rostenkowski, Dan (Ill.)	1721	4061			
Roudebush, Richard L. (Ind.)	1532	5037			
Roush, J. Edward (Ind.)	1407	3021			
Roybal, Edward R. (Calif.)	140	6235			
Rumsfeld, Donald (Ill.)	241	3711			
Ryan, William F. (N.Y.)	1517	6616			
St Germain, Fernand J. (R.I.)	1339	4911			
St. Onge, William L. (Conn.)	1405	2076			
Satterfield, David E., 3d (Va.)	337	2815			
Saylor, John P. (Pa.)	2351	2065			
Scheuer, James H. (N.Y.)	222	3816			
Schisler, Gale (Ill.)	208	5905			
Schmidhauser, John R. (Iowa)	134	6576			
Schneebeli, Herman T. (Pa.)	1328	4315			
Schweiker, Richard S. (Pa.)	1221	6111			
Scott, Ralph J. (N.C.)	2443	2515			
Secrest, Robert T. (Ohio)	1208	2015			
Selden, Armistead I., Jr. (Ala.)	2352	2665			
Senner, George F., Jr. (Ariz.)	444	4576			
Shipley, George E. (Ill.)	253	5001			
Shriver, Garner E. (Kans.)	1222	6216			
Sickles, Carlton R. (Md).	1507	5341			
Sikes, Robert L. F. (Fla.)	2269	4136			
Sisk, B. F. (Calif.)	2242	6131			
Skubitz, Joe (Kans.)	236	3911			
Slack, John M., Jr. (W. Va.)	126	2711			
Smith, H. Allen (Calif.)	2433	4176			
Smith, Henry P., 3d (N.Y.)	342	3231			
Smith, Howard W. (Va.)	1101	4376	Rules		
Smith, Neal (Iowa)	1233	4426			
Springer, William L. (Ill.)	2202	2371			
Stafford, Robert T. (Vt.)	1218	4115			
Staggers, Harley O. (W. Va.)	2366	4331			
Stalbaum, Lynn E. (Wis.)	315	3031			
Stanton, J. William (Ohio)	1626	5306			
Steed, Tom (Okla.)	2410	6165			
Stephens, Robert G., Jr. (Ga.)	357	4101			
Stratton, Samuel S. (N.Y.)	1229	5076			
Stubblefield, Frank A. (Ky.)	1514	3115			
Sullivan, Leonor K. (Mo.)	2344	2671			
Sweeney, Robert E. (Ohio)	1618	6205			
Talcott, Burt L. (Calif.)	120	2861			
Taylor, Roy A. (N.C.)	252	6401			
Teague, Charles M. (Calif.)	1414	3601			
Teague, Olin E. (Tex.)	2311	2002	Veterans' Affairs.		
Tenzer, Herbert (N.Y.)	423	3811			

REPRESENTATIVES—Continued

Name	Office building		Chairmanship	Capitol	
	Room	Phone		Location	Phone
Thomas, Albert (Tex.)	2408	4901			
Thompson, Clark W. (Tex.)	2217	4511			
Thompson, Frank, Jr. (N.J.)	2442	3765			
Thompson, T. Ashton (La.)	2430	2031			
Thomson, Vernon W. (Wis.)	1115	5506			
Todd, Paul H., Jr. (Mich.)	316	5011			
Toll, Herman (Pa.)	1428	4661			
Trimble, James W. (Ark.)	1201	4301			
Tuck, William M. (Va.)	2429	4711			
Tunney, John V. (Calif.)	1322	2305			
Tupper, Stanley R. (Maine)	206	6116			
Tuten, J. Russell (Ga.)	425	6531			
Udall, Morris K. (Ariz.)	456	4065			
Ullman, Al (Oreg.)	2439	5711			
Utt, James B. (Calif.)	2346	5611			
Van Deerlin, Lionel (Calif.)	1641	5672			
Vanik, Charles A. (Ohio)	2463	6331			
Vigorito, Joseph P. (Pa.)	220	5406			
Vivian, Weston E. (Mich.)	118	4401			
Waggonner, Joe D., Jr. (La.)	1237	2777			
Walker, E. S. Johnny (N. Mex.)	434	2365			
Walker, Prentiss (Miss.)	409	5031			
Watkins, G. Robert (Pa.)	138	5761			
Watts, John C. (Ky.)	2411	4706			
Weltner, Charles L. (Ga.)	218	3801			
Whalley, J. Irving (Pa.)	1230	4676			
White, Compton I., Jr. (Idaho).	133	6611			
White, Richard C. (Tex.)	407	4831			
Whitner, Basil L. (N.C.)	2422	2071			
Whitten, Jamie L. (Miss.)	2413	4306			
Widnall, William B. (N.J.)	2329	4465			
Williams, John Bell (Miss.)	2370	5865			
Willis, Edwin E. (La.)	2135	4031	Un-American Activities.		
Wilson, Bob (Calif.)	2235	3201			
Wilson, Charles H. (Calif.)	1117	5425			
Wolff, Lester L. (N.Y.)	1629	5956			
Wright, James C., Jr. (Tex.)	2459	5071			
Wyatt, Wendell (Oreg.)	1030	2206			
Wydler, John W. (N.Y.)	417	5516			
Yates, Sidney R. (Ill.)	1713	2111			
Young, John (Tex.)	2419	2831			
Younger, J. Arthur (Calif.)	2234	5411			
Zablocki, Clement J. (Wis.)	2184	4572			

EXECUTIVE

417

THE CABINET

Secretary of State_____ DEAN RUSK, of New York, 4980 Quebec Street.

Secretary of the Treasury_____ HENRY H. FOWLER, of Virginia, 209 South Fairfax Street, Alexandria, Va.

Secretary of Defense_____ ROBERT S. MCNAMARA, of Michigan, 2412 Tracy Place.

Attorney General_____ NICHOLAS deB. KATZENBACH, of Illinois, 3141 Highland Place.

Postmaster General_____ *Lawrence F. O'Brien*
~~JOHN A. GRONOUSKI~~, of Wisconsin, 6133 33d Street.

Secretary of the Interior_____ STEWART L. UDALL, of Arizona, 4551 Crest Lane, McLean, Va.

Secretary of Agriculture_____ ORVILLE L. FREEMAN, of Minnesota, 2805 Daniel Road, Chevy Chase, Md.

Secretary of Commerce_____ JOHN T. CONNOR, of New Jersey, 2429 Kalorama Road.

Secretary of Labor_____ W. WILLARD WIRTZ, of Illinois, 5009 39th Street.

Secretary of Health, Education, and Welfare. *John W. Gardner*
~~ANTHONY J. CELEBREZZE~~, of Ohio, 7207 Pomander Lane, Chevy Chase, Md.

418

EXECUTIVE

THE PRESIDENT

LYNDON BAINES JOHNSON, Democrat, of Johnson City, Tex., President of the United States; born near Johnson City, Tex., August 27, 1908; B.S. degree, Southwest Texas State Teachers College at San Marcos, 1930; attended Georgetown Law School, 1935; honorary doctor of laws degrees from Southwestern University, 1943, Howard Payne College, Brownwood, Texas, 1957, Brown University, Providence, R.I., 1959, Bethany College, Bethany, W. Va., 1959, Gallaudet College, Washington, D.C., 1961, East Kentucky State College, Richmond, Ky., 1961, University of Hawaii, Honolulu, Hawaii, 1961, University of the Philippines, Quezon City, Philippines, 1961, William Jewell College, Liberty, Mo., 1961, Elon College, N.C., 1962, Southwest Texas State Teachers College, 1962, Wayne State University, Detroit, Mich., 1963, Jacksonville University, Jacksonville, Fla., 1963, MacMurray College, Jacksonville, Ill., 1963, University of Maryland, College Park, Md., 1963, Tufts University, Medford, Mass., 1963, University of California, Los Angeles, Calif., 1964, University of Texas, Austin, Tex., 1964, Syracuse University, Syracuse, N.Y., 1964, Georgetown University, Washington, D.C., 1964, and honorary doctor of humane letters degree from Oklahoma City University, Oklahoma City, Okla., 1960, Yeshiva University, New York City, 1961; honorary doctor of literature, St. Mary's College of California, 1962; honorary doctor of civil law, University of Michigan, Ann Arbor, Mich., 1964, Holy Cross College, Mass., 1964; elected to the 75th Congress at a special election held April 10, 1937; reelected to the 76th, 77th, 78th, 79th, and 80th Congresses; elected to the United States Senate, November 2, 1948, for the term ending January 3, 1955; reelected November 2, 1954, for term ending January 3, 1961; reelected November 8, 1960, for term ending January 3, 1967, resigning January 3, 1961, immediately following taking the oath of this office having been elected Vice President of the United States for the 44th term on November 8, 1960, taking oath of office January 20, 1961; parents, Sam Ealy and Rebekah Baines Johnson; married Lady Bird Taylor, November 17, 1934; daughter, Lynda Bird Johnson, born March 19, 1944; daughter, Lucy Baines Johnson, born July 2, 1947; elected Democratic Whip, January 2, 1951; elected Democratic Leader, January 3, 1953, and reelected each succeeding Congress; Chairman, National Aeronautics and Space Council; Chairman, President's Committee on Equal Employment Opportunity; Chairman, National Advisory Council of the Peace Corps. Acceded to the Presidency November 22, 1963, on the death of President John F. Kennedy. Elected to the Presidency November 3, 1964.

EXECUTIVE OFFICE OF THE PRESIDENT

THE WHITE HOUSE OFFICE

1600 Pennsylvania Avenue, 20500.   Phone, 456-1414

Special Assistant to the President.—McGeorge Bundy, 5225 Partridge Lane, 20016.

Special Assistant to the President.—Horace Busby, Jr., 4805 Newport Avenue, 20016.

Special Assistant to the President.—S. Douglass Cater, Jr., 4905 Maury Lane, Alexandria, Va.

Special Assistant to the President.—Richard N. Goodwin, The White House Office.

Special Assistant to the President.—Donald F. Hornig, 2810 Brandywine Street, 20008.

Special Assistant to the President.—David L. Lawrence, The White House Office.

Special Assistant to the President.—Bill D. Moyers, The White House Office.

Special Assistant to the President.—Lawrence F. O'Brien, The White House Office.
  Administrative Assistant to the President.—Mike N. Manatos, 5341 Nevada
    Avenue, 20015.
  Administrative Assistant to the President.—Henry Hall Wilson, Jr., 654 Queen
    Anne Terrace, Falls Church, Va.
Special Assistant to the President.—Jack J. Valenti, The White House Office.
Special Assistant to the President.—W. Marvin Watson, 4509 Frazier Lane,
    McLean, Va.
Press Secretary to the President.—George E. Reedy, 3135 Highland Place.
Special Counsel to the President.—Lee C. White, 7573 Alaska Avenue.
Special Assistant to the President—Director, Food for Peace.—Richard W. Reuter,
    5421 Duvall Drive, 20016.
Special Assistant to the President on the Arts.—Roger L. Stevens, The White
    House Office.
Advisor for National Capital Affairs.—Charles A. Horsky, 1227 Pinecrest Circle,
    Silver Spring, Md., 20910.
Military Aide to the President.—Maj. Gen. Chester V. Clifton, USA, 2743 Raleigh
    Road, Annandale, Va.
Physician to the President.—Vice Adm. George G. Burkley (MC), USN, 3507
    Preston Court, Chevy Chase, Md., 20015.
Personal Secretary to the President.—Juanita Duggan Roberts, 6915 Braddock
    Road, Alexandria, Va., 22312.
Press Secretary and Staff Director for the First Lady.—Elizabeth S. Carpenter,
    4701 Woodway Lane, 20016.
Social Secretary.—Bess Abell, 4506 49th Street, 20016.
Executive Clerk.—William J. Hopkins, 814 Rowen Road, Silver Spring, Md.,
    20910.
Chief Usher.—J. Bernard West, 1101 North Ohio Street, Arlington, Va., 22205.

BUREAU OF THE BUDGET

Executive Office Building, 20503.   Phone, EXecutive 3-3300 (Code 128)

Director.—Kermit Gordon, 7311 River Road, Bethesda, Md., 20014.
Deputy Director.—Elmer B. Staats, 5011 Overlook Road, 20016.
Assistant Director.—William M. Capron, 3205 Pickwick Lane, Chevy Chase, Md.,
    20015.
Assistant Director.—Henry S. Rowen, 3307 Newark Street, 20008.
Assistant Director.—[Vacant.]
Executive Assistant Director.—William D. Carey, 3724 Northampton Street, 20015.
Special Assistant to the Director.—Roger W. Jones, 3912 Leland Street, Chevy
    Chase, Md., 20015.
General Counsel.—Arthur B. Focke, 5619 Western Avenue, 20015.
Assistant to the Director.—Joseph Laitin, 7204 Exfair Road, Bethesda, Md., 20014.
Administrative Assistant to the Director.—E. Charles Woods, 307 South St. Asaph
    Street, Alexandria, Va., 22314.
Administrative Services Officer.—Philip A. Langehough, 1527 North Patrick Henry
    Drive, Arlington, Va., 22205.
Budget and Management Officer.—Edward F. Kelley, 1911 Hawthorne Avenue,
    Alexandria, Va., 22311.
Information Officer.—Virginia M. de Pury, 1801 16th Street, 20009.
Personnel Officer.—Velma N. Baldwin, 2034 48th Street, 20007.
Assistant Director for Budget Review.—William F. McCandless, 6203 Welborn
    Drive, Wood Acres, Md., 20016.
Assistant Director for Legislative Reference.—Phillip S. Hughes, 3710 Taylor
    Street, Chevy Chase, Md., 20015.
Assistant Director for Management and Organization.—Harold Seidman, 200 C
    Street SE., 20003.
Assistant Director for Statistical Standards.—Raymond T. Bowman, 9609 Dewmar
    Lane, Byeforde, Kensington, Md., 20795.
Chief, Office of Financial Management.—William J. Armstrong, 9601 Hillridge
    Drive, Kensington, Md., 20795.
Chief, Commerce and Finance Division.—Sam R. Broadbent, 4201 Cathedral
    Avenue, No. 716W., 20016.
Chief, International Division.—Robert Amory, Jr., 4833 Dexter Terrace, 20007.

Executive Office 421

Chief, Labor and Welfare Division.—Hirst Sutton, 206 Buxton Road, Falls Church, Va., 22042.
Chief, Military Division.—Ellis H. Veatch, 1580 Mount Eagle Place, Alexandria, Va., 22302.
Chief, Resources and Civil Works Division.—Carl H. Schwartz, Jr., 3407 Alabama Avenue, Alexandria, Va., 22305.

COUNCIL OF ECONOMIC ADVISERS

Executive Office Building. Phone, EXecutive 3-3300 (Code 128, extension 22282)

Chairman.—Gardner Ackley, 3689 North Harrison Street, Arlington, Va., 22207.
Member.—Otto Eckstein, 4816 Alton Place, 20016.
Member.—Arthur M. Okum, 5035 Macomb Street, 20016.
Assistant to the Chairman.—Lewis J. Spellman, 1193 North Van Dorn, Alexandria, Va., 22302.

NATIONAL SECURITY COUNCIL

Executive Office Building. Phone, 393-3111 (Code 128, extension 21877)

Lyndon B. Johnson, President of the United States (Chairman).
Hubert H. Humphrey, Vice President.
Dean Rusk, Secretary of State.
Robert S. McNamara, Secretary of Defense.
Buford Ellington, Director, Office of Emergency Planning.
Special Assistant to the President for National Security Affairs.—McGeorge Bundy.
Executive Secretary.—Bromley Smith.

CENTRAL INTELLIGENCE AGENCY

Washington, D.C., 20505. Phone, 351-1100 (Code 143)

Director of Central Intelligence.—~~John A. McCone~~, 351-6363.
Deputy Director.—~~Lt. Gen. Marshall S. Carter~~, USA, 351-6464.
Legislative Counsel.—John S. Warner, 351-6121.

NATIONAL AERONAUTICS AND SPACE COUNCIL

Executive Office Building, 20502. Phone, 382-2203 (Code 128, extension 22203)

Chairman.—Hubert H. Humphrey (Vice President of the United States).
Members:
  Dean Rusk (Secretary of State).
  Robert S. McNamara (Secretary of Defense).
  James E. Webb (Administrator, National Aeronautics and Space Administration).
  Glenn T. Seaborg (Chairman, Atomic Energy Commission).
Executive Secretary.—Edward C. Welsh.

OFFICE OF ECONOMIC OPPORTUNITY

1200 19th Street. Phone, EXecutive 3-3111 (Code 128, extension 5216)

Director.—Robert Sargent Shriver, Jr., Timberlawn, Edson Lane, Rockville, Md., 20852.
Deputy Director.—~~Jack T. Conway, 3606 35th Street, 20016.~~
Executive Secretary.—Ferdinand Nadherny, 10805 South Glen Road, Potomac, Md., 20850.
Assistant Director for Community Action Programs.—Theodore M. Berry.
Assistant Director for Jobs Corps.—Otis Singletary, 1400 20th Street, 20036.
Assistant Director for Volunteers in Service to America.—Glenn W. Ferguson, 5311 Massachusetts Avenue, 20016.

Assistant Director for Program Planning, Analysis and Research.—Joseph A. Kershaw.

General Counsel.—Donald M. Baker, 1350 4th Street, 20024.

Assistant Director for Management.—William P. Kelly, Jr., 7608 Marshall Drive, Annandale, Va., 22003.

Assistant Director for Congressional Relations.—Gillis W. Long, 3340 Reservoir Road, 20007.

Assistant Director for Interagency Relations.—Lisle C. Carter, 234 G Street, 20024.

Assistant Director for Inspection.—William F. Haddad, 289 G Street, 20024.

Assistant Director for Private Groups.—Hyman H. Bookbinder, 6308 Bannock-burn Drive, Bethesda, Md., 20034.

Assistant Director for Public Affairs.—Holmes M. Brown, 1701 Massachusetts Avenue, 20036.

OFFICE OF EMERGENCY PLANNING

Executive Office Building Annex, 20504.   Phone, EXecutive 3-3300 (Code 128, extension 22201)

Director.—Buford Ellington, The Towers, 4201 Cathedral Avenue NW., 20016.

Deputy Director.—Franklin B. Dryden, 5128 37th Road North, Arlington, Va., 22207.

Assistant Director.—Charles S. Brewton, 233 Belle Haven Road, Alexandria, Va., 22307.

Assistant Director.—John E. Cosgrove, 3953 Lantern Drive, Silver Spring, Md., 20902.

Assistant Director/Director of Telecommunications Management.—James D. O'Connell, 1400 20th Street, 20036.

Legal Adviser.—Mordecai M. Merker, 407 Regent Drive, Alexandria, Va., 22307.

Health Adviser.—Dr. James K. Shafer, 5100 Hampden Lane, Bethesda, Md., 20014.

Director, Analysis and Research Office.—John C. Green, Box 246, Joyce Lane, Arnold, Md., 21012.

Director, Economic Affairs Office.—G. Lyle Belsley, 3277 Rittenhouse Street, 20015.

Director, Government Readiness Office.—Robert Y. Phillips, 2000 North Adams Street, Arlington, Va., 22201.

Director, Program Development Office.—Robert W. Stokley, 4617 Clark Place, 20007.

Director, Program Evaluation Office.—Eugene J. Quindlen, 1007 Cedar Lane, Falls Church, Va., 22042.

Director, Resource Readiness Office.—Edward L. Keenan, 5928 Kirby Road, Falls Church, Va., 22043.

Director of Liaison and Public Affairs.—Hubert R. Gallagher, 5416 Burling Road, Bethesda, Md., 20014.

Director of Information.—Emmet Riordan, 1016 17th Street, 20036.

Director of Administration.—William B. Rice, 11 Overhill Road, Falls Church, Va., 22042.

REGIONAL OFFICES

Regional Office 1—Connecticut, Maine, Massachusetts, New Hampshire, New Jersey, New York, Rhode Island, Vermont, Puerto Rico, Virgin Islands.— Albert D. O'Connor, Director, Regional Office 1, Office of Emergency Planning, Oak Hill Road, Harvard, Mass., 01451.

Regional Office 2—Delaware, District of Columbia, Kentucky, Maryland, Ohio, Pennsylvania, Virginia, West Virginia.—Robert J. Carmody, Director, Regional Office 2, Office of Emergency Planning, Olney, Md., 20832.

Regional Office 3—Alabama, Florida, Georgia, Mississippi, North Carolina, South Carolina, Tennessee, Canal Zone.—John J. Pilcher, Director, Regional Office 3, Office of Emergency Planning, P.O. Box 108, Thomasville, Ga., 31792.

Regional Office 4—Illinois, Indiana, Michigan, Missouri, Wisconsin.—Frank P. Bourgin, Director, Regional Office 4, Office of Emergency Planning, Federal Center, Battle Creek, Mich., 49016.

Regional Office 5—Arkansas, Louisiana, New Mexico, Oklahoma, Texas.—George E. Hastings, Director, Regional Office 5, Office of Emergency Planning, Denton Federal Center, Denton, Tex., 75202.

Regional Office 6—Colorado, Kansas, Iowa, Minnesota, Nebraska, North Dakota, South Dakota, Wyoming.—John F. Sullivan, Jr., Director, Regional Office 6, Office of Emergency Planning, Denver Federal Center, Building 50, Denver, Colo., 80225.

Regional Office 7—Arizona, California, Hawaii, Nevada, Utah, American Samoa, Guam.—George M. Grace, Director, Regional Office 7, Office of Emergency Planning, Santa Rosa, Calif., 95401.

Regional Office 8—Alaska, Idaho, Montana, Oregon, Washington.—Creath Tooley, Director, Regional Office 8, Office of Emergency Planning, Everett, Wash., 95201.

OFFICE OF SCIENCE AND TECHNOLOGY
Executive Office Building, 20506.   Phone, 393-3300 (Code 128-22415)

Director.—Donald F. Hornig, 2810 Brandywine Street, 20008.

Deputy Director.—Colin M. MacLeod, 2702 Dumbarton Avenue, 20007.

Assistant to the Director.—David Z. Beckler, 117 Duvall Street, Fairfax, Va., 22030.

Special Assistant to the Director.—Robert Barlow, 121 Woodside Drive, McLean, Va., 22101.

Executive Secretary, Federal Council for Science and Technology.—Charles V. Kidd, 8000 Springer Road, Bethesda, Md., 20034.

OFFICE OF THE SPECIAL REPRESENTATIVE FOR TRADE NEGOTIATIONS
Executive Office Building, 20500.   Phone, 382-1914 (Code 128)

Special Representative for Trade Negotiations.—Christian A. Herter, 3108 P Street, 20007.

Deputy Special Representative for Trade Negotiations.—W. Michael Blumenthal, U.S. Mission, Geneva, Switzerland.

Deputy Special Representative for Trade Negotiations.—William M. Roth, 3005 O Street, 20007.

Executive Assistant.—Kenneth Auchincloss, 3757 Ramleigh Road, McLean, Va.

General Counsel.—John B. Rehm, 5200 Saratoga Avenue, Chevy Chase, Md., 20015.

Assistant General Counsel.—Robert E. Hudec, 4202 Oakridge Lane, Chevy Chase, Md., 20015.

Agricultural Trade Specialist.—Irwin R. Hedges, 3648 North Oakland Street, Arlington, Va.

Chief Economist.—Theodore R. Gates, 5810 Surrey Street, Chevy Chase, Md., 20015.

Senior Economist.—Harald B. Malmgren, 1251 35th Street, 20007.

Economist.—Norman S. Fieleke, 5703 Sangar Avenue, Alexandria, Va.

Chairman, Trade Staff Committee.—Bernard Norwood, 6409 Majory Lane, Bethesda, Md., 20034.

Alternate Chairman, Trade Staff Committee.—Albert J. Powers, 509 Highland Road, Fairfax, Va.

Assistant to Chairman of Trade Staff Committee.—Joseph Simanis, 2116 F Street.

Chairman, Trade Information Committee.—Louis C. Krauthoff II, 3317 O Street.

Executive Secretary, Trade Information Committee.—Sidney I. Picker, Jr., 1900 South Eads Street, Arlington, Va.

Public Affairs Adviser.—David C. Williams, 4305 Elm Street, Chevy Chase, Md., 20015.

Staff Assistant to Ambassador Blumenthal.—Courtenay P. Worthington, U.S. Mission Geneva, Switzerland.

DEPARTMENT OF STATE

2201 C Street, 20520. Phone, REpublic 7-5600 (Code 182)

DEAN RUSK, Secretary of State; born February 9, 1909, Cherokee County, Ga.; son of Robert Hugh and Frances Elizabeth (Clotfelter) Rusk; married Virginia Foisie of Seattle, Wash., June 19, 1937; children: David Patrick, Richard Geary, and Margaret Elizabeth; education: A.B., Davidson College (Phi Beta Kappa) 1927–31; Rhodes Scholar, St. John's College, Oxford University, 1931–34; awarded Cecil Peace Prize 1934; Bernard Baruch Distinguished Service Medal, 1962; LL.D. (honorary) Mills College; LL.D. (honorary) Davidson College; LL.D. (honorary) University of California at Berkeley; LL.D. (honorary) Emory University; LL.D. (honorary) Princeton University; LL.D. (honorary) Louisiana State University; LL.D. (honorary) Amherst College; L.H.D. (honorary) Westminster College; D.C.L. (honorary) Oxford University; LL.D. (honorary) Columbia University; LL.D. (honorary) Harvard University; LL.D. (honorary) Rhode Island University; L.H.D. (honorary) Hebrew Union College; LL.D. (honorary) Valparaiso University; LL.D. (honorary) Williams College; LL.D. (honorary) University of North Carolina; Associate Professor of Government and Dean of Faculty, Mills College; entered U.S. Army as Captain (Infantry Reserve) December 1940; discharged as Colonel February 1946; awarded Legion of Merit and Oak Leaf Cluster; Assistant Chief, Division of International Security Affairs, Department of State, 1946; Special Assistant to Secretary of War, 1946–47; Director, Office of Special Political Affairs, Department of State, 1947–48; Director, Office of United Nations Affairs, Department of State, 1948; Assistant Secretary for United Nations Affairs, Department of State, 1949; Deputy Under Secretary, Department of State, 1949–50; Assistant Secretary for Far Eastern Affairs, Department of State, 1950–52; president, The Rockefeller Foundation, 1952–61; appointed Secretary of State and took oath of office on January 21, 1961; member: Council on Foreign Relations, American Political Science Association, American Society for International Law; residence: 4980 Quebec Street, 20016.

Secretary of State.—Dean Rusk.
> *Special Assistant to the Secretary.*—Edward S. Little, 311 Franklin Street, Alexandria, Va., 22307.
> *Personal Assistant to the Secretary.*—Carolyn J. Proctor, 2100 Massachusetts Avenue, 20008.
> *Ambassador at Large.*—Llewellyn E. Thompson, 1913 23d Street, 20008.
> *Ambassador at Large.*—W. Averell Harriman, 3038 N Street, 20007.

Under Secretary of State.—George W. Ball, 3100 35th Street, 20016.
> *Special Assistants to the Under Secretary.*—George S. Springsteen, 5115 Baltimore Avenue; Robert Anderson, 4546 Cathedral Avenue, 20016.
> *Special Assistant to the Secretary and Executive Secretary of the Department.*—Benjamin H. Read, 1739 Crestwood Drive, 20011.
>> *Deputy Executive Secretary.*—Grant G. Hilliker, 604 Abbott Lane, Falls Church Va., 22046.
>> *Deputy Executive Secretary and Director of the Operations Center.*—Lewis Hoffacker, 2836 Albermarle Street, 20008.

Under Secretary of State for Economic Affairs.—Thomas C. Mann, 4355 Lowell Street, 20016.
> *Special Assistant to the Under Secretary for Economic Affairs.*—Davis E. Boster, 916 Lakeview Drive, Falls Church, Va., 22041.
> *Special Assistant to the Secretary and Coordinator of International Labor Affairs.*—George P. Delaney, 2946 McKinley Street, 20015.
> *Special Assistant to the Under Secretary for Fisheries and Wildlife.*—William C. Herrington, 6025 North 23d Street, Arlington, Va., 22205.

Deputy Under Secretary of State for Political Affairs (Acting).—Llewellyn E. Thompson, 1913 23d Street, 20008.
  Special Assistant to the Deputy Under Secretary for Political Affairs.—Windsor G. Hackler, 9504 Burning Tree Road, Bethesda, Md., 20034.
  Deputy Assistant Secretary for Politico-Military Affairs.—Jeffrey C. Kitchen, 10401 Riverwood Drive, Rockville, Md., 20854.

Deputy Under Secretary of State for Administration.—William J. Crockett, 3329 Reservoir Road, 20016.
  Special Assistants to the Deputy Under Secretary for Administration.—Frederick Irving, 9622 Culver Street, Kensington, Md., 20795; William R. Little, (Congressional Relations-Appropriations), 3736 Gunston Road, Alexandria, Va., 22302.
  Chief of Protocol.—Lloyd N. Hand, 4603 Hardy Drive, McLean, Va., 22101.
  Administrator, Bureau of Security and Consular Affairs.—Abba P. Schwartz, 3306 R Street, 20007.
  Director General of the Foreign Service.—Joseph Palmer 2nd, 5414 Kirkwood Drive, Springfield, Md., 20016.
  Inspector General, Foreign Service Inspection Corps.—Fraser Wilkins, 4332 Garfield Street, 20007.
  Director, Foreign Service Institute.—George A. Morgan, 2812 34th Place, 20007.
  Deputy Assistant Secretary for Security.—G. Marvin Gentile, 14808 Claude Lane, Silver Spring, Md., 20904.
  Deputy Assistant Secretary.—Mrs. Katie Louchheim, 2824 O Street, 20007.
  Deputy Assistant Secretary.—Mrs. Lee Walsh, 3123 Dumbarton Avenue, 20007.
  Deputy Assistant Secretary.—Michel Cieplinski, 730 24th Street, 20037.

Counselor and Chairman of Policy Planning Council.—Walt Whitman Rostow, 3414 Lowell Street, 20016.
  Deputy Counselor.—Henry D. Owen, 2946 University Terrace, 20016.

Legal Adviser (Acting).—Leonard C. Meeker, 3000 Chain Bridge Road, 20016.
  Deputy Legal Adviser.—Richard D. Kearney, 1316 Fourth Street SW., 20024.
  Deputy Legal Adviser for Administration.—J. Edward Lyerly, 3707 Taylor Street, Chevy Chase, Md., 20015.
  Deputy Legal Adviser (Acting).—Andreas F. Lowenfeld, 4410 Greenwich Parkway, 20007.
  Executive Assistant.—Jac. H. Bushong, 7103 Connecticut Avenue, Chevy Chase, Md., 20015.
  Assistant Legal Adviser for African Affairs.—Charles Runyon III, 5114 Cathedral Avenue, 20016.
  Assistant Legal Adviser for Inter-American Affairs.—Marjorie M. Whiteman, 5021 Glenbrook Broad, 20016.
  Assistant Legal Adviser for International Claims.—George W. Spangler, 4545 Connecticut Avenue, 20008.
  Assistant Legal Adviser for Cultural Relations and Public Affairs.—Fred T. Teal, 6501 Third Avenue, Takoma Park, Md., 20012.
  Assistant Legal Adviser for Economic Affairs.—Andreas F. Lowenfeld, 4410 Greenwich Parkway, 20007.
  Assistant Legal Adviser for European Affairs.—Herbert K. Reis, 2727 29th Street, 20008.
  Assistant Legal Adviser for Far Eastern Affairs.—Carl F. Salans, 409 Beechwood Road, Hollin Hills, Alexandria, Va., 22307.
  Assistant Legal Adviser for Military and Economic Regional Affairs.—Ely Naurer, 1023 Forest Glen Road, Silver Spring, Md., 20901.
  Assistant Legal Adviser for Near Eastern and South Asian Affairs.—Donald A. Wehmeyer, 742 Ivydale Drive, Annandale, Va., 22003.
  Assistant Legal Adviser for Security and Consular Affairs.—Frederick Smith, Jr., 606 Juniper Lane, Falls Church, Va., 22044.
  Assistant Legal Adviser for Special Functional Problems.—Raymund T. Yingling, 3040 Idaho Avenue, 20016.
  Assistant Legal Adviser for Treaty Affairs.—Charles I. Bevans, 2221 North Madison Street, Arlington, Va., 22205.
  Assistant Legal Adviser for United Nations Affairs.—Stephen M. Schwebel, 824 New Hampshire Avenue, 20007.
  General Counsel Visa Office.—James J. Hines, 3120 North Inglewood Street, Arlington, Va., 22207.

Assistant Secretary of State for Congressional Relations.—Douglas MacArthur II, 2236 Q Street, 20007.
  Deputy Assistant Secretary for Congressional Relations.—Robert E. Lee, 2813 Q Street, 20007.
  Deputy Assistant Secretary for Congressional Relations.—John P. White, 10201 Grosvenor Place, Rockville, Md., 20014.

Assistant Secretary of State for Economic Affairs.—G. Griffith Johnson, 6412 Garnet Drive, Chevy Chase, Md., 20015.
  Deputy Assistant Secretary for Economic Affairs.—Philip H. Trezise, 6900 Broxburn Drive, Bethesda, Md., 20034.
  Deputy Assistant Secretary for Economic Affairs.—Jerome Jacobson, 3215 Rowland Place, 20008.
  Executive Staff: Director (Acting).—Frances M. Wilson, 5400 Brookeway Drive, 20016.
  Office of International Trade Director.—Joseph Greenwald, 2900 Connecticut Avenue, 20008.
  Office of International Finance and Economic Analysis: Director.—Benjamin Caplan, 4201 Cathedral Avenue, 20016.
  Office of International Resources: Director.—Stanley Nehmer, 9007 Kirkdale Road, Bethesda, Md., 20034.
  Office of International Aviation: Coordinator.—Allen R. Ferguson, 5817 Marbury Road, Bethesda, Md., 20034.
  Office of Telecommunications and Maritime Affairs: Director.—Paul F. Geren, 4914 Upton Street, 20016.

Assistant Secretary of State for Educational and Cultural Affairs.—Harry C. McPherson, Jr., 24 Sixth Street SE., 20003.
  Deputy Assistant Secretary for Educational and Cultural Affairs.—Arthur W. Hummel, Jr., 4923 Essex Avenue, Somerset, Md., 20015.
  Deputy Assistant Secretary for Educational and Cultural Affairs.—Catherine D. Norrell, 2559 Waterside Drive, 20008.
  Public Information and Reports Staff: Director.—Hugh B. Sutherland, 2709 34th Place, 20007.
  Policy Review and Coordination Staff: Director.—Francis J. Colligan, 5200 Oakland Road, Chevy Chase, Md., 20015.
  Executive Director.—Theo E. Hall, 5100 Dorset Avenue, Chevy Chase, Md., 20015.
  Office of African Programs: Director.—J. Roland Jacobs, 3024 Arizona Avenue, 20007.
  Office of European Programs: Director.—Joseph M. Roland, 5040 Albemarle Street, 20016.
  Office of Far Eastern Programs: Director.—Harold E. Howland, 406 Dove Circle, Vienna, Va., 22180.
  Office of Inter-American Programs: Director.—Jacob Canter, 5209 38th Street, 20015.
  Office of Near Eastern and South Asian Programs: Director.—Henry T. Smith, 6438 Lakeview Drive, Lake Barcroft, Falls Church, Va., 22041.
  Office of Cultural Presentations: Director.—Charles M. Ellison, 7011 Westbury Road, McLean, Va., 22101.
  Office of U.S. Programs and Services: Director.—Frank S. Hopkins, 5108 Lawton Drive, 20016.
  Multilateral and Special Activities: Director.—Douglas N. Batson, 141 12th Street SE., 20003.

The Director of Intelligence and Research.—Thomas L. Hughes, 3602 Shepherd Street, Chevy Chase, Md., 20015.
  Deputy Director of Intelligence and Research.—George C. Denney, Jr., 2604 36th Street, 20007.
  Deputy Director for Research.—Allan Evans, 3206 Reservoir Road, 20007.
  Deputy Director for Coordination.—Murat W. Williams, 1529 29th Street, 20007.
  Executive Staff: Director.—Edward C. Wilson, 5002 Nahant Street, Bethesda, Md., 20016.
  Office of Current Intelligence Indications: Director.—William M. Marvel, 5303 Duvall Drive, 20016.
  Office of Research and Analysis for American Republics: Director.—Gregory B. Wolfe, 10401 Lloyd Road, Potomac, Md., 20854.

The Director of Intelligence and Research—Continued

    Office of Research and Analysis for Far East: Director.—Allen S. Whiting, 3509 McKinley Street, 20015.

    Office of Research and Analysis for Africa: Director (Acting).—Robert D. Baum, 1106 Seaton Lane, Falls Church, Va., 22046.

    Office of Research and Analysis for Soviet Bloc: Director.—Howard Trivers, 3729 North Oakland Street, Arlington, Va., 22207.

    Office of Research and Analysis for Western Europe: Director.—David E. Marck, 8314 Loring Drive Bethesda, Md., 20034.

    Office of Research in Economics and Science: Director.—Meredith B. Givens, Cosmos Club, 2121 Massachusetts Avenue, 20008.

    Office of Research and Analysis for Near East and South Asia: Director.—James W. Spain, 2244 Cathedral Avenue, 20008.

    The Geographer.—Dr. G. Etzel Pearcy, 2426 I Street, 20037.

Assistant Secretary of State for International Organization Affairs.—Harlan Cleveland, 2738 McKinley Street, 20015.

    Deputy Assistant Secretary for International Organization Affairs.—Joseph J. Sisco, 5205 Portsmouth Road, Westmoreland Hills, Md., 20016.

    Deputy Assistant Secretary for International Organization Affairs.—Richard N. Gardner, 3417 R Street, 20007.

    Executive Director.—Oscar H. Nielson, 1217 Admiral Drive, Alexandria, Va., 22307.

    Office of United Nations Political Affairs: Director.—William B. Buffum, 5806 McKinley Street, Bethesda, Md., 20034.

    Office of International Economic and Social Affairs: Director.—William J. Stibravy, 6205 Goldsboro Road, Bethesda, Md., 20034.

    Office of International Administration: Director.—Virginia C. Housholder, 2611 North Upland Street, Arlington, Va., 22207.

    Office of International Conferences: Director.—Francis Cunningham, 3906 Kincaid Terrace, Kensington, Md., 20795.

Director of International Scientific Affairs.—[Vacant.]

    Deputy Director of International Scientific Affairs (Acting).—Herman Pollack, 7000 Selkirk Drive, Bethesda, Md., 20034.

    Executive Director.—Arthur E. Pardee, Jr., 10104 Kohler Road, Silver Spring, Md., 20902.

Inspector General of Foreign Assistance.—J. K. Mansfield, 1069 Thomas Jefferson Street, 20007.

    Deputy Inspector General of Foreign Assistance.—Howard E. Haugerud, 2609 South Hayes Street, Arlington, Va., 22202.

Assistant Secretary of State for Public Affairs.—James L. Greenfield, 3310 N Street, 20007.

    Deputy Assistant Secretary for Public Affairs.—Richard I. Phillips, 3701 Massachusetts Avenue, 20016.

    Deputy Assistant Secretary for Public Affairs.—Raymond E. Lisle, 8051 Parkside Lane, 20012.

    Deputy Assistant Secretary for Public Affairs.—Mrs. Charlotte M. Hubbard, 1830 16th Street, 20009.

    Executive Director.—Francis T. Murphy, 8602 Irvington Avenue, Bethesda, Md., 20034.

    Office of News: Director.—Robert J. McCloskey, 110 Hesketh Street, Chevy Chase, Md., 20015.

    Office of Public Services: Director.—John E. Horner, 5700 Broad Branch Road, 20015.

    Office of Media Services: Director.—William D. Blair, Jr., 125 Hesketh Street, Chevy Chase, Md., 20015.

    Historical Office: Director.—William M. Franklin, 6617 Barnaby Street, 20015.

Assistant Secretary of State for African Affairs.—G. Mennen Williams, 1401 31st Street, 20007.

    Deputy Assistant Secretary for African Affairs.—J. Wayne Fredericks, 4530 Lowell Street, 20016.

    Deputy Assistant Secretary for African Affairs.—Henry J. Tasca, 2142 Wyoming Avenue, 20008.

Assistant Secretary of State for African Affairs—Continued

    Deputy Assistant Secretary for African Affairs.—Samuel Z. Westerfield, Jr., 4801 Colorado Avenue, 20011.

    Executive Director.—Edward P. Dobyns, 7721 Old Chester Road, Bethesda, Md., 20034.

      Office of Central African Affairs: Director.—James L. O'Sullivan, 5040 Klingle Street, 20016.

      Office of Eastern and Southern African Affairs: Director.—Jesse M. Mac-Knight, 8318 Haddon Drive, Takoma Park, Md., 20012.

      Office of Inter-African Affairs: Director.—Fred L. Hadsel, 3432 Ashley Terrace, 20008.

      Office of Northern African Affairs: Director.—David D. Newsom, 3308 Woodley Road, 20008.

      Office of West African Affairs: Director.—William C. Trimble, 2535 Queen Anne's Lane, 20037.

Assistant Secretary of State for European Affairs.—William R. Tyler, 2627 Dumbarton Avenue, 20007.

    Deputy Assistant Secretary for European Affairs.—Richard H. Davis, 3410 Q Street, 20007.

    Deputy Assistant Secretary for European Affairs.—J. Robert Schaetzel, 2 Bay Tree Lane, 20016.

    Deputy Assistant Secretary for European Affairs.—Robert C. Creel, 2717 36th Place, 20007.

    Executive Director.—Seaborn P. Foster, 3708 Livingston Street, 20015.

      Office of British Commonwealth and Northern European Affairs: Director.—J. Harold Shullaw, 3704 Leland Street, Chevy Chase, Md., 20015.

      Office of Eastern European Affairs: Director.—Harold C. Vedeler, 403 South Fairfax Street, Alexandria, Va., 22314.

      Office of German Affairs: Director.—Alfred Puhan, 5701 Hazel Lane, McLean, Va., 22101.

      Office of Soviet Union Affairs: Director.—David H. Henry 2d, 415 Brentwood Place, Hollin Hills, Alexandria, Va., 22306.

      Office of Western European Affairs: Director.—David H. McKillop, 5169 Tilden Street, 20016.

      Office of Atlantic Political and Military Affairs: Director.—David H. Popper, 6116 33d Street, 20015.

      Office of Atlantic Political-Economic Affairs: Director.—Deane R. Hinton, 6025 Dellwood Place, Bethesda, Md., 20034.

      Soviet and Eastern European Exchanges Staff: Director.—Frank G. Siscoe, 3422 Garfield Street, 20007.

Assistant Secretary of State for Far Eastern Affairs.—William P. Bundy, 3500 Lowell Street, 20016.

    Deputy Assistant Secretary for Far Eastern Affairs.—Leonard Unger, 12701 Circle Drive, Rockville, Md., 20850.

    Deputy Assistant Secretary for Far Eastern Affairs.—Marshall Green, 5063 Millwood Lane, 20016.

    Deputy Assistant Secretary for Far Eastern Affairs.—Robert W. Barnett, 5205 Abingdon Road, 20016.

    Executive Director.—Marshall P. Jones, 5414 Newington Road, Bethesda, Md., 20016.

      Office of Regional Affairs: Director.—Joseph A. Mendenhall, 503 Sleepy Hollow Road, Falls Church, Va., 20022.

      Office of Asian Communist Affairs: Director.—Lindsey Grant, 411 Rucker Place, Alexandria, Va., 22301.

      Office of East Asian Affairs: Director.—Robert A. Fearey, 5104 Cammack Drive, 20016.

      Office of Southeast Asian Affairs: Director.—William C. Trueheart, 5149 Tilden Street, 20016.

      Office of Southwest Pacific Affairs: Director.—David C. Cuthell, 6616 Barnaby Street, 20015.

Assistant Secretary of State for Near Eastern and South Asian Affairs.—Phillips Talbot, 3634 Upton Street, 20008.

    Deputy Assistant Secretary for Near Eastern and South Asian Affairs.—John D. Jernegan, 3257 Worthington Street, 20015.

    Deputy Assistant Secretary for Near Eastern and South Asian Affairs.—William J. Handley, 3818 North Oakland Street, Arlington, Va., 22207.

Assistant Secretary of State for Near Eastern and South Asian Affairs—Continued
  Executive Director (Acting).—Martin G. Manch, 4814 Lochraven Drive, Mc-
    Lean, Va., 22101.
    Office of Near Eastern Affairs: Director.—Rodger P. Davies, 5315 Duvall
      Drive, 20016.
    Office of Greek, Turkish and Iranian Affairs: Director.—Katherine W.
      Bracken, 4201 Cathedral Avenue, 20016.
    Office of South Asian Affairs: Director.—Turner C. Cameron, Jr., 1565 33d
      Street, 20007.
    Office of Near Eastern and South Asian Regional Affairs: Director.—Guy A.
      Lee, 3715 Thornapple Street, Chevy Chase, Md., 20015.

Deputy Assistant Secretary of State for Administration.—W. T. M. Beale, 1661
  Crescent Place, 20009.
  Executive Director for Administration.—Victor Purse, Alvictus, Lake Jackson,
    Manassas, Va., 22110.
  Deputy Assistant Secretary for Budget and Finance.—Verne B. Lewis, 9704
    Stoneham Terrace, Bethesda, Md., 20034.
    Office of Budget: Director.—Paul G. Sinderson, 5913 Cheshire Drive, Bethesda,
      Md., 20014.
    Office of Finance: Director.—Anthony Novak, 5511 North 24th Street,
      Arlington, Va., 22205.
  Deputy Assistant Secretary for Foreign Buildings.—James R. Johnstone, 8616
    Ewing Drive, Bethesda, Md., 20034.
  Deputy Assistant Secretary for Management.—Ralph S. Roberts, 6400 31st
    Place, 20015.
  Deputy Assistant Secretary for Communications.—John W. Coffey, 4220 North
    25th Street, Arlington, Va., 22207.
  Office of Personnel: Director.—Harvey R. Wellman, 4108 Dunel Lane, Kensing-
    ton, Md., 20795.
  Office of Operations: Director.—Winson O. Trone, 5612 Massachusetts Avenue,
    Falls Church, Va., 22043.

Administrator, Bureau of Security and Consular Affairs.—Abba P. Schwartz, 3306
  R Street, 20007.
  Deputy Administrator.—Charles Hoyt Mace, 4300 47th Street, 20016.
  Adviser, Refugee and Migration Affairs.—George L. Warren, Sr., 4000 Cathedral
    Avenue, 20016.
  Executive Director.—Seymour Levenson, 9619 Alta Vista Terrace, Bethesda,
    Md., 20014.
    Passport Office: Director.—Frances G. Knight, 2445 Wyoming Avenue,
      20008.
    Visa Office Director.—Allen B. Moreland, 4620 North 35th Street, Arlington,
      Va., 22207.
    Office of Special Consular Services: Director.—Allyn C. Donaldson, 2405
      South Joyce Street, Arlington, Va., 22202.
    Office of Refugee and Migration Affairs: Director.—Elmer M. Falk, 105
      Virginia Avenue, Wellington, Alexandria, Va., 22308.

**BUREAU OF INTER-AMERICAN AFFAIRS (STATE) AND BUREAU FOR LATIN AMERICA
(AGENCY FOR INTERNATIONAL DEVELOPMENT)**

*Assistant Secretary of State for Inter-American Affairs and U.S. Coordinator,
  Alliance for Progress.*—Jack Hood Vaughn, Room 6260, Department of
  State.
  Deputy Assistant Secretary of State for Inter-American Affairs.—Robert W.
    Adams, 8939 Colesbury Place, Fairfax, Va., 22030.
  Deputy U.S. Coordinator.—William D. Rogers, 304 Beechwood Drive, Alex-
    andria, Va., 22307.
  Deputy Assistant Secretary of State for Inter-American Affairs.—Anthony M.
    Solomon, 2535 Massachusetts Avenue, 20008.
  *Executive Director and Deputy Assistant Administrator for Management and
    Operations.*—Rodger C. Abraham, 4305 Lynbrook Drive, Bethesda, Md.,
    20014.
    Office of Argentine-Paraguayan-Uruguayan Affairs: Director.—Henry A.
      Hoyt, 5037 Westpath Terrace, 20016.

Department of State

431

Assistant Secretary of State for Inter-American Affairs and U.S. Coordinator, Alliance for Progress—Continued

Office of Bolivian-Chilean Affairs: Director.—William T. Dentzer, Jr., 3512 North Military Road, Arlington, Va., 22207.

Office of Brazil Affairs: Director.—Jack Kubish, 4700 Rodman Street, 20008.

Office of Caribbean Affairs: Director.—Kennedy M. Crockett, 1632 Devine Street, McLean, Va., 22101.

Office of Central American Affairs: Director.—Oliver L. Sause, 3014 Dent Place, 20007.

Office of Colombian-Venezuelan Affairs: Director.—Daniel F. Margolies, 802 Third Street, 20024.

Office of the Coordinator of Cuban Affairs: Coordinator.—John H. Crimmins, 4112 Dana Court, Kensington, Md., 20795. Liaison Office (Miami): Director.—Godfrey H. Summ, 524 Warren Lane, Key Biscayne, Miami, Fla.

Office of Ecuadorean-Peruvian Affairs: Director (Acting).—Malcolm R. Barnebey, 2828 23d Road North, Arlington, Va.

Office of Mexican Affairs: Director—Terrance Leonhardy, 3117 38th Street, 20016.

Office of Panamanian Affairs: Director.—Edward W. Clark, 5407 Center Street, Chevy Chase, Md., 20015.

Office of Regional Political Affairs: Director.—Ward P. Allen, 11 Shenandoah Road, Alexandria, Va., 22308.

Office of Regional Economic Policy: Director.—Donald K. Palmer, 5404 Greystone Street, Chevy Chase, Md., 20015.

Office of Development Planning and Programs: Deputy Assistant Administrator.—Reuben Sternfeld, 333 I Street SW., 20024.

Office of Institutional Development: Director.—Irving G. Tragen, 4201 Cathedral Avenue, 20016.

Office of Capital Development: Deputy Assistant Administrator.—Philip Glaessner, 9019 Burdette Road, Bethesda, Md., 20034.

UNITED STATES MISSION TO THE UNITED NATIONS
799 United Nations Plaza, New York, N.Y.

United States Representative to the United Nations.—Adlai E. Stevenson, Waldorf Towers, New York, N.Y., 10022.

Deputy United States Representative to the United Nations.—Francis T. P. Plimpton, 1165 Fifth Avenue, New York, N.Y., 10029.

Deputy United States Representative to the United Nations.—Charles W. Yost, 1165 Fifth Avenue, New York, N.Y., 10029.

United States Representative on the Trusteeship Council.—Marietta P. Tree, 123 East 79th Street, New York, N.Y., 10021.

United States Representative on the Economic and Social Council.—Franklin H. Williams, 501 East 87th Street, New York, N.Y., 10028.

Deputy United States Representative on the Economic and Social Council.—Walter M. Kotschnig, 3518 Bradley Lane, Chevy Chase, Md., 20015.

Counselor of Mission.—Richard F. Pedersen, 1 Lexington Avenue, New York, N.Y., 10010.

Deputy Counselor.—Seymour M. Finger, 476 Morris Avenue, Rockville Center, Long Island, N.Y., 11570.

Chief Administrative Officer.—Edward J. Gaumond, 8 Mildred Parkway, New Rochelle, N.Y., 10804.

United Nations Military Staff Committee:

Army:
Representative and Chairman, United States Delegation.—Lt. Gen. Robert W. Porter, Jr., USA, Quarters 1, Governors Island, New York, N.Y., 10004.

Navy:
Representative and Vice Chairman, United States Delegation.—Vice Adm. Harold T. Deutermann, USN, Quarters A, New York Naval Shipyard, Brooklyn, N.Y., 11201.

Air Force:
Representative.—Lt. Gen. William H. Blanchard, USAF, c/o U.S. Delegation, UNMSC, 799 UN Plaza, New York, N.Y., 10017.

BOARDS AND COMMISSIONS

Board of the Foreign Service:
  Chairman.—William J. Crockett (Deputy Under Secretary of State for Administration).
  Executive Secretary.—Edward T. Walters.
Board of Examiners for the Foreign Service:
  Chairman.—Joseph Palmer 2nd (Director General of the Foreign Service, Department of State).
  Vice Chairman.—Harvey R. Wellman (Director, Office of Personnel, Department of State).
  Executive Secretary.—Donovan Q. Zook.
Board of Foreign Scholarships:
  Chairman.—John M. Stalnaker, 990 Grove Street, Evanston, Ill.
  Executive Secretary.—Ralph H. Vogel, 313 Maple Avenue, Falls Church, Va., 22046.
U.S. Advisory Commission on International Educational and Cultural Affairs:
  Chairman.—Homer D. Babbidge, Jr., Storrs, Conn., 06268.
  Director, Secretariat.—James A. Donovan, Jr., 1616 Ripon Place, Parkfairfax, Alexandria, Va., 22302.
Advisory Committee on the Arts: Chairman.—Roy E. Larsen, 4900 Congress Street, Fairfield, Conn.
U.S. National Commission for UNESCO:
  Executive Secretary.—L. Arthur Minnich, Jr., 8611 Brook Road, McLean, Va., 22101.

AGENCY FOR INTERNATIONAL DEVELOPMENT

Twenty-first and Virginia Avenue, 20523. Phone, REpublic 7-5600 (Code 182)

Administrator.—David E. Bell, 5801 Bent Branch Road, Tulip Hill, Md., 20016.
  Deputy Administrator.—William S. Gaud, 5053 Glenbrook Terrace, 20016.
  Assistant Administrator for Administration.—William O. Hall, 2231 Bancroft Place, 20008.
  Executive Secretary.—Frederick F. Simmons, 1304 Fourth Street SW., 20024.
  Assistant Administrator for Program Coordination (acting).—Bartlett Harvey, 1506 Turkey Run Road, McLean, Va., 22101.
  Information Staff: Director.—Michael W. Moynihan, 3130 Macomb Street, 20016.
  Congressional Liaison Staff: Director.—William C. Gibbons, 1101 Prince Street, Alexandria, Va., 22314.
  General Counsel.—Thomas L. Farmer, 3456 Macomb Street, 20016.
  Management Inspection Staff: Director.—Thomas A. Kennedy, 218 Chichester Lane, Fairfax, Va., 22030.
  Assistant Administrator for Near East and South Asia.—William B. Macomber, 4200 Cathedral Avenue, 20016.
  Deputy U.S. Coordinator for Alliance for Progress.—William D. Rogers, 304 Beechwood Drive, Alexandria, Va., 22307.
  Assistant Administrator for Africa.—Edmond C. Hutchinson, 9619 Hillridge Drive, Kensington, Md., 20795.
  Assistant Administrator for Far East.—Rutherford M. Poats, 423 Crosswoods Drive, Falls Church, Va., 22044.
  Assistant Administrator for Material Resources.—Herbert J. Waters, 5721 Little Falls Road, Arlington, Va., 22207.
  Assistant Administrator for Development Finance and Private Enterprise.—Donald W. Hoagland, 3500 Macomb Street, 20016.
  Assistant Administrator for Technical Cooperation and Research.—Dr. Leona Baumgartner, 56 Washington Mews, New York, N.Y., 10003.
  Office of Engineering: Director.—L. M. Hale, 4301 Columbia Pike, Arlington, Va., 22204.
  Office of Labor Affairs: Director.—George P. Delaney, 2946 McKinley Street, 20015.
  Office of Public Safety: Director.—Byron Engle, 2500 Q Street, 20007.
  Office of the Controller: Controller.—Charles F. Flinner, 2004 Glen Ross Road, Silver Spring, Md., 20910.
  Office of Personnel Administration: Director.—L. Wade Lathram, 5829 Doris Drive, Alexandria, Va., 22311.

Administrator—Continued
  Office of Management Planning: Director.—Harry H. Fite, 3311 P Street, 20007.
  Office of International Training: Director.—Robert W. Kitchen, 4800 17th Street, 20011.
  Office of Security: Director.—John G. Bradley, 2406 North Upton Street, Arlington, Va., 22207.
  Statistics and Reports Division: Chief.—Frank M. Charrette, 1118 Walters Woods Drive, Falls Church, Va., 22044.
  General Services Division: Chief.—Anthony J. Mulvaney, 1721 North Vietch Street, Arlington, Va., 22201.

ADVISORY COMMITTEE ON VOLUNTARY FOREIGN AID

Chairman.—Charles P. Taft, 6 Burton Woods Lane, Cincinnati, Ohio.
  Vice Chairman.—William L. Batt, 710 South Ocean Boulevard, Delray Beach, Fla.
  Executive Director.—Howard S. Kresge, 5011 46th Street, 20016.

COOPERATIVE ADVISORY COMMITTEE

Ex-Officio Chairman.—Herbert J. Waters, 5712 Little Falls Road, North Arlington, Va., 22207.

DEVELOPMENT LOAN COMMITTEE

Chairman.—David E. Bell, 5801 Bent Branch Road, Tulip Hill, 20016.
Members:
  Donald W. Hoagland, 3500 Macomb Street, 20016.
  G. Griffith Johnson, 6412 Garnett Drive, Chevy Chase, Md., 20015.
  Harold F. Linder, 1901 24th Street, 20008.
  Merlyn N. Trued, 2020 F Street, 20006.

PEACE CORPS

806 Connecticut Avenue.   Phone, EXecutive 3–3111 (Code 128)

Director.—Robert Sargent Shriver, Jr., Edson Lane, Rockville, Md., 20852.
  Deputy Director.—[Vacant.] Warren W. Wiggins   5/17/65
  Executive Secretary.—Gerald W. Bush, 406 Colin Lane, Vienna, Va.
  General Counsel.—William H. Josephson, 1854 Wyoming Avenue, 20009.
  Associate Director for Management.—Max Medley, 6858 Riverdale Road, Lanham, Md., 20022.
  Associate Director for Peace Corps Volunteers (Acting).—F. Kingston Berlew, 5110 Wissioming Road, Bethesda, Md., 20016.
  Associate Director for Planning and Evaluation.—Harris L. Wofford, 200 Primrose Street, Chevy Chase, Md., 20015.
  Associate Director for Program Development and Operations.—Warren W. Wiggins, 1207 Rebecca Drive, Hollin Hills, Alexandria, Va., 22307.
  Associate Director for Public Affairs.—Charles C. Woodard, Jr., 1255 Rebecca Drive, Hollin Hills, Alexandria, Va., 22307.

DEPARTMENT OF THE TREASURY

Fifteenth Street and Pennsylvania Avenue, 20220
Phone, Executive 3-6400 (Code 184, extension 2117)

HENRY HAMILL FOWLER, of Alexandria, Va. (209 South Fairfax Street), son of Mack Johnson and Bertha Browning Fowler, born in Roanoke, Va., September 5, 1908; graduated from Jefferson High School, Roanoke, Va.; A.B. 1929, LL.D. 1962, Roanoke College; LL.B. 1932 and J.S.D. 1933, Yale University Law School; married Trudye Pamela Hathcote, October 19, 1938; children: Marianne Fowler Smith and Susan Maria Fowler; attorney in private law practice in Washington with Covington & Burling and with various government agencies, 1933–41; Assistant General Counsel, Office of Production Management and War Production Board, 1941–44; Economic Advisor, U.S. Mission for Economic Affairs, London, 1944; Special Assistant to Administrator, Foreign Economic Administration, 1945; private law practice as senior member of Fowler, Leva, Hawes and Symington, Washington, D.C., 1946–51; Deputy Administrator, National Production Administration, 1951; Administrator, National Production Authority, 1952; Administrator, Defense Production Administration, 1952–53; Director, Office of Defense Mobilization, and Member of National Security Council, 1952–53; private law practice as senior member with Fowler, Leva, Hawes and Symington, 1953–61; Under Secretary of the Treasury, 1961–64; private law practice as senior member with Fowler, Leva, Hawes and Symington, 1964–65; awards: distinguished alumni award Tau Kappa Alpha, 1958; Alexander Hamilton Award, 1964.

The Secretary:
Special Assistant to the Secretary.—Robert Carswell, 3022-B Q Street.
Confidential Assistant to the Secretary.—Dorothy deBorchgrave, 4200 Cathedral Avenue.
Under Secretary.—[Vacant.] *Joseph U. Barr (4/28/10)*
Special Assistant to the Under Secretary.—Douglass Hunt, 3617 Gunston Road, Alexandria, Va.
Under Secretary for Monetary Affairs.—Frederick L. Deming, Room 3312, Treasury Department.
Deputy Under Secretary for Monetary Affairs.—Paul A. Volcker, 4621 Chevy Chase Boulevard, Chevy Chase, Md.
Deputy Director, Office of Financial Analysis.—John H. Auten, 208 Holmes Run Road, Falls Church, Va.
Director, Office of Domestic Gold and Silver Operations.—Leland Howard, 3835 Lorcum Lane, Arlington, Va.
Director, Office of Debt Analysis.—R. Duane Saunders, 408 Daphne Lane, Hollin Hills, Alexandria, Va.
Assistant to the Secretary (Debt Management).—Daniel S. Ahearn, 2116 F Street, 20037.
Acting General Counsel.—Fred B. Smith, 5205 Battery Lane, Bethesda, Md., 20014.
Deputy General Counsel.—Fred B. Smith, 5205 Battery Lane, Bethesda, Md., 20014.
Assistant General Counsel (Chief Counsel, Internal Revenue Service).—Mitchell Rogovin, 4100 Duncan Drive, Annandale, Va., 22003.
Assistant General Counsels:
Roy T. Englert, 7353 Hastings Street, Springfield, Va., 22150.
Edwin F. Rains, 217 East Marshall Street, Falls Church, Va., 22042.
Hugo A. Ranta, 12031 Remington Drive, Silver Spring, Md., 20902.
George F. Reeves, 1135 16th Street, 20036.
Director, Office of Practice.—Thomas J. Reilly, 4000 Massachusetts Avenue, 20009.

Assistant Secretary.—Stanley S. Surrey, 4632 Reservoir Road.
  Deputy Assistant Secretary and Director, Office of Tax Analysis.—Jacob A. Stockfisch, 4705 Kellogg Drive, McLean, Va.
  Director, Office of International Tax Affairs.—Nathan N. Gordon, 5215 31st Road North, Arlington, Va.
  Tax Legislative Counsel.—Lawrence M. Stone, 720 Third Street SW., 20024.
    Associate Tax Legislative Counsel and Special Assistant to Assistant Secretary.—Richard O. Loengard, Jr., 1245 35th Street, 20007.
    Associate Tax Legislative Counsels:
      William T. Gibb III, 9810 Culver Court, Kensington, Md., 20795.
      George E. Zeitlin, 4117 Saul Road, Kensington, Md., 20795.

Assistant Secretary.—James A. Reed, 10 Snows Court.
  Deputy Assistant Secretary.—James P. Hendrick, 3303 Volta Place.
  Director, Office of Law Enforcement Coordination.—Arnold Sagalyn, 3006 Albemarle Street.
  Aide to Assistant Secretary.—Comdr. G. H. Patrick Bursley, USCG, 5905 Beech Avenue, Bethesda, Md.

Assistant Secretary.—Robert A. Wallace, 7 Carderock Court, Bethesda, Md.
  Special Assistant to Assistant Secretary.—Thomas W. Wolfe, 3810 Denfeld Avenue, Kensington, Md.
  Director, Employment Policy Program.—Mrs. Mary F. Nolan, 3911 Ravensworth Place, Alexandria, Va.

Acting Assistant Secretary for International Affairs.—Merlyn N. Trued, 2020 F Street.
  Deputy Assistant Secretary for International Affairs.—Merlyn N. Trued, 2020 F Street.
  Deputy to the Assistant Secretary, for International Monetary Affairs.—George H. Willis, 2480 16th Street.
  Deputy to the Assistant Secretary, for International Financial, and Economic Affairs.—Ralph Hirschtritt, 1712 Republic Road, Silver Spring, Md.
  Director, Office of Balance of Payments Programs, Operations and Statistics.—Philip P. Schaffner, 4200 Cathedral Avenue, Apartment 519.
  Director, Office of International Financial Policy Coordination and Operations.—Charles R. Harley, 5016 Hampden Lane, Bethesda, Md.
  Director, Office of Latin America.—Henry J. Costanzo, 8216 West Beach Drive.
  Director, Office of Industrial Nations.—F. Lisle Widman, 1606 Wilson Place, Silver Spring, Md.
  Director, Office of Developing Nations.—Bernard Zagorin, 1314 Fiddlers Green, Falls Church, Va.
  Director, Office of International Gold and Foreign Exchange Operations.—Thomas Page Nelson, 4825 Davidson Road, McLean, Va.
  Director, Office of International Economic Activities.—William W. Diehl, 4528 26th Street North, Arlington, Va.

Fiscal Assistant Secretary.—John K. Carlock, 2116 F Street.
  Deputy Fiscal Assistant Secretary.—George F. Stickney, 5023 Riverdale Road, Riverdale, Md.
  Assistant Fiscal Assistant Secretary.—Hampton A. Rabon, Jr., 5501 Nevada Avenue.

Assistant Secretary for Administration.—A. E. Weatherbee, 12613 Springloch Court, Silver Spring, Md.
  Deputy Assistant Secretary for Administration and Director, Office of Budget and Finance.—Ernest C. Betts, Jr., 815 26th Street South, Arlington, Va.
  Director, Office of Management and Organization.—James H. Stover, Route 4, Box 375, Vienna, Va.
  Director, Office of Personnel.—Amos N. Latham, Jr., 6 Perrott Court, Fairfax, Va.
  Director, Office of Security.—Thomas M. Hughes, 4000 Massachusetts Avenue.
  Director, Office of Administrative Services.—Paul McDonald, 1400 North Edison Street, Arlington, Va.

Assistant to the Secretary (Congressional Relations).—Joseph M. Bowman, Jr., 3204 Old Dominion Boulevard, Alexandria, Va.

Assistant to the Secretary (Public Affairs).—Dixon Donnelley, 2551 Waterside Drive.
  Deputy Assistant to the Secretary (Public Affairs).—Stephen C. Manning, Jr., 1496 Fort Hunt Road, Alexandria, Va.
Assistant to the Secretary.—Charles A. Sullivan, 2810 Dumbarton Avenue.
  National Security Affairs Adviser.—Bradley H. Patterson, Jr., 6705 Pemberton Street, Bethesda, Md.
  Director, Foreign Assets Control.—Mrs. Margaret W. Schwartz, 4215 Vacation Lane, Arlington, Va.
Special Assistants to the Secretary:
  Tom Killefer, 4201 Kirby Road, McLean, Va.
  William B. Dale, 6008 Landon Lane, Bethesda, Md.
Senior Consultant to the Secretary.—Seymour E. Harris, 8450 El Paseo Grande, La Jolla, Calif.
Director, Executive Secretariat and Special Assistant to the Secretary.—Donald I. Lamont, 2031 Crossley Place, Alexandria, Va.

INTERNAL REVENUE SERVICE
Internal Revenue Building, Twelfth and Constitution Avenue, 20224
Phone, EXecutive 3-6400 (Code 184, extension 2117)

Commissioner.—Sheldon S. Cohen, 5518 Trent Street, Chevy Chase, Md., 20015.
Deputy Commissioner.—Bertrand M. Harding, 1304 Park Terrace Drive, Alexandria, Va.
Assistant Commissioner (Administration).—Edward F. Preston, 1203 Rebecca Drive, Alexandria, Va.
Assistant Commissioner (Compliance).—Donald W. Bacon, 4813 Cola Drive, McLean, Va.
Assistant Commissioner (Data Processing).—Robert L. Jack, 302 Ravenwood Drive, Falls Church, Va.
Assistant Commissioner (Inspection).—Vernon D. Acree, 7900 Cross Street, Lanham, Md.
Assistant Commissioner (Planning and Research).—William H. Smith, 4912 Longfellow Court, McLean, Va.
Assistant Commissioner (Technical).—Harold T. Swartz, 1555 Mount Eagle Place, Alexandria, Va.
Assistant to the Commissioner.—Edwin M. Perkins, 5330 Neptune Drive, Alexandria, Va.
Director, Public Information Division.—Joseph S. Rosapepe, 3636 16th Street.
Chief Counsel.—Mitchell Rogovin, 4100 Duncan Drive, Annandale, Va.

BUREAU OF CUSTOMS
2100 K Street. Phone, EXecutive 3-6400 (Code 184, extension 2117)

Acting Commissioner.—Lester D. Johnson, 203 Windsor Road, Belle Haven, Alexandria, Va.
Confidential Assistant to the Commissioner.—James M. Harkless, 301 G Street SW.
Acting Chief Counsel.—F. M. Ivey, 5316 43d Street.
Deputy Commissioner, Office of Administration.—Norbert G. Strub, 8806 West Parliament Drive, Springfield, Va.
Deputy Commissioner, Office of Investigations.—Lawrence Fleishman, 4201 Cathedral Avenue, Apt. 1010–East.
Acting Deputy Commissioner, Office of Operations.—David C. Ellis, 200 Merimac Drive, McLean, Va.
Acting Deputy Commissioner, Office of Regulations and Rulings.—Donald L. E. Ritger, 3300 Woodbine Street, Chevy Chase, Md.

CUSTOMHOUSE
1221 Thirty-first Street.   Phone, FEderal 3–2193 or 3–2195

Deputy Collector in Charge.—Robert E. Werner, 12027 Livingston Street, Wheaton, Md.

UNITED STATES SAVINGS BOND DIVISION
1111 Twentieth Street.   Phone, EXecutive 3–6400 (Code 184, extension 2117)

National Director.—William H. Neal, 4101 Cathedral Avenue.
Assistant National Director.—Bill McDonald, 3200 16th Street.
Assistant to the National Director.—Harold B. Master, 5603 Harwick Road, Woodacres, 20016.
Director of Sales.—Elmer L. Rustad, 3901 Lorraine Avenue, Falls Church, Va.
Director of Advertising and Promotion.—Edmund J. Linehan, 6333 22d Street North, Arlington, Va.

COAST GUARD HEADQUARTERS
Old Southern Railway Building, 1300 E Street.   Phone, EXecutive 3–6400 (Code 184, extension 2641)

OFFICE OF THE COMMANDANT

The Commandant.—Adm. Edwin J. Roland, 2931 Cathedral Avenue, 20008.
Assistant Commandant.—Vice Adm. William D. Shields, 633 Woodland Circle, Falls Church, Va., 22041.
Congressional Liaison Officer.—Capt. William L. Morrison, 500 McCauley Street, Washington Grove, Md., 20880.
Administrative Aide.—Cdr. John D. McCann, 5619 Johnson Avenue, Bethesda, Md., 20014.
Personal Aide to the Commandant.—Lt. Thomas W. Kirkpatrick, 5619 Bradley Boulevard, Bethesda, Md., 20014.
Flag Pilot.—Lt. David P. Bosomworth, 5771 Sanger Avenue, Alexandria, Va., 22311.
Chief Counsel.—Kenneth S. Harrison, Parkfairfax Apartments, 3403 Valley Drive, Alexandria, Va.
Chief Hearing Examiner.—James H. Molloy, 2945 Upton Street.
Inspector General.—Capt. Edward P. Chester, Jr., 204 Ross Avenue, Vienna, Va., 20034.
Chairman, Merchant Marine Council.—Rear Adm. Charles P. Murphy, Valley Drive, Glen Hills, Rockville, Md., 20850.

CHIEF OF STAFF

Chief of Staff.—Rear Adm. Paul E. Trimble, 109 Lucas Lane, Bethesda, Md., 20014.
Deputy Chief of Staff.—Capt. Richard R. Smith, 4264 25th Street North, Arlington, Va., 22207.
Chief, Administrative Management Division.—Capt. Harry L. Morgan, 11601 Rokeby Avenue, Kensington, Md., 20795.
Chief, Headquarters Services Division.—Cdr. William Miller, 3501 Sussex Road, Baltimore, Md., 21207.
Chief, Legal Division.—Kenneth S. Harrison, Parkfairfax Apartments, 3403 Valley Drive, Alexandria, Va., 22302.
Chief, Program Analysis Division.—Capt. Edward D. Scheiderer, 5426 Richenbacher Avenue, Alexandria, Va., 22304.
Chief, Public Information Division.—Capt. Warner K. Thompson, 1310 Fiddler's Green, Falls Church, Va., 22043.

OFFICE OF ENGINEERING

Chief. Office of Engineering.—Rear Adm. John B. Oren, 5539 Columbia Pike, Arlington, Va., 22204.
Deputy Chief, Office of Engineering.—Capt. Douglas B. Henderson, 826 Aster Boulevard, Woodley Gardens, Rockville, Md., 20850.
Chief, Aeronautical Engineering Division.—Cdr. Joseph R. Steele, 1756 North Troy St., Arlington, Va., 22201.
Chief, Civil Engineering Division.—Capt. Thomas R. Sargent III, 4103 Canterbury Terrace, Rockville, Md., 20853.
Chief, Electronics Engineering Division.—Capt. Harold T. Hendrickson, 4406 Saul Road, Kensington, Md., 20795.
Chief, Naval Engineering Division.—Capt. Cornelius G. Houtsma, 9701 Bellevue Drive, Bethesda, Md., 20014.
Chief, Testing and Development Division.—Capt. Clinton E. McAuliffe, 9006 Grant Avenue, Bethesda, Md., 20034.

OFFICE OF COMPTROLLER

Comptroller.—Rear Adm. Joseph R. Scullion, 4221 Brookside Road., McLean, Va., 22101.
Deputy Comptroller.—Capt. James A. Hyslop, 5123 Manning Drive, Bethesda, Md., 20014.
Chief, Accounting Division.—Seymour Steiglitz, 4407 Bestor Drive, Rockville, Md., 20853.
Chief, Budget and Cost Analysis Division.—Cdr. William H. Boswell, 6808 Clay Drive, Oxon Hill, Md., 20021.
Chief, Data Processing Division.—Cdr. Otto F. Unsinn, BOQ South Area, Fort Myer, Va., 20044.
Chief, Internal Audit Division.—Ray M. Thompson, 5158 38th Street North, Arlington, Va., 22207.
Chief, Payment and Claims Division.—Marvin B. Hopkins, 10313 Inwood Avenue, Silver Spring, Md., 20902.
Chief, Supply Division.—Capt. Roger H. Banner, 5412A Sanger Avenue, Alexandria, Va., 22311.

OFFICE OF OPERATIONS

Chief, Office of Operations.—Rear Adm. William W. Childress, 7207 Thomas Branch Drive, Bethesda, Md., 20034.
Deputy Chief, Office of Operations.—Capt. Wayne L. Goff, 7507 Springlake Drive, Apt. C2, Bethesda, Md., 20034.
Assistant Chief for Roles and Missions.—Capt. William F. Cass, 3203 Turner Lane, Chevy Chase, Md., 20015.
Assistant Chief for Facilities and Services.—Capt. Paul E. G. Prins, 6016 Bradley Boulevard, Bethesda, Md., 20034.
Chief, Auxiliary Division.—Capt. Albert A. Heckman, Park Arlington Apts., 1200 North Nash Street, Arlington, Va., 22209.
Chief, Intelligence Division.—Capt. William D. Strauch, The Diplomat, Apt. 306, 2420 16th Street, 20009.
Chief, Search and Rescue Division.—Capt. John M. Waters, Jr., 1317 22d Street South, Arlington, Va., 22202.
Chief, Port Security and Law Enforcement Division.—Capt. Albert Frost, 4618 Woodfield Road, Parkwood, Bethesda, Md., 20014.
Chief, Aids to Navigation Division.—Capt. Billy R. Ryan, 914 Country Club Drive, Vienna, Va., 22180.
Chief, Operational Readiness Division.—Capt. Robert P. Cunningham, 5550 Columbia Pike, Arlington, Va., 22204.
Chief, Recreational Boating Safety Division.—Capt. David W. Sinclair, 5800 Conway Road, Falls Church, Va., 22042.
Chief, Shore Units Division.—Capt. Elmer A. Crock, 4613 Woodfield Road, Bethesda, Md., 20014.

Chief, Floating Units Division.—Capt. Francis X. Riley, 107 Mayflower Drive, McLean, Va., 22101.
Chief, Aviation Units Division.—Capt. Benjamin F. Engel, 6009 Berkshire Drive, Bethesda, Md., 20014.
Chief, Communications Division.—Capt. Charles Dorian, 4444 Chesapeake Street, 20016.

OFFICE OF MERCHANT MARINE SAFETY

Chief, Office of Merchant Marine Safety.—Rear Adm. Charles P. Murphy, Valley Drive, Glen Hills, Rockville, Md., 20850.
Deputy Chief, Office of Merchant Marine Safety.—Capt. Benjamin D. Shoemaker, Jr., 5108 Manning Drive, Bethesda, Md., 20014.
Chief, Merchant Marine Technical Division.—Capt. James B. McCarty, Jr., 908 Prince William Drive, Fairfax, Va.. 22030.
Chief, Merchant Vessel Inspection Division.—Capt. William C. Foster, 6220 Rockhurst Road, Bethesda, Md., 20014.
Chief, Merchant Vessel Personnel Division.—Capt. Lynn Parker, 7720 Lamar Drive, Springfield, Va., 22150.

OFFICE OF PERSONNEL

Chief, Office of Personnel.—Rear Adm. George A. Knudsen, 5033 29th Street, 20015.
Deputy Chief, Office of Personnel.—Capt. William B. Ellis, 3814 Williams Lane, Chevy Chase, Md., 20015.
Chief, Civilian Personnel Division.—Dewey A. Queen, 503 Nutley Street, Fairfax, Va., 22030.
Chief, Enlisted Personnel Division.—Capt. Benjamin P. Clark, 8765 Preston Place, Chevy Chase, Md., 20014.
Chief, Medical Division.—Rear Adm. Howard D. Fishburn, 5007 Danbury Court, Bethesda, Md., 20014.
Chief, Personnel Services Division.—Capt. James C. Waters, 112 Flagpole Lane, Fairfax, Va.
Chief, Officer Personnel Division.—Capt. Victor Pfeiffer, 618 Whispering Lane, Falls Church, Va.
Chief, Training and Procurement Division.—Capt. Joseph J. McClelland, 4523 Dorset Avenue, Chevy Chase, Md., 20015.

OFFICE OF RESERVE

Chief, Office of Reserve.—Rear Adm. Charles Tighe, Jr., U.S. Coast Guard Headquarters.
Deputy Chief, Office of Reserve.—Capt. E. G. Cardwell, 1201 South Scott Street, Apt. 333, Arlington, Va., 22204.
Reserve Programs Division.—Cdr. Wesley J. Quamme, 5115 Banger Road, Kensington, Md., 20795.
Reserve Administration Division.—Cdr. Harold R. Cotton, 1020 North Quincy Street, Apt. 608, Arlington, Va., 22201.
Reserve Training Division.—Cdr. Orland D. French, 3910 Spruell Drive, Kensington, Md., 20795.

WELFARE

President, Coast Guard Welfare.—Adm. Edwin J. Roland, 2931 Cathedral Avenue.
Executive Vice President, Coast Guard Welfare.—Capt. James C. Waters, 112 Flagpole Lane, Fairfax, Va.

OFFICE OF THE COMPTROLLER OF THE CURRENCY

Fifteenth Street and Pennsylvania Avenue. Phone, EXecutive 3-6400 (Code 184, extension 2117)

Comptroller of the Currency.—James J. Saxon, 6024 Western Avenue, Chevy Chase, Md., 20015.

Administrative Assistant to the Comptroller.—A. J. Faulstich, 505 Elderwood Road, Silver Spring, Md.

First Deputy Comptroller.—William B. Camp, 9518 Kentstone Drive, Bethesda, Md.

Deputy Comptroller for Bank Supervision and Examination.—Justin T. Watson, 5825 Osceola Road, Bethesda, Md.

Deputy Comptroller for New Charters.—Thomas G. DeShazo, 612 South University Drive, Fairfax, Va.

Deputy Comptroller for Trusts.—Dean E. Miller, 129 Duvall Street, Fairfax, Va.

Deputy Comptroller for Mergers and Branches.—Richard J. Blanchard, 427 St. Lawrence Drive, Silver Spring, Md.

Deputy Comptroller for Domestic Bank Operations.—R. Coleman Egertson, 3705 Lyons Lane, Alexandria, Va.

Deputy Comptroller for International Banking and Finance.—E. Radcliffe Park, 1020 Allan Avenue, Falls Church, Va.

Chief National Bank Examiner.—Daniel D. Moore, 4750 Kenmore Avenue, Alexandria, Va.

Special Assistant to the Comptroller (Public Affairs).—W. Robert Grubb, 3005 Cathedral Avenue.

Special Assistance to the Comptroller.—E. E. Cox, 715 Lakeview Drive, Falls Church, Va.

Deputy Administrative Assistant to the Comptroller.—Anthony G. Chase, 6617 Tulip Hill Terrace, Bethesda, Md.

DIVISION CHIEFS

Law Department.—Chief Counsel, Robert Bloom, 1516 16th Road North, Arlington, Va.

  Associate Chief Counsel.—R. J. Gerber, 3400 Toledo Terrace, Apt. C, West Hyattsville, Md.

  Associate Chief Counsel.—C. H. McEnerney, 2795 28th Street.

Organization Division.—Thaddeus M. Brezinski, 4891 Homer Avenue SE.

  Assistant Director.—B. G. Glisson, 6521 Washington Drive, Falls Church, Va.

Trust Department.—P. P. Kellogg, 2712 Wisconsin Avenue.

  Assistant Chief Representative.—R. P. St. Pierre, 2019 Holly Lane, Falls Church, Va.

BUREAU OF ENGRAVING AND PRINTING

Fourteenth and C Streets SW. Phone, EXecutive 3-6400 (Code 184, extension 7214)

Director.—Henry J. Holtzclaw, 2231 Sudbury Road.

Assistant Director.—Frank G. Uhler, 5404 Richenbacher Avenue, Alexandria, Va.

Controller.—Charles E. Deery, 4859 27th Street North, Arlington, Va.

Director of Manufacturing.—James A. Conlon, Lee Chapel Road, Burke, Va.

BUREAU OF THE MINT

Director.—Eva Adams, Apt. 1221-W, The Towers, 4201 Cathedral Avenue, 20016.

Assistant Director.—Frederick W. Tate, 3515 North Washington Boulevard, Arlington, Va., 22201.

BUREAU OF NARCOTICS

633 Indiana Avenue. Phone, EXecutive 3-6400 (Code 184, extension 2117)

Commissioner of Narcotics.—Henry L. Giordano, 9609 New Hampshire Avenue, Silver Spring, Md.
Deputy Commissioner.—George H. Gaffney, 6814 Greyswood Road, Bethesda, Md.
Assistant Deputy Commissioner.—Ernest M. Gentry, 4201 31st Street South, Arlington, Va.
Assistant to the Commissioner.—John R. Enright, 4108 Breezewood Lane, Annandale, Va.
Chief Counsel.—Donald E. Miller, 5936 First Street North, Arlington, Va.

UNITED STATES SECRET SERVICE

Chief.—James J. Rowley, 3501 Rittenhouse Street.
Deputy Chief.—Paul J. Paterni, 5717 33d Street.
Assistant Chief.—E. A. Wildy, 4618–B, 36th Street South, Arlington, Va.
Chief Inspector.—Jackson N. Krill, 5007 Randall Lane.

FISCAL SERVICE

BUREAU OF ACCOUNTS

Commissioner of Accounts.—Sidney S. Sokol, 7777 Maple Avenue, Takoma Park, Md.
Acting Assistant Commissioner.—L. D. Mosso, 8622 Piccadilly Place, Springfield, Va.
Chief Disbursing Officer, Division of Disbursement.—C. O. Bryant, 8104 Jansen Drive, Springfield, Va.
Deputy Commissioner in Charge of Central Accounts and Reports.—Howard A. Turner, 4740 Bradley Boulevard, Apt. A–17, Chevy Chase, Md.
Deputy Commissioner in Charge of Systems.—Ray T. Bath, 10225 Kensington Parkway, Apt. 206, Kensington, Md.
Chief Auditor, Division of Internal Audits.—Steve L. Comings, 7904 West Park Drive, Hyattsville, Md.
Deputy Commissioner in Charge of Deposits, Investments and Surety Bonds.—Sidney Cox, 3817 Wendy Lane, Silver Spring, Md.
Assistant Commissioner for Administration.—John H. Henriksen, 2500 20th Road North, Apt. 401, Arlington, Va.
Director, Defense Lending.—Robert M. Seabury, 4750 Chevy Chase Drive, Chevy Chase, Md.

BUREAU OF THE PUBLIC DEBT

Commissioner.—Donald M. Merritt, 5202 Abingdon Road, Westmoreland Hills, Md.
Assistant Commissioner.—Ross A. Heffelfinger, 4427 Davenport Street.
Deputy Commissioner.—Michael E. McGeoghegan, 4427 Arnold Road, Suitland, Md.
Deputy Commissioner in Charge, Chicago Office.—Jack P. Thompson, 6229 North Winthrop Avenue, Chicago, Ill.
Director, Parkersburg Office.—Frank Armfield, Jr., 4410 10th Avenue, Vienna, W. Va.
Chief of Division of—
  Loans and Currency.—Harold M. Stephenson, 512 Howsen Avenue, Fairfax, Va.
  Accounts and Audit.—Delmar A. Stacy, 4549 South Chelsea Lane, Bethesda, Md.
  Retired Securities.—Settle Headley, 2504 41st Street.
Chief Counsel.—Thomas J. Winston, Jr., 104 East Melbourne Avenue, Silver Spring, Md.

OFFICE OF THE TREASURER OF THE UNITED STATES

Treasurer.—Mrs. Kathryn O'Hay Granahan, The Mayflower, 20036.
    Deputy Treasurer.—William T. Howell, 1169 North Van Dorn Street, Alexandria, Va.
    Assistant Deputy Treasurer.—Willard E. Scott, 3930 Mackall Avenue, McLean, Va.
    Assistant to the Deputy Treasurer.—Hayden E. Isaacs, 4720 Chevy Chase Drive, Chevy Chase, Md.
    Assistant to the Deputy Treasurer.—D. A. Pagliai, 10606 Dunkirk Drive, Silver Spring, Md.
Operations Divisions:
    Cash.—Wilbur E. Beall, 330 Onondaga Drive, Forest Heights, Md.
    Check Accounting.—Peter E. Traver, 6306 31st Street North, Arlington, Va.
    Check Claims.—Walter J. Herron, 989 North Potomac Street, Arlington, Va.
    Currency Redemption.—Leon Betensky, 3901 Alton Place.
    Electronic Data Processing.—Roy O. Conner, 2905 Weller Road, Silver Spring, Md.
    General Accounts.—Estil J. Kious, 5811 Lone Oak Drive, Bethesda, Md.
    Securities.—Howard M. Annis, 4614 19th Street North, Arlington, Va.
Services Divisions:
    Administrative.—R. Glenn Hawthorne, 303 Monroe Street, Herndon, Va.
    Examiner of Questioned Documents.—Alwyn Cole, 2730 Blaine Drive, Chevy Chase, Md.
    Internal Audit.—Marshall T. Gould, 6540 Beaver Dam Road, Beltsville, Md.
    Management Analysis.—Orion H. Tomkinson, 12027 Berry Street, Silver Spring, Md.
    Personnel Administration.—John T. Burns, Jr., 2712 Elnora Street, Silver Spring, Md.

NATIONAL ADVISORY COUNCIL ON INTERNATIONAL MONETARY AND FINANCIAL PROBLEMS

Department of the Treasury. Phone, EXecutive 3-6400 (Code 184, extension 2748)

Chairman.—Henry H. Fowler, (Secretary of the Treasury).
    Dean Rusk (Secretary of State).
    John T. Connor (Secretary of Commerce).
    William McC. Martin, Jr. (Chairman, Board of Governors of the Federal Reserve System).
    Harold F. Linder (President and Chairman, Export-Import Bank of Washington).
Secretary.—Charles R. Harley (Director, Office of International Financial Policy Coordination and Operations, Treasury Department).

DEPARTMENT OF DEFENSE

Phones, OXford or Code 11

(All offices located at the Pentagon, Washington, D.C., 20301, unless otherwise stated)

ROBERT S. McNAMARA, Secretary of Defense; born in San Francisco, Calif., June 9, 1916, son of Robert James and Clara Nell (Strange) McNamara; University of California, A.B.; Harvard, MBA; University of Alabama, LL.D. (honorary); Phi Beta Kappa; married Margaret Craig, August 13, 1940; children— Margaret Elizabeth, Kathleen, Robert Craig; assistant professor of business administration, Harvard, 1940–43; Ford Motor Co., 1946 to January 3, 1961, elected president on November 9, 1960; formerly member of board of directors of Scott Paper Co.; active duty in the Air Force 1943 to 1946; awarded Legion of Merit; sworn in as Secretary of Defense January 21, 1961; home: Ann Arbor, Mich.; Washington address: 2412 Tracy Place, 20008.

CYRUS ROBERTS VANCE, Deputy Secretary of Defense; born in Clarksburg, W. Va., March 27, 1917, son of Mrs. Amy (Roberts) Vance and the late John C. Vance; was graduated from Kent School, 1935; B.A., Yale University, 1939; LL.B., Yale Law School, 1942; honorary LL.D., Marshall University, 1963; married Grace Elsie Sloane, February 15, 1947; children: Elsie Nicoll, Amy Sloane, Grace Roberts and Camilla (twins), and Cyrus, Jr.; served as lieutenant in the United States Navy, primarily in destroyers in both the Atlantic and Pacific, 1942–46; assistant to the President, The Mead Corporation, 1946–47; entered practice of law with Simpson, Thacher and Bartlett, New York City, 1947, partner of the firm, 1956–61; Special Counsel, Preparedness Investigating Subcommittee, Senate Armed Services Committee, 1957–60; Consulting Counsel, Special Senate Committee on Space and Astronautics, 1958; General Counsel of the Department of Defense, January 29, 1961 to June 30, 1962; Secretary of the Army, July 1, 1962 to January 28, 1964; sworn in as Deputy Secretary of Defense, January 28, 1964; member, American Bar Association, New York State Bar Association and Association of the Bar of the City of New York; admitted to U.S. Supreme Court, 1960; Fellow, American College of Trial Lawyers, 1962; Trustee, Kent School; former Director and Chairman of the Board, Union Settlement Association, Inc., 1953–61; Trustee, The Boys' Club of New York, 1959–61; member, Executive Committee, Yale Law School Association; homes: 3060 Foxhall Road, Washington, D.C., and 2 East 93d Street, New York City.

IMMEDIATE OFFICE OF THE SECRETARY

The Secretary of Defense.—Robert S. McNamara, rm 3E880, Ext. 55261.
  The Special Assistant to the Secretary and Deputy Secretary of Defense.—Joseph A. Califano, Jr., rm 3E941, Ext. 76351; 4704 Albemarle Street, 20016.
  Legislative Assistant.—David E. McGiffert, rm 3E944, Ext. 76211; 3524 P Street, 20007.
  Military Assistant.—Col. Alfred J. F. Moody, USA, rm 3E800, Ext. 55261; 32 Littleton Lane, Fairfax Va., 22030.
  Secretary to the Secretary of Defense.—Margaret S. Stroud, rm 3E880, Ext. 55261; 1500 Arlington Boulevard, Arlington, Va., 22209.
The Deputy Secretary of Defense.—Cyrus R. Vance, rm 3E925, Ext. 56352.
  Military Assistant.—Rear Adm. Ralph W. Cousins, USN, rm 3E925, Ext. 71509; 2316 Kalorama Road, 20008.
  Military Assistant.—Lt. Col. DeWitt C. Smith, Jr., USA, rm 3E925, Ext. 77845; 3816 North Dittmar Road, Arlington, Va., 22207.
  Secretary to the Deputy Secretary.—Velma Cameron, rm 3E925, Ext. 56352; 2800 Woodley Road, 20008.
  Secretary to the Deputy Secretary.—Gwen Kinkead, rm 3E925, Ext. 56352; 2000 South Eads Street, Arlington, Va., 22022.

ARMED FORCES POLICY COUNCIL

Chairman.—Robert S. McNamara, Secretary of Defense.
Members:
  Cyrus R. Vance, Deputy Secretary of Defense.
  Stephen Ailes, Secretary of the Army.
  Paul H. Nitze, Secretary of the Navy.
  Eugene M. Zuckert, Secretary of the Air Force.
  Harold Brown, Director of Defense Research and Engineering.
  Gen. Earle G. Wheeler, USA, Chairman, Joint Chiefs of Staff.
  Gen. Harold K. Johnson, USA, Chief of Staff, Army.
  Adm. David L. McDonald, USN, Chief of Naval Operations.
  Gen. John P. McConnell, USAF, Chief of Staff, Air Force.
  Gen. Wallace M. Greene, Jr., USMC, Commandant of the Marine Corps (on
    Marine Corps matters only).

DIRECTOR OF DEFENSE RESEARCH AND ENGINEERING

Director.—Harold Brown, rm 3E1006, Ext. 79111; 416 Argyle Drive, Alexandria,
    Va., 22305.
  Secretary to the Director.—Jean M. Bederski, rm 3E1006, Ext. 79111; 2926
    South Buchanan Street, Arlington, Va., 22206.
  Executive Assistant.—Samuel E. Clements, rm 3E1006, Ext. 56556; 7913 Park
    Overlook Drive, Carderock Springs, Bethesda, Md.
  Special Assistant.—Capt. Roger W. Paine, Jr., USN, rm 3E1030, Ext. 71282;
    4456 20th Road North, Arlington, Va., 22207.
  Special Assistant (Command and Control).—James M. Bridges, rm 3D1085,
    Ext. 77922; 6601 31st Street North, Arlington, Va., 22213.
  Special Assistant (Intelligence and Reconnaissance).—Bruno W. Augenstein,
    rm 3E120, Ext. 73712; 3815 Ridgeview Road, Arlington, Va., 22207.
  Assistant Secretary of Defense (Deputy Director).—Eugene G. Fubini, rm 3E1014,
    Ext. 57178; 9000 Bronson Drive, Potomac, Md., 20854.
    Executive Assistant.—Col. John R. Deane, Jr., USAF, rm 3E1014, Ext. 57178;
      507 Canterbury Lane, Alexandria, Va., 22314.
  Deputy Director (Administration and Management).—Lt. Gen. William J. Ely,
    USA, rm 3E1030, Ext. 74176; Quarters 11–A, Fort Myer, Va., 22211.
  Assistant Director.—Rear Adm. Vincent P. de Poix, USN, rm 3E1030, Ext.
    59284; 2782 North Wakefield Street, Arlington, Va., 22207.
  Director, Office of Review and Services.—Ben G. Huff, rm 3E1019, Ext. 72525;
    400 South Fenwick Street, Arlington, Va., 22206.
  Director of Technical Information.—Walter M. Carlson, rm 3E112, Ext. 74789;
    3916 Linda Lane, Annandale, Va., 22003.
  Assistant Director (Engineering Management).—James W. Roach, rm 3D1028,
    Ext. 79125; 4101 Cathedral Avenue, 20016.
  Assistant Director (Plans and Policy).—Paul J. Sturm, rm 3E1082, Ext. 72433;
    5956 Searl Terrace, Bethesda, Md., 20016.
  Executive Assistant (Manpower).—Mrs. Astrid W. Kraus, rm 3D1014, Ext.
    78155; 3101 Highland Place, 20008.
  Deputy Director (Research and Technology).—Chalmers W. Sherwin, rm 3E1060,
    Ext. 74172; 3540 36th Road North, Arlington, Va., 22207.
  Assistant Director (Chemical Technology).—Nicholas T. Samaras, rm 3D129,
    Ext. 59604; 2754 South Ives Street, Arlington, Va., 22202.
  Assistant Director (Communications and Electronics).—Thomas F. Rogers, rm
    3D1047, Ext. 57245; 4390 Lorcom Lane, Arlington, Va., 22207.
  Assistant Director (Materials).—Earl T. Hayes, rm 3D117, Ext. 76933; 517
    Gilmoure Drive, Silver Spring, Md., 20901.
  Assistant Director (Research).—Edward M. Reilley, rm 3E1060, Ext. 74197;
    8420 Wendell Drive, Alexandria, Va., 22308.

Deputy Director (Space).—Albert C. Hall, rm 3E144, Ext. 57345; Route 2, Box 245, Joyce Lane, Arnold, Md., 21012.

  Assistant Director (Ranges and Space Ground Support).—Col. Clifford J. Kronauer, USAF, rm 3E144, Ext. 79203; 4704 Kellogg Drive, McLean, Va., 22101.

  Assistant Director (Space Technology).—Starr J. Colby, rm 3E153, Ext. 72467; 4300 Ivanhoe Place, Alexandria, Va., 22304.

Deputy Director (Strategic and Defensive Systems).—Fred A. Payne, Jr., rm 3E130, Ext. 79386; 102 G Street SW., 20024.

  Assistant Director (Defensive Systems).—Daniel J. Fink, rm 3D138, Ext. 57327; 503 Crosswoods Drive, Falls Church, Va., 22044.

  Assistant Director (National Military Command System (Technical Support)) and Strategic Command and Control.—Robert H. Scherer, rm 3D1082, Ext. 57936, 409 Vista Drive, Falls Church, Va., 22041.

  Assistant Director (Strategic Weapons).— Richard D. Geckler, rm 3E130, Ext. 74931; 1400 South Joyce Street, Arlington, Va., 22202.

Deputy Director (Tactical Warfare Programs).—Thomas P. Cheatham, Jr., rm 3E1040, Ext. 59713; 520 East Boulevard Drive, Alexandria, Va., 22308.

  Special Assistant (Counterinsurgency).—Seymour J. Deitchman, rm 3E1040, Ext. 71421; 3606 Stewart Drive, Chevy Chase, Md.

  Assistant Director (Combat Systems).—Samuel O. Perry, rm 3D1067, Ext. 52754; 388 N Street SW., 20024.

  Assistant Director (Undersea Warfare and Battle Support Systems).—James H. Probus, rm 3D1048, Ext. 72205; 5506 Bargo Court, Falls Church, Va., 22043.

  Director of Aeronautics.—Thomas C. Muse, rm 3E1047, Ext. 53015; 3501 North Peary Street, Arlington, Va., 22207.

  Director of Ordnance.—Melvin Bell, rm 3D122, Ext. 73459; 8821 Bellwood Road, Bethesda, Md., 20034.

Assistant Director (International Programs).—Ronald M. Murray, rm 3D1060, Ext. 71644; 3147 O Street, 20007.

Director, Office of Atomic Programs.—John E. Jackson, rm 3E1071, Ext. 77166; 4800 Old Dominion Drive, Arlington, Va., 22207.

Defense Science Board:

  Chairman.—Frederick Seitz, rm 3D1040, Ext. 54157; 3327 N Street, 20007.

  Executive Secretary.—William W. Hammerschmidt, rm 3D1040, Ext. 54147; 2434 Holmes Run Drive, Falls Church, Va., 22042.

Advanced Research Projects Agency:

  Director.—Robert L. Sproull, rm 3E160, Ext. 78255; 4921 Seminary Road, Alexandria, Va., 22311.

  Deputy Director.—Charles M. Herzfeld, rm 3E160, Ext. 57105; 811 Hyde Road, Silver Spring, Md., 20902.

  Director (Program Management).—Donald K. Hess, rm 3E163, Ext. 57063; 5318 Glenwood Road, Bethesda, Md.

  Director (Ballistic Missile Defense Research).—Samuel J. Rabinowitz, rm 3D157, Ext. 57026; 5311 Pooks Hill Road, Bethesda, Md.

  Director (Materials Sciences).—Edward L. Salkovitz, rm 3D156, Ext. 56607; 5454 30th Street, 20015.

  Director (Nuclear Test Detection).—Robert A. Frosch, rm 3D170, Ext. 57060; 10105 Hurst Street, Bethesda, Md., 20014.

  Director (Remote Area Conflict).—Maj. Gen. Robert H. Wienecke, USA, rm 3E172, Ext. 57151; 627 29th Street South, Arlington, Va., 22202.

  Director (Behavioral Sciences).—Lee W. Huff, rm 3E175, Ext. 57068; 1400 South Joyce Street, Arlington, Va., 22202.

  Director (Information Processing Techniques).—Ivan E. Sutherland, rm 3D200, Ext. 78654; 1716 Fort Hunt Road, Alexandria, Va., 22308.

Weapons Systems Evaluation Group:

  Director.—Lt. Gen. Joseph R. Holzapple, USAF, 400 Army-Navy Drive, Ext. 76335; 2712 South Ives Street, Arlington, Va., 22202.

  Director, Institute for Defense Analyses/Weapons Systems Evaluation Division.— Bernard O. Koopman, 400 Army-Navy Drive, Ext. 54188; 6911 Oakridge Avenue, Chevy Chase, Md.

  Executive Secretary.—Col. Robert O. Fricks, USAF, 400 Army-Navy Drive, Ext. 76336; 7518 Cayuga Avenue, Bethesda, Md.

ASSISTANT SECRETARY OF DEFENSE (ADMINISTRATION)

Assistant Secretary of Defense.—Solis Horwitz, rm 3E822, Ext. 78225; 1000 Sixth Street, 20024.
 Secretary to the Assistant Secretary.—Bernice M. Hill, rm 3E822, Ext. 78225; 1400 South Joyce Street, Arlington, Va., 22202.
 Executive Assistant.—Col. Herbert D. Raymond, Jr., USMC, rm 3E822, Ext. 54506; 6833 Old Stage Road, Rockville, Md., 20852.
 Deputy Assistant Secretary (Administrative Services).—John C. Airhart, rm 3E822, Ext. 54436; 17 Seventh Street NE., 20002.
 Executive Assistant.—Shirley E. Meyer, rm 3E827, Ext. 56936; 6606 Hillmead Road, Bethesda, Md., 20034.
 Director, Administrative Management Division.—Charles V. Brewer, rm 3C916, Ext. 73111; 8912 Ridge Place, Bethesda, Md., 20034.
 Director, Budget and Finance Division.—L. Frank Waller, rm 3C916, Ext. 76760; 7402 Elgar Street, Springfield, Va., 22151.
 Director, Correspondence and Directives Division.—Maurice W. Roche, rm 3D949, Ext. 78261; 308 Burke Road, Fairfax, Va., 20030.
 Director, Facilities and Services Division.—Raymond J. Hayden, rm 3C921, Ext. 77241; 2400 32d Street SE., 20020.
 Director, Personnel Services Division.—John E. Moore, rm 3A918, Ext. 73723; Route 2, Box 443, Old Georgetown Pike, McLean, Va., 22101.
 Director, Security Division.—William C. Hunt, rm 3B916, Ext. 77171; 5712 Cromwell Drive, 20016.
 Historian.—Rudolph A. Winnacker, rm 3B915, Ext. 74216; 7002 Hillcrest Place, Chevy Chase, Md., 20015.
Director of Inspection Services.—Lt. Gen. James V. Edmundson, USAF, rm 3E988, Ext. 78650; 4004 Watkins Trail, Annandale, Va., 22003.
 Deputy Director.—Brig. Gen. Edwin A. Machen, Jr., USA, rm 3D993, Ext. 54924; Dorchester Apartments, 2005 Columbia Pike, Arlington, Va., 22204.
 Deputy Director.—Rear Adm. C. Edwin Bell, Jr., USN, rm 3E993, Ext. 54489; 1428 Cavalier Corridor, Falls Church, Va., 22044.
Director of Organization and Management Planning.—Capt. David O. Cooke, USN (acting), rm 3E827, Ext. 54278; 30 South Park Drive, Arlington, Va., 22204.
National Communications Systems Staff:
 Military Assistant.—Col. William G. McDonald, USAF, rm 3E993, Ext. 53136; 4311 Bradley Lane, Chevy Chase, Md.
 Technical Advisor.—David L. Solomon, rm 3E993, Ext. 53136; Route 5, 1109 Janet Lane, Vienna, Va., 22180.

ASSISTANT SECRETARY OF DEFENSE (COMPTROLLER)

Assistant Secretary of Defense.—Charles J. Hitch, rm 3E854, Ext. 53237; 5406 Albemarle Street, 20016.
 Secretary to the Assistant Secretary.—Betty M. Meints, rm 3E854, Ext. 53237; 333 South Glebe Road, Arlington, Va., 22204.
 Special Assistant.—Maj. Gen. Robert S. Moore, USA, rm 3E854, Ext. 54845; 2126 Connecticut Avenue, 20008.
 Economic Advisor.—Henry E. Glass, rm 3D855, Ext. 78191; 2104 North Quintana Street, Arlington, Va., 22205.
 Deputy Assistant Secretary (Budget).—Joseph S. Hoover, rm 3E843, Ext. 59252; 3221 Military Road, 20015.
 Deputy Assistant Secretary (Management).—W. Carl Blaisdell, rm 3E838, Ext. 78580; 209 Fairfax Road, Alexandria, Va., 22308.
 Deputy Comptroller for Management and Data Services.—Edmund B. Gifford, rm 3A862, Ext. 53147; 1206 Chestnut Avenue, Falls Church, Va., 22042.
 Directorate for Statistical Services.—Foster Adams, rm 4B938, Ext. 76107; 1527 Mount Eagle Place, Alexandria, Va., 22302.
 Deputy Comptroller for Internal Audit.—G. C. Gardner, Jr., rm 407 Donata Building, Ext. 79108; 2709 North Brandywine Street, Arlington, Va., 22207.

Assistant Secretary of Defense.—Continued
  Deputy Assistant Secretary (Accounting and Audit Policy).—Henry W. Sweeney, rm 3A882, Ext. 53424; 1111 Army-Navy Drive, Arlington, Va., 22202.
    Deputy Comptroller for Accounting and Finance Policy.—Melvin K. Zucker (Acting), rm 3C883, Ext. 76837; 953 North Lebanon Street, Arlington, Va., 22205.
    Deputy Comptroller for Audit Policy.—Kenneth K. Kilgore, rm 5A870, Ext. 56931; 4104 Downing Street, Annandale, Va., 22003.
    Directorate for External Audit Reports.—James L. Brewer, Jr., rm 5A862, Ext. 78281; 6103 Dorchester Street, Springfield, Va., 22150.
  Deputy Assistant Secretary (Programming).—Harold Asher, rm 3A882, Ext. 57341; 1020 North Quincy Street, Arlington, Va., 22201.
    Deputy Comptroller for Programming.—Willard L. Johnson, Jr., rm 3A882, Ext. 57451; 303 Jackson Street, Falls Church, Va., 22046.
    Directorate for Cost and Economic Analysis.—Saul Hoch, rm 3B863, Ext. 54177; 7777 Maple Avenue, Apt. 1101, Takoma Park, Md., 20012.
    Directorate for Program Operations and Review.—Henry G. Puppa, rm 3B862, Ext. 76556; 4608 Albemarle Street, 20016.
  Deputy Assistant Secretary (Systems Analysis).—Alain G. Enthoven, rm 3E838, Ext. 57191; 3203 Alabama Avenue, Alexandria, Va., 22305.
    Deputy Comptroller for General Purpose Forces.—Russell Murray 2d, rm 3C856, Ext. 73521; 213 Wilkes Street, Alexandria, Va., 22314.
    Deputy Comptroller for Strategic Programs.—Fred S. Hoffman, rm 3B852, Ext. 53380; 6309 Dahlonega Road, 20016.

ASSISTANT SECRETARY OF DEFENSE (INSTALLATIONS AND LOGISTICS)

Assistant Secretary of Defense.—Paul R. Ignatius, rm 3E808, Ext. 55254; 3650 Fordham Road, 20016.
  Secretary to the Assistant Secretary.—Sally J. Moser, rm 3E808, Ext. 55254; 1200 South Court House Road, Arlington, Va., 22204.
  Special Assistant.—Robert C. Unkrich, rm 3E794, Ext. 57402; 6314 Green Spring Road, Alexandria, Va., 22312.
  Director, Economic Adjustment.—Donald F. Bradford, rm 3E787, Ext. 55175; 1122 St. Andrews, Fairfax, Va., 22030.
  Director, Technical Logistics Data and Standardization Policy.—Brig. Gen. Allen T. Stanwix-Hay, USA, rm B–110, Cameron Station, Ext. 88101; 114 Olin Drive, Falls Church, Va., 22044.
  Deputy Assistant Secretary.—Glenn V. Gibson, rm 3E808, Ext. 71163; 9322 Parkhill Drive, Bethesda, Md.
    Directorate for International Programs.—Donald S. Cuffe, rm 3D823, Ext. 75981; 1821 North Jackson Street, Arlington, Va., 22201.
    Directorate for Research and Special Projects.—Nathan Brodsky, rm 3C846, Ext. 57175; 2840 Lorcom Lane, Arlington, Va., 22207.
  Deputy Assistant Secretary (Procurement).—G. C. Bannerman, rm 3E760, Ext. 78177; 3506 T Street, 20007.
    Directorate for Contract Administration Services.—Col. Donald E. Sowle, USAF, rm 1E836, Ext. 54137; 325 Capitol View Drive, McLean, Va., 22101.
    Directorate for Procurement Analysis and Planning.—Richard W. Webb, rm 3E821, Ext. 76907; 5538 10th Street North, Arlington, Va., 22205.
    Directorate for Procurement Management.—Robert D. Lyons, rm 3E773, Ext. 56705; 504 Crosswoods Drive, Lake Barcroft, Falls Church, Va., 22040.
    Directorate for Procurement Policy.—Brig. Gen. Robert H. McCutcheon, USAF, rm 3E773, Ext. 77909; 4030 North Tazewell Street, Arlington, Va., 22207.
    Directorate for Small Business and Economic Utilization.—Albert C. Lazure, rm 3D779, Ext. 79383; 2430 North George Mason Drive, Arlington, Va., 22207.
    Assistant for Contract Finance Policy.—John S. Bachman, rm 3E773, Ext. 76832; 4524 32d Road North, Arlington, Va., 22207.

Assistant Secretary of Defense.—Continued

Deputy Assistant Secretary (*Supply and Services*).—Paul H. Riley, rm 3E808, Ext. 74157; 1127 Lake Boulevard, Annandale, Va., 22003.

Cost Reduction Coordinator.—Col. Jack H. Alston, USAF, rm 2D779, Ext. 50337; 9 White Oaks Drive, Alexandria, Va., 22306.

Directorate for Petroleum Logistics Policy.—Lt. Gen. William O. Senter, USAF, rm 3C830, Ext. 59844; Quarters 66, Bolling Air Force Base, 20332.

Directorate for Supply Management Policy.—Hyman S. Zaretzky, rm 1E800, Ext. 79238; 303 Quaker Court, Falls Church, Va., 22042.

Directorate for Telecommunications Policy.—M. E. Curts, Building 12, Navy Service Center, Room 4205, Ext. 41157; 2652 South June Street, Arlington, Va., 22202.

Directorate for Transportation and Warehousing Policy.—Vincent F. Caputo, rm 2C769, Ext. 77191; 5711 Noble Drive, McLean, Va., 22101.

Deputy Assistant Secretary (*Properties and Installations*).—Edward J. Sheridan, rm 3E760, Ext. 79155; 2711 Sycamore Street, Alexandria, Va., 22305.

Directorate for Construction.—John Heard, rm 3E763, Ext. 79381; 104 East Melrose Street, Chevy Chase, Md., 20015.

Directorate for Real Property Management.—Allen W. Fore, rm 3E752, Ext. 54258; 106 East Braddock Road, Alexandria, Va., 22301.

Deputy Assistant Secretary (*Weapons Acquisition and Industrial Readiness*).— [Vacant], rm 3E784, Ext. 71368.

Directorate for Weapons Systems, Scheduling and Analysis.—Eckhard Bennewitz, rm 3E784, Ext. 56322; 7317 Broxburn Court, Bethesda, Md.

Directorate for Industrial Readiness.—Henry A. Damminger, rm 3E784, Ext. 56322; 4823 Lockraven Drive, McLean, Va., 22101.

Assistant for Industrial Plant Equipment.—A. Howard Millbourn, rm 5E687, Ext. 73503; 5101 23d Road North, Arlington, Va., 22207.

Deputy Assistant Secretary (*Equipment Maintenance and Readiness*).—George E. Fouch, rm 3E784, Ext. 79251; 6859 Tulip Hill Terrace, 20016.

Special Assistant.—Lee S. Harding, rm 3E791, Ext. 52198; Lake Hill Motel, Woodbridge, Va., 22191.

Assistant for Industrial Management Practices.—A. William Buschman, rm 3E784, Ext. 75530; 6630 Joallen Drive, Lake Barcroft Estates, Falls Church, Va., 22044.

Directorate for Maintenance Policy.—John R. Taylor, rm 5E679, Ext. 76191; 3708 Battery Road, Alexandria, Va., 22308.

Directorate for Quality and Reliability Assurance.—John J. Riordan, rm 5E725, Ext. 59537; 4201 Massachusetts Avenue, 20016.

Directorate for Value Engineering and Productivity.—Col. Arthur D. Powers, USAF, rm 5E723, Ext. 50121; 7715 Rowan Court, Annandale, Va., 22003.

Deputy Assistant Secretary (*Family Housing*).—John J. Reed, rm 3E772, Ext. 57804; 2109 Cyrus Place, Alexandria, Va., 22308.

Directorate for Programming.—John H. Arrington, rm 3C800, Ext. 76231; 4200 Cathedral Avenue, 20016.

Directorate for Management and Evaluation.—Arthur B. Crap, rm 3D763, Ext. 74329; 601 19th Street, 20006.

Directorate for Standardization and Design.—Sigmund I. Gerber, rm 3E781, Ext. 57612; 6817 Algonquin Avenue, Bethesda, Md.

ASSISTANT SECRETARY OF DEFENSE (INTERNATIONAL SECURITY AFFAIRS)

Assistant Secretary of Defense.—John T. McNaughton, rm 4E806, Ext. 54351; 5031 Lowell Street, 20016.

Secretary to the Assistant Secretary.—Thelma E. Stubbs, rm 4E806, Ext. 54351; 1850 Columbia Pike, Arlington, Va., 22204.

Special Assistant.—Daniel Ellsberg, rm 4E806, Ext. 56273; 1400 South Joyce Street, Arlington, Va., 22202.

Assistant Secretary of Defense.—Continued

Executive Officer.—Col. Jack A. Rogers, USA, rm 4E810, Ext. 79729; 2706 North Pollard Street, Arlington, Va., 22207.

Assistant for Counterinsurgency.—George A. Carroll, rm 4D832, Ext. 74882; 728 Center Building, Hunting Towers, Alexandria, Va., 22314.

Deputy Assistant Secretary.—Peter Solbert, rm 4E813, Ext. 57273; 3107 Garfield Street, 20008.

    Special Assistant.—Col. Fred E. Haynes, USMC, rm 4E813, Ext. 56274; 1001 North Lebanon Street, Arlington, Va., 22205.

    Regional Director, Far East.—Rear Adm. Francis J. Blouin, USN, rm 4D761, Ext. 54175; 3807 Underwood Street, Chevy Chase, Md., 20015.

Deputy Assistant Secretary (Planning and North Atlantic Affairs).—Henry S. Rowen, rm 4E828, Ext. 72307; 3307 Newark Street, 20008.

    Director, Policy Planning Staff.—Brig. Gen. John W. Vogt, USAF, rm 4E842, Ext. 79347; 702 Tarpon Lane, Alexandria, Va., 22309.

    Regional Director, Europe.—Brig. Gen. J. T. Folda, USA, rm 4D770, Ext. 77207; 2800 Woodley Road, 20008.

    Regional Director, Sino-Soviet.—Col. Melvin J. Nielsen, USAF, rm 4D781, Ext. 74689; 1600 South Joyce Street, Arlington, Va., 22202.

Deputy Assistant Secretary (Regional Affairs).—Alvin Friedman, rm 4E820, Ext. 78101; 4125 25th Place North, Arlington, Va., 22207.

    Regional Director, Western Hemisphere.—Brig. Gen. William M. Fondren, USA, rm 4C839, Ext. 77588; 3703 Cameron Mills Road, Alexandria, Va., 22305.

    Director, Foreign Economic Affairs.—Joseph W. Darling, rm 4C763, Ext. 74625; 423 New Jersey Avenue SE., 20003.

Deputy Assistant Secretary (Overseas Forces and Facilities).—William E. Lang, rm 4E820, Ext. 75334; 1200 North Nash Street, Arlington, Va., 22209.

    Regional Director, Africa.—Col. Irwin H. Dregne, USAF, rm 4C826, Ext. 77836; 4201 31st Street South, Arlington, Va., 22206.

    Director, Foreign Military Rights.—Ray W. Bronez, rm 4D800, Ext. 56386; 315 Westmoreland Road, Alexandria, Va., 22308.

Deputy Assistant Secretary (Near East, South Asia and Military Assistance Program Policy Review).—Townsend W. Hoopes, rm 4B737, Ext. 72291; Box 456, Route 2, McLean, Va., 22101.

    Regional Director, Near East and South Asia.—Brig. Gen. Eugene L. Strickland, USAF, rm 4C836, Ext. 71335; 511 Thrasher Road, McLean, Va., 22101.

Deputy Assistant Secretary (Arms Control).—Arthur W. Barber, rm 4E832, Ext. 75146; 7666 Hemlock Street, Bethesda, Md.

    Director, Arms Control.—Col. Jack J. Wagstaff, USA, rm 4E829, Ext. 57315; 648 Timberbranch Parkway, Alexandria, Va., 22302.

Director of Military Assistance.—Gen. Robert J. Wood, USA, rm 4C762, Ext. 53291; Quarters 7, Fort Lesley J. McNair, SW.

    Deputy Director.—William M. Leffingwell, rm 4C762, Ext. 57013; 2601 Woodley Place, 20008.

    Assistant for Systems Control.—Kenneth L. Lee, rm 4B742, Ext. 78181; 8908 Hickory Hill Avenue, Lanham, Md., 20801.

    Assistant for Special Projects.—Col. Forrest I. Rettgers, USA, rm 4C774, Ext. 79753; 8414 Camden Street, Alexandria, Va., 22308.

    Director, Plans and Programs Division.—Brig. Gen. Gladwyn E. Pinkston, USAF, rm 4B683, Ext. 78000; 1600 South Joyce Street, Arlington, Va., 22202.

    Director, Administration and Management Division.—Col. Lincoln A. Simon, USA, rm 4B714, Ext. 55459; 6912 Montrose Street, Alexandria, Va., 22312.

    Military Assistance Comptroller.—W. Arthur Comer, rm 4B724, Ext. 74758; 4208 23d Street North, Arlington, Va., 22207.

Deputy Assistant Secretary (International Logistics Negotiations).—Henry J. Kuss, Jr., rm 4B652, Ext. 59562; 7318 Chatham Street, North Springfield, Va., 22151.

ASSISTANT SECRETARY OF DEFENSE (MANPOWER)

Assistant Secretary of Defense.—Norman S. Paul, rm 3E966, Ext. 52334; 3035 Chain Bridge Road, 20016.

Secretary to the Assistant Secretary.—Virginia Joseph, rm 3E966, Ext. 52334; 2826 28th Street, 20008.

Special Assistant.—Stephen S. Jackson, rm 3E966, Ext. 79158; Apt. A–1611, River House, 1400 South Joyce Street, Arlington, Va., 22202.

Deputy Coordinator, Federal Voting Assistance Program.—James W. Platt, rm 3C170, Ext. 79141; 2205 Valley Circle, Alexandria, Va., 22302.

Director for Civil Affairs.—Leslie V. Dix, rm 3C170, Ext. 75556; 428 Springman Drive, Fairfax, Va., 22030.

Executive Assistant.—John L. Fallon, rm 3E966, Ext. 73137; 801 Hobbs Drive, Silver Spring, Md., 20904.

Military Assistant.—Col. James F. Lawrence, Jr., USMC, rm 3E966, Ext. 73137; 804 Waterford Road, Alexandria, Va., 22308.

Deputy Assistant Secretary (Civilian Personnel, Industrial Relations, and Civil Rights).—Stephen N. Shulman, rm 3C232, Ext. 76381; 3732 North Oakland Street, Arlington, Va., 22207.

Directorate for Civilian Personnel.—Leon L. Wheeless, rm 3C242, Ext. 55348; 4309 Rosemary Street, Chevy Chase, Md., 20015.

Directorate for Industrial Relations.—Samuel Silver, rm 3C232, Ext. 74854; 8808 Spring Valley Road, Chevy Chase, Md., 20015.

Assistant for Civil Rights.—L. Howard Bennett, rm 3C255, Ext. 50110; 3636 16th Street, 20011.

Counselor for Civil Rights.—James C. Evans, rm 3B254, Ext. 52431; 3533 Warder Street, 20010.

Deputy Assistant Secretary (Education).—[Vacant.] Rm 3D260, Ext. 57579.

Directorate for Education Programs.—Col. J. A. Bowman, USAF, rm 3D267, Ext. 74184; 322 Anneliesse Drive, Falls Church, Va., 22044.

Directorate for Manpower Resources.—Albert Kay, rm 3D261, Ext. 72091; 204 East Columbia Street, Falls Church, Va., 22046.

Directorate for Armed Forces Information and Education.—John C. Broger, rm 3D253, Ext. 76125; 6904 Greentree Drive, Falls Church, Va., 22041.

Deputy Assistant Secretary (Health and Medical).—Shirley C. Fisk, M.D., rm 3B269, Ext. 72111; 3039 West Lane Keys, 20007.

Staff Director.—Rear Adm. William N. New, USN, rm 3B265, Ext. 56281; 2701 South Grove Street, Arlington, Va., 22202.

Deputy Assistant Secretary (Military Personnel Policy).—Col. William W. Berg, USAF, rm 3C961, Ext. 74166; 517 Dalebrook Drive, Alexandria, Va., 22308.

Directorate for Compensation Affairs.—Col. John E. Kirk, USA, rm 3C980, Ext. 79191; 2008 Fort Hunt Drive, Alexandria, Va., 22308.

Directorate for Management Affairs.—Capt. G. D. Williams, USN, rm 3C975, Ext. 77197; 6100 North Washington Boulevard, Arlington, Va., 22205.

Deputy Assistant Secretary (Reserve Affairs).—Col. James F. Hollingsworth, USA, rm 3C956, Ext. 74222; 639 Pullman Place, Alexandria, Va., 22305.

Directorate for Reserve Policy.—Capt. S. W. Gavitt, USN, rm 3C966, Ext. 74334; 303 Capitol View Drive, McLean, Va., 22101.

Directorate for Reserve Mobilization Policy.—Col. Edward M. Geary, USA, rm 3C966, Ext. 74334; 5550 Columbia Pike, Arlington, Va., 22204.

Deputy Assistant Secretary (Security Policy).—Walter T. Skallerup, Jr., rm 3C275, Ext. 78233; 4555 Crest Lane, McLean, Va., 22101.

Directorate for Classification Management.—George MacClain, rm 3C285, Ext. 73969; 2646 Fort Scott Drive, Arlington, Va., 22202.

Directorate for Security Plans and Programs.—Charles M. Trammell, Jr., rm 3C272, Ext. 50122; 6534 Wiscasset Road, 20016.

Directorate for Industrial Personnel Access Authorization Review.—Herbert Lewis, rm 3C239, Ext. 73256; 6519 East Halbert Road, Bethesda, Md.

Deputy Assistant Secretary (Special Studies and Requirements).—William Gorham, rm 3D970, Ext. 54593; 1561 35th Street, 20007.

Directorate for Manpower Requirements and Utilization.—Gus C. Lee, rm 3D970, Ext. 78244; 5309 Falmouth Road, 20016.

Directorate for Policy Planning.—Harold Wool, rm 3D973, Ext. 56940; 6716 Brigadoon Drive, Bethesda, Md.

Director, Equal Employment Opportunity Program.—Ralph Horton, Jr., rm 3C200, Ext. 50107; 700 South Court House Road, Arlington, Va., 22204.

Assistant Secretary of Defense.—Continued
  Chairman, Reserve Forces Policy Board.—John Slezak, rm 3A926, Ext. 75253; 711 West Street, Sycamore, Ill.
    Military Executive.—Maj. Gen. Ralph A. Palladino, USAR, rm 3Z926, Ext. 75253; 3199 North Pollard Street, Arlington, Va., 22207.
  Chairman, Armed Forces Chaplains Board.—Rear Adm. J. Floyd Dreith (CH), USN, rm G–803, Arlington Annex, Ext. 42347; Route 2, Box 184, Vienna, Va., 22180.
    Executive Director.—Col. John I. Rhea, USA, rm 3C170, Ext. 79015; 3305 North Nottingham Street, Arlington, Va., 22207.

ASSISTANT SECRETARY OF DEFENSE (PUBLIC AFFAIRS)

Assistant Secretary of Defense.—Arthur Sylvester, rm 2E800, Ext. 79312; 203 Crystal House, 2000 South Eads Street, Arlington, Va., 22202.
  Secretary to the Assistant Secretary.—Violet L. Bryan, rm 2E800, Ext. 79312; 1101 South Washington Street, Alexandria, Va., 22314.
  Deputy Assistant Secretary.—Nils A. Lennartson, rm 2E800, Ext. 53381; 214–M Fort Hunt Road, Alexandria, Va., 22307.
  Military Assistant.—Capt. Hugh M. Robinson, USN, rm 2E782, Ext. 59032; 6206 29th Street North, Arlington, Va., 22207.
  Special Assistant.—Orville S. Splitt, rm 2E780, Ext. 76648; 2603 Rodes Court, Annandale, Va., 22003.
  Special Assistant for Vietnam.—Col. Rodger R. Bankson, USA, rm 2E789, Ext. 73532; 7 Dearborn Drive, Falls Church, Va., 22044.
  Executive Assistant.—Maj. Clarence S. Weaver, USA, rm 2E800, Ext. 79143; 4421 31st Street South, Arlington, Va., 22206.
  Chief, Media Accreditation and Tours.—Lt. Col. Richard P. Taffe, USA, rm 2D757, Ext. 76005; 819 South Barton Street, Arlington, Va., 22204.
  Directorate for Plans and Programs.—Col. Charles F. Heasty, Jr., USA, rm 2E776, Ext. 71346; 2403 Wemberly Way, McLean, Va., 22101.
  Directorate for Information Services.—William E. Odum, rm 2E761, Ext. 59082; 3936 Legation Street, 20015
  Directorate for Community Relations.—Col. Julian B. Cross, USAF, rm 2E772, Ext. 52113; 3201 Landover Street, Alexanderia, Va., 22305.
  Directorate for Security Review.—Charles W. Hinkle, rm 1E771, Ext. 74325; 905 Birchwood Road, Falls Church, Va., 22041.
Assistant Secretary of Defense.—Eugene G. Fubini, rm 3E1009, Ext. 57178; 9000 Bronson Drive, Potomac, Md., 20854.
Assistant for Special Intelligence.—John F. O'Gara, rm 3E1083, Ext. 78970; 410 Slade Run Drive, Falls Church, Va., 22042.

GENERAL COUNSEL

General Counsel.—[Vacant], rm 3E980, Ext. 53341.
  Secretary to the General Counsel.—[Vacant], rm 3E980, Ext. 53341.
  Deputy General Counsel.—Leonard Niederlehner, rm 3E980, Ext. 77248; 3709 North Nelson Street, Arlington, Va., 22207.
    Assistant General Counsel (Logistics).—Jack L. Stempler, rm 3D937, Ext. 75073; 1202 Trinity Drive, Alexandria, Va., 22314.
    Assistant General Counsel (Manpower).—Frank A. Bartimo, rm. 3E963, Ext. 79341; 513 Eppard Street, Falls Church, Va., 22044.
    Assistant General Counsel (Fiscal Matters).—Maurice H. Lanman, rm 3D961, Ext. 77228; 4416 Westbrook Lane, Chevy Chase View, Kensington, Md., 20795.
    Assistant General Counsel (International Affairs).—Benjamin Forman, rm 3D918, Ext. 78343; 1111 Army-Navy Drive, Apt. B–1201, Arlington, Va., 22202.
    Assistant General Counsel (Administration).—James J. Kearney, rm 3B279, Ext. 56804; 7700 Persimmon Tree Lane, Bethesda, Md., 20034.
  Director, Legislative Reference Service.—Frank J. Sherlock, rm 3C940, Ext. 71305; 1633 Hickory Hill Road, Falls Church, Va., 22042.

ASSISTANTS TO THE SECRETARY OF DEFENSE

Assistant to the Secretary of Defense (Atomic Energy).—William J. Howard, rm 3E1074, Ext. 56639; 6627 Joallen Drive, Falls Church, Va., 22044.

Military Assistants:

Capt. F. Costagliola, USN, rm 3E1074, Ext. 75161; 307 Gibbon Street, Alexandria, Va., 22314.

Col. W. H. Fleming, USAF, rm 3E1074, Ext. 75161; 528 Waterway Drive, Falls Church, Va., 22044.

Col. C. M. Davenport, Jr., USA, rm 3E1074, Ext. 75161; 7206 Blair Road, 20012.

Assistant to the Secretary of Defense (Legislative Affairs).—David E. McGiffert, rm 3E944, Ext. 76211; 3524 P Street, 20007.

Special Assistant.—Charles N. Gregg, Jr., rm 3E967, Ext. 72365; Box 462, Route 2, Swinks Mill Road, McLean, Va., 22101.

Deputy.—Brig. Gen. Charles R. Roderick, USAF, rm 3E944, Ext. 75381; 700 South Court House Road, Arlington, Va., 22204.

Director, Office of Legislative Liaison.—Brig. Gen. Charles R. Roderick, USAF, rm 3E944, Ext. 75381; 700 South Court House Road, Arlington, Va., 22204.

Deputy (ISA, PA).—Col. Clyde M. Dillender, Jr., USA, rm 3E940, Ext. 57104; 1600 South Joyce Street, Arlington, Va., 22202.

Deputy (Installations).—James F. Shumate, Jr., rm 3D940, Ext. 55497; 1611 Roundtree Road, Falls Church, Va., 22042.

Deputy (Manpower).—Lt. Col. William W. Wander, USMC, rm 3D940, Ext. 54131; 5893 First Street South, Arlington, Va., 22204.

Deputy (Logistics, DSA, DCA).—Cdr. Michael F. Durkin, USN, rm 3D940, Ext. 79369; 7603 Newcastle Drive, Annandale, Va., 22003.

Deputy (R&E, AE, DIA).—Maj. Everette L. Harper, USAF, rm 3D940, Ext. 54132; Featherstone Farm, Woodbridge, Va., 22191.

Deputy (Senate Liaison).—Col. Ralph E. Vandervort, Jr., USA, rm 3E967, Ext. 73782; 621 Midday Lane, Alexandria, Va., 22306.

Deputy (House Liaison).—Maurice G. Burnside, rm 3E967, Ext. 73344; 800 Crescent Drive, Alexandria, Va., 22302.

Special Projects.—Lt. Col. Margaret P. Shroyer, USA, rm 3D940, Ext. 79166; 5539 Columbia Pike, Arlington, Va., 22204.

Director, Office of Plans and Coordination.—Capt. Oscar N. Hibler, Jr., USN, rm 3D919, Ext. 57470; 1828 Beverly Avenue, McLean, Va., 22101.

Defense Representative, North Atlantic and Mediterranean Areas/U.S. Regional Office, Defense Advisor.—John A. Hooper, rm 4E806, Ext. 54351.

Assistant to the Deputy Secretary.—Samuel W. Crosby, rm 3E925, Ext. 72059; 4421 31st Street South, Arlington, Va., 22206.

JOINT CHIEFS OF STAFF

Chairman.—Gen. Earle G. Wheeler, USA, rm 2E873, Ext. 79121; Quarters 6, Fort Myer, Arlington, Va., 22211.

Chief of Staff, U.S. Army.—Gen. Harold K. Johnson, USA, rm 3E668, Ext. 52077; Quarters 1, Fort Myer, Arlington, Va., 22211.

Chief of Naval Operations.—Adm. David J. McDonald, USN, rm 4E660, Ext. 56007; Admiral's House, Quarters A, U.S. Naval Observatory, 20390.

Chief of Staff, U.S. Air Force.—Gen. John P. McConnell, USAF, rm 4E929, Ext. 79225; Quarters 7, Fort Myer, Arlington, Va., 22211.

Commandant of the Marine Corps.—Gen. Wallace M. Greene, Jr., USMC (on Marine Corps matters only), rm 2004, Arlington Annex, Ext. 42500; Commandant's House, Marine Barracks, Eighth and I Streets SE., 20003.

JOINT STAFF

Director.—Lt. Gen. David A. Burchinal, USAF, rm 2E936, Ext. 74084; 65 Westover Avenue, Bolling AFB, 20332.

Vice Director.—Maj. Gen. Ashton H. Manhart, USA, rm 2E932, Ext. 71297; 1623 35th Street, 20007.

Director.—Continued

Deputy Director.—Rear Adm. Louis J. Kirn, USN, rm 2E937, Ext. 76628; River House, Apt. C-1515, 1600 South Joyce Street, Arlington, Va., 22202.

Director, J-1 (Personnel).—Brig. Gen. William A. Tope, USAF, rm 2E824, Ext. 73062; 107 Langdon Court, McLean, Va., 22101.

Director, J-3 (Operations).—Vice Adm. Lloyd M. Mustin, USN, rm 2D876, Ext. 73702; 500 West Taylor Run Parkway, Alexandria, Va., 22314.

Director, J-4 (Logistics).—Lt. Gen. Richard D. Meyer, USA, rm 2E832, Ext. 52732; 1403 Evening Lane, Alexandria, Va., 22306.

Director, J-5 (Plans and Policy).—Lt. Gen. Paul S. Emrick, USAF, rm 2E1000, Ext. 55618; 7402 Dulany Drive, McLean, Va., 22101.

Director, J-6 (Communications-Electronics).—Rear Adm. Theodore A. Torgerson, USN, rm 1D776, Ext. 71998; 2600 Fort Scott Drive, Arlington, Va., 22202.

Special Assistant for Counterinsurgency and Special Activities.—Maj. Gen. Rollen H. Anthis, USAF, rm 1E962, Ext. 59852; 310 Vassar Road, Alexandria, Va., 22314.

Special Assistant for Military Assistance Affairs.—Maj. Gen. Joseph T. Kingsley, Jr., USAF, rm 1E843, Ext. 75225; 1421 29th Street, 20007.

Secretary, Joint Chiefs of Staff.—Col. Robert C. Forbes, USA, rm 2E935, Ext. 72700; 652 South Illinois, Arlington, Va., 22204.

JOINT SERVICE SCHOOLS

THE NATIONAL WAR COLLEGE
Washington, D.C., 20315

Commandant.—Vice Adm. Fitzhugh Lee, USN, rm 105, National War College, OX 5-8315; Quarters 6, Fort Lesley J. McNair, 20315.

Deputy Commandant for Academic Affairs.—Maj. Gen. Sidney C. Wooten, USA, rm 101, National War College, OX 5-8203; Quarters 12, Fort Lesley J. McNair, 20315.

Deputy Commandant for Foreign Affairs.—Hon. Samuel Berger, rm 103, National War College, OX 5-8204; Quarters 15, Fort Lesley J. McNair, 20315.

Executive Officer.—Col. Jacob K. Rippert, USA, rm 107, National War College, OX 5-8318; Quarters 3-B, Apt. 2, Fort Lesley J. McNair, 20315.

INDUSTRIAL COLLEGE OF THE ARMED FORCES
Washington, D.C., 20315

Commandant.—Lt. Gen. August Schomburg, USA, rm 202, OX 5-8311; Quarters 13, Fort Lesley J. McNair, 20315.

Deputy Commandant.—Maj. Gen. William S. Steele, USAF, rm 226, OX 5-8332; Quarters 3, Fort Lesley J. McNair, 20315.

Secretary.—Col. Roberts H. Billingsley, USA, rm 206, OX 5-8305; 917 North Overlook Drive, Alexandria, Va., 22305.

ARMED FORCES STAFF COLLEGE
Norfolk, Va., 23511

Commandant.—Maj. Gen. J. Stanley Holtoner, USAF, rm A201, Normandy Hall, 444-5302; Illinois House, 478 Powhatan Street, Naval Station, Norfolk, Va., 23511.

Deputy Commandant for Navy.—Capt. James S. Gray, Jr., USN, rm E208, Normandy Hall, 444-5305; Quarters B, Porter Road, Armed Forces Staff College, Norfolk, Va., 23511.

Deputy Commandant for Army.—Col. Thomas Dooley, USA, rm E212, Normandy Hall, 444-5307; Quarters A, Porter Road, Armed Forces Staff College, Norfolk, Va., 23511.

Deputy Commandant for Air Force and Executive.—Col. John C. Jennison, USAF, rm E204, Normandy Hall, 444-5676; Quarters D, Porter Road, Armed Forces Staff College, Norfolk, Va., 23511.

456 Congressional Directory

DEFENSE ATOMIC SUPPORT AGENCY

Director.—Lt. Gen. Harold C. Donnelly, USAF, rm 1B668, Ext. 56375; Qtrs 57A Westover Avenue, Bolling AFB, Washington, D.C., 20332.
  Executive.—Col. Donald G. Williams, USA, rm 1B668, Ext. 55338; 1400 South Joyce Street, Apt. C–512, Arlington, Va., 22202.
  Assistant Executive.—Lt. Col. James M. Harris, USAF, rm 1B668, Ext. 54454; 6300 Gormley Place, Springfield, Va., 22150.
  Comptroller.—Capt. John M. Gore, USN, rm 1B729, Ext. 52350; 2605 23d Road North, Arlington, Va., 22207.
  Public Information Officer.—Lt. Col. James H. Dickson, Jr., USA, rm 1B915, Ext. 77626; 7102 Hillcrest Road, Alexandria, Va., 22312.
  Deputy Director (Operations and Administration).—Brig. Gen. Kenneth F. Dawalt, USA, rm 1B671, Ext. 75181; 3617 Oval Drive, Alexandria, Va., 22305.
    Operations Division.—Col. Willard M. Shankle, USAF, rm 1B665, Ext. 53111; 6118 Massachusetts Avenue, 20016.
    Plans Division.—Col. Elba W. Bowen, USA, rm 1B669, Ext. 54125; 6902 Lupine Lane, McLean, Va., 22101.
    Requirements Division.—Col. Wilmer K. Benson, USA, rm 1B730, Ext. 53638; 7535 Spring Lake Drive, Bethesda, Md., 20034.
    Personnel and Administrative Division.—Col. Harry E. Morrill, USAF, rm 1B664, Ext. 74874; 201 Raymond Avenue, McLean, Va., 22101.
    Security Division.—Col. Norman A. Skinrood, USA, rm 1B684, Ext. 75277; 3723 North Oakland Street, Arlington, Va., 22207.
    Logistics Division.—Col. John E. Minahan, USA, rm 1B744, Ext. 71354; 732 Mosby Woods Drive, Fairfax, Va., 22030.
  Deputy Director (Scientific).—Dr. Theodore B. Taylor, rm 1B677, Ext. 57153; 7604 Glennon Drive, Bethesda, Md., 20034.
    Radiation Division.—Col. Howard C. Rose, USAF, rm 1B674, Ext. 71516; 1620 Vagabond Drive, Falls Church, Va., 22042.
    Analysis and Programs Division.—Col. Charles S. Brice, Jr., USA, rm 1B672A, Ext. 77025; 1304 Scarlet Circle, Fairfax, Va., 22030.
    Blast and Shock Division.—Col. George E. Hesselbacher, Jr., USA, rm 1B689, Ext. 71300; 902 Allison Street, Alexandria, Va., 22302.
    Medical Division.—Col. Gerrit L. Hekhuis, USAF, rm 1B685, Ext. 52793; 4326 24th Street North, Arlington, Va., 22207.

JOINT TASK FORCE EIGHT
Tempo E, 4th and Adams Drive SW.

Commander, Joint Task Force Eight.—Maj. Gen. John D. Stevenson, USAF, Ext. 61381, Wg. 8; 2000 South Eads Street, Apt. 827, Arlington, Va.
  Deputy Commander.—Brig. Gen. Charles F. Mudgett, Jr., USA, Wg. 8, Ext. 68653; 1108 Beverly Drive, Alexandria, Va.

ARMED FORCES RADIOBIOLOGY RESEARCH INSTITUTE
National Naval Medical Center Building 42

Director, Armed Forces Radiobiology Research Institute.—Col. James T. Brennan, USA, rm 1018, Ext. 1223x312; 10204 Tyburn Terrace, Bethesda, Md.

DEFENSE COMMUNICATIONS AGENCY
Building 12, Navy Department Service Center, 8th and South Court House Road, Arlington, Va.

Director.—Lt. Gen. Alfred D. Starbird, USA, rm 4120, Ext. 43155; Quarters 11A, Fort Lesley J. McNair, 20315.
  Chief of Staff.—Rear Adm. Jack S. Dorsey, USN, rm 4130, Ext. 43158; 2707 George Mason Place, Alexandria, Va., 22305.

Director.—Continued
  Deputy Director, Defense Communications System.—Maj. Gen. George E. Pickett, USA, rm 4160, Ext. 42135; 2316 South Arlington Ridge Road, Arlington, Va., 22202.
  Deputy Director, National Military Command System.—Maj. Gen. John B. Bestic, USAF, rm 4140, Ext. 41753; 2525 North Ridgeview Road, Arlington, Va., 22207.
  Deputy Director, Communications Satellite Project Office.—Rear Adm. Francis D. Boyle, USN, rm 4730, Ext. 42251; 2001 Columbia Pike, Arlington, Va., 22204.
  Assistant Director, Administrative Services.—Col. Elwyn M. Stimson, USMC, rm 3470, Ext. 41014; 518 Antietam Avenue, Fairfax, Va., 22030.
  Comptroller.—Thomas D. Moran, Jr., rm 4670, Ext. 42761; 205 Waynewood Boulevard, Alexandria, Va., 22308.

DEFENSE INTELLIGENCE AGENCY

Director.—Lt. Gen. Joseph F. Carroll, USAF, rm 3E258, Ext. 57353; 64 Westover Avenue, Bolling Air Force Base, 20332.
  Deputy Director.—Lt. Gen. Alva R. Fitch, USA, rm 3E258, Ext. 75128; Qtrs 23-A, Fort Myer, Arlington, Va., 22211.
  Chief of Staff.—Rear Adm. Allan L. Reed, USN, rm 3E261, Ext. 57380; 2203 Shipman Lane, McLean, Va., 22101.

DEFENSE SUPPLY AGENCY
Cameron Station, Alexandria, Va., 22314

Director.—Vice Adm. Joseph M. Lyle, USN, rm 135A, Bldg. 3, Ext. 81111; Dorchester Towers, Apt. 303, 2001 Columbia Pike, Arlington, Va., 22204.
  Deputy Director.—Maj. Gen. Francis C. Gideon, USAF, rm 135A, Bldg. 3, Ext. 81113; 808 Rose Lane, Annandale, Va., 22003.
  Executive.—Col. E. M. Teeter, USA, rm 135A, Bldg. 3, Ext. 81115; 3105 Towanda Road, Alexandria, Va., 22303.
  Special Assistant to the Director.—Dr. W. J. Garvin, rm 132B, Bldg. 3, Ext. 81131; 1213 Radnor Place, Falls Church, Va., 22042.
  Special Assistant for Public Affairs.—Eugene F. Hart, rm 134B, Bldg. 3, Ext. 81135; 107 Lemon Road, Falls Church, Va., 22043.
  Inspector General.—Col. Talbert I. Martin, USA, rm 139C, Bldg. 3, Ext. 81057; 4921 Seminary Road, Apt. 830, Alexandria, Va., 22311.
  Counsel.—Robert M. Lemke, rm 110C, Bldg. 3, Ext. 81156; 6104 Cromwell Drive, 20016.
  Deputy Director for Contract Administration Services.—Maj. Gen. William W. Veal, USAF, rm 129C, Bldg. 4, Ext. 88091; 1903 Alyce Place, Alexandria, Va., 22308.
  Assistant Director for Plans, Programs and Systems.—Maj. Gen. Victor J. MacLaughlin, USA, rm 127D, Bldg. 3, Ext. 81271; 313 Crown View Drive, Alexandria, Va., 22314.
  Comptroller.—Robert C. Moot, rm 106E, Bldg. 3, Ext. 81201; 2 Woolls Place, Annandale, Va., 22003.
  Staff Director, Administration.—Col. O. R. Rumph, USA, 4m 135F, Bldg. 3, Ext. 81003; 4817 27th Road South, Arlington, Va., 22206.
  Staff Director, Military Personnel.—Lt. Col. Robert F. Askey, USA, rm 116F, Bldg. 3, Ext. 81137; 6309 Joslyn Place, Cheverly, Md., 20785.
  Staff Director, Civilian Personnel.—Walter G. Ingerski, rm 104A, Bldg. 3, Ext. 81025; 945 North Quantico Street, Arlington, Va., 22205.
  Staff Director, Installations and Services.—Capt. Gardiner T. Pollich, USN, rm 112D, Bldg. 4, Ext. 81355; 5007 Regency Place, Alexandria, Va., 22304.
  Executive Director, Supply Operations.—Brig. Gen. John M. Kenderdine, USA, rm 114B, Bldg. 4, Ext. 81101; 941 West Van Dorn Street, Alexandria, Va., 22304.

Director.—Continued

Executive Director, Procurement and Production.—Rear Adm. Charles A. Blick, USN, rm 105B, Bldg. 4, Ext. 81401; 2001 Columbia Pike, Apt. 806, Arlington, Va., 22204.

Executive Director, Technical and Logistics Services.—Maj. Gen. Bruce E. Kendall, USA, rm 102E, Bldg. 4, Ext. 81771; 4843 Dodson Drive, Alexandria, Va., 22003.

MILITARY LIAISON COMMITTEE TO THE ATOMIC ENERGY COMMISSION

Chairman.—William Jack Howard, rm 3E1074, Ext. 56639; 6627 Joallen Drive, Falls Church, Va., 22044.

Members:

Army:

Maj. Gen. Austin W. Betts, USA, rm 3E412, Ext. 78187; 4822 Old Dominion Drive, Arlington, Va., 22207.

Maj. Gen. Lloyd E. Fellenz, USA, rm 3A480, Ext. 57728; 5339 Holmes Run Parkway, Alexandria, Va., 22304.

Navy:

Rear Adm. Thomas F. Connolly, USN, rm 4E552, Ext. 54611; 2741 South Ives Street, Arlington, Va., 22202.

Capt. Harry B. Hahn, USN, rm 5D816, Ext. 52143; Stratford Apts., 4901 Seminary Road, Alexandria, Va., 22311.

Air Force:

Maj. Gen. Arthur C. Agan, Jr., USAF, rm 4E1020, Ext. 79811; 1401 Juliana Place, Alexandria, Va., 22304.

Maj. Gen. Andrew J. Kinney, USAF, rm 4E334, Ext. 76518; 2343 South Nash Street, Arlington, Va., 22202.

Executive Secretary.—Col. Sidney C. Bruce, USAF, rm C–425, AEC Headquarters Building, Germantown, Md., 20545, 973, Ext. 3462; 1107 West Boulevard Drive, Alexandria, Va., 22308.

ARMED SERVICES BOARD OF CONTRACT APPEALS
Room 3C749, Pentagon Building

Chairman.—Louis Spector, 6710 Joallen Drive, Falls Church, Va., 22041.

Vice-Chairman.—Carl A. Turmo, 4301 Columbia Pike, Arlington, Va., 22207.

Recorder.—George L. Hawkes, 3717 North Vernon Street, Arlington, Va., 22207.

DEPARTMENT OF THE ARMY

The Pentagon, 20310. Phone, LIberty 5-6700 (Code 11)

STEPHEN AILES, of West Virginia, Secretary of the Army, was sworn into office January 28, 1964 (4521 Wetherill Road); born in Romney, W. Va., March 25, 1912, son of Eugene E. Ailes and Sallie (Cornwell) Ailes; was graduated from the Episcopal High School in Alexandria, Va., in 1929, from Princeton University (B.A.) 1933, and from West Virginia University Law School (LL. B.) 1936; admitted to West Virginia bar 1936, District of Columbia bar 1946; assistant professor of law at West Virginia University, 1937–1940; practiced law in Martinsburg, W. Va., 1936–37, 1940–42; served with the Federal Government on the legal staff of the Office of Price Administration and was Assistant General Counsel, Consumer Goods Price Division, 1942–1946; returned to private law practice with the law firm of Steptoe & Johnson, Washington, D.C., 1946; took leave of absence from law practice to go to Greece as Counsel to the American Economic Mission, 1947; returned to private practice of law with Steptoe & Johnson and became a partner in the firm, 1948–Feb. 1, 1961; served as a legal consultant to Mr. Michael DiSalle, Director of the Office of Price Stabilization, during Korean Conflict, 1951; nominated Under Secretary of the Army by President Kennedy, February 9, 1961, and served until his appointment as Secretary of the Army by President Johnson; member of the American Bar Association; Clubs: Chevy Chase, Burning Tree, and Metropolitan (Washington, D.C.); married Helen Wales, June 24, 1939; four children—Hester, Stephen C., Walter, and Richard.

Under Secretary of the Army.—[Vacant.]

Assistant Secretary of the Army (Research and Development).—Willis M. Hawkins, 2507 Spencer Road, McLean, Va., 22101.

Assistant Secretary of the Army (Installations and Logistics).—Daniel M. Luévano, 7001 Oak Forest Lane, Bethesda, Md., 20034.

Assistant Secretary of the Army (Financial Management).—[Vacant.]

Director of Civil Defense.—William P. Durkee, 3429 34th Street, 20008.

General Counsel.—Alfred B. Fitt, 3501 Macomb Street, 20016.

Chief of Public Information.—Maj. Gen. George V. Underwood, Jr., Quarters 20B, Fort Myer, Va., 22211.

Chief of Legislative Liaison.—Maj. Gen. Frederic W. Boye, Jr., Quarters 22A, Fort Myer, Va., 22211.

Administrative Assistant.—James C. Cook, 5403 Bradley Boulevard, Bethesda, Md., 20014.

OFFICE OF THE SECRETARY OF THE ARMY

Executive.—Col. George S. Blanchard, 5931 Lemon Road, McLean, Va., 22101.

Military Assistants to the Secretary of the Army.—Col. Clayton M. Gompf, 1801 Hamilton Drive, Fairfax, Va., 22030; Maj. Philo A. Hutcheson, 2310 Chester Drive, Annandale, Va., 22003.

Military Aide to the Secretary of the Army.—Lt. Col. Frank R. Pagnotta, 4226 Dalmatian Drive, McLean, Va., 22101.

Personal Secretaries.—Marilyn L. Howard, 6102 27th Avenue, 20031; Hulda I. Strand, 3411 P Street, 20007.

OFFICE OF THE UNDER SECRETARY OF THE ARMY

Immediate Office of the Under Secretary:

 Executive.—Col. Paul V. Hannah, 2924 South Grant Street, Arlington, Va., 22202.

 Military Aide.—Maj. Charles B. Tharp, 7817 Bristow Drive, Annandale, Va., 22003.

 Secretaries.—Virginia L. Wright, 1624 Kenwood Avenue, Alexandria, Va., 22302; Dolores M. Goode, 611 North Pickett Street, Alexandria, Va., 22304.

Deputy Under Secretary of the Army (Manpower & Reserve Forces).—Arthur W. Allen, Jr., 4000 Massachusetts Avenue, 20016.

 Executive.—Col. Joseph L. Knowlton, 2239 North Quincy, Arlington, Va., 22207.

Deputy Under Secretary of the Army (Personnel Management).— Roy K. Davenport, 230 G Street SW., 20024.

 Executive.—Col. Paul C. Bender, 5306 Juliet Street, Springfield, Va., 22151.

Deputy Under Secretary of the Army (International Affairs).—John M. Steadman, 4820 Upton Street, 20016.

 Executive.—Col. John P. Sheffey III, 1313 Kingston Avenue, Alexandria, Va., 22302.

Special Assistant.—Francis X. Plant, 3218 Ravensworth Place, Alexandria, Va., 22302.

Special Assistant.—C. Owen Smith, 37 West Irving Street, Chevy Chase, Md., 20015.

OFFICE OF THE ASSISTANT SECRETARY OF THE ARMY
(INSTALLATIONS AND LOGISTICS)

Deputy Assistant Secretary (Logistics).—A. Tyler Port, 6515 Hillmead Road, Bethesda, Md., 21811.

Deputy Assistant Secretary (Installations).—Eugene H. Merrill, 615 Juniper Lane, Falls Church, Va., 22040.

 Executive.—Col. Walter J. Woolwine, 307 Crown View Drive, Alexandria, Va., 22300.

Assistant Executive (Military Assistant).—CWO Philip W. Uebelein, 1408 28th Street South, Arlington, Va., 21917.

Assistant Executive (Logistics).—Lt. Col. Jefferson T. Holman, 2409 South Inge Street, Arlington, Va., 22202.

Assistant Executive (Installations).—Col. Douglas K. Blue, 6208 18th Road North, Arlington, Va., 22200.

Special Assistant for Planning.—William F. Lipman, 602 E Street SE., 20003.

Director of Procurement.—Brig. Gen. John A. Goshorn, 4524 LaSalle Avenue, Alexandria, Va., 22304.

Director of Supply and Maintenance.—Joseph C. Zengerle, Jr., 303 South Frederick Avenue, Gaithersburg, Md., 20760.

Director of Military Construction and Real Property.—Col. Robert C. Pfeil, 314 Churchill Road, McLean, Va., 22101.

Director of Programs and Requirements.—Vincent P. Huggard, 826 Wayne Avenue, Silver Spring, Md., 20900.

Secretary.—Penelope Dammann, 800 4th Street SW., 20024.

OFFICE OF THE ASSISTANT SECRETARY OF THE ARMY
(FINANCIAL MANAGEMENT)

Deputy Assistant Secretary.—John H. Fitch, 30 West Grove Drive, Alexandria, Va., 22307.

Executive.—Col. Robert A. Martin, 4901 Seminary Road, Alexandria, Va., 22311.

Assistant Executive.—CWO S. T. Stagg III, 5436 North Carlyn Springs Road, Arlington, Va., 22203.

Chief, Fiscal and Accounting Policy.—W. Russell Roane, 1718 North Inglewood Street, Arlington, Va., 22205.

Chief, Budget and Funding.—Theodore A. Janssen, 10515 DeNeane Road, Silver Spring, Md., 20903.

Chief, Office of Programming.—Lt. Col. Marvin S. Weinstein, 5209 Ravensworth Road, Springfield, Va., 22151.
Chief, Office of Management Information.—Robert E. McKelvey, 7405 Fairfax Parkway, Alexandria, Va., 22312.
Chief, Office of Working Capital Funds.—James C. Jenkins, 5934 Lemon Road, McLean, Va., 22101.
Special Assistant for Operations Research.—Dr. Wilbur B. Payne, 6801 Buttermere Lane, Bethesda, Md., 20034.
Special Assistant for Aviation.—Col. Jack K. Norris, 1907 Felton Lane, Alexandria, Va., 22308.
Secretaries.—Mrs. Mildred V. Tanner, 3507 N Street, 20007; Mrs. Constance G. Bender, 5306 Juliet Street, Springfield, Va., 22151.

OFFICE OF THE DIRECTOR OF CIVIL DEFENSE

Secretaries to the Director.—Eloise Harris, 200 South Jackson Street, Arlington, Va., 22204; Betty Lou Stone, 4025 Davis Place, 20007.
Executive Assistant.—Robert E. Young, 5142 33d Street North, Arlington, Va., 22207.
Special Assistant to the Director.—George W. Mundy, 3801 24th Street North, Arlington, Va., 22207.
Deputy Directors of Civil Defense.—Hubert A. Schon, 984 Ramsgate Terrace, Alexandria, Va., 22309; Jane F. Hanna, 4000 Massachusetts Avenue, 20016.
General Counsel.—Charles M. Manning, 301 Old Courthouse Road NE., Vienna, Va., 22801.
Assistant Director of Civil Defense (Policy and Programs).—Joseph Romm, 6705 Pyle Road, Bethesda, Md., 20014.
Assistant Director of Civil Defense (Plans and Operations).—John W. McConnell, 6714 Greeley Boulevard, Springfield, Va., 22150.
Assistant Director of Civil Defense (Technical Services).—Ren F. Read, 1415 Pinecastle Road, Falls Church, Va., 22403.
Assistant Director of Civil Defense (Public Information) (acting).—Charles J. Arnold, 2365 North Quincy Street, Arlington, Va., 22207.
Assistant Director of Civil Defense (Management).—Robert E. Holt, 408 Bay Tree Lane, Barcroft Woods, Falls Church, Va., 22041.
Comptroller.—Troy V. McKinney, 4 Tansey Drive, Falls Church, Va., 22042.
Assistant Director of Civil Defense (Research).—Walmer E. Strope, 1514 Half Moon Drive, Falls Church, Va., 22044.
Assistant Director of Civil Defense (Industrial Participation).—Virgil L. Couch, 4906 28th Street North, Arlington, Va., 22207.
Assistant Director of Civil Defense (Technical Liasion).—Gerald R. Gallagher, 2937 W Street SE., 20020.

OFFICE OF THE ASSISTANT SECRETARY OF THE ARMY
(RESEARCH AND DEVELOPMENT)

Deputy Assistant Secretary.—Charles L. Poor, 5001 Nahant Street, 20016.
Assistant for Communications and Avionics Systems.—Howard P. Gates, Jr., 217 Waterway Drive, Falls Church, Va., 22044.
Assistant for Programs.—Charles R. Woodside, 3607 Dorado Court, Fairfax, Va., 22030.
Assistant for Research.—Col. Kary C. Emerson, 2511 North Jefferson, Arlington, Va., 22207.
Assistant for Guided Missiles.—Lt. Col. John B. Bond, 4124 25th Place North, Arlington, Va., 22207.
Executive and Assistant for Air Mobility.—Col. Allen M. Burdett, Jr., 1427 Cavalier Corridor, Falls Church, Va., 22044.
Assistant Executive and Assistant for Infantry Weapons and Vehicles.—Lt. Col. Stanley Y. Kennedy, 209 Elizabeth Drive, McLean, Va., 22101.
Secretary.—Mrs. Thelma P. Leach, 1801 North Inglewood, Arlington, Va., 22205.

OFFICE OF THE GENERAL COUNSEL

Deputy General Counsel.—R. Tenney Johnson, 424 Magruder Mill Court, Bethesda, Md., 20034.
Assistant General Counsel.—Bruce M. Docherty, 1011 Arlington Boulevard, Arlington, Va., 22209.
Chief, Civil Functions.—Richard A. Hertzler, 1915 Anesbury Lane, Alexandria, Va., 22308.

OFFICE OF THE CHIEF OF LEGISLATIVE LIAISON

Deputy Chief.—Brig. Gen. Howard W. Penney, 515 Robinson Court, Alexandria, Va., 22302.
Assistant Chief.—Col. Roger M. Currier, 172 Normandy Hill Drive, Alexandria, Va., 22304.
Executive.—Lt. Col. Randall Kelly, 1426 21st Street South, Arlington, Va., 22202.
Chief, Plans and Projects Division.—Col. Howard D. Balliett, 4404 Rupert Street, McLean, Va., 22101.
Chief, Legislative Division.—Col. Richard deF. Cleverly, 2800 South Ives Street, Arlington, Va., 22202.
Chief, Congressional Liaison and Inquiry Division.—Col. Ben L. Anderson, 3166 20th Street North, Arlington, Va., 22201.
Chief, Congressional Investigations Division.—Col. Roy H. Steele, 2920 Dartmouth Road, Alexandria, Va., 22314.
Chief, Special Operations Division.—Col. Rex R. Sage, 1808 South Lynn Street, Arlington, Va., 22202.

OFFICE OF THE ADMINISTRATIVE ASSISTANT TO THE SECRETARY OF THE ARMY

Deputy Administrative Assistant.—John G. Connell, Jr., 302 Clover Way, Alexandria, Va., 22314.
Assistant for Management.—Roswell M. Yingling, 213 South Royal Street, Alexandria, Va., 22314.
Coordinator for Headquarters Services—Washington.—Everett L. Butler, 1017 Allison Street, Alexandria, Va., 22302.
Director, Defense Telephone Service—Washington.—James T. Bedsole, 3906 Stratford Lane, Alexandria, Va., 22308.
Director, Defense Supply Service—Washington.—Chelsea L. Henson, 106 Cedar Lane, Fairfax, Va., 22030.
Director, Civilian Employees Security Program.—Beatty R. Julien, 5801 33d Street, 20015.

ARMY STAFF

Chief of Staff, United States Army.—Gen. Harold K. Johnson, Quarters 1, Fort Myer, Arlington, Va., 22211.
Vice Chief of Staff, United States Army.—Gen. Creighton W. Abrams, Jr., Quarters 8, Fort Lesley J. McNair, 20315.
Secretary of the General Staff.—Maj. Gen. Vernon P. Mock, Quarters 21A, Fort Myer, Arlington, Va., 22211.
Chairman, General Staff Committee on Army National Guard Policy.—Maj. Gen. Francis W. Billado, 864 South Prospect Street, Burlington, Vt., 05401.
Chairman, General Staff Committee on Army Reserve Policy.—Maj. Gen. J. W. Kaine, 208 Bengeyfield Drive North, East Williston, Long Island, N.Y., 14449.
Special Assistant to the Chief of Staff for Special Warfare Activities.—Maj. Gen. William R. Peers, 1512 22d Street South, Arlington, Va., 22202.
Director of Special Studies.—Lt. Gen. Charles H. Bonesteel III, Quarters 16B, Fort Myer, Va., 22211.

Secretary of the General Staff.—Continued

Director of Army Programs.—Maj. Gen. Frank W. Norris, 2909 Garfield Terrace NW., 20008.

Special Assistant to the Chief of Staff for Army Information and Data Systems.—Maj. Gen. James E. Landrum, Jr., 500 Sleepy Hollow Road, Falls Church, Va., 22042.

Director of Coordination and Analysis.—Brig. Gen. Charles A. Corcoran, 305 Rose Lane, Falls Church, Va., 22042.

Deputy Secretary of the General Staff (Staff Services) and White House Liaison Officer.—Col. D. H. McGovern, 5903 Essex Avenue, Springfield, Va., 22150.

Deputy Secretary of the General Staff (Staff Action Control).—Col. Richard M. Lee, 5905 Engle Drive, McLean, Va., 22101.

Deputy Chief of Staff for Military Operations.—Lt. Gen. Bruce Palmer, Jr., Quarters 2, Fort Myer, Arlington, Va., 22211.

Chief of Communications—Electronics.—Maj. Gen. David P. Gibbs, Route 1, Box 431, McLean, Va., 22101.

Chief of Military History.—Brig. Gen. Hal C. Pattison, 703 Glenbrook Road, Fairfax, Va., 22030.

Deputy Chief of Staff for Personnel.—Lt. Gen. J. L. Richardson, Quarters 8, Fort Myer, Arlington, Va., 22211.

Director, United States Women's Army Corps.—Col. Emily C. Gorman, 4764 Reservoir Road, 20007.

The Adjutant General.—Maj. Gen. Joe C. Lambert, 1400 South Joyce Street, Arlington, Va., 22202.

The Surgeon General.—Lt. Gen. Leonard D. Heaton, 1 Main Drive, Walter Reed Army Medical Center, 20012.

Chief of Chaplains.—Maj. Gen. Charles E. Brown, Jr., 5005 14th Street North, Arlington, Va., 22205.

The Provost Marshal General.—Maj. Gen. Carl C. Turner, 6804 Floyd Avenue, Springfield, Va., 22150.

Chief of Personnel Operations.—Maj. Gen. Julian A. Wilson, 6935 Pinetree Terrace, Falls Church, Va., 22041.

Deputy Chief of Staff for Logistics.—Lt. Gen. L. J. Lincoln, Quarters 5, Fort Myer, Arlington, Va., 22211.

Chief of Engineers.—Lt. Gen. W. K. Wilson, Jr., Quarters 1, Fort Belvoir, Va. 22060.

Chief of Support Services.—Col. John W. Hanger, 1711 Fairwood Lane, Falls Church, Va., 22042.

Comptroller of the Army.—Lt. Gen. Robert Hackett, Quarters 17, Fort Myer, Arlington, Va., 22211.

Director of Army Budget.—Maj. Gen. B. F. Taylor, Quarters 28, Fort Myer, Arlington, Va., 22211.

Chief of Finance.—Maj. Gen. William C. Haneke, 840 South Dickerson Street, Apt. 311, Arlington, Va., 22204.

Chief, U.S. Army Audit Agency.—Maj. Gen. Thomas J. Sands, 2615 O Street, 20007. *Chief of Research and Development.*—Lt. Gen. William W. Dick, Jr., Quarters 12A, Fort Myer, Arlington, Va., 22211.

Chief, Office of Reserve Components.—Lt. Gen. W. H. S. Wright, Quarters 15A, Fort Myer, Arlington, Va., 22211.

Chief, Army Reserve.—Maj. Gen. William J. Sutton, River House, B611, 1111 Army–Navy Drive, Arlington, Va., 22202.

Assistant Chief of Staff for Force Development.—Lt. Gen. Ben Harrell, Quarters 11B, Fort Myer, Arlington, Va., 22211.

Acting Assistant Chief of Staff for Intelligence.—Brig. Gen. Charles J. Denholm, 809 Clovercrest Drive, Alexandria, Va., 22314.

The Judge Advocate General.—Maj. Gen. Robert H. McCaw, 4604 26th Street North, Arlington, Va., 22207.

The Inspector General.—Maj. Gen. H. Dudley Ives, 5300 Albemarle Street, 20016.

Chief, National Guard Bureau.—Maj. Gen. Winston P. Wilson, 4311 Loyola Avenue, Alexandria, Va., 22304.

Chief of Information.—Maj. Gen. G. V. Underwood, Jr., Quarters 20–B, Fort Myer, Arlington, Va., 22211.

HEADQUARTERS, U.S. ARMY SECURITY AGENCY
Arlington, Va., 22212

Chief.—Maj. Gen. William H. Craig, Quarters 1, Arlington Hall Station, Arlington, Va., 22212.
Deputy Chief.—Brig. Gen. Dayton W. Eddy, 7739 Dockser Terrace, Falls Church, Va., 22041.

HEADQUARTERS, U.S. CONTINENTAL ARMY COMMAND
Fort Monroe, Va., 23351

Commanding General.—Gen. Paul L. Freeman, Jr.
Deputy Commanding General.—Lt. Gen. Harvey H. Fischer.
Chief of Staff.—Maj. Gen. George T. Duncan.
USCONARC Liaison Officer (The Pentagon, Washington, D.C., 20310).—Col. J. C. Sandlin.
Continental U.S. Armies and Military District of Washington, U.S. Army:
    First U.S. Army (Hq. Governors Island, N.Y., 10004).—Lt. Gen. Thomas W. Dunn.
    Second U.S. Army (Hq. Fort George G. Meade, Md., 20755).—Lt. Gen. William F. Train.
    Third U.S. Army (Hq. Fort McPherson, Ga., 20330).—Lt. Gen. Charles W. G. Rich.
    Fourth U.S. Army (Hq. Fort Sam Houston, Tex., 78234).—Lt. Gen. Robert W. Colglazier, Jr.
    Fifth U.S. Army (Hq. Chicago, Ill., 60615).—Lt. Gen. Charles G. Dodge.
    Sixth U.S. Army (Hq. Presidio of San Francisco, Calif., 94129).—Lt. Gen. Frederick J. Brown.
    Military District of Washington, U.S. Army (Tempo Bldg. B, 2d and R Streets, SW., 20315.—Maj. Gen. Philip C. Wehle.

HEADQUARTERS, U.S. ARMY MATERIEL COMMAND
Washington, D.C., 20315

Commanding General.—Gen. Frank S. Besson, Jr., Quarters 9A, Fort Lesley J. McNair, 20315.
Deputy Commanding General.—Maj. Gen. William B. Bunker, 1201 South Scott Street, Arlington, Va., 22204.
Chief of Staff.—Maj. Gen. Selwyn D. Smith, Jr., 1409 Pinecastle Road, Falls Church, Va., 22043.
Deputy Commanding General for Western Operations (Oakland Army Terminal, Calif., 94129).—Brig. Gen. Raymond C. Conroy.
Major Subordinate Commands:
    U.S. Army Supply and Maintenance Command (Washington, D.C., 20315):
        Commanding General.—Lt. Gen. Jean E. Engler, Quarters 27A, Fort Myer, Va., 22211.
        Deputy Commanding General.—Maj. Gen. Robert C. Kyser, 4764 33d Street North, Arlington, Va., 22207.
    U.S. Army Mobility Command (Center Line, Mich., 48090).—Maj. Gen. William J. Lapsley.
    U.S. Army Missile Command (Redstone Arsenal, Huntsville, Ala., 35809).—Maj. Gen. John G. Zierdt.
    U.S. Army Weapons Command (Rock Island, Ill., 61202).—Brig. Gen. Roland B. Anderson.
    U.S. Army Munitions Command (Dover, N.J., 07801).—Maj. Gen. Floyd A. Hansen.
    U.S. Army Electronics Command (Fort Monmouth, N.J., 07703).—Maj. Gen. Frank W. Moorman.
    U.S. Army Test and Evaluation Command (Aberdeen Proving Ground, Md., 21005).—Maj. Gen. James W. Sutherland, Jr.

HEADQUARTERS, U.S. ARMY COMBAT DEVELOPMENTS COMMAND
Fort Belvoir, Va., 22060

Commanding General.—Lt. Gen. Dwight E. Beach.
Deputy Commanding General.—Maj. Gen. Charles Billingslea.
Chairman, Advanced Tactics Project.—Maj. Gen. Thomas H. Lipscomb.
Chief of Staff.—Brig. Gen. George B. Pickett, Jr.
USACDC Liaison Officer (The Pentagon, Washington, D.C., 20310).—Lt. Col.
Eugene C. Prather.

HEADQUARTERS, U.S. ARMY STRATEGIC COMMUNICATIONS COMMAND
Washington, D.C., 20315

Commanding General.—Maj. Gen. Richard J. Meyer, 860 South Greenbrier, Apt.
619, Arlington, Va., 22204.
Deputy Commander.—Col. Wallace M. Lauterbach, 5125 37th Street North,
Arlington, Va., 22207.
Chief of Staff.—Col. Lawrence W. Bengel, 120 Longview Drive, Alexandria, Va.,
22314.

HEADQUARTERS, U.S. ARMY INTELLIGENCE CORPS COMMAND
Fort Holabird, Md., 21219

Commanding General.—Maj. Gen. Charles F. Leonard, Jr.
Deputy Commander.—Col. Bernard P. Major.
Chief of Staff.—Col. Charles R. Etzler.
USAINTCC Liaison Officer (The Pentagon, Washington, D.C., 20310).—Maj.
A. A. Rickert, Jr.

UNITED STATES MILITARY ACADEMY
West Point, N.Y., 10996

Superintendent.—Maj. Gen. James B. Lampert.
Commandant of Cadets.—Brig. Gen. Richard P. Scott.

DEPARTMENT OF THE ARMY BOARDS, EXEMPTED STATIONS, MILITARY MISSIONS, AND COMMISSIONS

The following boards, exempted stations, military missions, and commissions
are under the jurisdiction of the authority indicated after their respective names:

Title	*Responsible Authority*
Army Board for Correction of Military Records.	Under Secretary of the Army.
Army Council of Review Boards	Under Secretary of the Army.
Beach Erosion Board	Chief of Engineers.
Board of Commissioners, United States Soldiers' Home.	Secretary of the Army.
Board of Engineers for Rivers and Harbors.	Chief of Engineers.
Military Missions	Deputy Chief of Staff for Military Operations.
Mississippi River Commission	Chief of Engineers.
National Board for the Promotion of Rifle Practice.	Assistant Secretary of the Army (Financial Management).
United States Military Academy, West Point, N.Y.	Assistant Chief of Staff for Force Development.

DEPARTMENT OF THE NAVY

Pentagon Building, 20350. Phone, OXford 5-3131 (Code 11)

PAUL HENRY NITZE, Secretary of the Navy (3120 Woodley Road, 20008), was sworn into office on November 27, 1963; born in Amhurst, Mass., on January 16, 1907, the son of Anina and William A. Nitze; graduated from Harvard, B.A. degree, cum laude, 1928; served as Vice President, Dillon Read & Co., investment brokers, New York, 1928–37 and 1939–40; President, P. H. Nitze & Co., Inc., 1938–39; Financial Director, Office of the Coordinator of Inter-American Affairs, 1941–42; Chief, Metals and Minerals Branch, Board of Economic Warfare, 1942–43; Director, Foreign Procurement and Development Branch, Foreign Economic Administration, 1943–44; from 1944–46 served as Vice Chairman of the U.S. Strategic Bombing Survey, for which service was awarded Medal of Merit by President Truman; Deputy Director, Office of International Trade Policy, Department of State, 1946–48; Deputy to Assistant Secretary of State for Economic Affairs, 1948–49; Deputy (1949–50) and then Director (1950–53), Policy Planning Staff, Department of State; served concurrently as President, Foreign Service Educational Foundation, and Associate of the Washington Center of Foreign Policy Research of the School of Advanced International Studies, The Johns Hopkins University, Washington, D.C., 1953–61; in January 1961 was appointed Assistant Secretary of Defense (International Security Affairs); married to the former Phyllis Pratt; they have four children—Heidi, Peter, William II, and Phyllis Anina.

Under Secretary of the Navy.—Kenneth E. BeLieu, 413 West Grove Boulevard, Alexandria, Va., 22307.
Assistant Secretary of the Navy (Financial Management).—Victor M. Longstreet, 3337 Reservoir Road, 20007.
Assistant Secretary of the Navy (Research and Development).—Robert W. Morse, 2646 South June Street, Arlington, Va., 22202.
Assistant Secretary of the Navy (Installations and Logistics).—Graeme C. Bannerman, 3506 T Street NW., 20007.
The Special Assistant to the Secretary of the Navy.—Howard W. Merrill, 501 Wyngate Road, Timonium, Md., 21093.

OFFICE OF THE SECRETARY OF THE NAVY

Naval Aide and Executive Assistant to the Secretary of the Navy.—Capt. E. R. Zumwalt, Jr., USN, 2708 Pickett Court, Annandale, Va., 22003.
Marine Corps Aide to the Secretary of the Navy.—Col. Ross T. Dwyer, Jr., USMC, Apt. 413, 1850 Columbia Pike, Arlington, Va., 22204.
Administrative Aide to the Secretary of the Navy.—Cdr. Richard E. Nicholson, USN, 7727 Heritage Drive, Annandale, Va., 22002.
Special Assistant for Public Affairs.—Cdr. William Thompson, USN, 1900 Devine Street, McLean, Va., 22101.
Special Assistant to the Secretary of the Navy.—David M. Clinard, 6814 Meadow Lane, Chevy Chase, Md., 20015.
Special Assistant for Counsel.—Cdr. Horace B. Robertson, USN, 3313 North Kensington Street, Arlington, Va., 22207.
Assistant for Office Management.—Lt. Lucy E. Zierdt (W), USN, 955 South Columbus Street, Arlington, Va., 22204.
Assistant for Administration.—Lt. R. W. Cavin, USN, 1330 South Columbus Street, Arlington, Va., 22204.
Private Secretary to the Secretary of the Navy.—Mrs. Margaret S. Martin, 1207 Powhatan Street, Alexandria, Va., 22314.

OFFICE OF THE UNDER SECRETARY OF THE NAVY

Naval Aide and Executive Assistant to the Under Secretary of the Navy.—Capt. David H. Bagley, USN, Old Court House Road, Vienna, Va., 22180.

Marine Corps Aide and Special Assistant to the Under Secretary of the Navy.—Col. William C. Chip, USMC, 1502 North Ivanhoe Street, Arlington, Va., 22205.

Personal Aide to the Under Secretary of the Navy.—Lt. Col. Patrick J. Hagarty, USMC, 612 Rose Lane, Annandale, Va., 22003.

Special Assistant and Aide to the Under Secretary of the Navy.—Cdr. John N. Longfield, USN, 6631 JoAllen Drive, Falls Church, Va., 22044.

Special Assistant for Civilian Personnel Requirements.—William K. Bassett, 7409 Beverly Road, Bethesda, Md., 20014.

Special Assistant for Legal Matters.—Capt. Robert H. Keehn, USN, 5905 South Maxwell Court, McLean, Va., 22101.

Special Assistant for Civilian Personnel Matters.—Charles R. Peck, 4917 Rockwood Parkway, 20016.

Special Assistant for Naval Personnel Matters.—Cdr. Albert M. Sackett, USN, 1801 Wesleyan Street, Vienna, Va., 22180.

Special Assistant for Civilian Management Training and Executive Development.—Frederick C. Dyer, 4509 Cumberland Avenue, Chevy Chase, Md., 20015.

Special Assistant to the Under Secretary of the Navy.—Capt. John B. Cline, USN, 1005 West Braddock Road, Alexandria, Va., 22302.

Special Assistant to the Under Secretary of the Navy.—Robert A. Carl, 1301 South Scott Street, Arlington, Va., 22204.

Assistant for Administration.—Lt. (jg) Clyde Wilson, USN, 815 Gordon Avenue, Falls Church, Va., 22046.

Private Secretary to the Under Secretary of the Navy.—Mrs. Louise L. Yarbrough, 1538 44th Street, 20007.

OFFICE OF THE ASSISTANT SECRETARY OF THE NAVY
(FINANCIAL MANAGEMENT)

Naval Aide and Executive Assistant to the Assistant Secretary of the Navy (Financial Management).—Cdr. James W. Montgomery, USN, 3606 North Nelson Street, Arlington, Va., 2207.

Marine Corps Aide to the Assistant Secretary of the Navy (Financial Management).—Lt. Col Robert T. Bell, USMC, Building T-606, South Post, Fort Myer, Arlington, Va., 22208.

Special Assistant to the Assistant Secretary of the Navy (Financial Management).—Harold R. Spiegel, 3702 Corey Place, 20016.

Private Secretary to the Assistant Secretary of the Navy (Financial Management.)—Elois S. Texter, 11714 Highview Avenue, Wheaton, Md., 20902.

OFFICE OF THE ASSISTANT SECRETARY OF THE NAVY
(RESEARCH AND DEVELOPMENT)

Naval Aide and Executive Assistant to the Assistant Secretary of the Navy (Research and Development).—Capt. Earl P. Yates, USN, 1818 South Lynn Street, Arlington, Va., 22202.

Marine Corps Aide to the Assistant Secretary of the Navy (Research and Development).—Maj. William E. H. Fitch, USMC, 7431 Murillo Street, Springfield, Va., 22151.

Special Assistants to the Assistant Secretary of the Navy (Research and Development).—Cdr. J. Edward Snyder, Jr., USN, 1712 Glenbrook Road, Mantua Hills, Fairfax, Va., 22030; Cdr. Theodore C. Lonnquest, Jr., USN, 4214 Thornapple Street, Chevy Chase, Md., 20015; Dr. William P. Raney, 14 Wilton Road, Alexandria, Va., 22310.

Private Secretary to the Assistant Secretary of the Navy (Research and Development).—Janice S. Gemmell, 3724 Columbia Pike, Arlington, Va., 22204.

OFFICE OF THE ASSISTANT SECRETARY OF THE NAVY
(INSTALLATIONS AND LOGISTICS)

Naval Aide and Executive Assistant to the Assistant Secretary of the Navy (Installations and Logistics).—Capt. Brian McCauley, USN, 2501 49th Street, 20007.

Aide and Special Assistant to the Assistant Secretary of the Navy (Installations and Logistics).—Cdr. William J. Robinson (SC), USN, 5002 Richenbacker Avenue, Alexandria, Va., 22304.

Marine Corps Aide/Liaison Officer to the Assistant Secretary of the Navy (Installations and Logistics).—[Vacant.]

Director of Installations and Facilities.—William J. Gregg, 12604 Pentenville Drive, Silver Spring, Md., 20904.

Director of Procurement.—M. E. Jones, 4221 Panarama Court, McLean, Va., 22101.

Director of Equal Employment Opportunity.—G. P. Clark, 3105 Naylor Road SE., 20020.

Assistant for Congressional Liaison.—Bernard L. Flanagan, 7419 Keystone Lane, Forestville, Md., 20028.

Special Assistant (Small Business).—Moris Questal, 1108 North Belgrade Road, Silver Spring, Md., 20902.

Administrative Officer to the Assistant Secretary of the Navy (Installations and Logistics).—CWO Donald A. Aemmer, USN, 134 Fairview Drive, Fairfax, Va., 22030.

Private Secretary to the Assistant Secretary of the Navy (Installations and Logistics).—[Vacant.]

OFFICE OF THE SPECIAL ASSISTANT TO THE SECRETARY OF THE NAVY

Military Assistant to The Special Assistant to the Secretary of the Navy.—Cdr. H. D. Train II, USN, 5526 39th Street, 20015.

Management Assistants.—Samuel V. Moore, 4104 Pine Ridge Drive, Annandale, Va., 22003; Allan G. Patterson, 2420 Kelford Lane, Bowie, Md., 20715; John Strohlein, 720 Carper Drive, McLean, Va., 22101.

Secretary to The Special Assistant to the Secretary of the Navy.—Mrs. Jane C. Curtin, 4000 Massachusetts Avenue, 20016.

DEPARTMENT OF THE NAVY STAFF OFFICES

ADMINISTRATIVE OFFICE, NAVY DEPARTMENT
Room 0014, Main Navy Building

The Administrative Officer, Navy Department.—John H. Walter, 10800 Montrose Avenue, Garrett Park, Md., 20766.

Staff Assistant.—W. J. Barrett, 103 West Maple Street, Alexandria, Va., 22301.

Comptroller.—Anthony Yannella, 6301 31st Street North, Arlington, Va., 22207.

Director, Departmental Civilian Personnel Division.—E. A. Wiggenhorn, 1414 Upshur Street, 20011.

Director, Departmental Facilities and Services Division.—S. O. Goode, Jr., 2202 Sorrel Street, McLean, Va., 22101.

Director, Administrative Procedures Division.—Robert S. Hagan, 4448 20th Road North, Arlington, Va., 22209.

Navy Department Provost Marshal.—Col. John H. Jones, USMC, 4854 North Rock Spring Road, Arlington, Va., 22207.

BOARD FOR CORRECTION OF NAVAL RECORDS
Room 4417, Arlington Annex

Chairman.—Jesse S. Eberdt, 2607 North Quincy Street, Arlington, Va., 22207.

Recorder.—Charles E. Curley, 2827 North Underwood Street, Arlington, Va., 22213.

BOARD OF DECORATIONS AND MEDALS
Room G-704, Arlington Annex

Senior Member.—Col. James N. Cupp, USMC, 33 Sharon Road, Triangle, Va., 22172.
Recorder and Member.—Cdr. M. M. Arthurs, USN, 4023 25th Road North, Arlington, Va., 22207.

NAVY COUNCIL OF PERSONNEL BOARDS
Room G-074A, Arlington Annex

Director.—Capt. C. W. Travis, USN, 24 Wardour Drive, Annapolis, Md., 21401.
Deputy Director.—Capt. G. T. Shirley, USN, 3812 23d Street North, Arlington, Va., 22207.

NAVAL EXAMINING BOARD (LINE)
Room G-077, Arlington Annex

President.—Capt. C. W. Travis, USN, 24 Wardour Drive, Annapolis, Md., 21401.
Recorder.—Lt. Cdr. William L. McNamara, USN, 11500 Elkin Street, Wheaton, Md., 20902.

NAVAL PHYSICAL DISABILITY REVIEW BOARD
Room G-077, Arlington Annex

President.—Capt. C. W. Travis, USN, 24 Wardour Drive, Annapolis, Md., 21401.
Deputy President.—Maj. Gen. John H. Masters, USMC, 2400 North Lincoln Street, Arlington, Va., 22207.
Recorder.—Lt. Cdr. William L. McNamara, USN, 11500 Elkin Street, Wheaton Md., 20902.

NAVAL CLEMENCY BOARD
Room G-703, Arlington Annex

Senior Member.—Capt. C. W. Travis, USN, 24 Wardour Drive, Annapolis, Md., 21401.
Recorder.—Alan W. Langworthy, 35 Wellington Lane, Alexandria, Va., 22308.

NAVY DISCHARGE REVIEW BOARD
Room G-709, Arlington Annex

President.—Capt. D. W. Bowman, USN, 3548 North Valley Street, Arlington, Va., 22207.
Secretary.—Cdr. E. I. Carson, USNR, 375 South George Mason Drive, Arlington, Va., 22204.

OFFICE OF MANAGEMENT INFORMATION
Room 4E777, Pentagon Building

Director.—Rear Adm. H. N. Wallin, CEC, USN, 9504 Columbia Boulevard, Silver Spring, Md., 20910.
Executive Assistant.—Col. David M. McFarland, USMC, 117 Skyview Drive, Alexandria, Va., 22309.
Director, Systems Development Division.—Earl H. Kuhl, 1309 Grass Hill Terrace, Falls Church, Va., 22044.
Director, Progress Appraisal Division.—Houston W. McClary, 7806 Jay Miller Drive, Falls Church, Va., 22041.
Director, Systems Automation Division.—W. Henry Hill, 1 Daybreak Court, Alexandria, Va., 22306.

Department of the Navy 471

OFFICE OF THE COMPTROLLER
Room 4E748, Pentagon Building

Comptroller of the Navy.—Victor M. Longstreet, 3337 Reservoir Road, 20007.
Deputy Comptroller.—Rear Adm. M. A. Hirsch, USN, 2625 South June Street, Arlington, Va., 22202.
Assistant Comptroller, Director of Budget and Reports.—Rear Adm. F. G. Bennett, USN, 3709 Cameron Mills Road, Alexandria, Va., 22305.
Assistant Comptroller, Accounting and Disbursing.—Philip L. O'Connell, 6218 Green Tree Road, Bethesda, Md., 20034.
Assistant Comptroller, Field Activities.—Capt. Francis B. Grubb, SC, USN, 646 Sleepy Hollow Road, Falls Church, Va., 22042.
Auditor General of the Navy.—Capt. C. M. Grassino, SC, USN, 5908 Maxwell Court, South, McLean, Va., 22101.
Counsel for Office of the Navy Comptroller.—Dr. Lawrence E. Chermak, 2725 29th Street, 20008.

OFFICE OF THE GENERAL COUNSEL
Room 2034, Main Navy Building

General Counsel.—Meritt H. Steger, 745 Morningside Drive, Fairfax, Va., 22030.
Deputy General Counsel.—Albert H. Stein, 8007 Whittier Boulevard, Bethesda, Md., 20034; John J. Phelan, Jr., 12629 Safety Turn, Belair Estates, Bowie, Md., 20715; Stanley P. Hebert, 4811 Blagden Avenue, 20011.
Assistants to the General Counsel.—Albert C. Kornblum, 1736 Columbia Road, 20009; George W. Markey, Jr., 8503 Carroll Avenue, Silver Spring, Md., 20912; Charles Goodwin, 3047 Porter Street, 20008.
Counsel for Bureaus and Offices.—Naval Weapons—Frederick Sass, Jr., 10730 River Road, Potomac, Md., 20854; Military Sea Transportation Service—Wilbur L. Morse, 3408 North George Mason Drive, Arlington, Va., 22207; Personnel—George E. Mackey, 1300 Locust Road, 20012; Ships—Samuel Pinn, Jr., 6677 32d Street, 20015; Supplies and Accounts—William Sellman, Route 5, Cedar Lane, Oakdale Park, Vienna, Va., 22180; Yards and Docks—Harold Gold, 7012 Richard Drive, Bethesda, Md., 20034; Office of the Comptroller—Lawrence E. Chermak, 2725 29th Street, 20008; Office of Naval Research—D. Allen Pace, 6405 Brookside Drive, Alexandria, Va., 22312; Marine Corps—Robert S. Hatch, 8711 Brierly Court, Chevy Chase, Md., 20015; European Branch, OGC—Donald M. Stearns, 1 Grosvenor Gardens, Mews North, London SW. 1, England; New York Branch OGC—James C. Adams, 430 East 20th Street, New York City.

OFFICE OF INDUSTRIAL RELATIONS
Room 222, Pentagon Annex Number 1

Chief of Industrial Relations.—Rear Adm. R. L. Moore, Jr., USN, Amberly, R.F.D. 2, Box 31 Annapolis, Md., 21401.
Deputy Chief of Industrial Relations.—Capt. P. A. Gisvold, USN, 9515 Justine Drive, Annandale, Va., 22003.
Director, Administrative Division.—Daniel H. Bonham, 447 Vista Drive, Falls Church, Va., 22041.
Director, Training and Development Division.—Ray A. Crosby, 5828 Doris Drive, Dowden Terrace, Alexandria, Va., 22311.
Director, Safety Division.—Capt. George T. Swiggum, CEC, USN, 10201 Grosvenor Place, Rockville, Md., 20852.
Director, Personnel Studies Division.—Margaret E. Moore, 1109 Cross Drive, Alexandria, Va., 22302.
Assistant Chief of Industrial Relations (Employment).—William E. Gerow, 810 Hillsboro Drive, Kemp Mill Estates, Silver Spring, Md., 20902.
Assistant Chief of Industrial Relations (Wage and Classification).—Thomas L. Gardner, 612 Gordon Street, Falls Church, Va., 22041.

OFFICE OF INFORMATION
Room 4C725, Pentagon Building

Chief of Information.—Rear Adm. William P. Mack, USN, 3308 Alabama Avenue, Alexandria, Va., 22305.

Aide.—Lt. Frederic M. Clark, USN, 7304 Hogarth Avenue, North Springfield, Va., 22151.

Deputy Chief of Information.—Capt. James S. Dowdell, USN, Apt. C–1415, River House, 1600 South Joyce Street, Arlington, Va., 22202.

Plans Division.—Cdr. Robert S. Jones, USN, 8518 Lancashire Drive, North Springfield, Va., 22151.

Administrative Division.—Cdr. Jesse B. Cobb, USN, 5526 Eastbourne Drive, North Springfield, Va., 22151.

Media Relations Division.—Capt. Hardy Glenn, USN, 600 Third Street SW., 20024.

Civil Relations Division.—Capt. Jack H. Crawford, USN, 4903 Walden Drive, McLean, Va., 22101.

Internal Relations Division.—Capt. John H. Dinneen, USN, 1500 North Jackson Street, Arlington, Va., 22201.

OFFICE OF LEGISLATIVE AFFAIRS
Room 5C760, Pentagon Building

Chief of Legislative Affairs.—Rear Adm. C. B. Jones, USN, 1111 Army-Navy Drive, River House #1, Apt. C–312, Arlington, Va., 22202.

Deputy Chief of Legislative Affairs.—Capt. C. R. Kear, USN, 6303 Broad Branch Road, Chevy Chase, Md., 20015.

Executive Deputy Chief and Coordinator Congressional Relations.—Capt. John Sweeny, USN, 3512 Sterling Avenue, Alexandria, Va., 22304.

Director, Legislative Division.—Capt. M. K. Disney, USN, 608 Niblick Drive SE., Vienna, Va., 22180.

Director of Congressional Investigations.—Capt. S. E. Robbins, USN, 607 Lakeview Drive, Lake Barcroft, Falls Church, Va., 22041.

Director, Congressional Information Division.—Cdr. M. E. Michaels (W), USN, 1500 Arlington Boulevard, Arlington, Va., 22209.

Director, Special Projects.—Capt. C. R. Frazier, USN, 6615 Nevius Street, Falls Church, Va., 22041.

Administrative Officer.—Mrs. C. P. Abbott, 7307 Statecrest Drive, Annandale, Va., 22003.

OFFICE OF NAVAL PETROLEUM AND OIL SHALE RESERVES
Room 2434, Munitions Building

Director.—Capt. Kenneth C. Lovell, CEC, USN, 3948 Garrison Street, 20016.

Deputy Director and Counsel.—Cdr. Richard E. Blair, USN, 207 Elizabeth Drive, McLean, Va., 22101.

Assistant Director and Consultant Engineer.—Eugene P. Bowler, 5620 Newington Court, 20016.

OFFICE OF NAVAL RESEARCH
Room 0449, Main Navy Building

Chief of Naval Research.—Rear Adm. John K. Leydon, USN, 4512 Lowell Street, 20016.

Deputy and Assistant Chief.—Capt. Edmund J. Hoffman, USN, 3218 Leland Street, Chevy Chase, Md., 20015.

Deputy and Chief Scientist.—Dr. F. Joachim Weyl, 3025 Macomb Street, 20008.

Counsel.—D. A. Pace, 6405 Brookside Drive, Alexandria, Va., 22312.

Comptroller.—R. C. Warsing, 664 South Illinois Street, Arlington, Va., 22204.

Assistant Chief for Patents.—Capt. Jack C. Davis, USN, 4 Eppard Street, Falls Church, Va., 22040.

Assistant Chief for Research.—Capt. Winfred E. Berg, USN, 2417 Coventry Road, Alexandria, Va., 22306.

Research Director.—Dr. Sidney G. Reed, Jr., 4625 Rosedale Avenue, Bethesda, Md., 20014.

Director, Naval Applications Group.—Capt. Lewis B. Melson, USN, 1600 Cedar Park Road, Annapolis, Md., 20401.

Director, Naval Analysis Group.—Dr. Marshall C. Yovits, 805 Lamberton Drive, Silver Spring, Md., 20902.

Director, Civilian Personnel and Services Division.—E. McCrensky, 6909 Wilson Lane, Bethesda, Md., 20034.

Director, Procurement Services.—Capt. Wilbert W. Lenox, USN, 6325 19th Street North, Arlington, Va., 22205.

Director, Military Services Division.—Capt. L. B. Blocker, USN, 220 Waterway Drive, Falls Church, Va., 22044.

Director, Naval Research Laboratory.—Capt. T. B. Owen, USN, 5400 Greystone Street, Chevy Chase, Md., 20015.

Commanding Officer and Director, Naval Training Device Center.—Capt. J. K. Sloatman, Quarters, U.S. Naval Training Device Center, Port Washington, N.Y., 11050.

OFFICE OF PROGRAM APPRAISAL
Room 4D730, Pentagon Building

Director.—Rear Adm. Draper L. Kauffman, USN, 5704 Rockmere Drive, 20016.

Deputy Director.—Wells H. Thomsen, 1509 Mount Eagle Place, Alexandria, Va., 22302.

Special Assistant to the Director.—A. David Brownlie, 7717 Dockser Terrace, Falls Church, Va., 22041.

Deputy for Systems Analysis.—Dr. James R. Larkin, 1520 Barbour Road, Falls Church, Va., 22043.

Deputy for Marine Corps Matters.—Col. Perry L. Shuman, USMC, 6417 Glen Forest Drive, Falls Church, Va., 22041.

Assistant Director, Program Administration and Appraisal Division.—Capt. Harry L. Harty, USN, 1035 26th Street South, Arlington, Va., 22202.

Assistant Director, Special Studies and Objectives Division.—Capt. Gerald S. Norton, USN, 411 Lyric Lane, Falls Church, Va., 22044.

OFFICE OF THE JUDGE ADVOCATE GENERAL OF THE NAVY
Room 2E338, Pentagon Building

Judge Advocate General.—Rear Adm. Wilfred Hearn, USN, 1116 Beverly Drive, Alexandria, Va., 22302.

Deputy Judge Advocate General.—Rear Adm. Robert H. Hare, USN, 3719 Fourth Street North, Arlington, Va., 22203.

Assistant Judge Advocate General (International and Administrative Law).—Capt. Carlton F. Alm, USN, 5001 Seminary Road, Alexandria, Va., 22311.

Assistant Judge Advocate General (Personnel, Reserve and Planning).—Capt. Thomas P. Smith, Jr., USN, 624 Pulman Place, Alexandria, Va., 22305.

Assistant Judge Advocate General (Military Justice).—Capt. George F. O'Malley, USN, 4604 Dorset Avenue, Chevy Chase, Md., 20015.

Assistant for Administration.—David R. Spain, 1903 Lilac Lane, Alexandria, Va., 22308.

Director, International Law Division.—Capt. Geoffrey E. Carlisle, USN, 4224 Columbia Pike, Apt. 1A, Arlington, Va., 22204.

Director, Admiralty Division.—Capt. C. A. Blocher, USN, 8605 Thames Street, Springfield, Va., 22151.

Director, Civil Law Division.—Capt. Warren C. Kiracofe, USN, 3731 39th Street, 20016.

Director, Administrative Law Division.—Capt. Merlin H. Staring, USN, 6318 Park Street, Alexandria, Va., 22312.

Director, Litigation and Claims Division.—Capt. Gale E. Krouse, USN, 1400 South Joyce Street, Apt. A1714, Arlington, Va., 22202.

Director, Military Personnel Division.—Capt. L. L. Milano, USN, 3860 Columbia Pike, Arlington, Va., 22204.

Director, Administrative Management Division.—David R. Spain, 1903 Lilac Lane, Alexandria, Va., 22308.

Director, Naval Reserve Division.—Capt. Eugene Harmon, USNR, 4506 Mayfield Drive, Annandale, Va., 22003.

Director, Legal Assistance Division.—Cdr. James J. Cross, Jr., USNR, Merrybrook, Route No. 1, Herndon, Va., 22070.

Director, Appellate Defense Division.—Capt. Charles Timblin, USN, 3150 North Pollard Street, Arlington, Va., 22207.

Director, Appellate Government Division.—Capt. James A. Potter, USN, 4606 19th Street North, Arlington, Va., 22207.

Director, Military Justice Division.—Capt. D. M. Wheat, USN, 3119 17th Street North, Arlington, Va., 22201.

Director, Investigations Division.—Cdr. G. T. Boland, USN, 4335 Wedgewood Drive, Annandale, Va., 22003.

HEADQUARTERS, U.S. MARINE CORPS
Room 2004, Arlington Annex

Commandant.—Gen. Wallace M. Greene, Jr., USMC, Commandant's House, Eighth and I Streets SE., 20003.

Assistant Commandant.—Lt. Gen. Charles H. Hayes, USMC, Quarters 1, Marine Barracks, Eighth and I Streets, SE., 20003.

Military Secretary.—Col. James O. Appleyard, USMC, 5203 Heming Avenue, Springfield, Va., 22151.

Legislative Assistant.—Brig. Gen. William G. Thrash, USMC, 6904 Mansfield Road, Falls Church, Va., 22041.

Aide-De-Camp.—Lt. Col. Jack D. Spaulding, USMC, 1036 Byrd Drive, Fairfax, Va., 22030.

Aide-De-Camp.—Cdr. Mark G. Tremaine, USN, 9108 Braeburn Drive, Annandale, Va., 22003.

Counsel for the Commandant.—Robert S. Hatch, 8711 Brierly Court, Chevy Chase, Md., 20015.

Staff Chaplain.—Capt. Loren M. Lindquist, CHC, USN, 1712 Oakcrest Drive, Springfield, Va., 22150.

Staff Medical Officer.—Capt. George Donabedian, MC, USN, 2502 Valley Drive, Alexandria, Va., 22312.

Staff Dental Officer.—Capt. William E. Ludwick, DC, USN.

Chief of Staff.—Lt. Gen. Leonard F. Chapman, USMC, Quarters 4, Marine Barracks, Eighth and I Streets SE., 20003.

Deputy Chief of Staff (Plans and Programs).—Lt. Gen. Henry W. Buse, Jr., USMC, Quarters 2, Marine Barracks, Eighth and I Streets SE., 20003.

Deputy Chief of Staff (R.D. & S.).—Brig. Gen. Wood B. Kyle, USMC, 3157 North Pollard Street, Arlington, Va., 22207.

Deputy Chief of Staff (Air).—Maj. Gen. Louis B. Robertshaw, USMC, 412 Shady Lane, Falls Church, Va., 22042.

Marine Corps Command Center.—Col. Frederick R. Dowsett, USMC, 729 Warren Drive, Annapolis, Md.

Assistant Chief of Staff, G-1.—Brig. Gen. Ormond R. Simpson, USMC, 3812 24th Street, North Arlington, Va., 22207.

Assistant Chief of Staff, G-2.—Col. Randolph C. Berkeley, Jr., USMC, 4313 Softwood Trail, McLean, Va., 22101.

Assistant Deputy Chief of Staff, Plans Director Joint Planning Group.—Brig. Gen. Charles J. Quilter, USMC, 4101 Cathedral Avenue, 20016.

Assistant Chief of Staff, G-3.—Maj. Gen. Richard G. Weede, USMC, 203 Vassar Place, Alexandria, Va., 22314.

Assistant Chief of Staff, G-4.—Brig. Gen. Melvin D. Henderson, USMC, 428 Valley Lane, Falls Church, Va., 22044.

Inspection Division.—Maj. Gen. Raymond L. Murray, USMC, 306 Emerald Drive, Alexandria, Va., 22308.

Fiscal Division.—James F. Wright, RFD 2, Sterling, Va., 22170.

Division of Information.—Brig. Gen. Arthur H. Adams, USMC, 4534 37th Street North, Arlington, Va., 22207.

Division of Reserve.—Brig. Gen. Joseph L. Stewart, USMC, 2202 Alden Road, Alexandria, Va., 22308.
Administrative Division.—Col. Robert E. Collier, USMC, 5909 Frederick Street, Springfield, Va., 22150.
Data Systems Division.—Col. Charles H. Greene, Jr., USMC, 1008 North Arlington Mill Drive, Arlington, Va., 22205.
Director of Women Marines.—Col. Barbara J. Bishop, USMC, 1200 South Nash Street, Arlington, Va., 22202.
Policy Analysis Division.—Col. Cecil W. Shuler, USMC, 37 Woodmount Road, Alexandria, Va., 22307.

PERSONNEL DEPARTMENT

Director of Personnel.—Maj. Gen. Lewis J. Fields, USMC, 3712 North Albermarle Street, Arlington, Va., 22207.
Assistant Director of Personnel.—Brig. Gen. Raymond G. Davis, USMC, 1905 Alyce Place, Alexandria, Va., 22308.
Assistant Director of Personnel.—Col. Cliff Atkinson, Jr., USMC, 5925 Lemon Road, McLean, Va., 22101.

SUPPLY DEPARTMENT

Quartermaster General.—Maj. Gen. Paul R. Tyler, USMC.
Assistant Quartermaster General.—Maj. Gen. John H. Masters, USMC, 2400 North Lincoln Street, Arlington, Va., 22207.

NAVAL EXAMINING BOARD (MARINE CORPS)

President.—Brig. Gen. Melvin D. Henderson, USMC, 428 Valley Lane, Falls Church, Va., 22044.
Recorder.—Maj. Albin L. Lindall, Jr., 2746 South Ives Street, Arlington, Va., 22202.

MARINE BARRACKS
Eighth and I Streets SE., 20003

Commanding Officer.—Col. Robert B. Carney, Jr., USMC, Quarters 3, Marine Barracks, Eighth and I Streets SE., 20003.

BUREAU OF MEDICINE AND SURGERY
Potomac Annex, Twenty-third and E Streets

Chief of Bureau.—Rear Adm. R. B. Brown, MC, USN, Surgeon General, Quarters A, NNMC, Bethesda, Md., 20014.
Deputy and Assistant Chief of Bureau.—Rear Adm. R. O. Canada, MC, USN, 3 Orchard Way, North, Falls Orchard, Rockville, Md., 20854.
Special Assistant to the Surgeon General.—Capt. E. F. Haase, MSC, USN, 4949 Battery Lane, Bethesda, Md., 20014.
Inspector General, Medical.—Rear Adm. Cecil D. Riggs, MC, USN, 206 Vassar Place, Alexandria, Va., 22314.
Editor, Navy Medical News Letter.—Capt. M. W. Arnold, MC, USN (ret.), 4407 Clearbrook Lane, Kensington, Md., 20795.
Comptroller.—T. J. Hickey, 6109 29th Street, 20015.
Legal Assistant.—Loren B. Poush, 1001 North Quantico Street, Arlington, Va., 22205.
National Coordinator, Medical Education for National Defense.—Capt. B. F, Avery, MC, USN, 8010 Bradley Boulevard, Bethesda, Md., 20034.

Assistant Chief for Personnel and Professional Operations.—Rear Adm. H. H. Eighmy, MC, USN, 4717 River Road, 20016.

Director, Professional Division.—Capt. B. L. Canaga, Jr., MC, USN, Apt. 830, 4000 Tunlaw Road, 20007.

Director, Nursing Division.—Capt. R. A. Erickson, NC, USN, Apt. C–1513, River House, 1600 South Joyce Street, Arlington, Va., 22202.

Director, Physical Qualifications and Medical Records Division.—Capt. P. R. Engle, MC, USN, 425 Cross Woods Drive, Falls Church, Va., 22044.

Director, Hospital Corps Division.—Capt. H. G. Edrington, MSC, USN, 6536 Fairlawn Drive, McLean, Va., 22101.

Director, Medical Service Corps Division.—Capt. R. S. Herrmann, MSC, USN, 4914 Aspen Hill Road, Rockville, Md., 20853.

Director, Naval Reserve Division.—Capt. C. Cummings, MC, USNR, 11701 Farmland Drive, Old Farm, Rockville, Md., 20852.

Director, Publications Division.—Capt. M. W. Arnold, MC, USN (ret.), 4407 Clearbrook Lane, Kensington, Md., 20795.

Assistant Chief for Planning and Logistics.—Rear Adm. Cecil D. Riggs, MC, USN, 206 Vassar Place, Alexandria, Va., 22314.

Executive Assistant.—Cdr. C. R. McMillin, MSC, USN, 7202 Fairland Street, Alexandria, Va., 22312.

Director, Planning Division.—Capt. R. Penington, Jr., MC, USN, 5345 Taney Avenue, Alexandria, Va., 22304.

Director, Material Division.—Capt. J. L. Conley, MC, USN, 3102 Cathedral Avenue, 20008.

Washington Contact.—Lt. Cdr. G. E. Elliott, MSC, USN, 7309 Long Pine Drive, North Springfield, Va., 22151.

Staff Director, Defense Medical Materiel Board.—Col. N. R. Drummond, MC, USAF, 3502 Preston Court, Chevy Chase, Md., 20015.

Director, Hospital Administration Division.—Cdr. L. W. Burr, MSC, USN, Apt. 402, 259 Congressional Lane, Rockville, Md., 20852.

Director, Administration Division.—L. P. Fern, 24 Lakeside Drive, Greenbelt, Md., 20770.

Director, Comptroller Division.—T. J. Hickey, 6109 29th Street, 20015.

Director, Data Processing Division.—Lt. Cdr. J. E. Wells, MSC, USN, 9 Maxim Lane, Rockville, Md., 20852.

Assistant Chief for Aviation Medicine.—Capt. W. M. Snowden, MC, USN, Apt. 622, 1021 Grosvenor Lane, Rockville, Md., 20014.

Director, Aviation Medicine Operations Division.—Capt. J. W. Weaver, MC, USN, 5103 Acacia Avenue, Bethesda, Md., 20014.

Director, Aviation Medicine Technical Division.—Capt. C. E. Wilbur, MC, USN, 3708 Kenilworth Driveway, Chevy Chase, Md., 20015.

Assistant Chief for Dentistry.—Rear Adm. F. M. Kyes, DC, USN, 5807 Osceola Road, 20016.

Chief, Dental Division.—Rear Adm. F. M. Kyes, DC, USN, 5807 Osceola Road, 20016.

Inspector General, Dental.—Rear Adm. E. C. Raffetto, DC, USN, 3900 Watson Place, Apt. 2–G, Bldg. B., 20016.

Assistant Chief for Research and Military Medical Specialties.—Rear Adm. L. C. Newman, MC, USN, Apt. C–1615, River House, 1600 South Joyce Street, Arlington, Va., 22202.

Director, Research Division.—Capt. J. P. Pollard, MC, USN, 4909 Brookway Drive, 20016.

Director, Occupational Health Division.—Cdr. N. E. Rosenwinkel, MC, USN, 7267 Gallows Road, Annandale, Va., 22003.

Director, Submarine and Radiation Medicine Division.—Cdr. J. H. Schulte, MC, USN, 8609 Brandt Place, Bethesda, Md., 20014.

NAVAL DISPENSARY
Rear Ninth Wing, Main Navy Building

Commanding Officer.—Capt. E. G. Hurlburt, MC, USN, 1013 26th Street South, Arlington, Va., 22202.

Administrative Officer.—Capt. W. G. McGehee, MSC, USN, 4211 Woodley Road, McLean, Va., 22101.

NATIONAL NAVAL MEDICAL CENTER
Bethesda, Md., 20014

Commanding Officer.—Rear Adm. C. L. Andrews, MC, USN, Quarters B, NNMC, Bethesda, Md., 20014.
Deputy Commanding Officer.—Capt. G. M. Davis, MC, USN, Quarters E, NNMC, Bethesda, Md., 20014.
Aide to the Commanding Officer.—Lt. W. R. Parrish, MSC, USN, White Grounds Road, Boyds, Md., 20720.
Administrative Officer.—Capt. C. W. Ferber, MSC, USN, BOQ, NNMC, Bethesda, Md., 20014.

NAVAL HOSPITAL
National Naval Medical Center, Bethesda, Md., 20014

Commanding Officer.—Capt. G. M. Davis, MC, USN, Quarters E, NNMC, Bethesda, Md., 20014.

NAVAL MEDICAL SCHOOL
National Naval Medical Center, Bethesda, Md., 20014

Commanding Officer.—Capt. J. H. Stover, Jr., MC, USN, 6002 Beech Avenue, Bethesda, Md., 20034.

NAVAL MEDICAL RESEARCH INSTITUTE
National Naval Medical Center, Bethesda, Md., 20014

Commanding Officer.—Capt. J. R. Seal, MC, USN, 4517 Cumberland Avenue, Chevy Chase, Md., 20015.

NAVAL DENTAL SCHOOL
National Naval Medical Center, Bethesda, Md., 20014

Commanding Officer.—Capt. A. R. Frechette, DC, USN, 5905 McKinley Street, Bethesda, Md., 20034.

NAVAL SCHOOL OF HOSPITAL ADMINISTRATION
National Naval Medical Center, Bethesda, Md., 20014

Commanding Officer.—Cdr. Emmett L. Van Landingham, Jr., MSC, USN, 4320 Rosedale Avenue, Bethesda, Md., 20014.

U.S. NAVY TOXICOLOGY UNIT
National Naval Medical Center, Bethesda, Md., 20014

Officer-in-Charge.—Capt. Jacob Siegel, MSC, USN, Apt. 507, 4857 Battery Lane, Bethesda, Md., 20014.

ARMED FORCES RADIOBIOLOGY RESEARCH INSTITUTE
National Naval Medical Center, Bethesda, Md., 20014

Director.—Col. J. T. Brennan, MC, USA, 10204 Tyburn Terrace, Bethesda, Md., 20014.

MILITARY SEA TRANSPORTATION SERVICE
Room 4006, T-8 Building, 3800 Newark Street, 20016

Commander.—Vice Adm. G. R. Donaho, USN, Quarters F, Washington Navy Yard SE., 20390.

Deputy Commander and Chief of Staff.—Rear Adm. W. S. Post, Jr., USN, **1678** 32d Street, 20007.

OFFICE OF THE CHIEF OF NAVAL OPERATIONS
Room 4E660, Pentagon Building

Chief of Naval Operations.—Adm. David L. McDonald, USN, Admiral's House, Naval Observatory, 20390.

Vice Chief of Naval Operations.—Adm. Horacio Rivero, Jr., USN, Quarters A, 2300 E Street SE., 20037.

Deputy Chief of Naval Operations (Personnel and Naval Reserve).—Vice Adm. Benedict J. Semmes, Jr., USN, Quarters G, Washington Navy Yard SE., 20390.

Deputy Chief of Naval Operations (Fleet Operations and Readiness).—Vice Adm. Alfred G. Ward, USN, 3701 Nebraska Avenue, 20016.

Deputy Chief of Naval Operations (Logistics).—Vice Adm. Lot Ensey, USN, Quarters C, Washington Navy Yard SE., 20390.

Deputy Chief of Naval Operations (Air).—Vice Adm. Paul H. Ramsey, USN, Quarters C, 2300 E Street SE., 20037.

Deputy Chief of Naval Operations (Plans and Policy).—Vice Adm. Andrew McB. Jackson, Jr., USN, Quarters B, Washington Navy Yard SE., 20390.

Deputy Chief of Naval Operations (Development).—Rear Adm. Charles T. Booth II, USN, 4740 Connecticut Avenue, 20008.

Assistant Vice Chief of Naval Operations/Director of Naval Administration.—Rear Adm. Roy S. Benson, USN, Quarters O, Washington Navy Yard SE., 20390.

Chief of Information.—Rear Adm. William P. Mack, USN, 3308 Alabama Avenue, Alexandria, Va., 22305.

BUREAU OF NAVAL PERSONNEL
Room 2072, Arlington Annex

Chief of Naval Personnel.—Vice Adm. B. J. Semmes, Jr., USN, Quarters G, Washington Navy Yard, SE., 20390.

Deputy and Assistant Chief of Naval Personnel.—Rear Adm. J. O. Cobb, USN, 6907 JoAllen Drive, Falls Church, Va., 22041.

Administrative Aide.—Cdr. R. B. Baldwin, USN, 731 Tarpon Lane, Alexandria, Va., 22309.

Administrative Officer.—C. B. MacLean, 921 North Lebanon Street, Arlington, Va., 22205.

Inspector General.—Capt. J. E. Hackett, USN, 4408 Kurpiers Court, McLean, Va., 22101.

Special Assistant for Leadership.—Capt. J. E. Godfrey, USN, 4911 37th Street North, Arlington, Va., 22207.

Special Assistant for Liaison and Technical Information.—Cdr. C. H. Klindworth, USN, 702 Pioneer Lane, Falls Church, Va., 22043.

Special Assistant for Surface Missile Systems Programs.—Rear Adm. E. T. Reich, USN, 4606 Langdrum Lane, Chevy Chase, Md., 20015.

Director, Personnel Research Division.—Cdr. L. A. Wilder, USN, 2701 North Somerset Street, Arlington, Va., 22213.

Director, Manpower Information Division.—Capt. N. Brango, USN, 1712 Swinburne Court, Mantua Hills, Fairfax, Va., 22030.

Assistant Chief for Plans.—Capt. B. H. Shupper, USN, 5539 Columbia Pike, Arlington, Va., 22204.

Assistant Chief for Personnel Control.—Rear Adm. W. L. Curtis, Jr., USN, 2000 South Eads Street, Arlington, Va., 22202.

Assistant Chief for Education and Training.—Rear Adm. M. B. Freeman, USN, 1421 22d Street South, Arlington, Va., 22202.

Assistant Chief for Naval Reserve and Naval District Affairs.—Rear Adm. W. C. Hughes, USNR, 1714 Lexington Road, Falls Church, Va., 22043.

Assistant Chief for Records.—Capt. C. E. Jackson, USN, 5005 Richenbacker Avenue, Alexandria, Va., 22304.

Assistant Chief for Performance.—Capt. R. J. Badger, USN, 926 26th Street South, Arlington, Va., 22202.
Assistant Chief for Morale Services.—Capt. J. W. Higgins, Jr., USN, 4808 14th Street North, Arlington, Va., 22205.
Assistant Chief for Finance and Comptroller.—Capt. A. W. Gardes, USN, 4828 27th Place North, Arlington, Va., 22207.
Chief of Chaplains.—Rear Adm. J. F. Dreith, USN, Route No. 2, Box 184, Vienna, Va., 22180.
Assistant Chief of Women.—Capt. V. B. Sanders (W), USN, 4000 Tunlaw Road, 20007.
Assistant Chief for Property Management.—Capt. R. A. Haase, USN, 500 Roosevelt Boulevard, Falls Church, Va., 22044.
Assistant Chief for Personnel Program Management.—Capt. W. R. McQuilkin, USN, 305 46th Street, Virginia Beach, Va., 23451.

OFFICE OF SAVINGS BONDS

Director.—Cdr. Norman J. Mills, USNR, 6302 Alberta Street, Springfield, Va., 22150.

U.S. NAVAL ACADEMY
Annapolis, Md.

Superintendent.—Rear Adm. Charles S. Minter, Jr., USN, 1 Buchanan Road, Annapolis, Md., 21402.
Commandant of Midshipmen.—Capt. S. H. Kinney, USN, 14 Porter Road, Annapolis, Md., 21402.

OFFICE OF NAVAL MATERIAL
Room 2010, Main Navy Building

Chief of Naval Material.—Vice Adm. I. J. Galantin, USN, Quarters H, Washington Navy Yard SE., 20390.
Vice Chief and Deputy Chief (Programs and Financial Management).—Rear Adm. R. L. Shifley, USN, 4738 Tilden Street, 20016.
Administrative Aide.—Cdr. E. L. Cochrane, Jr., USN, 7703 Viceroy Street, Springfield, Va., 22151.
Deputy Chief (Material and Facilities).—Rear Adm. B. H. Bieri, Jr., SC, USN, 4507 32d Road North, Arlington, Va., 22207.
Deputy Chief (Development).—Rear Adm. E. A. Ruckner, USN, 1904 Ashwood Drive, Alexandria, Va., 22308.
Acting Deputy Chief (Management and Organization).—Capt. W. J. Keim, USN, 5722 Old Chesterbrook Road, McLean, Va., 22101.
Legislative and Congressional Liaison Officer.—W. T. Ryan, 1410 North Meade Street, Arlington, Va., 22209.
Project Manager (F111B)—TFX Weapons System).—Capt. J. R. Rees, USN, 605 Dead Run Road, McLean, Va., 22101.
Project Manager (Surface Missile Systems).—Rear Adm. E. T. Reich, USN, 4606 Langdrum Lane, Chevy Chase, Md., 20015.
Project Manager (Anti-Submarine Warfare Systems).—Rear Adm. C. A. Karaberis, USN, 1405 23d Street, South, Arlington, Va., 22202.
Project Manager (Instrumentation Ships).—Capt. A. F. Hancock, USN, 20 Blowing Rock Road, Alexandria, Va., 22309.
Project Manager (All-Weather Carrier Landing System).—Capt. F. R. Fearnow, USN, 5945 Lemon Road, McLean, Va., 22101.
Project Manager (Fleet Ballistic Missile).—[Vacant.]

BUREAU OF NAVAL WEAPONS
Room 2082, Main Navy Building

Chief of Bureau.—Rear Adm. Allen M. Shinn, USN, Quarters M-1, Washington Navy Yard SE., 20390.

Deputy Chief of Bureau.—Rear Adm. E. R. Eastwold, USN, 409 Underhill Place, Alexandria, Va., 22305.

Assistant Chief for Plans and Programs.—Rear Adm. E. E. Christensen, USN, 4615 38th Street North, Arlington, Va., 22207.

Inspector General and Assistant Chief for Administration.—Rear Adm. F. L. Pinney, Jr., USN, 6345 Western Avenue, 20015.

Assistant Chief for Fleet Readiness and Training.—Rear Adm. T. S. King, Jr., USN, 8400 Whitman Drive, Bethesda, Md., 20034.

Assistant Chief for Financial Management (Comptroller).—Capt. J. A. Ferguson, USN, 1352 28th Street South, Arlington, Va., 22206.

Assistant Chief for Contracts.—Capt. W. H. Schleef (SC), USN, 405 Warbler Lane, McLean, Va., 22101.

Assistant Chief for Production and Quality Control.—Rear Adm. J. P. Sager, USN, 9902 Carter Road, Bethesda, Md., 20034.

Assistant Chief for Research, Development, Test and Evaluation.—Rear Adm. E. E. Fawkes, USN, 2757 South Ives Street, Arlington, Va., 22202.

Assistant Chief for Field Support.—Capt. C. M. MacDonald, USN, 11640 Glen Road, Potomac, Md., 20854.

Counsel for the Bureau.—Frederick Sass, Jr., 10730 River Road, Potomac, Md., 20854.

Patent Counsel.—C. J. Rubens, 8304 Melody Court, Bethesda, Md., 20034.

BUREAU OF SHIPS
Room 3046, Main Navy Building

Chief of Bureau.—Rear Adm. W. A. Brockett, USN, Quarters E, Washington Navy Yard SE., 20390.

Deputy Chief of Bureau.—Rear Adm. C. A. Curtze, USN, 519 Valley Lane, Falls Church, Va., 22044.

Special Assistant and Administrative Aide to Chief of Bureau.—Capt. R. W. King, USN, 8108 Thoreau Drive, Bethesda, Md., 20034.

Special Assistants to Chief of Bureau for Legislation and Special Matters.—Charles F. Elliott, Box 124, Oakton, Va., 22124; James W. Beatman, 1427 Oliver Avenue, Annandale, Va., 22003.

Assistant Chief for Research and Development.—Capt. W. C. Bennett, Jr., USN, 306 Wasp Lane, McLean, Va., 22101.

Assistant Chief for Design, Shipbuilding and Fleet Maintenance.—Rear Adm. J. A. Brown, USN, 2700 North Wakefield Street, Arlington, Va., 22207.

Assistant Chief for Technical Logistics.—Rear Adm. R. B. Fulton, USN, 9912 Old Spring Road, Kensington, Md., 20795.

Assistant Chief for Field Activities and Inspector General.—Rear Adm. W. F. Petrovic, USN, 904 Prince William Drive, Fairfax, Va. 22030.

Assistant Chief for Shore Electronics.—Rear Adm. J. E. Rice, USN, Crystal Spring Farm Road, Annapolis, Md., 21403.

Assistant Chief for Nuclear Propulsion.—Vice Adm. H. G. Rickover, USN (ret.), 4801 Connecticut Avenue, 20008.

Assistant Chief for Plans, Programs and Financial Management.—Rear Adm. J. J. Fee, USN, 1600 South Joyce Street, Arlington, Va., 22202.

Director of Management Services.—Capt. W. N. Price, USN, 3841 Calvert Street, 20007.

Director of Contracts.—Capt. G. C. Wells, USN, 8785 Preston Place, Chevy Chase, Md., 20015.

Comptroller.—Capt. C. N. Payne, USN, 8106 Thoreau Drive, Bethesda, Md., 20034.

BUREAU OF SUPPLIES AND ACCOUNTS
Room 0026, Main Navy Building

Chief of Bureau.—Rear Adm. J. W. Crumpacker, SC, USN, Quarters R, Washington Navy Yard SE., 20390.

Deputy Chief of Bureau.—Rear Adm. H. J. Goldberg, SC, USN, 210 Wilkes Street, Alexandria, Va., 22314.

Assistant Chief of Bureau for Supply Management.—Rear Adm. I. F. Haddock, SC, USN, 913 North Kemper Street, Alexandria, Va., 22304.
Assistant Chief of Bureau for Transportation and Facilities.—Rear Adm. H. J. P. Foley, Jr., SC, USN, 4705 Mori Avenue, McLean, Va., 22101.
Assistant Chief of Bureau for Purchasing.—Capt. H. E. Beckmeyer, SC, USN, 1711 Glenbrook Road, Fairfax, Va., 22030.
Assistant Chief of Bureau for Research and Development.—Capt. E. K. Scofield, SC, USN, 1007 Ampthill Drive, Alexandria, Va., 22312.
Assistant Chief of Bureau for Policy and Plans.—Capt. G. V. Clark, SC, USN, 2728 North Oakland Street, Arlington, Va., 22207.
Assistant Chief of Bureau for Resale Programs.—Rear Adm. J. J. Appleby, SC, USN, Quarters I, New York Naval Shipyard, Brooklyn, N.Y., 11251.
Assistant Chief of Bureau for Navy Service Programs.—Capt. John C. Herron, SC, USN, 5 Brown's Court SE., 20003.
Director, Resale Program Assistance Staff.—Cdr. William T. Hamill, SC, USN, 5007 Killebrew Drive, Annadale, Va., 22003.
Comptroller of the Bureau.—Capt. F. W. Martin, SC, USN, 2810 Farm Road, Alexandria, Va., 22302.
Inspector General of the Supply Corps.—Capt. S. B. Lee, SC, USN, 4320 Old Dominion Drive, Arlington, Va., 22207.
Director of Publications and Technical Information.—Capt. R. L. Daniels, SC, USN, 5420 19th Street North, Arlington, Va., 22205.
Director of Supply Corps Personnel.—Capt. William F. Harvey, SC, USN, 304 Skyhill Road, Alexandria, Va., 22314.
Director of Industrial Relations.—W. J. Hurd, 5 Christine Place, Alexandria, Va., 22311.
Director of Navy Publications and Printing Service.—A. N. Spence, 211 West Walnut Street, Alexandria, Va., 22301.
Director of Management Engineering.—Capt. L. M. Detweiler, SC, USN, 118 Van Winkle Drive, Falls Church, Va., 22044.
Counsel.—William Sellman, Route 5, Cedar Lane, Oakdale Park, Vienna, Va., 22180.
Small Business Specialist.—H.G. Fowler, Burke Lake Road, Route 645, Burke, Va., 22015.

NAVY PUBLICATIONS AND PRINTING SERVICE
Building 157, Washington Navy Yard

Director.—A. N. Spence, 211 West Walnut Street, Alexandria, Va., 22301.
Deputy Director.—T. G. Maynard, 3806 Thornapple Street, Chevy Chase, Md., 20015.
Assistant to the Director.—H. Kamien, 3116 Fayette Road, Kensington, Md., 20795.
Director, Management Programs Division.—J. E. Monahan, 3418 Old Dominion Boulevard, Alexandria, Va., 22305.
Director, Program Analysis Division.—L. R. Potter, R.F.D. 1–36, Brookeville, Md., 20729.

BUREAU OF YARDS AND DOCKS
Yards and Docks Annex, Arlington, Va.

Chief of Bureau.—Rear Adm. P. Corradi, CEC, USN, Quarters N, Washington Navy Yard SE., 20390.
Deputy and Assistant Chief of Bureau.—Rear Adm. A. C. Husband, CEC, USN, Apt. 401, 750 South Dickerson Street, Arlington, Va., 22204.
Executice Assistant to Chief of Bureau.—Cdr. J. E. Powell, CEC, USN, Apt. 202, 5402 Richenbacker Avenue, Alexandria, Va., 22304.
Counsel.—Harold Gold, 7012 Richard Drive, Bethesda, Md., 20034.
Inspector General.—Capt. L. P. Frate, CEC, USN, 609 Norman Avenue, Fairfax, Va., 22030.
Directorate for Programs and Comptroller.—Capt. J. G. Dillon, CEC, USN, 1004 Terrace Drive, Annandale, Va., 22003.
Directorate for Facilitate Engineering.—Capt. P. E. Seufer, CEC, USN, 4405 41st Street North, McLean, Va., 22101.

Directorate for Facilitate Management.—Capt. N. M. Martinsen, CEC, USN, Apt. 807, 2001 Columbia Pike, Arlington, Va., 22204.

U.S. NAVAL STATION
Mount Howard Road, Anacostia, SE.

Commanding Officer.—Capt. H. F. Rommel, USN, Quarters A, Washington Navy Yard SE., 20390.

Executive Officer.—Cdr. W. C. Avery, USN, Quarters B, Anacostia Annex SE., 20390.

Naval Station Representative (Washington Navy Yard).—Lt. R. W. Smiley, USN, 5628 Alice Avenue, Oxon Hill, Md., 20021.

Naval Station Representative (Anacostia Annex).—Lt. Cdr. J. P. Ashford, USN, Quarters Q-4, Washington Navy Yard SE., 20390.

Naval Station Representative (Arlington Barracks Annex).—Lt. W. B. Hale, USN, BOQ, Naval Station SE., 20390.

Naval Station Representative for Women.—Lt. C. J. MacLean (W), USN, 1918 Columbia Pike, Arlington, Va., 22204.

Industrial Relations Officer.—Charles J. Famosa, 5506 25th Avenue, Hillcrest Heights, Md., 20031.

Legal Officer.—Cdr. R. W. Glasgow, USN, 866 North Ohio Street, Arlington, Va., 22205.

Comptroller.—Lt. Cdr. J. M. McDaniel, USN, 5604 Goodfellow Drive SE., 20023.

Administrative Officer.—Cdr. C. K. Hoffman, USN, Quarters A, Anacostia Annex SE., 20390.

Operations Officer.—Cdr. J. B. Meehan, USN, 3300 Circle Hill Road, Alexandria, Va., 22305.

Public Works Officer.—Capt. J. A. Dougherty, CEC, USN, Quarters Q-3, Washington Navy Yard SE., 20390.

Supply Officer.—Capt. W. W. Hyland, SC, USN, Quarters J-3, Washington Navy Yard SE., 20390.

Medical Officer.—Capt. C. R. Longenecker, MC, USN, Quarters K, Washington Navy Yard SE., 20390.

HEADQUARTERS, NAVAL DISTRICT WASHINGTON
Washington Navy Yard, Eighth and M Streets SE., 20390

Commandant.—Rear Adm. A. J. Hill, USN, Quarters A, Tingey House, Washington Navy Yard SE., 20390.

Chief of Staff.—Capt. George A. O'Connell, Jr., USN, Quarters L, Washington Navy Yard SE., 20390.

Aide to the Commandant.—Lt. R. A. Kenney, USN, Quarters T, Washington Navy Yard SE., 20390.

Public Information Officer.—Lt. (jg) R. Krebs, USNR, 405 Second Street SE., 20003.

Assistant Chief of Staff for Administration.—Capt. Emory C. Smith, USN, 2118 49th Street, 20007.

DEPARTMENT OF THE AIR FORCE

Department of Defense Building, The Pentagon, 20330.   Phone, LIberty 5–6700 (Code 11)

EUGENE MARTIN ZUCKERT, Secretary of the Air Force (141 Hesketh Street, Chevy Chase, Md.), was born November 9, 1911, in New York City and is the son of Harry M. and Eugenie Adrienne Pincoffs Zuckert (deceased); attended public elementary and high schools of suburban New York, received preparatory education at the Salisbury School, Salisbury, Conn., and obtained his B.A. from Yale University in 1933; in 1937 received LL.B from Yale with a certificate for completion of the combined law-business course at Harvard and Yale; at Yale was a member of Beta Theta Pi Fraternity; has received an honorary LL.D. degree from George Washington University and an honorary doctor of engineering degree from Clarkson College, N.Y.; member of the bar in Connecticut, New York, and the District of Columbia and has practiced law in these States; most of professional career has been devoted to public service; from 1937 to 1940, was attorney for the U.S. Securities and Exchange Commission at Washington and New York; from 1940 to 1944 was an instructor in relations between government and business at the Harvard Graduate School of Business Administration, advancing to assistant professor and later to assistant dean of the school; during this period also served as administrative head of the first advanced management course given at the Harvard Graduate School; in 1944, entered the U.S. Navy on military duty and served in the office of the Chief of Naval Operations as a lieutenant (j.g.); on September 26, 1947, was appointed Assistant Secretary of the Air Force under Secretary of the Air Force Stuart Symington; was appointed a member of the U.S. Atomic Energy Commission on January 21, 1952, and served until June 30, 1954; returned to the private practice of law specializing as a consultant in the field of atomic energy; coauthored with Arnold Kramish, the book, *Atomic Energy For Your Business;* is a Director of the People-to-People Health Foundation, Inc., a nonprofit organization which is operating the *Hope* ship as part of the President's People-to-People program; member of the Executive Council of the Yale Law School Association; was sworn in as Secretary of the Air Force on January 24, 1961; married the former Barbara Jackman of Newburyport, Mass.; has three children, two daughters, Adrienne K. and Gene, and a son, Robert B.

Under Secretary of the Air Force.—Brockway McMillan, 2524 44th Street, 20007.
Assistant Secretary of the Air Force (Research and Development).—Alexander H. Flax, 3032 New Mexico Avenue, 20016.
Assistant Secretary of the Air Force (Installations and Logistics).—Robert H. Charles, 3214 S Street, 20007.
Assistant Secretary of the Air Force (Financial Management).—Leonard Marks, Jr., 4 Park Overlook Court, Carderock Springs, Bethesda, Md., 20034.
Special Assistant for Manpower, Personnel and Reserve Forces.—Benjamin W. Fridge, 2709 South Hayes Street, Arlington, Va. 22202.
Special Assistant for Public and Legislative Affairs.—Ralph R. Harding, 482 North Owen Street, Alexandria, Va., 22304.
Military Assistant to the Secretary.—Col. William V. McBride, 8034 Jansen Drive, Springfield, Va., 22150.
Administrative Assistant to the Secretary.—John A. Lang, Jr., 2430 32d Street SE., 20020.
General Counsel.—Gerritt W. Wesselink, 5103 Baltimore Avenue, 20016.
Director of Legislative Liaison.—Maj. Gen. Perry M. Hoisington II, 1111 Army-Navy Drive, Apt. A–1009, Arlington, Va., 22202.
Director of Information.—Maj. Gen. Eugene B. LeBailly, 405 Windsor Road, Alexandria, Va., 22307.
Director of Space Systems.—Brig. Gen. James T. Stewart, 4 Nemeth Court, Alexandria, Va., 22306.

OFFICE OF THE SECRETARY OF THE AIR FORCE

Executive Assistant.—Col. Buddy R. Daughtrey, 457 Argyle Drive, Alexandria, Va.
Deputy Executive Assistant.—Col. Brian S. Gunderson, 203 Waynewood Boulevard, Alexandria, Va.
Military Aide.—Col. John W. Mitchell, 3617 Wagon Wheel Road, Alexandria, Va.
Private Secretary.—Harriet Zimmerly, 2800 Quebec Street, 20008.

OFFICE OF THE UNDER SECRETARY OF THE AIR FORCE

Deputy Under Secretary of the Air Force.—Philip F. Hilbert, Hedgeland, Waterford, Va.
Executive Assistant.—Col. John H. Strand, 3101 North Quincy Street, Arlington, Va.
Deputy Executive Assistant.—Maj. Lawrence A. Skantze, 12908 Margot Drive, Rockville, Md.
Private Secretary.—Mary Kay Tompkins, 1600 South Joyce Street, Arlington, Va.

OFFICE OF THE ASSISTANT SECRETARY OF THE AIR FORCE
(RESEARCH AND DEVELOPMENT)

Deputy for Development.—Joe C. Jones, 909 Hyde Park Road, Silver Spring, Md.
Deputy for Engineering.—Thomas H. Dalehite, 4214 Selkirk Drive, Fairfax, Va.
Deputy for Requirements.—Franklin J. Ross, 2816 North Dinwiddie Street, Arlington, Va.
Deputy for Research.—Harry Davis, 6927 Pinetree Terrace, Falls Church, Va.
Executive.—Col. Valin R. Woodward, Arlington Towers, Apt. 1003–M, Arlington, Va.
Private Secretary.—Marie Miles, 1313 Park Terrace Drive, Alexandria, Va.

OFFICE OF THE ASSISTANT SECRETARY OF THE AIR FORCE
(INSTALLATIONS AND LOGISTICS)

Deputy Assistant Secretary.—Donald R. Jackson, 4100 Everett Street, Kensington, Md.
Deputy for Procurement Management.—Aaron J. Racusin, 6512 Kenhowe Drive, Bethesda, Md.
Deputy for Supply and Maintenance.—Hugh E. Witt, 913 Cameron Street, Alexandria, Va.
Deputy for Installations.—Lewis E. Turner, 3539 North Valley Street, Arlington, Va.
Deputy for Transportation and Communications.—John W. Perry, 3511 Idaho Avenue.
Executive.—Col. Allen B. Gaston, 1616 34th Street, 20007.
Private Secretary.—Dorothy M. Olsen, 2831 28th Street, 20008.

OFFICE OF THE ASSISTANT SECRETARY OF THE AIR FORCE
(FINANCIAL MANAGEMENT)

Deputy Assistant Secretary.—Robert D. Benson, 3506 Manor Road, Chevy Chase, Md.
Deputy for Financial Analysis.—John J. Holleran, 3324 North Rochester Street, Falls Church, Va.
Deputy for Management Systems.—J. Ronald Fox, 1301 Delaware Avenue SW., 20024.
Executive.—Col. James C. Snipes, 2112 South Columbus Street, Arlington, Va.
Private Secretary.—Helen B. Harpold, 6707 Haven Place, Falls Church, Va.

OFFICE OF THE SPECIAL ASSISTANT FOR MANPOWER, PERSONNEL AND RESERVE FORCES

Deputy for Manpower, Personnel and Organization.—James P. Goode, 5113 Marlyn Drive, Massachusetts Hills, 20016.

Deputy for Security Programs.—John E. Whalan, Jr., 610 Tyler Street, Falls Church, Va.
Deputy for Reserve and ROTC Affairs.—Dr. Theodore C. Marrs, 302 Rose Lane, Falls Church, Va.
Secretary of the Air Force Personnel Council:
   Director.—Maj. Gen. Turner C. Rogers, 12 Statendam Court, McLean, Va.
   Deputy Director.—Col. Henry G. MacDaniel, 5928 Merritt Place, Falls Church, Va.
   Executive.—Lt. Col. Marshal H. Cruse, 1600 South Joyce Street, Apt. B–311, Arlington, Va.
Executive.—Col. Raymond F. Wisniewski, 7854 Oreana Drive, Annandale, Va.
Private Secretary.—Glee Foster, 1200 Mason Road, Falls Church, Va.

OFFICE OF THE ADMINISTRATIVE ASSISTANT

Deputy Administrative Assistant.—Joseph P. Hochreiter, 5109 Blue Ridge Avenue, Annandale, Va.
Executive.—Lt. Col. Frank J. Simokaitis, 4812 Woodmoor Lane, McLean, Va.

OFFICE OF THE GENERAL COUNSEL

Assistant General Counsel (Fiscal).—Murray Comarow, 1715 Mayhew Drive, Silver Spring, Md.
Assistant General Counsel (Installations).—Samuel Hanenberg, 306 Annelliese Drive, Falls Church, Va.
Assistant General Counsel (Personnel and Administration).—Hugh R. Gilmore, 130 South Highland Street, Arlington, Va.
Assistant General Counsel (Procurement).—William Munves, 8204 Bryant Drive, Bethesda, Md.
Assistant General Counsel (International and Civil Aviation).—William Hancock, 1511 34th Street, 20007.
Executive.—Maj. James L. Gagnier, 4112 Saul Road, Kensington, Md.

OFFICE OF LEGISLATIVE LIAISON

Deputy Director.—Brig. Gen. Thomas G. Corbin, Quarters 58B, Bolling Air Force Base, 20332.
Deputy Director.—Col. George M. Lockhart, 600 North Pickett Street, Alexandria, Va.
Assistant Director for Legislation and Investigations.—Col. James M. McGarry, Jr., 6415 24th Street North, Arlington, Va.
Chief, Congressional Inquiry Division.—Col. Donald W. Paffel, 6615 North 32d Street, Arlington, Va.
Chief, Congressional Legislation Division.—Col. Joseph J. F. Clark, 7713 LaMar Drive, Springfield, Va.
Chief, Congressional Investigations Division.—Col. Richard L. Coons, 5311 Easton Drive, North Springfield, Va.
Chief, Senate Liaison Office.—Col. William F. Pitts, 2500 North Randolph Street, Arlington, Va.
Chief, House Liaison Office.—Col. John M. Chapman, 1600 South Joyce Street, Apt. B–1710, Arlington, Va.
Chief, Plans Group.—Col. James A. Darby, 213 South Fairfax Street, Alexandria, Va.
Executive Assistant.—Lt. Col. Leslie J. Campbell, Jr., 1111 Army-Navy Drive, Apt. C–411, Arlington, Va.
Executive.—Maj. Jack R. Benson, 6204 Charnwood Street, Springfield, Va.

OFFICE OF INFORMATION

Deputy Director.—Brig. Gen. Maurice F. Casey, 4819 Cola Drive, McLean, Va.
Assistant Director.—Col. Max B. Boyd, 4625 30th Street.

Chief, Reserve Forces Liaison.—Lt. Col. Robert S. Russell, 3910 Stratford Lane, Alexandria, Va.
Chief, Community Relations Division.—Col. William H. Huntley, Jr., 4420 Ramshorn Drive, McLean, Va.
Chief, Public Information Division.—Col. Jesse Stay, 1763 Roanoke, Woodbridge, Va.
Chief, Plans and Programs Division.—Col. Carl R. Carlson, 5622 9th Street North, Arlington, Va.
Chief, Internal Information Division.—Col. Bishop M. Kilgore, 409 Potomac Lane, Alexandria, Va.
Executive.—Lt. Col. Kenneth L. Sandvig, 8035 Anson Court, Springfield, Va.

OFFICE OF SPACE SYSTEMS

Executive.—Lt. Col. Robert A. Van Arsdall, 5938 Strata Street, McLean, Va.

AIR STAFF

Chief of Staff.—Gen. John P. McConnell, Quarters 7, Fort Myer, Va.
Executive to the Chief of Staff.—Col. James F. Kirkendall, 6916 Greentree Drive, Falls Church, Va.
Aide-de-Camp.—Maj. William B. Frasca, 1400 South Joyce Street, Apt. B–801, Arlington, Va.
Chief Scientist.—Dr. Winston Markey, 4409 Dexter Street.
Vice Chief of Staff.—Gen. William H. Blanchard, Quarters 62, Bolling Air Force Base, 20332.
Assistant Vice Chief of Staff.—Lt. Gen. Hewitt T. Wheless, 68 Westover Avenue, Bolling Air Force Base, 20332.
Director, Vice Chief of Staff Special Studies Group.—Maj. Gen. John S. Samuel, 1321 Stoneybrae Drive, Falls Church, Va., 22044.
Executive.—Col. Albert J. Bowley, 503 Canterbury Lane, Alexandria, Va.
Aide-de-Camp.—Lt. Col. Travis R. McNeil, 6811 Clay Drive, Oxon Hill, Md.
Chairman, Scientific Advisory Board.—Dr. H. Guyford Stever, 87 Rutledge Road, Belmont, Mass.
Military Director, Scientific Advisory Board.—Lt. Gen. James Ferguson, Quarters 72, Bolling Air Force Base, 20332.
Secretary, Scientific Advisory Board.—Col. Robert J. Burger, 7309 Chesterfield Drive SE., 20031.
Technical Director, Scientific Advisory Board.—Chester N. Hasert, 2475 Virginia Avenue, 20007.
Chief, Operations Analysis Office.—Paul A. Hower, 4416 Volunteer Drive, Alexandria, Va., 22309.
The Inspector General, USAF.—Lt. Gen. William K. Martin, Quarters 59B, Bolling Air Force Base, 20332.
Deputy, The Inspector General.—Maj. Gen. John B. Henry, Jr., 5152 38th Street North, Arlington, Va., 22207.
Assistant for Inquiries and Complaints.—Col. Thomas J. Rogers, 5074 Livingston Terrace, Oxon Hill, Md., 20021.
Assistant for Inspection and Safety Services.—Col. Dyson W. Cox, 1016 San Marcos Drive, Fairfax, Va., 22030.
Director of Special Investigations.—Col. Joseph J. Cappucci, 200 Valley Brook Drive, Falls Church, Va.
Director of Security and Law Enforcement.—Col. Charles W. Howe, 4989 Battery Lane, Bethesda, Md., 20034.
Deputy, The Inspector General (Norton AFB).—Maj. Gen. Bertram C. Harrison, Quarters 85, Norton Air Force Base, Calif.
Director of Inspection.—Brig. Gen. Henry C. Newcomer, 1817 Century Club Drive, Redlands, Calif.
Director of Aerospace Safety.—Brig. Gen. Jay T. Robbins, Quarters 83, Norton Air Force Base, Calif.
Director of Nuclear Safety.—Brig. Gen. Charles B. Stewart, 2240 Stockton Loop, Kirtland Air Force Base, N. Mex.
Assistant for Medical Services.—Brig. Gen. William F. Cook, Quarters 79, Norton Air Force Base, Calif.

The Judge Advocate General, USAF.—Maj. Gen. Robert W. Manss, 1687 North Longfellow Street, Arlington, Va.
Assistant Judge Advocate General.—[Vacant.]
Director of Civil Law.—Col. James H. Cowan, 1701 Chesterfield Avenue, McLean, Va.
Director of Military Justice.—Col. James S. Cheney, 2411 North Quincy Street, Arlington, Va.
Surgeon General, USAF.—Maj. Gen. Richard L. Bohannon, 5301 Westpath Way, 20016.
Deputy Surgeon General.—Brig. Gen. Kenneth E. Pletcher, 2933 Cathedral Avenue, 20008.
Assistant Surgeon General for Dental Services.—Brig. Gen. Benjamin W. Dunn, 7700 Massena Road, Bethesda, Md.
Director of Plans and Hospitalization.—Col. Robert A. Patterson, 3800 30th Street North, Arlington, Va.
Director of Professional Services.—Brig. Gen. Don S. Wenger, 8901 Burning Tree Road, Bethesda, Md.
Chief of Aerospace Medicine Division.—Brig. Gen. John M. Talbot, R.F.D. 3, Annapolis, Md.
Chief Medical Consultant to the Surgeon General.—Col. Henry C. Dorris, 5305 Massachusetts Avenue.
Director of Medical Staffing and Education.—Brig. Gen. Thomas H. Crouch, 5001 River Hill Road.
Assistant Surgeon General for Veterinary Services.—Col. Charles H. Snider, 9304 Chanute Drive, Bethesda, Md.
Assistant Chief of Staff for Reserve Forces.—Maj. Gen. Curtis R. Low, 3601 North Abingdon Street, Arlington, Va., 22206.
Assistant Chief of Staff for Intelligence.—Maj. Gen. Jack E. Thomas, 1400 South Joyce Street, Arlington, Va.
Deputy Assistant Chief of Staff for Intelligence.—Brig. Gen. Prentiss D. Wynne, 4000 Massachusetts Avenue.
Director of Collection.—Col. Harry O. Patteson, 19 Great Neck Court, Alexandria, Va.
Director of Estimates.—Col. Ralph L. Michaelis, 5913 Espey Lane, McLean, Va.
Chief of Chaplains.—Maj. Gen. Robert P. Taylor, 593 Lido Place, Mantua Hills, Fairfax, Va.
Deputy Chief of Chaplains.—Brig. Gen. Edwin R. Chess, 4200 Cathedral Avenue, Apt. 816, 20016.
Secretary of the Air Staff.—Col. Benjamin B. Cassiday, Jr., 623 Lakeview Drive, Falls Church, Va., 22041.
Director of Administrative Services.—Col. Robert J. Pugh, 5111 Eighth Road South, Arlington, Va., 22204.

THE COMPTROLLER OF THE AIR FORCE

The Comptroller of the Air Force.—Lt. Gen. Jack G. Merrell, Quarters 73, Bolling Air Force Base, 20332.
Acting Deputy Comptroller.—Arnold G. Bueter, 1311 Fiddlers Green, Falls Church, Va., 22044.
Director of Data Automation.—Maj. Gen. Elbert Helton, 2812 North Dinwiddie Street, Arlington, Va., 22207.
Director of Accounting and Finance.—Brig. Gen. George E. Brown, Crystal House II, Apt. 614, 2000 South Eads Street, Arlington, Va.
Auditor General.—Maj. Gen. Don Coupland, 2815 Fort Scott Drive, Arlington, Va., 22202.
Director of Management Analysis.—Col. Jerome P. Dufour, 704 Tarpon Lane, Alexandria, Va., 22309.
Director of Budget.—Maj. Gen. Duward L. Crow, 616 Pulman Place, Alexandria, Va., 22305.

DEPUTY CHIEF OF STAFF, PERSONNEL

Deputy Chief of Staff, Personnel.—Lt. Gen. William S. Stone, Quarters 71, Bolling Air Force Base, 20332.

Assistant Deputy Chief of Staff, Personnel.—Maj. Gen. William B. Kiefer, Apt. C–1015, River House, Arlington, Va.
Director of WAF.—Col. Elizabeth Ray, 2500 Q Street.
Assistant for Personnel Systems.—Col. Arthur K. Swanson, 3305 North George Mason Drive, Arlington, Va.
Director of Personnel Planning.—Maj. Gen. Thomas E. Moore, 1225 23d Street South, Arlington, Va.
Director of Military Personnel.—Maj. Gen. George B. Greene, Jr., Dorchester Towers Apartments, 2005 Columbia Pike, Arlington, Va.
Director of Personnel Training and Education.—Maj. Gen. James C. McGehee, 2741 South Grove Street, Arlington, Va.
Director of Civilian Personnel.—John A. Watts, 2475 Virginia Avenue, Potomac Plaza, Apt. 810.

DEPUTY CHIEF OF STAFF, PLANS AND OPERATIONS

Deputy Chief of Staff, Plans and Operations.—Lt. Gen. Keith K. Compton, Quarters 69, Bolling Air Force Base, 20332.
Assistant Deputy Chief of Staff, Plans and Operations.—Maj. Gen. Arthur C. Agan, Jr., 1401 Juliana Place, Alexandria, Va.
Assistant Deputy Chief of Staff, Plans and Operations for JCS Matters.—Maj. Gen. John W. Carpenter III, 448 Schley Road, Annapolis, Md.
Director of Operations.—Maj. Gen. R. J. Clizbe, 707 Eighth Street, Alexandria, Va.
Director of Plans.—Maj. Gen. Seth J. McKee, The Prospect House, Apt. 1124, 1200 North Nash Street, Arlington, Va., 22209.

DEPUTY CHIEF OF STAFF, PROGRAMS AND REQUIREMENTS

Deputy Chief of Staff, Programs and Requirements.—Lt. Gen. Robert J. Friedman, MOQ 1306–1, Andrews Air Force Base.
Assistant Deputy Chief of Staff, Programs and Requirements.—[Vacant.]
Director of Aerospace Programs.—Maj. Gen. John D. Lavelle, 9904 Marquette Drive, Bethesda, Md.
Director of Command Control and Communications.—Maj. Gen. J. Francis Taylor, Jr., 5335 37th Street North, Arlington, Va.
Director of Civil Engineering.—Maj. Gen. Robert H. Curtin, 801 South Overlook Drive, Alexandria, Va.
Director of Manpower and Organization.—Maj. Gen. Benjamin O. Davis, Jr., Quarters 61B, Bolling Air Force Base, 20332.

DEPUTY CHIEF OF STAFF, SYSTEMS AND LOGISTICS

Deputy Chief of Staff, Systems and Logistics.—Lt. Gen. Thomas P. Gerrity, Quarters 67, Bolling Air Force Base, 20332.
Assistant Deputy Chief of Staff, Systems and Logistics.—Maj. Gen. Robert G. Ruegg, 5224 Little Falls Road, Arlington, Va.
Assistant for Logistics Planning.—Brig. Gen. Timothy F. O'Keefe, 322 Leesburg Pike, Falls Church, Va.
Assistant for Mutual Security.—Col. George M. Johnson, Jr., 4030 24th Road North, Arlington, Va.
Director of Maintenance Engineering.—Brig. Gen. Charles G. Chandler, Jr., 307 White Street, Falls Church, Va.
Director of Transportation.—Maj. Gen. Richard T. Coiner, Jr., 26 Kalorama Circle.
Director of Supply and Services.—Brig. Gen. Ernest L. Ramme, 5402 Easton Drive, Springfield, Va.
Director of Procurement Policy.—Col. Robert E. Lee, 6012 Kelly Court, Alexandria, Va.

Director of Production and Programming.—Maj. Gen. Harry E. Goldsworthy, 6821 Joallen Drive, Falls Church, Va.

DEPUTY CHIEF OF STAFF, RESEARCH AND DEVELOPMENT

Deputy Chief of Staff, Research and Development.—Lt. Gen. James Ferguson, Quarters 72, Bolling Air Force Base, 20332.

Assistant Deputy Chief of Staff, Research and Development.—Maj. Gen. Andrew J. Kinney, 2343 Nash Street South, Arlington, Va.

Director of Development.—Brig. Gen. Andrew J. Evans, 512 Bay Tree Lane, Falls Church, Va.

Director of Development Plans.—Maj. Gen. Richard D. Curtin, 2001 Columbia Pike, Arlington, Va.

Director of Science and Technology.—Brig. Gen. Edward B. Giller, Route 4, Box 30, Fairfax, Va.

Assistant for Research and Development Programming.—Col. Harold C. Teubner, 6012 Westchester Court, 20031.

Assistant for Manned Space Flight.—Col. Kenneth W. Schultz, 1137 North Ivanhoe Street, Arlington, Va.

Assistant for Foreign Development.—Col. Raymond P. Klein, 9308 Rosewood Street, Annandale, Va.

Director of Operational Requirements.—Maj. Gen. Jack J. Catton, 3545 36th Road North, Arlington, Va.

MAJOR AIR COMMANDS
CONTINENTAL COMMANDS

North American Air Defense Command (Ent Air Force Base, Colo.).—Gen. Dean C. Strother.

Air Defense Command (Ent Air Force Base, Colorado Springs, Colo.).—Lt. Gen. Herbert B. Thatcher.

Air Force Communications Service (Scott Air Force Base, Ill.).—Maj. Gen. Kenneth P. Bergquist.

Air Force Logistics Command (Wright-Patterson Air Force Base, Dayton, Ohio).—Gen. Mark E. Bradley, Jr.

Air Force Systems Command (Andrews Air Force Base, Camp Springs, Md.).—Gen. Bernard A. Schriever.

Air Training Command (Randolph Air Force Base, Tex.).—Lt. Gen. William W. Momyer.

Air University (Maxwell Air Force Base, Montgomery, Ala.).—Lt. Gen. Ralph P. Swofford, Jr.

Continental Air Command (Robins Air Force Base, Ga.).—Lt. Gen. Edward J. Timberlake.

Headquarters Command, USAF (Bolling Air Force Base 20332, D.C.).—Maj. Gen. Brooke E. Allen.

Military Air Transport Service (Scott Air Force Base, Belleville, Ill.).—Gen. Howell M. Estes, Jr.

Strategic Air Command (Offutt Air Force Base, Omaha, Nebr.).—Gen. John D. Ryan.

Tactical Air Command (Langley Air Force Base, Hampton, Va.).—Gen. Walter C. Sweeney, Jr.

USAF Security Service (San Antonio, Tex.).—Maj. Gen. Richard P. Klocko.

OVERSEAS COMMANDS

Alaskan Air Command (Elmendorf Air Force Base, Alaska).—Maj. Gen. James C. Jensen.

United States Air Force Southern Command (Albrook Air Force Base, Balboa, Canal Zone).—Maj. Gen. Robert A. Breitweiser.

Pacific Air Forces (Hickam Air Force Base, Hawaii).—Gen. Hunter Harris, Jr.

United States Air Forces in Europe (Wiesbaden, Germany).—Gen. Gabriel P. Disosway.

SEPARATE OPERATING AGENCIES

Air Force Accounting and Finance Center (3800 York Street, Denver, Colo.).—Brig. Gen. Thomas P. Corwin.

Aeronautical Chart and Information Center (St. Louis, Mo.).—Col. John G. Eriksen.

Office of Aerospace Research (Washington, D.C.).—Maj. Gen. Don R. Ostrander.

UNITED STATES AIR FORCE ACADEMY

Superintendent.—Maj. Gen. Robert H. Warren.

Commandant of Cadets.—Brig. Gen. Robert W. Strong, Jr.

DEPARTMENT OF JUSTICE

Constitution Avenue between Ninth and Tenth Streets, 20530
Phone, REpublic 7-8200

NICHOLAS deB. KATZENBACH, Attorney General of the United States; born Philadelphia, Pa., January 17, 1922; graduated Phillips Exeter Academy, Exeter, N.H.; B.A. cum laude, Princeton University, 1945; LL.B. cum laude, Yale University Law School, 1947; Rhodes Scholar, Oxford University (1947–1949); admitted to New Jersey State Bar, 1950 and Connecticut State Bar, 1955; associate in law firm of Katzenbach, Gildea and Rudner (1950); attorney adviser, Office of General Counsel to the Secretary of the Air Force (1950–1952); associate professor of law, Yale University (1952–1956); professor of law, University of Chicago (1956–1961); Assistant Attorney General, Office of Legal Counsel, Department of Justice (1961–1962); Deputy Attorney General, Department of Justice (1962–1965); Democrat; married to Lydia Phelps Stokes; children: Christopher, John, Maria, Anne; served in the United States Air Force (1942–1945).

Personal Secretary to the Attorney General—Carolyn M. MacMullan, 5415 Lincoln Street, Bethesda, Md.
Executive Assistant to the Attorney General.—Harold F. Reis (acting), 3330 Stephenson Place.
Director of Public Information.—Jacob Rosenthal, 103 G Street SW.
Assistant Director of Public Information.—Edward W. Edstrom, 4201 Cathedral Avenue.

OFFICE OF THE DEPUTY ATTORNEY GENERAL

Deputy Attorney General.—Ramsey Clark, 714 Lakeview Drive, Falls Church, Va.
Assistant Deputy Attorney General.—Harold Barefoot Sanders, Jr., 7706 Aqua Terrace, Falls Church, Va.
Assistant Deputy Attorney General.—William A. Geoghegan, 9612 Accord Drive, Potomac, Md.
Executive Assistant.—John T. Duffner, 3802 Ridge Road, Annandale, Va.
Head of Executive Office for United States Attorneys.—William J. Brady, Jr., 2331 49th Street.
Head of Executive Office for United States Marshals.—James J. P. McShane, 1325 North VanDorn Street, Alexandria, Va.
Chief, Legal and Legislative Section.—Herbert E. Hoffman, 4424 N. 25th Street, Arlington, Va.

OFFICE OF THE SOLICITOR GENERAL

Solicitor General.—Archibald Cox, Meadow House, South Down, Great Falls, Va.
First Assistant.—Ralph S. Spritzer, 4823 Alton Place.
Second Assistant.—Daniel M. Friedman, 325 Constitution Avenue NE.

ANTITRUST DIVISION

Assistant Attorney General.—William H. Orrick, Jr., 4856 Rockwood Parkway.
First Assistant.—Robert L. Wright, 7937 Deepwell Drive, Bethesda, Md.
Second Assistant.—Larry L. Williams, 1624 Vagabond Drive, Falls Church, Va.
Chief of Field Operations.—Gordon B. Spivak, 1650 Mt. Eagle Place, Alexandria, Va.
Director of Policy Planning.—Murray H. Bring, 507 South Lee Street, Alexandria, Va.

491

Administrative.—[Vacancy.]
Appellate.—Robert B. Hummel, 6213 Dahlonega Road, Bethesda, Md.
Economic.—Lewis Markus, 4501 Connecticut Avenue.
General Litigation.—Allen A. Dobey, 4442 Vacation Lane, Arlington, Va.
Judgments and Judgment Enforcement.—William D. Kilgore, Jr., 4410 Albemarle Street.
Special Trial.—Donald F. Melchior, 120 South Hudson Street, Arlington, Va.
Special Litigation.—Lewis Bernstein, 123 Northway, Greenbelt, Md.
Trial.—Baddia J. Rashid, 5804 Tanglewood Drive, Bethesda, Md.
Foreign Commerce.—Wilbur L. Fugate, 3404 Saylor Place, Alexandria, Va.
Evaluation.—[Vacancy].

CIVIL DIVISION

Assistant Attorney General.—John W. Douglas, 5700 Kirkside Drive, Chevy Chase, Md.
First Assistant.—J. William Doolittle, 19 Seventh Street NE.
Second Assistant.—Carl Eardley, 7832 Hampden Lane, Bethesda, Md.
Executive Assistant.—Joseph D. Guilfoyle, 1622 Montague Street.

SECTION CHIEFS

Administrative.—Annetta M. Sanford, 4205 Franklin Street, Kensington, Md.
Admiralty and Shipping.—Leavenworth Colby, 4101 Cathedral Avenue.
Appellate.—Morton Hollander, 4511 Avamere Street, Bethesda, Md.
Court of Claims.—Irving Jaffe, 9105 LeVelle Drive, Chevy Chase, Md.
Frauds.—Frederick N. Curley, 3033 North Florida Street, Arlington, Va.
General Litigation.—Harland F. Leathers, 4613 31st Road South, Arlington, Va.
General Claims.—B. Russell Chapin, 5611 McLean Drive, Bethesda, Md.
Patent.—T. Hayward Brown, 3850 Calvert Street.
Torts.—John G. Laughlin, 2005 Sycamore Drive, Falls Church, Va.
Office of Alien Property.—Anthony L. Mondello, 5608 Namakagan Road.

CIVIL RIGHTS DIVISION

Assistant Attorney General.—[Vacancy].
First Assistant.—John Doar, 4514 Drummond Street, Chevy Chase, Md.
Second Assistant.—St. John Barrett, 6520 Western Avenue, Chevy Chase, Md.
Executive Assistant.—James N. McCune, 4713 Hummer Road, Annandale, Va.

SECTION CHIEFS

Appeals and Research.—Harold H. Greene, 6417 Tone Drive, Bethesda, Md.
General Litigation.—John L. Murphy, 2819 Sudberry Lane, Bowie, Md.
Voting and Elections.—[Vacancy.]

CRIMINAL DIVISION

Assistant Attorney General.—Herbert John Miller, Jr., 10100 Chapel Road Potomac, Md.
First Assistant.—Howard P. Willens, 5002 Hurst Terrace.
Executive Assistant.—[Vacancy.]
Staff Assistant.—[Vacancy.]

SECTION CHIEFS

Administrative.—James W. Muskett, 5012 North Carlyn Spring Road, Arlington, Va.
Administrative Regulation.—Harold P. Shapiro, 4629 Chesapeake Street.

Appeals and Research.—Robert S. Erdahl, 7072 Wyndale Street.
Trial Staff.—[Vacancy.]
General Crimes.—Carl W. Belcher, 1417 Burtonwood Drive, Alexandria, Va.
Fraud.—Nathaniel E. Kossack, 7109 Oakridge Avenue, Chevy Chase, Md.
Organized Crime and Racketeering.—William G. Hundley, 1618 Roundtree Road, Falls Church, Va.

INTERNAL SECURITY DIVISION

Assistant Attorney General.—J. Walter Yeagley, Riverbend Road, Box 475-A, Rt. 1, Great Falls, Va.
First Assistant.—John F. Doherty, 614 Dead Run Drive, McLean, Va.
Executive Assistant.—Thomas K. Hall, 613 Dead Run Drive, McLean, Va.
Confidential Assistant.—Oran H. Waterman, 405 Prosperity Avenue, Fairfax, Va.

SECTION CHIEFS

Administrative.—Robert J. Stubbs, 1254 South Taylor Street, Arlington, Va.
Civil.—Francis X. Worthington, 2805 Botany Lane, Bowie, Md.
Criminal.—John H. Davitt, 3617 Shepherd Street, Chevy Chase, Md.
Registration.—Nathan B. Lenvin, 2940 26th Street North, Arlington, Va.
Appeals and Research.—Kevin T. Maroney, 2704 Finch Street, Silver Spring, Md.
Departmental Security Officer.—Clifford J. Nelson, 3826 Garfield Street.

LANDS DIVISION

Assistant Attorney General.—[Vacancy.]
First Assistant.—J. Edward Williams, 4630 River Road, 20016.

SECTION CHIEFS

Administrative.—Henry D. Rogers, 1114 North Inglewood Street, Arlington, Va.
Land Acquisition.—Harold S. Harrison, 1800 North Huntington Street, Arlington, Va.
Appraisal.—Robert H. Alsover, 1317 Park Terrace Drive, Alexandria, Va.
General Litigation.—David R. Warner, 5402 Cromwell Drive, Springfield, Va.
Appellate.—Roger P. Marquis, 1034 North Quincy Street, Arlington, Va.
Indian Claims.—Ralph A. Barney, 3743 McKinley Street.

TAX DIVISION

Assistant Attorney General.—Louis F. Oberdorfer, 4828 W Street.
First Assistant.—John B. Jones, 2960 Newark Street.
Second Assistant.—Richard M. Roberts, 5111 Nahant Street.
Assistant for Civil Trials.—C. Moxley Featherston, 3904 Lorraine Avenue, Falls Church, Va.
Executive Assistant.—C. Guy Tadlock, 3409 Thornapple Street, Chevy Chase, Md.

SECTION CHIEFS

Appellate.—Lee A. Jackson, 810 Glovercrest Drive, Alexandria, Va.
General Litigation.—Frederick B. Ugast, 5704 Kirkside Drive, Chevy Chase, Md.
Review.—Abbott M. Sellers, 1104 Marlan Drive, Alexandria, Va.
Criminal.—Fred G. Folsom, 3705 Corey Place.
Court of Claims.—Lyle M. Turner, 6240 Utah Avenue.
Refund Trial #1.—David A. Wilson, Jr., 4816 Hutchins Place.
Refund Trial #2.—Myron C. Baum, 402 Hinsdale Court, Silver Spring, Md.
Refund Trial #3.—Jerome Fink, 4726 Merivale Road, Chevy Chase, Md.

OFFICE OF LEGAL COUNSEL

Assistant Attorney General.—Norbert A. Schlei, 3618 Prospect Street, 20007.
First Assistant.—Harold F. Reis, 3330 Stephenson Place.
Second Assistant.—Leon Ulman, 4838 Langdrum Lane, Chevy Chase, Md.
Director, Office of Administrative Procedure.—Webster P. Maxson, 5423 Beech Avenue, Bethesda, Md.
Chief, Conscientious Objector Section.—T. Oscar Smith, 4879 Old Dominion Drive, Arlington, Va.

ADMINISTRATIVE DIVISION

Assistant Attorney General for Administration.—S. A. Andretta, 2500 Q Street.
First Assistant.—John W. Adler, 4903 Brookeway Drive.
Chief, Budget and Accounts Office.—John C. Brown, Jr., 7413 Blair Road.
Chief, Legal and Legislative Office.—Ralph C. Jackson, 1619 Sherwood Road, Silver Spring, Md.
Chief, Management Office.—Bennett Willis, Jr., 3611 Rockland Terrace, McLean, Va.
Chief, Administrative Services Office.—Edgar M. Ford, 4413 Ridge Road, Chevy Chase, Md.
Chief, Records Administration Office.—Armando diGirolamo, 7101 Edgemoor Lane, Alexandria, Va.
Librarian.—Marvin P. Hogan, 7305 Foxe Place, Springfield, Va.

OFFICE OF THE PARDON ATTORNEY
131 Indiana Avenue

Pardon Attorney.—Reed Cozart, 808 Chalfonte Drive, Alexandria, Va.
Assistant Pardon Attorney.—Kenneth Van Keuren Harvey, 10225 Kensington Parkway, Kensington, Md.

FEDERAL BUREAU OF INVESTIGATION
Phone, EXecutive 3-7100

Director.—J. Edgar Hoover, 4936 30th Place, 20008.
Associate Director.—Clyde A. Tolson, 4000 Massachusetts Avenue, 20016.
Assistant to the Director.—Alan H. Belmont, 2711 North Yucatan Street, Arlington, Va., 22213.
Assistant to the Director.—John P. Mohr, 3427 North Edison Street, Arlington Va., 22207.
Administrative Division—Assistant Director.—Nicholas P. Callahan, 5611 Chesterbrook Road, 20016.
Training Division—Assistant Director.—Joseph J. Casper, 604 Kenbrook Drive, Silver Spring, Md., 20902.
FBI Laboratory—Assistant Director.—Ivan W. Conrad, 810 Crescent Drive, Alexandria, Va., 22302.
Crime Records Division—Assistant Director.—Cartha D. DeLoach, 107 Morningside Drive, Alexandria, Va., 22308.
Inspection Division—Inspector-in-Charge.—W. Mark Felt, 1208 Musket Court, Fairfax, Va., 22030.
Special Investigative Division—Assistant Director.—James H. Gale, 916 Rocky Mount Road, Fairfax, Va., 22030.
General Investigative Division—Assistant Director.—Alex Rosen, Dorchester House, 20009.
Domestic Intelligence Division—Assistant Director.—William C. Sullivan, 2810 64th Avenue, Cheverly, Md., 20785.
Files and Communications Division—Assistant Director.—William S. Travel, 4117 Woodacre Drive, McLean, Va., 22101.
Identification Division—Assistant Director.—C. Lester Trotter, 110 Iroquois Way, Forest Heights, Md., 20021.

IMMIGRATION AND NATURALIZATION SERVICE

119 D Street NE.   Phone, LIncoln 7-9000

Commissioner.—Raymond F. Farrell, 2500 Q Street.
Executive Assistant to the Commissioner.—James L. Hennessy, 3000 Russell Road, Alexandria, Va.
Associate Commissioner, Management.—Edward A. Loughran, 2266 Cathedral Avenue.
Associate Commissioner, Operations.—Mario T. Noto, 9512 Byeforde Road, Kensington, Md.
General Counsel.—L. Paul Winings, 3541 Brandywine Street.

BOARD OF IMMIGRATION APPEALS

H.O.L.C. Building, 101 Indiana Avenue

Chairman.—Thomas G. Finucane, 5415 Surrey Street, Chevy Chase, Md.
Members.—
  Thomas J. Griffin, 1701 Fairlawn Drive, McLean, Va.
  Robert E. Ludwig, 4509 18th Street North, Arlington, Va.
  Louisa Wilson, 2818 Wisconsin Avenue.
  Allen R. Cozier, 6335 Utah Avenue.
Executive Assistant.—Anthony L. Montaquila, 5148 South Dakota Avenue NE.

BUREAU OF PRISONS

H.O.L.C. Building, 101 Indiana Avenue

Director.—Myrl E. Alexander, 201 Massachusetts Avenue NE.
Assistant Directors.—
  Herman G. Moeller, 422 Tyler Place, Alexandria, Va
  John J. Galvin, 5946 Strata Street, McLean, Va.
  John C. Taylor, 201 Massachusetts Avenue NE

BOARD OF PAROLE

H.O.L.C. Building, 101 Indiana Avenue

Chairman.—Richard A. Chappell, 3601 Connecticut Avenue.
Members.—
  Charlotte P. Groshell, 2500 Q Street.
  Lewis J. Grout, 2601 North Jefferson Street, Arlington, Va.
  William F. Howland, Jr., 1301 Dogwood Drive, Alexandria, Va.
  Gerald E. Murch, 412 Deerfield Street, Silver Spring, Md.
Chairman, Youth Correction Division.—James A. Carr, Jr., 37 Pond View Avenue, Jamaica Plain, Mass.
Members.—
  Homer L. Benson, 811 Booker Place, Seat Pleasant, Md.
  Zeigel W. Neff, 9424 Locust Hill Road, Bethesda, Md.
Staff Director.—James C. Neagles, 5701 Mark Drive, Camp Springs, Md.
Parole Executive.—Joseph N. Shore, 6206 East Halbert Road, Bethesda, Md.
Youth Division Executive.—Claude S. Nock, Jr., 7623 Highland Avenue, Silver Spring, Md.

FEDERAL PRISON INDUSTRIES, INC.

H.O.L.C. Building, 101 Indiana Avenue

(Corporation authorized by act of Congress, approved June 23, 1934, and created by Executive Order No. 6917 of December 11, 1934)

Officers and Directors:
  President.—Sanford Bates, 12 Baldwin Street, Pennington, N.J., representing the Attorney General.

Officers and Directors—Continued

Vice President.—Emil Schram, Hillcrest, Peru, Ind., representing agriculture.

George Meany, President, American Federation of Labor and Congress of Industrial Organization, Washington, D.C., representing labor.

John Marshal Briley, R.R. 2, Perrysburg, Ohio, representing Secretary of Defense.

James L. Palmer, 921 North Hawthorne Place, Lake Forest, Ill., retailers and consumers.

Berry N. Beaman, Universal Vise & Tool Co., Parma, Mich., representing industry.

Commissioner of Industries.—Myrl E. Alexander, 201 Massachusetts Avenue NE.

Associate Commissioner of Industries.—T. Wade Markley, 13112 Andrew Drive, Silver Spring, Md.

Deputy Associate Commissioner.—[Vacancy.]

Assistant Commissioner.—Andrew W. Cleland, 4825 Kurtz Road, McLean, Va.

Secretary of Corporation.—Harold W. Reep, 8004 Powhatan Street, Hyattsville, Md.

Assistant Secretary.—John J. Maloney, 5403 56th Avenue, Riverdale, Md.

UNITED STATES ATTORNEYS OFFICE

United States Courthouse. Phone, STerling 3-5700

United States Attorney, District of Columbia.—David C. Acheson, 3101 Garfield Street.

UNITED STATES MARSHAL'S OFFICE

United States Courthouse. Phone, STerling 3-5700

United States Marshal, District of Columbia.—Luke C. Moore, 1303 Trinidad Avenue NE.

POST OFFICE DEPARTMENT

Pennsylvania Avenue, between Twelfth and Thirteenth Streets, 20260

Phone, STerling 3-3100 (Code 177)

JOHN A. GRONOUSKI, Postmaster General; born October 26, 1919, Dunbar, Wis., son of John A. (deceased) and Mary Riley Gronouski; reared and educated in Oshkosh, Wis., St. Peter's elementary and high school and Oshkosh State Teachers College; graduate of University of Wisconsin; economics with major in public finance; Bachelor Degree in 1942; Masters Degree in 1947; Doctorate in 1955; entered Army Air Corps in April 1942 as private and later served as navigator holding rank of first lieutenant; 24 combat missions in European Theater of Operations; honorable discharge in 1945; taught public finance, money, and banking at University of Maine from February 1948 to June 1950; from November 1952 to August 1956, was research associate for Federation of Tax Administrators doing research on state tax administration; during part of this time (1953–56) taught statistics at Roosevelt College Evening School; participated in study of Wisconsin income tax administration from September 1956 to August 1957 as research associate at University of Wisconsin; from September 1957 to January 1959 taught public finance, state and local finance, and money and banking at Wayne State University, Detroit, Mich.; at same time was on research staff of Michigan tax study; February 1959 became Research Director for Wisconsin Department of Taxation and Research Director of University of Wisconsin Tax Impact Study; in October 1959, named Executive Director for continuing Revenue Survey Commission established by Governor Gaylord Nelson; January 1960, appointed by Governor Nelson to be Wisconsin Commissioner of Taxation; nominated by President John F. Kennedy to be Postmaster General of the United States, September 9, 1963, confirmed by U.S. Senate on September 24, 1963; member of Executive Board, National Association of Tax Administrators; Editorial Advisory Board, National Tax Journal; American Economic Association; National Tax Association; the University Club; Board of Directors of the Pulaski Foundation; Polish Institute of the Arts and Sciences; honorary cochairman of the Committee for the Endowed Chair in Polish Studies, University of Chicago; trustee of the John F. Kennedy Library; representative of President Johnson at the International Trade Fair, Poznan, Poland, in 1964; a Catholic; married to Mary Louise Metz of Madison, Wis., on January 24, 1948; two daughters, Stacy, 12, and Julie, 9; residence at 6133 33d Street, 20015.

FREDERICK C. BELEN, Deputy Postmaster General; born December 25, 1913, Lansing, Mich., son of C. F. and Elizabeth L. Belen; attended Lansing schools; graduated Michigan State University, 1937, A.B. degree; LL.B., George Washington University 1942; admitted to practice before the Michigan, District of Columbia, and U.S. Supreme Court bars; in the 75th Congress, served as Secretary to former Congressman Andrew J. Transue and in the 77th Congress was secretary to the late Congressman George D. O'Brien, both from Michigan; entered U.S. Army as lieutenant July 1941, developed the security program for the Ports of Embarkation of the Army as well as the wartime security system for the Pentagon (WD & C of S Hdqtrs.); discharged as lieutenant colonel April 1946; joined staff of House Post Office and Civil Service Committee and became chief counsel and staff director, 1946–1961; nominated by President John F. Kennedy to be Assistant Postmaster General, Bureau of Operations, January 1961; nominated by President Lyndon B. Johnson to be Deputy Postmaster General, February 1964; member of American Society for Public Administration, American Legion, Board of Directors of Multiple Sclerosis Society; elder of Little Falls (Va.) Presbyterian Church; married Opal Sheets of Parsons, W. Va., February 1943; one son, Frederick C. Belen, Jr., 17.

OFFICE OF THE POSTMASTER GENERAL

Executive Assistant to the Postmaster General.—Michael Monroney, 5300 Westbard Avenue, Bethesda, Md., 20016.
Special Assistant to the Postmaster General (Public Information).—Ira Kapenstein, 9410 Woodland Drive, Silver Spring, Md., 20910.
Confidential Assistant to the Postmaster General.—Mrs. Norma L. Eroen, 2116 F Street, 20037.
Judicial Officer.—Reva Beck Bosone, Room 3358, Post Office Building, 20260.
Director, Office of Regional Administration.—John P. Carter, 3328 Northampton Street, 20015.

ADVISORY BOARD

Chairman.—John A. Gronouski (Postmaster General).
Vice Chairman.—Frederick C. Belen (Deputy Postmaster General).
Members:
  Charles H. Earl, 32 Edgehill Road, Little Rock, Ark., 72207.
  Fred Gates, 5249 Ewing Avenue South, Minneapolis, Minn., 55410.
  Robert E. MacNeal, The Kenilworth, Alden Park, Philadelphia, Pa., 19144.
  Carl Murphy, 2406 Overland Avenue, Baltimore, Md., 21214.
  Paul Perocchi, 144 Chestnut Street, Andover, Mass., 01810.
Executive Secretary.—William H. Snyder (Director, Executive Secretariat, Office of the Deputy Postmaster General).

OFFICE OF THE DEPUTY POSTMASTER GENERAL

Executive Assistant to Deputy Postmaster General.—John P. Doran, 12908 Goodhill Road, Silver Spring, Md., 20906.
Director, Headquarters Services Division.—Charles E. Carpenter, Route 1, Box 86, Broad Run, Va., 22014.

BUREAU OF OPERATIONS

Assistant Postmaster General.—William M. McMillan, 1200 North Nash Street, Arlington, Va., 22209.
Deputy Assistant Postmaster General for Field Operations.—August C. Hahn, 1368 Fourth Street SW., 20024.
Deputy Assistant Postmaster General for Postmasters and Patron Relations.— Charles H. Ryan, 1108 Marilta Court, Fairfax, Va., 22030.
Executive Assistant to the Assistant Postmaster General.—[Vacant.]
Special Assistant for Policy and Projects.—Edward V. Dorsey, 3708 Rectory Lane, Upper Marlboro, Md., 20870.
Staff Assistant to the Deputy Assistant Postmaster General.—Roger F. King, 2410 Davis Avenue, Alexandria, Va., 22301.
Installations Management Division:
  Director.—John D. Swygert, 7211 Pomander Lane, Chevy Chase, Md., 20015.
Classification and Special Services Division:
  Director.—Edwin A. Riley, 5702 Maiden Lane, Bethesda, Md., 20034.
Customer Relations Division:
  Director.—Robert M. Huse, 6812 Algonquin Avenue, Bethesda, Md., 20014.
Distribution and Delivery Division:
  Director.—Mike E. Chapin, 5725 Robinwood Lane, Falls Church, Va., 22041.
Space and Mechanization Requirements Division:
  Director.—[Vacant.]
Postmasters and Rural Appointments Division:
  Director.—W. Carson Browning, Jr., 3207 Wake Drive, Kensington, Md., 20795.

BUREAU OF TRANSPORTATION AND INTERNATIONAL SERVICES

Assistant Postmaster General.—William J. Hartigan, 2019 Scroggins Road, Alexandria, Va., 22302.

Executive Assistant (Acting).—G. Allan Brown, 907 Parkside Terrace, Fairfax, Va., 22030.

   Administrative Office, Director.—Edward J. Chaszar, 3 Accotink Road, Alexandria, Va., 22308.

   Control Officer.—William J. Forbes, 3343 Legation Street, 20015.

Deputy Assistant Postmaster General.—Frederick E. Batrus, 7124 Fairfax Road, Bethesda, Md., 20014.

   Research and Development Division:

      Director.—William L. Tobin, 3901 31st Street North, Arlington, Va., 22207.

      Director, Research Branch.—Beatrice Aitchison, 1929 S Street, 20009.

      Director, Railway Development.—[Vacant.]

      Director, Air and International Development.—James E. Gildea, 5619 33d Street North, Arlington, Va., 22207.

      Director, Highway Development.—Paul F. Achstetter, 6307 Stoneham Road, Bethesda, Md., 20034.

   International Service Division:

      Director.—Greever P. Allan, 800 South Pitt Street, Alexandria, Va., 22314.

      Deputy Director.—Francis L. Coolidge, 2905 32d Street, 20008.

      Assistant Director.—Cornelius Petersen, 308 Grant Avenue, Takoma Park, Md., 20012.

Deputy Assistant Postmaster General.—[Vacant.]

   Domestic Transportation Division:

      Director.—Joseph F. Jones, 5704 Euclid Street, Cheverly, Md., 20785.

      Director, Railway Transportation Branch.—Joseph E. Flory, 1905 North Hollister Street, Arlington, Va., 22205.

      Director, Highway Transportation Branch.—Laurence A. Woods, 8115 15th Avenue, Langley Park, Hyattsville, Md., 20783.

      Director, Air Transportation Branch.—Willis B. Henderson, 6715 Queens Chapel Road, Hyattsville, Md., 20782.

      Director, Mail Equipment Transportation Branch.—Arnold G. Aulick, 1845 Summit Place, 20009.

   Distribution and Routing Division:

      Director.—Charles A. McIntyre, 301 Cheryl Drive, Falls Church, Va., 22044.

      Director, Schemes and Routing Branch.—William E. Corrigan, 10029 Brunett Avenue, Silver Spring, Md., 20901.

      Director, Transportation Requirements Branch.—John C. Miller, 737 Morningside Drive, Fairfax, Va., 22030.

      Director, Transit Organization Control Branch.—Glen R. Wester, 6054 North Morgan Street, Alexandria, Va., 22312.

BUREAU OF FINANCE

Assistant Postmaster General.—Ralph W. Nicholson, 15 Fourth Street SE., 20003.

Deputy Assistant Postmaster General and Controller.—Eugene B. Crowe, 5151 Williamsburg Boulevard, Arlington, Va., 22207.

Deputy Assistant Postmaster General for Administration.—James R. Thomason, 1211 Burketon Road, Hyattsville, Md., 20783.

   Executive Assistant to Assistant Postmaster General.—Carlton H. Jencks, 4245 Susquehannock Drive, McLean, Va., 22101.

   Special Assistant to Assistant Postmaster General.—Emerson Markham, 5408 Keppler Road, 20031.

   Administrative Officer.—Joseph P. Griffin, 2873 South Abingdon Street, Arlington, Va., 22206.

   Postal Rates Division:

      Director.—Arthur Eden, 9708 Dameron Drive, Silver Spring, Md., 20910.

Assistant Controller for Accounting.—William E. Wootton, 8609 Melwood Road, Bethesda, Md., 20034.

   Accounting Division:

      Director.—Herschel Harris, 2417 Lilliam Drive, Silver Spring, Md., 20902.

   Data Processing Division:

      Director.—John Kangas, 152 North Columbus Street, Arlington, Va., 22203.

   Systems and Procedures Division:

      Director.—Clifton H. Brown, 8030 Jansen Drive, Springfield, Va., 22150.

Assistant Controller for Budget.—Clarence N. Bruce, 7505 Essex Avenue, Springfield, Va., 22150.

   Program Reports Division:

      Director.—Stanley K. Day, 801 Roberts Road, Fairfax, Va., 22030.

Statistical Programs Officer.—Benjamin J. Mandel, 6101 16th Street, 20011.
  Cost Analysis Division:
    Director.—Thomas F. McCormack, 10101 Greenock Road, Silver Spring, Md., 20901.
  Cost Ascertainment Division:
    Director.—Lewis W. Hicks, 732 Glenbrook Place, Fairfax, Va., 22030.
  Statistics and Economics Division:
    Director.—Milton A. Schwartz, 13010 Flack Street, Silver Spring, Md., 20906.
Finance Officer.—J. Harold Marks, 4400 34th Street South, Arlington, Va., 22206.
  Postal Funds Division:
    Director.—James M. Bell, 508 Blick Drive, Silver Spring, Md., 20904.
  Money Order Audit Division:
    Director.—Orion F. Schaffer, 9519 Avenel Road, Silver Spring, Md., 20903.
ADP Management Division:
    Director.—Douglass M. Parnell Jr., 2201 Wilkinson Place, Alexandria, Va., 22306.
Management Systems Division:
    Director.—Herbert S. Becker, 1600 South Joyce Street, Arlington, Va., 22202.

BUREAU OF FACILITIES

Assistant Postmaster General.—Tyler Abell, 4506 49th Street, 20016.
Deputy Assistant Postmaster General.—Amos J. Coffman, 324 Anneliese Drive, Falls Church, Va., 22044.
Deputy Assistant Postmaster General.—[Vacant.]
Executive Assistant to Assistant Postmaster General.—Joseph P. Doherty, 14209 Chadwick Lane, Rockville, Md., 20853.
Special Assistant to Assistant Postmaster General.—Joseph C. Russo, Jr., 2806 Key Boulevard, Arlington, Va., 22201.
Maintenance Division:
  Director.—Charles A. Dieman, 9216 Quintana Drive, Bethesda, Md., 20034.
Procurement Division:
  Director.—Conrad L. Trahern, 13011 Narada Street, Rockville, Md., 20853.
Realty Division:
  Director.—Dennis A. Jensen, 11702 Ibsen Drive, Rockville, Md., 20852.

BUREAU OF PERSONNEL

Assistant Postmaster General.—Richard James Murphy, 9912 Harrogate Road, Bethesda, Md., 20034.
Deputy Assistant Postmaster General (Industrial Relations).—James J. La Penta, Jr., 5018 57th Avenue, Bladensburg, Md., 20710.
Deputy Assistant Postmaster General (Personnel Plans and Programs).—Richard E. Orton, 2106 North Ohio Street, Arlington, Va., 22205.
Executive Assistant to Assistant Postmaster General (Personnel).—Fred E. Cashman, 1019 North Noyes Drive, Silver Spring, Md., 20910.
Employee Relations Division:
  Director.—James K. Sullivan, 11211 Monticello Avenue, Silver Spring, Md., 20902.
Compensation Division:
  Director.—Herbert Block, 1010 Playford Lane, Silver Spring, Md., 20901.
Departmental Personnel Division:
  Director.—Harry W. Hobbs, 315 Adrienne Drive, Alexandria, Va., 22309.
Employment and Placement Division:
  Director.—[Vacant.]
Safety and Health Division:
  Director.—Edward B. Landry, 12 Kentbury Way, Bethesda, Md., 20014.
Suggestions and Awards Division:
  Director.—Richard J. Payne, 2511 Plyers Mill Road, Silver Spring, Md., 20902.
Training and Development Division:
  Director.—Francis J. Mahaney, 4325 Dresden Street, Kensington, Md., 20795.
Board of Appeals and Review:
  Appeals Officer.—Hollis B. Bach, 5423 Sanger Avenue, Alexandria, Va., 22311.
  Appeals Officer.—Elmer W. McLain, 1000 6th Street SW., 20024.
  Appeals Officer.—John G. Werner, 6665 32d Place, 20015.

BUREAU OF THE CHIEF POSTAL INSPECTOR

Chief Postal Inspector.—Henry B. Montague, 1020 North Quincy Street, Arlington, Va., 22201.

Deputy Chief Postal Inspector.—Donald D. Duggan, 5151 Tenth Road North, Arlington, Va., 22205.

Assistant Chief Postal Inspector.—James F. Buckely, 418 Carolyn Drive, Falls Church, Va., 22044.

Staff Assistant to Chief Postal Inspector.—Edward W. Cummins, 1514 Dauphine Drive, Falls Church, Va., 22042.

Director, Mail Loss and Depredations Division.—Marlin W. Brown, 3819 Bound Brook Lane, Alexandria, Va., 22309.

Director, Fraud and Mailability Investigations Division.—William F. Callahan, 408 Pershing Drive, Silver Spring, Md., 20910.

Director Financial Investigations Division.—John F. Free, 5730 27th Street, 20015.

Director, Service Investigations and Inspections Division.—Norval W. Woodworth, 4624 Ninth Street South, Arlington, Va., 22204.

Director, Identification Laboratory.—Albert W. Somerford, Clarksburg, Md., 20734.

Director, Internal Audit Division.—Stancil M. Smith, 810 Waterford Road, Alexandria, Va., 22308.

Assistant to Chief Postal Inspector.—Paul R. Andrews, 4601 Brandywine Street, 20016.

Director Personnel Security.—Michael L. Keefe, 8510 Loughborough Place, Chevy Chase, Md., 20015.

OFFICE OF THE GENERAL COUNSEL

General Counsel.—Louis J. Doyle, 616 Woodside Parkway, Silver Spring, Md., 20910.

Deputy General Counsel.—Harvey H. Hannah, 3907 Turbridge Lane, Alexandria, Va., 22308.

Legal Counsel (Opinions-Real Property).—Adam G. Wenchel, 3803 Blackthorn Street, Chevy Chase, Md., 20015.

Opinions Division:
   Assistant General Counsel.—Jack T. DiLorenzo, 3801 Connecticut Avenue, 20008.

Real Property Division:
   Assistant General Counsel.—James J. Wilson, 6401 Tone Drive, Bethesda, Md., 20034.

Associate General Counsel (Litigation-Claims).—Paul Meininger, 5616 Southwick, Bethesda, Md., 20034.

Litigation Division:
   Assistant General Counsel.—Julian T. Cromelin, 3119 Rittenhouse Street, 20015.

Claims Division:
   Assistant General Counsel.—Earle D. Goss, 9700 Fernwood Road, Bethesda, Md., 20034.

Associate General Counsel (Legislative-Mailability).—William F. Lawrence, 1035 Crest Haven Drive, Silver Spring, Md., 20903.

Legislative Division:
   Assistant General Counsel.—Felix E. Sklagen, 4514 Connecticut Avenue, 20008.

Mailability Division:
   Assistant General Counsel.—Saul J. Mindel, 9621 Flower Avenue, Silver Spring, Md., 20901.

OFFICE OF RESEARCH AND ENGINEERING

Director.—Edward E. Harriman, 2 Holiday Drive, Alexandria, Va., 22308.

Deputy Director.—[Vacant.]

Manager, Operations Research.—L. Rex Landis, Hunting Towers East, Alexandria, Va., 22314.

Manager, Field Engineering.—James A. Burns, 8511 Hazelwood Drive, Bethesda, Md., 20014.
Assistant Director for Programming and Control.—Virgil C. Stone, 9903 Sidney Road, Silver Spring, Md., 20901.
  Acting Chief, Administrative Management Division.—Raymond B. Robinson, 9308 Saybrook Avenue, Silver Spring, Md., 20901.
  Acting Chief, Program Management Division.—Edward M. Tamulevich, 5208 Sangamore Road, 20016.
  Chief, Program Coordination Division.—[Vacancy.]
Assistant Director for Research and Development.—Harold W. Lieske, 414 Waterford Road, Silver Spring, Md., 20901.
  Chief, Research Division.—Richard W. Hessinger, 7509 Wellesley Drive, College Park, Md., 20741.
  Chief, Development Division.—E. C. Kautt, 20 Tansy Drive, Falls Church, Va., 22042.
  Acting Chief, Postal Laboratory.—Robert C. Wilbur, 1081 North Manchester Street, Arlington, Va., 22205.
  Chief, Automotive Division.—George C. Nield, 5104 Rappahannock Place, Annandale, Va., 22003.
Assistant Director for Management Engineering.—Walter R. Masters, 713 Tarpon Drive, Alexandria, Va., 22309.
  Chief, Project Engineering Division.—Fred W. Shaffer, 12609 Bluhill Road, Wheaton, Md., 20906.
  Chief, Industrial Engineering Division.—George M. Beck, 1703 East-West Highway, Silver Spring, Md., 20910.
  Chief, Systems Analysis Division.—Walter I. Jones, 6016 Kingsford Road, Bethesda, Md., 20034.
  Chief, Mechanization Utilization Division.—Edward R. Dunzweiler, 4914 Jamestown Road, Washington, D.C., 20016.
Assistant Director for Construction Engineering.—James M. Lowe, 9408 Riley Place, Silver Spring, Md., 20910.
  Chief, Architectural Division.—David Bregman, 8201 16th Street, Silver Spring, Md., 20910.
  Chief, Process Machinery Division.—Eugene A. Kafka, Route 1, Box 180, Kenmore, Great Falls, Va., 22066.
  Chief, Utilities Division.—W. Norman Meyer, 9401 Overlea Drive, Rockville, Md., 20850.
  Chief, Project Construction Division.—Patrick H. Sandlin, Jr., 5911 Maxwell Court South, McLean, Va., 22101.

REGIONAL OFFICES

Atlanta Region—Georgia, Florida, North Carolina, South Carolina.—Charlton B. Gladden, Regional Director, Federal Annex Building, Atlanta, Ga., 30304.
Boston Region—Massachusetts, Maine, Vermont, New Hampshire, Connecticut, Rhode Island.—Donald P. Steele, Regional Director, Post Office and Courthouse Building, Boston, Mass., 02109.
Chicago Region—Illinois and Michigan.—Donald L. Swanson, Regional Director, Main Post Office Building, Chicago, Ill., 60699.
Cincinnati Region—Indiana, Ohio, and Kentucky.—Joseph P. Nolan, Regional Director, Main Post Office Building, P.O. Box 1999, Cincinnati, Ohio, 45201.
Dallas Region—Texas and Louisiana.—William M. McMillan, Regional Director, Main Post Office Building, Dallas, Tex., 75221.
Denver Region.—Colorado, Utah, Arizona, New Mexico, and Wyoming.—Clifford G. Crossan, Regional Director, P.O. Box 1979, Denver, Colo., 80201.
Memphis Region—Tennessee, Alabama and Mississippi.—Isaac C. Pattison, Jr., Regional Director, Post Office Building, Memphis, Tenn., 38101
Minneapolis Region—Minnesota, North Dakota, South Dakota, Wisconsin.—Adrian P. Winkel, Regional Director, 512 Nicollet Avenue, Minneapolis, Minn., 55425.
New York Region—New York, Puerto Rico, Virgin Islands.—Sean P. Keating, Regional Director, Main Post Office Building, New York, N.Y., 10098.
Philadelphia Region—Pennsylvania, New Jersey, and Delaware.—James J. Doherty, Regional Director, Main Post Office Building, Philadelphia, Pa., 19104.
Saint Louis Region—Missouri, Iowa, Arkansas.—John F. Dee, Regional Director, 1114 Market Street, St. Louis, Mo., 63199.

San Francisco Region—California, Nevada, Hawaii, and all Pacific Possessions.— Raymond R. Holmquist Regional Director, 79 New Montgomery Street, San Francisco, Calif., 94106.

Seattle Region—Idaho, Montana, Oregon, Washington, and Alaska.—James J. Symbol, Regional Director, New Republic Building, Box 3900, Seattle, Wash., 98124.

Washington Region—Virginia, West Virginia, Maryland, the District of Columbia.—Andrew E. Newton, Regional Director, City Post Office Building, Washington, D.C., 20269.

Wichita Region—Kansas, Nebraska, and Oklahoma.—Charles W. Shoemake, Regional Director, Main Post Office Building, Wichita, Kans., 67225.

POSTAL DATA CENTERS

Atlanta Postal Data Center—Atlanta, Washington (Richmond), and Philadelphia.— Robert W. Bass, Director, Postal Data Center, Post Office Department, Federal Annex Building, Atlanta, Ga., 30335.

Dallas Postal Data Center—Dallas, Denver, and Wichita.—James R. Martin, Director, Postal Data Center, Post Office Department, Box 1557, Main Post Office Building, Dallas, Tex., 75299.

Minneapolis Postal Data Center—Chicago and Minneapolis.—Clifford W. LaMar, Director, Postal Data Center, Post Office Department, Main Post Office, Box 63, Minneapolis, Minn., 55470.

New York Postal Data Center—Boston and New York.—Joseph Klegman, Director, Postal Data Center, Post Office Department, Main Post Office Building, New York, N.Y., 10099.

Saint Louis Postal Data Center—Cincinnati, Memphis, and Saint Louis.—Milton L. Healy, Director, Postal Data Center, Post Office Department, Post Office Building, Saint Louis, Mo., 63180.

San Francisco Postal Data Center—San Francisco and Seattle.—John P. Miele, Director, Postal Data Center, Post Office Department, Post Office Box 3700, San Francisco, Calif., 94119.

DEPARTMENT OF THE INTERIOR

Interior Building, 20240.   Phone, 343-1100 (Code 183, extension 70)

STEWART L. UDALL, of Tucson, Ariz.; born in St. Johns, Ariz., January 31, 1920, son of the late Levi S. Udall, Arizona Supreme Court Chief Justice, and Louise Lee Udall; attended public schools of St. Johns, and received LL.B. degree at University of Arizona in 1948; member, L.D.S. (Mormon) Church; married Ermalee Webb of Mesa, Ariz., in 1947; six children—Thomas, Scott, Lynn, Lori, Denis, and James; as enlisted gunner flew tour with 15th Air Force, Italy, 1944; elected to the 84th Congress November 2, 1954; reelected to the 85th, 86th, and 87th Congresses; became Secretary of the Interior January 21, 1961.

Secretary of the Interior.—Stewart L. Udall.
Under Secretary.—John A. Carver, Jr., 6605 16th Street North, Arlington, Va., 22205.
Assistant Secretary (Water and Power).—Kenneth Holum, 8132 West Beach Drive, 20012.
Assistant Secretary (Public Land Management).—[Vacant.]
Assistant Secretary (Mineral Resources).—John M. Kelly, 4201 Cathedral Avenue, 20016.
Assistant Secretary for Fish and Wildlife.—Frank P. Briggs, 4740 Connecticut Avenue, 20008.
Assistant Secretary for Administration.—D. Otis Beasley, 4418 Davenport Street, 20016.
Assistant to the Secretary.—Orren Beaty, Jr., Route 4, Box 341, Vienna, Va.
Assistant to the Secretary and Legislative Counsel.—Max N. Edwards, 4000 Massachusetts Avenue, 20016.
Assistant to the Secretary for Land Utilization.—Karl S. Landstrom, 5400 North Carlyn Springs Road, Arlington, Va., 22200.
Assistant to the Secretary and Director of Information.—Charles K. Boatner, 3304 Woodbine Street, Chevy Chase, Md., 20015.
Assistant to the Secretary.—Walter I. Pozen, 3415 Raymond Street, Chevy Chase, Md., 20015.
Special Assistant to the Secretary (Liaison for Atomic Energy Agency).—Charles F. MacGowan, 18 Park Valley Road, Silver Spring, Md.
Director, Office of Water Resources Research.—Roland R. Renne, 2645 North Van Dorn Street, Alexandria, Va., 22302.
Assistant and Science Advisor to the Secretary.—[Vacant.]
Assistant to the Secretary (Congressional Liaison).—Robert C. McConnell, 9210 Manchester Road, Silver Spring, Md.
Executive Assistant to the Secretary.—Anna K. Life, 2223 North Military Road, Arlington, Va., 22207.
Oil Import Appeals Board:
  Chairman.—Henry C. Rubin, 2421 Lillian Drive, Silver Spring, Md.
  Members:
    Department of Commerce.—James F. Collins, Administrator, Business and Defense Services Administration, 3039 Dent Place, 20007.
    Department of Defense.—Paul H. Riley, Deputy Assistant Secretary of Defense (Supply and Services OASD (I. & L.)), 1127 Lake Boulevard, Annandale, Va.
Office of the Under Secretary:
  Deputy Under Secretary.—Moris Burge, 2601 Woodley Place, 20008.
Office of the Assistant Secretary (Water and Power):
  Deputy Assistant Secretary.—Robert W. Nelson, 1012 Crane Drive, Falls Church, Va., 22042.
  Assistant and Engineering Research Advisor to Assistant Secretary.—Morgan D. Dubrow, 6824 Williamsburg Boulevard, Arlington, Va., 22213.
  Director, Office of Saline Water.—Frank C. DiLuzio, 9504 Barroll Lane, Kensington, Md., 20795.
  Administrator, Defense Electric Power Administration.—Leslie N. Jochimsem, 1600 South Joyce Street, Arlington, Va., 22202.

Office of the Assistant Secretary (Public Land Management):
  Deputy Assistant Secretary.—Robert M. Mangan, Route 5, Box 88F, Vienna, Va., 22180.
Office of the Assistant Secretary (Mineral Resources):
  Deputy Assistant Secretary.—John F. O'Leary, Shady Oaks Manor, West River, Md., 20881.
  Director, Office of Coal Research.—George Fumich, Jr., 510 North Montana Street, Arlington, Va., 22203.
  Director, Office of Geography.—Meredith F. Burrill, 5503 Grove Street, Chevy Chase, Md., 20015.
  Director, Office of Minerals Exploration.—[Vacant.]
  Director, Office of Minerals and Solid Fuels.—William E. S. Flory, Bel Air, Woodbridge, Va., 22191.
  Director, Office of Oil and Gas.—Rear Adm. Onnie P. Lattu, 3600 Ordway Street, 20016.
  Administrator, Oil Import Administration.—J. Cordell Moore, 4301 Massachusetts Avenue, 20016.
Office of the Assistant Secretary for Fish and Wildlife:
  Deputy Assistant Secretary.—Robert M. Paul, 7707 Heming Place, Springfield, Va., 22151.
Office of the Assistant Secretary for Administration:
  Deputy Assistant Secretary for Administration.—George E. Robinson, 1517 North Kentucky Street, Arlington, Va., 22205.
  Director of Management Operations.—N. O. Wood, Jr., 3410 Macomb Street, 20016.
  Director of Survey and Review.—W. Darlington Denit, 3406 Jefferson, Hyattsville, Md., 20780.
  Director of Budget.—Sidney D. Larson, 4511 Kerby Parkway SE., 20022.
  Director of Management Research.—Arthur B. Jebens, 5437 Mohican Road, 20016.
  Director of Personnel.—Newell B. Terry, 7411 Grace Street, Springfield, Va., 22150.
Solicitor.—Frank J. Barry, 5712 Maryland Avenue, Falls Church, Va., 22043.
  Deputy Solicitor.—Edward Weinberg, 9619 Cottrell Terrace, Silver Spring, Md., 20903.
  Legislative Counsel.—Max N. Edwards, 4000 Massachusetts Avenue, 20016.
  Associate Solicitor (Indian Affairs).—Henry E. Hyden, 4801 Kenmore Avenue, Alexandria, Va., 22304.
  Associate Solicitor (Mineral Resources).—A. Bruce Wright, 6216 Wedgewood Road, Bethesda, Md., 20034.
  Associate Solicitor (Public Lands).—Thomas J. Cavanaugh, 1708 Reed Road, Falls Church, Va., 22043.
  Associate Solicitor (Territories, Wildlife and Parks).—Lewis S. Flagg III, 800 4th Street SW., 20024.
  Associate Solicitor (Water and Power).—Harry J. Hogan, 4424 Volta Place NW., 20007.
Director, Resources Program Staff.—Henry P. Caulfield, Jr., 6625 31st Street., 20015.
  Field Committees:
    Alaska.—Burke Riley, regional coordinator, Alaska Region and Chairman, P.O. Box 711, Juneau, Alaska, 99801.
    Missouri Basin.—Harrell F. Mosbaugh, regional coordinator, Missouri Basin Region and chairman, P.O. Box 2530, Billings, Mont., 59101.
    North Central.—Harold C. Jordahl, Jr., cochairman, 303 Price Place, Madison, Wis., 53705; Fred Wampler, cochairman, Federal Bldg., 550 Main Street, Cincinnati, Ohio, 45202.
    Northeast.—Mark Abelson, regional coordinator, Northeast Region and chairman, 59 Temple Place, Boston, Mass., 02111.
    Pacific Northwest.—Paul T. Quick, acting regional coordinator, Pacific Northwest Region, P.O. Box 3621, Portland, Oreg., 97208.
    Pacific Southwest.—William T. Davoren, regional coordinator, Pacific Southwest Region and chairman, 125 South State Street, Salt Lake City, Utah, 84111.
    Southwest.—Kenneth D. McCall, regional coordinator, Southwest Region and chairman, Federal Building, P.O. Box 1467, Muskogee, Okla., 74402.

Department of the Interior
507

BOARD ON GEOGRAPHIC NAMES

Chairman.—Edward P. Cliff, 221 North Royal Street, Alexandria, Va., 22314.
Executive Secretary.—Dr. Meredith F. Burrill, 5503 Grove Street, Chevy Chase, Md., 20015.
Executive Secretary for Domestic Names.—Jerome O. Kilmartin, 1800 North Inglewood Street, Arlington, Va., 22205.
Members:
 Department of State.—Dr. G. Etzel Pearcy, 1101 New Hampshire Avenue, 20037; Dr. Robert D. Hodgson, 103 Joyce Drive, Fairfax, Va., 22030, deputy.
 Department of the Army.—Frank C. Shepard, 3519 Cummins Lane, Chevy Chase, Md., 20015; George E. Thornton, 9306 Piney Branch Road, Silver Spring, Md., 20903, deputy.
 Department of the Navy.—W. G. Watt, 1600 North Highland Street, Arlington, Va., 22201; Charles D. Rouse, 7307 Elmhurst Street, 20028, deputy.
 Department of the Air Force.—Edward M. Thompson, 1028 Tulip Lane, Ellisville, Mo., 63024, deputy; Robert Y. Ota, 4 Charen Court, Potomac, Md., 20677, deputy.
 Post Office Department.—Boyd W. Fielder, 5608 19th Street North, Arlington, Va., 22205; Madeline Biscoe, 3619 Third Street South, Arlington, Va., 22204, deputy.
 Department of the Interior.—Arthur A. Baker, 5201 Westwood Drive, 20016; Robert H. Lyddan, 3101 Beech Street, 20015, deputy.
 Department of Agriculture.—Edward P. Cliff, 221 North Royal Street, Alexandria, Va., 22314; Fred W. Grover, 2323 North Utah Street, Arlington, Va., 22207, deputy.
 Department of Commerce.—Dr. A. Joseph Wraight, 5431 Connecticut Avenue, 20015.
 Government Printing Office.—Aaron S. Blauer, 2102 Rolander Street, Adelphi, Md., 21710; Leslie P. Cox, Jr., 7002 21st Avenue, Lewisdale, Md., 20783, deputy.
 Library of Congress.—Dr. Walter W. Ristow, 320 Ingleside Avenue, McLean, Va., 22101; Dr. Charles C. Bead, 4201 Massachusetts Avenue, 20016, deputy.
 Central Intelligence Agency.—
 Department of Defense.—Harry Coggin, 1509 West Street, Falls Church, Va., 22046; Raymond Gornitzky, 8104 Beech Tree Road., Bethesda, Md., 20034, deputy.

FISH AND WILDLIFE SERVICE
Interior Building.   Phone, 343-1100 (Code 183, extension 70)

Commissioner of Fish and Wildlife.—Clarence F. Pautzke, 2430 Pennsylvania Avenue, 20037.
Bureau of Commercial Fisheries:
 Director.—Donald L. McKernan, 4100 North Richmond Street, Arlington, Va., 22207.
 Deputy Director.—Harold E. Crowther, 7105 Claymore Avenue, West Hyattsville, Md., 20782.
Bureau of Sport Fisheries and Wildlife:
 Director.—John S. Gottschalk, 305 Creswell Drive, Falls Church, Va., 22044.
 Deputy Director.—Abram V. Tunison, 304 Sleepy Hollow Road, Falls Church, Va., 22042.
 Associate Director.—Lansing A. Parker, 4819 24th Road North, Arlington, Va., 22207.

GEOLOGICAL SURVEY
General Services Building.   Phone, 343-1100 (Code 183, extension 70)

Director.—Thomas B. Nolan, 2219 California Street, 20008.
Associate Director.—Arthur A. Baker, 5201 Westwood Drive, Westmoreland Hills, Md., 20016.
Assistant Director.—Robert H. Lyddan, 3101 Beech Street, 20015.
Executive Officer.—Glendon J. Mowitt, 3115 Worthington Street, 20015.
Information Officer.—Frank H. Forrester, 4808 Longfellow Court, McLean, Va., 22101.
Chief, Geologic Division.—William T. Pecora, 4572 Indian Rock Terrace, 20007.

Chief, Water Resources Division.—Luna B. Leopold, 5705 Springfield Drive, Springfield, Md., 20016.
Chief, Topographic Division.—George D. Whitmore, 6806 Florida Street, Chevy Chase, Md., 20015.
Chief, Conservation Division.—Harold J. Duncan, 1613 Mount Eagle Place, Parkfairfax, Alexandria, Va., 22302.
Chief, Publications Division.—Robert L. Moravetz, 3813 Fourth Street North, Arlington, Va., 22203.

BUREAU OF INDIAN AFFAIRS
Interior Building.   Phone, 343-1100 (Code 183, extension 70)

Commissioner.—Philleo Nash, 800 Fourth Street SW., 20024.
Deputy Commissioner.—John O. Crow, 2386 North Edgewood Street, Arlington, Va., 22207.
Associate Commissioner.—James E. Officer, 320 N Street SW., 20024.
Assistant Commissioner (Administration).—Fred H. Massey, 2231 Bancroft Place, 20008.
Assistant Commissioner (Economic Development).—E. Reeseman Fryer, Route 1, Chantilly Woods, Chantilly, Va., 22021.
Assistant Commissioner (Community Services).—Selene Gifford, 802 Crescent Drive, Alexandria, Va., 22304.
Assistant Commissioner (Legislation).—Graham E. Holmes, 1117 Roan Lane, Alexandria, Va., 22302.
Public Information and Reports Officer.—Virginia S. Hart, 4107 North 27th Road, Arlington, Va., 22207.

AREA OFFICES

Aberdeen.—Martin N. B. Holm, 1220 North Third Street, Aberdeen, S. Dak., 57401.
Anadarko.—Leslie P. Towle, 602 Mission Terrace, Anadarko, Okla., 73005.
Billings.—James F. Canan, 1810 Iris Lane, Billings, Mont., 59101.
Gallup.—Fredrick M. Haverland, 631 McKee Drive, Gallup, N. Mex., 87301.
Juneau.—Robert L. Bennett, 1214 Fifth Street, Douglas, Alaska, 99801.
Minneapolis.—Paul L. Winsor, 14521 Moonlight Hill Road, Hopkins, Minn., 55345.
Muskogee.—Virgil N. Harrington, 221 South 12th Street, Muskogee, Okla., 74401.
Phoenix.—W. Wade Head, 1342 East Georgia, Phoenix, Ariz., 85011.
Portland.—Robert D. Holtz, 10830 S. W. Berkshire Street, Portland, Oreg., 97225.
Sacramento.—Leonard M. Hill, 4505 Argonaut Way, Sacramento, Calif., 95825.

INDIAN ARTS AND CRAFTS BOARD

Chairman.—F. J. Dockstader, 165 West 66th Street, New York City, 10006.
Members:
Rene d'Harnoncourt, 333 Central Park West, New York City, 10024.
Vincent Price, 580 North Beverly Glen Boulevard, Los Angeles, Calif., 90024.
Erich Kohlberg, 130 South Eudora, Denver, Colo., 80222.
Lloyd H. New Kiva, 75 West 5th Avenue, Scottsdale, Ariz., 85251.
General Manager.—Robert G. Hart, 2202 North Charles Street, Baltimore, Md., 21218.

BUREAU OF LAND MANAGEMENT
Interior Building.   Phone, 343-1100 (Code 183, extension 70)

Director.—Charles H. Stoddard, 4422 Volta Place, 20007.
Associate Director.—Harold R. Hochmuth, 4127 34th Road North, Arlington, Va., 22207.
Assistant Director (Administration).—James P. Beirne, 10622 Gatewood Avenue, Silver Spring, Md., 20903.

Assistant Director (Lands and Minerals).—Luther T. Hoffman, 5201 Glenwood Road, Bethesda, Md., 20014.

Assistant Director (Resource Management).—Eugene V. Zumwalt, 1934 Columbia Pike, Arlington, Va., 22204.

Assistant to the Director.—Robert E. Wolf, 5824 Carlyle Street, Cheverly, Md., 20785.

Office of Appeals and Hearings.—James F. Doyle, 2005 Columbia Pike, Arlington, Va., 22204.

Office of Legislation and Cooperative Relations.—Jerry A. O'Callaghan, 5607 Chesterbrook Road, 20016.

Office of Program Development.—Robert A. Jones, 8729 Cheltonham Place, Annandale, Va., 22003.

State Directors:

Alaska.—Roger R. Robinson, 406 10th Avenue, Anchorage, Alaska, 99501.

Arizona.—Fred J. Weiler, 724 East Hayward, Phoenix, Ariz., 85021.

California.—Neal D. Nelson, 2800 Azalea Road, Sacramento, Calif., 95825.

Colorado.—Lowell M. Puckett, 1035 South Elizabeth, Denver, Colo., 80209.

Idaho.—Joseph T. Fallini, 2324 North Pendleton Drive, Boise, Idaho, 83705.

Montana.—E. I. Rowland, 2611 Sunnyview Lane, Billings, Mont., 59102.

Nevada.—J. Russell Penny, 1200 Alturas, Reno, Nev., 89503.

New Mexico.—W. J. Anderson (acting), 1307 Declovina, Santa Fe, N. Mex., 87502.

Oregon.—Russell E. Getty, Route 3, Box 468, Dundee, Oreg., 97115.

Utah.—Robert D. Nielson, 3648 Furtuna Circle, Salt Lake City, Utah, 84117.

Wyoming.—Ed Pierson, Route 1, Box 525, Cheyenne, Wyo., 82001.

BUREAU OF MINES

Interior Building. Phone, 343–1100 (Code 183, extension 70)

Director.—[Vacant.]

Deputy Director.—Frank C. Memmott, Park Arlington Apartments, Arlington, Va., 22201.

Chief, Office of Mineral Reports.—Allan Sherman, 8318 Draper Lane, Silver Spring, Md., 20910.

Chief, Office of Program Coordination.—Richard H. Mote, 206 Brook Road, McLean, Va., 22101.

Assistant Director—Administration.—Carl Rampacek, 125 North Ripley Street, Alexandria, Va., 22304.

Chief, Division of Automatic Data Processing.—William A. Yost (acting), 14211 Dennington Place, Rockville, Md., 20853.

Chief, Division of Budget.—Elwood Thomson, 4449–20th Road North, Arlington, Va., 22207.

Chief, Division of Finance.—Kenfield Bailey, 5822 Westchester Drive, Alexandria, Va., 22310.

Chief, Division of Management Analysis.—Warren L. Dahlstrom, Box 319A, Route 4, Vienna, Va., 22180.

Chief, Division of Personnel.—Harvey V. Pearce, 503 Twinbrook Parkway, Rockville, Md., 20851.

Chief, Division of Procurement and Property Management.—Charles J. Hann, 5001 Seminary Road, Apt. 820, Alexandria, Va., 22311.

Chief, Division of Publication Services.—Robert P. Willing, 303 Whitestone Road, Silver Spring, Md., 20901.

Assistant Director—Health and Safety.—James Westfield, 5550 Columbia Pike, Arlington, Va., 22204.

Chief, Division of Accident Prevention and Health.—Earle P. Shoub, 545 North Pollard Street, Arlington, Va., 22203.

Chief, Division of Coal Mine Inspection.—Harry F. Weaver, 2135 Tunlaw Road, 20007.

Assistant Director—Helium.—Henry P. Wheeler, Jr., 10222 Conover Drive, Silver Spring, Md., 20900.

Assistant Director.—Mineral Resource Development.—Paul Zinner, 6002 34th Place, 20015.

Chief, Division of Anthracite.—Joseph A. Corgan, 5605 Park Street, Chevy Chase, Md., 20015.

Assistant Director—Continued
　Chief, Division of Bituminous Coal.—T. Reed Scollon, 6319 Walhonding Road, 20016.
　Chief, Division of Economic Analysis.—William A. Vogely, 6504 Pyle Road, Bethesda, Md., 20014.
　Chief, Division of International Activities.—Virgil L. Barr, 9729 West Bexhill Drive, Kensington, Md., 20795.
　Chief, Division of Minerals.—Charles W. Merrill, 1554 44th Street, 20007.
　Chief, Division of Petroleum.—William C. Elliott, Jr., 9318 Fern Lane, Annandale, Va., 22003.
　Chief, Division of Statistics.—Paul W. Icke (acting), 1436 Stuart Place, Falls Church, Va., 22040.
Assistant Director—Minerals Research.—Joe B. Rosenbaum (acting).
　Director of Coal Research.—Harry Perry, 6713 Wilkins Drive, Falls Church, Va., 22040.
　Director of Metallurgy Research.—Joe B. Rosenbaum, 9101 Kensington Parkway, North Chevy Chase, Md., 20015.
　Director of Mining Research.—Thomas E. Howard, 9511 Nowell Drive, Bethesda Md., 20014.
　Director of Petroleum Research.—J. Wade Watkins, 5309 Easton Drive, Springfield, Va., 22151.

NATIONAL PARK SERVICE
Interior Building. Phone, 343-1170 (Code 183, extension 70)

Director.—George B. Hartzog, Jr., 4818 Old Dominion Drive, Arlington, Va. 22207.
Associate Director.—A. Clark Stratton, 1507 Cavalier Corridor, Falls Church, Va., 22044.
Assistant Director (Administration).—Clarence P. Montgomery, 3130 North Inglewood St., Arlington, Va., 22007.
Assistant Director (Operations).—Howard W. Baker, 6745 Algonquin Court, Annandale, Va., 22003.
Assistant Director (Design and Construction).—Johannes E. N. Jensen, 3114 Elba Road, Hollin Hills, Alexandria, Va., 22306.
Assistant Director (Specialized Service).—Jackson E. Price, 5129 Bradley Boulevard, Chevy Chase, Md., 20015.
Assistant Director (Resource Studies).—[Vacant.]
Assistant Director (Cooperative Activities). Theodor R. Swem, 4109 Watkins Trail, Annandale, Va., 22003.

REGIONAL OFFICES
Regional Directors:
　Southeast Region.—Elbert Cox, Federal Building, Box 10008, Richmond, Va., 23240.
　Midwest Region.—Lemuel A. Garrison, 1709 Jackson Street, Omaha, Nebr., 68102.
　Southwest Region.—Daniel B. Beard, Box 728, Santa Fe, N. Mex., 87501.
　Western Region.—Edward A. Hummel, 450 Golden Gate Avenue, P.O. Box 36063, San Francisco, Calif., 94102.
　Northeast Region.—Ronald F. Lee, 143 South Third Street, Philadelphia, Pa., 19106.
　National Capital Region.—T. Sutton Jett, 1100 Ohio Drive SW., 20242.

EASTERN, WESTERN, AND NATIONAL CAPITAL OFFICES OF DESIGN AND CONSTRUCTION

Chief, Eastern Office, Design and Construction.—Robert G. Hall, 143 South Third Street, Philadelphia, Pa., 19106.
Chief, Western Office, Design and Construction.—Sanford Hill, 450 Golden Gate Avenue, San Francisco, Calif., 94102.
Chief, National Capital Office, Design and Construction.—Robert W. Andrews, 1100 Ohio Drive SW., 20242.

NATIONAL PARK TRUST FUND BOARD

Henry H. Fowler, Secretary of the Treasury, 209 South Fairfax Street, Alexandria, Va.
Stewart L. Udall, Secretary of the Interior, 4551 Crest Lane, McLean, Va., 22101.
George B. Hartzog, Jr., Director, National Park Service, and Secretary, National Park Trust Fund Board, 4818 Old Dominion Road, Arlington, Va., 22207.
M. Donald Thurber, 798 Neff Road, Grosse Pointe, Mich.
Hugh D. Galusha, Jr., Box 1699, Helena, Mont., 59601.

ADVISORY BOARD ON NATIONAL PARKS, HISTORIC SITES, BUILDINGS, AND MONUMENTS

Chairman.—Dr. Stanley A. Cain, Resources for the Future, Inc., Room 725, 1755 Massachusetts Avenue, Washington, D.C., 20007.
Vice Chairman.—Dr. Wallace E. Stegner, 13456 South Fork Lane, Los Altos Hills, Calif., 94022.
Secretary.—Mrs. Marian S. Dryfoos, Director of Special Activities, *The New York Times*, New York, N.Y., 10036.
Members.—Dr. Joe B. Frantz, Chairman, Department of History, University of Texas, Austin, Tex.; Dr. Melville B. Grosvenor, President, National Geographic Society, 17th and M Streets, Washington, D.C., 20036; Dr. Emil W. Haury, Department of Anthropology, University of Arizona, Tucson, Ariz.; Edward J. Meeman, Editor Emeritus, *Memphis Press-Scimitar*, 495 Union Avenue, Memphis, Tenn., 38101; Sigurd F. Olson, Box 157, Ely, Minn., 55731; Paul L. Phillips, President, United Papermakers and Paperworkers, Paper Makers Building, Albany, N.Y., 12201; Dr. Robert G. Sproul, President Emeritus, The University of California, Berkeley, Calif., 94720; Dr. Robert L. Stearns, 1210 American National Bank Building, Denver, Colo., 80202.

BUREAU OF RECLAMATION

Interior Building. Phone, 343-1100 (Code 183, extension 70)

Commissioner.—Floyd E. Dominy, Route 1, Box 240, Oakton, Va., 22124.
Assistant Commissioner.—Newcomb B. Bennett, Jr., 6801 Wells Parkway, University Park, Md., 20782.
Assistant Commissioner.—Gilbert G. Stamm, 1605 Balls Hill Road, McLean, Va., 22101.
Assistant Commissioner.—Wilbur P. Kane, 1404 Moffett Road, Silver Spring, Md., 20903.
Chief, Division of Irrigation and Land Use.—Maurice N. Langley, 6825 Algonquin Avenue, Bethesda, Md., 20034.
Chief, Division of Project Development.—Daniel V. McCarthy, 4417 Dittmar Road, Arlington, Va., 22207.
Chief, Division of Power.—William H. Keating, 6503 Kentland Place, Springfield, Va., 22150.
Chief, Division of Program Coordination and Finance.—Bruce G. Davis, 9924 Carter Road, Bethesda, Md., 20034.
Chief, Division of Procurement and Property.—J. Carl Phillips, 3124 North Quincy Street, Arlington, Va., 22207.
Chief, Division of General Services.—Harold L. Byrd, 2712 Plyers Mill Road, Silver Spring, Md., 20902.
Chief, Division of Personnel.—Chester R. Baggs, Route 1, Box 86, Centreville, Va., 22020.
Chief, Division of Organization Management.—L. Ray Awtrey, 5304 Portsmouth Road, 20016.
Chief, Division of General Engineering.—Thaddeus W. Mermel, 4540 43d Street, 20016.
Chief, Division of Foreign Activities.—Leon W. Damours, 4390 Lorcom Lane, Arlington, Va., 22207.
Chief, Division of Audit and Financial Review.—James S. Reece, 5550 Columbia Pike, Arlington, Va., 22204.
Assistant to the Commissioner—Information.—Ottis Peterson, 4977 Battery Lane, Bethesda, Md., 20014.
Assistant to the Commissioner—Research.—Thaddeus W. Mermel, 4540 43d Street, 20016.

FIELD ORGANIZATION

Chief Engineer.—B. P. Bellport, Denver Federal Center, Denver, Colo., 80225.
Region 1.—Harold T. Nelson, Regional Director, Reclamation Building, Fairgrounds, Boise, Idaho, 83701.
Region 2.—Robert J. Pafford, Jr., Regional Director, Fulton and Marconi Avenues, Sacramento, Calif., 95811.
Region 3.—A. B. West, Regional Director, Administration Building, Boulder City, Nev., 89005.
Region 4.—F. M. Clinton, Regional Director, 125 South State Street, Salt Lake City, Utah, 84111.
Region 5.—Leon W. Hill, Regional Director, Seventh and Taylor, Amarillo, Tex., 79105.
Region 6.—Harold E. Aldrich, Regional Director, 709 Central Avenue, Billings, Mont., 59101.
Region 7.—Hugh P. Dugan, Regional Director, Building 46, Denver Federal Center, Denver, Colo., 80225.
Alaska District.—George N. Pierce, District Manager, 226 Seward Street, Juneau, Alaska, 99801.

OFFICE OF TERRITORIES

Interior Building. Phone, 343-1100 (Code 183, extension 70)

Director.—Ruth G. Van Cleve, 6304 Emory Street, Alexandria, Va., 22312.
Assistant Director for Virgin Islands and Guam.—John J. Kirwan, 1350 Monroe Street NE., 20017.
Assistant Director for American Samoa and Trust Territory of the Pacific Islands.—Martin P. Mangan, 7005 Montrose Street, Alexandria, Va., 22312.
Special Assistant.—Chester B. Leedom, 500 Dead Run Drive, McLean, Va., 22101.
Administrative Officer.—Juanita M. Vidi, 712 Quaint Acres Drive, Silver Spring, Md., 20904.

TERRITORIAL OFFICIALS

Governor of the Virgin Islands.—Ralph M. Paiewonsky, St. Thomas, V.I., 00802.
Government Secretary for the Virgin Islands.—Cyril E. King, St. Thomas, V.I., 00802.
Governor of Guam.—Manuel F. L. Guerrero, Agana, Guam, 96910.
Secretary of Guam.—Denver Dickerson, Agana, Guam, 96910.
Governor of American Samoa.—H. Rex Lee, Tutuila, American Samoa, 96920.
Secretary of American Samoa.—Owen S. Aspinall, Tutuila, American Samoa, 96920.
High Commissioner of the Trust Territory.—M. W. Goding, Saipan, Mariana Islands, 96950.
Deputy High Commissioner of the Trust Territory.—Richard F. Taitano, Saipan, Mariana Islands, 96950.

THE VIRGIN ISLANDS CORPORATION

General Office, St. Croix, V.I.

Members of the Board of Directors:
  Stewart L. Udall, 4451 Chain Bridge Road, McLean, Va., 22101.
  Orville L. Freeman, 2805 Daniel Road, Chevy Chase, Md., 20015.
  Eugene P. Foley, 9508 Burning Tree Road, Bethesda, Md., 20034.
  Ralph M. Paiewonsky, St. Thomas, V.I., 00802.
  Ward M. Canaday, 4455 Brookside Road, Toledo, Ohio, 43615.
  Robert F. Dwyer, 1500 S. E. Waverly Drive, Portland, Oregon, 97222.
Secretary to the Board of Directors.—Ruth G. Van Cleve, 6304 Emory Street, Alexandria, Va., 22312.
Officer:
  President.—Robert P. Cramer, St. Croix, V.I., 00820.

Department of the Interior   513

THE ALASKA RAILROAD
General Offices, Anchorage, Alaska, P.O. Box 7-2111.   Phone, Arco 411

General Manager.—John E. Manley, 1524 Hidden Lane, Anchorage, Alaska, 99501.
Assistant General Manager.—R. H. Bruce, 736 15th Street, Anchorage, Alaska, 99501.
Comptroller.—Leland P. Draney, 243 West Cook, Anchorage, Alaska, 99501.
Assistant to the General Manager, Washington, D.C., Interior Building.—Edwin M. Fitch, 4905 Longfellow Street, McLean, Va., 22101.
Assistant to the General Manager, Seattle, Wash.—A. R. Sessions, 601 East 78th Street, Seattle, Wash., 98115.

BONNEVILLE POWER ADMINISTRATION
P.O. Box 3621, Portland, Oreg., 97208.   Phone, 234-3361

Administrator.—Charles F. Luce, 7012 East Sleret Street, Vancouver, Wash., 98664.
Deputy Administrator.—Charles W. Kinney, 12235 N.E. Rose Parkway, Portland, Oreg., 97230.
General Counsel (Regional Solicitor).—John L. Bishop, 6020 S.W. Arrow Wood Lane, Portland, Oreg., 97223.
Assistant Administrator for Engineering.—Eugene L. White, 432 Country Club Road, Oswego, Oreg., 97034.
Assistant Administrator for Power Management.—Bernard Goldhammer, 3014 N.E. 30th Avenue, Portland, Oreg., 97214.
Assistant Administrator for Administrative Management.—Jack N. O'Neal, 8024 S.E. 32d Avenue, Portland, Oreg., 97211.
Assistant Administrator, Washington, D.C. Office, Interior Building.—George W. Toman, 9921 Georgia Avenue, Silver Spring, Md., 20902.

BONNEVILLE ADVISORY BOARD

Charles F. Luce, Administrator, Bonneville Power Administration, Portland, Oreg., 97208.
Brig. Gen. Peter C. Hyzer, Division Engineer, Corps of Engineers, Department of the Army, Portland, Oreg., 97209.
Harold T. Nelson, Regional Director, Bureau of Reclamation, Department of the Interior, Boise, Idaho, 83701.
Stewart Brown, Chief, Bureau of Power, Federal Power Commission. Washington, D.C., 20426.
Thomas P. Helseth, State Conservationist, Soil Conservation Service, Department of Agriculture, Portland, Oreg., 97204.

SOUTHEASTERN POWER ADMINISTRATION
Elberton, Ga.   Phone 283-3261, Area Code 404

Administrator.—Charles W. Leavy, 121 Edwards Street, Elberton, Ga.

SOUTHWESTERN POWER ADMINISTRATION
P.O. Drawer 1619, Tulsa, Okla., 74101.   Phone Area Code 918, LUther 4-7161

Administrator.—Douglas G. Wright, 1759 South Quincy, Tulsa, Okla., 74120.
Assistant Administrator.—Virgil B. Stanley, 319 E Street NW., Miami, Okla., 74354.
Assistant Administrator, Washington, D.C., Interior Building.—Knoland J. Plucknett, 742 Fontaine Street, Alexandria, Va., 22302.
Chief, Management Office.—E. Milford Rice, 638 North Vancouver Avenue, Tulsa, Okla., 74127.
Chief, Division of Power.—Floyd E. Conway, 3423 East 13th Street, Tulsa, Okla., 74112.

Assistant Chief, Division of Power.—George D. Simpson, 2156 South Florence Place, Tulsa, Okla., 74114.
Assistant to Chief, Division of Power.—Charlie F. Jack, 4620 South Jamestown, Tulsa, Okla., 74135.
Chief, Division of Administrative Services.—James V. Alfriend, 3823 East 11th Place, Tulsa, Okla., 74112.
Assistant Chief, Division of Administrative Services.—Philip J. Cassilly, 3111 East 26th Place, Tulsa, Okla., 74114.
Chief, Division of Planning and Resources.—Carl E. Roberts, 4405 South Sandusky, Tulsa, Okla., 74135.

BUREAU OF OUTDOOR RECREATION

Interior Building. Phone 343-1100 (Code 183, extension 70)

Director.—Edward C. Crafts, 7111 44th Street, Chevy Chase, Md., 20015.
Associate Director.—Lawrence N. Stevens, 1920 North Quintana Street, Arlington, Va., 22205.
Assistant to the Director.—Martha A. Combe, 5425 Connecticut Avenue, Washington, D.C., 20015.
Assistant to the Director.—Joseph F. Kaylor, 1515 Blair Mill Road, Silver Spring, Md., 20910.
Assistant Director for Administration.—Harry W. Rice, 1710 Burroughs Lane, Falls Church, Va., 22043.
Assistant Director for Federal Coordination.—John F. Shanklin, 4616 Van Ness Street, Washington, D.C., 20016.
Assistant Director for Planning and Research.—Daniel M. Ogden, Jr., 6402 Crane Terrace, Bethesda, Md., 20034.
Assistant Director for State, Local and Private Programs.—A. Heaton Underhill, 4345 Road North, Arlington, Va. 22207.
Chief, Office of Recreation Information.—Louis E. Reid, Jr., 5702 Mohican Place, Bethesda, Md., 20016.
Chief, Division of Federal Programs and Conservation Fund.—Howard E. Ball, 4809 Wrightson Drive, McLean, Va., 22101.
Chief, Division of Financial Operations.—[Vacant.]
Chief, Division of Grants-in-Aid, Land and Water Conservation Fund.—Maurice D. Arnold, 8919 Bradmore Drive, Bethesda, Md., 20034.
Chief, Division of Legislative Review.—Thomas A. Sullivan, 5163 37th Road North, Arlington, Va., 22207.
Chief, Division of Nationwide Planning and Surveys.—William C. Dent, 6732 31st Street, Arlington, Va., 22213.
Acting Chief, Division of Personnel Management and Organization.—Theodore C. Krell, 4127 North Glebe Road, Arlington, Va., 22207.
Acting Chief, Division of Program Development and Management Operations.— Warren J. Kelvie, 14408 Gaines Avenue, Rockville, Md., 20853.
Chief, Division of Recreation Advisory Council Services.—[Vacant.]
Chief, Division of Research and Education.—[Vacant.]
Chief, Division of State Planning and Technical Assistance.—William J. Duddleson, 3814 Jocelyn Street, 20015.
Chief, Division of Water Resources and Special Area Studies.—[Vacant.]

REGIONAL OFFICES

Regional Directors:
Pacific Northwest Region.—Fred J. Overly, 12024 Eighth NW, Seattle, Wash., 98177.
Pacific Southwest Region.—Frank E. Sylvester, 160 Duran Drive, San Rafael, Calif., 94903.
Mid-Continent Region.—Wilfred W. Dresskell, 3210 South University Boulevard, Denver, Colo., 80210.
Lake Central Region.—Roman H. Koenings, 306 Linda Vista Street, Ann Arbor, Mich., 48103.
Southeast Region.—Jerome F. Anderson, 6533 Cherry Tree Lane NE, Atlanta, Ga., 30328.
Northeast Region.—John L. Sullivan, 100 Chetwynd Drive, Rosemont, Pa., 19010.

DEPARTMENT OF AGRICULTURE

The Mall, between Twelfth and Fourteenth Streets SW., 20250.
Phone, REpublic 7-4142 (Code 111)

ORVILLE L. FREEMAN, of Minneapolis, Minn., Secretary of Agriculture (U.S. Department of Agriculture, Washington, D.C.); born at Minneapolis, May 9, 1918; educated at Seward Elementary and Central High Schools in Minneapolis; B.A. magna cum laude, University of Minnesota (1940); LL.B. (1946) from University of Minnesota Law School; admitted to Minnesota bar (1947); married Jane C. Shields, May 2, 1942; two children: Constance Jane (July 3, 1945, and Michael Orville (May 7, 1948); enlisted U.S. Marine Corps, August 1941; commissioned 2d lieutenant, Infantry, 9th Regiment, 3d Marine Division, February 2, 1942; wounded leading combat patrol on Bougainville Island, November 7, 1943; returned to U.S. and hospitalized 8 months, awarded Purple Heart; returned to duty in Washington, D.C., to help establish and administer Marine Corps veterans rehabilitation program; presently lieutenant colonel in U.S. Marine Corps Reserve; assistant to Mayor of Minneapolis (1945–49); chairman Minneapolis Civil Service Commission (1946–49); member of law firm: Larson, Loevinger, Lindquist, Freeman, & Fraser (1950–54); secretary, State Central Committee of Democratic Farm Labor Party (1946–48); chairman of the DFL State Executive Committee (1948–50); elected Governor of Minnesota in 1954, and reelected 1956 and 1958; member of following organizations: Alpha Zeta National Agricultural Honorary Fraternity; American Veterans Committee; Veterans of Foreign Wars; Disabled American Veterans; American Legion; Military Order of Purple Heart; Minnesota Bar Association; Minnesota Association Claimants Compensation Attorneys (past president); American Judicature Society; Minnesota United Nations; Minneapolis Family and Children's Service (ex-director); National Congress of Parents and Teachers; Americans for Democratic Action; Co-op Services, Inc., Phi Beta Kappa; Delta Theta Phi Law Fraternity; American Civil Liberties Union; Loyal Order of Moose; Order of Eagles; Sons of Norway, Vasa Order; University of Minnesota "M" Club and Alumni Association; Izaak Walton League; Boys Scouts National Council; Variety Club. Became Secretary of Agriculture January 21, 1961.

Under Secretary.—Charles S. Murphy, 5513 Nebraska Avenue, 20015.

Assistant Secretaries:
  John A. Baker, 6301 15th Road North, Arlington, Va., 22205.
  Dorothy H. Jacobson, 502 Blair Road, Falls Church, Va., 22041.
  George L. Mehren, 3601 Connecticut Avenue, 20008.

Director, Agricultural Economics.—John A. Schnittker, 2114 North Randolf, Arlington, Va., 22207.

Director of Science and Education.—Nyle C. Brady, 1300 South Arlington Ridge Road, Arlington, Va., 22202.

Assistant Secretary for Administration.—Joseph M. Robertson, 9409 Kingsley Avenue, Bethesda, Md., 20014.

General Counsel.—John C. Bagwell, 5511 18th Street North, Arlington, Va., 22205.

Inspector General.—Lester P. Condon, 1306 Janney's Lane, Alexandria, Va., 22302.

Executive Assistant to the Secretary.—Thomas R. Hughes, 9709 Culver Street, Kensington, Md., 20795.

Deputy Under Secretary.—James L. Sundquist, 3016 North Florida Street, Arlington, Va., 22207.

Assistant to the Secretary (Defense Mobilization Planning).—Robert S. Reed, 4014 Beechwood Road, Hyattsville, Md., 20782.

Assistant to the Secretary:
  Byron G. Allen, 1400 South Joyce, Arlington, Va., 22202.
  Kenneth M. Birkhead, 653 Queen Anne Terrace, Falls Church, Va., 22044.
  Rodney E. Leonard, 5410 Kingswood Road, Bethesda, Md., 20014.
  William M. Seabron, 1703 Taylor Street, 20011.

Judicial Officer.—Thomas J. Flavin, 4800 Dover Road, 20016.

STABILIZATION

The Mall, between Twelfth and Fourteenth Streets SW. Phone, REpublic 7-4142 (Code 111)

Under Secretary.—Charles S. Murphy, 5513 Nebraska Avenue, 20015.

AGRICULTURAL STABILIZATION AND CONSERVATION SERVICE

Administrator.—Horace D. Godfrey, 1906 Anesbury Lane, Alexandria, Va., 22308.
Associate Administrator.—Edwin A. Jaenke, 115 Worthington Circle, Falls Church, Va., 22044.
Deputy Administrator for Commodity Operations.—Roland F. Ballou, 5246 32d Street North, Arlington, Va.
Deputy Administrator for State and County Operations.—Ray Fitzgerald, 5900 Kimball Court, Falls Church, Va., 22041.
Deputy Administrator for Management.—Robert P. Beach, 6601 Kentland Street, Springfield, Va., 22150.
Executive Assistant to the Administrator.—Lionel C. Holm, 4840 Red Fox Drive, Annandale, Va., 22003.

CONSERVATION AND LAND USE POLICY STAFF

Director.—Fred G. Ritchie, 2245 North Quincy Street, Arlington, Va., 22207.

COTTON POLICY STAFF

Director.—Joseph A. Moss, 437 North Manchester Street, Arlington, Va., 22203.

GRAIN POLICY STAFF

Director.—Arthur T. Thompson, 2116 F Street, 20037.

LIVESTOCK AND DAIRY POLICY STAFF

Director.—Harlan J. Emery, 4900 27th Street North, Arlington, Va., 22207.

OILS AND PEANUT POLICY STAFF

Director.—J. E. Thigpen, 3043 North Stafford Street, Arlington, Va., 22207.

SUGAR POLICY STAFF

Director.—Tom Murphy, 4307 Woodacre Court, McLean, Va., 22101.

TOBACCO POLICY STAFF

Director.—Claude G. Turner, 1056 North Montana Street, Arlington, Va., 22205.

ADMINISTRATIVE SERVICES DIVISION

Director.—M. D. Kimball, 3911 Fourth Street North, Arlington, Va., 22203.

AERIAL PHOTOGRAPHY DIVISION

Director.—Joseph W. Clifton, 1040 Beacon Lane, Falls Church, Va., 22043.

BIN STORAGE DIVISION

Director.—T. Scott Mowry, 3006 Mosby Street, Alexandria, Va., 22305.

BUDGET DIVISION

Director.—Andrew J. Nemshick, 6921 Chaco Road, Alexandria, Va., 22312.

CONSERVATION AND LAND USE DIVISION

Director.—John B. Vance, 5505 Ferndale Street, Springfield, Va., 22151.

DISASTER AND DEFENSE SERVICES STAFF

Director.—Wilson E. Westbrook, 1120 Vermont Avenue, 20005.

FARMER PROGRAMS DIVISION

Director.—Everett H. F. Felber, 4111 Oliver Street, Chevy Chase, Md., 20015.

FISCAL DIVISION

Director.—J. J. Somers, 404 Woodland Terrace, Alexandria, Va., 22302.

INFORMATION DIVISION

Director.—M. L. Du Mars, 8412 Galveston Road, Silver Spring, Md., 20910.

INVENTORY MANAGEMENT DIVISION

Director.—C. Hilary Moseley, 7735 Donnybrook Court, Annandale, Va., 22003.

OPERATIONS ANALYSIS STAFF

Director.—Jerome A. Miles, 4411 Medford Drive, Annandale, Va., 22003.

PERSONNEL MANAGEMENT DIVISION

Director.—J. P. Haughey, 6917 JoAllen Drive, Falls Church, Va., 22041.

POLICY AND PROGRAM APPRAISAL DIVISION

Director.—J. Murray Thompson, 2 Midhurst Road, Silver Spring, Md.

PROCUREMENT AND SALES DIVISION

Director.—Clifford Pulvermacher, Broad Run Farms, RFD #2, Sterling, Va., 22170.

PRODUCER ASSOCIATIONS DIVISION

Director.—John I. Morton, 12 Anesbury Court, Alexandria, Va., 22308.

COMMODITY CREDIT CORPORATION
The Mall, between Twelfth and Fourteenth Streets SW. Phone, REpublic 7-4142 (Code 111)

Board of Directors:
  Chairman.—Orville L. Freeman, Secretary of Agriculture, 2805 Daniel Road, Chevy Chase, Md., 20015.
  Charles S. Murphy, 5513 Nebraska Avenue, 20015.
  John A. Baker, 6301 15th Road North, Arlington, Va., 22205.
  George L. Mehren, 3601 Connecticut Avenue, 20008.
  Dorothy H. Jacobson, 502 Blair Road, Falls Church, Va., 22041.
  Horace D. Godfrey, 1906 Anesbury Lane, Alexandria, Va., 22308.
  John A. Schnittker, 2114 North Randolph Street, Arlington, Va., 22207.

Officers:
　President.—Charles S. Murphy, 5513 Nebraska Avenue, 20015.
　Executive Vice President.—Horace D. Godfrey, 1906 Anesbury Lane, Alexandria, Va., 22308.
　Vice Presidents:
　　Raymond A. Ioanes, 107 Poplar Drive, Falls Church, Va., 22046.
　　S. R. Smith, 4507 31st Street South, Arlington, Va., 22206.
　　Edwin A. Jaenke, 115 Worthington Circle, Falls Church, Va., 22044.
　　Robert G. Lewis, 3512 Porter Street, 20016.
　　Ray Fitzgerald, 5900 Kimball Court, Falls Church, Va., 22041.
　　Robert P. Beach, 6601 Kentland Street, Springfield, Va., 22150.
　Secretary.—Lionel C. Holm, 4840 Red Fox Drive, Annandale, Va., 22003.
　Controller.—James J. Somers, 404 Woodland Terrace, Alexandria, Va., 22302.
　Treasurer.—Rulon Gibb, 5526 18th Street North, Arlington, Va., 22205.
　Chief Accountant.—J. W. Vaughan, 2806 Davis Avenue, Alexandria, Va., 22302.

FEDERAL CROP INSURANCE CORPORATION
Phone, REpublic 7-4142 (Code 111, extension 6795)

Manager.—John N. Luft, 1400 South Joyce Street, Arlington, Va., 22202.
Deputy Manager.—Jack H. Morrison, 5101 Eighth Road South, Arlington, Va., 22204.
Director, Actuarial Division.—Joe R. McWilliams, 3106 North Rochester Street, Arlington, Va., 22213.
Director, Administrative Division.—H. Eugene Harker, 5323 Massachusetts Avenue, 20016.
Director, Budget and Finance Division.—John P. Skeffington, 5710 Noble Drive, McLean, Va., 22101.
Director, Claims Management Division.—Ernest C. Neas, 6201 31st Street North, Arlington, Va., 22207.
Director, Program Development and Research Division.—Earll H. Nikkel, 3401–A South Stafford Street, Arlington, Va., 22206.
Director, Sales Management Division.—Ross A. Dimock, 13104 Jingle Lane, Silver Spring, Md., 20906.
Area Directors.—Ervin W. Anderson, 115 Jersey Street, Denver, Colo., 80220; Dean Bernitz, 744 College Heights Circle, Manhattan, Kans., 66502; Robert F. Bullard, 301 North Jackson Street, Nashville, Ga., 31639; Mervin J. Kassube, 3417 South Second Street, Springfield, Ill., 62703.

SCIENCE AND EDUCATION
The Mall, between Twelfth and Fourteenth Streets SW. Phone, REpublic 7-4142 (Code 111)

Director.—Nyle C. Brady, 1300 South Arlington Ridge Road, Arlington, Va., 22202.
Assistant Director.—James H. Starkey, RFD 1, Mitchellville, Md., 21109.

AGRICULTURAL RESEARCH SERVICE
The Mall, between Twelfth and Fourteenth Streets SW. Phone, DUdley 8-3656 (Code 111, extension 3656)
OFFICE OF THE ADMINISTRATOR

Administrator.—Byron T. Shaw, 4501 Connecticut Avenue, 20008.
Associate Administrator.—G. W. Irving, Jr., 4836 Langdrum Lane, Chevy Chase, Md., 20015.
Deputy Administrator, Farm Research.—H. A. Rodenhiser, 5805 Aberdeen Road, Bethesda, Md., 20034.
　Assistant Deputy Administrator.—E. R. Goode, 5705 Pontiac Street, College Park, Md., 20740.
Deputy Administrator, Marketing Research.—O. W. Herrmann, 4313 Elm Street, Chevy Chase, Md., 20015.
　Assistant Deputy Administrator.—E. R. Glover, 14507 Faraday Drive, Rockville, Md., 20853.

Deputy Administrator, Nutrition, Consumer and Industrial Use Research.—F. R. Senti, 2601 North Pollard Street, Arlington, Va., 22207.
  Assistant Deputy Administrator.—W. D. Maclay, 9302 Parkhills Terrace, Bethesda, Md., 20014.
  Assistant Deputy Administrator.—Miss Ruth M. Leverton, 3900 16th Street, 20011.
Deputy Administrator, Regulatory Programs.—R. J. Anderson, 2737 Bradley Circle, Annandale, Va., 22003.
  Assistant Deputy Administrator.—Eugene P. Reagan, 5910 Engel Drive, McLean, Va., 22101.
Deputy Administrator, Administrative Management.—F. H. Spencer, 4313 Knox Road, Apt. 601, College Park, Md., 20740.
  Assistant Deputy Administrator.—P. K. Knierim, Wilelinor Estates, RFD #2, Edgewater, Md., 21037.
Director, Emergency Programs Staff.—Frank A. Todd, 145 South Aberdeen Street, Arlington, Va., 22204.
Director, Legislation and Special Assignments.—H. Rothenbach, 11401 Rokeby Avenue, Garrett Park, Md., 20766.
Director, Foreign Research and Technical Programs Division.—G. E. Hilbert, 5325 McKinley Street, Bethesda, Md., 20014.
Director, Information Division.—E. G. Moore, 7705 Old Chester Road, Bethesda, Md., 20034.

MANAGEMENT DIVISIONS

Director, Administrative Services Division.—R. W. Sooy, 3537 South River Terrace, Edgewater, Md.
Director, Program Examination and Budget Development Division.—Edmund Stephens, 3044 North Peary Street, Arlington, Va., 22207.
Director, Finance Division.—Frank E. Dow, 713 Fontaine Street, Alexandria, Va., 22302.
Director, Personnel Division.—John P. McAuley, 6019 Hawthorne Street, Cheverly, Md., 20785.
Operations Analysis and Systems Development Staff.—S. P. Williams, 10821 Georgia Avenue, Silver Spring, Md., 20902.
Superintendent, Agricultural Research Center, Office of Operations.—C. A. Logan, Agricultural Research Center, Beltsville, Md., 20705.

RESEARCH DIVISIONS

Director, Agricultural Engineering Research Division.—E. G. McKibben, 4226 Longfellow Street, Hyattsville, Md., 20781.
Director, Animal Disease and Parasite Research Division.—Howard W. Johnson, 9634 Brunett Avenue, Silver Spring, Md., 20901.
Director, Animal Husbandry Research Division.—Ralph E. Hodgson, 7006 Wake Forest Drive, College Park, Md., 20740.
Director, Clothing and Housing Research Division.—Miss Esther L. Batchelder, 8 Devon Road, Silver Spring, Md., 20910.
Director, Crops Research Division.—H. Rex Thomas (acting), 3907 Beechwood Road, Hyattsville, Md., 20782.
Director, Eastern Utilization Research and Development Division.—P. A. Wells, 1223 Wheatsheaf Lane, Abington, Pa., 19001.
Director, Entomology Research Division.—Edward F. Knipling, 2623 Military Road, Arlington, Va., 22207.
Director, Consumer and Food Economics Research Division.—Miss Faith Clark, 5510 Surrey Street, Chevy Chase, Md., 20015.
Director, Human Nutrition Research Division.—Willis A. Gortner, 12701 Lacy Drive, Meadowood, Silver Spring, Md., 20904.
Director, Northern Utilization Research and Development Division.—Robert J. Dimler, 1102 West Loucks Avenue, Peoria, Ill., 61604.
Director, Soil and Water Conservation Research Division.—Cecil H. Wadleigh, 5621 Whitfield Chapel Road, Lanham, Md., 20801.
Director, Southern Utilization Research and Development Division.—C. H. Fisher, 1624 Mirabeau Avenue, New Orleans, La., 70122.
Director, Western Utilization Research and Development Division.—M. J. Copley, 862 Arlington Avenue, Berkeley, Calif., 94707.

REGULATORY DIVISIONS

Director, Animal Disease Eradication Division.—F. J. Mulhern, 2702 Oakwood Street, Annandale, Va., 22003.
Director, Animal Inspection and Quarantine Division.—L. C. Heemstra, 4503 Elmwood Road, Beltsville, Md., 20705.
Director, Plant Pest Control Division.—E. D. Burgess, 2454 North Utah Street, Arlington, Va., 22207.
Director, Plant Quarantine Division.—F. A. Johnston, 4224 East-West Highway, Chevy Chase, Md., 20015.
Director, Pesticides Regulation Division.—Justus C. Ward, 509 Faber Drive, Falls Church, Va., 22044.

COOPERATIVE STATE RESEARCH SERVICE

Administrator.—T. C. Byerly, 1311 Delaware Avenue SW., Apt. S-843, 20024.
Associate Administrator.—H. C. Knoblauch, 4103 Lawton Street, McLean, Va., 22101.

FEDERAL EXTENSION SERVICE

South Building, Fourteenth Street and Independence Avenue SW.
Phone, DUdley 8-3377 (Code 111, extension 3377)

Administrator.—Lloyd H. Davis, 6820 Mansfield Road, Falls Church, Va., 22041.
Deputy Administrator.—John A. Cox, 1000 Sixth Street SW., 20024.
Assistant Administrators:
　Charles W. McDougall, 918 Baylor Drive, Alexandria, Va., 22307.
　Luke M. Schruben, 4603 Morgan Drive, Chevy Chase, Md., 20015.
　Raymond C. Scott, 3606 North Monroe Street, Arlington, Va., 22207.
Division of Management Operations.—Jos. P. Flannery, 4819 Yuma Street, 20016
Division of Agricultural Science, Technology and Management.—Charles E. Bell, Jr., 904 Janneys Lane, Alexandria, Va., 22302.
Division of 4-H and Youth Development.—Mylo S. Downey, 4609 Beechwood Road, College Park, Md., 20740.
Division of Home Economics.—Margaret C. Browne, 1100 Sixth Street, 20024.
Division of Extension Research and Training.—Joseph L. Matthews, 4948 34th Road North, Arlington, Va., 22207.
Division of Information.—Walter W. John, 6219 31st Street North, Arlington, Va., 22207.
Division of Marketing and Utilization Sciences.—Sharon Q. Hoobler, 1033 Kling Drive, Alexandria, Va., 22312.
Division of Resource Development and Public Affairs.—Everett C. Weitzell, 722 Fontaine Street, Alexandria, Va., 22302.

NATIONAL AGRICULTURAL LIBRARY

South Building, Fourteenth Street and Independence Avenue SW. Phone, DUdley 8-3434 (Code 111)

Director of the Library.—Foster E. Mohrhardt, 2601 South Joyce Street, Arlington, Va., 22202.
Assistant Director for—
　Field and Special Services.—Kirby B. Payne, 6524 35th Road North, Arlington, Va., 22213.
　Public Services.—Angelina J. Carabelli, Batchelors Forest Road, R.D. 1, Olney, Md., 20832.
　Technical Services.—Bella E. Shachtman, 8201 16th Street, Silver Spring, Md., 20910.
　Program Coordination Services.—Blanche L. Oliveri, 1006 Brooks Road, Capitol Heights, Md., 20027.

INTERNATIONAL AFFAIRS

The Mall, between Twelfth and Fourteenth Streets SW. Phone, DUdley 8-3111 (Code 111, extension 3111)

Assistant Secretary.—Dorothy H. Jacobson, 502 Blair Road, Falls Church, Va., 22041.
Deputy Assistant Secretary.—Arthur Mead, 9507 Ocala Street, Silver Spring, Md., 20901.

INTERNATIONAL ORGANIZATIONS STAFF

Director.—Ralph W. Phillips, 2401 South Lynn Street, Arlington, Va., 22202.

FOREIGN AGRICULTURAL SERVICE
Phone, REpublic 7-4142 (Code 111)

OFFICE OF THE ADMINISTRATOR

Administrator.—Raymond A. Ioanes, 107 Popular Drive, Falls Church, Va., 22046.
Associate Administrator.—Clarence R. Eskildsen, 326 Grove Avenue, Falls Church, Va., 22046.
  General Sales Manager.—Frank M. LeRoux, The River House, 1600 South Joyce, Arlington, Va., 22202.
  Assistant Administrator for Export Programs.—David L. Hume, 5511 Trent, Chevy Chase, Md., 20015.
  Barter and Stockpiling Manager.—Thomas R. Rawlings, 2501 North Lincoln Street, Arlington, Va., 22207.
  Assistant Administrator for Commodity Programs.—Donald M. Rubel, 3889 30th Street North, Arlington, Va., 22207.
  Assistant Administrator for International Trade.—A. Richard DeFelice, 7822 Glenbrook Road, Bethesda, Md., 20014.
  Assistant Administrator for Agricultural Attaches.—Horace J. Davis, University Club, 1135 16th Street, 20005.
  Assistant Administrator for Management.—W. A. Minor, 435 Greenbrier Drive, Silver Spring, Md., 20910.
  Acting Assistant to the Administrator.—Arnold R. Beasley, 5820 Old Chesterbrook Road, McLean, Va., 22101.
  Assistant to the Administrator.—Philip E. Shapiro, 9420 Balfour Drive, Bethesda, Md., 20014.

GENERAL SALES MANAGER

Manager.—Frank M. LeRoux, The River House, 1600 South Joyce Street, Arlington, Va., 22202.
Deputy Manager.—John H. Dean, 4837 First Street South, Arlington, Va., 22204.

EXPORT PROGRAMS

Assistant Administrator.—David L. Hume, 5511 Trent, Chevy Chase, Md., 20015.
Deputy Assistant Administrator.—Richard H. Roberts, 2401 North Upshur Street, Arlington, Va., 22207.
Deputy Assistant Administrator.—Kenneth K. Krogh, 815 Waterford Road, Stratford Landing, Alexandria, Va., 22308.
  Director, Program Development Division.—Thomas E. Street, 309 Martha Road, Alexandria, Va., 22307.
  Director, Trade Projects Division.—James O. Howard, 4009 Woodacre Drive, McLean, Va., 22101.
  Director, International Trade Fairs Division.—J. Kendall McClarren, 3806 North Oakland Street, Arlington, Va., 22207.
  Director, Program Operations Division.—Dan L. Tierney, 1906 Neal Drive, Alexandria, Va., 22308.

BARTER AND STOCKPILING MANAGER

Manager.—Thomas R. Rawlings, 2501 North Lincoln Street, Arlington, Va., 22207.
Deputy Manager.—Francis A. Woodling, 2203 Prichard Road, Silver Spring, Md., 20902.
Deputy Manager.—Otto A. Atzert, 9204 Harvey Road, Silver Spring, Md., 20910.

Assistant Administrator.—Donald M. Rubel, 3889 30th Street North, Arlington, Va., 22207.
Deputy Assistant Administrator.—William F. Doering, 422 Carolyn Drive, Falls Church, Va., 22044.
  Director, Cotton Division.—Robert C. Sherman, 4000 Massachusetts Avenue, 20016.
  Acting Director, Dairy and Poultry Division.—Norman G. Paulhus, RFD 1, Box 039A, Derwood, Md., 20752.
  Director, Fats and Oils Division.—Walter W. Sikes, 1708 North Utah Street, Arlington, Va., 22207.
  Director, Fruit and Vegetable Division.—J. W. Stewart, 4733 34th Road North, Arlington, Va., 22207.
  Director, Grain and Feed Division.—Raymond E. Vickery, 601 Marshal Road, Vienna, Va., 22180.
  Director, Livestock and Meat Products Division.—James P. Hartman, 5107 Williamsburg Boulevard, Arlington, Va., 22207.
  Director, Tobacco Division.—Hugh C. Kiger, 1518 Barbour Road, Falls Church, Va., 22043.
  Director, Sugar and Tropical Products Division.—John C. Scholl, 305 Virginia Avenue, Alexandria, Va., 22302.

INTERNATIONAL TRADE

Assistant Administrator.—A. Richard DeFelice, 7822 Glenbrook Road, Bethesda, Md., 20014.
Deputy Assistant Administrator.—Howard L. Worthington, 2118 Rosehill Drive, Alexandria, Va., 22310.
  Director, Trade Policy Division.—Nicholas M. Thuroczy, 4457 MacArthur Boulevard, 20007.
  Director, Operations Analysis Division.—R. L. Gastineau, 5337 Taney Avenue, Apt. 301, Alexandria, Va., 22304.

AGRICULTURAL ATTACHES

Assistant Administrator.—Horace J. Davis, University Club, 1135 16th Street, 20005.
Deputy Assistant Administrator.—Elmer W. Hallowell, 3647 Trinity Drive, Alexandria, Va., 22304.
  European Area Officer.—Burl Stugard, 1111 Army-Navy Drive, Arlington, Va., 22202.
  Latin America Area Officer.—Dale E. Farringer, 908 Brenda Lane, Annandale, Va., 22003.
  Far East and So. Asia Area Officer.—Paul F. Taggart, 6010 Dellwood Place, Bethesda, Md., 20034.
  Near East and Africa Area Officer.—A. I. Tannous, 6912 Oak Lane, Annandale, Va., 22003.
  Field Reports.—Harald C. Larsen, 2808 Cameron Mills Road, Alexandria, Va., 22302.

MANAGEMENT

Assistant Administrator.—W. A. Minor, 435 Greenbrier Drive, Silver Spring, Md., 20910.
Deputy Assistant Administrator.—Kenneth F. McDaniel, 908 Ampthill Drive, Alexandria, Va., 22312.
  Director, Foreign Market Information Division.—Kenneth W. Olson, 123 Van Winkle Drive, Falls Church, Va., 22044.
  Director, Budget and Finance Division.—Thomas E. Morrow, 4355 Fessenden Street, 20016.
  Director, Personnel Division.—Joseph L. Phillips, 14 Foxcroft Road, Alexandria, Va., 22307.
  Director, Management Services Division.—Lee A. Dashner, 6501 Persimmon Tree Road, Bethesda, Md., 20034.

INTERNATIONAL AGRICULTURAL DEVELOPMENT SERVICE
Phone, REpublic 7-4142 (Code 111)

Administrator.—Matthew Drosdoff, 600 River Towers Drive, Alexandria, Va., 22307.
Deputy Administrator.—Gerald E. Tichenor, 2212 Olmstead Drive, Falls Church, Va., 22043.
Regional Coordinator, Latin America.—A. J. Nichols, 215 Van Buren Street, Falls Church, Va., 22046.
Regional Coordinator, Africa.—John R. Beasley, 1000 Sixth Street SW., 20024.
Regional Coordinator, Asia.—Eugene T. Ransom, 103 Woodcliff Drive, Alexandria, Va., 22308.
Director, Foreign Training Division.—Cannon C. Hearne, 4527 31st Street South, Arlington, Va., 22206.

MARKETING AND CONSUMER SERVICES
The Mall, between Twelfth and Fourteenth Streets SW. Phone, REpublic 7-4142 (Code 111)

Assistant Secretary.—George L. Mehren, 3601 Connecticut Avenue, 20008.
Deputy Assistant Secretary.—Trienah Meyers, 8600 16th Street, Silver Spring, Md., 20910.

CONSUMER AND MARKETING SERVICE
South Building, Fourteenth Street and Independence Avenue SW. Phone, REpublic 7-4142 (Code 111)

Office of Administrator:
Administrator.—S. R. Smith, 4507 31st Street South, Arlington, Va., 22206.
Associate Administrator.—Roy W. Lennartson, 8209 Woodhaven Boulevard, Bethesda, Md., 20034.
Deputy Administrator, Consumer Food Programs.—Howard P. Davis, 2401 North Stuart Street, Arlington, Va., 22207.
Assistant Deputy Administrator, Consumer Food Programs.—Samuel C. Vanneman (Acting), 316 Riley Street, Falls Church, Va., 22046.
Assistant Deputy Administrator, Consumer Food Programs.—Marvin M. Sandstrom (acting), 4149 Sixth Street South, Arlington, Va., 22204.
Deputy Administrator, Consumer Protection.—Robert K. Somers (acting), 5704 18th Road North, Arlington, Va., 22205.
Deputy Administrator, Marketing Services.—George R. Grange, 5008 Bradford Drive, Annandale, Va., 22003.
Deputy Administrator, Regulatory Programs.—Clarence H. Girard, 4325 Kentbury Drive, Bethesda, Md., 20014.
Assistant Deputy Administrator, Regulatory Programs.—John C. Blum, 7501 Walton Lane, Annandale, Va., 22003.
Deputy Administrator, Management.—Henry G. Herrell, 10116 Parkwood Terrace, Bethesda, Md., 20014.
Economist.—Harold F. Breimyer, 9516 Byeforde Road, Kensington, Md., 20795.
Special Assistant to the Administrator.—Nathan Koenig, 6411 33d Street, 20015.
Assistant to the Administrator.—Donald A. Russell, 3900 Hummer Road, Annandale, Va., 22003.
Director, Marketing Information Division.—Franklin Thackrey, 102 West Rosemary Lane, Falls Church, Va., 22046.
Director, Matching Fund Program.—George H. Goldsborough, 223 Patuxent Drive, Laurel, Md., 20810.
Consumer Food Programs—Division Directors:
Commodity Distribution.—Neill W. Freeman (acting), 5807 Old Chesterbrook Road, McLean, Va., 22101.
Food Stamp.—Isabelle M. Kelley (acting), 4201 Cathedral Avenue, 20016.
School Lunch.—Herbert D. Rorex (acting), 5806 Old Chesterbrook Road, McLean, Va., 22101.
Food Trades Staff.—Jacob L. Puterbaugh, 4514 Westbrook Lane, Kensington, Md., 20795.
Consumer Food Programs Services Staff.—Guy Carmack (acting), 8005 Powhaton Street, Carrollton, Hyattsville, Md., 20784.

Consumer Protection, Marketing Services and Regulatory Programs—Division Directors:

Cotton.—Stanley C. Rademaker, 5005 Terrell Street, Annandale, Va., 22003.
Dairy.—Herbert L. Forest, 5 Shenandoah Road, Alexandria, Va., 22308.
Fruit and Vegetable.—Floyd F. Hedlund, 4101 Cathedral Avenue, 20016.
Grain.—Edward J. Overby, 4504 Cedell Place SE., 20031.
Livestock.—David M. Pettus, Route 1, Box 414, Manassas, Va., 22110.
Meat Inspection.—C. H. Pals, 2338 South Ode Street, Arlington, Va., 22202.
Packers and Stockyards.—Donald A. Campbell, 804 Whispering Lane, Falls Church, Va., 22041.
Poultry.—Hermon I. Miller, 5116 Moorland Lane, Bethesda, Md., 20014.
Special Services.—George A. Dice, 3852 Calvert Street, 20007.
Tobacco.—Stephen E. Wrather, 818 Marshall Lane, Alexandria, Va., 22302.

Management—Division Directors:

Administrative Services.—L. Kenneth Wright, 3020 Porter Street, 20008.
Budget and Finance.—Arthur J. Holmaas, 1113 Aronow Drive, Falls Church, Va., 22042.
Operations Analysis Staff.—Ernest A. Jenkinson, 301 Roosevelt Court, Vienna, Va., 22180.
Personnel.—William C. Laxton, 5705 Harwick Road, 20016.

COMMODITY EXCHANGE AUTHORITY

Administration Building, Fourteenth Street and Independence Avenue SW.
Phone, REpublic 7-4142 (Code 111)

Administrator.—Alex C. Caldwell, 3200 Holly Street, Alexandria, Va., 22305.
Deputy Administrator.—Arthur R. Grosstephan, 928 South St. Asaph Street, Alexandria, Va., 22314.
Assistant Administrator.—Daniel A. Currie, 3419 Raymond Street, Chevy Chase, Md., 20015.
Director, Compliance Division.—Charles E. Robinson, 3207 Cummings Lane, Chevy Chase, Md., 20015.
Assistant Director, Compliance Division.—Neal H. Stults, 7603 Kedron Street, Springfield, Va., 22150.
Director, Accounting and Licensing Division.—Roy Tipton, 957 North Quantico Street, Arlington, Va., 22205.
Director, Trading Division.—Ronald C. Callander, 1804 Preston Road, Alexandria, Va., 22302.
Assistant Director, Trading Division.—R. Corbin Dorsey, 5539 Columbia Pike, Arlington, Va., 22204.

RURAL DEVELOPMENT AND CONSERVATION

The Mall, between Twelfth and Fourteenth Streets SW. Phone, REpublic 7-4142 (Code 111)

Assistant Secretary.—John A. Baker, 6301 15th Road North, Arlington, Va., 22205.
Deputy Assistant Secretary.—Alfred L. Edwards, 813 Delaware Avenue SW., 20024.

FARMER COOPERATIVE SERVICE

Administrator.—Joseph G. Knapp, 7119 Fairfax Road, Bethesda, Md., 20014.
Deputy Administrator.—Martin A. Abrahamsen, 10305 Parkman Road, Silver Spring, Md., 20903.
Director, Management Services Division.—Job K. Savage, 1850 Columbia Pike, Arlington, Va., 22204.
Director, Marketing Division.—J. Kenneth Samuels, 2905 McKinley Street, 20015.
Director, Purchasing Division.—Homer J. Preston, 1303 Flintlock Road, Fairfax, Va., 22030.
Assistant to Administrator.—Harold D. Walker, 1709 Fairlawn Drive, McLean, Va., 22101.
Assistant Director, Marketing Division.—Stanley S. Cross, 5301 32d Street North, Arlington, Va., 22207.

FARMERS HOME ADMINISTRATION
Administrator's Office: South Building, Fourteenth Street and Independence Avenue SW.
Phone, DUdley 8-4574 (Code 111)

Administrator.—Howard Bertsch, 419 N Street SW., 20024.

Deputy Administrator.—Floyd F. Higbee, 1001 Third Street SW., 20024.

Assistant Administrator (Operating Loans).—J. Virgil Highfill, 3937 36th Street North, Arlington, Va., 22207.

Assistant Administrator (Community Services).—Bernard H. Polk, 6007 Hanover Avenue, Springfield, Va., 22150.

Assistant Administrator (Real Estate Loans).—Julian Brown, 1001 Third Street SW., 20024.

Assistant Administrator (Management).—Robert C. Leary, 10108 Pierce Drive, Silver Spring, Md., 20901.

Assistant Administrator (Insured Loan Funds).—Lawrence Brock, 1201 South Courthouse Road, Arlington, Va., 22204.

Assistant to the Administrator (Farm Planning and Supervision Staff).—Odom Stewart, 3424 South Stafford Street, Arlington, Va., 22206.

Assistant to the Administrator (Program Development and Administrative Coordination Staff).—Edward M. Newton, 3237 Gunston Road, Alexandria, Va., 22302.

Special Assistant for Economic Opportunity Programs.—Joseph C. Doherty, 2714 Poplar Street, 20007.

Director of Association Loan Division.—Henry A. Palm, 5533 Queensbury Avenue, Springfield, Va., 22151.

Director of Budget Division.—James T. Holliday, 8606 Beach Tree Road, Bethesda, Md., 20034.

Director of Business Services Division.—Cylar H. Van Natta, 2801 63d Avenue, Cheverley, Md., 20785.

Director of Emergency Loan Division.—Jack Frost, 3679 Alabama Avenue SE., 20020.

Director of Farm Ownership Loan Division.—Harold J. Finegan, 4359 Americana Drive, Annandale, Va., 22003.

Director of Information Division.—Philip S. Brown, 7914 Sleaford Place, Bethesda, Md., 20014.

Director of Operating Loan Division.—M. H. Williams, 1515 Dauphine Drive, Falls Church, Va., 22042.

Director of Personnel Division.—James A. Somerville, 509 Yorktown Drive, Alexandria, Va., 22313.

Director of Rural Housing Loan Division.—Louis D. Malotky, 3013 North Toronto Street, Alexandria, Va., 22210.

Director of Rural Renewal Division.—John Lovorn, 403 Darby Street, Fairfax, Va., 22030.

Director of Finance Office.—William B. Wood, 716 South Gore Street, Webster Groves, Mo., 63119.

FOREST SERVICE
South Building, Twelfth Street and Independence Avenue SW., 20250.
Phone, REpublic 7-4142 (Code 111)

Chief.—Edward P. Cliff, 221 North Royal Street, Alexandria, Va., 22314.

Assistant to the Chief.—Philip L. Thornton, 7407 Hamlett Street, North Springfield, Va., 22151.

Program Planning and Legislation:

Deputy Chief.—Hamilton K. Pyles, 116 Van Winkle Drive, Falls Church, Va., 22044.

Division of Legislative Reporting and Liaison.—Reynolds G. Florance, 510 South Abingdon Street, Arlington, Va., 22204.

Division of Program Planning and Special Projects.—Adrian M. Gilbert.

National Forest Resource Management Divisions:

Deputy Chief.—Arthur W. Greeley, 8312 Thoreau Drive, Bethesda, Md., 20034.

Associate Deputy Chief.—Burnett H. Payne, 916 South 26th Place, Arlington, Va., 22202.

Staff Assistant.—Leon R. Thomas, 4109 Wadsworth Court, Annandale, Va., 22003.

Staff Assistant.—Albert Arnst, P.O. Box 762 Benjamin Franklin Station, 20044.

National Forest Resource Management Divisions—Continued
> *Division of Timber Management.*—Ira J. Mason, 5305 Hampden Lane, Bethesda, Md., 20014.
> *Division of Range Management.*—Reginald M. DeNio, 4228 Columbia Pike, Arlington, Va., 22204.
> *Division of Recreation and Land Uses.*—Richard J. Costley, 2213 Shipman Lane, McLena, Va., 22101.
> *Division of Wildlife Management.*—D. Irvin Rasmussen, 4421 South 31st Street, Arlington, Va., 22206.
> *Division of Watershed Management.*—Byron B. Beattie, 6044 Rossmore Drive, Bethesda, Md., 20014.

National Forest Protection and Development Divisions:
> *Deputy Chief.*—M. M. Nelson, 4512 South 31st Street, Arlington, Va., 22206.
> *Associate Deputy Chief.*—Edward W. Schultz, 901 10th Street, Alexandria, Va., 22307.
> *Division of Land Classification.*—Frederick W. Grover, 2323 North Utah Street, Arlington, Va., 22207.
> *Division of Land Adjustments.*—Russell P. McRorey, 412 Randolph Drive, Annandale, Va., 22003.
> *Division of Fire Control.*—Merle S. Lowden, 3511 Shepherd Street, Chevy Chase, Md., 20015.
> *Division of Engineering.*—James J. Byrne, 257 Sharptown Street, Maryland City, Laurel, Md., 20810.

State and Private Forestry Divisions:
> *Deputy Chief.*—Boyd Rasmussen, 5539 Columbia Pike, Arlington, Va., 22204.
> *Associate Deputy Chief.*—Arthur R. Spillers, 503 West Windsor Avenue, Alexandria, Va., 22301.
> *Division of Cooperative Forest Fire Control.*—E. M. Bacon, 4106 Watkins Trail, Annandale, Va., 22003.
> *Division of Forest Pest Control.*—Warren V. Benedict, 5311 Sangamore Road, 20016.
> *Division of Flood Prevention and River Basin Programs.*—Warren T. Murphy, 6207 Crathie Lane, 20016.
> *Division of Cooperative Forest Management.*—Edward G. Grest, 1527 North Ivanhoe Street, Arlington, Va., 22205.

Forest Research Divisions:
> *Deputy Chief.*—V. L. Harper, 6409 Winston Drive, Bethesda, Md., 20034.
> *Associate Deputy Chief.*—George M. Jemison, 423 Hillmoor Drive, Silver Spring, Md., 20901.
> *Staff Assistant.*—Robert D. McCulley, 2941 Hickory Street, Alexandria, Va., 22305.
> *Staff Assistant.*—Thomas C. Nelson, 2800 Dartmouth Road, Alexandria, Va., 22314.
> *Biometrical Studies.*—George M. Furnival, Route 2, Springfield Road, Herndon, Va., 22070.
> *Foreign Forestry Services.*—Robert K. Winters, 5400 Moorland Lane, Bethesda, Md., 20014.
> *Division of Timber Management Research.*—Carl E. Ostrom, 4016 North Richmond Street, Arlington, Va., 22207.
> *Division of Watershed, Recreation, and Range Research.*—Herbert C. Storey, 611 Landon Lane, Bethesda, Md., 20034.
> *Division of Forest Protection Research.*—R. Keith Arnold, 809 Murray Lane, Annandale, Va., 22003.
> *Division of Forest Products and Engineering Research.*—Herbert O. Fleisher, 1019 27th Street South, Arlington, Va., 22202.
> *Division of Forest Economics and Marketing Research.*—H. R. Josephson, 5504 Burling Court, Bethesda, Md., 20034.

Administrative Divisions:
> *Deputy Chief.*—Clare W. Hendee, 4812 Essex Avenue, Chevy Chase, Md., 20015.
> *Associate Deputy Chief.*—Gordon D. Fox, 6215 Dahlonega Road, 20016.
> *Staff Assistant.*—Roy W. Olson, 6001 Landon Lane, Bethesda, Md. 20034.
> *General Inspector.*—Russell B. McKennan, 6318 11th Road North, Arlington, Va, 22205.
> *Division of Budget and Finance.*—Glenn C. Todd, 5420 Sanger Avenue, Alexandria, Va., 22311.
> *Division of Administrative Management.*—Chester A. Shields, 8110 Gosport Lane, Springfield, Va., 22151.

Administrative Divisions—Continued
  Associate Deputy Chief—Continued
    Division of Administrative Services.—Don Williamson, Roosevelt Towers, 500 North Roosevelt Boulevard, Falls Church, Va., 22042.
    Division of Information and Education.—Clint Davis, 9403 Columbia Boulevard, Silver Spring, Md., 20910.
    Division of Personnel Management.—Chalmer K. Lyman, 2117 Holmes Run Drive, Falls Church, Va., 22042.

RURAL COMMUNITY DEVELOPMENT SERVICE
Fourteenth Street and Independence Avenue SW.

Administrator.—Robert G. Lewis, 3512 Porter Street, 20016.
Deputy Administrator.—A. T. Mace, 909 North Montana Street, Arlington, Va., 22205.

RURAL ELECTRIFICATION ADMINISTRATION
Administrator's Office: South Building, Fourteenth Street and Independence Avenue SW.
Phone, DUdley 8-5123 (Code 111, extension 5123)

OFFICE OF THE ADMINISTRATOR

Administrator.—Norman M. Clapp, 1704 St. Marks Place, Fairfax, Va., 22030.
Deputy Administrator.—Richard A. Dell, 1308 Rusticway Lane, Falls Church, Va. 22044.
Assistant Administrator, Electric.—Richard H. Wood, 4608 North 26th Street, Arlington, Va., 22207.
Assistant Administrator, Telephone.—Edgar F. Renshaw, 2130 North Early Street, Alexandria, Va., 22302.
Assistant Administrator, Operations.—John W. Scott, 510 Yorktown Drive, Alexandria, Va., 22308.
Director, Rural Areas Development Staff.—Richard M. Hausler, 122 Country Hill, Drive, Fairfax, Va., 22030.

ELECTRIFICATION ACTIVITIES

Assistant Administrator.—Richard H. Wood, 4608 North 26th Street, Arlington, Va., 22207.
Deputy Assistant Administrator.—Edward F. Wilson, 5301 Saratoga Avenue, Chevy Chase, Md.
Director, Northeast Area Office.—William H. Callaway, 5722 Arlington Boulevard, Arlington, Va., 22204.
Director, Southeast Area Office.—Hubert Wales, 2112 Van Buren Street, Hyattsville, Md., 20782.
Director, North Central Area Office.—Everett R. Brown, 2556 Gallows Road, Falls Church, Va., 22042.
Director, Western Area Office.—Gerald F. Diddle, 634 Edmonston Drive, Rockville, Md., 20851.
Director, Southwest Area Office.—Richard F. Richter, 219 North Wakefield Street, Arlington, Va., 22203.
Director, Power Supply Division.—Hoburg B. Lee, 6305 Landon Lane, Bethesda, Md., 21814.
Director, Electric Distribution Division.—J. B. McCurley, 7508 Glendale Road, Chevy Chase, Md., 20015.
Director, Electric Standards Division.—J. E. O'Brien, 4723 Cumberland Avenue, Chevy Chase, Md., 20015.

TELEPHONE ACTIVITIES

Assistant Administrator.—Edgar F. Renshaw, 2130 North Early Street, Alexandria, Va., 22302.
Deputy Assistant Administrator.—Walter L. Wolff, 602 Beverly Drive, Alexandria, Va.

Director, Northeast Area Office.—Edward F. Maddox, 511 South Abingdon Street, Arlington, Va., 22204.
Director, Southeast Area Office.—Harold F. Clark, 1920 North Hollister Street, Arlington, Va., 22205.
Director, North Central Office.—Arthur H. Schartner, 5601 21st Avenue, Hillcrest Heights, Md.
Director, Western Area Office.—Donnan E. Basler, 5046 35th Road North, Arlington, Va., 22207.
Director, Southwest Area Office.—Walter E. Rich, 4958 35th Street North, Arlington, Va., 22207.
Director, Telephone Engineering and Operations Division.—Raymond W. Lynn, 902 Glaizewood Avenue, Takoma Park, Md., 20012.
Director, Telephone Standards Division.—Thomas J. McDonough, 6214 Stoneham Road, Bethesda, Md., 20034.

OPERATIONS

Assistant Administrator.—John W. Scott, 510 Yorktown Drive, Alexandria, Va., 22308.
Controller.—Leslie Surginer, 4115 34th Street North, Arlington, Va., 22207.
Director, Information Services Division.—William E. Spivey, 4367 North Pershing Drive, Arlington, Va., 22203.
Director, Personnel Management Division.—Henry C. Starns, 4112 North Randolph Street, Arlington, Va., 22207.
Director, Program Services Division.—Robert T. Beall, 5809 Doris Drive, Alexandria, Va., 22311.

SOIL CONSERVATION SERVICE

Executive Offices: South Building, 12th and Independence Avenues SW.
Phone, DUdley 8-4531 (Code 111, extension 4531)

Administrator.—Donald A. Williams, 5135 15th Street North, Arlington, Va., 22205.
Associate Administrator.—Gladwin E. Young, 5526 16th Street North, Arlington, Va., 22205.
Assistant to Associate Administrator.—Herschel E. Hecker, 6903 General Duff Drive, Falls Church, Va., 22041.
Assistant to Administrator for Great Plains.—Norman Berg, 7008 22d Avenue, West Hyattsville, Md., 20783.
Assistant to Administrator.—Raymond W. Heinen, 2306 Hildarose Drive, Silver Spring, Md., 20902; Lloyd E. Partain, 22 Dearborn Drive, Falls Church, Va., 22044; Frederick Prange, 618 Melrose Street, Alexandria, Va., 22302.
Field Representatives.—E. A. Norton, 4702 Morgan Drive, Chevy Chase, Md., 20015; H. E. Tower, 2515 North Quincy Street, Arlington, Va., 22207; Harvey G. Bobst, 1850 Columbia Pike, Executive North, Apt. 608, Arlington, Va., 22204; Thomas L. Gaston, Jr., 4700 Connecticut Avenue, 20008; Steven J. Kortan, 5535 Columbia Pike, Windsor Towers, Arlington, Va., 22204.
Deputy Administrator for Watersheds.—Hollis R. Williams, 218 North Columbus Street, Arlington, Va., 22203.
Assistant Deputy Administrator for Watersheds.—Richard M. Dailey, 5539 Columbia Pike, Windsor Towers, Arlington, Va., 22204.
Assistant to Deputy Administrator for Watersheds.—Ellis L. Hatt, 1006 Sixth Street SW., Apt. 505-W, 20024.
Watershed Planning Division.—John H. Wetzel, 6311 Dahlonega Road, 20016.
River Basins Division.—George R. Phillips, 4612 Harrison Street, Chevy Chase, Md., 20015.
Deputy Administrator for Field Services.—Jefferson C. Dykes, 4511 Guilford Road, College Park, Md., 20740.
Resource and Development Division.—Valentine W. Silkett, 5466 30th Street, 20015.
Engineering Division.—Chester J. Francis, 4118 North Richmond Street, Arlington, Va., 22207.
Hydrology Branch.—Harold O. Ogrosky, 1004 North Livingston Street, Arlington, Va., 22205.
Design Branch.—Melvin M. Culp, 1125 Cresthaven Drive, Silver Spring, Md., 20903.

Administrator—Continued
  Deputy Administrator for Field Services—Continued
    Engineering Division—Continued
      Construction Engineering.—Paul E. Nylander, 9531 Justine Drive, Annandale, Va., 22003.
      Water Supply Forecasting Branch.—William G. Shannon, 2700 Elnora Street, Wheaton, Md., 20909.
      Irrigation Engineering.—Tyler H. Quackenbush, 10107 Crestwood Road, Kensington, Md., 20795.
      Drainage Engineering.—John G. Sutton, 6300 Crathie Lane, Fairway Hills, 20016.
      Agricultural Engineering.—James J. Coyle, 1510 Dale Drive, Silver Spring, Md., 20910.
      Sedimentation Geology.—John W. Roehl, 5359 Taney Avenue, Alexandria, Va., 22304.
      Engineering and Groundwater Geology.—Alfonso F. Geiger, 101 Lakeside Drive, Greenbelt, Md., 20770.
      Engineering Plans.—Clarence E. Ghormley, 1201 South Scott Street, Arlington, Va., 22204.
    Plant Science Division.—Darnell M. Whitt, 7010 Wake Forest Drive, College Park, Md., 20740.
      Agronomy.—Burdette D. Blakely, 2105 Prichard Road, Wheaton, Md., 20902.
      Range Conservation.—Berten W. Allred, 4100 W Street, 20007.
      Woodland Conservation.—Theodore B. Plair, 113 Third Street NE., 20002.
      Biology.—Lawrence V. Compton, 2841 Beechwood Circle, Arlington, Va. 22207.
      Plant Materials.—Donald S. Douglas, 5928 Third Street North, Arlington, Va., 22204.
  Deputy Administrator for Soil Survey.—Charles E. Kellogg, 4100 Nicholson Street, Hyattsville, Md., 20782.
    Cartographic Division.—Charles W. Koechley, 2415 59th Avenue, Cheverly, Md., 20785.
    Soil Survey Operations.—Roy D. Hockensmith, 2832 McKinley Place, 20015.
    Soil Survey Interpretation.—Albert A. Klingebiel, 915 Newhall Street, Silver Spring, Md., 20901.
    Soil Survey Investigations.—Guy D. Smith, 6407 40th Avenue, University Park, Md., 20782.
    Soil Classification and Correlation.—Roy W. Simonson, 4613 Beechwood Road, College Park, Md., 20740.
  Deputy Administrator for Management.—William R. Van Dersal, 6 South Kensington Street, Arlington, Va., 22204.
    Administrative Services Division.—Gerald E. Ryerson, 202 Apple Grove Road, Silver Spring, Md., 20904.
      Budget and Finance Division.—Carl H. Dorny, 7412 Oak Lane, Chevy Chase, Md., 20015.
      Personnel Division.—Verna C. Mohagen, 4633 River Road, 20016.
      Information Division.—D. Harper Simms, 4410 38th Street North, Arlington, Va., 22207.

AGRICULTURAL ECONOMICS

Director, Agricultural Economics.—John A. Schnittker, 2114 North Randolph Street, Arlington, Va., 22207.

STAFF ECONOMIST GROUP

Lester R. Brown, 3716 Manor Road, Chevy Chase, Md.
Winn F. Finner, 400 Maple Avenue, Fairfax, Va., 22030.
Howard W. Hjort, 8013 Noel Street, Alexandria, Va., 22305.
Frank Lowenstein, 9205 Seven Locks Road, Bethesda, Md.

ECONOMIC RESEARCH SERVICE
OFFICE OF THE ADMINISTRATOR

Administrator.—Nathan M. Koffsky, 5515 Greystone Street, Chevy Chase, Md., 20015.

Deputy Administrator, Agricultural Economics.—Carl P. Heisig, 3125 North Nelson Street, Arlington, Va., 22207.

Deputy Administrator, Foreign Economics.—Sherman E. Johnson, 118 North Jackson Street, Arlington, Va., 22201.

Outlook and Situation Board.—Bushrod W. Allin, 5214 Goddard Road, Bethesda, Md., 20014.

AGRICULTURAL ECONOMICS DIVISIONS

Deputy Administrator.—Carl P. Heisig, 3125 North Nelson Street, Arlington, Va. 22207.

Director, Economic and Statistical Analysis.—James P. Cavin, 7605 Glennon Drive, Bethesda, Md., 20034.

Director, Farm Production Economics.—M. L. Upchurch, 5312 Thayer Avenue, Alexandria, Va., 22304.

Director, Marketing Economics.—Kenneth E. Ogren, 8904 Burbank Road, Annandale, Va., 22003.

Director, Resource Development Economics.—Harry A. Steele, 3600 North Rockingham Street, Arlington, Va., 22213.

FOREIGN ECONOMICS DIVISIONS

Deputy Administrator.—Sherman E. Johnson, 118 North Jackson Street, Arlington, Va., 22201.

Director, Development & Trade Analysis.—Kenneth L. Bachman, 845 Rose Lane, Annandale, Va., 22003.

Director, Regional Analysis.—Wilhelm Anderson, 2514 23d Road North, Arlington, Va., 22207.

STATISTICAL REPORTING SERVICE

Administrator.—Harry C. Trelogan, 3625 North Piedmont Street, Arlington, Va., 22207.

Deputy Administrator.—Glenn D. Simpson, 4425 49th Street, 20016.

Assistant to Administrator.—Christian A. Stokstad, 2703 Lockwood Lane, Annandale, Va., 22003.

Crop Reporting Board.—Glenn D. Simpson, 4425 49th Street, 20016.

Director, Agricultural Estimates Division.—Richard K. Smith, 12 Sunnyside Road, Silver Spring, Md., 20910.

Director, Field Operations Division.—Russell P. Handy, 4025 Forest Lane, McLean, Va., 22101.

Director, Standards & Research Division.—Earl E. Houseman, 1005 Hillwood Avenue, Falls Church, Va., 22042.

DEPARTMENTAL ADMINISTRATION

The Mall, between Twelfth and Fourteenth Streets SW. Phone, REpublic 7-4142 (Code 111)

Assistant Secretary for Administration.—Joseph M. Robertson, 9409 Kingsley Avenue, Bethesda, Md., 20014.

OFFICE OF BUDGET AND FINANCE

The Mall, between Twelfth and Fourteenth Streets SW. Phone, REpublic 7-4142 (Code 111)

Director of Finance and Budget Officer.—Charles L. Grant, 4922 27th Street North Arlington, Va., 22207.

Deputy Director.—Harry B. Wirin, 412 South Garfield Street, Arlington, Va., 22204.

Assistant Director.—John L. Wells, 2722 South Arlington Ridge Road, Arlington, Va., 22202.

Assistant to the Director.—Joseph P. Loftus, 7–J Crescent Road, Greenbelt, Md., 20770; William A. Carlson, 4620 Butterworth Place, 20016.

Program and Budget Analysis Staff.—James T. Caprio, Jr., 1208 North Powhatan Street, Arlington, Va., 22205; Robert A. Lerchen, 1302 Quincy Street, Alexandria, Va., 22302; Hartman Rector, Jr., 11204 Braddock Road, Fairfax, Va., 22030.

Division of Accounting Policies and Systems.—Chief, Charles I. Jenkins, 4535 North 19th Street, Arlington, Va., 22207.

Division of Budget Policies and Operations.—Chief, Sam H. Neel, 3009 Cheverly Avenue, Cheverly, Md., 20785.

Division of Budgetry and Financial Reporting.—Chief, Emmett B. Collins, 4101 25th Street North, Arlington, Va., 22207.

Division of Legislative Reporting.—Chief, Carl R. Sapp, 5534 18th Road North, Arlington, Va., 22205.

OFFICE OF HEARING EXAMINERS

The Mall, between Twelfth and Fourteenth Streets SW. Phone, DUdley 8-6383 or 6645 (Code 111)

Chief Hearing Examiner.—G. Osmond Hyde, 3944 Baltimore Street, Kensington, Md., 20795.

Hearing Examiners.—Jack W. Bain, Apt. 1508, 3110 Mount Vernon Avenue, Alexandria, Va., 22305; John J. Curry, 410 Cleve Drive, Falls Church, Va., 22042; Benj. M. Holstein, 628 South Royal Street, Alexandria, Va., 22314; Will Rogers, 2611 North Nelson Street, Arlington, Va., 22207.

OFFICE OF INFORMATION

The Mall, between Twelfth and Fourteenth Streets SW. Phone, REpublic 7-4142 (Code 111)

Director.—Harold R. Lewis, 22 Norman Avenue, Fairfax, Va., 22030.

Deputy Director.—Gordon Webb, 3004 South Abingdon Street, Arlington, Va., 22206.

Assistant Director (Visual Information).—J. H. McCormick, 5705 Cromwell Drive, 20016.

Executive Assistant to Director.—Francis A. Shea, 3605 Littledale Road, Kensington, Md., 20795.

Chief, Publications Division.—Harry P. Mileham, 912 Hillwood Avenue, Falls Church, Va., 22040.

Chief, Press Service.—Harry P. Clark, Jr., 1405 North Lancaster Street, Arlington, Va., 22205.

Chief, Special Reports.—Daniel D. Alfieri, 6749 Doane Avenue, Springfield, Va., 22150.

Chief, Radio and Television Service.—Layne Beaty, 1449 44th Street, 20007.

Chief, Arts and Graphic Division.—Elmo J. White, 310 Old Court House Road, Vienna, Va., 22180.

Chief, Exhibits Service.—David M. Granahan, 6715 Adelphi Road, University Park, Hyattsville, Md., 20782.

Chief, Motion Picture Service.—Calle A. Carrello, 5506 Parkland Courts SE., 20028.

Chief, Division of Photography.—Albert W. Matthews, 9316 Piney Branch Road, Silver Spring, Md., 20903.

OFFICE OF MANAGEMENT APPRAISAL AND SYSTEMS DEVELOPMENT

The Mall, between Twelfth and Fourteenth Streets SW. Phone, DUdley 8-3535

Director.—John C. Cooper, Jr., 5209 North 16th Street, Arlington, Va., 22205.

Assistant Director.—Charles C. Weaver, 812 Ferry Landing Road, Alexandria, Va., 22309.

OFFICE OF MANAGEMENT SERVICES

Director.—Charles F. Kiefer, 5302 18th Street North, Arlington, Va., 22205.
Chief, Administrative Services Division.—Stanley J. Dorick, 1708 Byrnes Drive, McLean, Va., 22101.
Chief, Budget and Finance Division.—John J. Kaminski, 2009 Chillum Road, Avondale, Hyattsville, Md., 20782.
Chief, Information Division.—Wayne V. Dexter, 1101 Jackson Court, Falls Church, Va., 22046.
Chief, Personnel Division.—Joseph P. Findlay, 4710 Yuma Street, 20016.
Assistant to the Director.—Charles J. Leman, 511 Patrick Henry Drive, Falls Church, Va., 22044.

OFFICE OF PERSONNEL

The Mall, between Twelfth and Fourteenth Streets SW. Phone, REpublic 7-4142 (Code 111)

Director of Personnel.—Carl B. Barnes, 123 Martha's Road, Hollin Hills, Alexandria, Va., 22307.
Deputy Director.—Max P. Reid, 146 East Rosemary Lane, Falls Church, Va., 22042.
Assistant Director, Program Planning.—Christopher O. Henderson, 5206 Western Avenue, Chevy Chase, Md., 20015.
Assistant to the Director, Manpower Utilization and Personnel Legislation.—Robert L. Hill, 6302 East Halbert Road, Bethesda, Md., 20034.
Chief, Personnel Research Staff.—Dr. Albert S. Glickman, 10117 Renfrew Road, Silver Spring, Md., 20901.
Chief, Classification, Organization & Standards Division.—Thomas T. Townsend, 4413 Brandywine Street, 20016.
Chief, Employee Appeals Division.—N. Robert Bear, 3290 Worthington Street, 20015.
Chief, Employee Development Division.—Dr. Erwin R. Draheim, 105 South Aberdeen Street, Arlington, Va., 22204.
Chief, Examination & Employment Division.—H. Reelf Peecksen, 7611 Lakeview Drive, Lake Barcroft, Falls Church, Va., 22041.
Chief, Health, Safety & Welfare Division.—Dr. Lee K. Buchanan, 4225 Sleaford Road, Bethesda, Md., 20014.
Chief, Policies & Procedures Division.—Dora E. Oliver, 1608 Cortland Road, Alexandria, Va., 22306.
Chief, Security and Employee Conduct Division.—John E. Francis, 5040 35th Road North, Arlington, Va., 22207.

OFFICE OF PLANT AND OPERATIONS

The Mall, between Twelfth and Fourteeth Streets SW. Phone, REpublic 7-4142 (Code 111)

Director.—Francis R. Mangham, 9634 Dewmar Lane, Kensington, Md., 20795.
Assistant Directors.—Samuel L. Gardiner, 6806 32d Street North, Falls Church, Va., 22046; Tony M. Baldauf, 6817 Mansfield Road, Falls Church, Va., 22041; Mackey W. White, 4000 Fitzhugh Drive, Annandale, Va., 22003.
Administrative Officer.—Hugh W. Berger, 917 Dale Drive, Silver Spring, Md., 20910.
Chief, Procurement and Contract Management Division.—V. Samuel Gunther, 4510 31st Street South, Arlington, Va., 22206.
Chief, Real Estate Management Division.—Clarence A. Salisbury, 1925 North Wayne Street, Arlington, Va., 22201.
Chief, Records Management Division.—Charles E. Wylie, 5502 Kempton Drive, Springfield, Va., 22151.
Chief, Secretary's Records and Communications Division.—James H. Austin, 13306 Lydia Street, Silver Spring, Md., 20906.
Chief, Service Operations Division.—Fred A. Hoyland, 4000 Cathedral Avenue, 20016.
Chief, Supply and Property Management Division.—Ralph G. McIntyre, 7511 Old Chester Road, Bethesda, Md., 20034.

OFFICE OF THE GENERAL COUNSEL

South Building, Fourteenth Street and Independence Avenue SW.
Phone, REpublic 7-4142 (Code 111, extension 3351)

General Counsel.—John C. Bagwell, 5511 18th Street North, Arlington, Va., 22205.
  Deputy General Counsel.—Edward M. Shulman, 6621 32d Street, 20015.
    Director, Commodity Stabilization Division.—George E. Cooper, 303 Buxton Road, Falls Church, Va., 22046.
    Director, Production Stabilization Division.—Howard Rooney, 2 Pike Branch Drive, Wilton Woods, Alexandria, Va., 22310.
    Director, Foreign Agricultural and Special Programs Division.—Claude T. Coffman, 1401 North Illinois Street, Arlington, Va., 22205.
Assistant General Counsels for—
  Marketing, Regulatory Laws, Research and Operations.—Charles W. Bucy, 4618 Langdrum Lane, Chevy Chase, Md., 20015.
    Director, Regulatory Division.—Carl R. Bullock, 9205 E. Parkhill Drive, Bethesda, Md., 20014.
    Director, Marketing Division.—J. Charles Krause, 9507 Hale Street, Silver Spring, Md., 20910.
    Director, Research and Operations Division.—Elmer Mostow, 3336 Runnymede Place, 20015.
  Litigation.—Neil Brooks, 3215 Morrison Street, 20015.
    Rural Development and Conservation.—Ralph F. Koebel, 8525 Spartan Road, Fairfax, Va., 22030.
    Director, Forestry and Soil Conservation Division.—Leroy M. Adams, 1111 Army Navy Drive, Arlington, Va., 22202.
    Director, Rural Electrification Division.—Louis Gorrin, 1020 19th Street, 20036.
    Director, Farmers Home Division.—Howard V. Campbell, 504 Lloyds Lane, Alexandria, Va., 22302.
Executive Assistant to the General Counsel.—W. Edward Bawcombe, 4310 34th Street South, Arlington, Va., 22206.

OFFICE OF THE INSPECTOR GENERAL

The Mall, between Twelfth and Fourteenth Streets SW.
Phone, DUdley 8-3306 (Code 111, extension 3306)

Inspector General.—Lester P. Condon, 1306 Janneys Lane, Alexandria, Va., 22302.
Executive Assistant to the Inspector General.—Smith Blair, Jr., 308 Leesburg Pike, Falls Church, Va., 22041.
Assistant Inspector General for Operations.—J. William Howell, 1012 North Powhatan Street, Arlington, Va., 22205.
Assistant Inspector General for Policy and Plans.—Leonard H. Greess, 2215 Westminister Court, Falls Church, Va., 22042.
Assistant Inspector General for Inspections and Special Projects.—Louis J. Roth, 1721 Fairwood Land, Falls Church, Va., 22046.
Assistant Inspector General for Analysis and Evaluation.—Benjamin F. Robinson, 9 Sudbury Place, Alexandria, Va., 22309.
Special Assistant to the Inspector General.—Richard W. Fitch, Jr., 4977 Battery Lane, Bethesda, Md., 20014.

DEPARTMENT OF COMMERCE

Commerce Building, Fourteenth Street between Constitution Avenue and E Street, 20230

Phone. STerling 3–9200 (Code 112)

JOHN T. CONNOR, Secretary of Commerce (2429 Kalorama Road); nominated as Secretary of Commerce by President Johnson on January 6, 1965; appointed January 18, 1965; born in Syracuse, N.Y., on November 3, 1914, the son of Michael J. and Mary (Sullivan) Connor; graduated from Holy Rosary High School, Syracuse, N.Y.; received an A.B. degree from Syracuse University (Magna cum laude) 1936, awarded an LL.B. degree by Harvard University's Law School in 1939; married the former Mary O'Boyle in 1940; three children, John T., Jr., Geoffrey, and Lisa Forrestal; associated with the New York City law firm of Cravath, de Gersdorff, Swaine & Wood from 1939 until 1942 when he became general counsel for the Office of Scientific Research and Development; joined the Marine Corps in 1944 as second lieutenant, served in the Pacific as Air Combat Intelligence Officer, was recalled to Washington in late 1945 and became Counsel, Office of Naval Research and later Special Assistant to the late James V. Forrestal, then Secretary of Navy; in 1947 he joined Merck & Co., Inc., as general attorney; later that year he was appointed secretary and counsel of the Company; in 1950 was made vice president; in 1955 he was selected president and chief executive officer of Merck & Co., Inc.; resigned from Merck & Co., Inc., just prior to his appointment as Secretary of Commerce.

Secretary.—John T. Connor, 2429 Kalorama Road, 20008.
   Assistant to the Secretary.—Lawrence C. McQuade, 3248 Prospect Street, 20007.
   Private Secretary to the Secretary.—Rachel H. Havnaer, 6006 Bowie Drive, Springfield, Va., 22150.
   Special Assistant to the Secretary for Textile Programs.—James S. Love, 4841 Sedgwick Street, 20016.
   Special Assistant to the Secretary for Congressional Relations.—Paul Southwick, 4012 Underwood Street, Chevy Chase, Md., 20015.
   Special Assistant to the Secretary for Public Affairs.—James G. Morton, Oregon Inlet Road, Nag's Head, N.C., 27954.
   Director, Office of Public Information.—Henry Scharer, 9105 East Parkhill Drive, Bethesda, Md., 20034.
   National Export Expansion Coordinator.—Daniel L. Goldy, 3605 Albermarle Street, 20008.
      Deputy National Export Expansion Coordinator.—Robert W. Barrie, 419 Fifth Street SE., 20014.
   Executive Secretariat.—Director, Margaret B. Tyler, 7200 Delfield Street, Chevy Chase, Md., 20015.
      Assistant Director and Chief Review Section.—Marion Meadows, 7009 Wells Parkway, College Heights Estates, Hyattsville, Md., 20782. *Le Roy Collin*
Under Secretary.—Franklin D. Roosevelt, Jr., 5188 Palisade Lane, 20016.
   Private Secretary to the Under Secretary.—Carol Ann Lammie, 1851 Columbia Road, 20009.
   Deputy to the Under Secretary.—John H. Royer, Jr., Bushy Park, Glenwood, Md., 21738. *alan S. Boyd 5/2/65*
Under Secretary for Transportation.—Clarence D. Martin, Jr., 6001 Wilson Lane, Bethesda, Md., 20034.
   Deputy Under Secretary for Transportation (Operations).—Lowell K. Bridwell, 147 D Street SE., 20003.
   Director, Transportation Research.—Robert A. Nelson, 4713 Yuma Street, 20016.
   Director, Office of Emergency Transportation.—[Vacant.]
   Deputy Director, Office of Emergency Transportation.—Carroll K. Faught, Jr., 5400 Pooks Hill Road, Linden Hill Towers, Apartment 620, Bethesda, Md., 20014.

Assistant Secretary for Administration.—Herbert W. Klotz, 4 Langley Place, McLean, Va., 22101.
    Deputy Assistant Secretary for Administration.—[Vacant.]
Assistant Secretary for Domestic and International Business.—Thomas G. Wyman, 2435 Tracy Place, 20008.
    Deputy Assistant Secretary for Domestic and International Business.—[Vacant.]
    Deputy Assistant Secretary for Financial Policy.—[Vacant.]
    Deputy Assistant Secretary for Trade Policy.—Robert L. McNeill, 7728 Old Chester Road, Bethesda, Md.
Assistant Secretary for Economic Affairs.—Andrew F. Brimmer, 861 Third Street SW., 20024.
    Deputy Assistant Secretary for Economic Affairs.—[Vacant.]
Assistant Secretary for Science and Technology.—J. Herbert Hollomon, 3650 Upton Street, 20008.
    Deputy Assistant Secretary for Science and Technology.—William W. Eaton, 215 Swithins Lane, Winchester-on-Severn, Annapolis, Md., 21406.
General Counsel.—Robert E. Giles, 4824 Upton Street, 20016.
    Deputy General Counsel.—Dean Lewis, 8215 Woodhaven Boulevard, Bethesda, Md.

OFFICE OF ASSISTANT SECRETARY FOR ADMINISTRATION

Office of Administrative Services:
    Director.—Donald B. Moore, 2710 Briggs Road, Silver Spring, Md., 20906.
    Deputy Director for Operations.—Bert Silver, 12810 Bushey Drive, Wheaton, Md., 20906.
Office of Audits:
    Director.—John R. Delmore, 4503 Edgefield Road, Kensington, Md., 20795.
    Deputy Director.—John R. Kurelich, 6729 Joallen Drive, Falls Church, Va., 22041.
Office of Budget and Finance:
    Director.—Lawrence E. Imhoff, 4540 Chesapeake Street, 20016.
    Deputy Director.—Charles H. Alexander, 5612 Greenleaf Road, Cheverly, Md., 20785.
Office of Emergency Readiness:
    Director.—Robert L. Hill, 1111 Army-Navy Drive, Arlington, Va., 22202.
Office of Investigations and Security:
    Director.—John W. Phillips, Clarksville, Md., 21029.
    Deputy Director.—Joseph M. Kelly, 7405 Jervis Street, Springfield, Va., 22151.
Office of Management and Organization:
    Director.—William F. Rapp, 2710 Donna Circle, Annandale, Va., 22003.
Office of Personnel:
    Director.—John Will, 8319 Ashwood Drive, Alexandria, Va., 22308.
    Associate Director.—John F. Lukens, 4514 Gretna Street, Bethesda, Md., 20014.
    Chief, Personnel Operations Division.—Francis X. Seymour, 12116 Hunter Lane, Rockville, Md., 20853.
Office of Publications:
    Director.—Herbert L. Brown, Jr., 2710 South Hayes Street, Arlington, Va., 22202.
    Deputy Director.—Paul A. Ziemer, 5818 Weaver Avenue, McLean, Va., 22101.
U.S. Commission.—New York World's Fair:
    Commissioner.—Norman K. Winston, 7 Sutton Square, New York, N.Y.
Appeals Board:
    Chairman.—Nathan Ostroff, 2914 Kanawha Street, 20015.

COMMUNITY RELATIONS SERVICE

Department of Commerce Building. Phone, WOrth 7–4894 (Code 112, extension 4894)

Director.—LeRoy Collins, 3116 P Street NW., 20007.
Deputy Director.—Calvin Kytle, 430 M Street SW., 20024.
Associate Director for Conciliation.—John A. Griffin, 1444 Rhode Island Avenue, 20005.
Assistant Director for Community Action.—Roger W. Wilkins, 201 G Street SW., 20024.

Assistant Director for Media Relations.—David H. Pearson, 2905 Farm Road, Alexandria, Va., 22302.
Chief Counsel.—Samuel W. Allen, 1100 Sixth Street SW., 20024.
Administrative Officer.—Richard H. Adams, 1358 Fourth Street SW., 20024.

PRESIDENT'S ADVISORY COMMITTEE ON LABOR-MANAGEMENT POLICY

Executive Secretary.—[Vacant.]

FEDERAL DEVELOPMENT PLANNING COMMITTEE FOR APPALACHIA

Chairman.—John L. Sweeney, 3717 Morrison Street, 20015.

FEDERAL FIELD COMMITTEE FOR DEVELOPMENT PLANNING IN ALASKA

Chairman.—Joseph H. Fitzgerald, Anchorage, Alaska.

INLAND WATERWAYS CORPORATION

Governor.—The Secretary of Commerce.
Chairman of the Advisory Board.—Clarence D. Martin, Jr., 6001 Wilson Lane, Bethesda, Md., 20034.

GREAT LAKES PILOTAGE ADMINISTRATION

Administrator.—Alfred T. Meschter, Box 373–M, Rt. 4, Vienna, Va., 22180.

UNITED STATES TRAVEL SERVICE

1666 Connecticut Avenue.   Phone, STerling 3–9200 (Code 112)

Acting Director.—John W. Black, 7025 31st Street, 20015.
Deputy Director.—John W. Black, 7025 31st Street, 20015.

OFFICE OF BUSINESS ECONOMICS

1832 M Street.   Phone, STerling 3–9200 (Code 112)

Director.—George Jaszi, 4910 Cumberland Avenue, Chevy Chase, Md., 20015.
Associate Director.—Louis J. Paradiso, 1004 Stirling Road, Silver Spring, Md., 20901.
Acting Associate Director.—Morris R. Goldman, 9626 Evergreen Street, Silver Spring, Md., 20901.
Deputy Director for Information and Administration.—James W. McNally, 3511 Porter Street, 20016.
Assistant Director (Chief Statistician).—Lawrence Grose, 4004 Woodlawn Road, Chevy Chase, Md., 20015.
Divisions:
  Balance of Payment.—Walther Lederer, Chief, 5 Westmoreland Road, Alexandria, Va., 22308.
  Business Structure.—Lawrence Bridge, Chief, 707 Cedar Lane, Falls Church, Va., 22042.
  Current Business Analysis.—Murray F. Foss, Chief, 6209 East Halbert Road, Bethesda, Md., 20034.
  National Economics.—Martin L. Marimont, Chief, 11512 Yates Street, Wheaton, Md., 20902.
  National Income.—Frederick M. Cone, Chief, 4502 Chase Avenue, Bethesda, Md., 20014.
  Regional Economics.—Robert E. Graham, Jr., Chief, 4851 28th Street North, Arlington, Va., 22207.

AREA REDEVELOPMENT ADMINISTRATION

Department of Commerce. Phone, STerling 3-9200 (Code 112, extension 5113)

Administrator.—William L. Batt, Jr., 6425 31st Street, 20015.
Deputy Administrator.—Harold W. Williams, 4 Bedford Lane, Alexandria, Va., 22307.
Chief Counsel.—Thomas W. Harvey, 4110 Thornapple Street, 20015.
Economic Adviser.—Victor Roterus, 5611 Overlea Road, 20016.
Congressional Liaison.—Francis X. Dooley, 1400 South Joyce Street, Arlington, Va., 22200.
Public Affairs.—William A. Platt, 800 Fourth Street SW., Apt. S-623, 20024.
Assistant Administrator for Administration.—Furniss L. Parnell (acting), 505 Mashie Drive SE., Vienna, Va., 22180.
Divisions:
  Chief, Accounting Division.—Edgar H. Dye, 5101 Dodson Drive, Annandale, Va., 22003.
  Chief, Budget Division.—Brinley J. Lewis, 3904 Foreston Road, Beltsville, Md., 20705.
  Chief, Program Evaluation and Reports Staff.—Eleanor K. Buschman, 6630 Joallen Drive, Falls Church, Va., 22044.
Assistant Administrator for Program Development.—Gordon E. Reckord, 400 Beechwood Road, Alexandria, Va., 22300.
  Deputy Assistant Administrator for Program Development.—Sidney R. Jeffers, 5426 Roanoke Avenue, Alexandria, Va., 22311.
Divisions:
  Chief, Designation Division.—Gladys F. Miller, 11603 Montgomery Road, Beltsville, Md., 20705.
  Chief, Research Division.—Roger A. Prior, 2130 N Street, 20009.
  Chief, Technical Projects Division.—Frank A. Cirillo, 6206 Fairhill Court, Kay Park, Md., 20023.
  Chief, Area Surveys Division.—Theodore K. Pasma, 5806 Augusta Lane, Glen Mar Park, Md., 20016.
  Chief, Program Analysis Division.—Frederick H. Eaton, 5830 Lowell Avenue, Alexandria, Va., 22300.
  Chief, Publications Division.—Zackary Metz, 12411 Stirrup Lane, Bowie, Md., 20715.
Assistant Administrator for Public Works Acceleration.—Johannes U. Hoeber, 1100 Sixth Street SW., 20024.
Assistant Administrator for Operations.—Sherwood Gates, 1727 Massachusetts Avenue, 20036.
  Deputy Assistant Administrator for Operations.—Ward Miller, Jr., 8804 Mead Street, Bethesda, Md., 20034.
Divisions:
  Chief, Northeast Division.—Anthony DeAngelo, 706 Boundary Avenue, Silver Spring, Md., 20910.
  Chief, Lake States Division.—Wilfred C. Leland, 4550 McArthur Boulevard, 20007.
  Chief, Appalachian Division.—George T. Karras, 148 11th Street, 20003.
  Chief, Southeast Division.—Richard G. Schmitt, Jr., 4017 Beechwood Road, University Park, Hyattsville, Md., 20782.
  Chief, Northwest Division.—Cecelia P. Galey, 1616 18th Street, 20009.
  Chief, Southwest Division.—Leon V. Langan, 7202 Lenhart Drive, Chevy Chase, Md., 20015.
Assistant Administrator for Financial Assistance.—James T. Sharkey, 3603 Underwood Street, Chevy Chase, Md., 20015.
Divisions:
  Chief, Financial Projects Division.—William F. Abell, 2804 East-West Highway, Chevy Chase, Md., 20015.
  Chief, Management Assistance.—William K. Holl, 4206 39th Street North, Arlington, Va., 22207.

BUREAU OF INTERNATIONAL COMMERCE

Department of Commerce Building. Phone, WOrth 7-5261 (Code 112, extension 5261)

Director.—Eugene M. Braderman, 1630 45th Street, 20007.
Deputy Director.—Archie M. Andrews, 222 Green Street, Alexandria, Va.

Assistant Director.—E. E. Schnellbacher, 4540 Warren Street, 20016.

Assistant Director.—J. Mishell George, 1022 Rynex Drive, Alexandria, Va., 22312.

ACEP Executive Secretary.—Theodore L. Thau, 8713 Sundale Drive, Silver Spring, Md., 20910.

Executive Secretary, Foreign Trade Zones Board.—Richard H. Lake, 4710 Surry Place, Alexandria, Va., 22304.

Director, International Organizations Staff.—Irwin Fine, Apt. S–602, 429 N Street SW., 20024.

Director, Office of Commercial and Financial Policy.—Lawrence A. Fox, 611 Lakeview Drive, Falls Church, Va., 22040.

Deputy Director.—Milton A. Berger, 6906 Greentree Drive, Falls Church, Va., 22040.

Director, Foreign Business Practices Division.—Vincent D. Travaglini, 413 Hanson Lane, Alexandria, Va., 22302.

Director, Trade and Commercial Policy Division.—Allen H. Garland, 2117 Saranac Street, Adelphi, Md., 20783.

Director, Transportation and Insurance Division.—Jerome Sachs, 4531 28th Street, 20008.

Director, International Finance Division.—Eugene A. Birnbaum, 6512 Elgin Lane, Bethesda, Md., 20034.

Director, International Resources Policy Division.—Donald Sham, 2124 I Street, 20037.

Director, Office of International Investment.—Robert L. Oshins, 2 Stanford Circle, Fall Church, Va., 22041.

Director, Investment Opportunities Division.—Charles W. Vear, 7324 Gallows Road, Annandale, Va., 22003.

Director, Investment Resources Division.—S. David Horner, 9904 Old Spring Road, Kensington, Md., 20795.

Director, Foreign Capital and Investment Services Division.—Frank W. Sheaffer, 1503 Sharon Drive, Silver Spring, Md., 20900.

Director, Office of International Regional Economics.—Robert E. Simpson, 10315 Riverwood Drive, Potomac, Md., 20854.

Assistant Director.—Murray P. Rennert, 2500 Wisconsin Avenue, 20007.

Special Assistant.—Frederick Strauss, 629 Lakeview Drive, Falls Church, Va.

Director, American Republics Division.—Claude W. Courand, 2433 Ft. Scott Drive, Arlington, Va., 22202.

Director, Africa Division.—Bernard Blankenheimer, 9508 Wadsworth Drive, Bethesda, Md.

Director, European Division.—Clarence S. Siegel, 6007 28th Street.

Director, Far Eastern Division.—Saul Baran, 34 Custis Street, Alexandria, Va.

Director, Sino-Soviet Division.—Ernest Rubin, 540 South Carlyn Spring Road, Arlington, Va., 22204.

Director, Near East-South Asia Division.—D. A. Kearns-Preston, 2001 Lucerne Avenue, Silver Spring, Md., 20910.

Director, International Trade Analysis Division.—Miss Frances L. Hall, 3025 Ontario Road, Apt. 207, 20009.

Director, Office of Export Control.—F. D. Hockersmith, 40 Littleton Lane, Fairfax, Va., 22030.

Deputy Director.—Rauer H. Meyer, 738 Kerns Road, Falls Church, Va.

Assistant Airector.—Wilson E. Sweeney, 5917 Kirby Road, Bethesda, Md., 20034.

Director, Technical Data and Services Division.—John W. Shepard, 3313 North Ohio Street, Arlington, Va., 22207.

Director, Operations Division.—Mrs. Geraldine S. DePuy, 2402 East-West Highway, Silver Spring, Md., 20910.

Director, Policy Planning Division.—Edward P. Walinsky, 6555 Marlo Drive, Falls Church, Va.

Director, Investigations Division.—Charles B. Clements, 6710 Renita Lane, Bethesda, Md., 20034.

Director, Scientific and Electronic Equipment Division.—John R. Collins, 2005 Hermitage Avenue, Silver Spring, Md., 20902.

Director, Production Materials and Consumer Products Division.—Livingston Goddard, 709 Lakeview Drive, Falls Church, Va., 22041.

Director, Capital Goods Division.—H. Leigh Brite, 4821 32d Street, 20008.

Director, Office of International Trade Promotion.—Ralph A. Bergsten, 48 G Street SW., 20024.

Deputy Director for Programs.—Paul E. Pauly, 309 Meadow View Road, Falls Church, Va., 22042.

Deputy Director for Operations.—John E. Orchard, 1915 Norvale Road, Silver Spring, Md.

Acting Assistant Director for Commercial Exhibits.—Edward J. Krause, 5301 Marlyn Drive, Glen Mar Park, Md., 20016.

Assistant Director for U.S. National Exhibits.—Thomas L. Craig, 200 C Street SE., 20003.

Director, Trade Missions Division.—Roy F. Gootenberg, 10805 Clermont Avenue, Garrett Park, Md., 20766.

Acting Director, Commercial Exhibits Division.—Earl W. Wade, 2808 North Van Buren, Arlington, Va., 22213.

Director, Exhibits Design Division.—Joseph W. Adams, 3415 Orchid Drive, Falls Church, Va.

Acting Director, U.S. National Exhibits Division.—Thomas L. Craig, 200 C Street SE.

Director, Commercial Intelligence Division.—Charles F. Boehm, 2127 Woodberry Lane, Falls Church, Va., 22040.

OFFICE OF FOREIGN COMMERCIAL SERVICES

Department of Commerce Building. Phone, WOrth 7-3320 (Code 112, extension 3320)

Director.—Donald S. Gilpatric, 6306 Carnegie Drive, Bethesda, Md., 20034.

Deputy Director.—Herbert P. VanBlarcom, 407 Jackson Place, Alexandria, Va., 22302.

Director, Overseas Personnel Division.—Donald O. Hays, 4000 Massachusetts Avenue, 20016.

Director, Foreign Activities Management Division.—Wayland B. Waters, 2580 Naylor Road SE., 20020.

Director, Performance Evaluation Division.—Herbert J. Cummings, 800 Fourth Street SW., 20024.

Director, Foreign Communications Division.—William R. Hayden, 1415 North Oak Street, Apt. 401, Arlington, Va., 22209.

Director, Training Programs Division.—Kenneth B. Atkinson, 11 Langley Hill Drive, McLean, Va.,

BUSINESS AND DEFENSE SERVICES ADMINISTRATION

Department of Commerce Building. Phone, WOrth 7-5491 (Code 112, extension 5491)

Administrator.—George Donat, 4836 Kellog Street, McLean, Va.

Deputy Administrator.—James F. Collins, 3039 Dent Place, 20007.

Office of Assistant Administrator for Business and Government Services.—[Vacant.]

Office of Assistant Administrator for Industrial Mobilization.—Anthony A. Bertsch, 4714 33d Street North, Arlington, Va., 22207.

Director, Industrial Materials Staff.—Thomas Curtis, 5015 Garfield Street, 20016.

Director, Mobilization Readiness Staff.—[Vacant.]

Director, Mobilization Plans and Control Staff.—Arthur U. Sufrin, 4000 Tunlaw Road, 20007.

Director, Industrial Evaluation Staff.—Kurt E. Rosinger, 3900 16th Street, 20011.

Office of Assistant Administrator for Industrial Analysis.—Paul W. McGann, 6307 Glenwood Place, Falls Church, Va.

Director, Industrial Analysis Staff.—Davis A. Portner, 2318 North Quantico, Arlington, Va. 22205.

Director, Industrial Growth and Research Staff.—Hyman B. Kaitz, 308 Beechwood Road, Hobbins Hills, Alexandria, Va., 22307.

Director, Statistical Operations and Analysis Staff.—Thomas E. Murphy, 4415 Glenridge Street, Parkwood, Kensington, Md., 20795.

Office of Distribution Services.—[Vacant.]

Director, Service Trades Division.—[Vacant].

Director, Service Industries Division.—Robert J. Bond, 210 South Oak Street, Falls Church, Va.

Director, Marketing Information Division.—[Vacant.]

Director, Water Industries and Engineering Services Division.—Konstantine L. Kollar, 1700 Overlook Drive, Hillandale, Silver Spring, Md., 20903.

Office of Chemicals and Consumer Products.—Edward R. Killam, 4813 Blackfoot Road, College Park, Md., 20740.

Director, Chemcial and Allied Products Division.—Wesley R. Koster, 5902 Ramsgate Road, 20016.

Director, Consumer Durables Division.—Kenneth B. Smith, 1009 Notley Road, Silver Spring, Md., 20904.
Director, Food Industries Division.—[Vacant.]
Acting Director, Food Industries Division.—Irving I. Kramer, 12919 Matey Road, Silver Spring, Md., 20906.
Director, Rubber, Leather and Allied Products Division.—[Vacant.]
Office of Industrial Equipment.—Erwin C. Hannum, 9815 Indian Queen Point Road, Oxon Hill, Md., 20022.
Director, Agriculture, Construction, Mining and Oil Field Equipment Division.—Charles R. Weaver, Apt. 603, 2828 Connecticut Avenue, 20008.
Director, General Industrial Equipment and Components Division.—[Vacant].
Director, Metalworking Equipment Division.—Philip A. Bennett, Apt. 305, 2000 F Street, 20006.
Director, Transportation Equipment Division.—Edward G. Smith, 5110 Lawton Drive, 20016.
Office of Metals and Minerals.—James M. Owens, 6315 Highland Street, Alexandria, Va.
Director, Aluminum and Magnesium Division.—John H. Styer, 4837 Langdrum Lane, Chevy Chase, Md., 20015.
Director, Copper Division.—William A. Meissner, Jr., 6200 Massachusetts Avenue., 20016.
Director, Iron and Steel Division.—[Vacant.]
Deputy Director, Iron and Steel Division.—Harry K. Herschman, 3349 Military Road, 20015.
Director, Miscellaneous Metals and Minerals Division.—Ewing J. Talbert, 7605 Granada Drive, Bethesda, Md., 20034.
Office of Scientific and Technical Equipment.—Donald S. Parris, 3144 North Pollard Street, Arlington, Va., 22207.
Director, Communications Industries Division.—Thomas Z. Corless, 7604 Charleston Drive, Bethesda, Md., 20034.
Director, Electronics Division.—E. MacDonald Nyhen, 1637 North Greenbrier Street, Arlington, Va., 22205.
Director, Power and Electrical Equipment Division.—Charley M. Denton, 2828 Connecticut Avenue, 20008.
Director, Scientific, Photographic and Business Equipment Division.—[Vacant.]
Assistant Director, Scientific, Photographic and Business Equipment Division.—James L. Oliver, 2042 Fort Davis Street SE., 20020.
Office of Construction and Materials Industries.—Charles A. Lewis, 2208 Richland Place, Silver Spring, Md., 20910.
Director, Building Materials and Construction Industries Division.—Lee N. Blugerman, Apt. 516, 2020 F Street, 20006.
Director, Containers and Packaging Division.—Osker C. Reynolds, 3914 West Baltimore Street, Kensington, Md., 20795.
Director, Forest Products Division.—Thomas C. Mason, 7606 Hammond Avenue, Takoma Park, Md., 20012.
Director, Printing and Publishing Industries Division.—Harold F. Drury, 304 East Building, Hunting Towers, Alexandria, Va., 22314.
Office of Trade Adjustment, Deputy Director.—George A. Lavallee, 6201 32d Place., 20015.
Office of Textiles.—Thomas J. Davis, 510 21st Street, 20006.
Director, Business Services and Analysis Division.—William W. Shoaf, 5315 North 16th Street, Arlington, Va., 22205.
Director, Market Analysis Division.—[Vacant.]
Director, Trade Analysis Division.—Emanuel A. Lipscomb, 2705 13th Street NE., 20019.

OFFICE OF FIELD SERVICES

Department of Commerce Building.   Phone, WOrth 7-3641 (Code 112, extension 3641)

Director.—Roy L. Morgan, 3900 Watson Place, Apt. 2A, Tower B, 20016.
Deputy Director.—Joseph A. Mack, 2332 Nebraska Avenue, 20016.
Assistant Director for Operations.—Roderick M. Gillies, 210 Barbara Lane, Fairfax, Va., 22030.
Director, Operations Division.—Paul H. Cullen, 225 Juniper Lane, Falls Church, Va., 22040.
Acting Director, Trade Conferences Division.—Jan B. Verschuur, 12309 Firtree Lane, Bowie, Md., 20715.

OFFICE OF PUBLICATIONS AND INFORMATION FOR DOMESTIC AND INTERNATIONAL BUSINESS

Department of Commerce Building.   Phone, STerling 3-9200 (Code 112, extension 5436)

Director.—Dean Smith, 2325 49th Street, 20007.
Deputy Director.—Charles T. Reyner, 4118 23d Street North, Arlington, Va., 22207.
Director, International Commerce.—Frederic S. Otis, 2408 North Dearing Street, Alexandria, Va., 22302.
Acting Director, Publications Division.—Roland J. Sawyer, 3017 44th Place, 20016.
Director, Information Division.—C. Alphonso Smith, 506 Eden Court, Alexandria, Va., 22308.
Director, Graphics Division.—Americo A. W. Favale, 2003 Iverson Street, Hillcrest Heights, 20031.

OFFICE OF ADMINISTRATION FOR DOMESTIC AND INTERNATIONAL BUSINESS

Department of Commerce Building.   Phone, WOrth 7-4106 (Code 112, extension 4106)

Director.—William I. Merkin, 3019 Crest Avenue, Cheverly, Md.
Deputy Director.—Richard M. Gottfried, 5021 Spring Drive, 20031.
Assistant Director.—Robert W. Newland, 5406 Christy Drive, 20016.
Director, Management and Organization Division.—John P. Eberle, 7901 Gateway Boulevard, District Heights, Md., 20028.
Director, Personnel Division.—James A. Mulcahy, 2727 29th Street, 20008.
Director, Budget and Finance Division.—Joe G. Keen, 9310 Reid Circle, 20022.

BUREAU OF THE CENSUS

Suitland, Md.   Phone, 735-2000 (Code 157, extension 576)

Director.—[Vacant]   (A. Ross Eckler, acting).
Deputy Director.—A. Ross Eckler, 3643 Brandywine Street, 20008.
Assistant Director for Administration.—Walter L. Kehres, 2912 73d Avenue, Landover, Md., 20785.
Assistant Director for Economic Fields.—Howard C. Grieves, 5611 Warwick Place, Chevy Chase, Md., 20015.
Assistant Director for Demographic Fields.—Conrad F. Taeuber, 4222 Sheridan Street, Hyattsville, Md., 20782.
Assistant Director for Research and Development.—Morris H. Hansen, 5212 Goddard Road, Bethesda, Md., 20014.
Assistant Director for Operations.—Charles B. Lawrence, Jr., 6505 Wiscassett Road, 20016.
Chief, Administrative Service Division.—Cecil B. Matthews, 5607 Lucente Avenue, 20023.
Chief, Agriculture Division.—Ray Hurley, Bell Station, Glenn Dale, Md., 20015.
Chief, Budget and Finance Division.—William E. Stiver, 4522 Kerby Parkway, Oxon Hill, Md., 20022.
Chief, Business Division.—Harvey Kailin, 5804 Johnson Avenue, Bethesda, Md., 20034.
Chief, Construction Statistics Division.—Samuel J. Dennis, 419 East Columbia Street, Falls, Church, Va., 22046.
Chief, Data Processing Systems Division.—Robert F. Drury, 3060 Oliver Street, 20015.
Chief, Demographic Operations Division.—Morton A. Meyer, 2303 Fairlawn Street SE., 20031.
Chief, Demographic Surveys Division.—Robert B. Pearl, 8504 16th Street, Silver Spring, Md., 20910.
Chief, Economic Operations Division.—M. D. Bingham, 427 Crosswoods Drive, Falls Church, Va., 22043.
Chief, Economic Research and Analysis Division.—Julius Shiskin, 8920 Whitney Street, Silver Spring, Md., 20901.
Chief, Field Division.—Jefferson D. McPike, 5506 Parkland Court SE., 20028.
Chief, Foreign Demographic Analysis Division.—Paul F. Myers, 12811 Crisfield Road, Silver Spring, Md., 20900.

Chief, Foreign Trade Division.—Dino S. Villa, 5009 Leeds Drive, 20023.
Chief, Geography Division.—William T. Fay, 225 Standish Drive, 20021.
Chief, Governments Division.—Allen D. Manvel, 6221 Western Avenue, 20015.
Chief, Housing Division.—Arthur F. Young, 5911 John Adams Drive SE., 20031.
Chief, Industry Division.—Maxwell R. Conklin, 4822 Cumberland Avenue, Chevy Chase, Md., 20015.
Chief, International Statistical Programs Office.—Calvert L. Dedrick, 6615 Western Avenue, 20015.
Chief, Management and Organization Division.—Samuel O. Maslak, 4305 Kingswood Drive, 20028.
Chief, Personnel Division.—James P. Taff, 5501 31st Street North, Arlington, Va., 22207.
Chief, Population Division.—Howard G. Brunsman, 5715 Ninth Street North, Arlington, Va., 22205.
Public Information Officer.—John C. Baker, 3107 Pearl Drive. Suitland, Md., 20023.
Chief, Statistical Methods Division.—Joseph Waksberg, 6302 Tone Drive, Bethesda, Md., 20034.
Chief, Statistical Reports Division.—Edwin D. Goldfield, 2809 Jasper Street SE., 20020.
Chief, Statistical Research Division.—William N. Hurwitz, 9324 Harvey Road, Silver Spring, Md., 20910.
Chief, Transportation Division.—Donald E. Church, 7313 Montrose Street, Alexandria, Va., 22312.

COAST AND GEODETIC SURVEY

Washington Science Center, Rockville, Md., 20852. Phone, 949-5310

Director.—Rear Adm. H. Arnold Karo, 6307 Kirby Road, Bethesda, Md., 20034.
Deputy Director.—Rear Adm. James C. Tison, Jr., 211 Wilkes Street, Alexandria, Va., 22314.
Assistant to the Director.—Capt. Edgar F. Hicks, Jr., 5813 Greentree Road, Bethesda, Md., 20034.
Program Planning Staff.—Capt. Harley D. Nygren, 5865 Lowell Avenue, Alexandria, Va., 22312.
Executive Assistant to the Director.—A. A. Stanley, 509 Springloch Road, Silver Spring, Md., 20904.
Public Information Officer.—Raymond Wilcove, 510 Fleetwood Street, Silver Spring, Md., 20910.

OFFICE OF ADMINISTRATION

Assistant Director.—[Vacant.]
Chief of Division of—
  Administrative and Technical Services.—Guy P. Meredith, 9720 Riggs Road, Adelphi, Md., 20783.
  Budget and Finance.—John M. Amstadt, 5813 Weaver Avenue, McLean, Va., 22101.
  Engineering.—Thomas J. Hickley, 10605 Amherst Avenue, Silver Spring, Md., 20902.
  Management and Organization.—Samuel C. Delfin, 11008 Lombardy Road, Silver Spring, Md., 20901.
  Personnel.—Leonard Zaciewski, 10317 Cherry Tree Lane, Silver Spring, Md., 20901.

OFFICE OF OCEANOGRAPHY

Assistant Director.—Capt. Max G. Ricketts, 7107 Connecticut Avenue, Chevy Chase, Md., 20015.
Chief of Division of—
  Operations.—Capt. Horace G. Conerly, 5300 Westbard Avenue, Bethesda, Md., 20016.
  Marine Data.—Cdr. William D. Barbee, 5703 Heming Avenue, Springfield, Va., 22151.
  Facilities.—Cdr. Allen L. Powell, 4811 Westmoreland Street, McLean, Va., 22101.

OFFICE OF PHYSICAL SCIENCES

Assistant Director.—Charles A. Whitten (acting), 9606 Sutherland Road, Silver Spring, Md., 20901.
Chief of Division of—
   Geodesy.—Capt. John O. Phillips, 911 Baylor Drive, Alexandria, Va., 22307.
   Photogrammetry.—Capt. Joseph E. Waugh, 4858 Battery Lane, Bethesda, Md., 20014.
   Geomagnetism.—James H. Nelson, 3041 North Pollard Street, Arlington, Va., 22207.
   Seismology.—Leonard M. Murphy, 4422 Montgomery Avenue, Bethesda, Md., 20014.
   Electronic Computing.—Rex B. Finley, 5311 T Street SE., 20027.

OFFICE OF CARTOGRAPHY

Assistant Director.—Capt. Raymond H. Tryon, Jr., 1921 North Quantico Street, Arlington, Va., 22205.
Chief of Division of—
   Nautical Chart.—Cdr. Lorne G. Taylor, 1013 Ampthill Drive, Alexandria, Va., 22312.
   Reproduction.—C. Walter Lane, Jr., 10301 Gary Road, Potomac, Md., 20854.
   Distribution.—Charles R. Bush, Jr., 4801 Kenmore Avenue, Alexandria, Va., 22304.
   Aeronautical Chart.—Granville K. Emminizer, Jr. (acting), 10800 Georgia Avenue, Silver Spring, Md., 20902.

OFFICE OF RESEARCH AND DEVELOPMENT

Assistant Director.—Dr. John S. Rinehart, 6424 Dahlonega Road, 20016.

MARITIME ADMINISTRATION

General Accounting Office Building.   Phone: STerling 3-5200 (Code 129, extension 5331)

Office of the Maritime Administrator:
   Maritime Administrator.—Nicholas Johnson, 5808 Augusta Lane, Glen Mar Park, Md., 20016.
   Deputy Maritime Administrator.—James W. Gulick, 312 Wood Road, Fairfax, Va., 22030.
   Assistant Deputy Maritime Administrator.—George R. Griffiths, 442 Fairview Place, Falls Church, Va., 22041.
   Secretary and Assistant to Deputy Administrator.—James S. Dawson, Jr., 123 South Washington Street, Rockville, Md., 20850.
   Chief Investigator and Security Officer.—W. George Goold, 4800 Cecile Street, McLean, Va., 22101.
   Chief Hearing Examiner.—Paul N. Pfeiffer, 412 Basset Street, Alexandria, Va., 22308.
   Special Assistant to the Maritime Administrator.—Maitland S. Pennington, 2901 Connecticut Avenue, 20008.
   Public Information Officer.—John K. Tennant, 8312 14th Avenue, Hyattsville, Md., 20783.
   Maritime Labor Adviser.—John P. Miraglia, 2109 34th Street SE., 20020.
   Confidential Assistant to the Maritime Administrator.—Stephen J. Friedman, 4600 Connecticut Avenue, 20008.
Office of Program Planning:
   Chief, Office of Program Planning.—Ira Dye, 809 Crescent Drive, Alexandria, Va., 22302.
   Deputy Chief, Office of Program Planning.—Walter B. Chambers, Jr., 313 Patrick Henry Drive, Falls Church, Va., 22044.
   Chief, Division of Ports.—Howard J. Marsden, 3230 Woodburn Road, Annandale, Va., 22003.
   Chief, Division of Planning and Economic Studies.—Carl L. Weir, 803 Leverton Road, Rockville, Md., 20852.

Office of Personnel Management:
  Personnel Officer.—Thomas F. Fay, 38 Pratt Street, Alexandria, Va., 22310.
  Chief, Division of Employment.—Charles C. E. Buhler, 4210 Swan Creek Road, 20022.
  Chief, Division of Classification and Wage Administration.—John J. Maxwell, 3813 57th Avenue, Hyattsville, Md., 20022.
Office of Budget and Management:
  Chief, Office of Budget and Management.—Philip G. Asher, 810 Park Avenue Falls Church, Va., 22046.
  Budget Officer and Deputy Chief, Office of Budget and Management.—Clyde L. Miller, 1706 Lexington Road, Falls Church, Va., 22043.
  Chief, Division of Management.—Anthony J. Ossi, 9620 Parkwood Drive, Bethesda, Md., 20014.
  Chief, Division of Internal Audits.—Frank J. Horuff, 2408 Crest Street, Alexandria, Va., 22302.
Office of Statistics:
  Chief, Office of Statistics.—Irwin M. Heine, 4000 Massachusetts Avenue, 20016.
  Chief, Division of Cargo Data.—Marlow F. Ladd, Route 1, Clifton, Va., 22024.
  Chief, Division of Ship Data.—Miss Ethel W. Herring, 2220 20th Street, 20009.
  Acting Chief, Division of Labor Data.—Henry F. Sickinger, 3772 W Street, 20007.
Office of the General Counsel:
  General Counsel.—Carl C. Davis, 2747 South Ives Street, Arlington, Va., 22202.
  Deptuy General Counsel.—Graydon L. Andrews, 6908 JoAllen Drive, Falls Church, Va., 22041.
  Chief, Division of Legislation.—William R. Burchill, 3228 Ravensworth Place, Alexandria, Va., 22302.
  Chief, Division of Construction Contracts.—John F. Harrell, Poolesville, Md., 20837.
  Chief, Division of Operating Subsidy Contracts.—Louis Zimmet, 733 Sligo Avenue, Silver Spring, Md., 20910.
  Chief, Division of Mortgage and Marine Insurance.—John R. Tankard, 2742 North Wakefield Street, Arlington, Va., 22207.
  Chief, Division of Litigation.—Hyman Wank, Hotel Bellevue, 15 E Street, 20001.
Office of the Comptroller:
  Comptroller.—Joseph R. Hock, 3201 Leland Street, Chevy Chase, Md., 20015.
  Deputy Comptroller.—Alfred L. Hedbawny, 1961 Owens Road, Oxon Hill, Md., 20021.
  Chief, Division of Accounts.—Vernon C. Richardson, 11520 Charlton Drive, Silver Spring, Md., 20902.
  Chief, Division of Audits.—Benjamin W. Harvey, 4333 Americana Drive, Annandale, Va., 22003.
  Chief, Division of Insurance.—William H. Lane, 4201 Massachusetts Avenue, 20016.
  Chief, Division of Credits and Collections.—Gordon B. Prowse, 2501 Crest Street, Alexandria, Va., 22302.
Office of Property and Supply:
  Chief, Office of Property and Supply.—Harold E. Steffes, 803 Jackson Street, Falls Church, Va., 22046.
  Chief, Division of Purchase and Sales.—John G. Conkey, 7610 Lynn Drive, Chevy Chase, Md., 20015.
  Chief, Division of Office Services.—Julian C. Himes, 1519 Windham Lane, Silver Spring, Md., 20902.
Office of Government Aid:
  Chief, Office of Government Aid.—Edward Aptaker, 301 Brookwood Drive, Fairfax, Va., 22030.
  Deputy Chief, Office of Government Aid.—Lemuel C. Smith, 1225 13th Street, 20005.
  Chief, Division of Operating Costs.—Stephen Hotsko, 1608 Myrtle Road, Silver Spring, Md., 20902.
  Chief, Division of Trade Routes.—Marion E. Parr, 26 Addison Road, Fairfax, Va., 22030.
  Chief, Division of Subsidy Contracts.—W. Carl Clark, RFD 5, Box 730, Fairfax, Va., 22030.

Office of Government Aid—Continued
  Chief, Division of Mortgage-Insurance Contracts.—Roy H. Yowell, 7052 31st Street, 20015.
  Chief, Division of Subsidy Operations Examining.—Toby Jaffe, 11725 Stonington Place, Silver Spring, Md., 20902.
Office of Ship Operations:
  Chief, Office of Ship Operations.—Martin I. Goodman, Springbrook Farm, Waterford, Va., 22190.
  Deputy Chief, Office of Ship Operations.—Randall G. Kriner, 14 North Summit Drive, Gaithersburg, Md., 20760.
  Chief, Division of Operating Agreements and Traffic.—Frederick Tirling, 323 Cree Drive, 20021.
  Chief, Division of Operations.—William G. Allen, 8306 Custer Road, Bethesda, Md., 20014.
  Chief, Division of Ship Repair and Maintenance.—Christopher N. Guckert, 3450 Toledo Terrace, West Hyattsville, Md., 20782.
  Chief, Division of Ship Custody.—Joseph W. Armbrust, 495 Pickett Street, Alexandria, Va., 22304.
Office of Research and Development:
  Chief, Office of Research and Development.—Edward M. MacCutcheon, 6405 Earlham Drive, 20034.
  Deputy Chief, Office of Research and Development.—E. Kemper Sullivan, 7306 Pyle Road, Bethesda, Md., 20014.
  Chief, Division of Power Research.—Carl M. Fixman, 5126 Wickett Terrace, Bethesda, Md., 20014.
  Chief, Division of Hull Research.—Richard W. Black, 3433 34th Street, 20008.
  Manager, Division of Nuclear Projects.—Delma L. Crook, 12507 Eastbourne Drive, Silver Spring, Md., 20904.
Office of Ship Construction:
  Chief, Office of Ship Construction.—Ludwig C. Hoffmann, 325 Harvey Road, McLean, Va., 22101.
  Deputy Chief, Office of Ship Construction.—Vito L. Russo, 2714 North Norwood, Arlington, Va., 22207.
  Chief, Division of Ship Design.—E. Scott Dillon, 9009 Linton Street, Silver Street, Silver Spring, Md., 20901.
  Chief, Division of Engineering.—Frank Grafton, 3055 Harrison Street, 20015.
  Chief, Division of Estimates.—Donald E. Frye, 1600 South Joyce Street, Arlington, Va., 22202.
  Chief, Division of Production.—Howard E. St. Clair, 3804 Annandale Road, Annandale, Va., 22003.
  Acting Chief, Division of Nuclear Activities.—Harry B. Stover, Route 3, Box 130, Annandale, Va., 22003.
  Chairman, Trial and Guarantee Survey Boards.—Robert L. Jack, Jr., 4720 Seventh Road North, Arlington, Va., 22203.

NATIONAL BUREAU OF STANDARDS

Connecticut Avenue and Van Ness Street, 20234. Phone, EMerson 2-4040 (Code 144, extension 7755)

Director.—A. V. Astin, 5008 Battery Lane, Bethesda, Md., 20014.
Senior Research Fellow.—Ugo Fano, 3510 Rodman Street, 20008.
Senior Research Fellow.—K. E. Shuler, 75 East Wayne Avenue, Silver Spring, Md., 20901.
Senior Research Fellow.—Churchill Eisenhart, 9629 Elrod Road, Kensington, Md., 20795.
Special Assistant for Automatic Data Processing.—W. H. Gammon, 5740 18th Street North, Arlington, Va., 22205.
Deputy Director.—Irl C. Schoonover, 9501 Stanhope Road, Rock Creek Hill, Kensington, Md., 20795.
Special Assistant to Deputy Director.—Paul Kratz, 8601 Fenway Road, Bethesda, Md., 20034.
Chief, Office of Radio Frequency Management.—Allen Barnabei, 200 East Wayne Avenue, Silver Spring, Md., 20901.
Chief, Office of Industrial Services.—Robert L. Stern, 3312 Highland Place, 20008.
Associate Director for Office of Program Planning, Review and Analysis.—Shirleigh Silverman, 9509 Saybrook Avenue, Silver Spring, Md., 20901.

Associate Director for Administration.—Robert S. Walleigh, 5701 Springfield Drive, 20016.
Chief of Division of—
  Accounting.—Jacob Seidenbert, 9230 East Parkhill Drive, Bethesda, Md., 20014.
  Administrative Services.—Harry P. Dalzell, 3608 T Street, 20007.
  Budget and Management.—James E. Skillington, 11701 Smoke Tree Road, Rockville, Md., 20854.
  Internal Audit.—Harold F. Whittington, 12527 Knowledge Lane, Bowie, Md., 20715.
  Personnel.—George R. Porter, 2602 Loma Street, Silver Spring, Md., 20902.
  Plant.—Hylton Graham, 10404 Naglee Road, Silver Spring, Md., 20903.
  Supply.—G. B. Kefover, 322 University Boulevard East, Silver Spring, Md., 20901.
Associate Director for Technical Support.—[Vacant.]
Chief of Division of—
  Technical Information and Publications.—W. R. Tilley, 2727 Washington Avenue, Chevy Chase, Md., 20015.
  Research Information.—[Vacant.]
  Office of Radiation Safety.—[Vacant.]
  Instrument Shops.—Frank P. Brown, Box 205 RFD 4, Woodford Road, Vienna, Va., 22180.
Director, Institute for Basic Standards.—Robert D. Huntoon, 4200 Saul Road, Kensington, Md., 20795.
Associate Director, Institute for Basic Standards.—W. A. Wildhack, 415 North Oxford Street, Arlington, Va., 22203.
Chief of Division of—
  Office of Standard Reference Data.—Edward L. Brady, 4501 Connecticut Avenue, 20008.
  Applied Mathematics.—Edward W. Cannon, 5 Vassar Circle, Glen Echo, Md., 20768.
  Electricity.—C. H. Page, 15400 Layhill Road, Silver Spring, Md., 20906.
  Metrology.—A. G. McNish, 4711 Essex Avenue, Chevy Chase, Md., 20015.
  Mechanics.—Bruce L. Wilson, 3117 Jennings Road, Kensington, Md., 20794.
  Radiation Physics.—H. W. Koch, 2922 Stanton Avenue, Silver Spring, Md., 20910.
  Heat.—Ralph P. Hudson, 3101 Aberfoyle Place, 20015.
  Atomic Physics.—Karl G. Kessler, 5927 Anniston Road, Bethesda, Md., 20034.
  Physical Chemistry.—M. B. Wallenstein, 6023 McKinley Street, Bethesda, Md., 20014.
Director, Institute for Materials Research.—Gordon K. Teal, 1800 R Street, 20009.
Chief of Division—
  Office of Standard Refersnce Materials.—W. Wayne Meinke, 8405 Tech Place, Bethesda, Md., 20034.
  Analytical Chemistry.—W. Wayne Meinke, 8405 Tech Place, Bethesda, Md., 20034.
  Polymers.—J. D. Hoffman, 6121 Maiden Lane, Bethesda, Md., 20034.
  Metallurgy.—Lawrence M. Kushner, 9628 Cottrell Terrace, Silver Spring Md., 20903.
  Inorganic Materials.—H. C. Allen, Jr., 13009 Carney Street, Silver Spring, Md., 20906.
  Reactor Radiations.—Carl O. Muelhause, 9105 Seven Locks Road, Bethesda, Md., 20034.
Director, Institute for Applied Technology.—Donald A. Schon, 5817 Plainview Road, Bethesda, Md., 20034.
Deputy Director, Institute for Applied Technology.—John P. Eberhard, 7521 Westfield Drive, Bethesda, Md., 20034.
Chief of Division of—
  Office of Invention and Innovation.—D. V. DeSimone, 2433 North Quantico Street, Arlington, Va., 22207.
  Office of Weights and Measures.—Malcolm W. Jensen, 11812 Seven Locks Road, Potomac, Md., 20854.
  Office of Engineering Standards (acting).—Donald McKay, RD1, Box 19CC, Boyds, Md., 20720.
  Clearinghouse for Federal Scientific and Technical Information.—Bernard Fry, 3205 Park View Road, Chevy Chase, Md., 20015.
  Building Research.—A. Allan Bates, 3342 Stephenson Place, 20015.

Chief of Division of—Continued
  Electronic Instrumentation.—Myron G. Domsitz, 11820 Glen Mill Road,
    Rockville, Md., 20854.
  Measurement Engineering Division.—G. Franklin Montgomery, 4115 Wisconsin
    Avenue, 20016.
  Transport Systems.—S. M. Bruening, 8109 Fenway Road, Bethesda, Md., 20034.
  Technical Analysis (acting).—Walter E. Cushen, 3921 Aspen Street, Chevy
    Chase, Md., 20015.
  Textiles and Apparel Technology Center.—George S. Gordon, 4845 Broad Brook
    Drive, Bethesda, Md., 20014.
  Information Technology.—Samuel N. Alexander, 4120 Standford Street, Chevy
    Chase, Md., 20015.
  Office of Technical Resources.—E. A. Tietz, 4612 West Virginia Avenue,
    Bethesda, Md., 20014.

BOULDER LABORATORIES

Manager, Boulder Laboratories.—Russell B. Scott, 2205 Balsam, Boulder, Colo.,
  80302.
Senior Research Fellow.—James R. Wait, 756 14th Street, Boulder, Colo., 80302.
Chief of Division of—
  Administrative Services.—Herbert D. Stansell, 40 South 38th Street, Boulder,
    Colo., 80302.
  Shops.—Rodney S. Perrill (assistant), 5211 East Laurel, Boulder, Colo., 80302.
  Plant.—Edgar A. Yuzwiak, 2595 Hawthorn, Boulder, Colo., 80302.
  Cryogenics.—Bascom W. Birmingham, 2210 Mariposa Avenue, Boulder, Colo.,
    80302.
  Director, Central Radio Propagation Laboratory.—C. Gordon Little, 2940 20th
    Street, Boulder, Colo., 80302.
  Ionospheric Telecommunications.—Richard C. Kirby, 2814 15th Street, Boulder,
    Colo., 80302.
  Tropospheric Telecommunications.—Robert S. Kirby, Route 2, Box 379, Boulder,
    Colo., 80302.
  Space Environment Forecasting.—Robert W. Knecht, 1702 Mariposa Avenue,
    Boulder, Colo., 80302.
  Aeronomy.—Ernest K. Smith, Jr., 3165 Fifth Street, Boulder, Colo., 80302.
  Radio Standards Laboratory.—John M. Richardson, 625 14th Street, Boulder,
    Colo., 80302.
  Radio Standards Physics.—Yardley Beers, 740 Willowbrook Road, Boulder,
    Colo., 80302.
  Radio Standards Engineering.—George E. Schafer, 3795 Britting Avenue,
    Boulder, Colo., 80302.
  Joint Institute for Laboratory Astrophysics (NBS Group).—Lewis M. Branscomb,
    205 Abbey Place, Boulder, Colo., 80302.

PATENT OFFICE

Department of Commerce Building, 20231.   Phone, STerling 3-9200 (Code 112, extension 5148)

Commissioner.—Edward J. Brenner, 6220 Plainview Road, Bethesda, Md., 20034.
First Assistant Commissioner.—Edwin L. Reynolds, 5326 Willard Avenue, Chevy
  Chase, Md., 20015.
Assistant Commissioner.—[Vacant.]
Assistant Commissioner for Research.—Ezra Glaser, 305 East George Mason Road,
  Falls Church, Va., 22042.
Solicitor.—Clarence W. Moore, 1351 Kalmia Road, 20012.
Deputy Solicitor.—Joseph Schimmel, 8019 Eastern Avenue, Silver Spring, Md.,
  20910.
Director, Office of Legislative Planning.—Kenneth F. McClure, 306 Lawton Street,
  Falls Church, Va., 22046.
Director, Office of Planning and Program Evaluation.—Joseph U. Damico, 601
  North Pickett Street, Alexandria, Va., 22304.

Board of Patent Appeals:
 Examiners-in-Chief.—N. A. Asp, 1826 Varnum Street, 20011; M. F. Bailey, 4616 Harrison Street, Chevy Chase, Md., 20015; James L. Brewrink, 6905 Wells Parkway, Hyattsville, Md., 20782; P. T. Dracopoulos, 7407 Bybrook Lane, Chevy Chase, Md., 20015; P. J. Federico, 3634 Jocelyn Street, 20016; M. H. Friedman, 3722 Appleton Street, 20016; J. E. Keely, 10204 Big Rock Road, Silver Spring, Md., 20901; L. F. Kreek, 4636 Verplanck Place, 20016; Herbert J. Lidoff, 6433 31st Place, 20015; H. Magil, 3400 Patterson Street, 20015; J. C. Manian, 7505 Arlington Road, Bethesda, Md., 20014; L. P. McCann, 4333 Third Street, 20011; M. C. Rosa, 1418 Juliana Place, Alexandria, Va., 22304.
Board of Patent Interferences.—James S. Bailey, 6007 Williamsburg Boulevard, Arlington, Va., 22207; George W. Boys, 4811 Wellington Drive, Chevy Chase, Md., 20015; A. Y. Casanova, Jr., 7911 13th Street, 20012; Maurice A. Crews, 7713 Radnor Road, Bethesda, Md., 20034; S. Levin, 7777 Maple Avenue, Takoma Park, Md., 20012; LaVerne Williams, 5913 Dinwiddie Street, Springfield, Va., 22150; W. H. Willner, Crownsville, Md., 21032.
Acting Superintendent, Patent Examining Corps.—Richard A. Wahl, 5705 Virginia Avenue, Falls Church, Va., 22043.
Director, Examining Control and Patent Academy.—George Hyman, 4961 Rock Creek Church Road, 20011.
Director, Chemical Examining Operation.—Philip E. Mangan, 6305 Alcott Road, Bethesda, Md., 20034.
Director, Electrical Examining Operation.—Norman H. Evans, 7902 Sleaford Place, Bethesda, Md., 20014.
Director, General Engineering and Industrial Arts Examining Operation.—Jacob A. Manian, 6402 33d Street, 20015.
Acting Director, Mechanical Engineering Examining Operation.—Frank H. Bronaugh, 7417 Lynnhurst Street, Chevy Chase, Md., 20015.
Members, Trademark Trial and Appeal Board.—Murrell B. Leach, 2704 Donna Lane, Annandale, Va., 22003; Saul Lefkowitz, 3509 Randolph Road, Silver Spring, Md., 20902; R. F. Shryock, 6213 Redwing Court, Bethesda, Md., 20034; H. Waldstreicher, 8513 Farrell Drive, Chevy Chase, Md., 20015.
Director, Trademark Examining Operation.—John H. Merchant, 447 North Grant Avenue, Manassas, Va., 22110.
Director, Office of Administration.—C. A. Kalk, 3219 Leland Street, Chevy Chase, Md., 20015.
 Budget Officer.—Richard L. Franz, 3050 South Woodrow Street, Arlington, Va., 22206.
 Chief Accountant.—Fred E. Bear, 105 Palmer Drive, Oakton, Va., 22124.
 Management Analysis Officer.—Ethan A. Hurd, 204 Niblick Drive, Vienna, Va., 22180.
 Personnel Officer.—W. E. Ingram, 1012 North Quantico Street, Arlington, Va., 22205.
 General Services Officer.—W. R. Armstrong, 4410 Puller Drive, Kensington, Md., 20795.
Information Officer, Office of Information.—Isaac Fleischmann, 315 Ravenwood Drive, Falls Church, Va., 22044.
Staff Director of Research.—Richard A. Spencer, 112 Newlands Street, Chevy Chase, Md., 20015.
Director, Office of Patent Classification.—George A. Gorecki, 6908 Anchorage Drive, Bethesda, Md., 20034.
Librarian.—W. R. Campbell, 6135 35th Street North, Arlington, Va., 22213.

BUREAU OF PUBLIC ROADS

Matomic Building, 1717 H Street. Phone, STerling 3-9200 (Code 112, extension 3421)

Federal Highway Administrator.—Rex M. Whitton, 4201 Cathedral Avenue, 20016.
Deputy Federal Highway Administrator.—Lawrence Jones, 5504 Westbard Avenue, 20016.
Chief Engineer.—Francis C. Turner, 2529 North Military Road, Arlington, Va., 22207.

Director in Charge of:
  Office of Administration.—Lawrence S. Casazza, 3009 Birch Street, 20015.
  Personnel and Training Division, Chief.—Edward J. Martin, Jr., 7504 Rocart Drive, Annandale, Va., 22003.
  Office of Engineering and Operations.—George M. Williams, 3540 Valley Drive, Alexandria, Va., 22302.
  Office of Highway Safety.—James K. Williams, 1616 18th Street, 20009.
  Office of Planning.—Edward H. Holmes, 4814 DeRussey Parkway, Chevy Chase, Md., 20015.
  Office of Research and Development.—Robert F. Baker, 9422 Holland Avenue, Bethesda, Md., 20014.
  Office of Audits and Investigations.—Joseph M. O'Connor, 11104 Woodson Avenue, Kensington, Md., 20795.
  Office of Right-of-Way and Location.—Edgar H. Swick, 1201 South Scott Street, Arlington, Va., 22204.
  General Counsel.—Dowell H. Anders, 6753 26th Street North, Arlington, Va., 22213.
  Regional Engineer in Charge of Eastern Federal Highway Projects Office.—Galyn A. Wilkins, 332 Leesburg Pike, Falls Church, Va., 22041.

WEATHER BUREAU

2400 M Street. Phone, 965-2400 (191-X327)

Chief of Bureau.—Robert M. White, 8306 Melody Court, Bethesda, Md., 20034.
Chief Scientist.—Verner E. Suomi, 2411 20th Street, 20009.
Executive Officer and Congressional Liaison.—John H. Eberly, 6526 Elgin Lane, Bethesda, Md., 20034.
Special Assistant, Resource Programming.—Theodore P. Gleiter, 806 Foxwood Nook, Falls Church, Va., 22041.
Special Assistant, Legislative Planning.—Paul L. Laskin, 2800 Quebec Street, 20008.
Special Assistant, Industrial Meteorology.—Loren W. Crow, 2001 North Adams Street, Arlington, Va., 22201.
Director, Aviation Weather Affairs.—Newton A. Lieurance, 1316 Great Falls Street, McLean, Va., 22101.
Acting Director, International Affairs.—Gordon D. Cartwright, 825 New Hampshire Avenue, 20037.
Director, Policy Planning.—Walter A. Hahn, 5905 Espey Lane, McLean, Va., 22101.
Acting Director, Public Information.—Herbert S. Lieb, 13115 Blue Hill Court, Silver Spring, Md., 20906.
Director, Hydrology.—William A. Hiatt, 6008 Benalder Drive, Fairway Hills, 20016.
Director, Climatology.—Helmut E. Landsberg, 5107 53d Avenue SE., 20031.
Director, National Meteorological Services.—George P. Cressman, 9 Old Stage Court, Rockville, Md., 20852.
Deputy Director, Operations.—Robert H. Simpson, 10201 Grosvenor Place, Rockville, Md., 20852.
Deputy Director, Service Programs.—Paul H. Kutschenreuter, 6011 Tyndale Drive, McLean, Va., 22101.
Director, National Meteorological Center.—Frederick G. Shuman, 7010 Rolling Ridge Drive, Seat Pleasant, Md., 20027.
Director, Meteorological Research.—Jerome Spar, 6816 Renita Lane, Bethesda, Md., 20034.
Director, Systems Development.—Merritt N. Techter, 3102 Dawson Avenue, Silver Spring, Md., 20902.
Director, Administration and Technical Services.—Russell C. Grubb, 9308 Parkhill Terrace, Bethesda, Md., 20014.
Manager, Personnel Division.—Guy H. Dorsey, 6320 Newburn Drive, 20016.
Director, National Weather Satellite Center.—David S. Johnson, 237 Panorama Drive, Oxen Hill, Md., 20021.
Meteorologist in Charge (Washington National Airport).—Reinhart C. Schmidt, 601 Gordon Street, Falls Church, Va., 22041.

DEPARTMENT OF LABOR

Department of Labor Building, Fourteenth Street and Constitution Avenue.
Phone, EXecutive 3-2420 (Code 110)

W. WILLARD WIRTZ, Secretary of Labor; born in De Kalb, Ill., March 14,
1912; son of William Wilbur and Alpha Belle (White) Wirtz; attended Northern
Illinois State Teachers College in De Kalb (1928–30), the University of California
in Berkeley (1930–31), and Beloit College in Beloit, Wis. (1931–33), where he
received a Bachelor of Arts degree; after teaching at Kewanee (Ill.) High School
(1933–34), he attended Harvard Law School from which he was graduated
(LL. B., 1937); taught law at the University of Iowa (1937–39), Northwestern
University School of Law as assistant professor (1939–42), and Northwestern
University as full professor of law (1946–54); served as assistant general counsel
of the Board of Economic Warfare (1942–43); public member, chairman of
Appeals Board, general counsel and disputes director of the National War Labor
Board (1943–45); public member and chairman of the National Wage Stabilization
Board (1946); permanent arbitrator for the U.S. Rubber Co. and United Rubber,
Cork, Linoleum and Plastic Workers of America (1947–50); member of the
Presidential emergency board in the Railroad case (1948–49); member of the
Taft-Hartley board of inquiry in the Coal case (1949–50); served on panel estab-
lished by Senate Committee on Labor and Public Welfare to make recommenda-
tions (1960); engaged in private practice of law with the firm of Stevenson,
Rifkind and Wirtz in Chicago (1955–61); served as Under Secretary of Labor
(1961–62); appointed Secretary of Labor (August 30, 1962); married Mary Jane
Quisenberry (1936); two sons, Richard and Philip.

OFFICE OF THE SECRETARY

Secretary.—W. Willard Wirtz, 5009 39th Street, 20016.
   Executive Assistant to the Secretary.—N. Thompson Powers, 5204 Keokuk
      Street, Chevy Chase, 20016.
   Special Assistant to the Secretary for Legislative Affairs.—Samuel V. Merrick,
      1305 Popkins Lane, Alexandria, Va., 22307.
      Legislative Liaison Officer.—Frank V. Cantwell, 5010 Fort Sumner Drive,
         20016.
      Legislative Liaison Officer.—Micah H. Maftalin, 3403 W. Coquelin Terrace,
         Chevy Chase, Md., 20015.
      Legislative Liaison Officer.—Anne S. Butler, 7520 Maple Avenue, Takoma
         Park, Md., 20012.
   Special Assistant to the Secretary for Economic Affairs.—Seymour L. Wolfbein,
      6305 Crathie Lane, Bethesda, Md., 20016.
   Special Assistant to the Secretary.—Arthur A. Chapin, 3301 13th Street NE.,
      20017.
   Special Assistant to the Secretary.—Roger F. Lewis, 3414 N Street, 20007.
Under Secretary.—John F. Henning, 6401 Western Avenue, 20015.
   Special Assistant to the Under Secretary.—D. Donald Glover (acting), 1449
      Leegate Road, 20012.
   Deputy Under Secretary.—Millard Cass, 2103 Plyers Mill Road, Silver Spring,
      Md., 20902.
   Assistant to the Under Secretary.—Robert K. Salyers, 5617 Fifth Road South,
      Arlington, Va., 22204.
Assistant Secretary for International Affairs.—George L-P Weaver, 3819 26th
   Street NE., 20018.
   Special Assistant to the Assistant Secretary.—Edward C. Sylvester, Jr., 769
      Delaware Avenue SW, 20024.
   Deputy Assistant Secretary.—Harry Weiss, 5803 Warwick Place, Chevy Chase,
      Md., 20015.

Assistant Secretary for Labor-Management Relations.—James J. Reynolds, 4201 Cathedral Avenue, 20016.

Special Assistant to the Assistant Secretary.—Eric Stevenson, 3614 Fulton Street, 20007.

Deputy Assistant Secretary.—John N. Gentry (acting), 1311 Delaware Avenue SW., 20024.

Assistant Secretary for Labor Standards.—Esther Peterson, 1650 Jonquil Street, 20012.

Deputy Assistant Secretary.—Morris Weisz, 7106 Wilson Lane, Bethesda, Md., 20014.

Assistant Secretary for Policy Planning and Research.—Daniel Patrick Moynihan, 3100 Macomb Street, 20008.

Deputy Assistant Secretary.—Philip Arnow, 412 Linden Lane, Falls Church, Va., 20042.

Consumer Program Adviser.—Aryness J. Wickens, Box 212, R.F.D. 2, Vienna, Va., 22180.

Solicitor.—Charles Donahue, 3005 Albemarle Street, 20008.

Deputy Solicitor.—Edward Friedmann, 10702 Weymouth Street, Garrett Park, Md., 20766.

Assistant Secretary for Administration.—Leo R. Werts, 4819 Cumberland Avenue, Chevy Chase, Md., 20015.

Deputy Assistant Secretary for Administration.—V. S. Hudson, 77 Dunkirk Road, Baltimore, Md., 21212.

Assistant Assistant Secretary for Administration.—Edward J. McVeigh, R.F.D. 1, Friends Road, Cape St. John, Annapolis, Md., 21401.

Office of Information:
Director.—John W. Leslie, 2417 North Taylor Street, Arlington, Va., 22207.

Deputy Director.—Joseph R. Judge, 11909 Rock Run Drive, Bethesda, Md., 20854.

MANPOWER ADMINISTRATION

Administrator.—Stanley H. Ruttenberg, 6310 Maiden Lane, Bethesda, Md., 20034.

Executive Officer.—Samuel Ganz, 6505 Marjory Lane, Bethesda, Md., 20034.

Deputy Administrator for Planning, Research, and Evaluation.—[Vacant.]

Deputy Administrator for Operations.—Robert C. Goodwin, 5304 Broad Branch Road, 20015.

Assistant Administrator for Special Assignments.—David E. Christian, 381 O Street SW., 20024.

Assistant Administrator for Youth Programs.—[Vacant.]

Assistant Administrator for Trade Adjustment Assistance.—Edgar I. Eaton (acting), 416 Lyric Lane, Falls Church, Va., 22044.

Information Services.—[Vacant.]

Office of Financial and Management Services:
Director.—Ross S. Shearer, 3125 North Abingdon Street, Arlington, Va., 22072.

Assistant Director.—Margaret E. Thomas, 4109 Great Oak Road, Manor Club, Rockville, Md., 20853.

Office of Manpower, Automation and Training:
Director.—John P. Walsh (acting), 379 O Street SW., 20024.

Deputy Director.—John P. Walsh, 379 O Street SW., 20024.

Assistant Director for Manpower and Automation Research.—Howard Rosen (acting), 5204 Wyoming Road, Glen Echo Heights, 20016.

Assistant Director for Manpower Development.—Francis A. Gregory, 4015 Massachusetts Avenue SE., 20019.

Neighborhood Youth Corps:
Director.—Jack Howard, 372 N Street SW., 20024.

Deputy Director.—Aryness Joy Wickens (acting), Box 212, RFD 2, Vienna, Va., 22180.

Assistant Director for Program Development.—Jildo Cappio (acting), 1606 Kenney Drive, Falls Church, Va., 22042.

Assistant Director for Field Operations.—Mark Battle (acting), 250 G Street SW., 20024.

Bureau of Apprenticeship and Training:
  Administrator.—Hugh C. Murphy, 1920 Columbia Pike, Arlington, Va., 22204.
    Deputy Administrator.—Ansel R. Cleary, 5622 Back Lick Road, Springfield, Va., 22150.
    Assistant Administrator.—William J. Moore, 806 Marshall Lane, Alexandria, Va., 22302.
    Assistant Administrator.—Elliott French, 8413 Park Crest Drive, Silver Spring, Md., 20910.
    Assistant Administrator.—John T. Douthit, 2000 South Eads Street, Arlington, Va., 22202.
    Chief, Division of Administrative Management.—Ralph E. French, 7413 Birch Avenue, Takoma Park, Md., 20012.
Bureau of Employment Security:
  Administrator.—Robert C. Goodwin, 5304 Broad Branch Road, 20015.
    Deputy Administrator.—William R. Curtis, 321 Cross Woods Drive, Falls Church, Va., 22044.
    Director, Administration and Management Service.—James V. Doucet, 1218 North Chambliss Street, Alexandria, Va., 22312.
    Director, Unemployment Insurance Service.—William U. Norwood, Jr., 6319 Haviland Drive, Bethesda, Md., 20014.
    Director, United States Employment Service.—Louis Levine, 6429 31st Street, 20015.
    Director, Veterans Employment Service.—Marshall Miller, 3022 North Florida Street, Arlington, Va., 22207.
    Director, Office of Farm Labor Service.—Frank Potter, 1600 South Joyce Street, Arlington, Va., 22202.

UNITED STATES EMPLOYMENT SERVICE FOR THE DISTRICT OF COLUMBIA
555 Pennsylvania Avenue, 20012.   Phone, 393-6151 (Code 1237, extension 354)

Director.—Fred Z. Hetzel, 3625 Yuma Street, 20008.

LABOR-MANAGEMENT SERVICES ADMINISTRATION

Administrator.—James J. Reynolds, 4201 Cathedral Avenue, 20016.
  Deputy Assistant Secretary for Labor-Management Relations.—John N. Gentry (acting), 1311 Delaware Avenue SW., 20024.
  Director, Office of Labor-Management Policy Development.—[Vacant.]
  Director, Office of Federal Employee-Management Relations.—Louis S. Wallerstein, 6813 Alter Street, Baltimore, Md., 21207.
  Director, Office of Labor-Management and Welfare-Pension Reports.—Frank M. Kleiler, 9100 Warren Street, Silver Spring, Md., 20910.
    Deputy Director.—John C. Shinn, 6805 32d Street North, Falls Church, Va., 22046.
  Director, Office of Veterans' Reemployment Rights.—Hugh W. Bradley, 4010 Londonderry Road, Alexandria, Va., 22308.
    Deputy Director.—W. J. R. Overath, 3505 Macomb Street, 20016.
  Director, Office of Administration and Management.—Albert L. Moore, Jr., 6454 Portal Avenue, Temple Hills, Md., 20031.

OFFICE OF THE SOLICITOR

Solicitor.—Charles Donahue, 3005 Albemarle Street, 20008.
  Special Assistant.—Joseph Goldberg, 6301 West Halbert Road, Bethesda, Md., 20014.
  Special Assistqnt.—Jacob J. Schalet, 1744 Riggs Place, 20009.
  Management Assistant.—Jeanne S. Trexler, Haviland Mill Road, Brinklow, Md., 20707.
  Deputy Solicitor.—Edward D. Friedman, 10702 Weymouth Street, Garrett Park, Md., 10014.

Solicitor—Continued
  Associate Solicitor.—James R. Beaird, 746 North Ashton Street, Alexandria, Va., 22312.
    Deputy Associate Solicitor.—Jacob L. Karro, 6514 East Halbert Road, Bethesda, Md., 20014.
  Associate Solicitor.—Edith N. Cook, 1830 R Street, 20009.
    Deputy Associate Solicitor.—Philip A. Yahner, 6009 Nagy Place, Alexandria, Va., 22312.
  Associate Solicitor.—Bessie Margolin, 2725 29th Street, 20008.
    Deputy Associate Solicitor.—James M. Miller, 3404 Pendleton Drive, Wheaton, Md., 20902.
  Associate Solicitor.—Harold C. Nystrom, 9020 Old Georgetown Road, Bethesda, Md., 20014.
    Deputy Associate Solicitor.—Albert D. Misler, 6101 16th Street, 20011.
  Associate Administrator for Wage Determinations.—E. Irving Manger, 810 Chalfonte Drive, Alexandria, Va., 22305.
  Administrative Officer.—J. J. Lafranchise, 1355 Lawrence Street NE., 20017.

OFFICE OF THE ASSISTANT SECRETARY FOR ADMINISTRATION

Assistant Secretary for Administration.—Leo R. Werts, 4819 Cumberland Avenue, Chevy Chase, Md., 20015.
  Deputy Assistant Secretary for Administration.—V. S. Hudson, 77 Dunkirk Road, Baltimore, Md., 21212.
  Assistant Assistant Secretary for Administration.—Edward J. McVeigh, R.F.D. 1, Friends Road, Cape St. John, Annapolis, Md., 21401.
  Librarian.—Margaret F. Brickett, 4201 Massachusetts Avenue, 20016.
  Director, Office of Personnel Policy and Standards.—Charles H. Roberts, 4212 Ingomar Street, 20012.
  Director, Office of Employee Utilization and Development.—John J. Bean, 2006 Lakota Road, Alexandria, Va., 22303.
  Chief, Central Personnel Services.—Raymond Sumser, 2441 Villanova Drive, Vienna, Va., 22180.
  Director, Office of Financial Management.—[Vacant.]
  Director, Office of Organization and Management.—Tom Kouzes, 624 Barkley Drive, Fairfax, Va., 22030.
  Director, Office of Administrative Services.—John Neafsey, 1900 South Eads Street, Arlington, Va., 22202.
  Director, Office of Budget Administration.—Richard Miller, 9404 Woodland Drive, Silver Spring, Md., 20910.
  Director, Office of Program Analysis and Evaluation.—Charles D. Carlson, 614 Poplar Drive, Falls Church, Va., 22046.
  Financial Audit Staff.—Louis P. Glenn, 3001 Branch Avenue SE., 20023.

INTERNATIONAL AFFAIRS

Bureau of International Labor Affairs:
  Administrator.—Harry Weiss, 5803 Warwick Place, Chevy Chase, Md., 20015.
  Deputy Administrator.—Edward C. Sylvester, Jr., 769 Delaware Avenue SW., 20024.

WAGE AND LABOR STANDARDS

Bureau of Labor Standards:
  Director.—Nelson M. Bortz, 7901 Greentree Road, Bethesda, Md., 20034.
  Deputy Director.—George T. Brown, 11301 Rokeaby Avenue, Garrett Park, Md., 20766.
  Assistant Director for Safety.—Robert D. Gidel, 5417 Neptune Drive, Yacht Haven, Alexandria, Va., 22300.
  Chief, Division of International Cooperation.—Roger W. Grant, Jr., Langley Lane, Route 3, Box 188, McLean, Va., 22101.
  Chief, Division of Reports and Public Service.—Lucille J. Buchanan, 2804 27th Street, 20008.
  Chief, Division of State Services.—Milton Brooke, 6310 Bannockburn Drive, Bethesda, Md., 20014.
  Chairman, Federal Safety Council.—Nelson M. Bortz, 7901 Greentree Road, Bethesda, Md., 20034.

Women's Bureau:
 Director.—Mary Dublin Keyserling, 2908 Albemarle Street, 20008.
  Deputy Director.—Mary N. Hilton (acting), 5022 Reno Road, 20008.
  Chief, Field Division.—Agnes M. Douty, 2951 Upton Street, 20008.
  Chief, Division of Information and Publications.—Eleanor M. Coakley, 1311 Delaware Avenue SW., 20024.
  Chief, International Division.—Mary M. Cannon, 1321 28th Street, 20007.
  Chief, Division of Legislation and Standards.—Alice Angus Morrison, 3582 Trinity Drive, Alexandria, Va., 22300.
  Chief, Division of Management Services.—Dorothy A. Carroll, 1920 Belmont Road, 20009.
  Chief, Division of Economic Status and Opportunities.—Mary N. Hilton, 5022 Reno Road, 20008.
  Executive Secretary, Interdepartmental Committee on the Status of Women.— Catherine S. East, 5212 32d Street North, Arlington, Va., 22207.
Wage and Hour and Public Contracts Divisions:
 Administrator.—Clarence T. Lundquist, 4822 Tilden Street, 20016.
  Deputy Administrator.—Duane A. Wendele, 4501 Connecticut Avenue, 20008.
  Technical Assistant to the Administrator.—Frederick J. Glasgow, 1508 Elson Street, Takoma Park, Md., 20012.
  Assistant Administrator (Compliance and Enforcement).—Francis J. Costello, 828 Pinewood Terrace, Falls Church, Va., 22040.
  Assistant Administrator (Research and Legislative Analysis).—Clara F. Schloss, 9515 Pin Oak Drive, Silver Spring, Md., 20900.
  Assistant Administrator (Wage Determinations and Regulations).—Max Schiferl, 9006 Manchester Road, Silver Spring, Md., 20901.
  Assistant Administrator (Planning and Management).—Irving Levine, 509 Waterford Road, Silver Spring, Md., 20900.
Bureau of Employees' Compensation:
 Director.—Thomas A. Tinsley, 6302 Frontier Drive, Springfield, Va., 22150.
  Deputy Director.—[Vacant.]
  Assistant Director, Administrative Management.—Leroy T. Minor, 3516 13th Street SE., 20032.
  Assistant Director, Federal Employees' Compensation Program.—John J. Newman, 5761 Sanger Avenue, Alexandria, Va., 22300.
  Assistant Director, Longshoremen's and Harbor Workers' Program.—John D. McLellan, Jr., 917 Bluedale Street, Alexandria, Va., 22300.
  Medical Director.—Dr. Ralph B. Snavely (acting), 3703 Albemarle Street, 20016.
  Chief, Division of Budget, Fiscal and Management Services.—[Vacant.]
  Chief, Division of Claims.—Wilfred J. Harren, 2325 42d Street, 20007.
  Chief, Division of Statistics.—Edward F. Brayer, 6723 44th Avenue, University Park, Md.
  Deputy Commissioner, District of Columbia Workmen's Compensation Act.— Theodore Britton, 1625 25th Street SE., 20032.
  Assistant Deputy Commissioner.—Albert Kline, 8101 15th Avenue, Hyattsville, Md.
Employees' Compensation Appeals Board:
 Chairman.—Theodore M. Schwartz, 1801 Clydesdale Place, 20009.
  Members:
   E. Gerald Lamboley, 21 Snows Court, 20037.
   James A. Broderick, 3515 Saylor Place, Alexandria, Va., 22304.

LABOR STATISTICS

Bureau of Labor Statistics:
 Commissioner.—Ewan Clague, 3821 Woodley Road, 20016.
  Deputy Commissioner.—Robert J. Myers, 2735 McKinley Street, 20015.
  Economic Consultant.—Hyman L. Lewis, 1640 Portal Drive, 20012.
  Special Assistants:
   Gertrude Bancroft, 3615 O Street, 20007.
   Joseph P. Goldberg, 707 Stonington Road, Silver Spring, Md., 20900.
   Walter G. Keim, 5006 Klingle Street, 20016.
   Kenneth G. Van Auken, 2929 University Boulevard West, Kensington, Md., 20795.

Bureau of Labor Statistics—Continued
  Commissioner—Continued
    Associate Commissioner, Office of Systems Analysis and Economic Growth.— [Vacant.]
      Chief, Division of Economic Growth.—Jack Alterman, 9015 Garland Avenue, Silver Spring, Md., 20900.
      Chief, Division of Statistical Standards.—Abe Rothman, 9407 Crosby Road, Silver Spring, Md., 20900.
      Departmental Statistical Officer.—John W. Gracza, 7513 Gresham Street, Springfield, Va., 22150.
    Associate Commissioner, Office of Program Planning and Publications.—Harry M. Douty, 4612 Butterworth Place, 20016.
      Deputy Associate Commissioner.—Peter Henle, 3219 North Wakefield, Arlington, Va., 22200.
      Chief, Division of Publications.—Lawrence R. Klein, 2600 North Upshur Street, Arlington, Va., 22200.
      Chief, Division of Foreign Labor Conditions.—William C. Shelton, 8208 Old Georgetown Road, Bethesda, Md., 20014.
    Associate Commissioner, Office of Administrative Management.—Paul R. Kerschbaum, 10405 Lloyd Road, Rockville, Md., 20850.
      Deputy Associate Commissioner for Administrative Management.—Edward L. Diamond, 4404 Dresden Street, Kensington, Md., 20795.
      Chief, Division of Fiscal Management and Services.—Ray S. Dunn, 421 Midday Lane, Alexandria, Va., 22300.
      Chief, Division of Personnel Management.—Stanton M. Strawson, 12805 Tamarack Road, Silver Spring, Md., 20904.
      Chief, Division of Management Analysis.—William T. Furman, 4012 35th Street North, Arlington, Va., 22207.
      Chief, Division of Data Processing.—Jesse R. Black, 7204 Everglade Drive, Alexandria, Va., 22300.
    Assistant Commissioner for Manpower and Employment Statistics.—Harold Goldstein, 7012 Wilson Lane, Bethesda, Md., 20014.
    Assistant Commissioner for Productivity and Technological Developments.— Leon Greenberg, 1821 Sanford Road, Silver Spring, Md., 20902.
      Chief, Division of Industrial Hazards.—Frank S. McElroy, 9233 Farnsworth Drive, Potomac, Md., 20854.
    Assistant Commissioner for Wages and Industrial Relations.—Leonard R. Linsenmayer, 7204 Kempton Road, Lanham, Md., 20801.
    Assistant Commissioner for Prices and Living Conditions.—Arnold E. Chase, 2405 North Upshur Street, Arlington, Va., 22200.

THE PRESIDENT'S COMMITTEE ON EQUAL EMPLOYMENT OPPORTUNITY

U.S. Department of Labor Building. Phone, WOrth 1-3603

Chairman.—Hubert H. Humphrey, Vice President of the United States.
Vice Chairman.—W. Willard Wirtz, Secretary of Labor, 5009 39th Street, 20016.
Executive Vice Chairman.—Hobart Taylor, Jr., 301 G Street SW., 20024.
Executive Assistant to the Executive Vice Chairman.—William J. Kendrick, 3210 Ravensworth Place, Alexandria, Va.
Special Counsel.—N. Thompson Powers, 5204 Keokuk Street, Chevy Chase, Md., 20015.
Special Assistant.—Percy H. Williams, 1700 Taylor Street, 20011.
Director (Federal Employment Program).—John Hope II, 360 N Street SW., 20024.
  Director of Administration.—Raymond C. Shelkofsky.
  Director (Contract Compliance Program).—Ward McCreedy.
  Director of Information.—Malcolm F. Wise.
  Director of Compliance Surveys.—David Mann.
  Director of Community Relations.—George O. Butler.
  Director of Labor Liaison.—Thomas McNamara.
  Director of Construction Industry Programs.—Vincent Macaluso.

THE PRESIDENT'S MISSILE SITES LABOR COMMISSION

Executive Secretary.—Julius E. Kuczma, 3602 Underwood Street, Chevy Chase, Md., 20015.
  Labor Relations Advisor.—Richard P. Chambers, 1108 Wendell Drive, Alexandria, Va., 22300.

THE PRESIDENT'S COMMITTEE ON MANPOWER

Executive Director.—Garth L. Mangum, 14917 Claude Lane, Silver Spring, Md., 20904.

NATIONAL COMMISSION ON TECHNOLOGY, AUTOMATION, AND ECONOMIC PROGRESS

Executive Secretary.—Garth L. Mangum, 14917 Claude Lane, Silver Spring, Md., 20904.
Deputy Executive Secretary for Manpower and Employment.—Frazier Kellogg, 7725 Tomlinson Avenue, Cabin John, Md., 20731.
Deputy Executive Secretary for Technology.—William D. Drake.

DEPARTMENT OF HEALTH, EDUCATION, AND WELFARE

330 Independence Avenue SW., 20201.   Phone, WOrth 3-1110 (Code 13, extension 22247)

ANTHONY J. CELEBREZZE, Secretary of Health, Education, and Welfare; born September 4, 1910, Anzi, Italy; married Anne Marco of Cleveland, Ohio; children: Anthony, Jr., Jean Anne, and Susan Marie; educated in the public schools of Cleveland, Ohio; attended John Carroll University; received LL.B. degree from Ohio Northern University, 1936; holds seven honorary degrees; admitted to Ohio State bar and served on legal staff of Ohio Bureau of Unemployment Compensation from 1936 to 1939; engaged in general practice of law 1939–53; served in United States Navy in World War II; elected to Ohio Senate in 1950 and 1952; served four terms as Mayor of Cleveland and was serving fifth term when appointed to Cabinet; president of American Municipal Association in 1958 and president and director of U.S. Conference of Mayors in 1962; appointed by both President Eisenhower and President Kennedy to serve as member of Advisory Commission on Intergovernmental Relations; took oath of office as Secretary of Health, Education, and Welfare on July 31, 1962.

OFFICE OF THE SECRETARY

Secretary.—Anthony J. Celebrezze, 72707 Pomander Lane, Chevy Chase, Md., 20015.

Secretary to the Secretary.—Edith S. Murphy, 3701 Connecticut Avenue, 20008.

Assistant to the Secretary.—F. Robert Meier, 7209 MacArthur Boulevard, Bethesda, Md., 20016.

Assistant to the Secretary (for Public Affairs).—Harold R. Levy, 1529 33d Street, 20007.

Assistant to the Secretary.—Joseph T. Ventura, 544 Dead Run Drive, McLean, Va., 22101.

Director, Public Information.—Harvey A. Bush, 3404 Halcyon Drive, Alexandria, Va., 22305.

Deputy Director, Public Information.—Samuel Botsford, 4601 Potomac Avenue, 20007.

Under Secretary.—Ivan A. Nestingen, 4821 Potomac Avenue, 20007.

Assistant to the Under Secretary.—Lloyd H. Rooney, 5603 Potomac Avenue, 20007.

Defense Coordinator.—Dean Snyder, 7 Hunting Cove Place, Alexandria, Va., 22307.

Director, Security.—Frederick H. Schmidt, 106 Devon Court, Silver Spring, Md., 20910.

Director, Field Administration.—Chester B. Lund, 4108 Forest Lane, McLean, Va., 22101.

Associate Director, Field Administration.—Harold B. Siegel, 8805 Leonard Drive, Silver Spring, Md., 20910.

Chief, Grant-in-Aid Audits.—Leonard J. Wilbert, 3224 Military Road, 20015.

Chief, State Merit Systems.—Albert H. Aronson, 5409 39th Street, 20015.

Chief, Surplus Property Utilization.—[Vacant.]

Assistant to the Under Secretary for Educational Television.—John W. Bystrom, 6401 31st Place, 20015.

Assistant to the Under Secretary (Manpower Training).—James J. Clarke, 1718 Mark Lane, Rockville, Md., 20852.

Special Assistant to the Secretary (Health and Medical Affairs).—Edward W. Dempsey, 3817 47th Street, 20016.

Assistant to the Special Assistant.—William H. Stewart, 9108 Ewing Drive, Bethesda, Md., 20034.

559

Under Secretary—Continued

Assistant Secretary (for Legislation).—Wilbur J. Cohen, 9819 Capitol View Avenue, Silver Spring, Md., 20910.

Deputy Assistant Secretary.—Philip H. DesMarais, 1529 44th Street, 20007.

Deputy Assistant Secretary (Legislative Services).—Dean Coston, 1303 Stoney Brae Drive, Falls Church, Va., 22044.

Assistant Secretary.—James M. Quigley, 9710 Carriage Road, Kensington, Md., 20795.

Deputy Assistant Secretary.—Shelton B. Granger, 1424 Hamilton Street, 20011.

Deputy Assistant Secretary for International Affairs.—Robert A. Kevan, A–1409, 1600 South Joyce Street, Arlington, Va., 22202.

International Program Relations Staff.—Laurence Wyatt, 10704 Shelley Court, Garrett Park, Md., 20766.

International Surveys Staff.—Ronald S. Kain, 3611 N Street, 20007.

General Counsel.—Alanson W. Willcox, 5073 Lowell Street, 20016.

Associate General Counsel (acting).—Reginald G. Conley, 12400 Columbia Pike, Silver Spring, Md., 20904.

Assistant General Counsel, Food and Drugs.—William W. Goodrich, 4833 30th Street North, Arlington, Va., 22207.

Assistant General Counsel, Legislation (acting).—Theodore Ellenbogen, 3500 30th Street, 20008.

Assistant General Counsel, Old-Age and Survivors Insurance.—Harold Packer, 2425 Lightfoot Drive, Baltimore, Md., 21209.

Assistant General Counsel, Public Health.—Edward J. Rourke, 2509 North Quincy Street, Arlington, Va., 22207.

Assistant General Counsel, Welfare and Education.—Edwin H. Yourman, 2825 Tennyson Street, 20015.

Assistant General Counsel, Business and Administrative Law.—Manuel B. Hiller, 8510 Leonard Drive, Silver Spring, Md., 20910.

Assistant Secretary for Administration.—Rufus E. Miles, Jr., 3309 Cummings Lane, Chevy Chase, Md., 20015.

Deputy Assistant Secretary for Administration and Comptroller.—James F. Kelly, 4108 Woodbine Street, Chevy Chase, Md., 20015.

Deputy Comptroller.—Loyal C. Fisher, 117 Van Winkle Drive, Falls Church, Va., 22044.

Director, Budget.—Daniel O. Mathewson, 11411 Nairn Road, Silver Spring, Md., 20902.

Director, Central Pay Roll.—Gregory T. Sheridan, 1644 21st Street, 20009.

Director, Fiscal Policy and Procedure.—Marvin W. Bingham, 6507 Nevius Street, Falls Church, Va., 22041.

Director, Operations Analysis.—Robert W. Cox, 3180 North Quincy Street, Arlington, Va., 22206.

Director Audit.—James L. Thompson, Jr., 217 East Franklin Avenue, Silver Spring, Md., 20901.

Director, Management Policy.—James W. Greenwood, Jr., 4020 Kennedy Street, Hyattsville, Md., 20781.

Assistant Director.—Paul W. Pyle, Jr., 2721 Donna Circle, Annandale, Va., 22003.

Director, General Services.—Dale S. Thompson, 3606 Arlington Boulevard, Arlington, Va., 22204.

Deputy Director, General Services.—E. Raymond Lannon, 7907 Legation Road, Carrollton, Hyattsville, Md., 20784.

Director, Personnel Management.—James C. O'Brien, 5002 Danbury Court, Bethesda, Md., 20014.

Deputy Director, Personnel Management.—Edmund J. Grant, 532 Paul Spring Parkway, Alexandria, Va., 22308.

REGIONAL OFFICES

Regional Directors:

Region I—Connecticut, Maine, Massachusetts, New Hampshire, Rhode Island, Vermont.—Walter W. Mode (acting director), 120 Boylston Street, Boston, Mass., 02116.

Region II—Delaware, New Jersey, New York, Pennsylvania.—Joseph B. O'Connor, Room 1200, 42 Broadway, New York, N.Y., 10004.

Region III—District of Columbia, Kentucky, Maryland, North Carolina, Virginia, West Virginia, Puerto Rico, Virgin Islands.—Edmund Baxter, 700 East Jefferson Street, Charlottesville, Va., 22901.

Region IV—Alabama, Florida, Georgia, Mississippi, South Carolina, Tennessee.—Richard H. Lyle, Room 404, 50 Seventh Street NE., Atlanta, Ga., 30323.

Region V—Illinois, Indiana, Michigan, Ohio, Wisconsin.—Melville H. Hosch, Room 712, New Post Office Building, 433 West Van Buren Street, Chicago, Ill., 60607.

Region VI—Iowa, Kansas, Minnesota, Missouri, Nebraska, North Dakota, South Dakota.—James W. Doarn, 560 Westport Road, Kansas City, Mo., 64111.

Region VII—Arkansas, Louisiana, New Mexico, Oklahoma, Texas.—James H. Bond, 1114 Commerce Street, Dallas, Tex., 75202.

Region VIII—Colorado, Idaho, Montana, Utah, Wyoming.—Dr. William T. Van Orman (acting director), Room 551, 621 17th Street, Denver, Colo., 80202.

Region IX—Alaska, Arizona, California, Hawaii, Nevada, Oregon, Washington, Guam, American Samoa.—Fay W. Hunter, Federal Office Building, 50 Fulton Street, San Francisco, Calif., 94102.

AMERICAN PRINTING HOUSE FOR THE BLIND

1839 Frankfort Avenue, Louisville, Ky., 40206

President.—J. McFerran Barr, Louisville, Ky.
Vice President and General Manager.—Finis E. Davis, Louisville, Ky.

GALLAUDET COLLEGE

Seventh and Florida Avenue NE., 20002. Phone, LIncoln 7-7200

Patron ex Officio.—Lyndon B. Johnson, President of the United States.
President.—Leonard M. Elstad, 1 Kendall Green NE.
Chairman of the Board of Directors.—Albert W. Atwood, Room I-648, Sheraton-Park Hotel.
Vice Chairman.—Linton M. Collins, 5025 Macomb Street, 20016.
Secretary.—George E. Muth, 5107 Allan Road, Westgate, 20016.
Treasurer.—Warren R. Forster, 4739 Massachusetts Avenue, 20016.
Assistant Secretary-Treasurer.—Sidney B. Cohen, 10117 Dallas Avenue, Silver Spring, Md.
Directors.—Albert W. Atwood; Linton M. Collins; Ancher Nelsen, House of Representatives; Leonard M. Elstad; Warren R. Forster; Bradshaw Mintener; George E. Muth; Nathan Poole; Hugh Carey, House of Representatives; George M. Ferris, Sr.; Robert C. Byrd, Senator from West Virginia; Edward W. Dempsey.

FOOD AND DRUG ADMINISTRATION

Federal Office Building No. 8, 200 C Street SW.
Phone, WOrth 3-1110 (Code 13, extension 22575)

Commissioner.—George P. Larrick, 4841 30th Street North, Arlington, Va., 22207.
Special Assistant to the Commissioner.—Kenneth L. Milstead, 4817 Dorset Avenue, Chevy Chase, Md., 20015.
Deputy Commissioner.—John L. Harvey, 709 South Wakefield Street, Arlington, Va., 22204.

Assistant Commissioner for Administration.—James B. Cardwell, 5213 Rayland Drive, Bethesda, Md., 20034.

Assistant Commissioner for Operations.—J. Kenneth Kirk, 5936 First Street South, Arlington, Va., 22204.

Assistant Commissioner for Planning.—Winton B. Rankin, 2716 North Yucatan Street, Arlington, Va., 22204.

Assistant Commissioner for Regulations.—Malcolm R. Stephens, 4814 Wellington Drive, Chevy Chase, Md., 20015.

Assistant Commissioner for Science Resources.—Oral L. Kline, 3509 Rodman Street, 20008.

Director of—

Emergency Preparedness.—H. G. Underwood, Post Office Box 417, Vienna, Va., 22180.

Federal-State Relations.—James C. Pearson, 4301 Columbia Pike, Arlington, Va., 22204.

Public Information.—Wallace F. Janssen, 3501 Raymond Street, Chevy Chase, Md., 20015.

Bureau of Education and Voluntary Compliance.—Shelbey T. Grey (acting director), 3814 Columbia Pike, Arlington, Va., 22204.

Division of Consumer Education.—James L. Trawick, 1104 Kennedy Lane, Falls Church, Va., 22042.

Division of Industry Advice.—Shelbey T. Grey (acting director), 3814 Columbia Pike, Arlington, Va., 22204.

Bureau of Medicine.—Joseph F. Sadusk, Jr., 7409 Haddington Place, Bethesda, Md., 20034.

Division of Antibiotic Drugs.—Raymond E. Barzilai (acting director), 7606 Honesty Way, Bethesda, Md., 20034.

Division of Medical Information.—Donald G. Levitt, 12901 Layhill Road, Silver Spring, Md., 20906.

Division of Medical Review.—Howard I. Weinstein, 8500 16th Street, Silver Spring, Md., 20910.

Division of New Drugs.—Ralph G. Smith, 1026 Noyes Drive, Silver Spring, Md., 20910.

Division of Veterinary Medicine.—Charles G. Durbin, 5705 Berwyn Road, College Park, Md., 20741.

Bureau of Regulatory Compliance.—Allan E. Rayfield, 22 North Granada Street, Arlington, Va., 22203.

Division of Case Supervision.—Morris L. Yakowitz, 4917 28th Parkway, Hillcrest Heights, Md., 20031.

Division of Field Operations.—Frederick M. Garfield, 2834 North Harrison Street, Arlington, Va., 22207.

Division of Review and Appraisal.—Kenneth R. Lennington, 411 North Nelson Street, Arlington, Va., 22203.

Bureau of Scientific Research.—William H. Summerson, 501 Gatewood Drive, Alexandria, Va., 22307.

Division of Color and Cosmetic Chemistry.—G. Robert Clark, Route 1, Box 479, Edgewater, Md., 21037.

Division of Food Chemistry.—Henry Fischbach, 3107 Grove Street, Alexandria, Va., 22302.

Division of Microbiology.—G. G. Slocum, 4204 Dresden Street, Kensington, Md., 20795.

Division of Nutrition.—P. L. Harris, 710 A Street SE., 20003.

Division of Pharmacology.—A. J. Lehman, 5615 Maryland Avenue, Falls Church, Va., 22040.

Division of Pharmaceutical Chemistry.—Jonas Carol (acting director), 609 Pershing Drive, Silver Spring, Md., 20910.

Bureau of Scientific Standards and Evaluation.—Robert S. Roe, 2807 Ridge Road Drive, Alexandria, Va., 22302.

Division of Antibiotics and Insulin Certification.—W. R. Jester, 2806 North 30th Street, Alexandria, Va., 22302.

Division of Color Certification and Evaluation.—Kenneth A. Freeman, Cape Ann, Churchton, Md., 20733.

Division of Food Standards and Additives.—L. M. Beacham, 2600 Valley Drive, Alexandria, Va., 22302.

Division of Toxicological Evaluation.—Bert J. Vos, Post Office Box 569, McLean, Va., 22101.

HOWARD UNIVERSITY

Howard Place and Georgia Avenue. Phone, DUpont 7-6100

Patron ex Officio.—Anthony J. Celebrezze, Secretary of Department of Health, Education, and Welfare.
Chairman, Board of Trustees.—Lorimer D. Milton, A.B., A.M.
President.—James M. Nabrit, Jr., A.B., J.D., LL.D., D.H.L.
Vice President for Special Projects.—William Stuart Nelson, A.B., B.D., LL.D.
Academic Vice President.—Stanton L. Wormley, A.B., M.A., Ph.D.
Secretary.—G. Frederick Stanton, B.S., M.A.
Treasurer and Chief Business and Financial Officer.—James B. Clarke, B.S., M.A.
Business Manager.—Wendell G. Morgan, B.A., M.A.

VOCATIONAL REHABILITATION ADMINISTRATION

Third Floor, Health, Education, and Welfare Building. Phone, WOrth 3-1110
(Code 13, extension 33155)

Commissioner.—Mary E. Switzer, 422 Underhill Place, Alexandria, Va., 22305.
  Deputy Commissioner.—Patrick J. Doyle, M.D., 3143 Davenport Street, Alexandria, Va., 22306.
  Assistant Commissioner, Legislation and Public Affairs.—Russell J. N. Dean, 1900 South Eades Street, Apt. 1228, Arlington, Va., 22202.
  Assistant Commissioner, Health and Medical Affairs.—[Vacant.]
  Assistant Commissioner, Program Services.—Joseph V. Hunt, 109 North George Mason Drive, Arlington, Va., 22203.
    Chief, Division of State Program Administration.—William M. Eshelman, 710 Woodside Parkway, Silver Spring, Md., 20910.
    Chief, Division of Services to the Blind.—Douglas C. MacFarland, 5510 Eastbourne Drive, Springfield, Va., 22151.
    Chief, Division of Disability Services.—Thomas J. Skelley, 406 Haynsworth Place, Fairfax, Va., 22030.
    Chief, Division of Rehabilitation Facilities.—Henry Redkey, 321 Bradley Avenue, Rockville, Md., 20851.
  Assistant Commissioner, Research and Training.—James F. Garrett, 204 Noland Street, Falls Church, Va., 22046.
    Chief, Division of Research Grants and Demonstrations.—William M. Usdane, 4015 Laird Place, Chevy Chase, Md., 20015.
    Chief, Division of Training.—Cecile M. Hillyer, 800 Fourth Street SW., Apt. So. 312, 20024.
    Chief, Division of International Activities.—Joseph LaRocca, 6 Wessex Road, Silver Spring, Md., 20910.
  Assistant Commissioner, Regional Operations.—Paul C. Howard, 5001 Brookdale Road, 20016.
  Assistant Commissioner, Management Services.—Samuel E. Martz, 1207 Stafford Road, Alexandria, Va., 22307.
    Chief, Division of Personnel and Administrative Services.—Margaret P. Bray, 10104 South Glen Road, Rockville, Md., 20854.
    Chief, Division of Budget and Fiscal Operations.—Edward G. Manning, 7109 Georgia Street, Chevy Chase, Md., 20015.
    Chief, Division of Statistics and Studies.—Sigmund Schor, 8605 Rayburn Road, Bethesda, Md., 20034.

OFFICE OF EDUCATION

400 Maryland Avenue SW., 20202. Phone, WOrth 3-1110

Commissioner.—Francis Keppel, 2800 O Street, 20007.
  Assistant to the Commissioner (Public Affairs).—John H. Naisbitt, 528 Cedar Street, 20012.
  Assistant to the Commissioner (Special Higher Education Projects).—Brodus N. Butler, 1427 Hamlin Street NE., 20017.
  Assistant to the Commissioner.—Lucille G. Anderson, 210 Hickory Hill Avenue, McLean, Va., 22101.

Deputy Commissioner.—Wayne O. Reed, 4800 Calvert Street, 20007.

   Executive Officer and Director, Office of Administration.—John F. Hughes, **776** Rollins Drive, Alexandria, Va., 22307.

   Director, Office of Legislation.—Samuel Halperin, 6812 Sixth Street, 20012.

   Director, Office of Information.—L. V. Goodman, 1101 Third Street SW., 20024

   Director, Office of Field Services.—Herman L. Offner, 603 Dead Run Drive, McLean, Va., 22101.

   Director, Programs for Education of the Disadvantaged.—J. William Rioux (acting), 6800 Sixth Street, 20012.

   Director, Office of Equal Educational Opportunities.—David S. Seeley (acting), 421 Whittier Street, 20012.

   Director, Office of Federal Education Activities.—Wayne O. Reed (acting), 4800 Calvert Street, 20007.

Associate Commissioner and Director, Bureau of Educational Research and Development.—Ralph C. M. Flynt, 72 Woodmont Road, Belle Haven, Alexandria, Va., 22307.

Deputy Associate Commissioner.—E. Glenn Featherston, 105 Quincy Place, Falls Church, Va., 22402.

   Director, Division of Educational Organization and Administration.—R. Orin Cornett, 5701 Wrightson Drive, McLean, Va., 22101.

   Director, Division of Educational Research.—Francis A. J. Ianni (acting), Route 1, Box 22, Fairfax Station, Va., 22039.

   Director, Division of Handicapped Children and Youth.—Morvin A. Wirtz, 9256 Edmonston Road, Greenbelt, Md., 20770.

   Director, Division of Library Services.—John G. Lorenz, 5629 Newington Road, 20016.

Associate Commissioner and Director, Bureau of International Education.—Oliver J. Caldwell (acting), 140 East Rosemary Lane, Falls Church, Va., 22042.

Deputy Associate Commissioner.—Thomas E. Cotner (acting), 228 Buxton Road, Falls Church, Va., 22046.

   Director, Division of International Studies and Services.—Fredrika M. Tandler, 5022 V Street, 20007.

   Director, Division of Technical Assistance and Exchange Programs.—Thomas E. Cotner (acting).

Associate Commissioner and Director, Bureau of Educational Assistance Programs.—Arthur L. Harris, 2630 South Ives Street, Arlington, Va., 22202

Deputy Associate Commissioner.—John R. Ludington, 7205 Exfair Road, Bethesda, Md., 20014.

   Assistant Commissioner and Director, Division of Vocational and Technical Education.—Walter M. Arnold, 1301 South Scott Street, Arlington, Va., 22204.

   Assistant Commissioner and Director, Division of School Assistance in Federally Affected Areas.—B. Alden Lillywhite, 519 North Oakland Street, Arlington, Va., 22203.

   Director, Division of State Grants.—Ralph J. Becker, 1935 Kimberly Road, Silver Spring, Md., 20902.

   Director, Division of College and University Assistance.—Kenneth W. Mildenberger, 4200 Cathedral Avenue, 20016.

Associate Commissioner and Director, Bureau of Higher Education.—Peter P. Muirhead, 230 West Hunting Towers, Alexandria, Va., 22314.

Deputy Associate Commissioner.—

   Director, Division of Undergraduate Academic Facilities.—Jay du Von, RFD 1, Box 82, Brook Farm, Manassas, Va., 22110.

   Director, Division of Graduate Academic Facilities.—John W. Ashton (acting), 1000 Sixth Street SW., 20024.

   Director, Division of Student Financial Aid.—Clarence E. Deakins (acting), 6011 Dempsey Street, McLean, Va., 22101.

Assistant Commissioner and Director, National Center for Educational Statistics.—Alexander M. Mood, 4701 Kenmore Avenue, Alexandria, Va., 22304.

   Director, Division of Data Sources and Standards.—Ivan N. Seibert (acting), 9311 Woodberry Street, Seabrook, Md., 20802.

   Director, Division of Statistical Services.—Virgil R. Walker (acting), 11306 Stephens Lane, Beltsville, Md., 20705.

   Director, Division of Statistical Analysis.—Louis H. Conger, Jr. (acting), 5006 Jamestown Road, 20016.

   Director, Division of Operations Analysis.—Arnold A. Heyl (acting), 117 Maple Lane, Fairfax, Va., 22030.

SAINT ELIZABETHS HOSPITAL

Nichols Avenue beyond Anacostia SE.   Phone, JOhnson 2-4000

Superintendent.—Dale C. Cameron, M.D., Saint Elizabeths Hospital, 20032.
Assistant Superintendent.—[Vacant.]
First Assistant Physician.—David W. Harris, M.D., Saint Elizabeths Hospital, 20032.
Executive Officer.—M. K. Madden, 4502 Middleton Lane, Bethesda, Md., 20014,
Assistant Executive Officer.—Robert K. Dean, 6457 Hemlock Place, Temple Hills, Md., 20031.
Registrar.—William F. Edwards, 1904 Merrimac Drive, Adelphi, Md., 20783.
Superintendent of Nurses.—Lavonne M. Frey, Saint Elizabeths Hospital, 20032
Personnel Officer.—Herman H. Wiebusch, 2480 16th Street, 20009.

PUBLIC HEALTH SERVICE

Health, Education, and Welfare Building, Fourth Street and Independence Avenue SW., and Health, Education, and Welfare Building South, Third and C Streets SW.: National Library of Medicine, 8600 Wisconsin Avenue, Bethesda, Md., phone, 656-4084 (Code 14, Extension 4084). National Institutes of Health, Bethesda, Md.; phone, OLiver 6-4000 (Code 14, Extension 62433).

Surgeon General.—~~Luther L. Terry~~, *William H. Stewart* *9/30/6* 105 South Van Buren Street, Rockville, Md., 20850.
Deputy Surgeon General.—David E. Price, 5215 Elsmere Avenue, Bethesda, Md., 20014.
Assistant Surgeon General.—James M. Hundley, 604 Rose Ann Place, Gaithersburg, Md., 20760.
Assistant Surgeon General.—M. Allen Pond, 7813 Moorland Lane, Bethesda, Md., 20014.
Executive Officer.—Donald F. Simpson, 5806 Broyhill Street, McLean, Va., 22101.
Assistant Executive Officer.—C. Robert Seater, 724 Chesapeake Street, Silver Spring, Md., 20910.
Chief Dental Officer.—Dr. Ralph S. Lloyd, 7801 Moorland Lane, Bethesda, Md., 20014.
Chief Sanitary Engineering Officer.—C. H. Atkins, 9518 East Stanhope Road, Kensington, Md., 20795.
Chief Nurse Officer.—Mrs. Lucile P. Leone, 3140 Wisconsin Avenue, 20016.
Assistant to the Surgeon General for Information.—J. Stewart Hunter, 1704 Oakcrest Drive, Alexandria, Va., 22302.

OFFICE OF THE SURGEON GENERAL

Chief, Division of Finance.—Harry L. Doran, 4302 Sleaford Road, Bethesda, Md., 20014.
Chief, Division of Administrative Services.—Kenneth W. Revell, 9311 Milroy Place, Bethesda, Md., 20014.
Chief, Office of Personnel.—Dr. Murray A. Diamond, 9105 Kirkdale Road, Bethesda, Md., 20034.
Deputy Chief, Office of Personnel.—Paul M. Camp, 101 Brookview Drive, Brookland Estates, Alexandria, Va., 22310.
Chief, Division of Public Health Methods.—Dr. Richard Prindle, 5118 Fairglen Lane, Chevy Chase, Md., 20015.
Director, Office of International Health.—Dr. James Watt, 2950 Macomb Street, 20008.
Acting Chief, Division of Health Mobilization.—Arnold H. Dodge, 4712 Little Falls Road, Arlington, Va., 22207.

NATIONAL CENTER FOR HEALTH STATISTICS

Director, National Center for Health Statistics.—Dr. Forrest E. Linder, 2122 California Street, 20008.
Executive Officer.—Louis R. Stolcis, 4004 Londonderry Road, Alexandria, Va., 22308.
Deputy Director.—Theodore D. Woolsey, 8121 Rayburn Road, Bethesda, Md., 20034.
Assistant Director.—Dr. O. K. Sagen, 210 Fifth Street SE., 20013.

NATIONAL LIBRARY OF MEDICINE

8600 Wisconsin Avenue, Bethesda, Md. Phone, 656-4084

Director.—Martin M. Cummings, 6 West Drive, Bethesda, Md., 20014.
Deputy Director.—Scott Adams, 4621 High Street, Chevy Chase, Md., 20015.
Executive Officer.—Ray W. Grim, 5418 Brown's Lane, Oxon Hill, Md., 20021.

BUREAU OF MEDICAL SERVICES

Chief.—Assistant Surgeon General Leo J. Gehrig, 4535 Alton Place, 20016.
Deputy Chief.—Assistant Surgeon General Andrew P. Sackett, 5108 Flanders Avenue, Kensington, Md., 20795.
Chief Medical Officer, U.S. Coast Guard.—Assistant Surgeon General Howard D. Fishburn, 5007 Danbury Court, Bethesda, Md., 20014.
Executive Officer.—Charles Hilsenroth, 9216 East Parkhill Drive, Bethesda, Md., 20014.
Chief, Division of Hospitals.—Assistant Surgeon General G. P. Ferrazzano, 7603 Newmarket Drive, Bethesda, Md., 20034.
Chief, Division of Foreign Quarantine.—Medical Director Louis Jacobs, 4600 Connecticut Avenue, 20008.
Chief, Division of Indian Health.—Assistant Surgeon General Carruth J. Wagner, 1 Ancel Street, Alexandria, Va., 22305.
Acting Medical Director, Bureau of Employees Compensation.—Medical Director Ralph B. Snavely, 3703 Albemarle Street, 20016.
Medical Director, Bureau of Prisons.—Medical Director Charles E. Smith, 5624 Lamar Road, 20016.

FREEDMEN'S HOSPITAL

Sixth and Bryant Streets. Phone, ADams 2-6262

Superintendent.—Charles E. Burbridge, 1639 Kalmia Road, 20012
Assistant to the Superintendent.—Houston A. Baker, 1441 Manchester Lane, 20011.
Medical Director.—Dr. R. Frank Jones, 1721 T Street, 20009.
Acting Airector of Nursing.—Mrs. Genevieve M. Brenner, 6606 Georgia Avenue, 20010.

NATIONAL INSTITUTES OF HEALTH

Director.—Assistant Surgeon General James A. Shannon, 12 North Drive, Bethesda, Md., 20014.
Deputy Director.—Assistant Surgeon General Stuart M. Sessoms, 9203 Bardon Road, Bethesda, Md., 20014.
Director of Laboratories and Clinics.—Dr. G. Burroughs Mider, 14 North Drive, Bethesda, Md., 20014.
Associate Director for Clinical Care Administration.—Assistant Surgeon General Jack Masur, 3710 Davenport Street, 20016.
Associate Director for Extramural Programs.—Dr. John F. Sherman, 9916 Wildwood Road, Kensington, Md., 20795.
Chief, Office of Program Planning.—Joseph S. Murtaugh, 10912 Clermont Avenue, Garrett Park, Md., 20766.
Chief, Office of Research Information.—Clifford Johnson, 4017 Byrd Road, Kensington, Md., 20795.
Chief, Office of International Research.—Dr. Charles L. Williams, Jr., 8016 Hampden Lane, Bethesda, Md., 20014.
Executive Officer.—Richard L. Seggel, 10310 Lloyd Road, Potomac, Md.
Director, Division of Biologics Standards.—Medical Director Roderick Murray, 5714 Springfield Drive, 20016.
Chief, Division of Research Grants.—Dr. Eugene A. Confrey, 6509 Laverock Lane, Bethesda, Md., 20034.
Chief, Division of Research Services.—Sanitary Engineer Director, Chris A. Hansen, 5615 Marengo Road, 20016.
Acting Chief, Division of Research Facilities and Resources.—Dr. Frederick L. Stone, 4807 Hampden Lane, Bethesda, Md., 20014.

Director, Clinical Center.—Assistant Surgeon General Jack Masur, 3710 Daven-
port, Street, 20016.
Director, National Cancer Institute.—Assistant Surgeon General Kenneth M.
Endicott, Ken-Milyn Farm, Dickerson, Md., 20753.
Director, National Heart Institute.—Medical Director Ralph E. Knutti, 9212
Aldershot Drive, Bethesda, Md., 20034.
Director, National Institute of Allergy and Infectious Diseases.—Medical Director
Dorland J. Davis, 4841 Broad Brook Drive, Bethesda, Md., 20014.
Director, National Institute of Arthritis and Metabolic Diseases.—Dr. G. Donald
Whedon, 5605 Sonoma Road, Bethesda, Md., 20034.
Director, National Institute of Dental Research.—Dental Director Francis A.
Arnold, Jr., 4 West Drive, Bethesda, Md., 20014.
Director, National Institute of Mental Health.—Assistant Surgeon General Stanley
F. Yolles, 5206 Locust Avenue, Bethesda, Md., 20014.
Director, National Institute of Neurological Diseases and Blindness.—Dr. Richard
L. Masland, 4700 Jamestown Road, Westmoreland Hills, 20016.
Director, National Institute of Child Health and Human Development.—[Vacant.]
Director, National Institute of General Medical Sciences.—Dr. Frederick L. Stone,
4807 Hampden Lane, Bethesda, Md., 20014.

BUREAU OF STATE SERVICES
ENVIRONMENTAL HEALTH

Chief.—Assistant Surgeon General Robert J. Anderson, 3624 36th Street North,
Arlington, Va., 22207.
Associate Chief for Environmental Health.—Assistant Surgeon General Harry G.
Hanson, 11824 Charen Lane, Rockville, Md., 20851.
Program Officer for Environmental Health.—Sanitary Engineer Director Earl H.
Arnold, 6602 Sulky Lane, Rockville, Md., 20852.
Executive Officer.—Lyman Moore, 7406 Hancock Avenue, Apt. 21, Takoma Park,
Md., 20012.
Assistant Executive Officer.—John H. Kelso, 2332 North Early Street, Alexandria,
Va., 22302.
Special Assistant to the Bureau Chief (EH) for Regional Office Liaison.—Sanitary
Engineer Director Hershel Engler, 3310 Camalier Drive, Chevy Chase, Md.,
20015.
Information Officer.—Francis J. Acosta, 323 Maple Avenue, Falls Church, Va.,
22406.
Chief, Office of Pesticides.—[Vacant.]
Assistant Chief, Office of Facilities Management.—Sanitary Engineer Harry C.
Vollrath 3d, 158 G Street SW., 20024.
Chief, Office of Resources Development.—Sanitary Engineer Director Harry P.
Kramer, Woodmont and Rigby Streets, Bethesda, Md., 20014.
Director, Arctic Health Research Center.—Medical Director A. B. Colyer, 2601
Foraker, Spenard, Alaska.
Director, Sanitary Engineering Center.—Sanitary Engineer Director Conrad P.
Straub, 4676 Columbia Parkway, Cincinnati, Ohio, 45226.
Chief, Division of Air Pollution.—Sanitary Engineer Director Vernon G.
MacKenzie, 2304 Benjamin Street, McLean, Va., 22101.
Chief, Division of Environmental Engineering and Food Protection.—Sanitary
Engineer Director Wesley E. Gilbertson, 5110 Fairglen Lane, Chevy Chase,
Md., 20015.
Chief, Division of Occupational Health.—Medical Director Murray C. Brown,
4409 Glenridge Street, Kensington, Md., 20795.
Chief, Division of Radiological Health.—Medical Director Donald R. Chadwick,
R.F.D. Box 4515, Upper Marlboro, Md., 20870.
Chief, Division of Water Supply and Pollution Control.—Assistant Surgeon General
Gordon E. McCallum, 9009 Spring Hill Lane, Chevy Chase, Md., 20015.

COMMUNITY HEALTH

Deputy Chief.—Assistant Surgeon General Aaron W. Christensen, Mountain Gap
Farm, Route 2, Leesburg, Va., 22075.
Acting Associate Chief for Community Health.—Assistant Surgeon General Paul
Q. Peterson, 8403 Whitman Drive, Bethesda, Md., 20034.

Associate Chief for Program.—Assistant Surgeon General Alan W. Donaldson, 7500 Sebago Road, Bethesda, Md., 20034.
Associate Chief for Grants (Community Health).—Sam A. Kimble, 509 Linden Lane, Falls Church, Va., 22042.
Associate Chief for Planning and Analysis (Community Health).—Stephen J. Ackerman, 1830 Plymouth Street, 20012.
Executive Officer for Community Health.—Richard W. Bunch, 5110 Rockwood Parkway, 20016.
Assistant Executive Officer for Community Health.—Harry C. Abernathy, 6218 27th Street North, Arlington, Va., 22207.
Acting Chief, Office of Grants Management.—Sam A. Kimble, 509 Linden Lane, Falls Church, Va., 22042.
Chief, Office of Research Grants.—Medical Director Gilbert R. Barnhart, 7108 Brenon Lane, Chevy Chase, Md., 20015.
Special Assistant in Mental Health.—Medical Director Mabel Ross, 101 North Carolina Avenue SE., 20003.
Chief, Division of Accident Prevention.—Medical Director Paul V. Joliet, 3309 Wake Drive, Kensington, Md., 20795.
Chief, Division of Chronic Diseases.—Medical Director Eugene H. Guthrie, 3908 Aspen Street, Chevy Chase, Md., 20015.
Chief, Communicable Disease Center.—Assistant Surgeon General James L. Goddard, 965 Clifton Road NE., Atlanta, Ga., 30307.
Chief, Division of Community Health Services.—Medical Director Burnet M. Davis, 4223 Leland Street, Chevy Chase, Md., 20015.
Chief, Division of Dental Public Health and Resources.—Assistant Surgeon General Donald J. Galagan, 9206 Farnsworth Drive, Potomac, Md., 20854.
Chief, Division of Hospital and Medical Facilities.—Assistant Surgeon General Harald M. Graning, 7915 Eastern Avenue, Silver Spring, Md., 20910.
Chief, Division of Nursing.—Nurse Director Jessie M. Scott, 710 North Wayne Street, Arlington, Va., 22201.

SOCIAL SECURITY ADMINISTRATION

Department of Health, Education, and Welfare Building, 330 Independence Avenue SW.; Phone, WOrth 2-3295; and Social Security Administration Headquarters Building, Baltimore, Md. 21235. Phone, 944-5000.

Commissioner.—Robert M. Ball, 4009 Villa Nova Avenue, Baltimore, Md., 21207.
Executive Assistant.—J. S. Futterman, 360 Chantel Court, Ellicott City, Md., 21042.
Director, Division of Accounting Operations.—Joseph L. Fay, 614 East Lake Avenue, Baltimore, Md., 21212.
Chief Actuary, Division of the Actuary.—Robert J. Myers, 9610 Wire Avenue, Silver Spring, Md., 20901.
Staff Director, Central Planning Staff.—George E. Rawson, 6826 Fox Meadow Road, Baltimore, Md., 21207.
Director, Division of Claims Control.—Richard E. Branham, 901 Nottingham Road, Baltimore, Md., 21229.
Director, Division of Claims Policy.—Thomas C. Parrott, 2326 Pickwick Road, Baltimore, Md., 21207.
Director, Division of Disability Operations.—Arthur E. Hess, 4805 Woodside Road, Baltimore, Md., 21229.
Director, Bureau of Federal Credit Unions.—J. Deane Gannon, 4806 Dover Road, 20016.
Director, Division of Field Operations.—Hugh F. McKenna, 224 Murdock Road, Baltimore, Md., 21212.
Director, Bureau of Hearings and Appeals.—Joseph E. McElvain, 4615 Brandy-wine Street, 20016.
Information Officer, Office of Information.—Roy L. Swift, 15 Seminole Avenue, Catonsville, Md., 21228.
Director, Division of Management.—Roy E. Touchet, 115 Maiden Choice Lane, Baltimore, Md., 21228.
Director, Division of Program Evaluation and Planning.—Alvin M. David, 4510 Wakefield Road, Baltimore, Md., 21216.
Director, Division of Research and Statistics.—Ida C. Merriam, 2908 Brandywine Street, 20008.

WELFARE ADMINISTRATION

Department of Health, Education, and Welfare Building, 330 Independence Avenue SW.

Phone, WOrth 3–1110 (Code 13, Extension 24265)

Commissioner.—Ellen Winston, 1601 18th Street, 20009.
Deputy Commissioner.—Joseph H. Meyers, 11800 Devilwood Drive, Rockville, Md., 20850.
  Executive Officer.—Roy L. Wynkoop, 785 Rollins Drive, Alexandria, Va., 22307.
  Legislative Reference Officer.—Charles E. Hawkins, 7900 Custer Road, Bethesda, Md., 20014.
  Information Officer.—Ruth Lauder, 2345 Nebraska Avenue, 20016.
  Director of Research.—Genevieve W. Carter, 1400 Joyce Street, Arlington, Va., 22202.
Chief, Children's Bureau.—Katherine B. Oettinger, 3027 Normanstone Terrace, 20008.
Director, Bureau of Family Services.—Fred H. Steininger, 800 Fourth Street SW., 20024.
Director, Office of Aging.—Donald P. Kent, 4314 Duncan Drive, Annandale, Va., 22003.
Director, Office of Juvenile Delinquency and Youth Development.—Bernard Russell, 205 Buxton Road, Falls Church, Va., 22046.
Director, Cuban Refugee Program.—John F. Thomas, 8335 East Beach Drive, 20012.

INDEPENDENT AGENCIES

INDEPENDENT AGENCIES

ADVISORY COMMISSION ON INFORMATION, UNITED STATES

1750 Pennsylvania Avenue, 20547.   Phone, DUdley 3-4910 (Code 182, extension 4910)

Chairman.—Frank Stanton, New York.
  Mrs. Dorothy B. Chandler, Los Angeles, Calif.
  Sigurd S. Larmon, New York, N.Y.
  Clark R. Mollenhoff, Washington, D.C.
  M. S. Novik, New York, N.Y.
Staff Director.—Louis T. Olon, 702 Poplar Drive, Falls Church, Va.
Executive Secretary.—Nancy B. Chappelear, 2475 Virginia Avenue, Washington, D.C., 20037.

ADVISORY COMMISSION ON INTERGOVERNMENTAL RELATIONS

1701 Pennsylvania Avenue, 20575.   Phone, DUdley 2-4953 (Code 128, extension 4953)

Private Citizens:
  Frank Bane, Virginia, Chairman.
  Thomas H. Eliot, Missouri, Vice Chairman.
  Mrs. Adelaide Walters, North Carolina.
Executive Branch:
  Orville L. Freeman, Minnesota.
  Robert C. Weaver, New York.
  [Vacancy.]
Governors:
  Carl E. Sanders, Georgia.
  Robert E. Smylie, Idaho.
  John Dempsey, Connecticut.
  [Vacancy.]
Members from United States Senate:
  Sam J. Ervin, Jr., North Carolina.
  Karl E. Mundt, South Dakota.
  Edmund S. Muskie, Maine.
Members from United States House of Representatives:
  Florence P. Dwyer, New Jersey.
  L. H. Fountain, North Carolina.
  Eugene J. Keogh, New York.
Mayors:
  Herman W. Goldner, Florida.
  [Vacancy.]
  [Vacancy.]
  [Vacancy.]
Members from State Legislative Bodies:
  Speaker Marion Crank, Arkansas.
  Senator C. George DeStefano, Rhode Island.
  Senator Charles R. Weiner, Pennsylvania.
Elected County Officers:
  Edward Connor, Wayne County, Michigan.
  Clair Donnenwirth, Plumas County, California.
  [Vacancy.]

STAFF

William G. Colman, executive director, 9805 Logan Drive, Potomac Md., 20850.
Norman Beckman, assistant director, 5943 Strata Street, McLean, Va., 22101.
L. Laszlo Ecker-Racz, assistant director, 1318 24th Street South, Arlington, Va., 22202.
Melvin W. Sneed, assistant director, 4770 Dexter Street, Washington, D.C., 20007.

AMERICAN BATTLE MONUMENTS COMMISSION

(Created by Public Law 534, 67th Cong., March 4, 1923)

Room 2018, Munitions Building. Phone, OXford 6-3683 (Code 11, extension 6-3683)

Chairman.—Gen. Jacob L. Devers, 1430 33d Street, 20007.
Vice Chairman.—Adm. Thomas C. Kinkaid, 2134 R Street, 20008.
   Leslie L. Biffle, 1028 Connecticut Avenue, 20006.
   Gen. Alexander A. Vandegrift, 640 Eldorado, Delray Beach, Fla., 33444.
   Charles E. Potter, 1411 K Street, 20005.
   Gen. Carl Spaatz, 5 Grafton Street, Chevy Chase, Md., 20015.
   Joseph C. Duke, Sheraton-Park Hotel, 20008.
   T. Harry Gatton, 2011 Stone Street, Raleigh, N.C., 27601.
   Mrs. Charles G. Peters, 805 Louden Heights Road, Charleston, W. Va., 25314.
   Sidney Salomon, Jr., 1006 Ambassador Building, St. Louis, Mo., 63101.
   Austin Thomas Walden, Suite 200, Walden Building, Atlanta, Ga., 30303.
Secretary.—Maj. Gen. Thomas North, U.S. Army

AMERICAN NATIONAL RED CROSS

Seventeenth and D Streets. Phone, REpublic 7-8300 (Code 170)

HONORARY OFFICERS

Honorary Chairman.—Lyndon B. Johnson, President of the United States.
Honorary Counselor.—Nicholas deB Katzenbach, Attorney General.
Honorary Treasurer.—Henry H. Fowler, Secretary of the Treasury.

OFFICERS

Chairman of the Board of Governors.—E. Roland Harriman.
Vice Chairmen of the Board of Governors:
   G. Gordon Copeland.
   Mrs. John W. Sheppard.
   Elisha Gray II.

BOARD OF GOVERNORS

Appointed by the President of the United States: E. Roland Harriman, Chairman of The American National Red Cross; Abba P. Schwartz, Administrator, Bureau of Security and Consular Affairs, Department of State; Frederick L. Deming, Under Secretary of the Treasury, Department of the Treasury; Cyrus R. Vance, Vance, Deputy Secretary of Defense, Department of Defense; Norman S. Paul, Assistant Secretary of Defense, Department of Defense; Dr. Shirley C. Fisk, Deputy Assistant Secretary of Defense, Department of Defense; W. Willard Wirtz, Secretary of Labor, Department of Labor; Anthony J. Celebrezze, Secretary of Health, Education, and Welfare, Department of Health, Education, and Welfare.

Elected by the chapters: Eldridge J. Butler, Forrest City, Ark.; Cornelius J. Byrne, Seattle Wash.; Warren H. Chase, Cleveland, Ohio; G. Gordon Copeland, New Haven, Conn.; Judge Fred Daugherty, Oklahoma City, Okla.; Martin C. Dondlinger, Wichita, Kans.; Mrs. Joseph H. Einhorn, Albany, N.Y.; Rev. John B. Fitz, Miles City, Mont.; Walter A. Giles, Albany, N.Y.; J. Shirley Gracy, St. Petersburg, Fla.; Joseph N. Greene, Birmingham, Ala.; Huntington Harris, Leesburg, Va.; Charles Heinz, Pittsburgh, Pa.; Marshall Hickson, Santa Monica, Calif.; William H. Johnson, San Francisco, Calif.; Kirtland J. Keve, Montpelier, Vt.; Joseph B. Lanterman, Chicago, Ill.; Mrs Emile R. Mayer, Denver, Colo.; Dr. Charles H. Morgan, Gastonia, N.C.;

Elected by the chapters—Continued
Mrs. Arthur C. Regan, Minneapolis, Minn.; Mrs. John T. Rodgers, Reedsville, Pa.; Mrs. John W. Sheppard, Greenwich, Conn.; Edward D., Smith, Atlanta, Ga.; David Steine, Nashville, Tenn.; James A. Swoboda, Milwaukee, Wis.; Mrs. Dorothy S. Thropp, Toms River, N.J.; Raymond E. Vester. Portland, Oreg.; J. Garneau Weld, St. Louis, Mo.; Dan C. Williams, Dallas, Tex.; John R. Woolford, Philadelphia, Pa.
Elected by the Board of Governors as members at large: Elisha Gray II, Benton Harbor, Mich.; Dorothy I. Height, Washington, D.C.; J. Victor Herd, New York, N.Y.; Dr. Jerome H. Hollans, Hampton, Va.; Frederick R. Kappel, New York, N.Y.; Harold B. Lee, Salt Lake City, Utah; George Meany, Washington, D.C.; Samuel W. Meek, New York, N.Y.; Howard J. Morgens, Cincinnati, Ohio; Jacob S. Potofsky, New York, N.Y.; Howard C. Sheperd, New York, N.Y.; Mrs. Joseph Willen, New York, N.Y.

EXECUTIVE AND ADMINISTRATIVE OFFICERS

Chairman.—E. Roland Harriman, Jefferson Hotel, 20006.
President.—Gen. James F. Collins, 2720 35th Place, 20007.
  Executive Assistant to the President.—Robert P. Rollins, 2903 Dartmouth Road, Alexandria, Va., 22314.
Executive Vice President.—John C. Wilson, 5124 Scarsdale Road, 20016.
Vice Presidents:
  Ramone S. Eaton, 1400 South Joyce Street, Arlington, Va., 22202.
  Frederic S. Laise, 3317 North Vermont Street, Arlington, Va., 22207.
  Robert C. Lewis, 2829 31st Street, 20008.
  Robert F. Shea, 2016 Scroggins Road, Alexandria, Va., 22304.
Secretary and Counselor.—Harold W. Starr, 5823 14th Street, 20011.
Treasurer.—Frederick L. Deming.
Comptroller.—Presnell K. Betts, 4106 Downing Street, Annandale, Va., 22003.

AREAS

Eastern Area.—Manager, Truman Solverud, 5700 Colfax Avenue, Alexandria, Va., 22311.
Southeastern Area.—Manager, Paul M. Moore, 3805 Ivy Road NE., Atlanta, Ga., 30305.
Midwestern Area.—Manager, Philip Schenkenberg, 340 Hillside, Webster Groves, Mo., 63119.
Western Area.—Manager, Donald W. Stout, 1805 Castenada Drive, Burlingame, Calif., 94011.

DIRECTORS OF SERVICES AND ACTIVITIES

Services to the Armed Forces and Veterans.—Vice President in Charge, Robert C. Lewis, 2829 31st Street, 20008.
Disaster Services.—Director, Robert C. Edson, 9109 Springhill Lane, Greenbelt, Md., 20770.
Nursing Services.—Director, Lucy Johns, 2000 South Eads Street, Arlington, Va., 22202.
Safety Services.—Director, Alfred W. Cantwell, 612 Juniper Lane, Falls Church, Va., 22042.
Blood Program.—Director, Dr. Sam T. Gibson, 5801 Rossmore Drive, Bethesda, Md., 20014.
Office of Volunteers.—Director, Mrs. Abbot L. Mills, 3345 Reservoir Road, 20007.
Office of Educational Relations.—Director, Dr. Garold D. Holstine, 311 Churchill Road, McLean, Va., 22101.
Office of Public Information.—Director, Neal English, 512 North Oakland Street, Arlington, Va., 22203.
Office of Publications.—Director, Paul Lawson, 601 19th Street, 20006.
Fund Raising.—Director, Robert L. Harry, 401 Basset Street, Alexandria, Va., 22308.
Service to Areas and Chapters.—Assistant to the Vice President, James B. Foley, 112 Falster Road, Alexandria, Va., 22308.
Personnel Services.—Director, Norman A. Durfee, 4814 15th Street North, Arlington, Va., 22205.

Convention.—Director, Robert O. Earl, 411 Warrington Place, Alexandria, Va., 22307.
Office of Accounting and Auditing.—General Accountant, Samuel M. Nichols, 1400 South Edgewood Street, Arlington, Va., 22204.
Office of Research Information.—Director, Clyde E. Buckingham, 812 Jefferson Avenue, Falls Church, Va., 22042.
General Supply Office.—General Supply Officer, William B. Lovejoy, 6217 Wedgewood Road, Bethesda, Md., 20034.
Office of International Relations.—Director, Samuel Krakow, 6809 Farragut Street, Hyattsville, Md., 20784.

ARMS CONTROL AND DISARMAMENT AGENCY, UNITED STATES

Department of State Building, 2201 C Street, Washington, D.C., 20451
Phone, REpublic 7-5690 (Code 182—0)

Director.—William C. Foster, 3304 R Street, 20007.
Deputy Director.—Adrian S. Fisher, 2721 N Street, 20007.
  Special Assistant to the Director and Executive Secretary.—Clement E. Conger, 320 Madison Drive, Alexandria, Va., 22302.
  Special Assistant to the Director.—George W. Rathjens, 2800 McKinley Place, 20015.
  Special Assistant to the Deputy Director.—Lawrence D. Weiler, 6045 Avon Drive, Bethesda, Md., 20014.
Assistant Director, International Relations Bureau.—Jacob D. Beam, 3129 O Street, 20007.
Deputy Assistant Director, International Relations Bureau.—Richard B. Freund, 3609 Edmunds Street, 20007.
  Chief, Political Affairs Division.—Samuel DePalma, 6707 Rannock Road, Bethesda, Md., 20852.
  Chief, Political Research and Analysis Division.—Marion W. Boggs, 11122 Whisperwood Lane, Rockville, Md., 20852.
Assistant Director, Science and Technology Bureau.—Herbert Scoville, Jr., 101 Old Georgetown Pike, McLean, Va., 22101.
Deputy Assistant Director, Science and Technology Bureau.—Sidney N. Graybeal, 11501 Parkedge Drive, Rockville, Md., 20852.
Assistant Director, Economics Bureau.—Archibald S. Alexander, 3333 Reservoir Road, 20007.
Deputy Assistant Director, Economics Bureau.—Robert L. Finley, 1622 32d Street, 20007.
Assistant Director, Weapons Evaluation and Control Bureau.—Lt. Gen. Fred M. Dean, 2346 South Nash Street, Arlington, Va., 22202.
Deputy Assistant Director, Weapons Evaluation and Control Bureau.—Israel I. Deutsch, 10412 Rockville Pike, Rockville, Md., 20852.
  Project Manager, Field Tests.—Maj. Gen. Douglass P. Quandt, 2022 Columbia Road, 20009.
General Counsel.—George Bunn, 3150 Highland Place, 20008.
Deputy General Counsel.—Charles N. Van Doren, 1387 Locust Road, 20012
Public Affairs Adviser.—Nedville E. Nordness, 70 Woodmont Road, Alexandria, Va., 22307.
Deputy Public Affairs Adviser.—Anne W. Marks, 2918 Olive Avenue, 20007.
Executive Director.—Joseph F. Donelan, Jr., 9220 East Parkhill Drive, Bethesda, Md., 20014.
Chief, Reference Research Staff.—Charles R. Gellner, 1211 Highland Drive, Silver Spring, Md., 20910.

GENERAL ADVISORY COMMITTEE

Chairman.—Mr. John J. McCloy, Milbank, Tweed, Hadley & McCloy, One Chase Manhattan Plaza, New York, N.Y.
  Roger Blough, Chairman of the Board, United States Steel Corporation, 71 Broadway, New York, N.Y.
  The Reverend Edward A. Conway, S.J., Creighton University, Omaha, Nebr.
  John Cowles, Minneapolis Star and Tribune, Minneapolis, Minn.

Chairman—Continued
    Dr. George B. Kistiakowsky, 12 Oxford Street, Cambridge, Mass.
    Dean McGee, Kerr-McGee Building, Oklahoma City, Okla.
    Ralph McGill, Atlanta Newspapers Inc., Atlanta, Ga.
    George Meany, AFL-CIO, 815 Sixteenth Street, Washington, D.C.
    Dr. James Perkins, President, Cornell University, Ithaca, N.Y.
    Herman Phleger, Brobeck, Phleger & Harrison, 111 Sutter Street., San Francisco, Calif.
    Dr. Isidor I. Rabi, Columbia University, New York, N.Y.
    Gen. Thomas D. White, USAF (Ret.), Room 4E929, The Pentagon, Washington, D.C.
    Dr. Herbert York, Chancellor, University of California, La Jolla, Calif.
Executive Secretary.—Mr. Clement E. Conger, U.S. Arms Control and Disarmament Agency, Room 5934, State Department Building, Washington, D.C.

ATOMIC ENERGY COMMISSION, UNITED STATES
Germantown, Md.
Mailing Address: Washington, D.C., 20545.   Phone: 973-1000 (Code 119-3414).   Individual extension may be reached by dialing 973 (Code 119) plus extension number

THE COMMISSION

Chairman.—Dr. Glenn T. Seaborg, 3825 Harrison Street, 20015.
    Dr. Mary I. Bunting, 4200 Cathedral Avenue, 20016.
    John G. Palfrey 3312, 35th Street, 20016.
    James T. Ramey, 6817 Hillmead Road, Bethesda, Md., 20034.
    Dr. Gerald F. Tape, 7705 Winterberry Place, Bethesda, Md., 20034.

OFFICE OF THE COMMISSION

Secretary to the Commission.—W. B. McCool, 7208 Selkirk Drive, Bethesda, Md., 20034.
Chief Hearing Examiner.—Samuel W. Jensch, P.O. Box 235, Gaithersburg, Md., 20760.
Chairman, AEC Board of Contract Appeals.—Paul H. Gantt, 4301 Massachusetts Avenue, 20016.
Controller.—John P. Abbadessa, 6900 Old Gate Lane, Rockville, Md., 20852.
General Counsel.—Joseph F. Hennessey, 7506 Honeywell Lane, Bethesda, Md., 20014.

OPERATING AND PROMOTIONAL FUNCTIONS

General Manager.—R. E. Hollingsworth, 6212 Bradley Boulevard, Bethesda, Md., 20034.
Deputy General Manager.—E. J. Bloch, 5524 Devon Road, Bethesda, Md., 20014.
Assistant General Manager.—Dwight A. Ink, 11708 Farmland Drive, Rockville, Md., 20852.
Assistant General Manager for Operations.—John A. Erlewine, 609 Hyde Road, Silver Spring, Md., 20902.
    Director, Office of Economic Impact and Conversion.—Clarence C. Ohlke, Route 1, Adamstown, Md., 21710.
    Director, Division of Construction.—John A. Derry, 5723 Ogden Road, 20016.
    Director, Division of Contracts.—[Vacant.]
    Director, Division of Labor Relations.—Oscar S. Smith, 311 Windsor Street, Silver Spring, Md., 20910.
    Director, Division of Operational Safety.—Dr. Nathan H. Woodruff, 9911 Julliard Drive, Bethesda, Md., 20034.
Assistant General Manager for Research and Development.—Dr. Spofford G. English, 8204 Thoreau Drive, Bethesda, Md., 20034.
    Director, Division of Biology and Medicine.—Dr. Charles L. Dunham, 5302 Carvel Road, 20016.
    Director, Division of Isotopes Development.—Dr. Paul C. Aebersold, 4811 Grantham Avenue, Chevy Chase, Md., 20015.
    Director, Division of Nuclear Education and Training.—Dr. Russell S. Poor, 10416 Montrose Road, Bethesda, Md., 20014.

Assistant General Manager for Researh and Development—Continued
> *Director, Division of Peaceful Nuclear Explosives.*—John S. Kelly, 25101 Woodfield Road, Damascus, Md., 20750.
> *Director, Division of Research.*—Dr. Paul W. McDaniel, 1854 North Herndon Street, Arlington, Va., 22201.

Assistant General Manager for Plans and Production.—George F. Quinn, Route 4, Mount Airy, Md., 21771.
> *Director, Division of Operations Analysis and Forecasting.*—Dr. Paul C. Fine, 3210 Wisconsin Avenue, Apt. 808, 20016.
> *Director, Division of Plans and Reports.*—William H. Slaton, 27100 Ridge Road, Damascus, Md., 20750.
> *Director, Division of Production.*—F. P. Baranowski, 9206 Laurel Oak Drive, Bethesda, Md., 20034.
> *Director, Division of Raw Materials.*—Rafford L. Faulkner, 8624 Beech Tree Road, Bethesda, Md., 20034.

Assistant General Manager for Reactors.—Dr. John A. Swartout, 120 North Langley Lane, McLean, Va., 22101.
> *Director, Division of Naval Reactors.*—Vice Adm. H. G. Rickover, 4801 Connecticut Avenue, 20008.
> *Director, Division of Reactor Development and Technology.*—Milton Shaw, 7309 Tomander Lane, Chevy Chase, Md., 20015.
> *Manager, Space Nuclear Propulsion Office.*—Harold B. Finger, 6908 Millwood Road, Bethesda, Md., 20034.

Assistant General Manager for International Activities.—John A. Hall, 8713 Cranbrook Court, Bethesda, Md., 20034.
> *Director, Division of International Affairs.*—Myron B. Kratzer, 7201 Selkirk Drive, Bethesda, Md., 20034.

Assistant General Manager for Administration.—Howard C. Brown, Jr., 9618 Carriage Road, Kensington, Md., 20795.
> *Director, Division of Classification.*—Charles L. Marshall, 4308 Lynbrook Drive, Bethesda, Md., 20014.
> *Director, Division of Headquarters Services.*—Edward H. Glade, 207 Spring Drive, Falls Church, Va., 22042.
> *Director, Division of Intelligence.*—Dr. Charles H. Reichardt, 3519 North Delaware Street, Arlington, Va., 22207.
> *Director, Division of Nuclear Materials Management.*—Douglas E. George, 975 North Rochester Street, Arlington, Va., 22205.
> *Director, Division of Personnel.*—Arthur L. Tackman, P. O. Box 6, Damascus, Md., 20750.
> *Director, Division of Public Information.*—Duncan C. Clark, Clarksburg, Md., 20734.
> *Director, Division of Security.*—John A. Waters, Jr., 3173 North 20th Street Arlington, Va., 22201.
> *Director, Division of Special Projects.*—Edward R. Gardner, 2500 Q Street, Apt. 702, 20007.
> *Director, Division of Technical Information.*—Edward J. Brunenkant, Jr., 8904 Honeybee Lane, Bethesda, Md., 20034.

Director, Division of Military Application.—Brig. Gen. Delmar L. Crowson, 209 Severn River Road, Severna Park, Md., 21146.
Director, Division of Industrial Participation.—Ernest B. Tremmel, 5908 Rossmore Drive, Bethesda, Md., 20014.
Director, Division of Inspection.—Curtis A. Nelson, 3139 Birch Street, 20015.
Director, Office of Congressional Relations.—John J. Burke, 10201 Grosvenor Lane, Rockville, Md., 20850.

LICENSING AND REGULATORY FUNCTIONS

Director of Regulations.—Harold L. Price, 4801 Drummond Avenue, Chevy Chase, Md., 20015.
Deputy Director.—Dr. Clifford K. Beck, Route 2, Shiloh Church Road, Boyds, Md., 20720.
Assistant Director.—Robert Lowenstein, 6601 Tulip Hill Terrace, 20016.
Assistant Director for Nuclear Safety.—Dr. M. M. Mann, 5607 Cromwell Drive, 20016.

Assistant Director for Administration.—C. L. Henderson, 611 Marcia Lane, Rockville, Md., 20851.
  Director, Division of Compliance.—Lawrence D. Low, Box 44, Damascus, Md., 20750.
  Director, Division of Reactor Licensing.—Dr. Richard L. Doan, 6601 Millwood Road, Bethesda, Md., 20034.
  Director, Division of Safety Standards.—Dr. Forrest Western, 104 Brookhaven Drive, McLean, Va., 22101.
  Director, Division of Materials Licensing.—Dr. John A. McBride, Rockville Plaza Motor Hotel, Rockville, Md., 20850.
  Director, Division of State and Licensee Relations.—Eber R. Price, 5904 Gloster Road, Wood Acres, Bethesda, Md., 20016.

FIELD OFFICES

Manager, Albuquerque Operations Office.—L. P. Gise, 3356 48th Loop, Sandia Base, Albuquerque, New Mexico, 87115.
Manager, Brookhaven Office.—E. L. Van Horn, 9 Bell Street, Bellport, Long Island, N.Y., 11713.
Manager, Chicago Operations Office.—Kenneth A. Dunbar, Route 3, Box 308, Naperville, Ill., 60540.
Manager, Grand Junction Office.—Allan E. Jones, 1244 Main Street, Grand Junction, Colo., 81501.
Manager, Richland Operations Office.—James E. Travis, 1218 Gowen Street, Richland, Wash., 99352.
Manager, Idaho Operations Office.—W. L. Ginkel, 2825 West Morningside Drive, Idaho Falls, Idaho, 83401.
Manager, New York Operations Office.—W. M. Johnson, 44 East 80th Street, Apt. 1A, New York, N.Y., 10021.
Manager, Oak Ridge Operations Office.—S. R. Sapirie, 100 Ogden Circle, Oak Ridge, Tenn., 37832.
Manager, Pittsburgh Naval Reactors Office.—Lawton D. Geiger, 60 Clover Drive, Pittsburgh, Pa., 15236.
Manager, San Francisco Operations Office.—Ellison C. Shute, 46 Arlington Avenue, Berkeley, Calif., 94706.
Manager, Savannah River Operations Office.—Robert C. Blair, Kalmia Hill, Aiken, S.C., 29801.
Manager, Schenectady Naval Reactors Office.—Stanley W. Nitzman, Route 2, Box 53, Swaggertown Road, Scotia, N.Y., 12302.
Manager, Nevada Operations Office.—James E. Reeves, 4994 Bock Street, Las Vegas, Nev., 89109.

DIVISION OF COMPLIANCE FIELD ORGANIZATION

Region I (New York).—Robert W. Kirkman, 232 Cambridge Avenue, Fair Haven, N.J., 07702.
Region II (Atlanta).—John G. Davis, 3473 Heritage Valley Road, S.W., Atlanta, Ga., 30331.
Region III (Chicago).—Roy C. Hageman, 241 South Lambert Road, Glen Ellyn, Ill., 60137.
Region IV (Denver).—Dr. Donald I. Walker, 12186 West 34th Place, Wheat Ridge, Colo., 80033.
Region V (San Francisco).—Richard W. Smith, 2768 Darnby Drive, Oakland, Calif., 94611.

GENERAL ADVISORY COMMITTEE

Chairman.—Dr. Lawrence R. Hafstad, Vice President, Research Laboratories, General Motors Corp., Warren, Mich., 48090.
  Dr. Manson Benedict, Professor of Nuclear Engineering, Massachusetts Institute of Technology, Cambridge, Mass., 02139.
  Dr. John C. Bugher, Director, Puerto Rico Nuclear Center, Bio-Medical Building, Caparra Heights Station, San Juan, P.R., 00902.
  Dr. Darol Froman, P.O. Box 428, Route, 1 Espanola, N. Mex., 87532.

Chairman—Continued

Dr. Stephen Lawroski, Argonne National Laboratory, 9700 South Cass Avenue Argonne, Ill., 60440.

Dr. K. S. Pitzer, President, Rice University, P.O. Box 1892, Houston, Tex., 77001.

Dr. Norman F. Ramsey, Department of Physics, Harvard University, Cambridge, Mass., 02138.

William Webster, Chairman, New England Electric System, 441 Stuart Street, Boston 16, Mass., 02116.

Dr. John H. Williams, School of Physics, University of Minnesota, Minneapolis, Minn., 55455.

Scientific Officer.—Duane C. Sewell, Lawrence Radiation Laboratory, University of California, P.O. Box 808, Livermore, Calif., 94551.

Secretary.—Anthony A. Tomei, General Advisory Committee, U.S. Atomic Energy Commission, P.O. Box 19029, Washington, D.C., 20036.

MILITARY LIAISON COMMITTEE

Chairman.—William Jack Howard, 6627 JoAllen Drive, Falls Church. Va., 22044.

Members:

Army:

Maj. Gen. Austin W. Betts, 4822 Old Dominion Drive, Arlington, Va., 22207.

Maj. Gen. Lloyd E. Fellenz, 5339 Holmes Run Parkway, Alexandria, Va., 22304.

Navy:

Rear Adm. Thomas F. Connolly, 2741 South Ives Street, Arlington, Va., 22202.

Capt. Harry B. Hahn, Stratford Apts., Apt. 1606, 49101 Seminary Road, Alexandria, Va., 22311.

Air Force:

Maj. Gen. Arthur C. Agan, Jr., 1401 Juliana Place, Alexandria, Va., 22304.

Maj. Gen. Andrew J. Kinney, 2343 South Nash Street, Arlington, Va., 22202.

Executive Secretary.—Col. Sidney C. Bruce, 1107 West Boulevard Drive, Alexandria, Va., 22308.

BOARD OF GOVERNORS OF THE FEDERAL RESERVE SYSTEM

Federal Reserve Building, Constitution, Avenue between Twentieth and Twenty-first Streets, 20551. Phone, REpublic 7-1100 (Code 147)

BOARD OF GOVERNORS

Chairman.—Wm. McC. Martin, Jr., 2861 Woodland Drive, 20008.

Private Secretary.—Margaret N. Muehlhaus, 3105 Patterson Street, 20015.

Vice Chairman.—C. Canby Balderston, 3337 P Street, 20007.

Private Secretary.—Helen B. Wolcott, 19 West Kirke Street, Chevy Chase, Md., 20015.

J. L. Robertson, 5114 Brookview Drive, Westhaven, Md., 20016.

Private Secretary.—Dorothy S. Mooney, 3833 Military Road, 20015.

Chas. N. Shepardson, 2475 Virginia Avenue, 20007.

Private Secretary.—Doreen M. Dippre, 3701 Connecticut Avenue, 20008.

George W. Mitchell, 1300 South Arlington Ridge Road, Arlington, Va., 22202.

Private Secretary.—Athens J. Messick, 3860 Columbia Pike, Arlington, Va., 22204.

J. Dewey Daane, 2500 Q Street, 20007.

Private Secretary.—Mrs. Dorothy B. Saunders, 200 University Avenue, Glen Echo, Md., 20768.

[Vacancy.]

OFFICERS

Advisers to the Board.—Ralph A. Young, 2836 Chesapeake Street, 20008; Guy E. Noyes, 3915 Huntington Street, 20015.

Legislative Counsel.—Robert L. Cardon, 2428 Executive Avenue, Falls Church, Va., 22242.

Assistants to the Board.—Charles Molony, 314 South Fairfax Street, Alexandria, Va., 22314; Clarke L. Fauver, 105 Normandy Drive, Silver Spring, Md., 20901.

Secretary.—Merritt Sherman, Route 2, Deakins Lane, Germantown, Md., 20767.

Assistant Secretaries.—Kenneth A. Kenyon, 105 Oxford Street, Chevy Chase, Md., 20015; Elizabeth L. Carmichael, 4740 Connecticut Avenue, 20008; Arthur L. Broida, 207 Martha's Road, Alexandria, Va., 22307; Karl E. Bakke, 1111 Arlington Boulevard, Arlington, Va., 22209.

General Counsel.—Howard H. Hackley, 5116 Marlyn Drive, 20016.

Assistant General Counsel.—David B. Hexter, 2480 16th Street, 20009; Thomas J. O'Connell, 9614 Carriage Road, Kensington, Md., 20795; Jerome W. Shay, 1607 North Jefferson Street, Arlington, Va., 22205; Wilson L. Hooff, 3312 Fessenden Street, 20008.

Director, Division of Research and Statistics.—Daniel H. Brill, 10414 Brookmoor Court, Woodmoor, Silver Spring, Md., 20901.

Associate Directors.—Robert C. Holland, 5907 Ramsgate Road, 20016; Albert R. Koch, 5009 Upton Street, 20016.

Advisers.—Frank R. Garfield, 5810 Warwick Place, Somerset, Chevy Chase, Md., 20015; J. Charles Partee, 1002 South Mansion Drive, Silver Spring, Md., 20910; Robert Solomon, 8502 West Howell Road, Bethesda, Md., 20014; Kenneth B. Williams, 4816 Cumberland Avenue, Somerset, Chevy Chase, Md., 20015,

Associate Adviser.—Lewis N. Dembitz, 3414 Garfield Street, 20007.

Director, Division of International Finance.—Ralph A. Young, 2836 Chesapeake Street, 20008.

Advisers.—A. B. Hersey, 3543 North Delaware Street, Arlington, Va., 22207; Samuel I. Katz, 2406 Benjamin Street, McLean, Va., 22101; Robert L. Sammons, 812 Tanley Road, Silver Spring, Md., 20904.

Associate Advisers.—Reed J. Irvine, 9326 Wilmer Street, Silver Spring, Md., 20901; John E. Reynolds, 3930 Huntington Street, 20015; Ralph C. Wood, 5917 Cheshire Drive, Wildwood Manor, Bethesda, Md., 20014.

Director, Division of Bank Operations.—John R. Farrell, 9500 Byeforde Road, Kensington, Md., 20795.

Assistant Directors.—Gerald M. Conkling, 7811 Marion Lane, Bethesda, Md., 20014; M. B. Daniels, 3701 Fordham Road, 20016; John N. Kiley, Jr., 5708 Colfax Avenue, Alexandria, Va., 22311.

Director, Division of Examinations.—Frederic Solomon, 5463 Nebraska Avenue, 20015.

Assistant Directors.—Glenn M. Goodman, 2000 Connecticut Avenue, 20008; Brenton C. Leavitt, 2020 F Street, 20006; James C. Smith, 5506 Cornish Road, Bethesda, Md., 20014; Andrew N. Thompson, 3067 North Oakland Street, Arlington, Va., 22207.

Chief Federal Reserve Examiner.—Lloyd M. Schaeffer, Federal Reserve Building.

Director, Division of Personnel Administration.—Edwin J. Johnson, 3800 52d Street, 20016.

Assistant Director.—H. Franklin Sprecher, Jr., 1415 Dilston Road, Silver Spring, Md., 20903.

Director, Division of Administrative Services.—Joseph E. Kelleher, 4613 40th Street North, Arlington, Va., 22207

Assistant Director.—Harry E. Kern, 3371 Denver Street SE., 20020.

Controller.—John Kakalec, 1405 Balls Hill Road, McLean, Va., 22101.

Assistant Controller.—Sampson H. Bass, 3025 W Street SE., 20020.

Coordinator, Office of Defense Planning.—Innis D. Harris, 3850 Tunlaw Road, 20007.

Director, Division of Data Processing.—Maurice H. Schwartz, 7924 Robison Road, Bethesda, Md., 20014.

Assistant Director.—Lee W. Langham, 415 Silver Spring Avenue, Silver Spring, Md., 20910.

CANAL ZONE GOVERNMENT

312 Pennsylvania Building, Washington, D.C., 20004. Phone, DIstrict 7-6984

Assistant to the Governor.—W. M. Whitman, 4309 Glenridge Street, Kensington, Md.

IN THE CANAL ZONE

Governor.—Maj. Gen. Robert J. Fleming, Jr., Balboa Heights, Canal Zone.
Lieutenant Governor.—Col. David S. Parker, Balboa Heights, Canal Zone.

CIVIL AERONAUTICS BOARD

Universal Building, 20428. Phone, EXecutive 3-3111 (Code 128, extension 7951)

Members:
  Chairman.—Alan S. Boyd, 1200 North Nash Street, Arlington, Va., 22209.
  Vice Chairman.—Robert T. Murphy, 7315 Lynnhurst Street, Chevy Chase, Md., 20015.
  Members:
    Whitney Gillilland, 4150 41st Street North, Arlington, Va., 22207.
    G. Joseph Minetti, 3032 24th Street NE., 20018.
    Chan Gurney, Army and Navy Club, Farragut Square and I Streets, 20006.
Executive Director.—Edward J. Driscoll, 4027 North Stuart Street, Arlington, Va., 22207.
Director, Office of Community and Congressional Relations.—John W. Dregge, 1687 32d Street, 20007.
Congressional Relations Officer.—Charles T. Donnelly, 8810 Maywood Avenue, Silver Spring, Md., 20910.
Planning Officer.—David W. Bluestone, 404 North George Mason Drive, Arlington, Va., 22203.
Information Officer.—Jack Yohe, 1928 Foxhall Road, Summer Hills, McLean, Va.
Secretary and Assistant Executive Director.—Harold R. Sanderson, 4125 North 34th Street, Arlington, Va., 22207.
Chief, Office of Administration.—John B. Russell, 1608 Highland Drive, Silver Spring, Md., 20910.
Director, Management and Programs.—Kermit W. Day, 8134 15th Avenue, Hyattsville, Md., 20783.
Director, Personnel and Security.—Marvin Bergsman, 2745 29th Street, 20008.
Comptroller.—Oscar C. Disler, 510 Highland Road, Fairfax, Va., 22030.
General Counsel.—John H. Wanner, 210 West Alexandria Avenue, Alexandria, Va., 22302.
Deputy General Counsel.—Joseph B. Goldman, 2920 Military Road, 20015.
Director, Bureau of Economic Regulation.—Irving Roth, 8204 Kenfield Court, Bethesda, Md., 20034.
Deputy Director, Bureau of Economic Regulation.—W. Fletcher Lutz, 809 Oakwood Drive, Falls Church, Va., 22041.
Director, Bureau of Safety.—Bobbie R. Allen, 4904 Kingston Drive, Annandale, Va.
Deputy Director, Bureau of Safety.—Marion F. Roscoe, Rock Creek Hotel, 1925 Belmont Road, 20009.
Assistant Director, Bureau of Safety.—Robert L. Froman, Ox Road, Fairfax Station, Va.
Director, Bureau of Enforcement.—John G. Adams, 3415 34th Place, 20016.
Associate Director, Bureau of Enforcement.—Robert N. Burstein, 2507 Leesburg Pike, Falls Church, Va., 22043.
Director, Bureau of International Affairs.—Joseph C. Watson, 4703 West Langley Lane, McLean, Va.
Chief, Office of Carrier Accounts and Statistics.—Warner H. Hord, Ivory Hill Farm, West Friendship, Md., 21794.
Associate Chief, Office of Carrier Accounts and Statistics.—Allan Craig, 8814 Walnut Hill Road, Chevy Chase, Md., 20015.
Chief Examiner.—Francis W. Brown, 3108 Worthington Street, 20015.
Associate Chief Examiner.—Thomas L. Wrenn, 4201 Massachusetts Avenue, 20016.

CIVIL SERVICE COMMISSION

Offices, 1900 E Street, 20415.   Phone, 343-1100 (Code 183)

Office of the Commissioners:
  Chairman.—John W. Macy, Jr., 201 North Langley Lane, McLean, Va., 22101.
  Commissioner.—Ludwig J. Andolsek, 9609 Bulls Run Parkway, Bethesda, Md., 20034.
  Commissioner.—Robert E. Hampton, 5804 Rossmore Drive, Bethesda, Md., 20014.
  Assistant to the Chairman.—Wilfred V. Gill, 8320 Fenway Road, Bethesda, Md., 20034.
  Executive Assistant to the Commissioners.—Mary V. Wenzel, 4226 East-West Highway, Chevy Chase, Md., 20015.
Office of the Executive Director:
  Executive Director.—Warren B. Irons, 3316 Gunston Road, Alexandria, Va., 22302.
  Deputy Executive Director.—Nicholas J. Oganovic, 2521 North Quebec Street, Arlington, Va., 22207.
  Appeals Examining Office, Chief.—James T. Masterson, 1122 Ware Street SW, Vienna, Va., 20018.
  Interagency Advisory Group, Executive Vice Chairman.—Irving Kator, 8005 Cindy Lane, Bethesda, Md., 20034.
  Hearing Examiners Office, Director.—Wilson M. Matthews, 5813 Doris Drive, Alexandria, Va., 22311.
General Counsel.—Lawrence V. Meloy, 5125 Scarsdale Road, 20016.
  Associate General Counsel.—Leo M. Pellerzi, 106 Indian Spring Drive, Silver Spring, Md., 20901.
  Assistant General Counsel.—John J. McCarthy, 3120 63d Avenue, Cheverly, Md., 20785.
Board of Appeals and Review:
  Chairman.—Edgar T. Groark, 1G Gardenway, Greenbelt, Md., 30770.
  Members:
    James W. McBee, 1401 North Inglewood Street, Arlington, Va., 22205.
    John O. Hardesty, 7509 Granada Drive, Landon Woods, Bethesda, Md., 20034.
    Leon S. Mapes, 9301 Chanute Drive, Bethesda, Md., 20034.
    Edward H. Bechtold, 4401 Woodfield Road, Kensington, Md., 20795.
    William P. Berzak, Apt. C–21, Hayes House, Presidential Gardens, Alexandria, Va., 22030.
    Philip J. LaMacchia, 6301 Pontiac Street, Berwyn Heights, Md., 20740.
International Organizations Employees Loyalty Board:
  Chairman.—Edgar T. Groark, 1G Gardenway, Greenbelt, Md., 20770.
  Executive Secretary.—Frederick D. Irwin, 5721 Fifth Road South, Arlington, Va., 22204.
Office of Career Development:
  Director.—J. Kenneth Mulligan, 4615 Hunt Avenue, Chevy Chase, Md., 20015.
  Deputy Director.—William T. McDonald, 7111 Broxburn Drive, Bethesda, Md., 20034.
Public Information Office, Chief.—Philip W. Schulte, 601 Woodside Parkway, Silver Spring, Md., 20910.
Bureau of Inspections:
  Director.—Seymour S. Berlin, 6410 Bannockburn Drive, Bethesda, Md., 20034.
  Deputy Director.—Gilbert A. Schulkind, 3121–2 University Boulevard West, Kensington, Md., 20795.
  Analysis and Development Division, Chief.—Arch S. Ramsay, 2455 Villanova Drive, Vienna, Va., 22180.
  Administrative Office, Chief.—Jacob J. Rutstein, 6505 Bannockburn Drive, Bethesda, Md., 20034.
  Program Evaluation Division, Chief.—Maurice L. Etzell, 3406 North Kensington Street, Arlington, Va., 22207.
  Classification Division, Chief.—Asa M. McCain, 10205 Gary Road, Rockville, Md., 20854.
  Classification Appeals Office, Chief.—John D. Glasheen, 9924 Brixton Lane, Bethesda, Md., 20034.

Bureau of Management Services:
  Director.—David F. Williams, 316 Williamsburg Drive, Silver Spring, Md., 20901.
  Deputy Director.—Charles J. Sparks, 5923 Fifth Road North, Arlington, Va., 22203.
  Budget and Finance Division, Chief.—W. B. Uhlenhop, 5453 Dawes Avenue, Alexandria, Va., 22311.
  Head Librarian.—Elaine Woodruff, 908 North Jacksonville Street, Arlington, Va., 22205.
  Management Systems Division, Chief.—Victor J. Cavagrotti, 517 Waterway Drive, Falls Church, Va., 22044.
  Office Services Division, Chief.—William E. Byram, 2700 North Underwood Street, Arlington, Va., 22213.
  Director of Personnel.—John W. Morgan, 5904 Dempsey Street, McLean, Va., 22101.
Bureau of Personnel Investigations:
  Director.—Kimbell Johnson, 3402 Rosemary Lane, Hyattsville, Md., 20782.
  Deputy Director.—Woodrow L. Browne, 609 Longstreet Drive, Manassas, Va., 22110.
  Security Appraisal Office, Chief.—Louis A. Mancusi, 1400 Ray Road, Hyattsville, Md., 20782.
Security Research Office, Chief.—Leonard B. Konkel, 2717 31st Street SE., 20020.
  Program Planning and Management Division, Chief.—Hugh P. Crowe, 2120 16th Street, Apt. 509, 20009.
  Operations Division, Chief. Pearley G. Buck, 2908 Edgehill Drive, Alexandria, Va., 22302.
  Reimbursable Investigations Division, Chief.—Walter I. Waldrop, 9810 Marquette Drive, Bethesda, Md., 20034.
  Adjudication Division, Chief.—Howard C. Bolton, 2421 South Dinwiddie Street, Arlington, Va., 22206.
  Washington Division of Investigations, Chief.—Joseph G. Campbell, 9522 Crosby Road, Silver Spring, Md., 20190.
Bureau of Programs and Standards:
  Director.—O. Glenn Stahl, 3600 North Piedmont Street, Arlington, Va., 22207.
  Deputy Director.—Evelyn Harrison, 327 A Street NE., 20002.
  Program Planning Division, Chief.—Harold H. Leich, 5606 Vernon Place, Bethesda, Md., 20034.
  Standards Division, Chief.—Raymond Jacobson, 6304 Bannockburn Drive, Bethesda, Md., 20034.
  Program Systems and Instructions Division, Chief.—John W. Steele, 9733 Bexhill Drive, Kensington, Md., 20795.
Bureau of Recruiting and Examining:
  Director.—Donald R. Harvey, 8503 Laverne Drive, Adelphi, Md., 20783.
  Deputy Director.—Edward A. Dunton, 6509 Wiscasset Road, 20016.
  Office of Analysis and Development, Director.—John E. Beckman, 4021 Byrd Road, Kensington, Md., 20795.
  Examining Review Board, Chairman.—Catherine R. Grant, 616 South Fairfax Street, Alexandria, Va., 22314.
  Office of College Relations and Recruitment, Director.—Robert F. Mello, 5008 Townsend Way, Bladensburg, Md., 20710.
  Office of Employment Information and Coordination, Director.—Betty F. Walker, 704 Sligo Creek Parkway, Takoma Park, Md., 20012.
  Office of Program Management, Director.—Donald J. Biglin, 9519 Edgerly Road, Bethesda, Md., 20014.
  Career Services Division, Chief.—Sam N. Wolk, 1416 Crestridge Drive, Silver Spring, Md., 20910.
  Operations Division, Chief.—Frederick H. MacIntyre, 2901 Landover Street, Alexandria, Va., 20045.
  Postal Examining Division, Chief.—Henry C. Roberson, 1514 Red Oak Drive, Silver Spring, Md., 20901.
  Washington Examining Division, Chief.—Raymond J. Mondor, 602 Perth Place, Silver Spring, Md., 20901.
  Civil Service Representative (Congressional).—Mary E. Conroy, 616 South Fairfax Street, Alexandria, Va., 22314.

Bureau of Retirement and Insurance:
   Director.—Andrew E. Ruddock, 208 Pathfinder Lane, McLean, Va., 22101.
   Deputy Director.—David F. Lawton, 3810 Reno Road, 20008.
   Assistant Director for Operations.—Charles F. Overend, 5715 Birch Avenue, McLean, Va., 22101.
   Contracts and Instructions Division, Chief.—Solomon Paperman, 508 East Indian Spring Drive, Silver Spring, Md., 20901.
   Chief Actuary.—Maurice S. Brown, 3608 Saul Road, Kensington, Md., 20795.
   Technical Advisor.—Richard M. Cody, 3424 Martha Custis Drive, Alexandria, Va., 22302.
   Systems and Audits Office, Chief.—Harold R. Hunsaker, 1731 North Greenbrier Street, Arlington, Va., 22205.
   Claims Division, Chief.—Jack Goldberg, 2500 Spencer Road, Silver Spring, Md., 20910.
   Fiscal Division, Chief.—Alva G. Freeman, 617 Crocus Drive, Rockville, Md., 20850.
   Medical Director.—Dr. Melvin T. Johnson, 3111 20th Street North, Arlington, Va., 22201.

REGIONAL OFFICES

Atlanta Region—North Carolina, South Carolina, Georgia, Florida, Alabama, Tennessee, Mississippi, Puerto Rico, and The Virgin Islands.—Hammond B. Smith, Director, Atlanta Merchandise Mart, 240 Peachtree Street NW, Atlanta, Ga., 30303.

Boston Region—Maine, New Hampshire, Vermont, Massachusetts, Rhode Island, and Connecticut.—Leonard F. Cronin, Director, Post Office and Courthouse Building, Boston, Mass., 02109.

Chicago Region—Wisconsin, Michigan, Illinois, Ohio, Indiana, and Kentucky.—Joseph A. Connor, Director, Main Post Office Building, 433 West Van Buren Street, Chicago, Ill., 60607.

Dallas Region—Texas, Louisiana, Arkansas, and Oklahoma.—Louis S. Lyon, Director, 1114 Commerce Street, Dallas, Tex., 75202.

Denver Region—Colorado, New Mexico, Utah, Wyoming, and Arizona.—William H. Rima, Jr., Director, Building 41, Denver Federal Center, Denver, Colo., 80225.

New York Region—New York and New Jersey.—Lawrence H. Baer, Director, News Building, 220 E. 42d Street, New York, N.Y., 10017.

Philadelphia Region—Pennsylvania, Delaware, Maryland, Virginia, and West Virginia.—Stephen P. Ryder, Director, Customhouse, Second and Chestnut Streets, Philadelphia, Pa., 19106.

St. Louis Region—Kansas, Missouri, Minnesota, North Dakota, South Dakota, Nebraska, and Iowa.—Albert H. Sonntag, Director, 1256 Federal Building, 1520 Market Street, St. Louis, Mo., 63103.

San Francisco Region—California, Nevada, Hawaii and the Pacific overseas area.—Asa T. Briley, Director, Federal Building, Box 36010, 450 Golden Gate Avenue, San Francisco, Calif., 94102.

Seattle Region—Montana, Oregon, Idaho, Washington, and Alaska.—John M. Young, Director, 302 Federal Office Building, First Avenue and Madison Street, Seattle, Wash., 98104.

COMMISSION OF FINE ARTS

7000 Interior Department Building.   Phone, 343-5324 (Code 183, extension 5324)

Chairman.—William Walton, Washington, D.C.
   Gordon Bunshaft, New York, N.Y.
   Burnham Kelly, Ithaca, N.Y.
   Theodore Roszak, New York, N.Y.
   Aline B. Saarinen, New Haven, Conn.
   Hideo Sasaki, Watertown, Mass.
   John Carl Warnecke, San Francisco, Calif.
Secretary and Administrative Officer.—Charles H. Atherton, 2122 Florida Avenue, 20008.

BOARD OF ARCHITECTURAL CONSULTANTS FOR THE OLD GEORGETOWN ACT

William M. Haussmann, Arlington, Va.
Frank Cole, Alexandria, Va.

COMMISSION ON CIVIL RIGHTS

1701 Pennsylvania Avenue, 20425. Phone, 382-1228 (Code 128, extension 21228)

Members:
  Chairman.—John A. Hannah, Michigan State University, East Lansing, Mich., 48824.
  Vice Chairman.—Eugene C. Patterson, Atlanta Constitution, Atlanta, Ga., 30302.
Commissioners:
  Theodore M. Hesburgh, Notre Dame University, Notre Dame, Ind., 46556.
  Erwin N. Griswold, Harvard University Law School, Cambridge, Mass., 02138.
  Robert S. Rankin, 1227 Vickers Avenue, Durham, N.C., 27707.
  Mrs. Frankie Muse Freeman, 1209 North Grand Boulevard, St. Louis, Mo., 63100.
Acting Staff Director.—Howard W. Rogerson, 3919 Cavendish Drive, Alexandria, Va., 22308.
Special Assistant to the Staff Director.—Warren I. Cikins, 2000 South Eads Street, Arlington, Va., 22202.
General Counsel.—William L. Taylor, 1325 Iris Street, 20012.
Director, Federal Programs Division.—F. Peter Libassi, 1317 Tuckerman Street, 20011.
Director, Field Services Division.—Samuel J. Simmons, 7244 15th Place, 20012.
Director, Research and Publications Division.—[Vacant.]
Director, Voting and Investigations Division.—Victor H. Wright, Jr., 5903 Espey Lane, McLean, Va., 22101.

COMMISSION ON INTERNATIONAL RULES OF JUDICIAL PROCEDURE

1701 Pennsylvania Avenue, Washington, D.C., 20448. Phone, 382-2650 (Code 128, extension 22650)

Commission Chairman.—Oscar Cox (Cox, Langford & Brown, 1521 New Hampshire Avenue, Washington, D.C., 20036), 1545 35th Street, Washington, D.C., 20007.
Commission Members:
  Charles D. Breitel (Associate Justice, Appellate Division, First Department, Supreme Court of the State of New York), 27 Madison Avenue, New York, N.Y.
  [Vacancy] (The Legal Adviser, Department of State).
  Archibald Cox (Solicitor General, Department of Justice), 4201 Forest Lane, McLean, Va.
  Abner V. McCall (President, Baylor University), 1001 Speight, Waco, Tex.
  Michael A. Musmanno (Justice, Supreme Court of Pennsylvania), 811 City-County Building, Pittsburgh, Pa.
  Norbert A. Schlei (Assistant Attorney General, Office of Legal Counsel, Department of Justice), 925 25th Street, Washington, D.C.
  Abba P. Schwartz (Administrator, Bureau of Security and Consular Affairs, Department of State), 3306 R Street, Washington, D.C.
  Bethuel M. Webster (Webster, Sheffield & Chrystie), One Rockefeller Plaza, New York, N.Y.
Director.—Harry LeRoy Jones, 1701 Pennsylvania Avenue, Washington, D.C. Phone, 382-2650 (Code 128, extension 22650); 1310 34th Street, Washington, D.C., 20007.
Assistant to the Director.—Mrs. Katherine Drew Hallgarten, 1701 Pennsylvania Avenue, Washington, D.C. Phone, 382-2650 (extension 2650); 3200 16th Street, Washington, D.C., 20010.
Advisory Committee Chairman.—Philip W. Amram (Amram, Hahn & Sundlun), 944 Washington Building, 15th and New York Avenue, Washington, D.C., 20006.

Advisory Committee Members:

Joe C. Barrett (Barrett, Wheatley, Smith & Deacon), Box 816, Jonesboro, Ark.

Maj. Gen. Charles L. Decker, American Bar Association Center, 1155 East 60th Street, Chicago, Ill.

Albert A. Ehrenzweig (professor, University of California Law School), Berkeley, Calif.

Robert Kramer (Dean, The George Washington University Law School), 720 20th Street, Washington, D.C.

Herbert S. Little (Little, Palmer, Scott & Slemmons), Hoge Building, Seattle, Wash.

Albert B. Maris (Senior United States Circuit Judge, United States Court of Appeals), 2070 United States Courthouse, Philadelphia, Pa.

Stanley F. Reed (Associate Justice (retired), Supreme Court of the United States), Washington, D.C.

James J. Robinson (Justice, Supreme Court of Libya), United Kingdom of Libya, Tripoli, Libya. (c/o American Embassy, APO 231, New York, N.Y.)

Ernest Schein (attorney at law), 1025 Connecticut Avenue, Washington, D.C.

Rudolf B. Schlesinger (professor, Cornell University Law School), Ithaca, N.Y.

F. Trowbridge vom Baur (vom Baur, Beresford & Coburn), 1700 K Street, Washington, D.C.

Hessel E. Yntema (professor emeritus, University of Michigan Law School), Ann Arbor, Mich.

Dr. Charles J. Zinn (Law Revision Counsel, House Committee on the Judiciary), the Calvert-Woodley, 2601 Woodley Place, Washington, D.C.

[One vacancy.]

COMMITTEE ON PURCHASES OF BLIND-MADE PRODUCTS

Room 1027, 1511 K Street, 20005. Phone, DIstrict 7-4918)

Chairman.—Anthony A. Bertsch, 4714 33d Street North Arlington, Va., 22207, representing the Department of Commerce.

Heinz A. Abersfeller, 8000 Overlook Drive, Alexandria, Va., 22305, representing the General Services Administration.

T. M. Baldauf, 6817 Mansfield Road, Falls Church, Va., 22041, representing the Department of Agriculture.

Rear Adm. John W. Crumpacker, Quarters R, Washington Navy Yard Annex, Naval Station, Washington, D.C., 20390, representing the Department of the Navy.

Miss Selene Gifford, 802 Crescent Drive, Alexandria, Va., 22302, representing the Department of the Interior.

Col. John W. Hanger, 1711 Fairwood Lane, Falls Church, Va., 22046, representing the Department of the Army.

Vice Adm. Joseph M. Lyle, Apt. 303, Dorchester Towers, 2001 Columbia Pike, Arlington, Va., 22204, representing the Defense Supply Agency.

Jansen Noyes, Jr., 299 Hollow Tree Ridge Road, Darien, Conn., 06820, private citizen.

Brig. Gen. Ernest L. Ramme, 5402 Easton Drive, Springfield, Va., 22151, representing the Department of the Air Force.

Executive Secretary.—L. F. Donahue.
Counsel.—William Sellman.

CONGRESSIONAL CLUB, THE

2001 New Hampshire Avenue, 20009. Phone, DEcatur 2-1155

OFFICERS FOR 1965 AND 1966

President.—Mrs. John C. Kunkel, Pennsylvania.
Vice Presidents:

Mrs. Edward V. Long, Missouri.

Mrs. Winston L. Prouty, Vermont.

Mrs. Robert E. Jones, Alabama.

Mrs. Thomas Pelly, Washington.

Mrs. Charles P. Vanik, Ohio.

Recording Secretary.—Mrs. Garner Shriver, Kansas.
Corresponding Secretary.—Mrs. John Dowdy, Texas.
Treasurer.—Mrs. Clark MacGregor, Minnesota.

COMMITTEES AND CHAIRMAN FOR 1965 AND 1966

Program.—Mrs. William H. Ayres, Ohio.
Membership.—Mrs. D. R. Matthews, Florida.
House.—Mrs. John W. Byrnes, Wisconsin.
Press.—Mrs. John J. Sparkman, Alabama.
Year Book.—Mrs. Roy Taylor, North Carolina.
Archives.—Mrs. Russell Mack, Washington.
Scrap Book.—The Misses Clements, Georgia.
Ways and Means.—Mrs. Odin E. S. Langen, Minnesota.
Hospitality.—Mrs. Jamie L. Whitten, Mississippi.
Hostess.—Mrs. Fred Schwengel, Chairman, Iowa; Mrs. Robert Ashmore, cochairman, South Carolina
Special Aides.—Mrs. Henry Talle, Chairman, Iowa; Mrs. James H. Morrison, Louisiana.
Cook Book.—Mrs. Clifford Davis, Tennessee, chairman.
Red Cross.—Mrs. Ben Reifel, South Dakota, chairman; Mrs. Durward G. Hall, Missouri, cochairman.
Associate Members.—Mrs. Richard Gordon Scott, Utah, chairman; Miss Mary O'Neal, cochairman, Kentucky.
Constitution and By-Laws.—Mrs. Wallace Bennett, chairman, Utah; Mrs. Omar Burleson, cochairman, Texas.
Music.—Mrs. James H. Davis, chairman, Kentucky; Mrs. Thomas A Wadden, cochairman, North Carolina.
Bridge.—Mrs. John S. Cross, chairman, Arkansas; Mrs. Patrick H. Mathews, cochairman, Arkansas.
Club Decorating.—Mrs. Thor Tollefson, chairman, Washington; Mrs. Russell Mack, cochairman, Washington.
Historian.—Mrs. Charles McLaughlin, Nebraska.
Parliamentarian.—Mrs. Omar Burleson, Texas.
Founder's Day Brunch.—Mrs. Daniel Flood, chairman, Pennsylvania.
Breakfast for First Lady.—Mrs. Alvin E. O'Konski, chairman, Wisconsin; Mrs. Chet Holifield, cochairman, California.
Diplomatic.—Mrs. Thomas Morgan, chairman, Pennsylvania; Mrs. Ross Adair, cochairman, Indiana.
Floral Arrangements.—Mrs. Joe L. Evins, chairman, Tennessee; Mrs. Abe McGregor Goff, cochairman, Idaho.
Children's Parties.—Mrs. John Foley, chairman, Maryland.
Receptions.—Mrs. Lawrence Smith, chairman, Wisconsin; Mrs. Charles R. Jonas, cochairman, North Carolina.
Teen-Age Activities.—Mrs. Lyle H. Boren, chairman, Oklahoma; Mrs. George Grant, cochairman, Alabama.
Telephone Committee.—Mrs. Albert W. Johnson, chairman, Pennsylvania; Mrs. Joseph M. McDade, cochairman, Pennsylvania.
Promotion of Museum.—Mrs. Wallace Bennett, chairman, Utah.

DISTRICT OF COLUMBIA ARMORY BOARD

Room 118-A, National Guard Armory. Phone, LIncoln 7-9077

Chairman.—Francis J. Kane, 3133 Connecticut Avenue.
  Walter N. Tobriner (President, D.C. Board of Commissioners), 6100 33d Street.
  Maj. Gen. William H. Abendroth (Commanding General, D.C. National Guard), 412 Lebanon Drive, Falls Church, Va.
Manager.—Arthur J. Bergman, 3910 Rosemary Street, Chevy Chase, Md.

DISTRICT OF COLUMBIA REDEVELOPMENT LAND AGENCY

919 Eighteenth Street, 20006.   Phone, DUdley 2-7704-5 (Code 128, extension 7704-5)

Chairman.—Neville Miller, 4715 Berkeley Terrace, 20007.
Vice Chairman.—Richard R. Atkinson, 422 Fifth Street SE., 20003.
   John S. Crocker, 1963 39th Street, 20007.
   John J. Gunther, 1696 31st Street, 20007.
   John L. Newbold, 2416 Tracy Place, 20008.
Executive Director.—[Vacant.]
Deputy Executive Director.—James A. Brown, 302 Dale Drive, Silver Spring, Md.
Assistant Executive Director.—Allan B. Elliot, 11711 Falls Road, Rockville, Md.
General Counsel.—George F. Riseling, 2217 Lakewood Street, Suitland, Md., 20023.
Financial Manager.—Arthur M. Zauft, 3705 Linda Lane, Annandale, Va., 22003.
Special Assistant to the Executive Director.—Anna S. Miller, 4600 Connecticut
   Avenue, 20008.
Chief, Rehabilitation and Conservation Division.—Carroll M. Meigs, 4000 Massa-
   chusetts Avenue, 20016.
Chief, Land Disposition Division.—Herbert L. Tyson, 5821 Westchester Drive,
   Alexandria, Va., 22310.
Chief, Real Estate Acquisition Division.—Vincent A. Holmes, 3517 Livingston
   Street, 20015.
Chief, Engineering Division.—James E. Linde, 3305 S. Stafford Street, Arlington,
   Va., 22206.
Chief, Project Design.—Stanley M. Sherman, 4516 Q Lane, 20007.
Chief, Relocation and Management Division.—Luther W. Hemmons, 1322
   Missouri Avenue, 20011.
Chief, Project Planning Division.—Daniel Driver, 306 N Street SW., 20024.

EXPORT-IMPORT BANK OF WASHINGTON

811 Vermont Avenue, 20571.   Phone, REpublic 7-7890 (Code 1246)

President and Chairman.—Harold F. Linder, 1901 24th Street, 20008.
   Special Assistant to the President.—John W. Donaldson, 3222 Scott Place,
   20007.
First Vice President and Vice Chairman.—Walter C. Sauer, 5118 Chevy Chase
   Parkway, 20008.
Directors:
   Charles M. Meriwether, 5737 MacArthur Boulevard, 20016.
   Elizabeth S. May, 1314 29th Street, 20007.
Executive Vice President.—R. H. Rowntree, 624 South Lee Street, Alexandria,
   Va., 22314.
Vice President for Program Planning and Information.—Glenn E. McLaughlin,
   3053 Ordway Street, 20008.
   Government Liaison Officer.—Seymour Pollack, 7815 Allan Sturges Terrace,
   Falls Church, Va., 22041.
   Business Liaison Officer.—Albert J. Redway, 2549 Waterside Drive, 20008
   Information Officer.—Albert H. Hamilton, 3034 Newark Street, 20008.
Vice President for Exporter Credits, Guarantees, and Insurance.—Raymond L.
   Jones, 9901 Old Georgetown Road, Bethesda, Md., 20014.
   Deputy to the Vice President.—Leonard R. Koser, 4804 Buchanan Street,
   McLean, Va., 22101.
   Chief, Exporter Credits and Guarantees Division.—Mahlon B. Beal, 5041 North
   Carlyn Springs Road, Arlington, Va., 22203.
   Chief, Exporter Insurance Division.—John W. Corbin, 5005 Margot Court,
   Rockville, Md., 20853.
General Counsel.—S. Douglas Shackleford, 18 Vernon Terrace, Belle Haven,
   Alexandria, Va., 22307.
   Assistant General Counsel.—Warren W. Glick, 10905 Fiesta Road, Silver Spring,
   Md., 20901.
Treasurer-Controller.—Clark L. Simpson, 6909 Dartmouth Avenue, College
   Park, Md., 20740.
Secretary.—Edward S. Conger, 6818 Oregon Avenue, 20015.
Engineer Officer.—A. Carl Cass, 37 Nicholson Street, 20011.

Administrative Officer.—John R. Crown, 7111 Longwood Drive, Bethesda, Md. 20034.
Chief, Europe and Africa Division.—William S. Balderston, 10527 Montrose Avenue, Bethesda, Md., 20014.
Chief, Far East Division.—Charles E. Houston, 6801 Hillmead Road, Bethesda, Md., 20034.
Chief, Eastern Latin America Division.—Eugene E. Oakes, 4801 Connecticut Avenue, 20008.
Chief, Western Latin America Division.—Charles J. Shohan, 1225 Stafford Road, Alexandria, Va., 22307.
Chief, Near East and South Asia Division.—William G. Welk, 1734 P Street, 20036.

FARM CREDIT ADMINISTRATION

South Agriculture Building, Fourteenth Street and Independence Avenue SW.
Phone, REpublic 7-4142 (Code 111)

FEDERAL FARM CREDIT BOARD

Members:
Julian B. Thayer, Middlefield, Conn.
William T. Steele, Jr., Richmond, Va.
Lorin T. Bice, Haines City, Fla.
Marion A. Clawson, Eaton, Ind.
L. C. Carter, Stuttgart, Ark.
Joe B. Zeug, Walnut Grove, Minn.
J. B. Fuller, Torrington, Wyo.
Kenneth T. Anderson, Emporia, Kans.
J. Pittman Stone, Coffeeville, Miss.
Glen R. Harris, Richvale, Calif.
David G. Gault, Manor, Tex.
Robert T. Lister, Prineville, Oreg.
Murray D. Lincoln, Gahanna, Ohio. (Representative of Secretary of Agriculture.)

OFFICIALS

Governor.—R. B. Tootell, 5104 Marlyn Drive, 20016.
Deputy Governor.—Harold T. Mason, 602 Malcolm Place, Alexandria, Va., 22302.
Deputy Governor and Director of Land Bank Service.—Glenn G. Browne, 5908 Lenox Road, Bethesda, Md., 20034.
Deputy Governor and Director of Short-Term Credit Service.—F. Vernon Wright, 5001 Sentinal Drive, 20016.
Deputy Governor and Director of Cooperative Bank Service.—Glenn E. Heitz, 4901 Scarsdale Road, 20016.
General Counsel.—Paul O. Ritter, 2651 16th Street, 20009.
Chief Examiner.—Walter L. Stovall, Jr., 1617-B North Van Dorn, Alexandria, Va., 22304.
Chief, Research and Information Division.—Lester L. Arnold, 8522 Adelphi Road, Adelphi, Md., 20783.
Director, Personnel Division.—Richard J. Petersen, 4301 Columbia Pike, Apt. 735, Arlington, Va., 22204.
Comptroller.—James E. Pitts, Jr., 1709 North Huntington Street, Arlington, Va., 22205.
Chief, Finance Division.—Robert C. Ferguson, Box 848, Route 3, Edgewater, Md., 21037.

FEDERAL AVIATION AGENCY

800 Independence Avenue SW., 20553. (Phone, WOrth 2-5166)

Administrator.—Najeeb E. Halaby, 800 Independence Avenue SW., 20553.
Deputy Administrator.—Lt. Gen. Harold W. Grant, 800 Independence Avenue SW., 20553.
Executive Secretary.—John R. Kennedy, 1609 Kennedy Place, 20011.

Associate Administrator for Administration.—Alan L. Dean, 3037 North Stafford Street, Arlington, Va., 22207.

Associate Administrator for Development.—Robert J. Shank, 2214 Massachusetts Avenue, 20008.

Associate Administrator for Programs.—David D. Thomas, 917 Rose Lane, Annandale, Va., 22003.

Deputy Administrator for Supersonic Transport Development.—Gordon M. Bain, 1600 South Joyce Street, Arlington, Va., 22202.

Director, Office of Policy Development.—Maurice C. Mackey, Jr., 4413 Yuma Street, 20016.

Federal Air Surgeon.—Maj. Gen. M. Samuel White, USAF, MC, 2785 North Wakefield, Arlington, Va., 22207.

Assistant Administrator for International Aviation Affairs.—[Vacant.]

Assistant Administrator for Appraisal.—Clarke H. Harper, 5607 Belmont Avenue, Chevy Chase, Md., 20015.

General Counsel.—Nathaniel H. Goodrich, 4705 Drummond Avenue, Chevy Chase, Md., 20015.

Executive Director, Regulatory Council.—William C. Jennings, 2234 North Quebec Street, Arlington, Va., 22207.

Director of Information Services.—Charles G. Warnick, 211 South Lee, Alexandria, Va., 22314.

Assistant Administrator for General Aviation Affairs.—William J. Schulte, 3706 Corey Place, 20016.

Director of Management Services.—John R. Provan, 5850 Doris Drive, Alexandria, Va., 22311.

Director of Budget.—Harold B. Alexander, 2309 Eccleston Street, Silver Spring, Md., 20902.

Assistant Administrator for Personnel and Training.—Robert H. Willey, 6708 Jansen Court, Springfield, Va., 22150.

Director of Compliance and Security.—James T. Murphy, 1416 Burton Wood Drive, Alexandria, Va., 22307.

Manager of Headquarters Operations—John B. Hogan, 913 Juniper Place, Alexandria, Va., 22304.

Director, Air Traffic Service.—Lee E. Warren, 3888 30th Street North, Arlington, Va., 22207.

Director, Flight Standards Service.—George S. Moore, 258 Glen Avenue, Vienna, Va., 22180.

Director, Systems Maintenance Service.—Bernard J. Vierling, 647 Oakland Terrace, Alexandria, Va., 22302.

Director, Airports Service.—Cole H. Morrow, 5503 MacArthur Drive, Falls Church, Va., 22043.

Director, Aircraft Development Service.—[Vacant.]

Director, Installation and Materiel Service.—Richard B. Leng, 3909 48th Street, 20016.

Director, Systems Research and Development Service.—Joseph D. Blatt, 4201 Cathedral Avenue, 20016.

Director, Bureau of National Capital Airports.—G. Ward Hobbs, Box 131, Hunter Mill Road, Oakton, Va., 22124

REGIONAL OFFICES

Director, Eastern Region.—Oscar Bakke, Kennedy International Airport, Jamaica, N.Y., 11430.

Director, Southern Region.—A. O. Basnight, P.O. Box 20636, Atlanta, Ga., 30320.

Director, Southwest Region.—Archie W. League, P.O. Box 1689, Fort Worth, Tex., 76101.

Director, Central Region.—Edward C. Marsh, 4825 Troost Avenue, Kansas City, Mo., 64110.

Director, Western Region.—Joseph H. Tippets, 5651 West Manchester Avenue, P.O. Box 90007, Los Angeles, Calif., 90009.

Director, Alaskan Region.—James G. Rogers, 632 Sixth Avenue, Anchorage, Alaska, 99501.

Director, Pacific Region.—Phillip Swatek, P.O. Box 4009, Honolulu, Hawaii, 96812.

Assistant Administrator for Europe, Africa, and Middle East.—Raymond B. Maloy, American Embassy, 24–32 Grosvenor Square, London W1, England.

Manager, Aeronautical Center.—Lloyd W. Lane, Will Rogers Field, P.O. Box 1082, Oklahoma City, Okla., 73101.
Manager, National Aviation Facilities Experimental Center.—William F. Harrison, Atlantic City, N.J., 08405.

FEDERAL COAL MINE SAFETY BOARD OF REVIEW

1701 Pennsylvania Avenue, Room 507.   Phone, EXecutive 3-3187 (Code 128, extension 5005)

Chairman.—Edward Steidle, 1104 Smithfield Street, State College, Pa.
Board Members:
  Charles R. Ferguson, 455 Fourth Avenue, New Kensington, Pa., 15068.
  George C. Trevorrow, 5941 Avon Drive, Bethesda, Md., 20014.
Executive Secretary.—Troy L. Back, 208 North Emerson Street, Arlington, Va., 22203.
General Counsel.—Robert J. Freehling, 8305 Still Spring Court, Bethesda, Md., 20034.

FEDERAL COMMUNICATIONS COMMISSION

New Post Office Building, Pennsylvania Avenue at Twelfth Street, 20554
Phone, EXecutive 3-3620 (Code 169)

Commissioners:
  Chairman.—E. William Henry, 3464 Macomb Street, 20016.
  Rosel H. Hyde, 2709 McKinley Street, 20015.
  Robert T. Bartley, 6801 Florida Street, Chevy Chase, Md., 20015.
  Robert E. Lee, 3147 Westover Drive SE., 20020.
  [Vacancy.]
  Kenneth A. Cox, 5836 Marbury Road, Bethesda, Md., 20034.
  Lee Loevinger, 5669 Bent Branch Road, 20016.
  Administrative Assistant to Chairman (Congressional Liaison).—John F. Cushman, 4312 Braeburn Drive, Fairfax, Va.
Office of Executive Director:
  Executive Director.—Curtis B. Plummer, 4521 Clark Place, 20007.
  Deputy Executive Director.—[Vacancy.]
Office of Secretary:
  Secretary.—Ben F. Waple, 2605 Avena Street, Wheaton, Md.
Office of the General Counsel:
  General Counsel.—Henry Geller, 3 Pickwick Lane, Alexandria, Va.
  Deputy General Counsel.—Daniel R. Ohlbaum, 280 Quebec Street, 20008.
  Associate General Counsels.—John H. Conlin, 806 Murray Lane, Annandale, Va.; Gerard M. Cahill, 5515 Grove Street, Chevy Chase, Md., 20015; Hilburt Slosberg, 7305 Brennon Lane, Chevy Chase, Md., 20015.
  Assistant General Counsels.—Robert D. Greenburg, 7101 Amy Lane, Bethesda, Md., 20034; John C. Harrington, 103 Lynmoor Drive, Silver Spring, Md.
Office of Chief Engineer:
  Chief Engineer.—Edward W. Allen, 100 Ichabod Place, Falls Church, Va., 22042.
  Associate Chief Engineer.—Ralph J. Renton, 321 East Greenway Boulevard, Falls Church, Va., 22042.
  Assistant Chief Engineers.—Edward W. Chapin, 6 Fairfield Drive, Catonsville, Md., 21228; William H. Watkins, 3210 Quesada Street, 20015; Julian T. Dixon 7524 Greenfield Road, Annandale, Va., 22003; Arnold G. Skrivseth, 203 Rogers Drive, Falls Church, Va., 22042.
Common Carrier Bureau:
  Chief of Bureau.—Bernard Strassburg, 9708 Saxony Road, Silver Spring, Md.
  Associate Chief of Bureau.—Asher H. Ende, 5845 Marbury Road, Bethesda, Md., 20014.
  Assistant Chief of Bureau.—John R. Lambert, 417 Regent Drive, Alexandria, Va.

Common Carrier Bureau—Continued
  Special Assistant to Chief.—Curtis M. Bushnell, 7112 Claymore Avenue, Hyattsville, Md., 20782.
Safety and Special Radio Services Bureau:
  Chief of Bureau.—James E. Barr, 3113 Helsel Drive, Silver Spring, Md.
  Assistant Chief of Bureau.—Irving Brownstein, 894 North Jefferson Street, Arlington, Va.
Broadcast Bureau:
  Chief of Bureau.—James B. Sheridan, 9807 Cottrell Terrace, Silver Spring, Md.
  Assistant Chiefs of Bureau.—James O. Juntilla, 6410 Marjory Lane, Bethesda, Md.; Wallace E. Johnson, 5512 Freedom Lane, Falls Church, Va., 22043; Hyman H. Goldin, 305 Belton Road, Silver Spring, Md.
Field Engineering and Monitoring Bureau:
  Chief of Bureau.—Frank M. Kratokvil, 11300 Montgomery Road, Beltsville, Md., 20705.
  Deputy Chief.—John R. Evans, 6041 Cheshire Drive, Bethesda, Md., 20014.
Office of Reports and Information:
  Chief of Office.—George O. Gillingham, 1322 Madison Street, 20011.
  Assistant Chief of Office.—Salina M. Lindo, 2800 Quebec Street, 20008.
Office of Hearing Examiners:
  Chief Hearing Examiner.—James D. Cunningham, 3606 16th Street, 20010.
  Assistant Chief Hearing Examiner.—Jay A. Kyle, 305 Mount Place, Alexandria, Va, 22305.
Office of Opinions and Review:
  Chief of Office.—Leonidas P. B. Emerson, 408 Colesville Manor Drive, Silver Spring, Md.
Review Board:
  Chairman.—Donald J. Berkemeyer, 205 Brook Road, McLean, Va.
  Members:
    Joseph N. Nelson, 2605 Holman Avenue, Silver Spring, Md.
    Dee W. Pincock, 9806 Kensington Parkway, Kensington, Md.
    Horace E. Slone, 6005 Landon Lane, Bethesda, Md., 20034.
    Sylvia D. Kessler, 2480 16th Street, 20009.

FEDERAL DEPOSIT INSURANCE CORPORATION

550 17th Street, 20429. Phone, 393-8400

Chairman.—Joseph W. Barr, 11001 Glen Road, Potomac, Md., 20854.
Comptroller of the Currency.—James J. Saxon, 6024 Western Avenue, Chevy Chase, Md., 20015.
Director.—Kenneth A. Randall, 12001 Old Bridge Road, Rockville, Md. 20852.
Assistant to the Chairman.—Timothy J. Reardon, Jr., 3134 Dumbarton Avenue, 20007.
Assistant to the Director.—John F. Lee, 12117 Whippoorwill Lane, Rockville, Md.
Chief, Division of Examination.—Edward H. DeHority, 3810 52d Street, 20016.
General Counsel, Legal Division.—William M. Moroney, 2913 University Terrace, 20016.
Controller.—Edward F. Phelps, Jr., 2800 Quebec Street, 20008.
Chief, Division of Liquidation.—A. E. Anderson, 3153 North Quincy Street, Arlington, Va., 22207.
Chief, Division of Research and Statistics.—Raymond E. Hengren, 11920 Glen Mill Road, Rockville, Md.
Chief, Audit Division.—James J. Bogart, 5615 Warwick Place, Chevy Chase, Md., 20015.
Secretary.—Miss E. F. Downey, 4470 Dexter Street, 20007.
Assistant to the Board.—Frank E. Tracy, 9210 Saybrook Avenue, Silver Spring, Md., 20901.
Assistant to the Board.—Raoul D. Edwards, 1402 Bren Mar Drive, Alexandria, Va., 22212.

FEDERAL HOME LOAN BANK BOARD

(Including Federal Savings and Loan Insurance Corporation)

Federal Home Loan Bank Board Building, 101 Indiana Avenue, 20552.
Phone, DUdley 6–3157 (Code 129, extension 3157)

Chairman.—John E. Horne, 415 Crown View Drive, Alexandria, Va., 22314.
[Vacancy, member.]
John deLaittre, member, 2800 R Street, 20007.
Administrative Assistant to the Chairman.—Robert N. Reeves, 4570 MacArthur Boulevard, 20007.
Executive Assistant to the Chairman.—Simon H. Trevas, 204 East Indian Spring Drive, Silver Spring, Md., 20901.
Secretary to the Board.—Harry W. Caulsen, 800 Fourth Street SW., 20024.
General Counsel.—Kenneth E. Scott, 4319 Reno Road, 20008.
Director, Office of Director of Audits.—William B. Martin, 112 Merrit Road, Alexandria, Va., 22312.
Director, Office of Administration.—Simon H. Trevas, 204 East Indian Spring Drive, Silver Spring, Md., 20901.
    Comptroller, Comptroller's Division.—Robert F. Quigley, 5101 Sargent Road NE., Apt. 304, 20017.
    Director, Administrative Services Division.—Charles M. Dulin, 4612 19th Road North, Arlington, Va., 22207.
    Director, Operating Analysis Division (Data Processing.)—James C. Byrnes, 210 Martha's Road, Alexandria, Va., 22307.
    Chief, Organization and Methods Division.—Richard E. Griebenow, 6613 22d Place, West Hyattsville, Md., 20782.
Director, Division of Federal Home Loan Bank Operations.—Lyndon R. Day, 3400 North Utah Street, Arlington, Va., 22207.
Director, Division of Regulations.—John M. Wyman, 11813 Magruder Lane, Rockville, Md., 20852.
Director, Office of Applications.—Clarence S. Smith, 5107 Lawton Drive, Sumner, Md., 20016.
Director, Division of Personnel.—Frank G. Healey, 7555 Kingman Drive, Annandale, Va., 22003.
Director, Office of Examinations and Supervision.—Nathaniel L. Armistead, 2500 Q Street, 20007.
    Deputy Director.—Lawrence M. Walters, 3218 45th Street, 20016.
Director, Office of Research and Home Finance.—Harry S. Schwartz, 8309 Loring Drive, Bethesda, Md., 20034.
Director, Office of Information. Clifford W. Patton, 3290 Aberfoyle Place, 20015.
Budget Officer.—Thaddeus Corcoran, 3800 Porter Street, 20016.
Executive Secretary, Federal Savings and Loan Advisory Council.—John J. Brady, 2705 Largo Place, Bowie, Md.
Secretary to the Board Chairman.—Jeanne F. Burleson, 5517 23d Parkway, 20031.

FEDERAL SAVINGS AND LOAN INSURANCE CORPORATION

Acting Director, Office of Director, FSLIC.—John A. O'Brien, 2914 Cortland Place, 20008.

FEDERAL MARITIME COMMISSION

1321 H Street, 20573. Phone, STerling 3–5200 (Code 129, extension-0)

Commissioners:
    Chairman.—Rear Adm. John Harllee, USN (retired), 1064 30th Street, 20007.
    Ashton C. Barrett, Dupont East, 1545 18th Street, 20006.
    James V. Day, 5524 Westbard Avenue, Bethesda, Md., 20014.
    George H. Hearn, 1414 Dilston Road, Silver Spring, Md., 20903.
    John S. Patterson, 4809 Drummond Avenue, Chevy Chase, Md., 20015.
Managing Director.—Timothy J. May, 5611 Namakagan Road, Sumner, Md., 20016.
Deputy Managing Director.—Earle J. Schweizer, 8011 Carroll Avenue, Takoma Park, Md., 20012.

Secretary.—Thomas Lisi, 120 North Columbus Street, Arlington, Va., 22203.
General Counsel.—James L. Pimper, 4320 Van Ness Street, 20016.
Solicitor.—Milan D. Miskovsky, 6141 31st Place 20015.
Chief Hearing Examiner.—Gus O. Basham, 717 25th Street South, Arlington, Va., 22202.
Director, Office of International Affairs and Relations.—Myer Trupp, 1129 Quebec Street, Silver Spring, Md., 20903.
Associate Director, Office of International Affairs and Relations.—Gerald W. Russell, 1934 Red Oak Drive, Hyattsville, Md., 20783.
Director, Bureau of Transport Economics.—Daniel H. Mater, 8101 MacArthur Boulevard, Bethesda, Md., 20034.
Director, Office of Administration.—Andrew Drance, 5419 North 20th Street, Arlington, Va., 22205.
Director, Bureau of Foreign Regulation.—William A. Stigler, Bishopsgate Chapel, Bluemont, Va., 22012.
Deputy Director, Bureau of Foreign Regulation.—Edward S. Johnson, 5223 Massachusetts Avenue, Westmoreland Hills, Md., 20016.
Director, Bureau of Domestic Regulation.—Edward Schmeltzer, 6708 Renita Lane, Bethesda, Md., 20034.
Deputy Director, Bureau of Domestic Regulation.—James A. Kempker, 918 North Quincy Street, Arlington, Va., 22203.
Director, Bureau of Hearing Counsel.—Robert J. Blackwell, 506 Warbler Place, McLean, Va., 22101.
Director, Bureau of Investigation.—Robert S. Pitzer, 11021 Ralston Road, Luxmanor, Rockville, Md., 20852.
Deputy Director, Bureau of Investigation.—Richard F. McIlwain, 127 C Street NE., 20002.
Director, Bureau of Financial Analysis.—James L. Wallace, 705 10th Street, Alexandria, Va., 22307.
Deputy Director, Bureau of Financial Analysis.—Charles J. Finegan, Fairfax Station, Va., 22039.

DISTRICT OFFICES

District Manager, Atlantic Coast Office.—Ralph M. Hylton, 40 Marlboro Road, Long Island, N.Y.
District Manager, Gulf Coast Office.—Ralph P. Dickson, 713 Wendy Lane, Jefferson Park, New Orleans, La.
District Manager, Pacific Coast Office.—Harvey P. Schneiber, 3165 Jordan Road, Oakland, Calif.

FEDERAL MEDIATION AND CONCILIATION SERVICE

Department of Labor Building.   Phone, EXecutive 3-7350 (Code 110, extension 3501)

Director.—William E. Simkin, 1100 Sixth Street, SW, 20024.
Deputy Director.—Robert H. Moore, 321 North Oakland Street, Arlington, Va., 22203.
Director of Mediation Activity.—Walter A. Maggiolo, 1619 North Nicholas Street, Arlington, Va., 22205.
Special Assistant to the Director.—Willoughby Abner, 1322 Fourth Street, SW., 20424.
General Counsel.—H. T. Herrick, 1308 Popkins Lane, Alexandria, Va., 22307.
Director of Special Activities.—Harold C. Munk, 7825 Jay Miller Drive, Lake Barcroft Estates, Falls Church, Va., 22041.
Director of Administrative Management.—Lawrence E. Eady, 1517 Red Oak Drive, Silver Spring, Md., 20910.
Public Affairs Officer.—Norman Walker, 3607 North Vernon Street, Arlington, Va., 22207.

NATIONAL LABOR-MANAGEMENT PANEL

Labor:
  H. S. Brown, President, Texas AFL–CIO, 402 West 13th Street, Austin 1, Tex.
  Jack T. Conway, Executive Director, Industrial Union Dept., AFL–CIO, 815 16th Street NW., Washington, D.C., 20006.

Labor—Continued

Cornelius J. Haggerty, President, Building and Construction Trades Dept., AFL–CIO, 815 16th Street NW., Washington, D.C., 20006.

Thomas E. Harris, Associate General Counsel, AFL–CIO, 815 16th Street NW., Washington, D.C., 20006.

John H. Lyons, General President, International Association of Bridge, Structural & Ornamental Iron Workers (AFL–CIO), 3615 Olive Street, St. Louis 8, Mo.

Marvin J. Miller, Assistant to the President, United Steelworkers of America (AFL–CIO), 1500 Commonwealth Building, Pittsburgh Pa., 15222.

Management:

Wayne T. Brooks, Director of Industrial Relations, Wheeling Steel Corp., Wheeling, W. Va.

J. V. Cairns, Director, Industrial Relations, The Firestone Tire & Rubber Co., 1200 Firestone Parkway, Akron, Ohio, 44317.

J. Curtis Counts, Director, Employe Relations, Douglas Aircraft Co., Inc., 3000 Ocean Park Boulevard, Santa Monica, Calif., 90406.

Jesse Freidin, Poletti, Freidin, Prashker, Feldman & Gartner, 777 Third Avenue, New York, N.Y., 10017.

Gerry E. Morse, Vice President, Honeywell, Inc., 2747 Fourth Avenue South, Minneapolis, Minn., 55408.

J. Paul St. Sure, President, Pacific Maritime Association, 16 California Street, San Francisco, Calif., 94111.

Willougby Abner, executive secretary to the panel.

REGIONAL DIRECTORS

Region 1.—Frank H. Brown, Room 1101, 11th Floor, East, 346 Broadway, New York, N.Y., 10013.

Region 2.—Robert W. Donnahoo, Room 5021, U.S. Courthouse and Post Office Bldg., 9th & Chestnut Streets, Philadelphia, Pa., 19107.

Region 3.—William S. Pierce, 154 Peachtree at Seventh Street Building, 50 Seventh Street NE., Atlanta, Ga., 30323.

Region 4.—James L. Macpherson, 2021 Superior Building, 815 Superior Avenue, NE., Cleveland, Ohio, 44114.

Region 5.—Cornelius K. Call, 1402 U.S. Courthouse and Federal Office Bldg., 219 South Dearborn Street, Chicago, Ill., 60604.

Region 6.—William F. White, 3266 Federal Building, 1520 Market Street, St. Louis, Mo., 63103.

Region 7.—Arthur C. Viat, Box 36007, 450 Golden Gate Avenue, San Francisco, Calif., 94102.

FEDERAL POWER COMMISSION

441 G Street, 20426. Phone, EXecutive 3–0100 (Code 129)

Commissioners:

Chairman.—Joseph C. Swidler, 9504 Michaels Court, Bethesda, Md., 20034.

Vice Chairman.—David S. Black, 6211 Wedgewood Road, Bethesda, Md., 20034.

Charles R. Ross, 10814 Alloway Drive, Potomac, Md., 20854.

Lawrence J. O'Connor, Jr., 2510 East Place, 20007.

Assistant to the Chairman.—S. David Freeman, 7211 Pyle Road, Bethesda, Md., 20034.

Executive Director.—Harry J. Trainor, 6 Sunnyside Road, Silver Spring, Md., 20910.

Secretary.—Joseph H. Gutride, The Albemarle House, 4501 Connecticut Avenue, 20008.

Assistant Secretary.—Gordon M. Grant, 972 North Rochester Street, Arlington, Va., 22205.

Office of Hearing Examiners:

Chief.—Joseph Zwerdling, 401 East Wayne Avenue, Silver Spring, Md., 20901.

Office of Special Assistants to the Commission:

Chief.—Theodore French, 7911 Glendale Road, Chevy Chase, Md., 20015.

Office of Economics:
   Chief.—Haskell P. Wald, 9528 Friars Road, Bethesda, Md., 20034.
   Assistant Chief.—J. Harvey Edmonston, 4307 Lynbrook Drive, Bethesda, Md., 20014.
Office of Personnel:
   Director.—William N. Campbell, 609 Gordon Street, Falls Church, Va., 22041.
   Assistant Director.—Claudius L. Fike, 2218 North Quincy Street, Arlington, Va., 22207.
Office of Management and Manpower Utilization:
   Chief.—Marsh H. Moy, 208 Ross Drive SW., Vienna, Va., 22180.
Office of Program, Budget and Financial Services:
   Chief.—Wesley Capar, 7156 Floyd Avenue, Springfield, Va., 22150.
Office of Administrative Operations:
   Chief.—Unger C. Murnan, Jr., 6057 25th Road North, Arlington, Va., 22207.
Bureau of Power:
   Chief (and Chief Engineer).—F. Stewart Brown, 1814 Highwood Drive, McLean, Va., 22101.
   Deputy Chief.—George E. Tomlinson, 4309 Crestwood Lane, McLean, Va., 22101.
   Assistant Chief.—Stewart P. Crum, 1111 Dunoon Road, Silver Spring, Md., 20903.
   Chief, Division of Electric Resources and Requirements.—Joseph J. A. Jessel, 4911 35th Road North, Arlington, Va., 22207.
   Chief, Division of River Basins.—James J. Stout, 2831 North Van Buren Street, Arlington, Va., 22213.
   Chief, Division of Rates and Corporate Regulation.—William W. Lindsay, 225 Whitmoor Terrace, Silver Spring, Md., 20901.
   Chief, Division of Licensed Projects.—Merle F. Thomas, 604 Longview Court, Vienna, Va., 22180.
Office of Accounting and Finance:
   Chief Accountant.—Arthur L. Litke, Edison Road, Potomac, Md., 20854.
   Deputy Chief Accountant.—John F. Utley, 3412 Javins Drive, Alexandria, Va., 22310.
   Chief, Division of Audits.—Gordon F. Heim, 6415 Adelphi Road, University Park, Hyattsville, Md., 20782.
   Chief, Division of Systems.—William J. Powell, 6905 Heidelburg Road, Lanham, Md., 20801.
   Chief, Division of Finance and Statistics.—C. Ford Blanchard, 2642 North Quantico Street, Arlington, Va., 22207.
   Western Audit Section.—John R. LaCamera, 555 Battery Street, Room 213, San Francisco, 94111.
Bureau of Natural Gas:
   Chief.—Frank F. Watters, 4220 Deer Drive, McLean, Va., 22101.
   Deputy Chief.—Louis W. Mendonsa, 4901 Seminary Road, Apt. 1601, Alexandria, Va., 22311.
   Assistant Chief (Staff Services).—Julian B. Turner, 5710 Chain Bridge Road, McLean, Va., 22101.
   Chief, Analysis and Procedures.—Joseph J. Curry, 2606 Evans Drive, Silver Spring, Md., 20902.
   Chief, Pipeline Division.—Louis Zanoff, 5908 Kirby Road, Bethesda, Md., 20034.
   Chief, Producer Division.—Edward M. McManus, 1407 Jefferson Street, Hyattsville, Md.
   Chief, Area Rate Division.—William H. Lyon, River House, 1111 Army-Navy Drive, Arlington, Va., 22202.
Office of General Counsel:
   General Counsel.—Richard A. Solomon, 6805 Delaware Street, Chevy Chase, Md., 20015.
   Deputy General Counsel.—John C. Mason, 1029 Poplar Drive, Falls Church, Va., 22046.
   Solicitor.—Howard E. Wahrenbrock, 103 Waverly Way, McLean, Va., 22101.
   Assistant General Counsels:
     Abraham R. Spalter, 10108 Georgia Avenue, Silver Spring, Md., 20902.
     Robert L. Russell, 8407 16th Street, Silver Spring, Md., 20910.
     Leo E. Forquer, 5903 Walton Road, Bethesda, Md., 20034.
     Peter A. Dammann, 2015 48th Street, 20007.
     David J. Bardin, 5520 Carolina Place, 20016.

Office of Public Information:
  Chief.—William L. Webb, 7712 Cayuga Avenue, Bethesda, Md., 20034.
Regional Offices and Regional Engineers:
  New York, N.Y.—Day J. Wait, 346 Broadway, 10013.
  Chicago, Ill.—Kenneth G. Tower, 610 South Canal Street, 60607.
  Atlanta, Ga.—Robert C. Price, 50 Seventh Street NE., 30323.
  Fort Worth, Tex.—Lenard B. Young, 100 North University Drive,76107.
  San Francisco, Calif.—M. Boyd Austin, 555 Battery Street, 94111.

FEDERAL TRADE COMMISSION

Pennsylvania Avenue at Sixth Street, 20580.   Phone, EXecutive 3–6800 (Code 1262)

Commissioners:
  Chairman.—Paul Rand Dixon, 5911 Carlton Lane, 20016.
    Philip Elman, 6719 Brigadoon Drive, Bethesda, Md., 20034.
    A. Everette MacIntyre, 1564 Colonial Terrace, Arlington, Va., 22209.
    John R. Reilly, 8103 Thoreau Drive, Bethesda, Md., 20034.
    Mary Gardiner Jones, 2821 Olive Avenue, 20007.
Assistant to the Chairman.—John V. Buffington, Clifton, Va., 22024.
Executive Director.—John N. Wheelock, 2100 Connecticut Avenue, 20008.
Office of Information, Director.—William F. Jibb, 4201 Cathedral Avenue, 20016.
Program Review Officer.—Philip R. Layton, 2220 20th Street, 20009.
Secretary and Congressional Liaison Officer.—Joseph W. Shea, 3067 Ordway Street, 20008.
  Assistant Secretary.—Joseph N. Kuzew, 2401 H Street, 20037.
  Assistant Secretary for Legal and Public Records.—Paul M. Trueblood, 707 15th Street, Alexandria, Va., 22307.
Office of Administration, Director.—John A. Delaney, 5928 Second Street North, Arlington, Va., 22203.
  Division of Administrative Services, Chief.—George F. Tucker, Jr., 4522 31st Street South, Arlington, Va., 22206.
  Librarian.—Amy R. Jennings, 417 Poplar Drive, Falls Church, Va., 22046.
  Division of Personnel, Chief.—Robert B. Sherwood, 1702 Lanham Road, Falls Church, Va., 22043.
  Management Officer.—Monroe F. Day, 305 Woodley Place, Falls Church, Va., 22046.
Comptroller.—William P. Glendening, 3815 Military Road, 20015.
  Division of Finance, Chief.—William H. Kephart, 392 Dranesville Road, Herndon, Va., 22070.
  Division of Data Processing, Chief.—Dale W. Johnson, 6010 Logan Way, Bladensburg, Md., 20710.
General Counsel.—James McI. Henderson, 5601 33d Street, 20015.
  Assistant to General Counsel.—John M. Lexcen, 8114 Carrick Lane, Springfield, Va., 22150.
  Assistant General Counsel, Appeals.—James B. Truly, 2823 Mosby Street, Alexandria, Va., 22305.
  Assistant General Counsel, Consent Orders.—Wayne Threlkeld, 7104 Edgevale Street, Chevy Chase, Md., 20015.
  Assistant General Counsel, Export Trade.—William A. Bailey, 4540 26th Street North, Arlington, Va., 22207.
  Assistant General Counsel, Legislation.—Fletcher G. Cohn, 2828 Connecticut Avenue, 20008.
  Assistant General Counsel.—Charles E. Grandey, 2808 North Underwood Street, Arlington, Va., 22304.
Office of Hearing Examiners, Director.—Edward Creel, 3369 Stuyvesant Place, 20015.
Bureau of Deceptive Practices, Director.—Daniel J. Murphy, 5009 Worthington Drive, Westmoreland Hills, Md., 20016.
  Assistant Director.—James A. Murray, 1900 South Eads Street, Arlington, Va., 22202.
  Assistant to Director.—Gale P. Gotschall, 2 Ridge Road, Falls Church, Va., 22042.
  Division of Compliance, Chief.—Berry W. Stanley, 5820 Danny's Lane, Alexandria, Va., 22311.

Bureau of Deceptive Practices—Continued

    Division of Food and Drug Advertising, Chief.—Charles A. Sweeny, 1600 South Joyce Street, Arlington, Va., 22202.

    Division of General Advertising, Chief.—John W. Brookfield, Jr., 607 Little Street, Alexandria, Va., 22301.

    Division of General Practices, Chief.—Michael J. Vitale, 2206 32d Place SE., 20020.

    Division of Scientific Opinions, Chief.—Frederick W. Irish, 5410 Connecticut Avenue, 20015.

Bureau of Economics, Director.—Willard F. Mueller, 357 O Street SW., 20024.

    Assistant Director.—Roy A. Prewitt, 4339 26th Street North, Arlington, Va., 22207.

    Assistant to Director.—Harrison F. Houghton, 4101 Oglethorpe Street, Hyattsville, Md., 20782.

    Division of Economic Evidence, Chief.—Harry Bender, 8413 Freyman Drive, Chevy Chase, Md., 20015.

    Division of Financial Statistics, Chief.—William Levin, 5423 33d Street, 20015.

    Division of Industry Analysis, Chief.—Stanley E. Boyle, 5908 Carlyn Springs Road, Bailey's Crossroads, Va., 22041.

Bureau of Field Operations, Director.—Samuel L. Williams, 25 Barlow Road, Fairfax, Va., 22030.

    Assistant Director for Deceptive Practices.—Charles R. Moore, 8607 Hempstead Avenue, Bethesda, Md., 20034.

    Assistant Director for Restraint of Trade.—Mason B. Bray, 10104 South Glen Road, Potomac, Md., 20854.

    Atlanta, Attorney in Charge.—Edward S. Ragsdale, 915 Forsyth Building, 86 Forsyth Street NW., 30303.

    Boston, Attorney in Charge.—John F. McCarty, Room 1001, 131 State Street, 02109.

    Chicago, Attorney in Charge.—William F. Lemke, Jr., Room 486, United States Courthouse and Federal Office Building, 219 South Dearborn Street, 60604.

    Cleveland, Attorney in Charge.—Vernon E. Taylor, 1128 Standard Building, 44113.

    Kansas City, Attorney in Charge.—Floyd M. Brown, 2806 Federal Office Building, 64106.

    Los Angeles, Attorney in Charge.—Robert E. O'Brien, Room 1212, 215 West Seventh Street, 90014.

    New Orleans, Attorney in Charge.—William B. Lott, 1000 Masonic Temple Building, 333 St. Charles Street, 70130.

        Houston, Assistant Attorney in Charge.—Jess C. Radnor, Room 10511, United States Courthouse Building, P.O. Box 61165, 77061.

    New York, Attorney in Charge.—Albert G. Seidman, 30 Church Street, 10007.

    San Francisco, Attorney in Charge.—Raymond J. Lloyd, 450 Golden Gate Avenue, P.O. Box 36005, 94102.

    Seattle, Attorney in Charge.—Walter W. Harris, 511 U.S. Court House, 98104.

    Washington Area, Attorney in Charge.—Herbert L. Propst, 450 West Broad Street, Falls Church, Va., 22046.

Bureau of Industry Guidance, Director.—Chalmers B. Yarley, 5700 Enterprise Avenue, McLean, Va., 22101.

    Assistant Director.—William B. Snow, Jr., 204 Waverly Way, McLean, Va., 22101.

    Division of Advisory Opinions, Chief.—George S. Rountree, 2613 North Military Road, Arlington, Va., 22207.

    Division of Trade Practice Conferences and Guides, Chief.—Edward M. Hall, 3805 Ingomar Street, 20015.

    Division of Trade Regulation Rules, Chief.—H. Paul Butz, 3116 North Military Road, Arlington, Va., 22207.

Bureau of Restraint of Trade, Director.—Joseph E. Sheehy, 5908 Harwick Road, 20016.

    Assistant Director.—Cecil G. Miles, 4532 32d Road North, Arlington, Va., 22207.

    Assistant to Director.—Henry I. Lipsky, 5924 Third Street North, Arlington, Va., 22203.

    Division of Accounting, Chief.—Melbourne C. Steele, 7404 Bybrook Lane, Chevy Chase, Md., 20015.

    Division of Compliance, Chief.—Joseph J. Gercke, 4004 Cleveland Street, Kensington, Md., 20015.

Bureau of Restraint of Trade—Continued
  Division of Discriminatory Practices, Chief.—Francis C. Mayer, 4910 Adrian Street, Rockville, Md., 20853.
  Division of General Trade Restraints, Chief.—Rufus E. Wilson, 3902 Lorraine Avenue, Falls Church, Va., 22043.
  Division of Mergers, Chief.—Robert A. Hammond, 3106 33d Place, 20016.
Bureau of Textiles and Furs, Director.—Henry D. Stringer, 3 Fairfax Court, Chevy Chase, Md., 20015.
  Assistant Director.—Charles F. Canavan, 7110 Pony Trail Lane, Hyattsville, Md., 20782.
  Division of Enforcement, Chief.—Eugene H. Strayhorn, 2622 North Florida Street, Arlington, Va., 22207.
  Division of Regulation, Chief.—Harold S. Blackman, 5504 Scioto Road, 20016.
  Charlotte Office, Investigator.—Robert C. Bledsoe, 327 North Tryon Street, Room 204 28202.
  Dallas Office, Investigator.—Benton R. Chism, 405 Thomas Building, 1314 Wood Street, 75202.
  Denver Office, Investigator.—Allen R. Franck, 647 Equitable Building, 730 17th Street, 80202.
  Miami Office, Investigator.—[Vacancy], 1308 New Federal Building, 51 SW First Avenue, 33130.
  Philadelphia Office, Investigator.—Charles J. Taggart, 53 Long Lane, Upper Darby, Pa., 19082.
  Portland Office, Investigator.—Richard Schultz, 231 United States Courthouse, 97205.
  St. Louis Office, Investigator.—Carl M. Bremer, 400 United States Court and Custom House, 1114 Market Street, 63101.

FOREIGN CLAIMS SETTLEMENT COMMISSION OF THE UNITED STATES

1111 20th Street, 20579.   Phone, DUdley 2-7700 (Code 128, extension 7700)

Chairman.—Edward D. Re, 4125 Military Road, 20015.
Commissioner.—Theodore Jaffe, 2727 29th Street, 20008.
Commissioner.—LaVern R. Dilweg, 1650 Harvard Street, 20009.

FOREIGN-TRADE ZONES BOARD

Room 6827, Commerce Building.   Phone, WOrth 7-4882 (Code 112, extension 4882)

Chairman.—John T. Connor, Secretary of Commerce.
Members:
  Henry H. Fowler, Secretary of the Treasury.
  Stephen Ailes, Secretary of the Army.
Executive Secretary.—Richard H. Lake, 4710 Surry Place, Alexandria, Va., 22304.
Staff Assistant.—Lena W. Carter, 215 Rogers Drive, Falls Church, Va., 22042.

GENERAL SERVICES ADMINISTRATION

General Services Building.   Phone, 343-1100 (Code 183, extension 4072)

OFFICE OF THE ADMINISTRATOR

Administrator (Acting).—Lawson B. Knott, Jr., 1712 North Highland Street, Arlington, Va., 22201.
  Administrative Assistant.—Patricia L. Walker, 3518 Martha Curtis Drive, Alexandria, Va., 22302.
Deputy Administrator.—Lawson B. Knott, Jr., 1712 North Highland Street, Arlington, Va., 22201.
  Administrative Assistant.—Hazel E. Miller, 2025 I Street, 20006.

Assistant Administrator.—Robert T. Griffin, 8003 Kerry Lane, Chevy Chase, Md., 20015.
Deputy Assistant Administrator.—John E. Byrne, 305 Martha's Road, Alexandria, Va., 22307.
  Director, Business Services and Small Business.—Henry A. Levy, 3112 Brooklawn Terrace, Chevy Chase, Md., 20015.
Assistant to the Assistant Administrator.—George J. Gilmore, 2300 Cheverly Avenue, Cheverly, Md., 20785.
Director of Legislation.—Robert T. Davis, 5518 Parkland Court SE., 20028.
Congressional Liaison Officer.—Kevin F. Flanagan, 9 Colonial Court, Rockville, Md., 20852.
Chairman, GSA Board of Contract Appeals.—Harold W. Sheehan, 3306 Valley Drive, Alexandria, Va., 22312.
Assistant Administrator for Finance and Administration.—William P. Turpin, 711 Santayana Drive, Mantua Hills, Fairfax, Va., 22030.
  Director of Data and Financial Management.—Jesse M. Merrell, Jr., 528 Military Drive, Falls Church, Va., 22044.
  Director of Manpower and Administration.—John H. Finlator, 2710 North Beechwood Place, Arlington, Va., 22207.
General Counsel.—Joe E. Moody, 9636 Parkwood Drive, Bethesda, Md., 20014.

PUBLIC BUILDINGS SERVICE
General Services Building. Phone, 343-1100 (Code 183, extension 4193)

Commissioner (Acting), Public Buildings Service.—William A. Schmidt, 5901 Cromwell Drive, Springfield, Md., 20016.
Deputy Commissioner, Public Buildings Service.—William A. Schmidt, 5901 Cromwell Drive, Springfield, Md., 20016.
Administrative Officer.—Charles A. Heffernan, 7604 Geranium Street, Bethesda, Md., 20034.
Director, Program Management Office.—Ferdinand Kaufholz, Jr., 5116 Palisades Lane, 20016.
Assistant Commissioner, Buildings Management.—Carl E. Rantzow, 305 Dalebrook Drive, Alexandria, Va., 22308.
  Deputy Assistant Commissioner.—John G. Wadsworth, 5550 Columbia Pike, Arlington, Va., 22204.
  Director, Operations Division.—Frank L. Capps, 3941 North Dumbarton Street, Arlington, Va., 22207.
  Director, Protection Division.—William H. Alexander, 1900 South Eads Street, Arlington, Va., 22202.
  Director, Repair and Improvement Division.—Thomas E. Crocker, 3026 N Street, 20007.
Assistant Commissioner, Design and Construction.—Karel H. Yasko, 7801 Green Twig Road, Bethesda, Md., 20034.
  Deputy Assistant Commissioner.—Charles G. Palmer, 4332 Clagett Road, Hyattsville, Md., 20782.
  Director, Design Division.—J. Rowland Snyder, 1840 47th Place, 20007.
  Director, Estimates Division.—James T. Redd, 34 North Granada Street, Arlington, Va., 22203.
  Director, Construction Division.—Howard K. Chapman, Jr., 7805 Stratford Road, Bethesda, Md., 20014.
Assistant Commissioner, Space Management.—John W. Chapman, Jr., 14505 Gilpin Road, Silver Spring, Md., 20906.
  Deputy Assistant Commissioner.—L. Anthony Ziernicki, 4315 13th Street NE., 20017.
  Director, Standards Staff.—Gerald S. Radley, 4504 Windom Place, 20016.
  Director, Appraisal Staff.—Richard H. Gaskins, 5821 Braddock Road, Alexandria, Va., 22312.
  Director, Lease Acquisition Division.—George F. Phillips, 104 Lyford Drive, Belvedere, Tiburon, Calif., 94920.
  Director, Site Acquisition Division.—John B. Huyett, Jr., 1400 North Ivanhoe Street, Arlington, Va., 22205.
  Director, Assignment and Utilization Division.—Raymond A. O'Brien, 5403 19th Avenue, Hyattsville, Md., 20782.
  Director, Space Requirements Division.—John F. Galuardi, 11120 Fawsett Road, Potomac, Md., 20854.

FEDERAL SUPPLY SERVICE

General Services Building.   Phone, 343-1100 (Code 183, extension 33265)

Commissioner, Federal Supply Service.—H. A. Abersfeller, 800 Overlook Drive, Alexandria, Va., 22305.

Deputy Commissioner, Federal Supply Service.—[Vacant.]

Administrative Officer.—D. O. Mathias, 5414 Glenallen Road, Springfield, Va., 22151.

Director of Program Management.—I. E. Friedlander, 916 Hyde Road, Silver Spring, Md., 20902.

Assistant Commissioner, Supply Distribution.—Lewis E. Spangler, 3904 West Underwood Street, Chevy Chase, Md., 20015.

Director, Distribution Programs Division.—George W. Saunders, 3409 Iverness Drive, Chevy Chase, Md., 20015.

Assistant to the Assistant Commissioner.—John R. Harkins, 878 North Kensington Street, Arlington, Va., 22205.

Director, Program Control and Evaluation Division.—Carl D. Yeakel, 9701 Watts Branch Drive, Rockville, Md., 20850.

Assistant Commissioner, Office of Procurement.—L. L. Dunkle, Jr., 4538 39th Street North, Arlington, Va., 22207.

Deputy Assistant Commissioner.—E. M. English, 1801 North Kenmore Avenue, Arlington, Va., 22207.

Assistant to the Assistant Commissioner.—S. Weinstein, 8500 16th Street, Silver Spring, Md., 20910.

Staff Assistant.—W. S. Dinsmore, 7823 Maryknoll Avenue, Bethesda, Md., 20023.

Director, Procurement Operations Division.—W. W. Warburton, 2001 Camp Alger Avenue, Falls Church, Va., 22042.

Director, Program Management Division.—L. F. Donahue, 13905 Ziglerway, Silver Spring, Md., 20904.

Acting Director, Inventory Management Division.—F. A. Brewer, 2325 South Buchanan Street, Arlington, Va., 22206.

Assistant Commissioner, Office of Standards and Quality Control.—George W. Ritter, 1150 Princess Anne Lane, Falls Church, Va., 22042.

Assistant to the Assistant Commissioner.—Walter F. Roberts, 3305 North Kensington Street, Arlington, Va., 22207.

Director, Quality Control Division.—Roger Carroll, 907 Country Club Drive, Vienna, Va., 22180.

Director, Standardization Division.—Willis S. MacLeod, 405 High Street, Alexandria, Va., 22302.

Assistant Commissioner, Office of Supply Management.—Loren L. Leeper, R.F.D., Ashburn, Va., 22011.

Deputy Assistant Commissioner.—John J. Mullen, 1027 Poplar Drive, Falls Church, Va., 22046.

Director, Supply Management Services Division.—Harry W. Tennant, 109 Maple Lane, Fairfax, Va., 22030.

Deputy Director, Supply Management Services Division.—Edwin L. Todd, 11 South Beaumont Avenue, Baltimore, Md., 21228.

Director, National Supply System Division.—Robert M. Oremland, 801 Spring Lake Terrace, Fairfax, Va., 22030.

Deputy Director, National Supply System Division.—John O. Tressler, 7403 Floyd Avenue, Springfield, Va., 22150.

Director, Supply Policy and Plans Division.—Robert J. Taylor, 1605 Crestwood Drive, Alexandria, Va., 22302.

Director, Supply Data Systems Staff.—Nelson B. Coon, 5226 Easton Drive, Springfield, Va., 22151.

DEFENSE MATERIALS SERVICE

General Services Building.   Phone, 343-1100 (Code 183, extension 4344)

Commissioner, Defense Materials Service.—Maurice J. Connell, 1400 South Joyce, Arlington, Va., 22202.

Deputy Commissioner, Defense Materials Service.—John G. Harlan, Jr., 8700 Fenway Drive, Bethesda, Md., 20034.

Assistant to the Deputy Commissioner.—Paul M. Haines, 4401 Van Buren Street, Hyattsville, Md., 20782.

Executive Officer.—Franklin J. Gutchess, 415 Glasgow Road, Alexandria, Va., 22307.

Administrative Officer.—Thomas J. Dolan, 4424 Aragona Drive, Oxon Hill, Md., 20022.

Technical Advisor (Marketing), Economics and Research Staff.—John Croston, 426 Sisson Street, Silver Spring, Md., 20902.

Assistant Commissioner, Materials Management.—George K. Casto, 5203 Westport Road, Chevy Chase, Md., 20015.

Director, Disposal Plans Division.—William W. Wickes, 4960 Rockwood Parkway, 20016.

Director, Inspection Division.—William K. Lazear, 4800 Sothoron Road, McLean, Va., 22101.

Director, Materials Division.—Chester S. Shade, 2324 Ashmead Place, 20009.

Assistant Commissioner, Storage Management.—Victor E. Johnson, 4732 Ellicott Street, 20016.

Director, Emergency Programs Division.—Sumner J. Maletz, 3808 Jenifer Street, 20015.

Director, Industrial Equipment Division.—Henry Greene, 225 North Galveston Street, Arlington, Va., 22203.

Director, Stockpile Division.—Hubert M. Kirtley, 2004 Bush Hill Drive, Alexandria, Va., 22310.

TRANSPORTATION AND COMMUNICATIONS SERVICE

General Services Building.   Phone, 343–1100 (Code 183, extension 5246)

Commissioner, Transportation and Communications Service.—Robert B. Conrad, 2819 Key Boulevard, Arlington, Va., 22201.

Deputy Commissioner, Transportation and Communications Service.—Malcolm D. Miller, 1701 North Huntington Street, Arlington, Va., 22205.

Assistant to the Commissioner.—Leonard R. Lief, 4740 Connecticut Avenue, 20008.

Executive Officer.—William H. Miller, 7111 Claymore Avenue, Hyattsville, Md., 20782.

Director, Program Management Office.—John L. Scott, 10706 Edgewood Avenue, Silver Spring, Md., 20901.

Assistant Commissioner for Transportation.—John W. Flatley, 6652 32d Street, 20015.

Deputy Assistant Commissioner for Transportation (Motor Equipment).—Sidney O. Farris, 709 Winhall Way, Silver Spring, Md., 20904.

Director, Motor Equipment Operations Division.—Carl J. B. Carlson, 522 Hawthorne Road, Linthicum Heights, Md., 21210.

Director, Motor Equipment Management Division.—Frank R. Carter, West River, Md., 20881.

Deputy Assistant Commissioner for Transportation (Transportation Management).—James K. Cowling, 101 Park Valley Road, Silver Spring, Md., 20910.

Director, Contract Administration Division.—Robert T. Bain, 6900 Jewel Street, Alexandria, Va., 22312.

Director, Rate and Routing Service Division.—John S. Peters, 4114 Gallatin Street, Hyattsville, Md., 20781.

Director, Transportation Management Division.—George S. Marsalek, 2211 Kentucky Avenue, Baltimore, Md., 21213.

Assistant Commissioner for Communications.—M. Lloyd Bond, 10914 Oakwood Street, Silver Spring, Md., 20902.

Deputy Assistant Commissioner for Communications (Operations).—Leonard Plotkin, 6102 Wilson Lane, Bethesda, Md., 20034.

Deputy Assistant Commissioner for Communications (Technical Coordination).—Robert F. Mundy, 3011 North Trinidad Street, Arlington, Va., 22213.

Director, Engineering Division.—Harold P. Belcher, 4516 New Hampshire Avenue, 20011.

Director, Operations Control Division.—Thomas G. Osterhoudt, 3527 Madison Place, West Hyattsville, Md., 20782.

Director, Planning and Requirements Division.—David B. Hall, Route 1, Box 274, Springfield, Va., 22150.

Director, Rates and Tariffs Division.—Richard Gabel, 3059 South Abingdon Street, Arlington, Va., 22206.

Assistant Commissioner for Communications—Continued
   Director, Systems Management Division.—Andrew A. Horner, 10920 New Hampshire Avenue, Silver Spring, Md., 20903.
   Director, Public Utilities Division.—H. Dean Miller, 22 Moller Parkway, Hagerstown, Md., 21741.

UTILIZATION AND DISPOSAL SERVICE

General Services Building.   Phone, 343-1100 (Code 183, extension 33104)

Commissioner, Utilization and Disposal Service.—Howard Greenberg, 7426 Arrowwood Road, Bethesda, Md., 20034.
Executive Officer.—Ernest Sullivan, 3630 Old Mount Vernon Road, Alexandria, Va., 22309.
Assistant Commissioner, Personal Property.—Curtis A. Roos, Route 1, Box 300, Great Falls, Va., 22066.
   Deputy Assistant Commissioner.—Lewis C. Tuttle, 9626 Cottrell Terrace, Silver Spring, Md., 20903.
   Director, Utilization Division.—Franklin P. Donaldson, 7100 Atlee Place, Springfield, Va., 22151.
   Director, Sales Division.—David W. Tompkins, 3919 Ryegate Lane, Alexandria, Va., 22308.
   Director, Property Rehabilitation Division.—William S. Eckert, 514 Shiloh Circle, Fairfax, Va., 22030.
   Director, Donation Division.—Howlett C. Kleinstuber, 8722 Milford Avenue, Silver Spring, Md., 20910.
Assistant Commissioner, Real Property.—Walter C. Moreland, 2942 Viewpoint Road, Alexandria, Va., 22314.
   Deputy Assistant Commissioner.—Melvin A. Norton, 832 South Ivy Street, Arlington, Va., 22204.
   Special Assistant to the Assistant Commissioner.—John R. Corridon, 2208 Apache Street, Hyattsville, Md., 20783.
   Acting Director, Eastern Division.—William P. Wolf, 9340 Columbia Boulevard, Silver Spring, Md., 20910.
   Director, Midwestern Division.—John L. Carroll, 5705 Hornet Lane, McLean, Va., 22101.
   Director, Southern Division.—Morgan Birge, 4540 34th Street South, Arlington, Va., 22206.
   Director, Western Division.—David C. Austin, 1020 19th Street, 20036.
   Director, Appraisal Staff.—Thomas L. Peyton, 3803 Saigon Road, McLean, Va., 22101.

NATIONAL ARCHIVES AND RECORDS SERVICE

National Archives Building.   Phone, WOrth 3-1110 (Code 13, extension 33434)

Archivist of the United States.—Wayne C. Grover, 2303 Linden Lane, Silver Spring, Md., 20910.
Deputy Archivist of the United States.—Robert H. Bahmer, 5603 Surrey Street, Chevy Chase, Md., 20015.
Administrative Officer.—Walter Robertson, Jr., 13245 Glenhill Road, Silver Spring, Md., 20904.
Executive Director (National Historical Publications Commission).—Oliver W. Holmes, 206 Waverly Way, McLean, Va., 22101.
Assistant Archivist, Office of Civil Archives.—G. Philip Bauer, 5209 Danbury Road, Bethesda, Md., 20014.
   Director, Archival Projects Division.—Kenneth W. Munden, 2673 North Upshur Street, Arlington, Va., 22207.
   Director, Exhibits and Publications Division.—Albert H. Leisinger, 5312 Wriley Road, 20016.
   Director, Reference Division.—G. Philip Bauer, 5209 Danbury Road, Bethesda, Md., 20014.
Assistant Archivist, Office of Military Archives.—Sherrod E. East, 2312 North Vernon Street, Arlington, Va., 22207.
   Director, Archival Projects Division.—Mabel E. Deutrich, 2801 Adams Mill Road, 20009.
   Director, Reference Division.—Sherrod E. East, 2312 North Vernon Street, Arlington, Va., 22207.

Assistant Archivist, Office of Federal Records Centers.—Herbert E. Angel, 8919 Brickyard Road, Potomac, Md., 20854.

    Director, Operations Division.—Charles A. Sterman, 8424 Donnybrook Drive, Chevy Chase, Md., 20015.

    Director, Records Appraisal Division.—Lewis J. Darter, Jr., 8909 Grant Street, Bethesda, Md., 20034.

Assistant Archivist, Office of Records Management.—Everett O. Alldredge, 1649 45th Street, 20007.

    Deputy Assistant Archivist.—Chester L. Guthrie, 5108 Westridge Drive, 20016.

    Director, Paperwork Standards and Automation Division.—Artel Ricks, 112 East Woodlawn Avenue, Falls Church, Va., 22042.

    Director, Program Evaluation Division.—Edward N. Johnson, 10610 Lexington Street, Kensington, Md., 20795.

    Director, Technical Assistance Division.—Harold E. Harriman, 5601 24th Avenue, Hillcrest Heights, Md., 20031.

Director, Federal Register.—David C. Eberhart, 955 South Columbus Street, Arlington, Va., 22204.

    Assistant to the Director.—Frank J. Nivert, 215 East Marshall Street, Falls Church, Va., 22042.

    Director, Presidential and Legislative Division.—Warren R. Reid, 307 Kentucky Avenue, Alexandria, Va., 22305.

    Director, Executive Agencies Division.—Kenneth K. Lawshe, 6207 Dahlonega Road, 20016.

Assistant Archivist, Office of Presidential Libraries.—Herman Kahn, 3238 38th Street, 20016.

    Director, Dwight D. Eisenhower Library.—William D. Aeschbacher, 1112 North Campbell Street, Abilene, Kans., 67410.

    Director, Herbert Hoover Library.—Franz G. Lassner, 312 South Downey Street, West Branch, Iowa, 52358.

    Director, Franklin D. Roosevelt Library.—Elizabeth B. Drewry, 25 Fuller Lane, Hyde Park, N.Y., 12538.

    Director, Harry S. Truman Library.—Philip C. Brooks, 701 Bellevista Drive, Independence, Mo., 64050.

REGIONAL ADMINISTRATORS

Region 1, Regional Administrator.—Paul Lazzaro, Post Office and Courthouse, Boston, Mass., 02109.

Region 2, Regional Administrator.—Arthur Miller, 30 Church Street, New York, N.Y. 10007.

Region 3, Regional Administrator.—David Phillips, 7th and D Streets, SW., Washington, D.C., 20407.

Region 4, Regional Administrator.—Wilbur H. Sanders, 1776 Peachtree Street NW., Atlanta, Ga., 30309.

Region 5, Regional Administrator.—Dominic A. Tesauro, 219 South Dearborn Street, Chicago, Ill., 60604.

Region 6, Regional Administrator.—William A. Holloway, 1500 East Bannister Road, Kansas City, Mo., 64131.

Region 7, Regional Administrator.—John M. McGee, 1114 Commerce Street, Dallas, Tex., 75202.

Region 8, Regional Administrator.—Gerald E. McNamara, Building 41, Denver Federal Center, Denver, Colo., 80225.

Region 9, Regional Administrator.—Thomas E. Hannon, 49 Fourth Street, San Francisco, Calif., 94103.

Region 10, Regional Administrator.—Eugene R. Thissen, GSA Center, Auburn, Wash., 98002.

FEDERAL RECORDS COUNCIL

Legislative Branch:

    Harley O. Staggers, Representative from West Virginia.

    James R. Grover, Jr., Representative from New York.

    Felton M. Johnston, Secretary of the Senate.

    Allen N. Humphrey, General Accounting Office.

Executive Branch:

    Department of the Air Force.—William Muller, Chief, Documentation Systems Division, Directorate of Administrative Services.

Executive Branch—Continued

    Department of Agriculture.—Samuel L. Gardiner, Assistant Director of Plant and Operations.

    Post Office Department.—Everett E. Sheats, Chief, Forms and Records Management Branch, Office of Management Services.

    Bureau of the Budget.—John B. Holden, Assistant Chief, Property and Supply Management Branch, Office of Management and Organization.

    Veterans Administration.—Blake E. Turner, Assistant Administrator for Management and Evaluation.

    Interstate Commerce Commission.—Bernard F. Schmid, Managing Director.

Judicial Branch:

    Supreme Court.—John F. Davis, Clerk.

    Administrative Office of U.S. Courts.—John C. Airhart, Assistant Director.

NATIONAL HISTORICAL PUBLICATIONS COMMISSION

Phone, WOrth 3–6488

Members.—Wayne C. Grover, Archivist of the United States (chairman); William M. Franklin, Director of the Historical Office, Department of State; Rudolph A. Winnacker, Historian for the Office of the Secretary of Defense, Department of Defense; David C. Mearns, Chief of the Manuscript Division, Library of Congress; Leverett Saltonstall, Senator from Massachusetts; George P. Miller, Representative from California; Arthur M. Schlesinger, Professor Emeritus of History, Harvard University; Boyd C. Shafer and Lyman H. Butterfield, members of the American Historical Association.

Executive Director.—Oliver W. Holmes, 206 Waverly Way, McLean, Va., 22101.

NATIONAL ARCHIVES TRUST FUND BOARD

Phone, WOrth 3–3434

Members.—The Archivist of the United States (chairman); the chairmen of the Senate Committee on Post Office and Civil Serice and the House Committee on Post Office and Civil Service.

Secretary.—Walter Robertson, Jr., Administrative Officer, National Archives and Records Service.

ADMINISTRATIVE COMMITTEE OF THE FEDERAL REGISTER

Phone, WOrth 3–3333

Members.—The Archivist of the United States (chairman); officer of the Department of Justice designated by the Attorney General; the Public Printer.

Secretary.—David C. Eberhart, Director, Office of the Federal Register, National Archives and Records Service.

FEDERAL FIRE COUNCIL

Room 4311, General Services Building. Phone, 343–2453

Governing Body:

    Maj. Gen. Robert H. Curtin, Director of Civil Engineering, Office, Deputy Chief of Staff, Operations, Headquarters, United States Air Force, Department of the Air Force, 801 South Overlook Drive, Alexandria, Va., 22305.

    Lt. Gen. Walter K. Wilson, Jr., Chief of Engineers, Department of the Army, Quarters 1, Fort Belvoir, Va., 22060.

    Rear Adm. P. Corradi, Chief, Bureau of Yards and Docks, Department of the Navy, Washington Navy Yard Annex, M at Eighth Street SE., 20390.

    Tyler Abell, Assistant Postmaster General, Bureau of Facilities, Post Office Department, 4506 49th Street, 20011.

    George B. Hartzog, Jr., Director, National Park Service, Department of the Interior, 2517 K Street, 20037.

    Dr. Allen V. Astin, Director, National Bureau of Standards, Department of Commerce, 5008 Battery Lane, Bethesda, Md., 20014.

    Dr. Wayne C. Grover, Archivist of the United States National Archives and Records Service, General Services Administration, 2303 Linden Lane Silver Spring, Md., 20910.

    [Vacancy], Commissioner, Public Buildings Service, General Services Administration, 20405.

Officers:
  Chairman.—[Vacancy], Commissioner, Public Buildings Service, General Services Administration, 20405.
  Deputy Chairman.—William A. Schmidt, Deputy Commissioner, Public Buildings Service, General Services Administration, 5901 Cromwell Drive, Springfield, Md., 20016.
  Secretary.—William L. Hanbury, Protection Division, Office of Buildings Management, Public Buildings Service, General Services Administration, 492 North Owen Street, Alexandria, Va., 22304.

GORGAS MEMORIAL INSTITUTE OF TROPICAL AND PREVENTIVE MEDICINE, INC.

Office, 1835 I Street, 20006.   Phone, MEtropolitan 8-1313

President.—Paul H. Streit, M.D., Major General, U.S.A. (Ret.), 4721 Falstone Avenue, Chevy Chase, Md.
Vice President and General Counsel.—Hon. Maurice H. Thatcher, 1801 16th Street.
Secretary.—Fred L. Soper, 4104 Rosemary Street, Chevy Chase, Md.
Assistant Secretary.—Gloriela Calvo, 3700 Massachusetts Avenue, 20016.

GORGAS MEMORIAL LABORATORY, PANAMA, R.P.

Director.—Martin D. Young, Sc. D., Panama, R.P.

HOUSING AND HOME FINANCE AGENCY

OFFICE OF THE ADMINISTRATOR

Normandy Building, 1626 K Street.   Phone, EXecutive 3-4160 (Code 128, extension 4486)

Mailing Address: 1626 K Street, 20410.

Administrator.—Robert C. Weaver, 4600 Connecticut Avenue, 20008.
Deputy Administrator.—Milton P. Semer, 2 Bedford Lane, Alexandria, Va., 22307.
General Counsel.—Milton P. Semer, 2 Bedford Lane, Alexandria, Va., 22307.
  Associate General Counsel.—Adolph H. Zwerner, 4201 Massachusetts Avenue, 20016.
  Associate General Counsel (Legislative).—Ashley A. Foard, 2250 North Powhatan Street, Arlington, Va.
  Associate General Counsel (Operations).—Hilbert Fefferman, 5661 Bent Branch Road, 20016.
Congressional Liaison Officer.—Charles M. Smith, 2 Potomac Court, Alexandria, Va., 22300.
Special Assistant to the Administrator.—Robert W. Murray, Jr., 206 G Street SW., 20024.
Special Assistant to the Administrator.—Edith P. L. Gilbert, 3336 O Street, 20007.
Assistant to the Administrator for Intergroup Relations.—Booker T. McGraw, 3036 Park Place, 20001.
Assistant to the Administrator for Consumer and Community Group Relations.—Flora Y. Hatcher, 4807 Dover Road, 20016.
Special Assistant to the Deputy Administrator.—Robert A. Sauer, 9411 Singleton Drive, Bethesda, Md., 20034.
Assistant Administrator (Community Programs).—Kermit G. Bailer, 755 Delaware Avenue SW.
Assistant Administrator (Housing for Senior Citizens).—Sidney Spector, 1209 Burton Street, Silver Spring, Md.
Acting Assistant Administrator (Public Affairs).—Robert W. Murray, Jr., 206 G Street SW., 20024.
Assistant Administrator (Program Policy).—Morton J. Schussheim, 9 Oxford Street, Chevy Chase, Md., 20015.
Assistant Administrator (International Housing).—James A. Moore, 3132 Elba Road, Alexandria, Va.
  Special Assistant, Office of International Housing.—George W. Snowden, 6307 13th Street, 20011.

Assistant Administrator (Transportation).—John C. Kohl, 1400 20th Street NW.
Assistant Administrator (Metropolitan Development).—Victor Fischer, 3516 Cummings Lane, Chevy Chase, Md., 20015.
Assistant Administrator (Administration).—Lewis E. Williams, 3819 48th Street, 20016.
Director, Division of Budget and Management.—John M. Frantz, 2934 Glover Driveway, 20016.
Director, Division of Personnel.—Douglas E. Chaffin, 5320 28th Street, 20015.
Director, Compliance Division.—Carl V. Ramey, 613 22d Street, 20007.
Director, Community Disposition Program.—Joseph P. Smith, Jr., 5013 Sargent Road NE., 20017.
Director, Audit Division.—Elmer W. Muhonen, 7214 Reservoir Road, Springfield, Va., 22150.

COMMUNITY FACILITIES ADMINISTRATION

1619 Massachusetts Avenue.   Phone, EXecutive 3–4160 (Code 128, extension 5634)

Mailing Address: 1626 K Street

Commissioner.—Clarence H. Osthagen, Franklin Park Hotel, 1332 I Street, 20005.
Deputy Commissioner.—Richard L. Still, 6801 Delaware Street, Chevy Chase, Md., 20015.
Assistant to the Commissioner.—Ludwig Caminita, Jr., Box 65, Sandy Spring, Md.
Assistant Commissioner for Operations and Engineering.—Allen Cywin, 35 Arcturus Lane, Alexandria, Va.
Assistant Commissioner for Management Control.—John R. Fernstrom, 5222 Colony Road, Oxon Hill, Md., 20021.
Assistant Commissioner (Program Development).—[Vacant.]
Chief Counsel.—[Vacant.]

URBAN RENEWAL ADMINISTRATION

Lafayette Building, 811 Vermont Avenue.   Phone EXecutive 3–4160 (Code 128, extension 3175)

Mailing Address: 1626 K Street

Commissioner.—William L. Slayton, 3411 Ordway Street, 20016.
Deputy Commissioner.—Howard J. Wharton, 8315 Taylor Drive, Annandale, Va., 22003.
Special Assistant to the Commissioner.—Andrew I. Hickey, 1803 Alcan Drive, Silver Spring, Md., 20902.
Assistant to the Commissioner for Intergroup Relations.— J. Lawrence Duncan, 1345 Childress Street NE., 20002.
Assistant Commissioner for Technical Standards.—John W. Shively, 383 O Street SW., 20024.
   Chief Finance Officer.—Max Lipowitz, 904 Buckingham Drive, Silver Spring, Md., 20901.
   Chief Real Estate Officer.—James E. McCormack, 3401 Alabama Avenue, Alexandria, Va., 22305.
   Director, Project Planning and Engineering Branch (Acting).—Dorn C. McGrath, Jr., 5128 Lipsner Court, Annandale, Va., 22003.
   Director, Redevelopment Branch.—Floyd B. Arms, 1311 Delaware Avenue SW., 20024.
Assistant Commissioner for Relocation and Rehabilitation.—Robert E. McCabe, 3121 33d Place, 20016.
   Deputy Assistant Commissioner, Relocation and Community Organization.—Hans B. Spiegel, 6621 First Street, 20012.
   Director, Relocation Branch.—Hilda M. James, 1620 Missouri Avenue, 20011.
   Director, Community Organization Branch.—[Vacant.]
Deputy Assistant Commissioner, Rehabilitation and Codes.—Leo Stern, 9808 Kensington Parkway, Kensington, Md., 20795.
   Director, Rehabilitation and Conservation Branch.—Leonard J. Czarniecki, 4813 Broad Brook Drive, Bethesda, Md., 20014.
   Director, Codes and Building Standards Branch.—Robert C. Reichel, 5307 Augusta Street, 20016.

Assistant Commissioner for Urban Planning and Community Development.—
Frederick O'R. Hayes, 412 Paul Spring Road, Alexandria, Va., 22307.
  Deputy Assistant Commissioner, Urban Planning.—Richard Ives, 4201 Cathedral
  Avenue, 20016.
    Director, Community Development Branch.—David A. Grossman, 6308 East
    Halbert Road, Bethesda, Md., 20034.
    Director, Urban Planning Assistance Branch.—Warren T. Zitzman, 3081
    North Pollard Street, Arlington, Va., 22207.
  Deputy Assistant Commissioner for Open-Space Land.—Arthur A. Davis, 3922
  Rickover Road, Wheaton, Md., 20902.
Assistant Commissioner for Program Planning.—Gordon E. Howard, 1316 Popkins
Lane, Hollin Hills, Alexandria, Va., 22307.
    Director, Legislative Policy Branch.—Frederick A. McLaughlin, Jr., 5805
    Namakagon Road, 20016.
    Director, Program Data and Evaluation Branch.—Peter P. Riemer, 2915 Elba
    Road, Alexandria, Va., 22306.
    Director, Demonstration Program Branch.—Howard Cayton, 3069 Canal Street,
    20007.
Assistant Commissioner for Field Operations.—Robert C. Robinson, 3908 Elby
Street, Wheaton, Md., 20906.
  Deputy Assistant Commissioner for Field Operations.—Howard W. Wolaver,
  9511 West Stanhope Road, Kensington, Md., 20795.
Chief Counsel.—S. Leigh Curry, Jr., 1716 Reddfield Drive, Falls Church, Va.,
22043.
Director, Public Affairs.—Sydney H. Kasper, 9622 Evergreen Street, Silver Spring,
Md., 20901.
Director, Division of Administrative Management.—William H. Gelbach, Jr., 1207
Lincoln Avenue, West Falls Church, Va., 22046.

HHFA REGIONAL OFFICES

Region I.—Connecticut, Maine, Massachusetts, New Hampshire, New York,
Rhode Island, Vermont.—Lester Eisner, Jr. (Regional Administrator), 346
Broadway, New York, N.Y., 10013.
Region II—New Jersey, Delaware, District of Columbia, Maryland, Pennsyl-
vania, Virginia, West Virginia.—Warren P. Phelan (Regional Administra-
tor), Chestnut and Juniper Streets, 10th Floor, Widener Building, Philadel-
phia, Pa., 19107.
Region III—Alabama, Florida, Georgia, Mississippi, South Carolina, Tennessee,
North Carolina, Kentucky.—Edward H. Baxter (Acting Regional Adminis-
trator), Peachtree Seventh Building, Atlanta, Ga., 30323.
Region IV—Illinois, Indiana, Iowa, Michigan, Minnesota, Nebraska, North
Dakota, Ohio, South Dakota, Wisconsin.—John P. McCollum (Regional
Administrator), Room 1500, 360 North Michigan Avenue, Chicago, Ill.,
60601.
Region V—Arkansas, Colorado, Louisiana, New Mexico, Oklahoma, Texas,
Missouri, Kansas.—William W. Collins, Jr. (Regional Administrator) Federal
Center, 300 West Vickery Boulevard, Fort Worth, Tex., 76104.
Region VI—Arizona, California, Idaho, Montana, Nevada, Oregon, Utah,
Washington, Wyoming, Guam, Alaska, Hawaii.—Robert B. Pitts (Regional
Administrator), 450 Golden Gate Avenue, Box 36003, San Francisco, Calif.,
94102.
Region VII—Puerto Rico, Virgin Islands.—Jose Febres-Silva (Regional Adminis-
trator), P.O. Box 9093, 1608 Ponce de Leon Avenue, Santurce, Puerto Rico,
00908.

FEDERAL HOUSING ADMINISTRATION

811 Vermont Avenue. Phone, EXecutive 3-4160 (Code 128, extension 4693)

Commissioner.—Philip N. Brownstein, 620 Sheridan Street, Hyattsville, Md.,
20783.
Deputy Commissioner.—Philip J. Maloney, 4520 Burlington Place, 20016.
Assistant Commissioner (Executive Officer).—Edwin G. Callahan, 906 28th Street
South, Arlington, Va., 22202.

Executive Assistant.—Agnes M. Cummings, 7200 Brookville Road, Chevy Chase, Md., 20015.
Assistant to the Commissioner (Intergroup Relations).—Oliver W. Hill, 741 Gresham Place, 20001.
General Counsel.—A. M. Prothro, 4724 Gilliams Road, McLean, Va., 22101.
Associate General Counsel.—John W. Kopecky, 3241 38th Street, 20016.
Assistant Commissioner for Programs.—M. Carter McFarland, 1140 Valley Drive, Alexandria, Va., 22312.
Director, Research and Statistics Division.—Allan F. Thornton, 4822 Upton Street, 20016.
Director, Program Division.—Robert C. Colwell, 422 Woodland Drive, Forest Heights, Md., 20021.
Director, International Division.—William T. Stansbury, 1381 Sheridan Street, 20011.
Assistant Commissioner-Comptroller.—Lester H. Thompson, Route 660, Fairfax Station, Va., 22039.
Associate Deputy Commissioner for Management.—M. Ray Niblack, 311 Vassar Road, Alexandria, Va., 22300.
Director of Compliance Coordination.—Albert E. Johnson, 5116 Cammack Drive, 20016.
Director, Audit and Examination.—Louis N. Teitelbaum, 1900 Rookwood Road, Silver Spring, Md., 20910.
Director, Audit Division.—John A. McAllister, 6207 Inwood Street, Cheverly, Md., 20785.
Director, Examination Division.—Raymond E. Crilley, 10240 Parkwood Drive, Kensington, Md., 20795.
Congressional Liaison Officer.—Burton C. Wood, 3001 P Street, 20000.
Public Information Officer.—Gerald E. Poston, 1802 Metzerott Road, Adelphi, Md.
Assistant Commissioner for Administration.—Horace B. Bazan, 11715 Magruder Lane, Rockville, Md., 20852.
Director, Budget Division.—Mason C. Doan, 9606 Merwood Lane, Silver Spring, Md., 20901.
Director, Personnel Division.—Joe B. Montgomery, 3931 Livingston Street, 20015.
Director, Management Division.—Louis•E. Walton, 501 North Manchester Street, Arlington, Va., 22203.
Director, General Services Division.—Osborne S. Koerner, 3753 North Woodrow Street, Arlington, Va., 22207.
Associate Deputy Commissioner for Operations.—[Vacant.]
Deputy Associate Deputy Commissioner for Operations.—Walter S. Newlin, 303 Hector Road, McLean, Va., 22101.
Assistant Commissioner for Home Mortgages.—J. Guy Arrington, 3909 Thornapple Street, Chevy Chase, Md., 20015.
Assistant Commissioner for Multifamily Housing.—C. Franklin Daniels, 783 Rollins Drive, Alexandria, Va., 22307.
Special Assistant for Armed Services Housing.—Jack Carter, 823 Crescent Drive, Alexandria, Va., 22302.
Special Assistant for Nursing Homes.—Helen F. Holt, 4225 49th Street, 20016.
Special Assistant for Elderly Housing.—Gracie B. Pfost, Hotel Congressional, 300 New Jersey Axenue SE., 20003.
Director, Rental Housing Division.—Marsh Cunningham, 5605 Shirley Street, McLean, Va., 22101.
Director, Urban Renewal Division.—Christian O. Christenson, 805 Sunrise Lane, Vienna, Va., 22180.
Director, Cooperative Housing Division.—Harry E. Johnson, 985 North Potomac Street, Arlington, Va., 22205.
Assistant Commissioner for Property Disposition.—Edward L. Tagwerker.
Assistant Commissioner for Property Improvement.—Harry A. Finney, RFD #1, Lovettsville, Va.
Assistant Commissioner for Technical Standards.—Richard J. Canavan, 3616 Rittenhouse Street, 20015.
Director, Architectural Standards Division.—Neil A. Connor, 2500 Q Street, 20007.
Director, Appraisal and Mortgage Risk Division.—Waldemar Weichbrodt, 4000 Cathedral Avenue, 20016.

Zone Operations Commissioners:
  Zone I. Joseph W. Maguire, Hunting Towers, C714, Alexandria, Va., 22314.
  Zone II. Charles W. Skinner, 1418 Oak Ridge Road, Falls Church, Va., 22042.
  Zone III. Stratford E. McKenrick, 1407 Boyce Avenue, Ruxton, Md., 21204.
  Zone IV. James F. Neville, 509 Juniper Lane, Falls Church, Va., 22040.
  Zone V. Carmen R. Pasquale, 9504 Caroline Avenue, Silver Spring, Md., 20901.

PUBLIC HOUSING ADMINISTRATION
1741 Rhode Island Avenue.   Phone, 382-4261 (Code 128, extension 4261)

Commissioner.—Marie C. McGuire, 1727 Massachusetts Avenue, 20006.
Deputy Commissioner.—Francis X. Servaites, 3162 Tennyson Street, 20015.
  Director of Labor Relations.—Raymond J. Dolan, 9509 Page Avenue, Bethesda, Md., 20014.
  Director of Intergroup Relations.—Philip G. Sadler, 2101 New Hampshire Avenue, 20009.
  Director of Internal Audit.—James F. Gore, 6712 North Williamsburg Boulevard, Arlington, Va., 22213.
General Counsel.—Joseph Burstein, 5725 26th Street, 20015.
  Associate General Counsel.—Frank L. Willingham, 6005 Cobalt Road, 20016.
  Associate General Counsel.—Arnold Coplan, 1437 Rittenhouse Street, 20011.
Congressional Liaison Officer.—Robert W. Notti, 2500 Q Street, 20007.
Director of Public Affairs.—Lee W. Schooler, 6702 41st Avenue, University Park, Md., 20782.
Assistant Commissioner for Administration.—H. L. Wooten, 6628 32d Street, 20015.
  Comptroller.—Patrick C. O'Leary, 8409 Galveston Road, Silver Spring, Md., 20910.
  Director of Administrative Planning.—Helen A. Halbig, 2500 Wisconsin Avenue, 20007.
  Director of Budget.—Nat A. Whitmire, 1100 6th Street SW., 20024.
  Director of Office Services.—Elmer F. Gustavson, 1611 31st Street, 20007.
  Director of Personnel.—Charles G. Stern, 401 Mansfield Road, Silver Spring, Md., 20910.
Assistant Commissioner for Development.—Thomas B. Thompson, 1745 N Street, 20036.
Deputy Assistant Commissioner for Development.—Charles B. Altman, 5310 Worthington Drive, 20016.
  Architectural Adviser.—Silver L. Tesone, 2829 O Street, 20007.
  Director of Design Services.—Archie P. Burgess, 1425 17th Street, 20036.
  Director of Planning and Production.—E. Stanton Foster, 7402 Ridgewood Avenue, Chevy Chase, Md., 20015.
Assistant Commissioner for Management.—Abner D. Silverman, 9908 Parkwood Drive, Bethesda, Md., 20014.
Deputy Assistant Commissioner for Management.—George O'B. Bailey, 3266 Worthington Street, 20015.
  Director of Fiscal Auditing.—Samuel S. Good, 3909 Northampton Street, 20015.
  Director of Fiscal Management.—Kenneth C. Cavanaugh, 4500 20th Street North, Arlington, Va., 22207.
  Director of General Management.—Harold Caden, 2219 Osborn Drive, Silver Spring, Md., 20910.
  Director of Maintenance Engineering.—Channing M. Bolton, 1003 Atlanta Street, Fairfax, Va., 22030.
Assistant Commissioner for Program Planning.—Sol Ackerman, 8000 Park Overlook Drive, Bethesda, Md., 20034.
  Director of Statistics.—Louis S. Katz, 1405 Primrose Road, 20012.

REGIONAL OFFICES

Atlanta—Alabama, Florida, Georgia, Kentucky, Mississippi, North Carolina, South Carolina, Tennessee.—Arthur R. Hanson, Peachtree-Seventh Street Building, 50 Seventh Street NE., Atlanta, Ga., 30323.
Chicago—Illinois, Indiana, Iowa, Michigan, Minnesota, Nebraska, North Dakota, Ohio, South Dakota, Wisconsin.—William E. Bergeron, 185 North Wabash Avenue, Chicago, Ill., 60601.

Fort Worth—Arkansas, Colorado, Kansas, Louisiana, Missouri, New Mexico, Oklahoma, Texas.—Thomas H. Callaham, 300 West Vickery Boulevard, Fort Worth, Tex., 76104.

New York—Connecticut, Maine, Massachusetts, New Hampshire, New Jersey, New York, Rhode Island, Vermont.—Herman D. Hillman, 346 Broadway, New York, N.Y., 10013.

Philadelphia—Delaware, Maryland, Pennsylvania, Virginia, West Virginia, the District of Columbia.—LeRoy A. Smith, 11th Floor Widener Building, Chestnut and Juniper Streets, Philadelphia, Pa., 19107.

Puerto Rico—Puerto Rico and the Virgin Islands.—Felipe Gorbea-Fernandez, Stop 23 Ponce de Leon Avenue, Santurce, Puerto Rico.

San Francisco—Alaska, Arizona, California, Idaho, Montana, Nevada, Oregon, Utah, Washington, Wyoming, Hawaii.—Louis B. Ambler, Jr., 450 Golden Gate Avenue, San Francisco, Calif., 94102.

FEDERAL NATIONAL MORTGAGE ASSOCIATION

Lafayette Building, 811 Vermont Avenue.   Phone, EXecutive 3-4160 (Code 128, extension 4212)

Board of Directors:
   Chairman: Robert C. Weaver (Housing and Home Finance, Administrator), 4600 Connecticut Avenue, 20008.
   J. Stanley Baughman, Member, 4702 Overbrook Road, 20016.
   [Vacant.]
   Milton P. Semer, Member, 2 Bedford Lane, Alexandria, Va., 22307.
   P. N. Brownstein, Member, 620 Sheridan Street, Hyattsville, Md., 20783.
President.—J. Stanley Baughman, 4702 Overbrook Road, 20016.
Vice President.—Harry M. Gilbert, 1400 Ivanhoe Street, Alexandria, Va., 22304.
Vice President and Loan Manager.—Allan C. Tyler, 34 West Spring Street, Alexandria, Va., 22301.
General Counsel.—Robert Newton Reid, The University Club, 1135 16th Street, 20006.
Secretary-Treasurer.—Arthur C. Hemstreet, 4405 East-West Highway, Apt. 601, Bethesda, Md., 20014.
Controller.—John L. Burke, 9201 Sudbury Road, Silver Spring, Md., 20901.
Director of Examination and Audit.—Alexander J. Sternberg, 2800 Quebec Street, 20008.
Public Information Officer.—Francis J. Nowak, 501 Lloyd Lane, Alexandria, Va., 22302.
Director of Personnel.—Glendon D. Willey, 8607 Victoria Road West, Springfield, Va., 22151.

AGENCIES

Philadelphia—Connecticut, Delaware, District of Columbia, Maine, Maryland, Massachusetts, New Hampshire, New Jersey, New York, Pennsylvania, Puerto Rico, Rhode Island, Vermont, Virgin Islands, Virginia, and West Virginia.—Arthur A. Gretz, Agency Manager, 211 South Broad Street, Philadelphia, Pa., 19107.

Atlanta—Alabama, Florida, Georgia, Kentucky, Mississippi, North Carolina, South Carolina, and Tennessee.—Frank H. Greer, Agency Manager, 34 Peachtree Street NE., Atlanta, Ga., 30303.

Chicago—Illinois, Indiana, Iowa, Michigan, Minnesota, Nebraska, North Dakota, Ohio, South Dakota, and Wisconsin.—Frank H. Bauman, Agency Manager, 72 West Adams Street, Chicago, Ill., 60603.

Dallas—Arkansas, Colorado, Kansas, Louisiana, Missouri, New Mexico, Oklahoma, and Texas.—Bertram A. Dietrich, Agency Manager, 1505 Elm Street, Dallas, Tex., 75201.

Los Angeles—Alaska, Arizona, California, Guam, Hawaii, Idaho, Montana, Nevada, Oregon, Utah, Washington, and Wyoming.—Paul Akin, Agency Manager, 3540 Wilshire Boulevard, Los Angeles, Calif., 90005.

INDIAN CLAIMS COMMISSION

General Accounting Office Building, 441 G Street. Phone, DUdley 6-4491 (Code 129, extension 4491)

Chief Commissioner.—Arthur V. Watkins, 1433 North Inglewood Street, Arlington, Va.
Associate Commissioners:
William M. Holt, 3935 Pennsylvania Avenue SE.
T. Harold Scott, 4125 Leland Street, Chevy Chase, Md.
Chief Clerk and Administrative Officer.—Jean R. Hanna, 1201 Plantation Parkway, Fairfax, Va., 22030.

INTERDEPARTMENTAL SAVINGS BONDS COMMITTEE

Civil Service Commission Building, 1900 E Street
Phone, Code 184, extension 2222

Chairman.—John W. Macy, Jr., 201 North Langley Lane, McLean, Va., 22101.
[The head of each agency in the Executive Branch of the Federal Government is ex officio a member of this committee by Presidential appointment.]

INTERSTATE COMMERCE COMMISSION

Interstate Commerce Commission Building, Twelfth Street and Constitution Avenue, 20423
Phone, NAtional 8-7460 (Code 156, extension 304)

Chairman.—Charles A. Webb, Route 1, Box 278, Great Falls, Va.
Vice Chairman.—John W. Bush, 4201 Cathedral Avenue.
Commissioners:
Howard G. Freas, 8 Kentbury Way, Bethesda, Md.
Kenneth H. Tuggle, 5200 Western Avenue, Chevy Chase, Md.
Everett Hutchinson, 5401 Albermarle Street.
Rupert L. Murphy, 1400 South Joyce Street, Arlington, Va.
Laurence K. Walrath, 5270 Loughboro Road, 20016.
Abe McGregor Goff, 5348 29th Street.
William H. Tucker, 5109 Brookeway Drive.
Paul J. Tierney, 7013 Beechwood Drive, Chevy Chase, Md.
Virginia Mae Brown, 600 River Towers Drive, Alexandria, Va.
Legislative Counsel.—Frank E. McCarthy, 4515 Harling Lane, Bethesda, Md.
Congressional Liaison Officer.—James T. Corcoran, 2020 F Street.
Office of the Managing Director:
Managing Director.—Bernard F. Schmid, 6803 Adelphi Road, University Park, Md.
Assistant to Managing Director.—Ernest Weiss, 3312 Brooklawn Terrace, Chevy Chase, Md.
Budget Officer.—J. Neil Ryan, 11008 Inwood Avenue, Silver Spring, Md.
Director of Personnel.—Curtis F. Adams, 5808 Lenox Road, Bethesda, Md.
Chief of Section of Administrative Services.—John A. Nolin, 6437 Burwell Street, Springfield, Va.
Office of the Secretary:
Secretary.—[Vacant].
Assistant Secretary.—Bertha F. Armes, 3801 Connecticut Avenue.
Public Information Officer.—Warner L. Baylor, 8700 Kenilworth Avenue, Springfield, Va.
Chief, Reference Service.—Walter W. Dwyer, 4901 Strathmore Avenue, Kensington, Md.
Librarian.—Glennie M. Norman, 4000 Tunlaw Road.
Office of the General Counsel:
General Counsel.—Robert W. Ginnane, 2533 North Upland Street, Arlington, Va.
Deputy General Counsel.—I. K. Hay, 9801 Wildwood Road, Bethesda, Md.

Bureau of Accounts:
    Director.—Matthew Paolo, 7311 Sara Street, Lanham, Md.
    Assistant Director.—Howard L. Domingus, 10316 Leslie Street, Silver Spring, Md.
    Assistant Director.—Richard J. Ferris, Route 1, Box 155C, Vienna, Va.
Bureau of Finance:
    Director.—Thaddeus W. Forbes, Clearview Avenue, Vienna, Va.
    Assistant Director.—Richard Block, Jr., 641 Sligo Avenue, Silver Spring, Md.
Bureau of Inquiry and Compliance:
    Director.—Asa J. Merrill, 4501 Connecticut Avenue.
    Assistant Director.—Bernard A. Gould, 9205 Sligo Creek Parkway, Silver Spring, Md.
    Assistant Director.—Marcus L. Meyer, 2301 Fort Scott Drive, Arlington, Va.
Bureau of Motor Carriers:
    Director.—Herbert Qualls, 5909 South Sixth Street, Falls Church, Va.
    Assistant Director.—George A. Meyer, 5033 Carlyn Spring Road North, Arlington, Va.
Bureau of Operating Rights:
    Director.—Bertram E. Stillwell, 4315 43d Street.
    Assistant Director.—Sheldon Silverman, 202 Hillsboro Drive, Kemp Mills, Silver Spring, Md.
Bureau of Rates and Practices:
    Director.—Alvin L. Corbin, 3000 Spencerville Road, Burtonsville, Md.
    Assistant Director.—Charlie H. Johns, 4111 Humer Road, Annandale, Va.
    Assistant Director.—Harold A. Downs, 421 Popkins Lane, Alexandria, Va.
Bureau of Safety and Service:
    Director.—Charles W. Taylor, 5515 18th Road North, Arlington, Va.
    Assistant Director.—Robert D. Pfahler, 4307 35th Street North, Arlington, Va.
    Assistant Director and Chief of Section of Car Service.—Paul J. Reider, 421 North Park Drive, Arlington, Va.
    Assistant Director and Chief of Section of Locomotive Inspection (Director of Locomotive Inspection).—John A. Hall, 713 Lincoln Avenue, Falls Church, Va.
    Assistant Director and Chief of Section of Railroad Safety.—H. R. Longhurst, 4704 30th Street South, Arlington, Va.
Bureau of Traffic:
    Director.—Edward H. Cox, 4925 Western Avenue.
    Assistant Director.—Robert Newel, 5918 Arlington Boulevard, Arlington, Va.
    Assistant Director and Chief of Section of Tariffs.—Grayson B. Robinson, Burke, Va.
    Assistant Director and Chief of Section of Rates and Informal Cases.—Radway R. Gibbs, 901 South Glebe Road, Arlington, Va.
Bureau of Transport Economics and Statistics:
    Director.—Edward Margolin, 8500 Freyman Drive, Chevy Chase, Md.
    Assistant Director.—Robert G. Rhodes, 704 Burtonwood Court, Alexandria, Va.
Bureau of Water Carriers and Freight Forwarders:
    Director.—Lee R. Nowell, 964 North Lebanon Street, Arlington, Va.
    Assistant Director.—Raymond Krebill, 7433 Baltimore Avenue, Takoma Park, Md.

REGIONAL OFFICES

Region 1: Boston, Mass. Covering Massachusetts, Maine, New Hampshire, Vermont, Rhode Island, New York, New Jersey, Connecticut.—Martin E. Foley, Regional Manager, Interstate Commerce Commission, B.F.S. Building, 30 Federal Street, Boston, Mass., 02110.
Region 2: Philadelphia, Pa. Covering Pennsylvania, Ohio, Virginia, West Virginia, Maryland, Delaware, District of Columbia.—Fred E. Cochran, Regional Manager, Interstate Commerce Commission, 900 U.S. Custom House, Second and Chestnut Streets, Philadelphia, Pa., 19106.
Region 3: Atlanta, Ga. Covering Kentucky, Tennessee, North Carolina, South Carolina, Georgia, Alabama, Mississippi, Florida.—James B. Weber, Regional Manager, Interstate Commerce Commission, 680 West Peachtree Street NW., Atlanta, Ga., 30308.
Region 4: Chicago, Ill. Covering Illinois, Indiana, Michigan, Wisconsin, Minnesota, North Dakota, South Dakota.—George L. Wilmot, Regional Manager, Interstate Commerce Commission, 1086 U.S. Custom House and Federal Office Building, 219 South Dearborn Street, Chicago, Ill., 60604.

Region 5: Fort Worth, Texas. Covering Missouri, Iowa, Nebraska, Kansas, Texas, Oklahoma, Arkansas, Louisiana.—Bernard H. English, Regional Manager, Interstate Commerce Commission, 816 Texas and Pacific Building, Throckmorton and Lancaster Streets, Fort Worth, Tex., 76102.
Region 6: Portland, Oregon. Covering Oregon, Washington, Idaho, Montana, Wyoming, Alaska.—Norman T. Harris, Regional Manager, Interstate Commerce Commission, 538 Pittock Block, 921 South West Washington Street, Portland, Oreg., 97205.
Region 7: San Francisco, Calif. Covering Arizona, California, Nevada, Colorado, Utah, New Mexico.—Philip J. Brannigan, Regional Manager, Interstate Commerce Commission, Federal Office Building, P.O. Box 36004, 450 Golden Gate Avenue, San Francisco. Calif., 94102.

NATIONAL ACADEMY OF SCIENCES AND NATIONAL RESEARCH COUNCIL

Constitution Avenue and Twenty-first Street, 20418. Phone, EXecutive 3–8100 (Code 1224)

President.—Frederick Seitz, 3327 N Street, 20007.
Vice President.—J. A. Stratton, Massachusetts Institute of Technology, Cambridge, Mass.
Foreign Secretary.—Harrison Brown, California Institute of Technology, Pasadena, Calif., and National Academy of Sciences.
Home Secretary.—Hugh L. Dryden, National Aeronautics and Space Agency.
Treasurer.—Lloyd V. Berkner, Graduate Research Center, Inc., Dallas, Tex.
Executive Officer.—S. D. Cornell, 3155 Highland Place, 20008.
Business Manager.—G. D. Meid, 3503 Cummings Lane, Chevy Chase, Md., 20015.

NATIONAL AERONAUTICS AND SPACE ADMINISTRATION

400 Maryland Avenue SW. Phone, EXecutive 3–3260

OFFICE OF THE ADMINISTRATOR

Administration.—James E. Webb, 2800 36th Street, 20007.
Deputy Administrator.—Dr. Hugh L. Dryden, 5606 Overlea Road, 20016.
Assistant Deputy Administrator.—Dr. George L. Simpson, Jr., 4515 Cathedral Avenue, 20016.
  Executive Officer.—Col. L. W. Vogel, 403 Springmann Drive, Fairfax, Va.
  Executive Secretary.—Col. C. J. George, 4104 Dana Court, Kensington, Md.
Associate Administrator.—Dr. Robert C. Seamans, Jr., 1503 Dumbarton Rock Court, 20007.
Deputy Associate Administrator.—Earl D. Hilburn, 412 Tudor Place, Alexandria, Va.
Deputy Associate Administrator for Programming.—DeMarquis D. Wyatt, 8407 Westmont Terrace, Bethesda, Md., 20034.
Deputy Associate Administrator for Industry Affairs.—George Freidl, 1400 South Joyce Street, Arlington, Va.
  Inventions and Contributions Board:
  Chairman.—[Vacant.]
    Executive Secretary.—Dr. James A. Hootman, 3118 Franconia Road, Alexandria, Va.
  Field Installation:
    Western Operations Office, Santa Monica, Calif.—Director—Robert W. Kamm, 22778 Liberty Bell Road, Woodland Hills, Calif.
Deputy Associate Administrator for Defense Affairs.—Adm. W. Fred Boone (ret.), 4000 Massachusetts Avenue, Apt. 916, 20016.
Deputy Associate Administrator for Administration.—John D. Young, 1014 Cedar Lane, Falls Church, Va., 22042.
General Counsel.—Walter D. Sohier, 1693 34th Street, 20007.
Deputy General Counsel.—Paul G. Dembling, 6303 Tone Drive, Bethesda, Md.
Assistant Administrator for Policy Planning.—Dr. George L. Simpson, 4515 Cathedral Avenue, 20016.

Assistant Administrator for Technology Utilization.—Breene M. Kerr, 3551 Spring-
land Lane, 20016.
Assistant Administrator for Management Development.—Gen. William F. McKee
(ret.), 2410 South Lynn Street, Arlington, Va.
Assistant Administrator for Legislative Affairs.—Richard L. Callaghan, 3210
Wisconsin Avenue, Apt. 403, 20016.
Assistant Administrator for Public Affairs.—Julian Scheer, 2511 Q Street, Apt.
106, 20007.
Assistant Administrator of International Programs.—Arnold W. Frutkin, 3702
Ingomar Street, 20016.
Chairman, Policy Planning Board.—Dr. Floyd L. Thompson, 94 Allegheny Road,
Hampton, Va.

OFFICE OF THE ASSOCIATE ADMINISTRATOR FOR MANNED SPACE FLIGHT

Associate Administrator for Manned Space Flight.—Dr. George E. Mueller, 3403
West Lane Keyes, 20007.
Deputy Associate Administrator for Manned Space Flight (Management).—William
B. Rieke, 5209 Bradley Boulevard, Bethesda, Md.
Deputy Associate Administrator for Manned Space Flight (Programs).—Gen.
David M. Jones, 1306–2 Vandenberg Drive, Andrews Air Force Base, 20331.
Assistant to the Associate Administrator for Manned Space Flight.—Paul E. Cotton,
5603 Glenwood Road, Bethesda, Md., 20034.
Director, Manned Space Flight Field Center Development.—Robert F. Freitag,
4110 Mason Ridge Drive, Annandale, Va.
Director, Manned Space Flight Program Control.—William E. Lilly, 3489 South
Utah Street, Arlington, Va.
Director, Manned Space Flight Management Operations.—Clyde B. Bothmer, 601
19th Street, 20006.
Director, Mission Operations.—E. E. Christensen, 5800 DeRussey Parkway,
Chevy Chase, Md., 20015.
Director, Space Medicine.—Dr. W. Randolph Lovelace II, 2815 Ridgecrest Drive
SE., Albequerque, N. Mex.
Director, Gemini Program (Acting).—Dr. George E. Mueller, 3043 West Lane
Keyes, 20007.
Deputy Director, Gemini Program.—William C. Schneider, 424 Ridge Road,
Greenbelt, Md.
Director, Apollo Program.—Maj. Gen. Samuel C. Phillips, 131 6th Street SE.,
20003.
Director, Advanced Manned Missions Program.—Edward Z. Gray, 4001 Wood
Acre Drive, McLean, Va., 22101.

FIELD INSTALLATIONS

George C. Marshall Space Flight Center, Huntsville, Ala.—Director.—Dr. Wernher
von Braun, P.O. Box 682, Huntsville, Ala.
John F. Kennedy Space Flight Center, Cocoa Beach, Fla.—Director.—Dr. Kurt H.
Debus, 100 North Riverside Drive, Patrick Air Force Base, Florida.
Manned Spacecraft Center, Houston, Tex.—Director.—Dr. Robert R. Gilruth,
5128 Park Avenue, Dickinson, Tex.

OFFICE OF THE ASSOCIATE ADMINISTRATOR FOR SPACE SCIENCE AND APPLICATIONS

Associate Administrator for Space Science and Applications.—Dr. Homer E.
Newell, 3704 33d Place, 20008.
Deputy Associate Administrator for Space Science and Applications.—Edgar M.
Cortright, 6909 Granby Street, Bethesda, Md., 20034.
Director of Sciences.—Dr. John F. Clark, 10709 Kinloch Road, Silver Spring, Md.
Director of Engineering.—Robert F. Garbarini, 7829 Cayuga Avenue, Bethesda,
Md.
Special Assistant.—James O. Spriggs, 9903 Thornwood Road, Kensington, Md.,
20795.
Director, Program Review and Resources Management.—Eldon D. Taylor, 7722
Jervis Street, Springfield, Va.
Director, Bioscience Programs.—Dr. Orr E. Reynolds, Route 1, Box 58, Green
Valley Road, Clarksburg, Md.

Director, Communication and Navigation Programs.—Leonard Jaffe, 418 Sisson Court, Silver Spring, Md.
Director, Physics and Astronomy Programs.—Dr. John E. Naugle, 111 Northwood Avenue, Silver Spring, Md.
Director, Grants and Research Contracts.—Dr. Thomas L. K. Smull, 4301 Massachusetts Avenue, 20016.
Director, Launch Vehicles and Propulsion Programs.—Vincent L. Johnson, 10241 Farnham Drive, Bethesda, Md.
Director, Lunar and Planetary Programs.—Oran W. Nicks, 5809 Wiltshire Drive, 20016.
Director, Manned Space Science.—Willis B. Foster, RFD No. 5, Box 875, Fairfax, Va., 22030.
Director, Meteorological Programs.—Dr. Morris Tepper, 107 Bluff Terrace, Silver Spring, Md.

FIELD INSTALLATIONS

Goddard Space Flight Center, Greenbelt, Md.—Director.—Dr. Harry J. Goett, 13319 Georgia Avenue, Silver Spring, Md.
Jet Propulsion Laboratory (Contractor Operated), Pasadena, Calif.—Director.—Dr. W. H. Pickering, 2514 North Highland Avenue, Altadena, Calif.
Pacific Launch Operations Office, Lompoc, Calif.—Director.—William H. Evans, 1719 LaMirada Drive, Carpenteria, Calif.
Wallops Station, Wallops Island, Va.—Director.—Robert L. Krieger, Quarters H-1, Munson Circle, Wallops Station, Wallops Island, Va.

OFFICE OF THE ASSOCIATE ADMINISTRATOR FOR ADVANCED RESEARCH AND TECHNOLOGY

Associate Administrator for Advanced Research and Technology.—Dr. Raymond L. Bisplinghoff, 405 DeWolfe Drive, Alexandria (Waynewood), Va., 22308.
Deputy Associate Administrator for Advanced Research and Technology (Operations).—Boyd C. Myers, 3902 Ryegate Lane (Stratford Landing), Alexandria, Va.
Deputy Associate Administrator for Advanced Research and Technology.—Dr. Alfred J. Eggers, Jr., 3671 North Harrison Street, Arlington, Va.
Director, Programs and Resources.—M. H. Mead, 3115 North Peary Street, Arlington, Va.
Director, Nuclear Systems and Space Power.—Harold B. Finger, 6908 Millwood Road, Bethesda, Md., 20034.
Director, Aeronautics.—C. W. Harper, 2522 Queen Ann's Lane.
Director, Space Vehicles.—Milton B. Ames, Jr., 3704 River Farm Drive, River Bend Estates, Alexandria, Va., 22306.
Director, Chemical Propulsion.—A. O. Tischler, 8408 Magruder Mill Court, Bethesda, Md.
Director, Electronics and Control (Acting).—F. J. Sullivan, 6892 Deland Drive, West Springfield, Va.
Director, Research.—Dr. Hermann H. Kurzweg, 731 Quaint Acres Drive, Silver Spring, Md., 20904.
Director, Biotechnology and Human Research (Acting).—W. L. Jones, 510 Bay Tree Court, Falls Church, Va.
Director, AEC-NASA Space Nuclear Propulsion Office.—Harold B. Finger, 6908 Millwood Road, Bethesda, Md., 20034.

FIELD INSTALLATIONS

Ames Research Center, Moffett Field, Calif.—Director.—Dr. Smith J. DeFrance, 12220 Fairway Drive, Los Altos, Calif.
Electronics Research Center, Cambridge, Mass.—Director.—Dr. Winston E. Koch, 980 Gale Street, Beverly Farms, Mass.
Flight Research Center, Edwards, Calif.—Director.—Paul F. Bikle, 44926 North Raysack Avenue, Lancaster, Calif.
Langley Research Center, Hampton, Va.—Director.—Dr. Floyd L. Thompson, 94 Allegheny Road, Hampton, Va.
Lewis Research Center, Cleveland, Ohio.—Director.—Dr. Abe Silverstein, 211 Seabury, Fairview Park, Ohio.

OFFICE OF TRACKING AND DATA ACQUISITION

Director, Tracking and Data Acquisition.—Edmond C. Buckley, 3501 Glenmoor Drive, Chevy Chase, Md., 20015.
Deputy Director, Tracking and Data Acquisition.—Gerald M. Truszynski, 3510 Dundee Driveway, Chevy Chase, Md.
Director, Program Support and Advanced Systems.—C. R. Morrison, RFD No. 1, Box 430, Chester, Va.
Director, Network Operations and Facilities.—H. R. Brockett, 9707 Stoneham Terrace, Bethesda, Md., 20034.

NATIONAL CAPITAL HOUSING AUTHORITY

1729 New York Avenue, 20430.   Phone, EXecutive 3-3111 (Code 128)

Chairman.—Walter N. Tobriner, President of the Board of Commissioners District of Columbia (6100 33d Street, 20015).
Vice Chairman.—Neville Miller, Chairman, District of Columbia Redevelopment Land Agency (4715 Berkeley Terrace, 20007).
Wesley S. Williams, President, District of Columbia Board of Education (1810 Randolph Street NE., 20018).
[Vacancy], Director, District of Columbia Department of Public Welfare.
James A. Washington, Jr., Chairman, Public Utilities Commission (4302 13th Street NE., 20017).
Wilmer C. Dutton, Jr., Director, National Capital Planning Commission (6513 41st Avenue, University Park, Md., 20782).
Executive Director.—Walter E. Washington, 408 T Street, 20001.
Deputy Executive Director.—Edward Aronov, 4600 Connecticut Avenue, 20008.
General Counsel.—William R. Simpson, Jr., 200 Williamsburg Drive, Silver Spring, Md., 20901.
Director of Administration.—Stuart R. Kerr, 2700 Beechwood Place, Arlington, Va., 22207.
Director of Management.—Harvey V. Everett, 5309 29th Avenue SE., 20031.
Acting Director of Project Development.—Joseph W. Hoban, Jr., 1000 Poplar Drive, Falls Church, Va., 22046.
Chief of Community and Social Services.—Olive W. Swinney, 3024 North Oakland Street, Arlington, Va., 22007.

NATIONAL CAPITAL PLANNING COMMISSION

1701 Pennsylvania Avenue, 20576.   Phone, 393-3300 (Code 128, extension 21161)

MEMBERS

Presidential Appointees:
Chairman.—Mrs. James H. Rowe, Jr., 3207 Highland Place, 20008.
Vice Chairman.—A. M. Woodruff, 40 Terry's Plain Road, Simsbury, Conn., 06070.
Walter C. Louchheim, Jr., 2824 O Street, 20007.
C. McKim Norton, 87 Lafayette Road, Princeton, N.J., 08541.
Paul Thiry, 1017 East Blaine Street, Seattle, Wash., 98102.

EX OFFICIO MEMBERS

Alan Bible, Chairman, Senate Committee on the District of Columbia.
John L. McMillan, Chairman, House Committee on the District of Columbia.
Brig. Gen. Charles, M. Duke, Engineer Commissioner, District of Columbia, 5712 26th Street, 20015.
Lt. Gen. Walter K. Wilson, Jr., Chief of Engineers, U.S. Army, Quarters No. 1, Fort Belvoir, Va., 22060.
George B. Hartzog, Jr., Director, National Park Service, Department of the Interior, 4818 Old Dominion Drive, Arlington, Va., 22210.
William A Schmidt, Acting Commissioner of Public Buildings, General Services Administration, 5901 Cromwell Drive, Springfield, Washington, D.C., 20016.

Rex M. Whitton, Federal Highway Administrator, Bureau of Public Roads, 4201 Cathedral Avenue, 20016.
C. Darwin Stolzenbach, Administrator, National Capital Transportation Agency, 10515 Meredith Avenue, Kensington, Md., 20795.

STAFF

Director.—W. C. Dutton, Jr., 6513 41st Avenue, University Park, Md., 20782.
Deputy Director.—Charles H. Conrad, 5030 27th Street North, Arlington, Va., 22207.
General Counsel and Secretary.—Daniel H. Shear, 3636 16th Street, 20016.
Assistant Director (Adm.).—John R. Pritchard, 711 North Pelham Street, Alexandria, Va., 22304.
Assistant Director for Comprehensive Planning.—Sydnor F. Hodges, 8001 Barron Street, Takoma Park, Md., 20012.
Assistant Director for Urban Renewal Planning.—Donald F. Bozarth, 2000 Sycamore Drive, Falls Church, Va., 22042.
Chief of District Planning.—William F. McIntosh, 7436 Hamlet Street, Springfield, Va., 22151.
Chief of Federal Planning.—[Vacant.]

NATIONAL CAPITAL REGIONAL PLANNING COUNCIL

1701 Pennsylvania Avenue, 20576.   Phone, 382–1114 (Code 128, extension 21114)

Chairman.—William J. Stevens, Prince Georges County nominee of the Maryland-National Capital Park and Planning Commission, 4410 Oglethorpe Street, Hyattsville, Md.
First Vice Chairman.—Mrs. James H. Rowe, Jr., ex officio: Chairman, National Capital Planning Commission, 3207 Highland Place.
Second Vice Chairman.—James R. F. Woods, Fairfax City nominee of the Northern Virginia Regional Planning and Economic Development Commission, 716 Pinehurst Avenue, Fairfax, Va.
Other Members:
Frank J. Lastner, nominated by the Prince Georges County Board of County Commissioners, 19–P Ridge Road, Greenbelt, Md.
Everett R. Jones, Montgomery County nominee of the Maryland-National Capital Park and Planning Commission, 9510 Main Street, Damascus, Md.
John H. Hiser, nominated by the Montgomery County Council, 8026 Glendale Road, Chevy Chase, Md.
Brig. Gen. Charles M. Duke, ex officio: Engineer Commissioner, District of Columbia, 5712 26th Street.
Mrs. Elizabeth Weihe, Arlington County nominee of the Northern Virginia Regional Planning and Economic Development Commission, 4133 33d Road North, Arlington, Va.
Harold Silverstein, Falls Church nominee of the Northern Virginia Regional Planning and Economic Development Commission, 203 West Marshall Street, Falls Church ,Va.
James R. F. Woods, Fairfax City nominee of the Northern Virginia Regional Planning and Economic Development Commission, 716 Pinehurst Avenue, Fairfax, Va.
Stuart T. DeBell, Fairfax County nominee of the Northern Virginia Regional Planning and Economic Development Commission, Centreville, Va.
Alternates:
Mrs. T. Paul Freeland, Montgomery County nominee of the Maryland-National Capital Park and Planning Commission, 5525 Pembroke Road, Bethesda, Md.
John A. Scheibel, Prince Georges County nominee of the Maryland-National Capital Park and Planning Commission, 5581 Branch Avenue, Camp Springs, Washington, D.C.
Miss Kathryn E. Diggs, nominated by the Montgomery County Council, 4705 Great Oak Road, Manor Club, Rockville, Md.
Thomas C. Kelly, nominated by the Prince Georges County Board of County Commissioners, 51–E Ridge Road, Greenbelt, Md.

Alternates—Continued
  Francis M. Coffey, Prince William County nominee of the Northern Virginia
    Regional Planning and Economic Development Commission, Dumfries, Va.
  John T. Ticer, Alexandria nominee of the Northern Virginia Regional Planning
    and Economic Development Commission, 512 Prince Street, Alexandria, Va.
  Donald A. Hagerich, Loudoun County nominee of the Northern Virginia Re-
    gional Planning and Economic Development Commission, Broad Run Farms,
    Sterling, Va.
  Samuel Epstein, At Large nominee of the Northern Virginia Regional Planning
    and Economic Development Commission, 207 Van Buren Street, Falls
    Church, Va.
  Col. John A. Israelson, ex officio: Assistant Engineer Commissioner, District
    of Columbia, 806 Shelby Lane, Falls Church, Va.
  A. M. Woodruff, ex officio: Vice Chairman, National Capital Planning Com-
    mission, 40 Terry's Plain Road, Simsbury, Conn.
Acting Director.—Harry A. Auerbach, 4844–A 28th Street South, Arlington, Va.

NATIONAL CAPITAL TRANSPORTATION AGENCY

1634 I Street. Phone, EXecutive 3–3111 (Code 128)

Administrator.—C. Darwin Stolzenbach, 3203 Oberon Street, Kensington, Md.,
    20795.
  Special Assistant to the Administrator.—Ellis S. Perlman, 4701 Kenmore Avenue,
    Alexandria, Va., 22304.
Deputy Administrator.—Warren D. Quenstedt, 1212 La Ronde Court, Alexandria,
    Va., 22307.
Acting General Counsel.—Owen J. Malone, 1200 Russell Road, Alexandria, Va.,
    22301.
Acting Director, Office of Engineering.—Howard W. Lyon, 6515 Dalroy Lane
    Bethesda, Md., 20034.
Acting Director, Office of Planning and Finance.—William I. Herman, 8405 Beech
    Tree Road, Bethesda, Md., 20034.
Director, Office of Administration.—J. Neal Tomey, 6004 Osceola Road, 20016.
Director, Office of Public Information and Community Services.—Cody Pfanstiehl,
    7514 Dundalk Court, Takoma Park, Md., 20012.

ADVISORY BOARD

Chairman.—Gerry Levenberg, 2846 28th Street, 20008.
Members:
  G. Franklin Edwards of the District of Columbia.
  Frederick Gutheim of Maryland.
  Edwin T. Holland of Virginia.
  Robert C. Wood of Massachusetts.

INTERSTATE COMPACT NEGOTIATIONS

Federal Representative.—Gregory B. Wolfe of Potomac, Md.

NATIONAL LABOR RELATIONS BOARD

1717 Pennsylvania Avenue, 20570. Phone, EXecutive 3–3111 (Code 128)

OFFICES OF THE BOARD

Chairman.—Frank W. McCulloch, 3642 Upton Street, 20008.
  Chief Counsel.—Arthur Leff, 2207 Richland Place, Silver Spring, Md.
  Confidential Staff Assistant.—Meta P. Barghausen, 5521 Colorado Avenue,
    20011.
  Confidential Assistant.—Elizabeth Summers, 3303 Oberon Street, Kensington,
    Md.

Members:
[Vacancy.]
   Chief Counsel.—Harry H. Kuskin, 2511 Harmon Road, Silver Spring, Md.
Howard Jenkins, Jr., 1333 Tuckerman Street, 20011.
   Chief Counsel.—Harry M. Leet, Gaithersburg, Md.
John H. Fanning, 5905 Welborn Drive, 20016.
   Chief Counsel.—William C. Baisinger, Jr., 2870 Arizona Terrace, 20016.
Gerald A. Brown, 6500 Marjory Lane, Bethesda, Md., 20034.
   Chief Counsel.—Ralph Winkler, 7801 Beech Tree Road, Bethesda, Md., 20034.
Executive Secretary.—Ogden W. Fields, 614 Greenbrier Drive, Silver Spring, Md.
   Associate Executive Secretary.—Howard W. Kleeb, 2450 North Powhatan Street, Arlington, Va.
   Associate Executive Secretary.—John C. Truesdale, 5123 Worthington Drive, 20016.
   Associate Executive Secretary.—George A. Leet, 5625 Overlea Road, Sumner, Md., 20016.
Solicitor.—William Feldesman, 7009 Connecticut Avenue, Chevy Chase, Md., 20015.
   Associate Solicitor.—Saul J. Jaffe, 6014 Maiden Lane, Bethesda, Md., 20034.
Chief Trial Examiner.—George Bokat, 7607 Holiday Terrace, Bethesda, Md.
   Associate Chief Trial Examiners:
   Sidney Lindner, 6314 Marjory Lane, Bethesda, Md., 20034.
   Charles W. Schneider, 7504 Glenside Drive, Takoma Park, Md.
   Wallace E. Royster, 50 Chumasero Drive, San Francisco, Calif., 94132.
Director, Division of Information.—Thomas W. Miller, Jr., 2317 North Early Street, Alexandria, Va., 22302.
   Associate Director.—Thomas P. Healy, 4113 Woodbine Street, Chevy Chase, Md., 20015.
   Associate Director.—Iliff McMahan, 1605 Byrnes Drive, McLean, Va., 22101.

OFFICES OF THE GENERAL COUNSEL

General Counsel.—Arnold Ordman, 3513 Randolph Road, Wheaton, Md., 20902.
   Special Assistant to the General Counsel.—William T. Evans, 3729 Reservoir Road, 20007.
   Executive Assistant to the General Counsel.—Robert H. Anderson, 5713 Wainright Avenue, Rockville, Md., 20851.
   Confidential Staff Assistant.—Yvonne M. Bradley, 2315 Lincoln Road NE., 20002.
   Secretarial Assistant.—Elsie E. Crowell, 1311 Delaware Avenue SW., 20024.
Associate General Counsel, Division of Litigation.—Dominick L. Manoli, 3114 North Inglewood Street, Arlington, Va., 22207.
Assistant General Counsels, Division of Litigation:
   Norton J. Come, 7044 Wilson Lane, Bethesda, Md., 20034.
   Marcel Mallet-Prevost, 11420 Old Georgetown Road, Rockville, Md., 20851.
   Julius G. Serot, 13005 Carney Street, Silver Spring, Md., 20902.
   Irving M. Herman, 5932 North 4th Street, Arlington, Va., 22203.
Associate General Counsel, Division of Operations.—H. Stephan Gordon, 2905 Covington Road, Forest Glen, Md., 20910.
   Deputy Associate General Counsel.—Joseph DeSio, 8109 Adair Lane, Springfield, Va., 22150.
Assistant General Counsels, Division of Operations:
   Gerald Brissman, 5318 Kepler Lane, Springfield, Va., 22150.
   Albert Colbert, 1608 Constance Street, Silver Spring, Md., 20902.
   John H. Fenton, 6410 Walhonding Road, Bethesda, Md., 20016.
   Thomas W. Kennedy, 1400 South Joyce Street, Riverhouse West, Arlington, Va., 22202.
   Elihu Platt, 503 Lamberton Drive, Silver Spring, Md., 20902.
Director, Division of Administration.—Clarence S. Wright, R.F.D. 5, Box 544, Fairfax, Va.

NATIONAL MEDIATION BOARD

1230 Sixteenth Street, Washington, D.C., 20572.   Phone, 393-3111 (Code 128)

Members:
Howard G. Gamser, chairman, 3236 Prospect Street, 20007.
Francis A. O'Neill, Jr., member, 2151 California Street, 20008.
Leverett Edwards, member, 5300 West Bard Avenue, Bethesda, Md., 20016.
Executive Secretary.—Thomas A. Tracy, 927 Oakwood Drive, Falls Church, Va.
Mediators.—A. Alfred Della Corte, Charles M. Dulen, Clarence G. Eddy, Lawrence Farmer, Eugene C. Frank, Arthur J. Glover, Edward F. Hampton, James M. Holaren, Matthew E. Kearney, Thomas C. Kinsella, Warren S. Lane, George S. MacSwan, Raymond McElroy, J. Earl Newlin, Michael J. O'Connell, William H. Pierce, Judson L. Reeves, C. Robert Roadley, Wallace G. Rupp, Tedford E. Schoonover, Frank K. Switzer, Eugene C. Thompson, Luther G. Wyatt.

NATIONAL SCIENCE FOUNDATION

1800 K Street, 20550.   Phone, 343-1100

Director.—Leland J. Haworth, 1600 South Joyce Street, Arlington, Va., 22202.
 Executive Assistant.—Franklin C. Sheppard, 1400 South Joyce Street, Arlington, Va., 22202.
Deputy Director.—John T. Wilson, 5611 Springfield Drive, 20016.
 Head, Office of International Science Activities.—Arthur Roe, 3113 38th Street, 20016.
 Deputy Head.—Philip Hemily, 3120 Dumbarton Avenue, 20007.
 Head, Office of Science Information Service.—Burton W. Adkinson, 5907 Welborn Drive, 20016.
 Deputy Head.—Henry J. Dubester, 6531 Elgin Lane, Bethesda, Md., 20034.
General Counsel.—William J. Hoff, 3041 N Street, 20087.
 Deputy.—Charles B. Ruttenberg, 4735 Butterworth Place, 20016.
Head, Office of Congressional and Public Affairs.—James F. King, 3801 Lorcom Lane, Arlington, Va., 22207.
 Congressional Liaison Officer.—James F. King, 3801 Lorcom Lane, Arlington, Va., 22207.
 Public Information Officer.—Roland D. Paine, Jr., 7363 Hastings, Springfield, Va., 22150.
Director, Mohole Project Officer.—Gordon G. Lill, 9617 E. Bexhill Drive, Kensington, Md., 20795.
Associate Director (Planning).—Bowen C. Dees, 2202 Wyoming Avenue, 20008.
 Head, Office of Science Resources Planning.—Henry David, 2139 Wyoming Avenue, 20008.
 Head, Office of Program Development and Analysis.—Louis Levin, 10201 Grosvenor Place, Rockville, Md., 20852.
 Head, Office of Economic and Manpower Studies.—Jacob Perlman, 9710 Singleton Drive, Bethesda, Md., 20034.
Associate Director (Education).—Henry W. Riecken, 7102 Borxburn Drive, Bethesda, Md., 20034.
 Director, Division of Pre-Collge Education in Science.—Keith R. Kelson, 5311 Baltimore Avenue, Chevy Chase, Md., 20015.
 Director, Division of Undergraduate Education in Science.—Leland Shanor, 1426 21st Street, 20036.
 Director, Division of Graduate Education in Science.—Thomas D. Fontaine, 5622 Ogden Road, Springfield, Md., 20016.
Associate Director (Research).—Randal M. Robertson, 6736 N. 26th Street, Arlington, Va., 22213.
 Head, Office of Antarctic Programs.—Thomas O. Jones, 7504 Holiday Terrace, Bethesda, Md. 20034.
 Director, Division of Institutional Programs.—Howard E. Page, 406 Westmoreland Street, Alexandria, Va., 22308.
 Deputy Division Director.—Denzel D. Smith, 3102 Lake Avenue, Cheverly, Md., 20785.

Associate Director Research—Continued
   Director, Division of Biological & Medical Sciences.—Harve J. Carlson, 5510 Hoover Street, Bethesda, Md., 20034.
     Deputy Division Director.—David D. Keck, 7227 Marbury Court, Bethesda, Md., 20034.
   Director, Division of Mathematical & Physical Sciences.—Geoffrey Keller, 5806 Johnson Avenue, Bethesda, Md., 20034.
   Director, Division of Engineering.—John M. Ide, 1068 30th Street, 20007.
   Director, Division of Social Sciences.—Howard H. Hines, 2020 F Street, 20006.
Administrative Manager.—Franklin C. Sheppard, 1400 South Joyce Street, Arlington, Va., 22202.
   Deputy.—Henry Birnbaum, 7007 Wake Forest Drive, College Park, Md., 20740.
   Head, Contracts Office.—Robert D. Newton, Route 2, Box 101 S, Lorton, Va., 22079.
   Head, Grants Office.——William E. Fee, Jr., 2820 28th Street, 20008.
   Head, Office Services.—Howard Tihila, 5100 Wehawken Road, 20016.
   Personnel Officer.—Calvin C. Jones, 5802 Felix Street, McLean, Va., 22101.
   Head, Management Analysis Office.—Lawrence W. Crain, 4512 North Dittmar Road, Arlington, Va., 22207.
Comptroller.—Aaron Rosenthal, 1010 Roswell Drive, Silver Spring, Md., 20901.
   Budget Officer.—Luther Schoen, R.F.D. 1, Box 193–B, Vienna, Va., 22180.
   Finance Officer.—Edward B. Garvey, 1015 Parker Street, Falls Church, Va., 22046.
   Head, Internal Audit.—Wilford G. Kener, 1016 North Quantico Street, Arlington, Va., 22205.

NATIONAL SCIENCE BOARD

Chairman.—Eric A. Walker, president, The Pennsylvania State University, 201 Old Main Building, University Park, Pa., 16802.
Vice Chairman.—Philip Handler, James B. Duke Professor and chairman, department of biochemistry, Duke University, Durham, N.C., 27706.
Members:
   W. O. Baker, vice president research, Bell Telephone Laboratories, Inc., Murray Hill, N.J., 07971.
   Harvey Brooks, Gordon McKay Professor of Applied Physics and dean of engineering and applied physics, 217 Pierce Hall, Harvard University, Cambridge, Mass., 02138.
   H. E. Carter, head, department of chemistry and chemical engineering, University of Illinois, 108 Noyes Laboratory, Urbana, Ill., 61803.
   Rufus E. Clement, president, Atlanta University, 223 Chestnut Street, SW., Atlanta, Ga., 30314.
   Henry Eyring, dean, Graduate School, University of Utah, Salt Lake City, Utah, 84112.
   Julian R. Goldsmith, associate dean, division of the physical sciences, University of Chicago, Chicago, Ill., 60637.
   William W. Hagerty, president, Drexel Institute of Technology, Philadelphia, Pa., 19104.
   Leland J. Haworth, director, National Science Foundation, Washington, D.C., 20550 (member ex officio).
   Theodore M. Hesburgh, C.S.C., president, The University of Notre Dame, Notre Dame, Ind., 46556.
   William V. Houston, honorary chancellor, William Marsh Rice University, Houston, Tex., 77001.
   Katharine E. McBride, president, Bryn Mawr College, Bryn Mawr, Pa., 19010.
   Edward J. McShane, professor of mathematics, department of mathematics, University of Virginia, Charlottesville, Va., 22903.
   Robert S. Morison, professor of biology, Cornell University, Ithaca, N.Y., 14850.
   Joseph C. Morris, vice president, Tulane University, Room 206 Gibson Hall, New Orleans, La., 70118.
   E. R. Piore, vice president and group executive, International Business Machines Corp., Armonk, N.Y., 10504.
   Mina S. Rees, dean of graduate studies, The City University of New York, 33 West 42d Street, New York, N.Y., 10036.

Members—Continued
   William W. Rubey, professor of geology and geophysics, department of geology and institute of geophysics, University of California, Los Angeles, Calif., 90024.
   John I. Snyder, Jr., chairman of the board and president, U.S. Industries, Inc., 250 Park Avenue, New York, N.Y., 10017.
   Julius A. Stratton, president, Massachusetts Institute of Technology, Cambridge, Mass., 02139.
   Edward L. Tatum, member, The Rockefeller Institute, York Avenue and 66th Street, New York, N.Y., 10021.
   F. P. Thieme, vice president, University of Washington, Seattle, Wash., 98105.
   Ralph W. Tyler, director, Center for Advanced Study in the Behavioral Sciences, 202 Junipero Serra Boulevard, Stanford, Calif., 94305.
   [One vacancy.]
   Vernice Anderson, secretary, National Science Board, National Science Foundation, Washington, D.C., 20550.

NATIONAL SELECTIVE SERVICE APPEAL BOARD
1724 F Street, 20435.   Phone, 343-7181

Chairman.—[Vacant.]
Board Members:
   Henry J. Gwiazda, 580 Shuttle Meadow Avenue, New Britain, Conn.
   [Vacancy.]
Executive.—Edwin J. Dentz, 7407 Floyd Avenue, Springfield, Va.

PANAMA CANAL COMPANY
312 Pennsylvania Building, Washington, D.C., 20004.   Phone, DIstrict 7-6984

Secretary.—W. M. Whitman, 4309 Glenridge Street, Kensington, Md.

IN THE CANAL ZONE

President.—Maj. Gen. Robert J. Fleming, Jr., Balboa Heights, C.Z.
Vice President.—Col. David S. Parker, Balboa Heights, C.Z.

PRESIDENT'S COMMISSION ON WHITE HOUSE FELLOWS
Executive Office Building.   Phone, 382-1613 (Code 128, extension 21614)

Chairman.—David Rockefeller, President, Chase Manhattan Bank, New York, N.Y.
Members:
   Ernest C. Arbuckle, Dean, Graduate School of Business, Stanford University, Stanford, Calif.
   James B. Carey, President, Electrical, Radio and Machine Workers, Washington, D.C.
   William C. Friday, President, University of North Carolina, Chapel Hill, N.C.
   John W. Gardner, President, Carnegie Foundation, New York, N.Y.
   William H. Hastie, Judge, Third U.S. Circuit Court of Appeals, Philadelphia, Pa.
   Francis Keppel, Commissioner, U.S. Office of Education, 2800 O Street.
   John W. Macy, Jr., Chairman, U.S. Civil Service Commission, 201 North Langley Lane, McLean, Va.
   John B. Oakes, Editorial Page Editor, *The New York Times*, New York, N.Y.
   Harry Ransom, Chancellor, University of Texas, Austin, Tex.
   Margaret Chase Smith, United States Senator, Maine.
   O. Meredith Wilson, President, University of Minnesota, Minneapolis, Minn.
Director: Thomas W. Carr, 3612 Shepherd Street, Chevy Chase, Md., 20015.

PRESIDENT'S COMMITTEE ON EMPLOYMENT OF THE HANDICAPPED

U.S. Department of Labor Building. Phone, EXecutive 3-2420 (Code 110, extension 3401)

Chairman.—Harold Russell, 18 Woodridge Road, Wayland, Mass., 01778.
Vice Chairman.—Gordon M. Freeman, 10103 East Bexhill, Kensington, Md., 20795.
Vice Chairman.—Leonard W. Mayo, Sturges Commons, Westport, Conn., 06882.
Vice Chairman.—Victor Riesel, 610 West End Avenue, New York, N.Y., 10024.
Vice Chairman.—Kenneth N. Watson, 3041 West Lane Keys, Washington, D.C., 20007.
Executive Secretary.—William P. McCahill, 2761 North Wakefield Street, Arlington, Va., 22207.

PRESIDENT'S COUNCIL ON PHYSICAL FITNESS

General Accounting Office Building. Phone, DUdley 6-6051

Special Consultant to the President.—Stan Musial.
Chairman.—Secretary of Health, Education, and Welfare.
Members:
  Secretary of the Interior.
  Secretary of Defense.
  Attorney General.
  Secretary of Agriculture.
  Secretary of Labor.
  Secretary of Commerce.
  Administrator, Housing and Home Finance Agency.

RAILROAD RETIREMENT BOARD

844 Rush Street, Chicago, Illinois, 60611. Phone, WHitehall 4-5500

Washington Liaison Office: The Pennsylvania Building, Room 444, 425 Thirteenth Street, 20004
Phone, REpublic 7-1780

Members:
  Howard W. Habermeyer (chairman), 175 Westlawn Avenue, Aurora, Ill.
    Assistant to the Chairman.—Joseph Duran.
  Thomas M. Healy, 302 17th Street, Wilmette, Ill.
    Administrative Officer.—Charles L. Culkin.
  A. E. Lyon, 938 Queens Lane, Glenview, Ill.
    Administrative Officer.—Gerald E. Woodcock.
Secretary of the Board.—Lawrence Garland.
Librarian.—Charlotte B. Stillwell.
Chief Executive Officer.—Frank J. McKenna, 1455 North Sandburg Terrace, Apt. 2609b, Chicago, Ill.
General Counsel.—Myles F. Gibbons.
Associate General Counsel.—David B. Schreiber.
Director, Management Control.—George W. Kenaga.
Director, Research.—Samuel Chmell.
Chief Actuary.—A. M. Niessen.
Director, Retirement Claims.—Donald M. Smith.
Director, Unemployment and Sickness Insurance.—H. L. Carter.
Director, Wage and Service Records.—Joseph V. Martin.
Director, Budget and Fiscal Operations.—Michael Rudisin.
Director, Personnel.—Clifford L. Rasmussen.
Chairman, Appeals Council.—Halbert W. Dodd.
Director, Supply and Service.—Harvey O. Lytle.
Washington Liaison Officer.—Jeremiah E. Walsh.

Regional Offices:
  Atlanta, Ga., 30302, 201–3 Ivy Street N.E.; H. H. Dashiell, director.
  Chicago, Ill., 60611, 844 Rush Street; Charles L. Holler, director.
  Cleveland, Ohio, 44113, Public Square Building; Frank J. Shea, director.
  Dallas, Tex., 75222, Fidelity Building, 1000 Main Street, P.O. Box 6314; Raymond W. Lusk, director.
  Kansas City, Mo., 64142, 911 Walnut Street, P.O. Box 2779; William R. Calwell, director.
  New York, N.Y., 10001, 341 Ninth Avenue, Room 920; John J. Finnerty, director.
  San Francisco, Calif., 94102, 450 Golden Gate Avenue, Box 36043; W. J. Macklin, director.

RENEGOTIATION BOARD

1910 K Street, 20446. Phone, 382–7052 (Code 128)

Chairman.—Lawrence E. Hartwig, 3520 39th Street, 20016.
Board Members:
  Thomas D'Alesandro, Jr., 245 Albemarle Street, Baltimore, Md., 21202.
  Herschel C. Loveless, 7523 17th Street, 20012.
  William M. Burkhalter, 5817 Madawska Road, 20016.
  Jack Beaty.
Secretary to the Board.—Nathan Bass, 3722 Gunston Road, Alexandria, Va., 22302.
Office of Administration.—[Vacant.]
Office of Economic Advisor.—George Lenches, economist, 2400 41st Street, 20007.
Office of General Counsel.—Howard W. Fensterstock, general counsel, 2360 North Quincy Street, Arlington, Va., 22207.
Office of Review.—Charles H. Swayne, director, Route 2, Box 94–A, Sterling, Va., 22170.
Office of Accounting.—Ross M. Girard, director, 2316 North Kentucky Street, Arlington, Va., 22205.
Office of Assignments.—Paul T. Semple, director, 4000 Tunlaw Road, 20007.

SAINT LAWRENCE SEAWAY DEVELOPMENT CORPORATION

Seaway Circle, Massena, N.Y., 13662. Phone, Area Code 315, 769–9941

Administrator.—Joseph H. McCann, 18205 Wildemere, Detroit, Mich., 48221.
Assistant Administrator.—Brendon T. Jose, 21 Sherwood Drive, Massena, N.Y., 13662.
Administrative Officer.—Roland W. Gleason, Riverdale Apartments, Massena, N.Y., 13662.
Counsel.—David C. Zimmermann, Riverdale Apartments, Massena, N.Y., 13662.
Superintendent, Operations and Maintenance.—William Grothaus, 45 Churchill Avenue, Massena, N.Y., 13662.

DETROIT OFFICE

401 Washington Boulevard, Detroit, Mich., 48226. Phone, Area Code 313, 961–7110

Assistant to the Administrator.—Willis H. Crosswhite, 27036 Timber Trail Drive, Dearborn, Mich., 48127.
Public Information Officer.—Richard H. Miller, 7320 Meurdale, Walled Lake, Mich., 48088.

SECURITIES AND EXCHANGE COMMISSION

425 Second Street, 20549. Phone, WOrth 3–1110 (Code 13)

Commissioners:
  Chairman.—Manuel F. Cohen, 6403 Marjory Lane, Bethesda, Md., 20034.
  Byron D. Woodside, Haymarket, Va., 22069.
  Hugh F. Owens, 4301 Massachusetts Avenue, 20016.

Commissioners—Continued
  Hamer H. Budge, 4101 Cathedral Avenue, 20016.
  Francis M. Wheat, 7310 Meadow Lane, Chevy Chase, Md., 20015.
Congressional Liaison:
  Administrative.—Orval L. DuBois, Secretary (Code 13, Ext. 35526).
  Legislative.—Philip A. Loomis, Jr., General Counsel (Code 13, Ext. 22331).
Executive Assistant to the Chariman.—Leonard M. Leiman, 3119 Rolling Road,
  Chevy Chase, Md., 20015.
Secretary.—Orval L. DuBois, 3067 North Quincy Street, Arlington, Va., 22207.
Assistant Secretary.—Nellye A. Thorsen, 1727 Massachusetts Avenue, 20036.
Management Analyst.—William E. Becker, 701 Downs Drive, Silver Spring, Md.,
  20904.
Comptroller.—Frank J. Donaty, 9202 Davidson St., College Park, Md., 21541.
Director of Personnel.—Harry Pollack, 1806 Metzerott Road, Adelphi, Md.,
  20783.
Records and Service Officer.—Ernest L. Dessecker, 4410 Oglethorpe Street, Hyatts-
  ville, Md., 20781.

DIVISION OF CORPORATION FINANCE

Director.—Edmund H. Worthy, 4607 Harrison Street, Chevy Chase, Md., 20015.
  Associate Director.—Robert H. Bagley, 108 Lyndale Drive, Wellington Heights,
    Alexandria, Va., 22308.
Executive Assistant Director.—Charles E. Shreve, 5314 Glenwood Road, Bethesda,
  Md., 20014.
Assistant Directors:
  Joseph Bernstein, 3040 North Harrison Street, Arlington, Va., 22207.
  Douglas M. Dunn, 7411 Buffalo Avenue, Takoma Park, Md., 20012.
  Ralph C. Hocker, 928 Nichols Drive, Laurel, Md., 20810.
  Benjamin Levy, 3140 Wisconsin Avenue, 20016.
  Herbert D. Miller, 5504 Fontana Place, Springfield, Va., 22151.
  Abraham Zwerling, 6637 Joallen Drive, Falls Church, Va., 22044.
Chief Counsel.—George P. Michaely, Jr., 415 Cynthia Lane, Vienna, Va.
Chief Accountant.—Sydney C. Orbach, 3140 Wisconsin Avenue, 20016.
Assistant Director in Charge of Administrative Proceedings.—Alan B. Levenson,
  1333 Leesburg Court, Alexandria, Va., 23302.

DIVISION OF CORPORATE REGULATION

Director.—Solomon Freedman, 4501 Middleton Lane, Bethesda, Md., 20014.
Associate Directors.—Harold V. Lese, 7706 13th Street, 20012; J. Arnold Pines,
  1405 Dilston Road, Silver Spring, Md., 20903.
Assistant Directors:
  John A. Dudley, 800 Fourth Street SW., 20024.
  Ralph C. Hocker, 928 Nichols Drive, Laurel, Md., 20810.
  Aaron Levy, 4609 Norwood Drive, Chevy Chase, Md., 20015.
Chief Counsel.—Alan R. Gordon, 409 Deerfield Avenue, Silver Spring, Md., 20910.
Chief Enforcement Attorney.—Sydney H. Mendelsohn, 11507 Lamberton Court,
  Silver Spring, Md., 20902.

DIVISION OF TRADING AND MARKETS

Director.—Ralph S. Saul, 511 Venice Street, Falls Church, Va., 22043.
Associate Director.—Irving M. Pollack, 13010 Carney Street, Wheaton, Md.,
  20906.
Assistant Director.—Thomas W. Rae, 301 G Street SW.
Assistant Director.—Mahlon M. Frankhauser, 7244 Long Pine Drive, Springfield,
  Va., 22151.
Assistant Director.—Frederick Moss, 8704 West Victoria Road, Springfield, Va.
Assistant Director.—Charles R. McCutcheon, 2024 North Scott Street, Arlington,
  Va.
Assistant Director.—Norman S. Poser, 3518 35th Street, 20016.
Chief Counsel.—Robert Block, 6308 31st Place, 20015.
Special Counsel to the Director.—David Silver, 4409 First Road South, Arlington,
  Va.

OFFICE OF THE GENERAL COUNSEL

General Counsel.—Philip A. Loomis, Jr., 7108 Beechwood Drive, Chevy Chase, Md., 20015.
Solicitor.—David Ferber, 3822 Livingston Street, 20015.
Associate General Counsel.—Walter P. North, 5100 Dorset Avenue, Chevy Chase, Md., 20015.
Assistant General Counsel.—Ellwood L. Englander, 4817 46th Street, 20016.

OFFICE OF THE CHIEF ACCOUNTANT

Chief Accountant.—Andrew Barr, 1135 16th Street, 20036.
Assistant Chief Accountant.—Lindsey J. Millard, 3613 Taylor Street, Chevy Chase, Md., 20015.

OFFICE OF POLICY RESEARCH

Director.—Walter Werner, 3234 Reservoir Road, 20009.
Chief Counsel.—Eugene H. Rotberg, 10822 Childs Court, Silver Spring, Md., 20909.

OFFICE OF OPINION WRITING

Director.—Leonard Helfenstein, 1371 Underwood Street, 20012.
Associate Director.—W. Victor Rodin, 5032 Fulton Street, 20016.
Assistant Director.—Alfred Letzler, 237 North Galveston Street, Arlington, Va., 22203.

REGIONAL AND BRANCH OFFICES

Region 1—New York Regional Office.—Llewellyn P. Young, regional administrator; John J. Devaney, Jr., associate regional administrator; Arthur Goldman and Richard V. Bandler, assistant regional administrators; 225 Broadway, New York, N.Y., 10007; phone, 732–6363; covering New York and New Jersey.
Region 2—Boston Regional Office.—Philip E. Kendrick, regional administrator; James E. Dowd, assistant regional administrator, Federal Building, Room 2004, Post Office Square, Boston, Mass., 02109; phone, 223–2721; covering Maine, New Hampshire, Vermont, Massachusetts, Connecticut, and Rhode Island.
Region 3—Atlanta Regional Office.—William Green, regional administrator; J. Cecil Penland, assistant regional administrator, Suite 138, 1371 Peachtree Street NE., Atlanta, Ga., 30309; phone 526–5844; covering North Carolina, South Carolina, Georgia, Florida, Alabama, Tennessee, Mississippi, and Louisiana.
Miami Branch Office.—Jule B. Greene, attorney-in-charge, Room 1504, 51 SW. First Avenue, Miami, Fla., 33230; phone, 350–5765.
Region 4—Chicago Regional Office.—Thomas B. Hart, regional administrator; John I. Mayer, assistant regional administrator, U.S. Court House and Federal Office Building, 219 Dearborn Street, Chicago, Ill., 60604; phone, 828–7390; covering Michigan, Ohio, Kentucky, Indiana, Illinois, Wisconsin, Minnesota, Iowa, and Missouri.
Cleveland Branch Office.—John W. Vogel, attorney-in-charge, 1628 Standard Building, 1370 Ontario Street, Cleveland, Ohio, 44113; phone, 241–3243.
Detroit Branch Office.—Edward H. Rakow, assistant regional administrator, Room 1503, Washington Boulevard Building, 234 State Street, Detroit, Mich., 48226; phone, 226–6070.
St. Paul Branch Office.—James M. Klees, attorney-in-charge, 1027 Main Post Office and Custom House, 180 East Kellogg Boulevard, St. Paul, Minn., 55101; phone, 228–7847.
St. Louis Branch Office.—William D. Goldsberry, attorney-in-charge, Room 4266A, Federal Building, 1520 Market Street, St. Louis, Mo., 63103; phone, 622–4872.
Region 5—Fort Worth Regional Office.—Oran H. Allred, regional, administrator, 301 U.S. Court House, 10th and Lamar Streets, Fort Worth, Tex., 76102; phone, 335–2611; covering Arkansas, Louisiana, Kansas, Oklahoma, and Texas.

Region 5—Continued
> *Houston Branch Office.*—Leo F. Wyrick, attorney-in-charge; 2226 Federal Office and Courts Building, 515 Rusk Avenue, Houston, Tex., 77002; phone, 228–4187.

Region 6—Denver Regional Office.—Donald J. Stocking, regional administrator, Joseph F. Krys, assistant regional administrator, 802 Midland Savings Building, 444 17th Street, Denver, Colo., 80202; phone, 297–4424; covering North Dakota, South Dakota, Nebraska, Wyoming, Colorado, New Mexico, and Utah.
> *Salt Lake Branch Office.*—Gordon G. Weggeland, attorney-in-charge, Room 8440, Federal Building, 125 South State Street, Salt Lake City, Utah, 84111; phone, 524–5796 and 5797.

Region 7—San Francisco Regional Office.—Arthur E. Pennekamp, regional administrator, W. Stevens Tucker, assistant regional administrator, Franklin E. Kennamer, Jr., assistant general counsel, Pacific Building, 821 Market Street, San Francisco, Calif., 94103; phone, 556–5264; covering Nevada, Arizona, California, and Hawaii.
> *Los Angeles Branch Office.*—Walter G. Holden, associate regional administrator, 309 Guaranty Bldg., 6331 Hollywood Blvd., Los Angeles, Calif., 90028; phone, 462–3242.

Region 8—Seattle Regional Office.—James E. Newton, regional administrator; John N. Fegan, assistant regional administrator; ninth floor, Hoge Building, 705 Second Avenue, Seattle, Wash., 98104; phone, 682–8200; covering Montana, Idaho, Washington, Oregon, and Alaska.

Region 9—Washington Regional Office.—Alexander J. Brown, Jr., regional administrator, 3937 Garrison Street, Washington, D.C., 20016; Paul F. Leonard, assistant regional administrator, 9905 Marquette Drive, Bethesda, Md., 20034; Office, 310 Sixth Street NW., Washington, D.C., 20549; phone 963–3151; covering Pennsylvania, Delaware, Maryland, Virginia, and West Virginia.

SELECTIVE SERVICE SYSTEM

National Headquarters, 1724 F Street, 20435. Phone, 343-8025 (Code 183, extension 38025)

Director.—Lt. Gen. Lewis B. Hershey, 5500 Lambeth Road, Bethesda, Md., 20014,
Deputy Director and General Counsel.—Col. Daniel O. Omer, 3616 Oval Drive. Alexandria, Va., 22305.
Assistant Director.—Col. Campbell C. Johnson, 800 Fourth Street SW., 20024.
Assistants to the Director.—Col. William S. Iliff, 3488 North Venice Street, Arlington, Va., 22207; Col. Frank R. Kossa, Building T–2, Fort Lesley J. McNair, 20024.
Chief, Office of Legislation, Liaison, and Public Information.—Col. Bernard T. Franck III, 6740 25th Street North, Arlington, Va., 22213.
Chief Medical Officer.—Dr. Robert A. Bier, 9028 Woodland Drive, Silver Spring, Md., 20910.
Chief Planning Officer.—Col. Joel D. Griffing, 3839 Rodman Street, 20016.
Office of the Adjutant General.—Col. Edwin Cash, 420 Monticello Boulevard, Alexandria, Va., 22305.
Division Chiefs:
> *Administrative Division.*—Col. Tom M. Pickle, 6800 33d Street, North Falls Church, Va., 22043.
> *Manpower Division.*—Col. E. Dee Ingold, 815 18th Street South, Arlington, Va., 22202.
> *Field Division.*—Col. William P. Averill, 1314 20th Street South, Arlington, Va., 22202.
> *Fiscal and Procurement Division.*—Col. Theron E. Roberts, 7 Elizabeth Lane, Fairfax, Va., 22030.
> *Communications and Records Division.*—Col. Charles R. Fox, 5606 Chesterbrook Road, 20016.
> *Research and Statistics Division.*—Kenneth H. McGill, Crystal Spring, Pa.

SMALL BUSINESS ADMINISTRATION

811 Vermont Avenue, 20416. Phone, EXecutive 3-3111 (Code 128)

Administrator.—Eugene P. Foley, 9508 Burning Tree Road, Bethesda, Md.
Executive Administrator.—Ross D. Davis, 3421 N Street, 20007.
Deputy Administrator for Financial Assistance.—Logan B. Hendricks, 5620 Lamar Road, 20016.
Deputy Administrator for Investment.—Richard E. Kelley, 2829 Connecticut Avenue, 20008.
Deputy Administrator for Procurement and Management Assistance.—Irving Maness, 7316 Durbin Terrace, Bethesda, Md.
General Counsel.—Philip F. Zeidman, 837 31st Street South, Arlington, Va., 22202.
Special Assistant to the Administrator.—Martin E. Underwood, 1900 South Eads Street, Arlington, Va., 22202.
Assistant Administrator for Administration.—K. L. Hanna, 615 Poplar Drive, Falls Church, Va., 22046.
Assistant Administrator for Economics.—Padraic P. Frucht, 414 Paul Spring Road, Alexandria, Va.
Director, Executive Secretariat.—Frances Pappas, 3636 16th Street.
Special Assistant to the Administrator for Advisory Councils.—Daniel J. Carr, 1456 South West Street, Falls Church, Va.
Special Assistant to the Administrator for Congressional Relations.—Robert T. Cochran, Jr., The Gralyn Hotel, 1745 N Street.
Special Assistant to the Administrator for Minority Groups.—Randall L. Tyus, 917 Saxony Road, Silver Spring, Md., 20910.
Deputy Assistant Administrator for Administration.—Paul S. Howell, 11022 Oakwood Street, Silver Spring, Md.
Assistant Deputy Administrator for Financial Assistance.—[Vacant.]
Assistant Deputy Administrator for Financial Assistance.—Harold A. Galloway, 4847 Bayard Boulevard, 20016.
Special Assistant for ARA.—Harold D. Brown, 3605 Norwood Place, Alexandria, Va.
Assistant Deputy Administrator for Investment.—Robert B. Leisy, 2216 Shipman Lane, McLean, Va., 22101.
Assistant Administrator for Management Assistance.—Gerald S. Fisher, 8512 Aragon Lane, Chevy Chase, Md., 20015.
Deputy Assistant Administrator for Management Assistance.—Thomas F. Shea, 1900 South Eads Street, Apt. 919, Arlington, Va.
Assistant Deputy Administrator for Procurement Assistance.—Ralph F. Turner, 9813 Singleton Drive, Bethesda, Md.
Director, Office of Administrative Operations Staff for Financial Assistance.—Robert J. Page, 6720 Greentree Road, Bethesda, Md., 20034.
Acting Director, Office of Administrative Operations Staff for Investment.—Stephen H. Bedwell, Jr., 2113 North Lincoln Street, Arlington, Va.
Director, Office of Administrative Operations Staff for Procurement and Management Assistance.—James Salisbury, Jr., 3003 Arlington Boulevard, Arlington, Va.
Director, Office of Administrative Services.—Norman J. Billingsley, 6912 Heidelberg Road, Lanham, Md.
Director, Office of Audits.—Joseph M. Hart, 8405 Cedar Street, Silver Spring, Md.
Director, Office of Budget.—John H. Barber, 4807 Taney Avenue, Alexandria, Va., 22304.
Director, Office of Business Advisory Services.—Grant C. Moon, 5229 Yorktown Boulevard, Arlington, Va., 22207.
Acting Director, Office of Chief Accountant.—Forest C. Brimacombe, 1701 White Oak Drive, Silver Spring, Md., 20910.
Acting Director, Office of Development Companies.—Thomas S. Francis, 4522 Drummond Avenue, Chevy Chase, Md., 20015.
Director, Office of Disaster Loans.—Clarence Cowles, 9100 16th Street, Silver Spring, Md.
Director, Office of Economic Opportunity Assistance.—Addison W. Parris, 12515 Shetland Lane, Bowie, Md.
Director, Office of Fiscal Operations.—Paul R. Redinger, 611 LaMarre Drive, Fairfax, Va., 22030.
Director, Office of Foreign Trade.—Samuel N. Klein, 5528 29th Street, 20015.

Acting Director, Office of Investment Company Operations, Eastern Area.—James T. Phelan, 8719 Milford Avenue, Silver Spring, Md., 20910.

Acting Director, Office of Investment Company Operations, Western Area.—John B. Morris, 3388 Martha Custis Drive, Alexandria, Va.

Acting Director, Office of Licensing.—Burrell F. Wicker, 2805 Nicholson Street, Apt. 103, West Hyattsville, Md., 20782.

Director, Office of Loan Administration.—William A. Chadwell, 409 North George Mason Drive, Arlington, Va., 22203.

Director, Office of Loan Appraisal.—James F. King, 6810 Nashville Road, Lanham, Md.

Director, Office of Loan Processing.—Pierron R. Leef, 1103 Burketon Road, Hyattsville, Md., 20783.

Director, Office of Management Analysis.—William C. Fisher, 3000 David Lane, Alexandria, Va., 22311.

Director, Office of Management Development.—Wendell O. Metcalf, 5111 Westridge Road, 20016.

Director, Office of Personnel.—Robert H. West, 75 Eldrid Road, Silver Spring, Md.

Director, Office of Procurement Services.—P. Herbert Pierce, 2222 North Roosevelt Street, Arlington, Va.

Director, Office of Production Facilities.—Sol Elson, 1366 Leegate Road, 20012.

Acting Director, Office of Program Development, Investment Division.—Lauren B. Hart, 9112 Fourth Street, Lanham, Md., 20801.

Director, Office of Public Information.—Rose McKee, 2 Snow's Court, 20037.

Acting Director, Office of Regulatory Activity.—Robert C. Downes, 1431 Martha Custis Drive, Alexandria, Va.

SMITHSONIAN INSTITUTION

The Mall, 20560. Phone, 628-1810 (Code 144)

Secretary.—Dr. S. Dillon Ripley, 2324 Massachusetts Avenue, 20008.

Assistant Secretary.—James Bradley, 9502 Columbia Boulevard, Silver Spring, Md., 20910.

Assistant to the Secretary.—Theodore W. Taylor, 706 North Frederick Street, Arlington, Va., 22203.

Assistant Secretary (Acting).—T. Dale Stewart, 4533 Crest Lane, McLean, Va., 22101.

Executive Assistant.—Robert W. Mason, 3706 R Street, 20007.

Special Assistant to the Secretary for Scientific Matters.—Philip Ritterbush, 1677 32d Street, 20007.

Special Assistant to the Secretary for Fine Arts.—Thomas M. Beggs, 6017 Hitt Avenue, McLean, Va., 22101.

Special Assistant to the Secretary for International Activities.—William W. Warner, 2243 47th Street, 20007.

Director of Education and Training.—Charles Blitzer (to assume duties of Director of Education and Training on July 1, 1965).

Assistant to the Secretary (Special Projects).—Robert N. Cunningham, 2629 O Street, 20007.

Special Assistant (Research Staff).—John Whitelaw, 2909 Brierdale Lane, Bowie, Md., 20715.

General Counsel.—Peter G. Powers, 3010 Cambridge Place, 20007.

Treasurer.—Otis O. Martin, 2000 South Eads Street, Arlington, Va., 22202.

Chief, Editorial and Publications Division.—Paul H. Oehser, Route 2, Box 396, McLean, Va., 22101.

Acting Librarian.—Mary A. Huffer, 6327 Hardwood Drive, Lanham, Md., 20801.

Liaison Librarian at Library of Congress.—Ruth E. Blanchard, 2500 Wisconsin Avenue, 20007.

Curator in charge, Smithsonian Museum Service.—G. Carroll Lindsay, 400 Carlisle Drive, Alexandria, Va., 23301.

Buildings Manager.—Andrew F. Michaels, 8509 Haskins Place, Takoma Park, Md., 20012.

Director of Personnel.—Joseph A. Kennedy, 1800 Cody Drive, Silver Spring, Md., 20902.

Chief, Supply Division.—Anthony W. Wilding, 6331 Tone Drive, Bethesda, Md., 20014.

Chief, Photographic Services Division.—Otis H. Greeson, 9513 49th Place, Berwyn, Md., 21541.
Budget Officer.—Maria M. Hoemann, 3804 South Capitol Street SE., 20032.
Chief, Organization and Methods Division.—Ann S. Campbell, 6401 Matthews Drive, Temple Hills, Md., 20031.

THE ESTABLISHMENT

President of the United States.
Vice President of the United States.
Chief Justice of the United States.
Secretary of State.
Secretary of the Treasury.
Secretary of Defense.
Attorney General.
Postmaster General.
Secretary of the Interior.
Secretary of Agriculture.
Secretary of Commerce.
Secretary of Labor.
Secretary of Health, Education, and Welfare.

BOARD OF REGENTS

Chancellor.—Earl Warren, Chief Justice of the United States.
Members of the Board.—Hubert H. Humphrey, Vice President of the United States; Clinton P. Anderson, Member of the Senate; J. W. Fulbright, Member of the Senate; Leverett Saltonstall, Member of the Senate; Frank T. Bow, Member of the House of Representatives; Michael J. Kirwan, Member of the House of Representatives; George H. Mahon, Member of the House of Representatives; John Nicholas Brown, citizen of Rhode Island (Providence); William A. M. Burden, citizen of New York; Robert V. Fleming, citizen of Washington, D.C.; Crawford H. Greenewalt, citizen of Delaware (Wilmington); Caryl P. Haskins, citizen of Washington, D.C.; Jerome C. Hunsaker, citizen of Massachusetts (Cambridge).
Executive Committee.—Robert V. Fleming, chairman; Caryl P. Haskins; Clinton P. Anderson.

BUREAUS UNDER DIRECTION OF SMITHSONIAN INSTITUTION

UNITED STATES NATIONAL MUSEUM

Director.—Frank A. Taylor, 6605 32d Street, 20015.
Registrar.—Helena M. Weiss, 2022 Columbia Road, 20009.

MUSEUM OF NATURAL HISTORY

Director.—T. Dale Stewart, 4533 Crest Lane, McLean, Va., 22101.
Assistant Director.—Richard S. Cowan, 4409 Tonquil Place, Beltsville, Md., 20705.
Assistant Director for Oceanography.—I. Eugene Wallen, 6310 12th Road North, Arlington, Va., 22205.
Acting Head, Office of Anthropology.—Waldo R. Wedel, 5432 30th Place, 20015.
Department Chairmen.—J. F. Gates Clarke, 5115 72d Avenue, Glenridge, Hyattsville, Md.; G. Arthur Cooper, 3425 Porter Street, 20016; G. S. Switzer, 5503 Yorktown Road, 20016; William L. Stern, 4157 Southern Avenue SE., 20020; Donald F. Squires, 4011 Byrd Road, Kensington, Md., 20795; Philip S. Humphrey, 5718 9th Road North, Arlington, Va., 22205.

MUSEUM OF HISTORY AND TECHNOLOGY

Director.—John C. Ewers, 4432 26th Road North, Arlington, Va., 22207.
Assistant Director.—[Vacant.]
Department Chairmen.—Philip W. Bishop, 8108 Hamilton Spring Road, Bethesda, Md., 20014; Richard H. Howland, 1516 33d Street, 20007; Robert P. Multhauf, 4100 W Street, 20007; Mendel L. Peterson, 102 Westgate Drive, Alexandria, Va., 20009.

ASTROPHYSICAL OBSERVATORY

Director.—Fred L. Whipple, 35 Elizabeth Road, Belmont, Mass., 02178.
Assistant Director.—Charles A. Lundquist, 218 Parker Street, Newton Center, Mass., 02159.
Assistant Director (Management).—Carlton W. Tillinghast, 30 Glen Road, Brookline, Mass., 02146.
Chief, Division of Radiation and Organisms.—William H. Klein, 7901 Kentbury Drive, Bethesda, Md., 20014.

NATIONAL COLLECTION OF FINE ARTS

Director.—David W. Scott, 3106 Cortland Place, 20008.
Acting Assistant to the Director.—Donald R. McClelland, 1616 19th Street, 20009.
Department Chairmen.—Richard P. Wunder, 3230 N Street., 20007; Harry Lowe, 1517 30th Street, 20007; Rowland Lyon, 3835 S Street, 20007.

FREER GALLERY OF ART

Director.—John A. Pope, 2425 California Street, 20008.
Assistant Director.—Harold P. Stern, 2122 Massachusetts Avenue, 20008.

NATIONAL AIR MUSEUM

Advisory Board—
Maj. Gen. Brooke E. Allen, representing the Chief of Staff, Department of the Air Force.
Vice Adm. William A. Schoech, representing the Chief of Naval Operations, Department of the Navy.
James Doolittle, citizen member.
Grover Loening, citizen member.
Secretary of the Smithsonian Institution.
Director.—S. Paul Johnston, 3713 Alton Place, 20016.
Head Curator.—Paul E. Garber, 310 South Jackson Street, Arlington, Va., 22204.

NATIONAL ZOOLOGICAL PARK

Adams Mill Road. Phone, COlumbia 5-0743

Director.—Theodore H. Reed, 5005 Baltimore Avenue, 20016.
Assistant Director.—J. Lear Grimmer, 5712 Bent Branch Road, 20016.

CANAL ZONE BIOLOGICAL AREA

Barro Colorado Island, Gatun Lake, Canal Zone

Director.—Martin H. Moynihan, Canal Zone Biological Area, Drawer C, Balboa, Canal Zone.

INTERNATIONAL EXCHANGE SERVICE

Chief.—Jeremiah A. Collins, 13 Montgomery Avenue, Takoma Park, Md., 20012.

NATIONAL PORTRAIT GALLERY

National Portrait Gallery Commission:
Catherine Drinker Bowen, 260 Booth Lane, Haverford, Pa., 19041.
Julian P. Boyd, 120 Breadmead, Princeton, N.J., 08541.
John Nicholas Brown, 50 South Main Street, Providence, R.I., 02903.
Lewis Deschler, 101 Lucas Lane, Bethesda, Md., 20014.
David E. Finley, 3318 O Street, 20007.
Wilmarth Sheldon Lewis, Farmington, Conn., 06032.
Richard H. Shryock, 104 South Fifth Street, Philadelphia, Pa., 19106.
Col. Frederick P. Todd, U.S. Military Academy, West Point, N.Y., 10996.
Ex Officio:
Chief Justice of the United States.
Secretary, Smithsonian Institution.
Director, National Gallery of Art.
Director.—Charles Nagel, 4806 De Russey Parkway, West Chevy Chase, Md., 20015.

NATIONAL ARMED FORCES MUSEUM ADVISORY BOARD

Chairman.—Dr. John Nicholas Brown, 50 South Main Street, Providence, R.I.
Ex Officio:
  Secretary of Defense.
  Secretary, Smithsonian Institution.
Members:
  Chief Justice of the United States.
  Secretary of Army.
  Secretary of Navy.
  Secretary of Air Force.
  Dr. David Lloyd Kreeger, 3201 Fessenden Street, 20008.
  Dr. Henry Bradford Washburn, Jr.—Museum of Science, Science Park, Boston, Mass., 02114.

NATIONAL GALLERY OF ART

[Under the direction of the Board of Trustees of the National Gallery of Art]

Constitution Avenue, between Fourth and Seventh Streets.   Phone, REpublic 7-4215

Board of Trustees:
  Chief Justice of the United States, chairman.
  Secretary of State.
  Secretary of the Treasury.
  Secretary of the Smithsonian Institution.
  Paul Mellon.
  John Hay Whitney.
  John Nichol Irwin II.
  Franklin D. Murphy.
  Lessing J. Rosenwald.
President.—Paul Mellon, Oak Spring, Upperville, Va., 22176.
Vice President.—John Hay Whitney, Room 4600, 110 West 51st Street, New York, N.Y., 10019.
Secretary-Treasurer.—Huntington Cairns, 2219 California Street, 20008.
Director.—John Walker, 2806 N Street, 20007.
Administrator.—Ernest R. Feidler, 1411 North Glebe Road, Arlington, Va., 22207.
General Counsel.—Huntington Cairns, 2219 California Street, 20008.
Chief Curator.—Perry B. Cott, 4201 Cathedral Avenue, 20016.
Assistant Director.—J. Carter Brown, 3330 Reservoir Road, 20007.

JOHN F. KENNEDY CENTER FOR THE PERFORMING ARTS

(Under the direction of the Board of Trustees of the John F. Kennedy Center for the Performing Arts)

1701 Pennsylvania Avenue.   Phone, 382-1933

BOARD OF TRUSTEES

Chairman.—Roger L. Stevens.
Ex Officio:
  Assistant Secretary of State for Cultural and Educational Affairs.
  Secretary, Smithsonian Institution.
  Commissioner, U.S. Office of Education.
  Chairman, Commission of Fine Arts.
  Secretary of Health, Education, and Welfare.
  Chairman, D.C. Recreation Board.
  President, D.C. Board of Commissioners.
  Librarian of Congress.
  Director, National Park Service.

U.S. Senate:
  Joseph S. Clark.
  J. W. Fulbright.
  Leverett Saltonstall.
  Robert F. Kennedy.

U.S. House of Representatives:
  Frank Thompson, Jr.
  James C. Wright, Jr.
  Charlotte T. Reid.

General:

Richard Adler.
Howard Ahmanson.
Floyd D. Akers.
Robert O. Anderson.
Ralph E. Becker.
K. LeMoyne Billings.
Mrs. Thomas Braden.
Ernest R. Breech.
Edgar M. Bronfman.
Mrs. George R. Brown.
Ralph J. Bunche.
Abe Fortas.
Leonard H. Goldenson.
Mrs. George A. Garrett.
Mrs. A. D. Lasker.

Erich Leinsdorf.
Sol Myron Linowitz.
George Meany.
Edwin Wendell Pauley.
Arthur Penn.
Richard S. Reynolds, Jr.
Frank H. Ricketson, Jr.
Richard Rodgers.
Arthur Schlesinger, Jr.
Mrs. Jouett Shouse.
Mrs. Jean Kennedy Smith.
Roger L. Stevens.
Edwin L. Weisl, Sr.
Robert W. Woodruff.

OFFICERS

Honorary Chairmen.—Mrs. Dwight D. Eisenhower, Mrs. Lyndon B. Johnson, Mrs. John F. Kennedy.
Chairman.—Roger L. Stevens, 745 Fifth Avenue, New York, N.Y., 10002.
Vice Chairman.—Robert O. Anderson, 410 East College Boulevard, Roswell, N. Mex., 88201.
Counsel.—Ralph E. Becker, 2916 32d Street, 20008.
Secretary.—K. LeMoyne Billings, 380 Madison Avenue, New York, N.Y., 10002.
Treasurer.—Daniel W. Bell, 3816 Gramercy Street, 20016.
Assistant Treasurer.—Herbert D. Lawson, 15th Street and Pennsylvania Avenue, 20005.
Assistant Treasurer.—Kenneth Birgfeld, 5116 West Ridge Road, 20016.

ADVISORY COMMITTEE ON THE ARTS

Chairman.—Robert W. Dowling, 978 Madison Avenue, New York, N.Y., 10002.

SOLDIERS' HOME, UNITED STATES
REGULAR ARMY—REGULAR AIR FORCE
BOARD OF COMMISSIONERS
United States Soldiers' Home.   Phone, RAndolph 6-9100

Gen. Wade H. Haislip, USA (retired), Governor of the Home.
Lt. Gen. Leonard D. Heaton, USA, The Surgeon General, USA.
Lt. Gen. Walter K. Wilson, Jr., USA, The Chief of Engineers, USA.
Maj. Gen. Richard L. Bohannon, USAF, The Surgeon General, USAF.
Maj. Gen. T. E. Moore, USAF, Director of Personnel Planning, USAF.
Maj. Gen. Robert H. McCaw, USA, The Judge Advocate General, USA.
Maj. Gen. Joe C. Lambert, USA, The Adjutant General, USA.
Maj. Gen. W. C. Haneke, USA, The Chief of Finance, USA.
Maj. Gen. Robert W. Manss, USAF, The Judge Advocate General, USAF.
Col. J. W. Hanger, USA, Chief of Support Services, USA.

OFFICERS OF THE HOME
Residing at the Home.   Phone, RAndolph 6-9100

Governor.—Gen. Wade H. Haislip, U.S.A. (retired).
Deputy Governor.—Brig. Gen. John F. Cassidy, U.S.A. (retired).
Secretary-Treasurer.—Col. Edward V. Freeman, U.S.A. (retired).
Chief Surgeon.—Brig. Gen. Harry D. Offutt, U.S.A. (retired).
Quartermaster and Purchasing Officer.—Col. Ivan W. Elliott, U.S.A. (retired).
Secretary Board of Commissioners.—Col. Edward H. Young, U.S.A. (retired).

SUBVERSIVE ACTIVITIES CONTROL BOARD

811 Vermont Avenue, 20445.   Phone, EXecutive 3-3151 (Code 128, extension 6224)

Members:
Francis Adams Cherry (Chairman), 5324 Albemarle Street, 20016.
Thomas J. Donegan, 3247 Chestnut Street, 20015.
Frank Kowalski, 405 Regent Drive, Alexandria, Va., 22307.
Leonard L. Sells, Auburn, North Post Office, Mathews County, Va., 23128.
Edward Cleaveland Sweeney, 3300 Nebraska Avenue, 20016.
Executive Secretary.—Robert K. Thurber, 6404 Winston Drive, Bethesda, Md., 20034.
General Counsel.—Frank R. Hunter, Jr., 3317 North George Mason Drive, Arlington, Va., 22207.

TARIFF COMMISSION, UNITED STATES

Tariff Commission Building, Eighth and E Streets, 20436.   Phone, NAtional 8-3947 (Code 1272)

Commissioners:
Ben D. Dorfman (chairman), of District of Columbia, 4719 30th Street, 20008.
Dan H. Fenn, Jr. (vice chairman), 4008 Everett Street, Kensington, Md., 20795.
Joseph E. Talbot, of Connecticut, 7809 14th Street, 20012.
[Vacant.]
Glenn W. Sutton, of Georgia, 2800 Adams Mill Road, 20009.
James W. Culliton, of Indiana, 917 North Van Dorn Street, Alexandria, Va., 22304.
Secretary.—Donn N. Bent, 2128 North Pollard Street, Arlington, Va., 22207.
  Assistant to the Secretary.—Edith L. Finch, 10610 Greenacres Drive, Hillandale, Md., 20903.
Director of Investigation.—Willard W. Kane, 933 Taylor Run Parkway, Alexandria, Va., 22302.
  Assistant to the Director of Investigation.—Oscar E. Kiessling, 217 Haycock Road, Falls Church, Va., 22043.
  Assistant to the Director of Investigation.—William W. Meyer, 6911 General Duff Drive, Falls Church, Va.
Chief, Economics Division.—David Lynch, 3679 Highwood Drive SE., 20020.
General Counsel.—Russell N. Shewmaker, 5857 Nebraska Avenue, 20015.
  Assistant General Counsel.—Charles W. Lucas, Route 5, Box 88L, Vienna, Va., 22180.
Chief of Technical Service.—John B. Howard, Boyds, Md., 20720.
  Assistant Chief of Technical Service.—Albert F. Parks, 2907 Edghill Drive, Alexandria, Va., 22302.
  Chiefs of Technical Divisions:
    Agricultural.—Hyman Leikind, 6902 Breezewood Terrace, Rockville, Md., 20852.
    Ceramics.—Ray T. Watkins, 3202 Pickwick Lane, Chevy Chase, Md., 20015.
    Chemicals.—Frank Gonet, 4007 North Woodstock Street, Arlington, Va., 22207.
    Lumber and Paper.—Edward P. Furlow, 4406 North Vacation Lane, Arlington, Va., 22207.
    Metals.—Nicholas Yaworski, Route 4, Box 538, McLean, Va., 22101.
    Sundries.—Walter L. Sanders, Jr., 200 Maple Avenue, Falls Church, Va.
    Textiles.—Roland L. Lee, Jr., 5610 Nebraska Avenue NW., Washington, D.C., 20015.
Director of Administration.—Richard O. Quill, 5910 Woodacres Drive, Woodacres, Md., 20016.
New York Office.—John J. Hughes, Chief, 437 Customhouse, New York City (Home address: 712 Washington Street, Carlstadt, N.J.).

TENNESSEE VALLEY AUTHORITY

Wilson Dam, Ala. Phone, Sheffield 383-4631; Knoxville, Tenn. Phone, 522-7181; Chattanooga, Tenn. Phone, 265-3551; Washington Office, Woodward Building. Phone, 343-4537

BOARD OF DIRECTORS

Chairman.—Aubrey J. Wagner, 1600 Cedar Lane, Knoxville, Tenn., 37918.
Vice Chairman.—A. R. Jones, Hamilton House, 1400 Kenesaw Avenue, Knoxville, Tenn., 37919.
Director.—Frank E. Smith, 204 Suburban Road, Knoxville, Tenn., 37919.
General Manager.—Louis J. Van Mol, 1309 Avonmouth Road, Knoxville, Tenn., 37914.
  Assistant General Manager.—Edwin A. Shelley, 3016 Gibbs Road, Knoxville, Tenn., 37918.
  Assistant to the General Manager (Budget and Planning).—E. Philip Ericson, 8616 Hempstead Drive, Knoxville, Tenn., 37919.
    Chief Budget Staff.—L. Edward Ellis, 328 Tedlo Lane, Knoxville, Tenn., 37920.
  Director of Information.—Paul L. Evans, 29 East Norris Road, Norris, Tenn., 37828.
  Power Financing Officer.—G. O. Wessenauer, 2931-N Nurick Drive NW., Chattanooga, Tenn., 37405.
  Washington Representative.—Marguerite Owen, 3000 39th Street, Washington, D.C., 20016.
General Counsel and Secretary to the Corporation.—Charles J. McCarthy, Route 10, Martin Mill Pike, Knoxville, Tenn., 37920.
Comptroller.—Gifford G. Cruze, 1109 Young Avenue, Maryville, Tenn., 37801.
Director of Health.—O. Merton Derryberry, M.D., 621 Mississippi Avenue, Signal Mountain, Tenn., 37377.
Director of Personnel.—John E. Massey, 1015 Kenesaw Avenue SW., Knoxville, Tenn., 37919.
Director of Property and Supply.—Ashford Todd, Jr., Sunset Road West, Lookout Mountain, Tenn., 37350.
Director of Purchasing.—Paul I. Fahey, 95 South Crest Road, Chattanooga, Tenn., 37404.
Acting Director of Reservoir Properties.—Claude W. Nash, 914 Green Ridge Circle, Knoxville, Tenn., 37919.
Director of Forestry Development.—Kenneth J. Seigworth, 100 West Norris Road, Norris, Tenn., 37828.
Project Manager, Land Between the Lakes Project.—Robert M. Howes, 5006 Jacksboro Pike, Knoxville, Tenn., 37918.
Director of Navigation Development.—J. Porter Taylor, 2909 Barber Hill Lane, Knoxville, Tenn., 37920.
Director of Tributary Area Development.—Richard Kilbourne, 27 Dogwood Road, Norris, Tenn., 37828.
Director of Water Control Planning.—Reed A. Elliot, 5600 Marilyn Drive, Knox, ville, Tenn., 37914.
Manager of Agricultural and Chemical Development.—Lewis B. Nelson, 1918 Courtney Avenue, Florence, Ala., 35630.
  Assistant Manager of Agricultural and Chemical Development.—John H. Walthall, Route 1, Wilson Lake, Sheffield, Ala., 35660.
  Director of Agricultural Development.—Gerald G. Williams, 825 Sherrod Avenue, Florence, Ala., 35630.
  Director of Chemical Development.—Travis P. Hignett, 704 Wilson Dam Circle, Sheffield, Ala., 35660.
  Director of Chemical Operations.—Stewart A. Harvey, 602 Wilson Dam Avenue, Sheffield, Ala., 35660.
Manager of Engineering Design and Construction.—George P. Palo, 8129 Chesterfield Drive, Knoxville, Tenn., 37919.
  Director of Construction.—Hendon R. Johnston, 6810 Haverhill Drive, Knoxville, Tenn., 37919.
  Director of Engineering Design.—Walter F. Emmons, 112 West Norris Road, Norris, Tenn., 37828.

Manager of Power.—G. O. Wessenauer, 2931–N Nurick Drive NW., Chattanooga, Tenn., 37405.

Assistant Manager of Power.—James E. Watson, 126 Norvell Drive, Signal Mountain, Tenn., 37377.

Director of Power Construction.—Worth B. Richardson, 1075 Druid Drive, Signal Mountain, Tenn., 37377.

Director of Power Marketing.—Paul S. Button, 3757 Queens Road, Chattanooga, Tenn., 37406.

Director of Power Planning and Engineering.—Fred Chambers, 4819 Lake Haven Drive, Chattanooga, Tenn., 37416.

Director of Power Production.—E. Floyd Thomas, 3589 Kings Road, Chattanooga, Tenn., 37406.

Director of Power System Operations.—Charles P. Almon, Jr., 405 Fern Train, Signal Mountain, Tenn., 37377.

TRADE INFORMATION COMMITTEE

Executive Office Building. Phone, 382–1911

MEMBERS

Louis C. Krauthoff II (chairman), 3317 O Street, 20007, Office of the Special Representative for Trade Negotiations.

Sidney Picker, Jr. (counsel and executive secretary), 1900 South Eads Street, Arlington, Va., 22202, Office of the Special Representative for Trade Negotiations.

John F. Hudson, 1035 Welsh Drive, Rockville, Md., International Economist, Trade Policy Division, Foreign Agricultural Service, Department of Agriculture.

Harold L. Lamar, 10242 Parkwood Drive, Kensington, Md., Director, Import Policy Staff, Trade and Commercial Policy Division, Bureau of International Commerce, Department of Commerce.

Joseph W. Darling, 423 New Jersey Avenue SE., 20003, Director, Office of Foreign Economic Affairs, Office of the Assistant Secretary of Defense, Department of Defense.

Morton Pomeranz, 4518 40th Street North, Arlington, Va., 22207, International Activities Assistant, Resources Program Staff, Office of the Secretary, Department of the Interior.

Herbert N. Blackman, 7004 Wilson Lane, Bethesda, Md., 20034, Acting Chief, Division of Foreign Economic Policy, Bureau of International Labor Affairs, Department of Labor.

James H. Lewis, 5331 Massachusetts Avenue, Deputy Director, Office of International Trade, Bureau of Economic Affairs, Department of State.

William H. Wynne, 3401 Thornapple Street, Chevy Chase, Md., 20015, Advisor on Financial Policy, Office of International Economic Affairs, Office of International Affairs, Department of the Treasury.

UNITED STATES INFORMATION AGENCY

1776 Pennsylvania Avenue. Phone, REpublic 7–8340 (Code 182)

Director.—Carl T. Rowan, 2832 Ellicott Street, 20008.

Executive Assistant.—Lester E. Edmond, 8901 Charred Oak Drive, Bethesda, Md., 20034.

Special Assistant.—Dennis Askey, 5227 Second Street, 20011. *Robert W. akers*

Deputy Director.—Donald M. Wilson, 5105 Lowell Lane, 20016.

Special Assistant to the Deputy Director.—Wilson P. Dizard, 2811 28th Street, 20008.

Deputy Director (Policy and Plans).—Burnett Anderson, 632 A Street SE., 20003.

General Counsel and Congressional Liaison.—Stanley Plesent, 3724 McKinley Street, 20015.

Assistant Director (Africa).—Mark B. Lewis, 1851 Redwood Terrace, 20012.

Assistant Director (Europe).—Robert A. Lincoln, 4101 Cathedral Avenue, 20016.

Assistant Director (Far East).—W. Kenneth Bunce, 3217 Old Dominion Boulevard, Alexandria, Va., 22305.

Assistant Director (Latin America).—Hewson A. Ryan, 6109 Robinwood Road, Bethesda, Md.,20034.

Assistant Director (Near East and South Asia).—William D. Miller, 120 Country-hill Drive, Fairfax, Va., 22030.

Assistant Director (Soviet Union and Eastern Europe).—Richard T. Davies, 3511 Leland Street, Chevy Chase, Md., 20015.

Assistant Director (Administration).—Ben Posner, 2405 Eccleston Street, Silver Spring, Md., 20902.

Agency Budget Officer.—Nancy G. Stephens, 7906 Takoma Avenue, Silver Spring, Md., 20910.

Director, Personnel and Training.—Lionel S. Mosley, 818 Glenmere Road, Fairfax, Va., 22030.

Director, Broadcasting Service.—Henry Loomis, Middleburg, Va., 22117.

Director, Information Center Service.—Reed Harris, 4905 Berkley Street, 20016.

Director, Motion Picture Service.—George Stevens, Jr., 1330 New Hampshire Avenue, 20036.

Director, Press and Publications Service.—Thomas L. Wright, 6019 Tyndale Street, McLean, Va., 22101.

Director, Television Service.—Alan Carter, 1802 Metzerott Road, A–1, Adelphi, Md., 20783.

Director, Office of Public Information.—Edward J. Savage, 3341 Prospect Street, 20007.

Director, Research and Reference Service.—Oren M. Stephens, 302 North Virginia Avenue, Falls Church, Va., 22043.

Acting Director, Office of Private Cooperation.—Richard T. Hamilton, 6512 Old Columbia Pike, Annandale, Va., 22003.

Director, Office of Security.—Paul J. McNichol, 200 River Towers Drive, 703, Alexandria, Va.

VETERANS ADMINISTRATION

Veterans Administration Building, Vermont at H Street, 20420.   Phone, EXecutive 3–4120 (Code 148)

Administrator of Veterans Affairs.—William J. Driver, 215 West Colombia Street, Falls Church, Va., 22046.

Executive Assistant to the Administrator.—L. J. Hook, 9719 West Bexhill Drive, Kensington, Md., 20795.

Special Assistant to the Administrator.—Esther M. LaMarr, 1444 Rhode Island Avenue, 20005.

Confidential Assistant to the Administrator.—P. E. Howard, 109 Olley Lane, Fairfax, Va., 22030.

Personal Assistant to the Administrator.—Mrs. Maxine P. Phillips, 2906 North Kensington Street, Arlington, Va., 22207.

Secretary to the Administrator.—Mrs. D. Jane Hudson, 2725 Fort Baker Drive SE., 20020.

Acting Deputy Administrator.—A. H. Monk, 2705 North Somerset Street, Arlington, Va., 22213.

Acting Associate Deputy Administrator.—A. T. McAnsch, 3417 Dent Place, 20007.

Chairman, Administrator's Advisory Council.—Paul N. Schmoll, 9914 Ashburton Lane, Bethesda, Md., 20014.

Chief Benefits Director.—Cyril F. Brickfield, 9615 Bellevue Drive, Bethesda, Md.

Chief Data Management Director.—P. J. Budd, 5536 Backlick Road, Springfield, Va.

Chief Medical Director.—Dr. J. H. McNinch, 6445 Luzon Avenue, 20012.

Controller.—John D. Shytle, 1512 Red Oak Drive, Silver Spring, Md.

General Counsel.—Robert C. Fable, Jr., 5118 Duvall Drive, 20016.

Assistant Administrator for Management and Evaluation.—Blake E. Turner, 318 Cabin Road SE., Vienna, Va.

Assistant Administrator for Construction.—Whitney Ashbridge, 3 Magnolia Parkway, Chevy Chase, Md., 20015.

Assistant Administrator for Personnel.—Willis O. Underwood, 3144 O Street, 20007.

Director, Information Service.—F. R. Hood, 513 Westcott Street, Falls Church, Va.

Chairman, Board of Veterans Appeals.—James W. Stancil, 100 Fourth Street NE., 20002.
Manager, Administrative Services.—Edward J. Gorman, 5415 Connecticut Avenue, 20015.

WASHINGTON NATIONAL MONUMENT SOCIETY

(Organized 1833; chartered 1859; acts of Congress August 2, 1876, October 2, 1888)

President ex Officio.—Lyndon B. Johnson, President of the United States.
Vice Presidents ex Officio.—The Governors of the several States.
First Vice President.—U.S. Grant 3d, 1135 21st Street, 20036.
Second Vice President.—John Lord O'Brian, 2123 California Avenue, 20008.
Treasurer.—Charles C. Glover, Jr., 4200 Massachusetts Avenue.
Secretary.—George B. Hartzog, Jr., 4818 Old Dominion Drive, Arlington, Va., 22207.
Members:
  Cloyd Heck Marvin; Benjamin M. McKelway; Colgate W. Darden, Jr.; Thomas C. Kinkaid; Charles S. Dewey; Chief Justice Earl Warren; Harry Flood Byrd; Corcoran Thom, Jr.; David E. Finley; Melville Grosvenor; Samuel Spencer; George Hamilton; Frederick M. Bradley. Members Emeritus: Samuel H. Kauffmann; Gilbert H. Grosvenor; Joseph C. Grew; C. R. Train; Conrad L. Wirth.

JUDICIARY

JUDICIARY

SUPREME COURT OF THE UNITED STATES

1 First Street NE., 20543.   Phone, EXecutive 3–1640 (Code 1207)

EARL WARREN, Chief Justice of the United States; born March 19, 1891, in Los Angeles, Calif., son of Methias H. and Christine (Hernlund) Warren; B. L., University of California, 1912; J. D. 1914; married Nina E. Meyers, October 14, 1925; children—James C., Virginia, Earl, Dorothy, Nina, and Robert; deputy and chief deputy district attorney, Alameda County, Calif., 1920–25; district attorney, 1925–39; attorney general of California, 1939–43; Governor of California, 1943–53; served as first lieutenant in Infantry, U. S. Army, 1917–18; nominated Chief Justice of the United States by President Eisenhower September 30, 1953; took oath of office and his seat on October 5, 1953; chancellor of the Board of Regents, Smithsonian Institution; chairman, Board of Trustees, National Gallery of Art.

HUGO LAFAYETTE BLACK, of Birmingham, Ala., Associate Justice of the Supreme Court of the United States; born in Clay County, Ala., February 27, 1886; was nominated by President Franklin D. Roosevelt on August 12, 1937, to be Associate Justice of the Supreme Court of the United States; confirmed by the Senate on August 17, 1937, and took his seat on October 4, 1937.

WILLIAM ORVILLE DOUGLAS, Associate Justice of the Supreme Court of the United States, was born at Maine, Minn., on October 16, 1898; graduated from Whitman College, Walla Walla, Wash., A. B., 1920, and from Columbia University Law School, LL. B., 1925; practiced law New York and Washington; member of law faculties, Columbia and Yale; member of Securities and Exchange Commission, 1936–39, chairman, 1937–39; nominated Associate Justice of the United States Supreme Court by President Roosevelt, March 20, 1939; confirmed by the Senate, April 4, 1939, and took his seat April 17, 1939.

TOM C. CLARK, Associate Justice of the Supreme Court of the United States; born September 23, 1899, in Dallas, Tex.; son of William H. and Jennie (Falls) Clark; Virginia Military Institute, 1917–18; A. B., University of Texas, 1921; LL. B., 1922; married Mary Ramsey, of Texas, November 8, 1924; children, William Ramsey, Mildred (Mrs. Thomas R. Gronlund), (Tom C., Jr., deceased); in private practice, Dallas, 1922–37 (civil district attorney, Dallas County, 1927–32); Department of Justice, Washington, D.C., 1937–43; Assistant Attorney General, 1943–45; Attorney General of the United States, 1945–49; nominated by President Truman to be Associate Justice of the Supreme Court of the United States August 2, 1949, confirmed by the Senate August 18, 1949, and took his seat October 3, 1949; home: 2101 Connecticut Avenue, Washington, D.C. Office: United States Supreme Court, Washington, D.C., 20543.

JOHN M. HARLAN, Associate Justice of the Supreme Court of the United States; born May 20, 1899, in Chicago, Ill.; A. B., Princeton University, 1920; B. A. in Jurisprudence in 1923, and M. A., Oxford University; LL. B., New York Law School, 1924; married Ethel Andrews of New Haven, Conn., November 10, 1928; has one daughter, Eve Harlan Newcomb (Mrs. W. A. Newcomb); joined firm of Root, Clark, Buckner & Howland (subsequently Root, Ballantine, Harlan, Bushby & Palmer), New York City, as associate in 1923; member from January 1931 to February 1954; Assistant United States Attorney, Southern District of New York, 1925–27; chief assistant special counsel to Commissioners Clarence E. Shearn and Judge Townsend Scudder, appointed by Governor Smith in 1928 in removal proceedings against the Borough President of Queens; appointed by Governor Smith special assistant attorney general, State of New York, 1928–30, in connection with Queens County sewer prosecutions; appointed by Governor Dewey as chief counsel to New York State Crime Commission in 1951; appointed by President Eisenhower to United States Court of Appeals, Second Circuit, on February 10, 1954, took oath of office on March 4, 1954; appointed by President

Eisenhower to Supreme Court of the United States on March 17, 1955, took oath of office on March 28, 1955; United States Army Air Force, England, 1943–45, colonel, United States Army, decorated United States Legion of Merit, and French and Belgian Croix de Guerre.

WILLIAM J. BRENNAN, JR., of Rumson, N. J., Associate Justice of the Supreme Court of the United States; born April 25, 1906, in Newark, N. J., son of William J. and Agnes (McDermott) Brennan; married Marjorie Leonard May 5, 1928; children—William J., Hugh Leonard, and Nancy; B. S. (with honors) Wharton School of Business, University of Pennsylvania 1928; LL. B., Harvard, 1931; joined firm Pitney, Hardin & Skinner, Newark, N. J., as associate in 1931; member from 1937–42 and again 1945–49, firm name Pitney, Hardin, Ward & Brennan; major, later colonel, United States Army, specializing in manpower and personnel work, 1942–45, awarded Legion of Merit; appointed by Governor Driscoll, New Jersey Superior Court, 1949, served as assignment judge, Hudson County, to 1951; appointed to Appellate Division of that court 1951; appointed by Governor Driscoll, associate justice of New Jersey Supreme Court, 1952; appointed as an Associate Justice of the Supreme Court of the United States by President Eisenhower, a recess appointment on October 15, 1956; took the oaths and his seat on October 16, 1956; was nominated by President Eisenhower on January 14, 1957; the nomination was confirmed by the Senate on March 19, 1957; was given a new commission on March 21, 1957, and again took the oaths on March 22, 1957.

POTTER STEWART, Associate Justice of the Supreme Court of the United States; born Jackson, Mich., January 23, 1915; Yale College, A.B., 1937, Yale Law School, LL.B., 1941; married Mary Ann Bertles, April 24, 1943; three children, Harriet, Potter, David; practiced law New York City and Cincinnati, Ohio, 1941–54; served 3 years active sea duty during World War II, discharged as lieutenant in 1945; appointed by President Eisenhower to United States Court of Appeals for the Sixth Circuit, April 27, 1954, and took oath of office and assumed duties as Circuit Judge, June 1, 1954; appointed from Ohio as an Associate Justice of the Supreme Court of the United States on October 14, 1958, during a recess of the Senate, and took the oaths of office and his seat on that day; was nominated by President Eisenhower on January 17, 1959, as an Associate Justice of the Supreme Court of the United States: was confirmed by the Senate on May 5, 1959, and took the oaths of office on May 15, 1959.

BYRON RAYMOND WHITE, Associate Justice of the Supreme Court of the United States; born in Ft. Collins, Colo., June 8, 1917; son of Alpha Albert White and Maude Burger White; elementary and high school, Wellington, Colo.; B.A., University of Colorado, 1938; Rhodes scholar, Oxford, England, 1939; LL.B., Yale Law School, 1946; married Marion Lloyd Stearns of Denver, Colo., June 15, 1946; children, Charles Byron and Nancy Pitkin; law clerk to Chief Justice of the Supreme Court of the United States, 1946–47; associate, Lewis, Grant, Newton, Davis & Henry (now Davis, Graham & Stubbs), 1947–50, partner, 1950–60; Deputy Attorney General of the United States, January 1961–April 1962; nominated Associate Justice of the Supreme Court of the United States by President Kennedy on April 3, 1962, confirmed by the Senate on April 11, 1962, and took the oaths of office and his seat on April 16, 1962; officer USNR May 1942–January 1946.

ARTHUR J. GOLDBERG, Associate Justice of the Supreme Court of the United States, was born in Chicago, Ill., August 8, 1908; son of Joseph and Rebecca Goldberg; received elementary education in Chicago public schools; graduated Benjamin Harrison High School (1924); attended Crane Junior College, a branch of the City College of Chicago; Bachelor of Science in Law (1929) and Doctor of Jurisprudence (1930) Northwestern University; editor-in-chief "Illinois Law Review"; admitted to practice before Illinois bar (1929); qualified for practice before the U.S. Supreme Court (1937); engaged in private law practice in Chicago (1929–48), member of the firm of Goldberg, Devoe, Shadur and Mikva, Chicago (1945–61); general counsel for Congress of Industrial Organizations (CIO) (1948–55) and United Steel Workers of America (1948–61); special counsel for AFL–CIO (1955–61); general counsel for Industrial Union Department, AFL–CIO (1955–61); legal adviser to several individual unions; practiced law with firm of Goldberg, Feller & Bredhoff, Washington, D.C. (1952–61); Secretary of Labor (1961–62); President Kennedy appointed him an Associate Justice of the United States Supreme Court on August 29, 1962. He was con-

firmed by the Senate on September 25, 1962, and took his oath of office and seat
on the Court on October 1, 1962; during World War II served as special assistant,
with ranks of captain and major, to Office of Strategic Services; author of articles
in American legal publications and journals of opinion; author of book "AFL–CIO;
Labor United" married Dorothy Kurgans, artist, 1931; they have two children,
a daughter, Barbara Cramer, and a son, Robert M. Goldberg; legal residence,
Illinois.

RETIRED JUSTICES

STANLEY FORMAN REED, Associate Justice of the Supreme Court of the
United States, retired; born in Mason County, Ky., December 31, 1884; A. B.,
Kentucky Wesleyan College, 1902; A. B., Yale, 1906 (Bennett prize); LL. D.,
1938; LL. D., Columbia University, 1940; University of Kentucky, 1940; Kentucky
Wesleyan College, 1941; University of Louisville, 1947; studied law at University
of Virginia, Columbia University, and University of Paris; married Winifred
Elgin, of Maysville, Ky.; has two sons, John A. and Stanley Forman, Jr.; general
practice Maysville and Ashland, Ky., 1910–29; member General Assembly of
Kentucky, 1912–16; American Legion; American Law Institute; counselor and
member, executive committee, American Red Cross, 1935–38; general counsel,
Federal Farm Board, 1929–32; general counsel, Reconstruction Finance Corporation, December 1932 to March 1935; Solicitor General of the United States, March
23, 1935, to January 31, 1938; nominated Associate Justice of the Supreme Court
of the United States by President Roosevelt, January 15, 1938; confirmed January 25, 1938, and took his seat January 31, 1938; retired February 25, 1957.

SHERMAN MINTON, Associate Justice of the Supreme Court of the United
States, retired; born in Georgetown, Ind., October 20, 1890; son of John Evan and
Emma (Livers) Minton; LL. B., Indiana University, 1915; LL. M., Yale, 1916;
LL. D., Indiana University, 1950; LL. D., University of Louisville, 1956; married
Gertrude Gurtz, August 11, 1917; children—Sherman, Jr., Mrs. J. H. Callanan,
John Evan; began practice at New Albany, 1916; member, Stotsenburg, Weathers
& Minton, 1922–25; member, Shutts & Bowen, Miami, Fla., 1925–28; returned to
New Albany, 1928; public counselor of Indiana, 1933–34; elected to the United
States Senate on November 6, 1934, for term ending January 3, 1941; served as
majority whip from April 1939 to January 3, 1941; appointed administrative as-
sistant to President Roosevelt January 8, 1941; nominated judge, United States
Court of Appeals for Seventh Circuit, May 7, 1941, took oath of office May 29,
1941; nominated Associate Justice of Supreme Court by President Truman September 15, 1949; confirmed October 4, 1949; took seat October 12, 1949; retired
October 15, 1956; served as captain, Infantry, United States Army, 1917–19;
member, Phi Delta Theta, Phi Delta Phi, Elks.

CHARLES EVANS WHITTAKER, Associate Justice of the Supreme Court
of the United States, retired; born in Doniphan County, Kans., on February 22,
1901, son of Charles E. and Ida E. Whittaker; resident of Kansas City, Mo., from
1920 until 1957; LL.B., Kansas City School of Law (since 1934 the Law School of
the University of Missouri at Kansas City), 1924; admitted to Missouri Bar in
1923; married Winifred R. Pugh of Kansas City on July 7, 1928; three sons,
Dr. Charles Keith Whittaker, Kent E. Whittaker and Gary T. Whittaker; junior
partner in law firm of Watson, Gage and Ess in 1928; member of the firm (Watson,
Ess, Whittaker, Marshall and Enggas) from 1932 until July 1954; appointed by
President Eisenhower as a United States District Judge for Western District of
Missouri on July 5, 1954, and took the oath of office and assumed duties on July 19,
1954; elevated to United States Court of Appeals, Eighth Circuit, by President
Eisenhower in May 1956, and took the oath of office and assumed duties on June
22, 1956; nominated by President Eisenhower as an Associate Justice of the
Supreme Court of the United States on March 2, 1957, and took the oath of office
and his seat on March 25, 1957; first Missourian in history to be named to the
United States Supreme Court, and also first native Kansan ever to serve on that
Court; was retired for physical disability on April 1, 1962.

RESIDENCES OF THE JUSTICES OF THE SUPREME COURT

[The * designates those whose wives accompany them]

*Mr. Chief Justice Warren, Sheraton-Park Hotel.
*Mr. Justice Black, 619 South Lee Street, Alexandria, Va.
*Mr. Justice Douglas, 4852 Hutchins Place.
*Mr. Justice Clark, 2101 Connecticut Avenue.
*Mr. Justice Harlan, 1677 31st Street.
*Mr. Justice Brennan, 3037 Dumbarton Avenue.
*Mr. Justice Stewart, 5136 Palisade Lane.
*Mr. Justice White, 2209 Hampshire Road, McLean, Va.
*Mr. Justice Goldberg, 2811 Albemarle Street.

RETIRED

*Mr. Justice Reed, the Mayflower.
*Mr. Justice Minton, Silver Hills, New Albany, Ind.
*Mr. Justice Whittaker, 615 Federal Courts Building, Kansas City, Mo.

OFFICERS OF THE SUPREME COURT

Clerk.—John F. Davis, 4704 River Road.
Deputy Clerk.—Edmund P. Cullinan, 4823 Reservoir Road.
Marshal.—T. Perry Lippitt, 6004 Corbin Road, Woodacres, Md.
Reporter of Decisions.—Henry Putzel, Jr., 3703 33d Place.
Librarian.—Helen Newman, 126 Third Street SE.
Press Information.—Banning E. Whittington, 6037 Fifth Road North, Arlington,
   Va.

UNITED STATES COURTS OF APPEALS

District of Columbia Judicial Circuit (District of Columbia).—Mr. Chief Justice Warren, Circuit Justice. *Chief Judge.*—David L. Bazelon. *Circuit Judges.*—Charles Fahy, George Thomas Washington, John A. Danaher, Walter M. Bastian, Warren E. Burger, J. Skelly Wright, Carl McGowan. *Clerk.*—Nathan J. Paulson, Washington, D.C.

First Judicial Circuit (Districts of Maine, New Hampshire, Massachusetts, Rhode Island, and Puerto Rico).—Mr. Justice Goldberg, Circuit Justice. *Chief Judge.*—Bailey Aldrich, Boston, Mass. *Circuit Judge.*—John P. Hartigan, Providence, R.I. *Clerk.*—Roger A. Stinchfield, Boston, Mass.

Second Judicial Circuit (Districts of Vermont, Connecticut, northern New York, southern New York, eastern New York, and western New York).—Mr. Justice Harlan, Circuit Justice. *Chief Judge.*—J. Edward Lumbard, New York, N.Y. *Circuit Judges.*—Sterry R. Waterman, St. Johnsbury, Vt.; Leonard P. Moore, New York, N.Y.; Henry J. Friendly, New York, N.Y.; J. Joseph Smith, Hartford, Conn.; Irving R. Kaufman, New York, N.Y.; Paul R. Hays, New York, N.Y.; Thurgood Marshall, New York, N.Y.; Robert P. Anderson, Hartford, Conn. *Clerk.*—A. Daniel Fusaro, New York, N.Y.

Third Judicial Circuit (Districts of New Jersey, eastern Pennsylvania, middle Pennsylvania, western Pennsylvania, Delaware, and the Virgin Islands).—Mr. Justice Brennan, Circuit Justice. *Chief Judge.*—John Biggs, Jr., Wilmington, Del. *Circuit Judges.*—Gerald McLaughlin, Newark, N.J.; Harry E. Kalodner, Philadelphia, Pa.; Austin L. Staley, Pittsburgh, Pa.; William Henry Hastie. Philadelphia, Pa.; J. Cullen Ganey, Philadelphia, Pa.; William F. Smith, Newark, N.J.; Abraham L. Freedman, Philadelphia, Pa. *Clerk.*—Mrs. Ida O. Creskoff, Philadelphia, Pa.

Fourth Judicial Circuit (Districts of Maryland, northern West Virginia, southern West Virginia, eastern Virginia, western Virginia, eastern North Carolina, middle North Carolina, western North Carolina, eastern South Carolina, and western South Carolina).—Mr. Chief Justice Warren, Circuit Justice. *Chief Judge.*—Clement F. Haynsworth, Jr., Greenville, S.C. *Circuit Judges.*—Simon E. Sobeloff, Baltimore, Md.; Herbert S. Boreman, Parkersburg, W. Va.; Albert V. Bryan, Alexandria, Va.; J. Spencer Bell, Charlotte, N.C. *Clerk.*—Maurice S. Dean, Richmond, Va.

Fifth Judicial Circuit (Districts of northern Georgia, middle Georgia, southern Georgia, middle Florida, northern Florida, southern Florida, northern Alabama, middle Alabama, southern Alabama, northern Mississippi, southern Mississippi, eastern Louisiana, western Louisiana, northern Texas, southern Texas, eastern Texas, western Texas, and Canal Zone).—Mr. Justice Black, Circuit Justice. *Chief Judge.*—Elbert Parr Tuttle, Atlanta, Ga. *Circuit Judges.*—Richard T. Rives, Montgomery, Ala.; Warren L. Jones, Jacksonville, Fla.; John R. Brown, Houston, Tex.; John Minor Wisdom, New Orleans, La.; Walter Pettus Gewin, Tuscaloosa, Ala.; Griffin B. Bell, Atlanta, Ga. *Clerk.*—Edward W. Wadsworth, New Orleans, La.

Sixth Judicial Circuit (Districts of northern Ohio, southern Ohio, eastern Michigan, western Michigan, eastern Kentucky, western Kentucky, eastern Tennessee, middle Tennessee, and western Tennessee).—Mr. Justice Stewart, Circuit Justice. *Chief Judge*, Paul C. Weick, Cleveland, Ohio. *Circuit Judges*—Shackelford Miller, Jr., Louisville, Ky.; Lester L. Cecil, Dayton, Ohio; Clifford O'Sullivan, Port Huron, Mich.; Harry Phillips, Nashville, Tenn.; George Clifton Edwards, Jr., Detroit, Mich. *Clerk.*—Carl W. Reuss, Cincinnati, Ohio.

Seventh Judicial Circuit (Districts of northern Indiana, southern Indiana, northern Illinois, eastern Illinois, southern Illinois, eastern Wisconsin, and western Wisconsin).—Mr. Justice Clark, Circuit Justice. *Chief Judge.*—John S. Hastings, Chicago, Ill. *Circuit Judges.*—F. Ryan Duffy, Milwaukee, Wis.; Elmer J. Schnackenberg, Chicago, Ill.; Win G. Knoch, Chicago, Ill.; Latham Castle, Chicago, Ill.; Roger J. Kiley, Chicago, Ill.; Luther M. Swygert, Chicago, Ill. *Clerk.*—Kenneth J. Carrick, Chicago, Ill.

Eighth Judicial Circuit (Districts of Minnesota, northern Iowa, southern Iowa, eastern Missouri, western Missouri, eastern Arkansas, western Arkansas, Nebraska, North Dakota, and South Dakota).—Mr. Justice White, Circuit Justice. *Chief Judge.*—Harvey M. Johnsen, Omaha, Nebr.; *Circuit Judges.*— Charles J. Vogel, Fargo, N. Dak.; Martin D. Van Oosterhout, Sioux City, Iowa; M. C. Matthes, St. Louis, Mo.; Harry A. Blackmun, Rochester Minn.; Albert A. Ridge, Kansas City, Mo.; Pat Mehaffy, Little Rock, Ark. *Clerk.*—Robert C. Tucker, St. Louis, Mo.

Ninth Judicial Circuit (Districts of Alaska, northern California, southern California, Oregon, Nevada, Montana, eastern Washington, western Washington, Idaho, Arizona, Hawaii, and Guam).—Mr. Justice Douglas, Circuit Justice. *Chief Judge.*—Richard H. Chambers, Tucson, Ariz. *Circuit Judges.*—Stanley N. Barnes, Los Angeles, Calif.; Frederick G. Hamley, San Francisco, Calif.; Gilbert H. Jertberg, Fresno, Calif.; Charles M. Merrill, San Francisco, Calif.; M. Oliver Koelsch, San Francisco, Calif.; James R. Browning, Great Falls, Mont.; Ben Cushing Duniway, San Francisco, Calif.; Walter Ely, Los Angeles, Calif. *Clerk.*—Frank H. Schmid, P.O. Box 547, San Francisco, Calif.

Tenth Judicial Circuit (Districts of Colorado, Wyoming, Utah, Kansas, eastern Oklahoma, western Oklahoma, northern Oklahoma, and New Mexico).— Mr. Justice White, Circuit Justice. *Chief Judge.*—Alfred P. Murrah, Oklahoma City, Okla. *Circuit Judges.*—John C. Pickett, Cheyenne, Wyo.; David T. Lewis, Salt Lake City, Utah; Jean S. Breitenstein, Denver, Colo.; Delmas C. Hill, Wichita, Kans.; Oliver Seth, Santa Fe, N. Mex. *Clerk.*—Robert B. Cartwright, Denver, Colo.

UNITED STATES COURT OF APPEALS

FOR THE DISTRICT OF COLUMBIA CIRCUIT

U.S. Courthouse, Third Street and Constitution Avenue.   Phone, STerling 3-5700 (Code 1204)

DAVID L. BAZELON, chief judge; was born in Superior, Wis., September 3, 1909, the son of Israel and Lena Bazelon; received degree of B.S.L. from Northwestern University in 1931; married to Miriam M. Kellner on June 7, 1936; children—James A., and Richard Lee; assistant United States Attorney for Northern District of Illinois 1935–40; senior member of firm of Gottlieb & Schwartz, 1940–46; appointed by President Truman as Assistant Attorney General, United States, in charge of lands division 1946–47, in charge of alien property 1947–49; member Illinois, Chicago, Federal, American, and District of Columbia Bar Associations; nominated by President Truman as Judge of the United States Court of Appeals for the District of Columbia Circuit, October 15, 1949; following adjournment of Senate on October 19, 1949, received recess appointment as such Judge under Commission of President Truman dated October 21, 1949, took oath of office and entered on duty November 1, 1949, nominated by President Truman as Judge of said Court January 5, 1950, confirmed by Senate February 8, 1950, and took oath of office February 24, 1950, under Commission of President Truman dated February 10, 1950, became chief judge October 9, 1962; Chairman, Task Force on Law and Public Awareness, President's Panel on Mental Retardation.

CHARLES FAHY, circuit judge; born Rome, Ga., August 27, 1892; son of Thomas and Sarah (Jonas) Fahy; married Mary Agnes Lane of Washington, D.C., June 26, 1929; children, Charles (Dom Thomas Fahy, Order of St. Benedict), Anne Marie (Mrs. Rourke J. Sheehan), Sarah Agnes (Sister Charles Mary, Sisters of Notre Dame de Namur), and Mary Agnes (Mrs. John Carroll Johnson); educated public schools and Darlington School, Rome, Ga.; University of Notre Dame, 1910–11; LL. B., Georgetown University, Washington, 1914; LL. D., 1942; admitted to District of Columbia Bar, 1914, and practiced in Washington until 1924, except service in naval aviation 1917–19, and from 1947 to 1949; practiced in Santa Fe, N. Mex., 1924–33; First Assistant Solicitor, Member and Chairman, Petroleum Administrative Board, 1933–35, Department of Interior, Washington; General Counsel, National Labor Relations Board, 1935–40; Assistant Solicitor General of the United States, 1940–41; member President's Naval and Air Base Commission to London, 1941; Solicitor General of the United States, 1941–45; Adviser to United States Delegation to San Francisco Conference, United Nations, 1945; the Legal Adviser, Military Governor, Germany, 1945–46; the Legal Adviser, Department of State, 1946–47; Adviser, United States Delegation to General Assembly, United Nations, 1946; Alternate Representative, United States Delegation to General Assembly, United Nations, 1947 and 1949; Chairman, Personnel Security Review Board, Atomic Energy Commission, 1949; Chairman, President's Committee on Equality of Treatment and Opportunity in the Armed Services, 1948–50 (Robert S. Abbot Memorial Award, 1951); President, Catholic Association for International Peace, 1950–51, Board of Governors, 1964–; nominated by President Truman as Judge October 15, 1949; entered on duty December 15, 1949, under recess appointment and on April 13, 1950, under permanent commission after Senate confirmation; President, Washington League of Laymen's Retreats, 1960–63; John Carroll Award, 1952 (Georgetown University); Russwurm Award, 1953; awarded Navy Cross by President Wilson; awarded Medal of Merit by President Truman.

GEORGE THOMAS WASHINGTON, circuit judge; born in Cuyahoga Falls, Ohio, June 24, 1908; educated in public schools in Ohio, Kentucky, and Michigan; attended Yale College, and graduated with Ph. B. degree, 1928; B. Litt. (law), Oxford University, 1931; LL. B. (cum laude), Yale Law School, 1932; married Helen Goodner of Washington, D.C., on July 18, 1953; practiced law in New York City, 1932–38, in association with Carter, Ledyard & Milburn, and with Root, Clark, Buckner & Ballantine; member faculty Cornell University Law School, 1938–42, appointed professor of law, 1942; author of Corporate Executives' Compensation, 1942; revised ed., 1962, and of numerous articles in legal periodicals; attorney, Office for Emergency Management, 1942; assisted in prosecution of eight Nazi saboteurs, 1942; United States Economic Representative, Baghdad, Iraq, 1942–43; Chief United States Lend-Lease Mission, Teheran, Iran, 1943–44; special assistant to the Attorney General, 1944–45; Chief Legal Consultant, 1945–46; appointed Assistant Solicitor General by President Truman on July 25, 1946, after confirmation by the Senate; served as acting Solicitor General of the United States, October 1946 to July 1947; legal adviser to the United States Delegation to the Conference on Freedom of Information and the Press, held in Geneva in April 1948; appointed in 1948 to President's Advisory Commission on the Relation of Federal Laws to Puerto Rico; member of Phi Beta Kappa, Order of the Coif, Society of the Cincinnati; member of the New York Bar, the District of Columbia Bar, and the United States Supreme Court Bar; member of the District of Columbia Bar Association; received a recess appointment as Judge of the United States Court of Appeals for the District of Columbia Circuit by President Truman October 21, 1949, took oath of office October 25, 1949, and entered on duty November 8, 1949; nominated by President Truman as Judge of said Court January 5, 1950, confirmed by Senate April 28, 1950, and took oath of office May 16, 1950, under Commission of President Truman dated May 1, 1950.

JOHN ANTHONY DANAHER, circuit judge; born in Meriden, Conn., January 9, 1899; son of Cornelius J. and Ellen Danaher; A.B., Yale College, 1920; Yale Law School, 1919–21; served clerkship with White & Case, New York, 1921; admitted to the bar in Connecticut January 17, 1922, and to the bar of the United States District Court in Connecticut February 28, 1922; Assistant United States Attorney, 1922–34; Secretary of State of Connecticut, 1933–35; United States Senator for Connecticut, 1939–45; appointed by President Truman in 1951 to the President's Commission on Internal Security and Individual Rights under the chairmanship of Fleet Admiral Chester W. Nimitz; appointed by President Eisenhower in 1953 as one of the 12 lawyer members of the President's Conference on Administrative Procedure; member of the bar in Connecticut and in the District of Columbia, in the United States District Court for the District of Connecticut and in the District of Columbia, in the United States Court of Appeals for the Second Circuit and the United States Court of Appeals for the District of Columbia Circuit as well as of the Supreme Court of the United States; served on various of the special committees of the American Bar Association and the District of Columbia Bar Association; married February 3, 1921, to Miss Dorothy E. King of Meriden; children, John A., Jr., Robert C. and Mrs. Jeanne D. Lennhoff; Beta Theta Pi, Elihu (Yale), Phi Delta Phi, Corbey Court (Yale Law School); American Legion, Knights of Columbus, Fourth Degree; member, District of Columbia Bar Association, Connecticut Bar Association, Hartford County Bar Association, American Bar Association; appointed United States Circuit Judge, United States Court of Appeals for the District of Columbia Circuit by President Eisenhower by commission dated October 1, 1953, and took oath of office November 20, 1953; legal residence, Groton, Conn.

WALTER MAXIMILLIAN BASTIAN, circuit judge, of Washington, D.C.; born in Washington, D.C., November 16, 1891; educated in public schools of Washington, D.C., and Georgetown University, receiving LL. B. in 1913; LL. D. National University, 1952; George Washington University, 1958; admitted to bar of District of Columbia 1913; married Eva A. Bastian; children—Walter Maximillian, Jr., and David Charles; served as first lieutenant in Chemical Warfare Service, World War I; chairman of Draft Board of Appeals, World War II; instructor at National University School of Law, 1920–44; trustee of George Washington University; treasurer of bar association of District of Columbia, 1931–35, president of that association in 1936; member of Committee on Admissions and Grievances of District of Columbia District Court, 1946–50; practiced law in District of Columbia 1913–50; member of house of delegates of American Bar Association 1936–53 and 1956–, treasurer 1945–50, member of Board of Governors 1950–53; appointed United States District Judge by President Truman, taking oath of office November 8, 1950; appointed by President Eisenhower as Circuit Judge of the United States Court of Appeals for the District of Columbia Circuit, taking oath of office December 15, 1954.

WARREN EARL BURGER, circuit judge; born St. Paul, Minn., 1907; son of Charles Joseph and Katharine Schnittger Burger; student, University of Minnesota G.E.D. 1925–27; St. Paul College of Law (now Mitchell College of Law), 1931, LL.B. (magna cum laude); married Elvera Stromberg, 1933; children—

Wade Allan, Margaret Elizabeth; admitted to Minnesota Bar, 1931; engaged in private general practice 1931–1953 as associate in Boyesen, Otis & Faricy, and partner in successor firms of Faricy, Burger, Moore & Costello; member faculty St. Paul College of Law (now Mitchell College of Law) 1931–1946 (contracts, trusts); post graduate studies New York University School of Law, Hague Academy of International Law, The Hague, Holland; member Federal Bar Association, American Bar Association, Minnesota State Bar Association, Bar Association of the District of Columbia, Inter-American Bar Association, International Bar Association; Institute of Judicial Administration; American Judicature Society; trustee, Federal Bar Foundation; trustee, Mayo Foundation, Rochester, Minn.; Agent of the United States in relation to claims of foreign governments and nationals; member U.S. Delegation and Legal Adviser International Labor Organization Conference, Geneva, Switzerland, 1954; U.S. participant International Congress of Judges, Rome, Italy, 1958 and 1963 at The Hague, Holland; Assistant Attorney General of the United States in charge of civil litigation of the United States and international litigation 1953–56; nominated by President Eisenhower January 1956 as Judge of the United States Court of Appeals (D.C. Circuit), confirmed March 1956 and qualified April 13, 1956.

JAMES SKELLY WRIGHT, circuit judge; born in New Orleans, La., January 14, 1911, son of James Edward and Margaret (Skelly) Wright; Ph. B., Loyola University, New Orleans, 1931; LL.B., 1934; LL.D., Yale University, 1961; LL.D., University of Notre Dame, 1962; LL.D., Howard University, 1964; married Helen Mitchell Patton, February 1, 1945; one son, James Skelly; high school teacher, 1931–35; lecturer, English history, Loyola University, 1936–37; member of faculty, Loyola University School of Law, 1950 to 1962; James Madison Lecturer, New York University, 1965; Assistant U.S. Attorney, New Orleans, 1937–46; private practice of law, Ingoldsby, Coles & Wright, Washington, 1946–48; U.S. Attorney, Eastern District of Louisiana, 1948–49; U.S. District Judge, Eastern District of Louisiana, 1949 to April 1962; U.S. Circuit Judge, Washington, D.C., April 1962 to date; member, Standing Committee on Rules of Practice and Procedure, Committee on Revision of the Laws and Ad Hoc Committee on Habeas Corpus of the Judicial Conference of the U.S.; member of American Law Institute; served as lieutenant commander, U.S. Coast Guard, 1942–45; observer, U.S. State Department International Fisheries Conference, London, 1943; member, Louisiana State Bar Association (Board of Governors), Federal Bar Association (President, New Orleans Chapter), Bar Association of District of Columbia, American Bar Association, New Orleans Bar Association; member, Alpha Delta Gamma (National President); member, Blue Key; honorary member, Phi Delta Phi; Roman Catholic; Democrat; home: 5317 Blackistone Road, Westmoreland Hills, Md., 20016; office: U.S. Courthouse, Washington, D.C., 20001.

CARL McGOWAN, circuit judge; born in Hymera, Ind., May 7, 1911; Dartmouth College, A.B., 1932; Columbia University, LL.B., 1936; member of the New York (1936), Illinois (1940), and District of Columbia (1948) bars; private practice in New York City (1936–39), Washington (1946–48), and Chicago (1953–63); United States Naval Reserve (1942–45); married in 1945 to Josephine Vail Perry, of Boston; children: Mary, Rebecca, John, and Hope; counsel to the Governor of Illinois (1949–52); member of the faculty of Northwestern University Law School (1939–42; 1948–49); member of the Council of the American Law Institute, and of the American and Chicago Bar Associations; took oath of office April 22, 1963, under commission issued by President Kennedy March 27, 1963.

SENIOR CIRCUIT JUDGES

HENRY W. EDGERTON, senior circuit judge; born in Rush Center, Kans., October 20, 1888; University of Wisconsin, 1905–7; special agent, United States Bureau of Corporations, 1908; A. B., Cornell University, 1910; law school of the University of Paris, 1910–11; LL. B., Harvard, 1914; LL. D., Yale, 1956; Howard, 1963; married Alice Durand June 28, 1913; children—John D., Ann (dec); practiced in Boston, Mass., 1916, 1918–21; member of law faculties of George Washington University (1921–29), University of Chicago (1928–29), and Cornell University (1916–18, 1929–38); special assistant to the Attorney General, 1934–35; nominated to the United States Court of Appeals by President Roosevelt November 26, 1937; confirmed by the Senate December 9, 1937; took oath of office February 1, 1938; chief judge May 30, 1955 to October 20, 1958; retired from regular active service April 22, 1963.

ELIJAH BARRETT PRETTYMAN, senior circuit judge; born in Lexington, Va., August 23, 1891; son of Forrest Johnston and Elizabeth Rebecca (Stonestreet) Prettyman; A.B. Randolph-Macon College, Ashland, Va., 1910, A.M., 1911; LL. B., 1915, LL. D., 1946, Georgetown University 1961—William Mitchell School of Law, 1961—Randolph-Macon College; married Lucy C. Hill of Baltimore, Md., September 15, 1917; children, Elizabeth Courtney and Elijah Barrett; admitted to Virginia bar, 1915; associate and member law firm of Butler Lamb, Foster & Pope, Chicago and Washington, D.C., 1920–33; general counsel to Bureau of Internal Revenue, Washington, 1933–34; corporation counsel of District of Columbia, 1934–36; member law firm of Hewes, Prettyman & Awalt, Washington, D.C., and Hartford, Conn., 1936–45; served in the United States Army, 1917–19, advancing to captain of infantry; trustee of Randolph-Macon College, Ashland, Va., and of American University, Washington, D.C.; Phi Beta Kappa, Kappa Sigma, Gamma Eta Gamma, Omicron Delta Kappa, Order of the Coif; nominated to the United States Court of Appeals for the District of Columbia by President Truman, September 12, 1945; confirmed by the Senate September 24, 1945; assumed duties October 17, 1945; chief judge October 21, 1958, to October 21, 1960; retired from regular active service April 16, 1962.

WILBUR K. MILLER, senior circuit judge; born in Owensboro, Ky., October 9, 1892; married Marie Louise Hager, June 2, 1917; county attorney of Davises County, Ky., 1922–30; chairman, Public Service Commission of Kentucky, 1934–35; judge of Special Court of Appeals of Kentucky, 1940–41; member: American Legion, Phi Kappa Sigma and Phi Delta Phi (honorary); nominated associate justice (now circuit judge) of the United States Court of Appeals by President Truman, September 12, 1945, confirmed by the Senate September 24, 1945, and entered upon the duties of that office October 16, 1945: served as chief judge of the Circuit from October 22, 1960, to October 9, 1962; retired from regular active service October 15, 1964.

RESIDENCES OF THE JUDGES OF THE UNITED STATES COURT OF APPEALS FOR THE DISTRICT OF COLUMBIA CIRCUIT

[The * designates those whose wives accompany them]

*Chief Judge David L. Bazelon, 3020 University Terrace, 20016.
*Senior Circuit Judge Wilbur K. Miller, 4000 Cathedral Avenue, 20016.
*Circuit Judge Charles Fahy, 5504 Chevy Chase Parkway, 20015.
*Circuit Judge George Thomas Washington, The Westchester, 20016.
*Circuit Judge John A. Danaher, 6694 32d Street, 20015.
*Circuit Judge Walter M. Bastian, 4000 Cathedral Avenue, 20016.
*Circuit Judge Warren E. Burger, 3111 Rochester Street North, Arlington, Va., 22213.
*Circuit Judge J. Skelly Wright, 5017 Blackistone Road, Westmoreland Hills, 20016.
*Circuit Judge Carl McGowan, 4717 Quebec Street, 20016.
*Senior Circuit Judge Henry W. Edgerton, 2925 Glover Driveway, 20016.
*Senior Circuit Judge E. Barrett Prettyman, 5306 Woodlawn Avenue, Kenwood, Chevy Chase, Md., 20015.

OFFICERS OF THE UNITED STATES COURT OF APPEALS FOR THE DISTRICT OF COLUMBIA CIRCUIT

Clerk.—Nathan J. Paulson, 2000 South Eads Street, Arlington, Va., 22202.
Chief Deputy Clerk.—Alexander L. Stevas, 5603 Maryland Avenue, Falls Church, Va., 22043.
Marshal.—Joseph N. Weis, 4404 Harrison Street, 20015.

UNITED STATES COURT OF CLAIMS

1325 K Street. Phone, 382-1984

WILSON COWEN, chief judge; born near Clifton, Tex., December 20, 1905; son of John R. and Florence (McFadden) Cowen; LL.B., University of Texas, 1928; married Florence Elizabeth Walker April 18, 1930; children, Wilson Walker and John Elwin; admitted to Texas bar in 1928; private practice in Dalhart, Tex., 1928–34; county judge, Dallam County, Tex., 1935–38; state director for Texas, 1938–40, and regional director, 1940–42, Farm Security Administration, Region XII; commissioner, United States Court of Claims, 1942–43; assistant administrator, War Food Administration, 1943–44; returned to the Court of Claims as commissioner in 1945, and was designated chief commissioner in 1959; nominated by President Lyndon B. Johnson as chief judge, United States Court of Claims, June 16, 1964, and assumed duties of the office July 14, 1964; home address: 6300 Poe Road, Bethesda, Md., 20034.

DON NELSON LARAMORE, judge; born at Hamlet, Starke County, Ind., December 22, 1906; son of Louis Nelson and Pearl (Stephenson) Laramore; admitted to the practice of law in Indiana April 18, 1931; Judge pro tempore, 44th Judicial Circuit of Indiana, 1942 to 1944; elected Judge, 44th Judicial Circuit of Indiana, November 1944 and November 1950; commissioned Judge, United States Court of Claims, March 17, 1954; married Charlotte Mary Schminke at Chicago, Ill., December 29, 1938; daughter, Prudence Ann, born July 25, 1945.

JAMES RANDALL DURFEE, judge; born in Oshkosh, Wis., November 3, 1897; son of Thomas Henry and Mary Rossiter Durfee; student Huron College, Huron, S. Dak. 1919–21; Marquette University, Milwaukee, Wis. 1923–26, LL.B. degree 1926; married Mona Burns of Antigo, Wis., 1933; children, Mary Burns (Mrs. David Clarke), James Randall, Jr., John Thomas; served in World War I 1917–19, Company C, 127th Machine Gun Battalion, 34th Division, A.E.F.; admitted to Wisconsin bar in 1927; member of American Legion; District Attorney, Langlade County, Wis. 1928–32; private practice in Antigo, Wis., 1932–51; appointed Commissioner, Public Service Commission of Wisconsin 1951, Chairman 1953–56; appointed Chairman United States Civil Aeronautics Board 1956–60; appointed Judge United States Court of Claims January 1960, confirmed by the U.S. Senate April 20, 1960, assumed duties of that office May 2, 1960; home address: No. 4 Carvel Circle, Westmoreland Hills, Washington, D.C., 20016.

OSCAR H. DAVIS, judge; born in New York, N.Y., February 27, 1914; son of Jacob and Minnie (Robison) Davis; educated in the public schools of Mount Vernon, N.Y., Harvard College, A.B., 1934, and Columbia University School of Law, LL.B., 1937; admitted to the practice of law in New York, February 1938; private practice New York, N.Y., 1937–39; attorney, Claims (now Civil) Division, United States Department of Justice, 1939–42; served in the Army of the United States 1942–46, ending as captain in the Army Air Forces; returned to the United States Department of Justice as attorney, Claims Division, 1946–48; served as an assistant to the Solicitor General, 1949–50, second assistant to the Solicitor General, September 1950–July 1954, first assistant to the Solicitor General, July 1954–April 1962; was Acting Solicitor General in July 1953, and July–August 1956; nominated by President Kennedy as associate judge, United States Court of Claims, January 31, 1962; confirmed by the Senate, April 12, 1962; commissioned April 12, 1962; assumed duties of the office April 26, 1961; home address, 1101 3d Street SW., Washington, D.C., 20024.

LINTON McGEE COLLINS, judge; born in Reidsville, Ga., June 21, 1902; son of Ernest Clyde and Beulah Edna (Rogers) Collins; Mercer University, A.B. 1921, M.A. 1922; LL.D., Gallaudet College, 1955; admitted to the bar of the States of Georgia in 1924, Florida 1925, District of Columbia 1947; married Josephine Staten Hardman, daughter of Dr. Lamartine G. Hardman, former Governor of Georgia, and Mrs. Hardman of Commerce, Ga., January 30, 1934; one daughter, Cynthia Hardman Collins, born February 6, 1945; private practice of law in Tampa and Miami, Fla., 1925–33; Personnel Director and Division Administrator, Public Agencies Division, National Recovery Administration, 1933–35; Special Assistant to the Attorney General and First Assistant, Office of Deputy Attorney General, U.S. Department of Justice, 1935–44; private practice,

Washington, D.C., 1944–64; appointed judge, U.S. Court of Claims, September 8, 1964; confirmed September 17, 1964; oath of office, October 1, 1964; home address: 5025 Macomb Street NW., Washington, D.C., 20016.

MARVIN JONES, senior judge; was born near Valley View, in Cooke County, Tex., son of Horace King and Dosia (Hawkins) Jones; was graduated from South-western University, Georgetown· Tex., with A.B. degree, and from University of Texas with LL.B. degree; was appointed chairman of the board of legal examiners for the seventh supreme judicial district of Texas; member American Legion; elected to the Sixty-fifth and to each succeeding Congress to and including the Seventy-sixth; chairman, House Committee on Agriculture, December 1931 to November 20, 1940; appointed judge of United States Court of Claims April 9, 1940; confirmed by United States Senate April 10, 1940; assumed duties of that office November 20, 1940; on leave beginning January 15, 1943, as adviser and assistant to Justice James F. Byrnes, Director of Economic Stabilization, to June 29, 1943; president, United Nations Conference on Food and Agriculture, Hot Springs, Va., May 18 to June 3, 1943; member, President's War Mobilization Committee; served as Administrator, United States War Food Administration, June 29, 1943, to July 1, 1945, then resumed duties as judge, United States Court of Claims; chief judge of United States Court of Claims from July 10, 1947 until July 14, 1964, at which time transferred to the position of senior judge.

BENJAMIN H. LITTLETON, senior judge, of Nashville, Tenn.; born in Weatherford, Tex., in 1889; educated in the public schools of Tennessee; LL.B., Cumberland University, Lebanon, Tenn., 1914; admitted to the bar in 1914 and practiced law at Nashville, Tenn.; appointed assistant United States attorney for the middle district of Tennessee, 1918; appointed special attorney, Treasury Department, 1921; appointed a member of the United States Board of Tax Appeals, July 16, 1924, for 2 years; reappointed June 6, 1926, for term of 10 years; elected chairman of the Board, April 1927; reelected chairman, April 1929; commissioned judge of the Court of Claims, November 6, 1929; retired from active service on October 31, 1958, and transferred to the roster of senior judges.

SAMUEL ESTILL WHITAKER, senior judge; born in Winchester, Tenn., September 25, 1886; son of Madison Newton and Florence Jarrett (Griffin) Whitaker; student Winchester (Tenn.) Normal College, 1902–5; University of Virginia, 1905–6; LL.B., University of Chattanooga, 1909; married Lillian Nelson Chambliss, daughter of Chief Justice and Mrs. Alexander W. Chambliss, of Chattanooga, June 30, 1913; children, Nelson Chambliss (Mrs. Paul Campbell, Jr.) and Samuel Estill, Jr.; admitted to Tennessee bar in 1909, and practiced in Chattanooga until outbreak of First World War; served as captain of Cavalry, later Field Artillery, United States Army, 1917–19; attorney, United States Department of Justice, 1919–20; attorney, Bureau of Internal Revenue, 1920; in private practice of law in Chattanooga, 1921–37; city attorney, Chattanooga, 1923; member of firm of Whitaker & Whitaker, 1924–37; mayor of Riverview, Tenn., 1925–29; employed from time to time as special assistant to the Attorney General of the United States, 1933–37; Assistant Attorney General of the United States, 1937–39; appointed judge, United States Court of Claims, July 13, 1939; retired on July 19, 1964, and on same date enrolled on roster of senior judges; home address: 4921 Quebec Street.

J. WARREN MADDEN, senior judge; born at Damascus, Stephenson County, Ill., January 17, 1890; son of William J. and Elizabeth Dickey (Murdaugh) Madden; country school; Freeport (Ill.) High School; Northern Illinois State Normal School, De Kalb, Ill., University of Illinois, A.B., 1911; University of Chicago, J.D., 1914; married Margaret Bell Liddell, of McAlester, Okla., 1913; children, Mary Esther (Mrs. David Persinger), Lt. Joseph Warren, Jr. (killed in military service, 1943), Capt. Robert Liddell, Margaret Elizabeth (Mrs. Edmond Sommer), Sgt. Murdaugh Stuart; admitted to bar of Illinois, 1914; Ohio, 1918; West Virginia, 1922; Pennsylvania, 1927; professor of law, University of Oklahoma, 1914–16; Ohio State University, 1917–21; University of Pittsburgh, 1927–37; visiting professor of law, University of Chicago, North Carolina, Cornell, Stanford, Yale, and Vanderbilt Universities; dean of Law School, West Virginia University, 1921–27; practiced law in Illinois and part time in Ohio, West Virginia, and Pennsylvania; adviser to Reporters in Property and Torts Restatements, American Law Institute; author treatise on domestic relations, case book on

Judiciary

655

domestic relations, coauthor case book on property; special assistant to Attorney General of the United States, 1920; member of Governor's Commission on Private Policing in Industry in Pennsylvania, 1933–34; chairman National Labor Relations Board, 1935–40; commissioned judge, Court of Claims, January 8, 1941; went to Germany in July 1945 and served as Associate Director of Legal Division, and in 1946 as Director of Legal Division and Legal Adviser to the U.S. Military Governor and the Deputy Military Governor, Office of Military Government for Germany; returned to Court of Claims, July 1946; retired from active service on August 15, 1961, and transferred to the roster of senior judges.

RESIDENCES OF THE JUDGES OF THE COURT OF CLAIMS

[The * designates those whose wives accompany them; the † those whose daughters accompany them]

*Chief Judge Wilson Cowen, 6300 Poe Road, Bethesda, Md., 20034.
*Judge Don N. Laramore, 5017 Scarsdale Road, Sumner, Washington, D.C., 20016.
*Judge James R. Durfee, 4 Carvel Circle, Westmoreland Hills, Washington, D.C., 20016.
*Jude Oscar H. Davis, 1101 Third Street SW., 20024.
*†Judge Linton M. Collins, 5025 Macomb Street, 20016.
Senior Judge Marvin Jones, University Club, 20006.
*Senior Judge Benjamin H. Littleton, 2737 Devonshire Place, 20008.
*Senior Judge Samuel E. Whitaker, 4921 Quebec Street, 20016.
*Senior Judge J. Warren Madden, Hastings College of The Law, 198 McAllister Street, San Francisco, Calif.

COMMISSIONERS OF THE COURT OF CLAIMS

W. Ney Evans, 4651 Kenmore Drive, 20007.
Marion T. Bennett, 3715 Cardiff Road, Chevy Chase, Md., 20015.
William E. Day, 3601 North Roberts Lane, Arlington, Va.
Roald A. Hogenson, 4416 Greenwich Parkway, 20007.
Paul H. McMurray, 4327 Reno Road, 20008.
C. Murray Bernhardt, 1727 Massachusetts Avenue, 20036.
Donald E. Lane, 5040 Loughboro Road, 20016.
Mastin G. White, 3920 Argyle Terrace, 20011.
S. R. Gamer, 2818 Kanawha Street, 20015.
Robert K. McConnaughey, 5220 Parkway Drive, Chevy Chase, Md., 20015.
Lloyd Fletcher, 4851 Maury Lane, Alexandria, Va.
Richard Arens, 12801 Bluhill Road, Wheaton, Md.
Franklin M. Stone, 2500 Wisconsin Avenue, 20007.
Herbert N. Maletz, 1919 Hawthorne Avenue, Alexandria, Va.
George Willi, 3915 North Woodstock Street, Arlington, Va.

OFFICERS OF THE COURT OF CLAIMS

Clerk.—Frank T. Peartree, 4663 Third Street South, Arlington, Va.
Chief Deputy Clerk.—David J. Clouser, 120 Tapawingo Road, Vienna, Va.
Marshal and Bailiff.—Roger L. Nieman, 9703 Wichita Avenue, College Park, Md., 20741.
Secretary to Court.—Dudley G. Skinker, 6510 Old Stage Road, Rockville, Md.
Financial Officer.—Grace E. Wray, 4700 Connecticut Avenue, 20008.
Reporter of Decisions.—Margaret H. Pierce, 3829 Garfield Street, 20007.

UNITED STATES COURT OF CUSTOMS AND PATENT APPEALS

Internal Revenue Building, 20439. Phone, NAtional 8-4696

EUGENE WORLEY, chief judge, of Shamrock, Tex.; born October 10, 1908 (Lone Wolf, Okla.); education: Shamrock public schools, Texas A. and M. College, and University of Texas School of Arts and Sciences and School of Law; member Texas Legislature 1935–40; married Ann Spivy of Bonham, Tex., 1937; three children; member American Legion and Veterans of Foreign Wars; elected to Seventy-seventh Congress; reelected to Seventy-eighth, Seventy-ninth, Eightieth, and Eighty-first Congresses; appointed judge of the United States Court of Customs and Patent Appeals by President Harry S. Truman March 9, 1950; resigned from Congress April 3, 1950; entered upon the duties of that office April 4, 1950; appointed chief judge by President Dwight D. Eisenhower April 13, 1959; entered upon duties of that office May 4, 1959.

GILES SUTHERLAND RICH, judge, of New York City; born May 30, 1904, in Rochester, N.Y., son of Giles Willard and Sarah Sutherland Rich; education: public and private schools in Rochester, Horace Mann School for Boys in New York, Harvard College, S. B. 1926, Columbia University School of Law, LL.B. 1929; admitted to the bar of the State of New York and commenced practice in New York City in 1929; married, 1931, Gertrude Verity Braun (deceased) of New York; one daughter Verity Sutherland Rich, born 1940; married, 1953, Helen Gill Field of Milton, Mass., and Washington, D. C.; practiced patent and trademark law in New York City as partner in the firms of Williams, Rich & Morse and Churchill, Rich, Weymouth & Engel; lecturer on patent law, Columbia University, 1942–56; appointed judge of the United States Court of Customs and Patent Appeals by President Eisenhower on July 19, 1956; assumed duties as judge July 20, 1956.

I. JACK MARTIN, judge, was born in Cincinnati, Ohio, July 18, 1908, son of Isaac M. and Clara (Huttenbauer) Martin; University of Pennsylvania; LL.B. University of Cincinnati 1932; married Barbara Cohn, April 11, 1937; children, Donald Jack and Judy Barbara; admitted to Ohio bar, 1932, practiced in Cincinnati, 1932–40; assistant prosecutor, Hamilton County, 1933–40; admitted to Pennsylvania bar, 1941; practiced in Philadelphia 1941–43; administrative assistant to Senator Robert A. Taft, 1944–53; administrative assistant to President Dwight D. Eisenhower, 1953–58; member Phi Epsilon Pi; Order of Coif; residence, 9614 Hillridge Drive, Rock Creek Hills, Kensington, Md.; appointed judge of the United States Court of Customs and Patent Appeals by President Eisenhower August 6, 1958; assumed duties as judge August 28, 1958.

ARTHUR M. SMITH, judge, of Dearborn, Mich.; born September 19, 1903, in Scott, La Grange County, Ind., son of Ora Lynn and Genevieve (Mumford) Smith; education: Ithaca, Mich., public schools, University of Michigan, A.B. 1924, LL.B. 1926; married Elizabeth Barbara Allan of Detroit, Mich., 1926; children, Carrol Jean (Mrs. Dwight A. Lewis) and Arthur Allan; admitted to the State bars of Michigan and Illinois, 1926; practiced patent, trademark, and copyright law in Chicago, Ill., 1926–29 and in Detroit and Dearborn, Mich., 1929–59; lecturer in patent law, University of Michigan 1951–59; author, *Patent Law, Cases, Comments and Materials*, 1954; *The Art of Writing Readable Patents*, 1958; coauthor, *Patent Licensing*, 1958; appointed judge of the United States Court of Customs and Patent Appeals by President Eisenhower on April 30, 1959; assumed duties as judge, May 4, 1959.

JAMES LINDSAY ALMOND, Jr., judge, son of a locomotive engineer, was born at Charlottesville, Va., June 15, 1898; when a small boy, he moved to his father's farm in Orange County, Va., and was reared on that farm; graduated from Orange High School in 1917; a veteran of World War I, former high school principal, Lutheran, Sunday school teacher, served as Sunday school superintendent, member of Church Council, and on various boards and agencies of his church; 33d degree Scottish Rite Mason, Shriner, Past Potentate Kazim Temple, Roanoke, Va.; member Kiwanis International, Fraternal Orders of Eagles, Moose, United Commercial Travelers, Delta Theta Phi Legal Fraternity, Alpha Kappa Psi and Omicron Delta Kappa; LL.D., college of William and Mary in

Virginia; graduated in law, LL.B. degree, from University of Virginia, June 1923; married Josephine Katherine Minter of Roanoke, August 15, 1925; practiced law at Roanoke, Va., August 1923 to January 1, 1930; assistant commonwealth's attorney, city of Roanoke, January 1, 1930, to February 1, 1933; judge, Hustings Court, city of Roanoke, February 1, 1933, to December 31, 1945; represented the Sixth Congressional District in the 79th and 80th Congresses, serving on the Military Affairs and Post Office and Civil Service Committees; Attorney General of Virginia, April 1948 to September 1957; elected Governor of Virginia on November 5, 1957, and inaugurated January 11, 1958, for a 4-year term; appointed judge of the United States Court of Customs and Patent Appeals by President Kennedy on October 24, 1962; assumed duties as judge on October 30, 1962.

RESIDENCES OF THE JUDGES OF THE UNITED STATES COURT OF CUSTOMS AND PATENT APPEALS

[The * designates those whose wives accompany them; the † those whose daughters accompany them]

*Chief Judge Eugene Worley, 4745 32d Street North, Arlington, Va.
*Judge Giles S. Rich, 4949 Linnean Avenue, 20008.
*Judge I. Jack Martin, 9614 Hillridge Drive, Rock Creek Hills, Kensington, Md.
*Judge Arthur M. Smith, 5043 Lowell Street, 20016.
*Judge J. Lindsay Almond, Jr., 208 Wexleigh Drive, Richmond, Va.
Judge Joseph R. Jackson (retired), Westchester Apartments, 20016.
*†Judge Noble J. Johnson (retired), 4318 Warren Street, 20016.

OFFICERS OF THE UNITED STATES COURT OF CUSTOMS AND PATENT APPEALS

Clerk.—George E. Hutchinson, 5031 Fulton Street, 20016.
First Assistant Clerk.—Ann Adams, 1600 River House, Arlington, Va.
Second Assistant Clerk.—Dorothy I. Myers, 3624 Connecticut Avenue, 20008.
Marshal-Reporter.—Robert R. Reque, 2475 Virginia Avenue, 20035.

UNITED STATES CUSTOMS COURT

201 Varick Street, New York City, N.Y., 10014. Phone, WAtkins 4-7800

WEBSTER J. OLIVER, chief judge; born in Brooklyn, N.Y., January 14, 1888; son of William P. and Frances L. (Fortune) O.; LL.B., St. Lawrence University (Brooklyn Law School), 1911; received the honorary degree of LL. D., St. Lawrence University, 1941; married Genevieve M. Carlin, June 27, 1917, one son, Robert W.; buyer for Oliver Bros., Inc., hardware, machinery, New York and Pittsburgh, 1902–11; admitted to New York bar, 1911; member of the firm of Oliver & McNevin; later member of the firm of Leubuscher, Kayser & Oliver; appointed special United States attorney, 1935; appointed Assistant Attorney General in Charge of Customs, 1938; appointed judge, United States Customs Court, 1940, by President Roosevelt; designated by him as presiding judge (now Chief Judge) on June 24, 1940; served as captain, Ordnance Reserve Corps, 1917–19; Democrat, Roman Catholic. Home address 180 Central Park South, New York, N.Y., 10019.

CHARLES DRUMMOND LAWRENCE, judge; native of North Yarmouth, Maine; graduated from North Yarmouth Academy, Yarmouth, Maine; Shaw's Business College, Portland, Maine; New York Law School, LL.B.; New York University Law School, LL.M.; served successively as assistant counsel for Treasury Department before Board of General Appraisers (now United States Customs Court); assistant solicitor of customs; United States special attorney, Customs Division, Department of Justice; legal aid to the Ways and Means Committee of the House of Representatives and the Committee on Finance of the Senate in drafting the Tariff Acts of 1922 and 1930; assistant attorney general in charge of Customs; special assistant to the Attorney General, until appointment as judge, United States Customs Court, February 1, 1943, by President Roosevelt.

PAUL P. RAO, judge; born in Prizzi, Italy, June 15, 1899; arrived in United States 1904; enlisted in the United States Navy, 1917–19; saw service in France, Italy, Africa, and the Azores; also served as official French interpreter with the French cruiser division; disabled while in the naval service of the United States; graduated from Fordham University Law School in 1923 with degree of LL.B.; admitted to the New York bar in January 1924; served as assistant district attorney, New York County, 1925–27; nominated by President Franklin Delano Roosevelt and confirmed by the United States Senate as Assistant Attorney General of the United States in Charge of Customs; served as Assistant Attorney General of the United States, Customs Division, from July 3, 1941 to July 1, 1948, under Attorneys General Robert H. Jackson, Francis Biddle, and Tom C. Clark; appointed by President Harry S. Truman as judge of the United States Customs Court, and took oath of office July 2, 1948; invested as a Knight of Malta at the American Chapter on January 15, 1962, at St. Patrick's Cathedral, New York, by His Eminence, Francis Cardinal Spellman; chairman of the legal committee of the New York County American Legion for 5 years; commander of the Col. Francis Vigo Post 1093, American Legion, for 6 years and a life member; served as vice commander of the New York County American Legion; honorary member of the New York County Press Association of the American Legion; grand marshal of the Loyalty Day Parade held in New York by the Veterans of Foreign Wars in 1960; honorary commander, New York County Council of the Veterans of Foreign Wars 1951–56, 1957–62; life member of the Adm. H. B. Wilson Post 196, Veterans of Foreign Wars, also member of Father Duffy Post 54, Catholic War Veterans; Pvt. Arthur Shatel Chapter 127, Disabled American Veterans; Cardinal Hayes Garrison, Army and Navy Union, U. S. A.; honorary member of the Tiro a Segno (New York Rifle Club); received Catholic War Veterans Americanism Award, April 28, 1949; honorary associate of the New York Department, Sons of Union Veterans of the Civil War, by resolution adopted at its 73d Annual Encampment in Lake Placid in 1956; made honorary member of Phi Alpha Delta Law Fraternity, Henry De Bracton Chapter, St. John's University School of Law on April 17, 1959; general president of the Holy Name Societies of the Archdiocese of New York (Italian-American branches); trustee, Church of Our Lady of Peace; trustee, Parkway Hospital; director of the Fordham Law Alumni Association; director, Brotherhood in Action, Inc.; member of the executive committee of the Federal Business Association of New York (the organization of the heads of all Federal Agencies in the New York area) and chairman of the nominating committee for said Association for the years 1958–61; director, Cardinal Spellman Servicemen's Club of the National Catholic Community Service; honorary member of the Catholic Court Attaches' Guild of the City of New York; vice president of the Historical Society of the New World; member of Metropolitan Hospital Lay Advisory Board, and vice president of the Columbus Citizens Committee, which is in charge of the annual Columbus Day celebration and parade in New York City up to May 24, 1963; received Knight of the Order of St. Hubert, April 23, 1946; received Papal decoration, Knight of Lateran, for distinguished service in behalf of charitable enterprises; Star of Solidarity awarded by the Italian Government on January 9, 1953, and forwarded to the State Department to be presented at such time as Congressional approval is given for acceptance of decoration; cited by U.S. Customs and affiliated Federal agencies of the Columbia Association on May 28, 1954, for defense of human rights and fight against bigotry and intolerance; received citation of Sons of Union War Veterans and made associate member on April 28, 1957; received loyalty citation from Veterans of Foreign Wars on April 19, 1957; cited for meritorious service to veterans by the Disabled American Veterans, Civil Service Chapter 77, on September 20, 1957; presented on December 14, 1957, with citation of honor by Congressman James J. Delaney on behalf of the George Mueller Post 1786, American Legion, for unqualified dedication of service, with fidelity, devotion and honor; cited by the Columbia Association of the Department of Correction, of which Association he is honorary president, on February 6, 1958, for outstanding devotion and assistance to members of that association; awarded the Star and Cross of Academic Honor by the American International Academy of the U. S. A., for great humanitarian accomplishments and outstanding preeminence, and made an honorary life member of that organization on May 21, 1958; received honorary degree of doctor of humanities conferred by Philathea College of London, Ontario, Canada, on May 21, 1958; cited on June 20, 1958, by New York City Pup Tent 11, Military Order of the Cooties of the United States, for his untiring efforts on behalf of the Veterans of Foreign Wars; received Grand Cross from the Eloy Alfaro International Foundation of the Republic of Panama on August 1, 1959; cited by the Federal Business Association (an organization of all Federal Agencies) on September 18, 1962, at the U.S. Naval Air Station, Floyd Bennett Field, Brooklyn, N.Y., for distinguished service rendered to the Federal Government; cited by the Belgian War Veterans of America, Inc., on October 18, 1962, for distinguished service and made Honorary Commander of that organization for life; decorated with "Military Order of Lafayette" at the United Nations, May 14, 1963; cited by Interfaith Movement, Inc. on September 22, 1963, and awarded a plaque for outstanding achievement in attaining the highest ideals of good will, equality and mutual respect; cited by the Gold Star Wives of America at its annual convention; admitted to practice in the United States Supreme Court, the United States Court of Customs and Patent Appeals, and United States District Courts; member of American Bar Association and Federal Bar Association of New York, New Jersey, and Connecticut; honorary member of the Brooklyn-Manhattan Trial Counsel Association; married to Grace S. Malatino; three children, Mrs. Nina Rao Cameron, Mrs. Grayce Rao Visconti, and Paul P. Rao, Jr. Residence: 210 East 61st Street, New York, N.Y., 10021.

MORGAN FORD, judge; born on a farm near Wheatland, North Dakota, September 8, 1911; son of Morgan J. and Mary Langer Ford; grandson of Frank J. Langer, a member of the first legislature of the State of North Dakota; nephew of William Langer, United States Senator from North Dakota; graduated from Casselton High School, Casselton, North Dakota, 1929; B.A., University of North Dakota, 1935; teacher in District 102, Everest Township, Cass County, North Dakota, 1933–34; LL.B., Georgetown University, Washington, D.C., 1938; State manager Royal Union Fund of Des Moines, Iowa, 1938–39; engaged in general law practice, Fargo, North Dakota, 1939–49; president, Surety Mutual Health & Accident Insurance Co., Fargo, North Dakota, 1939–49; city attorney, city of Casselton, North Dakota, 1942–48; vice president, First State Bank of Casselton, North Dakota, 1941–49; appointed by Governor Fred G. Aandahl of North Dakota as a member of the advisory board for registrants in selective service, 1942; nominated to be judge of the United States Customs Court by President Truman, June 22, 1949; entered upon the duties of that office on July 28, 1949; married to Margaret Duffy; three sons, William, Patrick, and Michael, and one daughter, Mary Ellen.

DAVID J. WILSON, judge; born at Midway, Utah, October 27, 1887; son of
James B. and Margaret Powell Wilson; early education Midway public schools
and Brigham Young University; B. S., Brigham Young University, 1914; J.D.,
University of California, 1919· Willard D. Thompson Scholarship, University
of California, 2 years; editor, California Law Review, 1918–19; head of English
Department, Weber Academy, 1914–16; admitted to Utah Bar, 1919, and practiced in Ogden, Utah, continuously until 1954; general practice, State and Federal
courts; member Weber County and Utah State Bar Associations; Weber County
attorney, 1921–25, and district attorney, Second District, Utah, 1929–33; member
Utah State Bar Commission, 1953–54; past president Weber County Bar; one of
organizers of Federal Building and Loan Association, and Associated Investment
Corp. of Ogden, Utah, and served companies as director, vice president, and
general counsel over 30 years; chairman, Advisory Board, Salvation Army,
Ogden, Utah, several years; helped organize Ogden Community Chest; served as
president, Lake Bonneville (formerly Ogden Area) Council, Boy Scouts of America,
and as member at large on National Council; holds Silver Beaver award; member,
L. D. S. Church in which organization he has held numerous administrative
positions; served as Republican chairman, Weber County, 1924–30; chairman,
First Congressional District, Utah, 1922–32; Utah Republican chairman, 1936–44;
delegate, party's national conventions, 1932 and 1940; party's candidate for Congress, Utah First District, 1946 and 1948; awarded degree Honorary Doctor of
Law, Brigham Young University 1963; married Mary Jacobs, May 31, 1916;
five children: Marian (Mrs. O. Meredith Wilson), D. Jay, L. Keith, Margaret
(Mrs. L. C. Barlow), and Don B.; appointed judge, United States Customs Court,
by President Eisenhower under commission issued July 26, 1954; residence:
3299 Cambridge Avenue, New York, N.Y., 10463.

MARY H. DONLON, judge; born in Utica, N.Y., daughter of Joseph M. and
Mary Coughlin Donlon; graduated from Utica Free Academy and Cornell Uni-
versity; honorary degrees Skidmore College, Nazareth College and Marquette
University; editor-in-chief Cornell Law Quarterly, 1920; admitted to New York
bar in 1921 and practiced law in New York City 1921–44, as member of firm of
Burke & Burke; appointed by Gov. Thomas E. Dewey in 1944 as chairman New
York State Industrial Board and in 1945 as chairman of the newly created New
York State Workmen's Compensation Board, serving in that office 1945 to 1955;
president International Association of Industrial Accident Boards and Commis-
sions 1947–48; appointed judge United States Customs Court by President Dwight
D. Eisenhower in 1955, took oath of office August 10, 1955; trustee of Cornell
University since 1937; delegate to Republican National Convention and member
Resolutions Committee 1944 and 1948; chairman Resolutions Committee New
York State Republican convention 1954; residence: 249 East 48th Street, New
York.

SCOVEL RICHARDSON, judge; born in Nashville, Tenn., February 4, 1912,
son of M. Scovel and Capitola W. (Taylor) Richardson; graduated from Wendell
Phillips High School, Chicago, Ill., 1930; A.B., 1934 and A.M., 1936, University
of Illinois; LL.B., 1937, Howard University; married Inez Williston; four children:
Elaine (Mrs. Lawrence B. Harrisingh), Alice Inez, Mary Louise and Marjorie
Linda (twins); admitted to Illinois bar 1938, U.S. Supreme Court bar 1943, and
Missouri bar 1945; practiced law in Chicago 1938–39; associate professor of law,
Lincoln University, St. Louis, Mo., 1939–43; senior attorney, Office of Price
Administration, Washington, D.C., 1943–44; dean of School of Law and professor
of law, Lincoln University, St. Louis, Mo., 1944–53; appointed member of United
States Board of Parole in the Department of Justice, Washington, D.C., by
President Dwight D. Eisenhower, August 5, 1953; appointed chairman of the
United States Board of Parole by Attorney General Herbert Brownell, Jr.,
September 28, 1954, and served as chairman until April 1957; reappointed a
member of United States Board of Parole by President Eisenhower for a 6-year
term, July 7, 1956; appointed judge of the United States Customs Court by
President Eisenhower, April 8, 1957; received annual alumni award by trustees
of Howard University for distinguished postgraduate achievement in law, March
2, 1958; trustee of Howard University since 1961; trustee of the National Council
on Crime and Delinquency since 1958; member of American Law Institute,
American Bar Association, American Judicature Society, National Bar Association, Federal Bar Association, Missouri Bar Association, Bar Association of
St. Louis, and judiciary member of the Association of the Bar of the City of New
York.

PHILIP NICHOLS JR., judge; born in Boston, Mass., in 1907; in 1929 received his A.B. degree from Harvard College, and LL.B. degree from Harvard Law School following in 1932; practiced law in Boston for 6 years and came to Washington in 1938, entering the Government service with the Lands Division, Justice Department; in January 1942 transferred to the War Production Board as a member of the Office of the General Counsel; from December 1943 to February 1946 on active duty as an officer in the U.S. Navy, and remained as civilian attorney to the Navy Price Adjustment Board until December 1946; during service with the Treasury Department from December 1946 to December 1951 was first Chief Counsel to the Bureau of Federal Supply, and later Assistant General Counsel for Customs and Narcotics; was chairman of the committee which had responsibility for drafting legislation to simplify Customs procedures; General Counsel with the Renegotiation Board until April 1954 when he returned to private law practice; practiced chiefly in the field of customs law, but was also a specialist in the field of Government contracts and profit controls; became a member of the law firm of Butler, Koehler and Tausig in 1957; was appointed Commissioner of Customs on March 24, 1961, succeeding the late Ralph Kelly who had resigned on January 20 of that year; during his tour of duty as Commissioner of Customs, the Bureau undertook a number of reforms all designed to reduce paperwork and simplify Customs procedures in keeping with the policies of the Administration; the Bureau has cooperated with the United States Travel Service in extending a welcome to foreign visitors to the United States; an oral baggage declaration was introduced in lieu of the old long written form; at the same time, the importance of effective enforcement of law received new recognition and support; on September 2, 1964, Secretary of the Treasury Douglas Dillon awarded then Commissioner Nichols an Exceptional Service Award "for his exceptional leadership and success as Commissioner of Customs in modernizing the United States Customs Service to cope with the demands of ever-growing, and increasingly complex, international travel and commerce"; Judge and Mrs. Nichols have hitherto resided in Alexandria, Va.; they were married in 1940 and have three children, Donald, Patricia, and Christopher; nominated by President Johnson in June and was confirmed by the United States Senate on September 15, 1964.

[One vacancy.]

OFFICERS OF THE UNITED STATES CUSTOMS COURT

Clerk.—Howard Basler.
Marshal.—Dante A. Robilotti.
Court Reporters.—DeVera Hill, Ferdinand Schwartz, Michael J. Russo, Alfred J. Policastro, Samuel Lerner, Alan Dunst.
Librarian.—Anna H. Olsen.

TAX COURT OF THE UNITED STATES

Constitution Avenue at 12th Street. Phone, NAtional 8-5771 (Code 184)

NORMAN O. TIETJENS, chief judge—Ohio—born 1903, Napoleon, Ohio; married Lucretia Larkin, 1936; two daughters; attended public schools in Napoleon; Brown University, Ph.B., 1925 (magna cum laude), M.A., 1927; University of Michigan, J.D., 1930; associate editor, Michigan Law Review, 1929–30; admitted to the bar, Ohio, 1930; United States Supreme Court, 1935; District of Columbia, 1949; instructor, Napoleon High School, 1925–26; practice of law, Toledo, Ohio (1930–32) and Napoleon (1932–33); special counsel, Federal Emergency Administration of Public Works, 1933–37; counsel, United States Maritime Commission, 1937–38; attorney, office of the general counsel, 1938–39, and assistant general counsel, 1939–50, Treasury Department; member: Order of the Coif, Phi Beta Kappa, Phi Delta Phi, and Sigma Nu; oath of office as judge, Tax Court of the United States, August 30, 1950; reappointed for succeeding term June 2, 1962; term expires June 1, 1974; served as Chief Judge 1961–63, and reelected as Chief Judge to serve for two-year term beginning July 1, 1963; residence: 3509 Overlook Lane, 20016.

ARNOLD RAUM, judge—Massachusetts—born 1908, Massachusetts; married Violet Gang Kopp: Harvard College, A.B. (summa cum laude), 1929, and Harvard Law School, LL.B. (magna cum laude), 1932; member of Phi Beta Kappa; member, Editorial Board of Harvard Law Review, 1930–32; traveling fellowship, Cambridge University, England, 1932; attorney, Reconstruction Finance Corporation, 1932–34; special assistant to attorney general, tax division, Department of Justice, 1934–39; in 1939, entered solicitor general's office, in charge of Government tax litigation and other types of cases in United States Supreme Court; has argued more tax cases in Supreme Court than anyone in history; assistant to solicitor general and acting solicitor general from time to time; lectured on taxation as a member of faculty at Harvard and Yale; United States military service, World War II, lieutenant commander, Coast Guard; oath of office as judge, Tax Court of the United States, September 19, 1950; reappointed for succeeding term June 2, 1960; term expires June 1, 1972; residence: 2622 31st Street, 20008.

JOHN GREGORY BRUCE, judge—Kentucky—born 1897, Edinburg, Ind.; married Zilpha Foster: three sons; attended schools in Indiana and Pineville, Ky.; Transylvania University, A.B., 1921, University of Ky., LL. B. (cum laude), 1924; editor-in-chief, Kentucky Law Journal; U.S. Naval Service, 1918–21; admitted to bar, Kentucky, 1923; member of bar, U.S. Supreme Court. U.S. Courts of Appeals for the Fourth, Sixth, Ninth, and Tenth Circuits, U.S. District Courts (Eastern District of Kentucky and Eastern District of Michigan); attorney, Fordson Coal Co. (subsidiary of Ford Motor Co.), Pineville, Ky. and Detroit, Mich., 1924–31; private practice Pineville, Ky., 1931–34; attorney, Department of Justice, 1934–36; chief, Trial Division, Bureau of War Risk Litigation, 1936–43; assistant chief, Frauds Section, Claims Division, 1943–51; chief, Frauds Section, 1951–52; member Order of the Coif, Phi Alpha Delta law fraternity, and Phi Kappa Tau; Mason (F. & A.M., R.A.M., and K.T.; Past Master and Past Commander, Pineville, Ky.); American and Federal Bar Associations; National Lawyers Club; trustee, Bethesda Christian Church; oath of office as judge, Tax Court, May 28, 1952; reappointed May 13, 1958, for succeeding 12-year term; present term expires June 1, 1970; residence: 5524 Pembroke Road, Bethesda, Md. 20034.

GRAYDON G. WITHEY, judge—Michigan—born 1910, Reed City, Mich.; married Edna B. Leonard; three daughters and two sons; attended public schools in Reed City and Flint, Mich.; studied law under his father, Charles A. Withey, circuit judge in the State of Michigan; admitted to the bar, Michigan, 1933; practice of law, Flint, 1933–37, 1939–49; chief assistant prosecuting attorney, Genesee County, Mich., 1937–38; nominated for prosecuting attorney, 1944; appointed Deputy Attorney General of Michigan, 1949; member: State Bar of Michigan, Genesee County, Mich., Bar Association, and American Bar Association; oath of office as judge, The Tax Court of the United States, June 16, 1952; reappointed for succeeding term June 2, 1960; term expires June 1, 1972; residence: 2011 North Quantico Street, Arlington, Va., 22205.

ALLIN H. PIERCE, judge—Illinois—born 1897, Graceville, Minn.; married
Florence Bennet; son, Allin H., Jr.; daughter, Isabel S.; attended public schools
in Minnesota and Fort Dodge, Iowa; Swarthmore College, A. B. 1919; University
of Chicago, J. D., cum laude, 1923; admitted to bar, Illinois, 1923, New York,
1937; member of bar, U.S. Supreme Court, various U.S. Courts of Appeals, U.S.
District Courts, and U.S. Court of Claims; practice of law, New York and
Chicago, with professional specialization in Federal taxation, 1923–55; special
attorney, Bureau of Internal Revenue, Washington, 1928–35; lectured extensively
on Federal taxation before various institutes, bar associations, and conferences;
U.S. military service: aviation cadet, U. S. Naval Reserve Force, 1918; member,
American Bar Association (section of taxation); Illinois State Bar Association;
Association of the Bar of the City of New York; Chicago Bar Association (chair-
man, committee on Federal taxation, 1949; grievance committee, 1950–53; com-
mittee on judiciary, 1955); member, Legal Club, Chicago; Federal Tax Forum,
Chicago; National Lawyers Club, Washington; Methodist; Mason; president,
Swarthmore College Alumni Association, 1939–40; Delta Upsilon; Phi Delta
Phi; Order of the Coif; Columbia Country Club; oath of office as judge, Tax
Court, March 21, 1955; reappointed for term expiring June 1, 1972; residence:
3700 University Avenue, 20016.

CRAIG S. ATKINS, judge—Maryland—born 1903, Greensboro, N.C.;
married Margaret Denty; son, Craig S., Jr. and daughter, Constance Atkins
McShulskis: public schools in Baltimore and Baltimore Polytechnic Institute;
University of N. C. and George Washington U., A.B. 1923, LL.B., 1925; admitted to bar, District of Columbia, 1925, U. S. Supreme Court. 1928: attorney,
U.S. Board of Tax Appeals (now the Tax Court), 1927–37; attorney and assistant
head, interpretative division, office of chief counsel, Internal Revenue Service,
1937–49; tax advisor to Economic Cooperation Administration mission to Greece,
1949–51; assistant head, interpretative division, office of chief counsel, Internal
Revenue Service, 1951–54; special assistant and assistant chief counsel, 1954–55;
member, American Bar Association, Masonic Fraternity, Sigma Phi Epsilon; oath
of office as judge, Tax Court, September 1, 1955; term expires June 1, 1974;
residence: 7004 Florida Street, Chevy Chase, Md., 20015.

JOHN E. MULRONEY, judge—Iowa—born 1896, Ruthven, Iowa; married
Martha O'Connor, 1929; son, Michael, two daughters, Patricia Mulroney Thom,
and Ann Katherine Mulroney Doud; attended Creighton University, Iowa, 1915;
Iowa University Law School, 1919–22; admitted to Iowa bar, 1923; county attorney, Webster County, Iowa, 1929–33; assistant attorney general of Iowa, 1939–
42; justice of Iowa Supreme Court, 1943–55; resigned from that office to accept
appointment to the Tax Court; military service, 1917–19; member of Iowa State
Bar Association, American Legion, Phi Delta Phi, Order of the Coif; oath of
office as judge, Tax Court of the United States, October 11, 1955; reappointed for
succeeding term June 2, 1956; term expires June 1, 1968; residence: 3200 16th
Street, 20010.

BRUCE M. FORRESTER, judge—Missouri—born December 26, 1908,
Kansas City, Mo., son of Mr. and Mrs. James M. Forrester; married to Anne
Lee Broaddus; three children: Anne Norris Forrester, Jean Bruce Forrester, and
Bruce M. Forrester, Jr.; attended Lawrenceville Preparatory School, Lawrence-
ville, N.J., Country Day School, Kansas City, Mo., and Glendale Union High
School, Glendale, Calif., graduated cum laude; LL.B., 1935, University of Missouri; President's Honor Roll; admitted to the bar, 1935; engaged in the practice of law since 1935 in Kansas City, Mo.; member of the law firm of Watson,
Ess, Groner, Barnett & Whittaker (now known as Watson, Ess, Marshall and
Enggas); military service: 1944–45, as ROTC instructor, Chicago; past president
and trustee of the Sigma Alpha Epsilon Club of Missouri, past director of Stockyards National Bank, Kansas City, Mo., trustee, Holton-Arms School, Washington, D.C.; member of American Bar Association, the A.B.A. Section of Taxation,
the American Law Institute, Missouri Bar Association, Kansas City Bar Association, Lawyers Association of Kansas City, Chancery, Kansas City Country
Club, and St. John's Church, Norwood Parish; appointed to the Tax Court of the
United States for the term expiring June 1, 1958; reappointed, term expiring
June 1, 1970; residence: 7017 Beechwood Drive, Chevy Chase, Md., 20015.

RUSSELL E. TRAIN, judge—District of Columbia—born 1920, Jamestown, R.I.; married Aileen Bowdoin; three daughters: Nancy L., Emily L., and Errol C., and one son, Charles Bowdoin; graduated from St. Albans School, Washington, D.C.; Princeton University, A.B. (cum laude), 1941; Columbia University Law School, LL.B., 1948; admitted to the Bar of the District of Columbia, 1949; attorney, Staff of the Joint Congressional Committee on Internal Revenue Taxation, 1949–53; Clerk, House Committee on Ways and Means, 1953–54; Minority Advisor, House Committee on Ways and Means, 1954–56; Assistant to the Secretary and Head of the Legal Advisory Staff, Treasury Department 1956–57; served as major, field artillery, World War II; trustee, Washington Cathedral Foundation; member: board of governors, Saint Albans School, Washington, D.C.; Vestry (Junior Warden) of St. John's Episcopal Church, Lafayette Square, Washington, D.C.; Metropolitan Club, Chevy Chase Club; honorary member, East African Professional Hunters' Association; President, African Wildlife Leadership Foundation; Vice President, World Wildlife Fund; trustee, Conservation Foundation; director, Friends of the National Zoo; honorary trustee, Tanzania National Parks; appointed to the Tax Court of the United States, for term expiring June 1, 1958; reappointed, term expiring June 1, 1970; residence: 3101 Woodland Drive, 20008.

WILLIAM MILLER DRENNEN, judge—West Virginia—born 1914, Jenkins, Ky.; married Margaret Morton, 1940; two daughters, Margaret Penelope, and Dale Louise, and two sons, William M., Jr., and David Holmes; attended public schools in Charleston, W. Va.; Denver, Colo.; Columbus, Ohio; Ohio State University, B.S., 1936, and LL.B., 1938; admitted to the bar, West Virginia, 1939; employed during law school years in office of Ohio State Tax Commissioner, and as assistant to the clerk of the Ohio Supreme Court; law clerk to judge of United States District Court for Southern District of West Virginia, 1938–40; associate and later partner in law office of Brown, Jackson & Knight (now Jackson, Kelly, Holt & O'Farrell), Charleston, W. Va., 1940–58; air combat intelligence officer, USNR, 1942–45; past president and member of board of West Virginia Tax Institute; member—city council of Charleston, W. Va.; board of directors of Charleston Chamber of Commerce; board of trustees Charleston Memorial Hospital; American Bar Association (section of taxation); West Virginia State Bar; West Virginia Bar Association; American Judicature Society, Beta Theta Pi and Phi Delta Phi fraternities; appointed to the Tax Court of the United States for the term expiring June 1, 1968, to succeed Judge Stephen E. Rice, deceased; residence: 8001 Aberdeen Road, Bethesda, Md., 20014.

IRENE FEAGIN SCOTT, judge—Alabama—born October 6, 1912, Union Springs, Ala., daughter of Arthur H. and Irene Peach Feagin; married 1939 to Thomas J. Scott; two children, Thomas J., Jr. and Irene; attended public school in Union Springs, Ala.; graduated Union Springs High School, 1929; A.B. University of Alabama, 1932; LL.B. University of Alabama, 1936; LL.M. Catholic University of America, 1939; admitted to Alabama bar 1936; attorney, Office of Chief Counsel, Internal Revenue Service, 1937–50; member, Excess Profits Tax Council, Internal Revenue Service, 1950–52; Special Assistant to Head of Appeals Division, Office of Chief Counsel, Internal Revenue Service, 1952–59; Staff Assistant to the Chief Counsel, Internal Revenue Service, 1959–60; member, American Bar Association, Kappa Delta, Kappa Beta Pi; oath of office as judge, Tax Court, May 31, 1960; term expires June 1, 1972; residence: 4815 25th Road North, Arlington, Va., 22207.

WILLIAM M. FAY, judge—Pennsylvania—born May 14, 1915, Pittston, Pa.; married 1945 to Jean M. Burke, Plainfield, N.J.; son, Michael, age 17; attended St. John's Academy, Pittston; Georgetown and Catholic Universities; LL.B., 1942; admitted to District of Columbia Bar, 1942, and United States Supreme Court, 1946; Assistant Counsel, United States Senate Atomic Energy Committee, 1946; Executive Secretary to Senator McMahon of Connecticut, 1946–48; Office of Chief Counsel, Internal Revenue Service, 1948–57, serving successively as Trial Attorney, Assistant Head of Civil Division, and Assistant Head of Appeals Division; Assistant Regional Counsel in charge of Washington office handling litigation before the Tax Court, 1957–61; military service: 1942–45 serving successively as Naval Intelligence Officer, Gunnery Officer in European theater, and Senior Legal Officer; member of the American Bar (Tax Section) the Federal Bar, and the District of Columbia Bar Associations; the United

States Senate Association of Administrative Assistants; and the Kenwood Country Club; appointed to the Tax Court of the United States for the term expiring June 1, 1968, to succeed Judge J. E. Murdock, retired; residence: 5809 Highland Drive, Kenwood, Chevy Chase, Md., 20015.

HOWARD A. DAWSON, JR., judge—Arkansas—born October 23, 1922, Okolona, Ark., son of Dr. and Mrs. Howard A. Dawson; married in 1946 to Marianne Atherholt; two daughters, Amy and Suzanne; Woodrow Wilson High School, Washington, D.C., 1940; University of North Carolina, B.S. in Business Administration, 1946; George Washington University Law School, LL.B. 1949; President, Case Club; Secretary-Treasurer, Student Bar Association; private practice of law, Washington, D.C., 1949–1950; served with the Internal Revenue Service as follows: Attorney, Civil Division, Office of Chief Counsel, 1950–1953; Civil Advisory Counsel, Atlanta District, 1953–56; Assistant Regional Counsel, 1957; Regional Counsel, Atlanta Region, 1958; Personal Assistant to Chief Counsel, December 1, 1958, to June 1, 1959; and Assistant to the Chief Counsel in charge of management and administration, June 1, 1959, to August 20, 1962; military service: U.S. Army Finance Corps, 1942–45; served in European Theater; Captain, U.S. Army Reserve; member of the District of Columbia Bar, Georgia Bar, American Bar Association (Section of Taxation), Federal Bar Association, National Lawyers Club, Delta Theta Phi Legal Fraternity, George Washington Unversity Law Alumni Association; appointed to the Tax Court of the United States on August 21, 1962, for term expiring June 1, 1970, to succeed Judge Bolon B. Turner, retired; residence: 7408 Nevis Road, Bethesda, Md.

AUSTIN HOYT, judge—Colorado—born 1915, Beacon, N.Y.; son of the late Judge Ferdinand A. and Beatrice Watson Hoyt; married Margaret Llewellyn Carter of Virginia, 1939; three children: son, John Carter Hoyt, and two daughters, Julia Hoyt Rolland and Dale Llewellyn Hoyt; attended University of Alabama and St. John's University; University of Virginia Law School, LL.B. 1938, Dean's List, Law Review Board, Order of the Coif; admitted to the bars of the District of Columbia, 1939; New York, 1940; and Colorado, 1949; attorney, REA, 1938–40; private practice of law, Beacon, New York, 1940–42; special attorney and assistant to the Attorney General, Antitrust, Criminal, and Tax Divisions, Department of Justice, 1942–49; member of firms of Ziegler and Hoyt, 1949–54, and Hoyt and Gallagher, 1954–59 and 1961–62, Colorado Springs, Colo.; district judge, Fourth Judicial District of Colorado, 1959–61; military service: USNR, Procurement Legal Division, Navy Department, 1944–45; and Flag Secretary, and Air Combat Intelligence Officer, Staff, ComCarDivs 4 and 5, U.S. Pacific Fleet, 1945–46; Lieutenant USNR (retired); member of El Paso County, Colo., American and Federal Bar Associations, and American Judicature Society; president Colorado Springs Symphony Orchestra Association, 1958–60, Colorado Springs School for Girls, 1961–62; member, Phi Delta Theta, Phi Alpha Delta, and Society of Mayflower Descendants; appointed to the Tax Court of the United States to succeed Judge John Worth Kern, retired; term expires June 1, 1974; residence: 502 Arcturus Lane, Alexandria, Va., 22308.

RETIRED JUDGES RECALLED TO PERFORM JUDICIAL DUTIES

CHARLES ROGERS ARUNDELL, judge—Oregon—born 1885, Washington, D.C.; married Alice W. Robinson, nee Wright, 1926; daughter, Elizabeth (Mrs. James H. Stallings, Jr.); attended public schools in Washington, D.C.; George Washington University, LL. B., 1908; alumni achievement award, 1939; admitted to the bar, District of Columbia, 1908, Oregon, 1910; practice of law, Portland, Oreg., 1910–15; chief, Alaskan Field Division, General Land Office, in charge of public lands of Alaska, 1916–19; special attorney and assistant solicitor, Bureau of Internal Revenue, Treasury Department, 1921–25; original appointment to the Tax Court of the United States (the Board of Tax Appeals), September 1, 1925; reappointed for three succeeding terms June 2, 1926, June 2, 1938, and June 2, 1950; served as chairman, U.S. Board of Tax Appeals, 1937–41; retired August 31, 1955; recalled to perform further judicial duties, September 1, 1955; member, American Bar Association, Federal Bar Association, Oregon Bar Association, National Press Club, National Lawyers Club; residence: 4930 Quebec Street, 20016.

J. EDGAR MURDOCK, judge—Pennsylvania—born 1894, Greensburg, Pa.; parents, Henry H. and Mary Martha (Machesney) Murdock; married 1923 to Sarah Lynch; son, John Edgar, Jr., Lt. Cdr., USN (retired), and daughters, Sarah Martha (Mrs. Joseph L. Bolster, Jr.) and Elizabeth (Mrs. Richard P. Matsch); attended public schools in Greensburg; Princeton University, Litt. B., 1916; University of Pittsburgh, LL.B. (cum laude), Order of the Coif 1921; admitted to bar of Pennsylvania, 1920; United States military service, 1917–19; commissioned first lieutenant, Infantry, 1917; captain, 1918; overseas service, 1918–19; Silver Star citation; appointed sceond assistant district attorney, Westmoreland county, Pa., 1922 and first assistant district attorney, 1925; original appointment to the United States Board of Tax Appeals (now the Tax Court), June 9, 1926; reappointed for three succeeding terms, June 2, 1932, June 2, 1944, and June 2, 1956; served as chairman and presiding judge, 1941–45; chief judge July 1, 1955 to June 30, 1961; retired June 30, 1961; recalled to perform further judicial duties January 5, 1962; member, American Bar Association, Princeton Club, Chevy Chase Club, Rolling Rock Club, formerly president and member of Children's Hospital Board, Washington, D.C.; residence: 2940 Foxhall Road, 20016.

EUGENE BLACK, judge—Texas—born 1879, Blossom, Tex.; attended law school, Cumberland University, Lebanon, Tenn., LL. B., 1905; admitted to bar of Texas 1905; practiced law at Clarksville, Tex.; elected Representative in Congress from First Congressional District of Texas in 1914; elected to Sixty-fourth Congress and served in each succeeding Congress until the conclusion of 70th Congress; received honorary degree of Doctor of Laws from Cumberland University 1937; original appointment to Tax Court of the United States (then Board of Tax Appeals), November 5, 1929; reappointed for two succeeding terms June 2, 1932, and June 2, 1944; served as chairman, Board of Tax Appeals, 1933–37; retired November 30, 1953; recalled to perform further judicial duties December 1, 1953; residence: 5206 Colorado Avenue, 20011.

BOLON B. TURNER, judge—Arkansas—born 1897, Pulaski County, Ark., married Essie Lee Pearson Tusler, 1950; attended University of Arkansas and George Washington Universtiy, A.B., LL.B., 1922, and LL.M., 1924, from latter; United States military service, World War I, attaining rank of second lieutenant; employed in income tax unit, Bureau of Internal Revenue, 1920–23; assisted in drafting of Revenue Act of 1924, and in the preparation of regulations under that act; attorney, United States Board of Tax Appeals, 1924–27; practice of law, Little Rock, Ark., 1927–33; in 1929, organized income tax division of the Department of Revenues, State of Arkansas, and supervised drafting of regulations under Arkansas Income Tax Act; appointed attorney, Office of Secretary of the Treasury, 1933, and employed chiefly on matters pertaining to revenue legislation, assisting in the drafting of the Revenue Act of 1934; original appointment to the Tax Court of the United States (then Board of Tax Appeals) June 11, 1934; reappointed for two succeeding terms, June 2, 1946, and June 2, 1958; retired April 15, 1962; recalled to perform further judicial duties April 16, 1962; served as chief judge of Tax Court, 1945–49; Baptist; Mason; member: American Bar Association; American Legion; Sigma Chi; Phi Alpha Delta; residence: 4801 Connecticut Avenue, 20008.

MARION J. HARRON, judge—California—born September 3, 1903, San Francisco; University of California, Berkeley, A.B. (cum laude), 1924; University of California School of Law, J.D. (thesis, *Dissenting Opinions of Justice Brandeis*), 1926; member, Phi Beta Kappa, Delta Sigma Rho, Phi Delta Delta Law Fraternity, Prytanean Society (University of California); admitted to the bar, California, 1926, United States Supreme Court, 1938; auditor of the California Industrial Welfare Commission, Minimum Wage Law Division, summers, 1924, 1925; Teaching Fellow, Department of Economics, University of California, 1924–25–26; practiced law in San Francisco; legal and economic consultant, New York laws regulating industry, and Federal anti-trust laws, National Industrial Conference Board, New York City, 1927–28; member of faculty, Institute for the Study of Law, Johns Hopkins University, 1928–29; author, *Research in Law in the United States*, Johns Hopkins U. Press, 1929; counsel to Manufacturers Trust Co., New York City, concerned with legal aspects of bank liquidations, refinancing of real estate syndicates and mortgage loans, reorganizations of corporations, corporate trusts, 1929–33; legal consultant taxation, "blue sky" laws, Cohen, Gutman, & Richter, New York City, 1932–33; senior attorney, legal adviser on codes for food, textile industries, National Recovery Administration, Washington, D.C., 1933–35; assistant counsel, Resettlement Administration, Washington, D.C., 1935; Regional Custodian of Rehabilitation Corporations, Western Region, Berkeley, Calif., Resettlement Administration, 1936; original appointment to the Tax Court of the United States (then the Board of Tax Appeals) by President Roosevelt, June 20, 1936; reappointed by President Truman to a succeeding term ending June 1, 1960; recalled to perform further judicial duties June 2, 1960; member: State Bar of California, Bar Association of San Francisco, Federal Bar Association, Women's Bar Association of the District of Columbia, National Association of Women Lawyers, International Federation of Women Lawyers, Los Angeles Business Women's Council, American Association of University Women, National Lawyers Club; residence: 3243 Quesada Street, Washington, D.C., 20015.

JOHN WORTH KERN, judge—Indiana—born 1900, Indianapolis, Ind.; married Bernice Winn, 1927; son, John W. Kern 3d; attended Washington and Lee University, A.B., 1920; Harvard Law School, LL.B., 1923; graduate student, University of Chicago Law School, summers 1933–34–36; admitted to Bar, Indiana, 1923, and practiced in Indianapolis; United States Commissioner, 1923–30; judge, Superior Court, Marion County, 1931–35; lecturer, University of Virginia Law School, 1948–49; mayor of Indianapolis, 1935–37; professor of law, Indiana Law School, 1925–35; member, American Bar Association, American Law Institute, Indianapolis Bar Association (secretary, 1924–30), Metropolitan Club, Chevy Chase Club, Farmington Country Club; Lake Placid Club; original appointment to the Tax Court of the United States (then Board of Tax Appeals), September 7, 1937; reappointed for two succeeding terms June 2, 1938, and June 2, 1950; served as chief judge, 1949–55; retired June 30, 1961; recalled to perform further judicial duties July 1, 1961; residence: 4407 Hadfield Lane, 20007.

OFFICERS OF THE COURT

Administrative Officer.—Otto W. Schoenfelder, 6437 Dahlonega Road, 20016.
Assistant Administrative Officer.—William F. Huffman, 316 Hannes Street, Silver Spring, Md.
Clerk.—Howard P. Locke, 3901 Connecticut Avenue, 20008.
Chief Deputy Clerk.—Ralph A. Starnes, Box 332, McLean, Va., 22101.
Commissioner and Special Assistant to Chief Judge.—Edward C. Radue, 3229 Reservoir Road, 20007.
Budget and Fiscal Officer.—Oliver A. Keeter, 5544 16th Street North, Arlington, Va., 22205.
Librarian.—Helen C. McLaury, 2200 19th Street, 20009.
Reporter.—Mrs. Ella C. Thomas, 10715 Rock Run Drive, 20854.

UNITED STATES DISTRICT COURT FOR THE DISTRICT OF COLUMBIA

United States Courthouse. Phone, STerling 3-5700 (Code 1204)

MATTHEW F. McGUIRE, chief judge; B.A. Holy Cross College, 1921; LL.B Boston University School of Law, 1926; honorary LL.D.. Holy Cross, 1941 Special Assistant to Attorney General of United States 1934-39; Special Assistant Attorney General 1939; The Assistant to Attorney General 1940-41 (Deputy Attorney General); U.S. Navy 1918; U.S. Navy Distinguished Civilian Service Medal 1945; married Eleanor G. McCarthy 1936; appointed by President Roosevelt judge of the United States District Court for the District of Columbia July 7 1941; entered on duty October 7, 1941; Chief Judge, October 1961.

DAVID A. PINE, judge (chief judge, August 6, 1959–September 22, 1961) born September 22, 1891, District of Columbia, son of David Emory and Charlotte McCormick Pine; educated in Washington public schools, Central High School, Georgetown University, District of Columbia, LL. B. 1913, postgraduate work 1913-14; honorary LL.D., Georgetown University, 1954, passed bar examination, June 1913; admitted to District of Columbia bar, October 1913; confidential clerk to United States Attorneys General McReynolds, and Gregory 1914-15; law clerk and assistant attorney, Department of Justice, 1916-17 lieutenant, United States Army, 1918; captain, United States Army, 1918-19; attorney, Department of Justice, 1919; special assistant to the United States Attorney General, 1919-21; engaged in Federal litigation in Colorado, Arizona, New Mexico California, and Nevada; in 1921, returned to the District of Columbia to engage in the private practice of law, and in 1925 became a member of the firm of Easby Smith, Pine & Hill; in 1929 this firm was dissolved; continued in private practice in the District of Columbia; February 1, 1934, became first assistant United States attorney for the District of Columbia; on December 31, 1937, appointed by the United States district court as United States attorney for the District of Columbia; later, nominated to this office by the President, confirmed by the Senate, and sworn in on March 9, 1938; on March 15, 1940, nominated associate justice (now judge) of the United States District Court for the District of Columbia and took office after confirmation by the Senate on April 2, 1940; married to Elizabeth Bradshaw (deceased), also a native Washingtonian; one daughter, Elizabeth Pine Dayton, wife of Dr. Glenn O. Dayton, Jr., Los Angeles, Calif., married to Elenore E. Townsend, of Washington, July 8, 1959; member of District of Columbia Bar Association, American Bar Association, Lawyers' Club, Washington (former president), the Barristers, Washington (former president), Metropolitan Club, Washington, Chevy Chase Club, Maryland, Delta Theta Phi, and Sigma Nu Phi (honorary); Episcopalian; Mason (former master of St. Johns' Lodge No. 11 District of Columbia). Home address, 3507 Lowell Street, Washington, D.C. 20016.

ALEXANDER HOLTZOFF, judge; was born on November 7, 1886; was educated in New York City schools; Columbia College, A.B., 1908; M.A., 1909 Columbia University School of Law, LL. B., 1911; admitted to New York bar 1911; was in private practice in New York City, 1911-24; in Army during First World War; was appointed special assistant to the then Attorney General of the United States, Harlan F. Stone, in 1924 and continued as such till 1945; was executive assistant to the Attorney General, 1945; represented the Attorney General on the President's Committee on Economic Security, which laid the groundwork for the Social Security Act; member and secretary of the Advisory Committee of the Supreme Court on Federal Rules of Criminal Procedure, 1942-45; member of War Department Committee on Military Justice, 1946, appointed by the Secretary of War to study the administration of justice within the Army and to recommend changes in the court-martial system; member of Committee on Revision of Naval Court Martial System, and was given the Navy Distinguished Public Service Award by the Secretary of the Navy; past commander of Department of Justice Post of American Legion, 1944-45; member, Phi Beta Kappa married to Louise J. Cowan of Brooklyn, N.Y., 1925; author and coauthor of several law books; was appointed United States district judge, September 28 1945; resides at the Broadmoor.

RICHMOND B. KEECH, judge; born in Washington, D.C., November 28, 1896; son of Leigh R. and Anne L. (Contee) Keech; married Alice Cashell, of Rockville, Md., September 24, 1957; Junior Warden, All Souls Episcopal Church; educated in the public schools of the District of Columbia and Georgetown University, LL. B. 1922, LL. M. 1923; served in the Navy, 1917–19; engaged in the private practice of law in Washington, D.C., 1922–25; assistant corporation counsel, District of Columbia, 1925–30; people's counsel, District of Columbia, 1930–34, appointed by President Hoover; vice chairman, Public Utilities Commission of the District of Columbia, 1934–40, appointed by President Roosevelt; corporation counsel, District of Columbia, 1940–45; an administrative assistant to the President of the United States, 1945–46; appointed justice (now district judge) of the United States District Court for the District of Columbia by President Truman and entered upon the duties of that office on November 1, 1946.

EDWARD M. CURRAN, judge; born in Bangor, Maine, May 10, 1903; son of Michael J. and Mary A. Curran; A.B., University of Maine, 1928; LL.B., Catholic University of America, Washington, D.C., 1927; admitted to the District of Columbia bar 1929 and engaged in practice of the law with Milton W. King until 1934; married Katherine C. Hand (deceased) June 6, 1934; married Margaret V. Carr December 30, 1963; served as assistant corporation counsel for the District of Columbia 1934–36; judge of the Police Court of the District of Columbia 1936–40; United States attorney for the District of Columbia 1940–46; appointed United States district judge by President Truman October 16, 1946; instructor in law, School of Law, Catholic University, 1930–35; professor of law, Georgetown University School of Law 1943–46; four children: Eileen Marie, Mary Catherine, Ann Elizabeth, Edward M., Jr.; member of the American Bar Association; District of Columbia Bar Association; former first vice president, Federal Bar Association; Phi Kappa Fraternity; Gamma Eta Gamma Legal Fraternity; the John Carroll Society; the Metropolitan Police Boys Club; the Merrick Boys Club; the Friendly Sons of St. Patrick; the Advisory Board of the Catholic University School of Law; Knights of Columbus, Fourth Degree; vice president and director, Ridgley School For Exceptional Children, Ridgley, Md.

EDWARD ALLEN TAMM, judge; born St. Paul, Minn., April 21, 1906; student Mount St. Charles College, Helena, Mont.; University of Montana; LL.B., Georgetown University, 1930; married Grace Monica Sullivan; children: Edward Allen, Jr., and Grace T. Escudero; with Federal Bureau of Investigation, 1930–48; member bar of Minnesota and Supreme Court of the United States; member American and Federal bar associations; honorary member District of Columbia Bar Association; appointed district judge of the United States District Court for the District of Columbia by President Truman and entered upon the duties of that office June 28, 1948.

BURNITA SHELTON MATTHEWS, judge; born in Copiah County, Mississippi, December 28, 1894; admitted to bar and began practice in District of Columbia, 1920; received a recess appointment as judge of the United States District Court for the District of Columbia by President Truman October 21, 1949, and took oath of office and entered on duty November 9, 1949; nominated by President Truman as judge of said court January 5, 1950, confirmed by Senate April 4, 1950, and took oath of office April 11, 1950.

LUTHER WALLACE YOUNGDAHL, judge; of Washington, D.C.; born in Minneapolis, Minn., May 29, 1896, son of John C. and Elizabeth Youngdahl; educated in the public schools of Minneapolis; served in the United States Army in First World War; received A.B. from Gustavus Adolphus College, Saint Peter, Minn., 1919; LL.B. from Minnesota College of Law, 1921; assistant city attorney, Minneapolis, 1921–24; married Irene Annet Engdahl of Ortonville Minn., 1923; children: Margaret, William, and David; practiced law in Minneapolis as a member of the firm of Judge M. C. Tifft, 1924–30; appointed municipal judge in Minneapolis, 1930; elevated to district court judgeship, 1936; in 1942 elected to supreme court of Minnesota; resigned from supreme court of Minnesota in 1946 to run for Governor of Minnesota; elected to three terms as Governor of Minnesota; resigned September 27, 1951, to accept appointment as judge of the United States District Court for the District of Columbia; presented the Grand

Cross of the Royal Order of the North Star by King Gustaf V of Sweden and a doctorate in humane letters and honorary doctor of laws degrees from 14 colleges and universities.

JOSEPH C. McGARRAGHY, judge; born in Washington, D.C., November 6, 1897, the son of Andrew and Mary Imogene McGarraghy; educated in local public schools; graduated from Georgetown University, Washington, D.C., 1921, LL.B.; served with Engineer Corps, U.S. Army, 1917–1920; Assistant Corporation Counsel, 1924–25; married to Marian Boyd Cameron, February 24, 1939; member law firm of Colladay, McGarraghy, Colladay & Wallace, 1925–1940; member law firm of Wilkes, McGarraghy & Artis, 1940–1954; president of The Barristers, 1937–38; first vice president D.C. Bar Association, 1941–42; chairman, Washington Committee, American Bar Association, 1948–54; president, Washington Board of Trade, 1946–47; chairman, Greater National Capital Committee, 1947–50; chairman, Republican State Committee in and for the District of Columbia, 1949–54; delegate to Republican National Convention, 1952; chairman, Eisenhower-Nixon Inaugural Committee, 1953; honorary member Gamma Eta Gamma; member, Capitol Hill Club, Columbia Country Club, Lawyers Club of Washington, Metropolitan Club, The Vinson Club; appointed judge of United States District Court for the District of Columbia by President Eisenhower, November 10, 1954, and confirmed by Senate on December 2, 1954; assumed duties December 17, 1954.

JOHN J. SIRICA, judge; born in Waterbury, Conn., March 19, 1904, son of Fred and Rose Sirica; attended public schools in Jacksonville, Fla., and New Orleans, La., received the degree of LL.B. from Georgetown University Law School in 1926; admitted to the Bar of the United States District Court for the District of Columbia in October 1926, and subsequently to the Bars of the United States Court of Appeals for the District of Columbia Circuit and the Supreme Court of the United States; engaged in private practice here until August 1, 1930, on which date was appointed Assistant United States Attorney for the District of Columbia; resigned on January 15, 1934, to resume the practice of law; in 1944 served as General Counsel to the House Select Committee to investigate the Federal Communications Commission; member of the law firm of Hogan & Hartson, 1949–57; married Lucile M. Camalier, February 26, 1952; children: John J., Jr., Patricia Anne and Eileen Marie; member of the American Bar Association, served as State Chairman for the District of Columbia, Junior Bar Conference of the American Bar Association during 1938–39; member of Phi Alpha Delta Law Fraternity, Congressional Country Club and the John Carroll Society; honorary member of the District of Columbia Bar Association, National Lawyers Club, and the Lido Civic Club; nominated judge, United States District Court for the District of Columbia, February 25, 1957, by President Eisenhower and entered upon the duties of that office on April 2, 1957.

GEORGE L. HART, JR., judge; born in Roanoke, Va., July 14, 1905; son of George L. and Lavela (Slicer) Hart; married Margaret Louise Neller, October 12, 1935; son George L. Hart III; educated elementary schools of Roanoke, Va.; Forest Park Academy, Roanoke, Va.; Virginia Military Institute, A. B. 1927; Harvard Law School LL. B. 1930; admitted to District of Columbia bar, 1930; engaged in private practice of law as partner in firm of Lambert & Hart, 1930–41; entered on active duty as captain, Field Artillery and served as battery commander, Second Armored Division, January 1941; took part in North African Invasion, November 8, 1942; remained overseas until October 1945, during which period took part in the invasions of Africa, Sicily, Salerno, Anzio and Southern France; participated in battle campaigns Algeria-French Morocco, Tunisia, Sicily, Naples-Foggia, Rome-Arno, Anzio, Southern France, Rhineland, Northern France, Central Europe; September 1944, promoted to colonel and made chief of staff, 12th Tactical Air Command; decorations: Legion of Merit, Bronze Star, Air Medal, Croix de Guerre avec Palme; reentered active practice of law, January 1946, as partner in law firm of Lambert, Hart & Nothrop and remained in active practice to October 1958; chairman, Council on Law Enforcement, District of Columbia, 1955–58; 1954–58, chairman of Republican State Committee in and for the District of Columbia; 1952–56, delegate to Republican National Convention;

Episcopalian; member of District of Columbia Bar Association, ABA, the Barristers, Palaver Club, National Press Club, Capitol Hill Club, Columbia Country Club; Lawyers Club; National Lawyers Club; received recess appointment as judge of the United States District Court for the District of Columbia by President Eisenhower on August 26, 1958; assumed duties October 7, 1958; took oath of office September 11, 1959, under permanent commission after Senate confirmation.

LEONARD PATRICK WALSH, judge; born March 10, 1904, Superior, Wis.; University of Minnesota; National University (LL.B., 1933); instructor, George Washington University School of Education, 1929–36; admitted to bar of District of Columbia (1933), United States Court of Appeals for the District of Columbia, The Supreme Court of the United States, and administrative agencies; in private practice, 1933–53; nominated by President Eisenhower, confirmed by Senate, as chief judge, The Municipal Court for the District of Columbia, and took oath in July 1953 (10-year term); nominated by President Eisenhower as judge, United States District Court, confirmed by Senate, and took oath September 21, 1959; professorial lecturer, The George Washington University School of Law, 1956 to 1964; member: Bar Association of the District of Columbia (member of Board of Directors; president 1951–52), American Bar Association, and Phi Delta Phi Legal Fraternity.

WILLIAM B. JONES, judge; born March 20, 1907, in Cedar Rapids, Iowa, son of James Patrick and Isabel Cecilia Blakely Jones; educated in primary and secondary schools in Denison, Iowa, and Sioux City, Iowa; Notre Dame University, A.B. 1929, LL.B. 1931; admitted to the bars of the State of Montana, District of Columbia, and Maryland; Special Assistant Attorney General, State of Montana, 1935–37; engaged in private practice of law in Montana, 1931–37; attorney, Department of Justice, 1937–43; Office of Price Administration, 1943; Executive Assistant to the American Chairman of the Joint British-American Patent Interchange Committee, 1943–46; engaged in the practice of law, District of Columbia, as a member of the firm of Hamilton and Hamilton, 1946 to May 14, 1962; appointed by President Kennedy judge of the United States District Court for the District of Columbia March 19, 1962, confirmed by the Senate and sworn in on May 14, 1962; married to Alice Danicich; one daughter, Barbara; member of the District of Columbia Bar Association, American Bar Association, Lawyers' Club of Washington; Judicial Fellow, American College of Trial Lawyers, Fellow, American Bar Foundation; member, Metropolitan Club of Washington, Columbia Country Club of Maryland and the National Lawyers Club of Washington.

SPOTTSWOOD W. ROBINSON III, judge; born in Richmond, Va., July 26, 1916; son of Spottswood W., Jr., and Inez C. Robinson; attended public schools of Richmond, Va., and Virginia Union University, Richmond, Va.; LL.B. (magna cum laude), Howard University, Washington, D.C., 1939; LL.D., Virginia Union University, 1955; married to Marian B. Wilkerson; two children, Spottswood W., IV, and Nina Cecelia (Mrs. Oswald G. Govan); admitted to Virginia Bar, 1943; member of faculty, School of Law, Howard University, 1939–48 (on leave 1947–8); practiced law in Richmond, Va., as member of firm of Hill & Robinson, later Hill, Martin & Robinson, 1943–55, and as sole practitioner, 1955–60; dean of School of Law, Howard University, 1960–63; member of United States Commission on Civil Rights, 1961–63; vice president and general counsel, Consolidated Bank and Trust Company, Richmond, Va., 1963–64; member of American Bar Association, National Bar Association, National Lawyers Club (honorary), Old Dominion Bar Association; nominated by President Kennedy as Judge of the United States District Court for the District of Columbia on October 1, 1963; following adjournment of the Senate, received recess appointment as Judge of the Court under Commission of President Johnson dated January 6, 1964, and took oath of office on January 7, 1964; nominated by President Johnson as Judge of the Court on February 3, 1964, confirmed by the Senate on July 1, 1964, and took oath of office on July 7, 1964, under Commission of President Johnson dated July 2, 1964.

[One vacancy.]

RESIDENCES OF THE JUDGES OF THE UNITED STATES DISTRICT COURT FOR THE DISTRICT OF COLUMBIA

Chief Judge.—Matthew F. McGuire, 2701 Connecticut Avenue, 20008.
Judges:
David A. Pine, 3507 Lowell Street, 20016.
Alexander Holtzoff, Broadmoor Apartments, 20008.
Richmond B. Keech, 2746 Woodley Place, 20008.
Edward M. Curran, 6607 Western Avenue, 20015.
Edward A. Tamm, 3353 Runnymede Place, 20015.
Mrs. Burnita Shelton Matthews, 4500 Connecticut Avenue, 20008.
Luther W. Youngdahl, 3636 16th Street, 20010.
Joseph C. McGarraghy, Sheraton-Park Hotel, 20008.
John J. Sirica, 5069 Overlook Road, 20016.
George L. Hart, Jr., 3901 Jenifer Street, 20015.
Leonard P. Walsh, 4625 Rockwood Parkway, 20016.
William B. Jones, 5516 Grove Street, Chevy Chase, Md., 20015.
Spottswood W. Robinson III, 5400 30th Street, 20015.

RETIRED

F. Dickinson Letts, Kennedy-Warren Apartments, 20008.
Henry A. Schweinhaut, 3601 Saul Road, Kensington, Md.
Charles F. McLaughlin, 2101 Connecticut Avenue, 20008.

OFFICERS OF THE UNITED STATES DISTRICT COURT FOR THE DISTRICT OF COLUMBIA

Auditor.—John W. Follin, 3416 North Westmoreland Street, Falls Church, Va.
Clerk.—Harry M. Hull, 3211 Quesada Street.
Chief Deputy Clerk.—Robert M. Stearns, 6101 Broad Branch Road.
Administrative Assistant to the Chief Judge.—Melvin J. Marques, 12420 Stony Creek Road, Rockville, Md.
Assignment Commissioner.—Richard L. Collins, 1949 Rosemary Hills Drive, Silver Spring, Md.
Assistant Assignment Commissioner.—Vernon E. Greaver, 734 South Royal Street, Alexandria, Va.
Chief Probation Officer.—Edward W. Garrett, 3909 Seventh Street South, Arlington, Va.
Deputy Chief Probation Officer.—George W. Howard, 4540 North Chelsea Lane, Bethesda, Md.

COMMISSION ON MENTAL HEALTH

New U.S. Court Building, 333 Constitution Avenue. Phone, STerling 3–3700 (Code 1204)

Chairman.—Arthur J. McLaughlin, 1301 15th Street.
Alternate.—Samuel Meyer Greenbaum, 2840 Brandywine Street.
Physicians (Psychiatrists):
Irma Belk Hobart, M.D., 5110 Manning Place.
Albert E. Marland, M.D., 1216 16th Street.
Charles Prudhomme, M.D., 1752 17th Street.
Marshall deG. Ruffin, M.D., 4831 Quebec Street.
Anna Coyne Todd, M.D., 7519 Broadview Road SE.
Dan F. Keeney, M.D., 1028 Connecticut Avenue.
Clarence E. Bunge, 1426 35th Street.
Jean H. Menetrez, 6101 16th Street.
Secretary.—Bernadette D. Chadwick, 8722 Colesville Road, Silver Spring, Md.

UNITED STATES COURT OF MILITARY APPEALS

Fifth and E Streets, 20442

Phone, OXford 6-5177 (Code 11, extension 65177)

ROBERT EMMETT QUINN, chief judge: born in Phenix, R.I., April 2 1894: son of Charles and Mary Ann (McCabe) Quinn: A.B., Brown University, 1915; LL.B., Harvard, 1918; married Mary Carter, August 3, 1923; children, Norma Marie, Robert Carter, Pauline Fulton, Cameron Peter, and Penelope Dorr; admitted to Rhode Island bar and practicing attorney at Providence, R. I., since 1917; member, United States Diplomatic Intelligence Service in England and France, 1917–19; member, Rhode Island Senate, 1923–25 and 1929–33; lieutenant governor, State of Rhode Island, 1933–36; Governor, State of Rhode Island, 1937–39; judge, Rhode Island Superior Court commencing May 1, 1941; legal officer, First Naval District, 1942–45; captain, United States Naval Reserve since February 1942; commanding officer, Naval Reserve Volunteer Legal Unit of Rhode Island, 1947–50; president, Kent County Bar Association; member, American and Rhode Island Bar Associations; member, Phi Kappa; member, Brown, Harvard, Wannamoisett, Turks Head, West Warwick Country and Army and Navy Clubs; nominated by President Truman to chief judge of the United States Court of Military Appeals May 22, 1951, for the term expiring May 1, 1966, confirmed by Senate June 19, 1951, and took oath of office June 20, 1951, under commission of President Truman dated June 20, 1951; Democrat; Roman Catholic.

HOMER FERGUSON, judge; born in Harrison City, Pa., son of Samuel and Margaret Ferguson; married Myrtle Jones, June 20, 1913, one daughter, married Mrs. Charles R. Beltz; attended University of Pittsburgh; LL.B. degree University of Michigan, 1913; admitted to bar of Michigan, 1913; practiced law, Detroit, 1913 to 1929; circuit Judge of the Circuit Court of Wayne County, Mich., 1929, elected 1930, and reelected 1935 and 1941; United States Senator from Michigan, 1943 to 1955; chairman Republican Policy Committee, 83d Congress; member Foreign Relations Committee and Appropriation Committee, 83d Congress; honorary degrees conferred by Detroit College of Law, Kalamazoo College, Michigan State College, Muhlenberg College, Allentown, Pa.; LL. D., University of Michigan, 1951; member of the second Hoover Commission; ambassador from the United States to the Philippines, March 22, 1955, to April 8, 1956, at which time resigned to accept Presidential appointment; nominated by President Eisenhower as judge of the United States Court of Military Appeals January 30, 1956, for terms expiring May 1, 1956, and May 1, 1971, unanimously confirmed by Senate February 17, 1956, and took oath of office April 9, 1956, administered by Chief Justice Warren; member of American and Michigan Bar Associations.

PAUL J. KILDAY, judge; born in Sabinal, Uvalde County, Tex., March 29, 1900, son of Pat and Mary (Tallant) Kilday; moved with his family to San Antonio, Tex., in 1904; attended the San Antonio public schools, St. Mary's Parochial School, and old St. Mary's College of San Antonio, Tex.; graduated from Maine Avenue High School and from Georgetown University, Washington, D.C., in 1922, with LL.B. degree; doctor of laws degree, St. Mary's University of San Antonio, Tex., 1963; admitted to bar of Texas in 1922; engaged in private practice at San Antonio from 1922 to 1935; First Assistant Criminal District Attorney of Bexar County (San Antonio) 1935 to 1938; member of bars of Texas District of Columbia, and Supreme Court of United States; member, Texas State, San Antonio, and American Bar Associations; married Miss Cecile Newton, of San Antonio, 1932, and they have two daughters—Mary Catherine and Betty Ann (Mrs. Fred W. Drogula); elected to the 76th Congress in 1938 and reelected to the 11 succeeding Congresses, serving from January 3, 1939, to September 24, 1961; member, Committee on Military Affairs, House of Representatives, 1939 to 1946, and Committee on Armed Services, 1946 to 1961; for 10 years, member Joint Committee on Atomic Energy; awarded "Citation of Honor" by the Air Force Association "for tireless efforts in building national armed strength and active participation in successful legislation to enhance the military service as a career" (1955); awarded "Army Times 1957 Accomplishment Award in recognition of his outstanding leadership in military personnel legislation and his unceasing concern for the welfare of the men and women of the Armed Forces";

awarded honorary membership by the Fleet Reserve Association (1958); awarded "Honor Bell" by the Military Order of The Carabao "for Distinguished Service" (1960); elected an Honorary Life Member of the Reserve Officers Association of the United States ((in Recognition of Outstanding Contributions to the Association's Programs" (1961); awarded Veterans of Foreign Wars Gold Medal of Merit "in recognition of his many outstanding historic contributions to national security" (1961); resigned from House of Representatives September 24, 1961, to accept Presidential appointment; nominated by President Kennedy as judge of the United States Court of Military Appeals, June 28, 1961, for the term expiring May 1, 1976, unanimously confirmed by Senate, July 17, 1961, and took the oath of office September 25, 1961, under commission of President Kennedy dated September 25, 1961; Democrat.

RESIDENCES OF THE JUDGES OF THE UNITED STATES COURT OF MILITARY APPEALS

(The * designates those whose wives accompany them)

*Chief Judge Robert E. Quinn, Fifth and E Streets, 20442.
*Judge Homer Ferguson, 5054 Millwood Lane, 20016.
*Judge Paul J. Kilday, 5115 Chevy Chase Parkway, 20008.

OFFICERS OF THE UNITED STATES COURT OF MILITARY APPEALS

Chief Commissioner.—Richard L. Tedrow, 17 Oxford Street, Chevy Chase, Md., 20015.
Clerk.—Alfred C. Proulx, 307 North Virginia Avenue, Falls Church, Va., 22046.
Deputy Clerk.—Frederick R. Hanlon, 3450 Toledo Terrace, Hyattsville, Md., 20782.

DISTRICT OF COLUMBIA COURT OF APPEALS

400 F Street, 20001. Phone, EXecutive 3-1463 or 1464

Chief Judge.—Andrew McCaughrin Hood, 2237 46th Street, 20007.
Associate Judges:
  Thomas D. Quinn, 4545 Connecticut Avenue, 20008.
  Frank H. Myers, 2851 Arizona Terrace, 20016.
  Nathan Cayton (retired), 2727 29th Street, 20008.
Clerk.—C. Newell Atkinson, 2841 University Terrace, 20016.

DISTRICT OF COLUMBIA COURT OF GENERAL SESSIONS

Civil Division Building, Fourth Street between E and F; Criminal Division Building, Fifth Street between E and F. Phone, REpublic 7-4575 (Code 1206)

Chief Judge.—John Lewis Smith, Jr., 2424 Tracy Place, 20008.
Judges:
  Milton S. Kronheim, Jr., 3020 Chesapeake Street, 20008.
  Mary C. Barlow, 3133 Connecticut Avenue, 20008.
  Thomas C. Scalley, 5019 41st Street, 20016.
  Andrew J. Howard, Jr., 1532 Upshur Street, 20011.
  John J. Malloy, 5806 Nevada Avenue, 20015.
  Edward A. Beard, 4619 Kenmore Drive, 20007.
  Harry L. Walker, 5404 Cromwell Drive, 20016.
  Austin L. Fickling, 1716 Allison Street, 20011.
  John H. Burnett, 4817 36th Street, 20008.
  Catherine B. Kelly, 4501 Connecticut Avenue, 20008.
  DeWitt S. Hyde, 5606 McLean Drive, Bethesda, Md., 20014.
  Joseph M. F. Ryan, Jr., 5441 Jordan Road, 20016.
  Joseph C. Waddy, 1804 Upshur Street NE., 20018.
  Edmond T. Daly, 2401 H Street, 20037.

RETIRED

George D. Neilson, 4000 Tunlaw Road, 20007.

Clerk of the Court.—Walter F. Bramhall, 532 Peabody Street, 20011.
Director of Probation.—Robert J. Conner, 719 North Jackson Street, Arlington, Va., 22201.
Assistant Director of Probation.—Robert R. Estep, 10111 Renfrew Road, Silver Spring, Md., 20901.
Administrative Officer.—Anna L. Callahan, 532 Peabody Street, 20011.
Assistant Administrative Officer.—Shirley I. Ward, 1715 North Nelson Street, Arlington, Va., 22204.
Chief Deputy Clerk, Criminal Division.—Joseph M. Burton, Jr., 5604 Sonoma Road, Bethesda, Md., 20034.
Assistant Chief Deputy Clerk, Criminal Division.—Roy G. Dickinson, 1307 Delafield Place, 20011.
Chief Deputy Clerk, Central Violations Bureau.—Wallace D. Cummins, 214 Park Terrace Court SE., Vienna, Va., 22180.
Assistant Chief Deputy Clerk, Central Violations Bureau.—Wilmer S. Schantz, 414 Irwin Street, Silver Spring, Md., 20901.
Chief Deputy Clerk, Civil Division.—William M. Nedrow, 5223 Fourth Street NE., 20011.
Assistant Chief Deputy Clerk, Civil Division.—Charles A. Clements, Jr., 507 Dennis Avenue, Silver Spring, Md., 20901.
Assignment Commissioner.—Edward M. Carr, 5612 Glenwood Road, Bethesda, Md., 20014.
Deputy Assignment Commissioner.—Joseph J. Snyder, 3520 Nimitz Road, Kensington, Md., 20795.
Chief Deputy Clerk, Domestic Relations Branch.—John M. Bischoff, Bowie-Laurel Road, Bowie, Md., 20715.

2

Assistant Chief Deputy Clerk, Domestic Relations Branch.—Leroy H. McCarthy, 3040 Idaho Avenue, 20016.
Chief Deputy Clerk, Small Claims Branch.—Charles P. Henry, Jr., 1109 Drake Street SW., Vienna, Va., 22180.
Assistant Chief Deputy Clerk, Small Claims Branch.—Kathryn Trammell, 4201 Massachusetts Avenue, 20016.

JUVENILE COURT

400 E Street. Phone, REpublic 7-8777 (Code 1623, extension 0)

Chief Judge.—Morris Miller, 5706 Broad Branch Road, 20015.
Associate Judge.—Orman W. Ketcham, 2 East Melrose Street, Chevy Chase, Md., 20015.
Associate Judge.—Marjorie McKenzie Lawson, 4402 29th Street, 20008.
Hearing Officer.—John J. Larkin, 3803 W Street, 20007.
Executive Director.—Louis Levathes, 7900 Sleaford Place, Bethesda, Md., 20014.
Clerk of the Court.—Charles J. Rumsey, 4644 Tilden Street, 20016.
Director, Office of Administration.—Leah L. Friedman, 325 Constitution Avenue NE., 20002.
Acting Director, Social Services.—Edgar Silverman, 8918 Whitney Street, Silver Spring, Md., 20901.
Director, Child Guidance Clinic.—Harold B. Blessing, 11842 Enid Drive, Potomac Hills, Md., 20854.

ADMINISTRATIVE OFFICE OF THE UNITED STATES COURTS

Supreme Court Building, 1 First Street NE. Phone, EXecutive 3-1640

Director.—Warren Olney III, 20 Third Street NE.
  Secretary to the Director.—Mrs. Elinor R. Denham, 4201 31st Street South, Arlington, Va.
Deputy Director.—William E. Foley, 5 East Melrose Street, Chevy Chase, Md.
  Secretary to the Deputy Director.—Mrs. Marjorie D. Williams, 5460 Sanger Avenue, Alexandria, Va.
Assistant Director.—William R. Sweeney, 7609 Exeter Road, Bethesda, Md.
Chief, Division of Procedural Studies and Statistics.—Ronald H. Beattie, 800 Fourth Street SW.
Chief, Division of Probation.—Louis J. Sharp, 9945 Cherrytree Lane, Silver Spring, Md.
Chief, Division of Bankruptcy.—Royal E. Jackson, 1708 White Oak Drive, Silver Spring, Md.
Chief, Division of Business Administration.—Wilson F. Collier, 5503 Cornish Road, Bethesda, Md.
Chief, Division of Personnel.—William T. Barnes, 5204 27th Avenue SE.

REGISTER OF WILLS AND CLERK OF THE PROBATE COURT

United States Courthouse. Phone, STerling 3-5700 (Code 1204)

Register and Clerk.—Theodore Cogswell, 806–M Arlington Towers, Arlington, Va., 22209.
Chief Deputy Register.—Frank J. Burkart, 4801 Connecticut Avenue, 20008.
Deputy Registers:
  Aliene M. Ivory, 4801 Connecticut Avenue, 20008.
  Eleanor L. Marron, 2935 Macomb Street, 20008.
  Arthur P. Smith, 2745 29th Street, 20008.
  Peter J. McLaughlin, 4100 W Street, 20007.

DISTRICT OF COLUMBIA

DISTRICT OF COLUMBIA

ORIGIN AND FORM OF GOVERNMENT

The District of Columbia was established under the authority and direction of acts of Congress approved July 16, 1790, and March 3, 1791, which were passed to give effect to a clause in the eighth section of the first article of the Constitution of the United States giving Congress the power—

"To exercise exclusive Legislation in all Cases whatsoever, over such District (not exceeding ten Miles square) as may, by Cession of particular States, and the Acceptance of Congress, become the Seat of the Government of the United States, and to exercise like authority over all Places purchased by the Consent of the Legislature of the State in which the Same shall be, for the erection of Forts, Magazines, Arsenals, dock-Yards, and other needful buildings;—"

The States of Maryland and Virginia made cessions contemplated by this clause in the years 1788 and 1789, respectively. From the cessions tendered by the two States was selected the territory for the permanent seat of the General Government. This territory was 10 miles square, lying on either side of the Potomac River at the head of navigation. Later, 1846, Congress retroceded to Virginia that portion ceded by it. The Maryland, or retained, portion is approximately 70 square miles.

The seat of government of the United States was first definitely named by the clause in the act entitled "An act providing a permanent form of government for the District of Columbia," approved June 11, 1878, as follows: "That all territory which was ceded by the State of Maryland to the Congress of the United States, for the permanent seat of government of the United States, shall continue to be designated as the District of Columbia" (20 Stat. 102), although it had been incidentally mentioned as such in several preceding statutes.

The land within the ceded territory was owned by a number of people. In Georgetown, President Washington negotiated with the proprietors or landowners of that portion of the ceded territory selected as the site of the city of Washington, which comprised about 10 percent of the area of the present District of Columbia. On the second day, March 30, 1791, he concluded an agreement which was put in writing and signed by the proprietors. By it the President was given sole power to lay off streets as he pleased. These proprietors conveyed their holdings to trustees named by the President to hold title to the same during the laying out of the Federal city and then convey as agreed to the United States and the proprietors respectively. Under this agreement the proprietors donated to the United States all of the lands for the streets and one-half of the city lots throughout the entire city. Sites reserved by the United States for the public buildings, parks, and other public purposes were paid for by the United States in Maryland money the equivalent to $66.66 per acre. Such payment, amounting to $36,099, was made out of the proceeds from the sale of some of the lots which these proprietors had donated to the United States. This was the only purchase price paid by the United States for any part of the entire acquisition of 5,128 acres for the purpose of building the Capital City.

The land within the original city of Washington comprised a total of 6,111 acres and was divided to the United States 4,147 acres—3,606 acres for streets and 541 acres for public purposes. The remaining 1,964 acres was divided into squares and the squares into lots. The whole number of lots was 20,272—10,136 to the United States and the same number to the proprietors.

Thomas Jefferson, then Secretary of State, declared the liberality of the proprietors was "noble."

The United States lots were sold from time to time, chiefly before 1800 and up to 1835, and brought $740,024.45 (S. Doc. 247, 64th Cong., 1st sess., p. 23). This was a considerable sum as compared with the average annual income of the Federal Government during the 12 years from 1789 to 1800, it being about 13 percent of that average of about $5,600,000. The lots which still remained the property of the United States after gifts of them to charitable and literary institutions were sold about September 1865 for a moderate sum.

The proceeds from the sales of the Government lots were largely applied to the erection of the original Government buildings and improvements in their immediate neighborhood. The funds for these buildings were supplemented by grants of $120,000 by the State of Virginia and $72,000 by the State of Maryland (H. R. Report 269, 21st Cong., 1st sess., Doc. No. 5, p. 47). Both President Washington and President Jefferson expected the sale of these lots, if properly conserved, would not only provide ample funds for the erection of the public buildings without charge upon the lean Federal Treasury but would leave what Jefferson termed "the residuary interest of the city" which was intended to be used for streets and other city improvements. The failure of the Government to make these expected improvements so retarded the appreciation of values of the lots that the Government's prospective income from this source fell far short of expectations. The landowners who had so generously given their land to the Government as well as those who had been induced to purchase failed to realize the enhancement of value of their lots because of the failure of expected abutting and community improvements. The faith of Mr. Jefferson and the proprietors matched, but their fond hopes were not realized. The original proprietor of the land whereon is the Capitol Building, Daniel Carroll, of Duddington, in 1837 wrote "that the unfortunate proprietors are generally brought to ruin," who "were so wild as to suppose that the donation was so great the Government might pave the streets with ingots of gold or silver."

The city was planned and partly laid out by Maj. Pierre Charles L'Enfant, a French engineer. This work was perfected and completed by Maj. Andrew Ellicott. The building of the city and the erection of the public buildings were in charge of three commissioners selected by the President and subject to his direction.

When the Government establishment was moved in 1800, there existed within the 10 miles square two municipal corporations: the corporation of the city of Alexandria, incorporated by Virginia, and the corporation of the city of Georgetown, incorporated by Maryland.

The act of February 27, 1801, was the first legislation by Congress for the government of the District of Columbia following the removal to the permanent seat of government. While this act failed to set up a complete local government, it declared all of the laws of the States of Maryland and Virginia as then existing to be in force in the parts of the District ceded by the respective States. It created two counties, Washington County being the area outside of the cities of Washington and Georgetown on the Maryland side of the river, and Alexandria County being the area beyond the limits of the city of Alexandria on the Virginia side of the river. It also created the circuit court, the office of marshal of the District, the office of United States attorney for the District, justices of the peace for the two counties, a register of wills, and a judge of the orphans' court (2 Stat. 103).

The first government of the city of Washington consisted of a mayor appointed by the President of the United States and a city council elected by the people of the city. This was in 1802. The act chartering the city of Washington also created the levy courts, consisting originally of the justices of the peace of the respective counties (2 Stat. 115; 2 Stat. 773; 3 Stat. 195; 9 Stat. 230; 12 Stat. 384). The levy courts were given broad administrative powers over the counties of Washington and Alexandria, but had no judicial functions. At a later date the levy court of Washington County was composed of nine members appointed by the President (12 Stat. 799). Thus, there were within the 10 miles square five distinct local administrative units, namely (1) the corporation of Washington, (2) the corporation of Georgetown, (3) the county of Washington, (4) the corporation of Alexandria, and (5) the county of Alexandria. These were reduced to three units in 1846 with the retrocession of Alexandria city and county to the State of Virginia (9 Stat. 35; 9 Stat. 1000). The members of the city councils of the three municipalities were elected as were the mayors of Georgetown and Alexandria. In 1812 the city council was permitted to elect the mayor of Washington and in 1820 and thereafter the mayor was elected by the people (3 Stat. 583). The term of the mayor of Washington was for 2 years. This government continued until 1871.

By an act of Congress of February 21, 1871, the corporation of Washington, the corporation of Georgetown, and the levy court for Washington County were abolished, and the administration consolidated into a so-called territorial form of government. This government consisted of a governor, a board of public works, a board of health, and a legislative assembly. This legislative assembly consisted of a council of 11 members and a house of delegates of 22 members. The District then also had a Delegate in the House of Representatives of the United States. The Governor, the board of public works, and council were appointed by the President of the United States, by and with the advice and consent of the Senate. The 22 members of the house of delegates and the Delegate in Congress were elected by the people. The District had a Delegate in Congress until March 4, 1875.

This form of government lasted for 3 years, until June 20, 1874, when Congress provided that the District should be governed by three commissioners, appointed by the President. This was known as the temporary form of government and lasted until July 1, 1878, when the present permanent commission government was set up (18 Stat. 116). In the creation of the temporary commission form of government in 1874 and the permanent form in 1878 no provision was made for the franchise, and for the first time in three-quarters of a century no part of the District exercised the right of suffrage. The present form of government was created by act of Congress approved June 11, 1878 (20 Stat. 102).

The District of Columbia has an area of 69.245 square miles, of which 60.1 square miles are land. The river boundary is high-water mark along the Virginia shore of the Potomac River.

The local government of the District of Columbia is a municipal corporation having jurisdiction over the territory which was "ceded by the State of Maryland to the Congress of the United States for the permanent seat of the Government of the United States" (20 Stat. 102). This government is administered by a board of three Commissioners having general equal powers and duties (20 Stat. 103).

Two of these Commissioners, who must have been actual residents of the District for 3 years next before their appointment and have during that period claimed residence nowhere else, are appointed from civil life by the President of the United States and confirmed by the Senate for the term of 3 years each and until their successors are appointed and qualified.

The other Commissioner is detailed from time to time by the President of the United States from the Corps of Engineers of the United States Army, and shall not be required to perform any other military duty (ib.). This Commissioner shall be selected from the captains or officers of higher grade having served at least 15 years in the Corps of Engineers of the Army of the United States (26 Stat. 1113).

Three officers of the same corps, junior to said Commissioner, may be detailed to assist him by the President of the United States (26 Stat. 246). The senior officer of the Corps of Engineers of the Army, who for the time being is detailed to act as assistant (and in case of his absence from the District, or disability, the junior officer so detailed), shall, in event of the absence from the District or disability of the Commissioner, who shall for the time being be detailed from the Corps of Engineers, perform all the duties imposed by law upon said Commissioner (26 Stat. 1113).

One of said Commissioners shall be chosen president of the Board of Commissioners at their first meeting and annually and whenever a vacancy shall occur (20 Stat. 103).

The Commissioners are in a general way vested with jurisdiction covering all the ordinary features of municipal government and are also members of the Zoning Commission (37 Stat. 974).

The expenditures of the District of Columbia are based upon estimates prepared annually by the Commissioners and submitted by them to Congress through the Bureau of the Budget. To the extent to which it shall approve of said estimates, Congress shall appropriate a portion out of the Treasury of the United States. The remainder of the amount of such approved estimates shall be levied and assessed upon the taxable property and privileges in said District other than the property of the United States and of the District of Columbia (act approved June 11, 1878; 20 Stat. 104). "All taxes collected shall be paid into the Treasury of the United States, and the same as well as the appropriations to be made by the Congress as aforesaid shall be disbursed for the expenses of said District, on itemized vouchers, which have been audited and approved by the auditor of the District of Columbia, certified by said Commissioners or a majority of them" (ib. 105). This act also provided that the cost of operation, development, and maintenance of the District of Columbia should be borne jointly by the United States and the District of Columbia upon a 50–50 basis. This ratio was in 1922 changed to a payment of 60 percent from the revenues of the District of Columbia and 40 percent by the United States and this provision was repealed by act of Congress approved May 16, 1938. The act of July 16, 1947, provided for the fiscal year ending June 30, 1948, and for each fiscal year thereafter, that there was authorized to be appropriated as the annual payment by the United States toward defraying the expenses of the Government of the District of Columbia, the sum of $12,000,000. By the act of May 18, 1954, Public Law 364, 83d Congress, this amount was increased to $20,000,000, and further increased to $23,000,000 by the Act of March 31, 1956, Public Law 460, 84th Congress. The remainder of the local expenses are borne by the revenues of the District of Columbia derived from taxation of private property and privileges.

Congress has by sundry statutes empowered the Commissioners to make building regulations, plumbing regulations, to make and enforce all such reasonable and usual police regulations as they may deem necessary for the protection of lives, limbs, health, comfort, and quiet of all persons, and the protection of all property within the District, and other regulations of a municipal nature.

While the District has a municipal form of government, Congress by various statutory enactments has treated it as a branch of the United States Government by including it in legislation applying to the executive departments, such as the Budget and Accounting Act, the act classifying the salaries of Federal employees, and the act providing for retirement of Federal employees.

All legislation affecting the District of Columbia must be passed by Congress under the provisions of the Constitution. The advice of the Commissioners is usually asked before such legislation is enacted.

DISTRICT GOVERNMENT

District Building, Pennsylvania Avenue and Fourteenth Street
Phone, NAtional 8–6000 (Code 137)

EXECUTIVE OFFICES

Commissioner.—Walter N. Tobriner, 6100 33d Street, 20015.
 Special Assistant.—Richard S. Townsend, 7225 Marywood Street, Hyattsville, Md.
 Private Secretary.—Dorothy G. Allen, 4707 Connecticut Avenue, 20008.
Commissioner.—John B. Duncan, 5330 Second Street, 20011.
 Special Assistant.—Carl D. Coleman, 2 Elwyn Court, Silver Spring, Md. 20910.
 Private Secretary.—Grace V. Ellis, 8001 14th Street, 20012.
Engineer Commissioner.—Brig. Gen. Charles M. Duke, 5712 26th Street, 20015.
 Special Assistant.—Donald B. Rideout, 1117 Westbriar Court, Vienna, Va., 22180.
 Private Secretary.—Ethel H. Downing, 1850 Columbia Pike, Arlington, Va., 22204.
Assistants to Engineer Commissioner.—Col. John A. Israelson, 806 Shelby Lane, Falls Church, Va., 22043; Lt. Col. Victor O. Wilson, No. 4 Washington Circle, Alexandria, Va., 22305; Lt. Col. Edwin C. Adams, 606 South Woodstock Street, Arlington, Va., 22204.
Secretary to the Board.—F. E. Ropshaw, 7816 Libeau Lane, Annandale, Va.
 Assistant Secretary.—F. L. Timmons, Jr., 3210 Wheeler Road SE., 20032.
 Attorney Editor, Codification of D.C. Regulations and Publication of D.C. Register.—Paul Flaherty, 3701 Connecticut Avenue, 20008.
Administrative Assistant.—Lettie L. Leizear, 2032 Belmont Road, 20009.
 Administrative Aide.—Dorothy S. Busch, 8505 Flower Avenue, Takoma Park, Md., 20012.

DEPARTMENT OF GENERAL ADMINISTRATION

OFFICE OF THE DIRECTOR

Director.—Schuyler Lowe, 4715 Sedgwick Street, 20016.
Executive Assistant.—Ernest S. Miller, 5614 61st Place, East Riverdale, Md., 20804.

ADMINISTRATIVE SERVICES OFFICE

Administrative Services Officer.—James L. McCallister, 5312 36th Street North, Arlington, Va., 22207.
Deputy Administrative Services Officer.—William P. Bogardus, 5804 Felix Street, McLean, Va., 22101.

BUDGET OFFICE

Budget Officer.—David P. Herman, 2713 Branch Avenue SE., 20020.
Deputy Budget Officer.—John P. Sykes, 606 Eppard Circle, Falls Church, Va., 22044.
Deputy Budget Officer.—Richard F. Harris, 5901 North Second Street, Arlington, Va., 22203.

FINANCE OFFICE

Finance Officer.—Kenneth Back, 4620 Brandywine Street, 20016.
Deputy Finance Officer.—Clifford R. Barnes, 1301 Delaware Avenue SW., 20024.

Accounting Division

Chief.—Arthur R. Pilkerton, 4601 Western Avenue, 20016.
Deputy Chief.—Barney Farber, 101 G Street, SW., 20024.

Enforcement Division

Chief.—Samuel J. Kidd, 14613 Peach Orchard Road, Silver Spring, Md., 20904.

Data Processing Division

Chief.—Thomas L. Younger, 640 North Harrison Street, Arlington, Va.

Property Tax Division

Chief.—John C. Ahearn, 5205 11th Street NE., 20011.
Real Property Assessments:
  Supervisor.—[Vacant.]
  Personal Propery Assessments:
  Supervisor.—Laurence J. Eagan, 3850 Tunlaw Road, 20007.
Property Tax Records:
  Supervisor.—Roy W. Jones, 8601 Hartsdale Avenue, Bethesda, Md., 20034.
Special Assessments:
  Supervisor.—Dorothy M. Durkin, 4054 Fessenden Street, 20016.

Revenue Division

Chief.—Charles A. Beard, Jr., 108 Upton Street, Rockville, Md., 20850.
Income and Franchise Taxes:
  Supervisor.—Leo J. Ehrig, Jr., 1815 Sudbury Road, 20012.
Sales, Use and Excise Taxes:
  Supervisor.—Walter C. Thompson, 3300 Martha Custis Drive, Alexandria Va., 22302.
Inheritance and Estate Taxes:
  Supervisor.—William R. Mason, 203 Upton Street, Rockville, Md., 20850.

Treasury Division

Chief.—John W. West, 6266 29th Street, 20015.
Collection:
  Supervisor.—Allison Shell, 3804 Veazy Street, 20016.
Disbursing:
  Supervisor.—Francis X. Heard, 5415 Connecticut Avenue, 20015.

INTERNAL AUDIT OFFICE

Internal Audit Officer.—Frank M. Hally, 5218 Marly Drive, Glen Mar Park, 20016.
Deputy Internal Audit Officer.—Orlando J. Pulzone, 610 McNeill Road, Silver Spring, Md., 20910.
Deputy Internal Audit Officer.—David Legge, Route 1, Oakton, Va., 22124.

MANAGEMENT OFFICE

Management Officer.—Joseph C. Chicherio, 306 Charlton Court, Silver Spring, Md., 20902.

PERSONNEL OFFICE

Personnel Officer.—Henry F. Hubbard, 3133 Connecticut Avenue, 20008.
Chief, Administration and Safety Division.—Clifford K. Dodd, 1024 Indian Run Parkway, Alexandria, Va., 22312.
Chief, Employment and Training Division.—Albert T. Greenwood, 7810 Powhatan Street, Hyattsville, Md., 20784.
Chief, Classification and Wage Administration.—John H. Eaton, 83 Brandywine Heights Road, Brandywine, Md., 20613.

PROCUREMENT OFFICE

Procurement Officer.—Rexford G. Wessells, 5121 North 37th Road, Arlington, Va., 22207.
Deputy Procurement Officer.—Francis H. Herold, 1900 South Eads Drive, Arlington, Va., 22202.

ALCOHOLIC BEVERAGE CONTROL BOARD

Joy R. Simonson, chairman, 2929 University Terrace, 20016.
James G. Tyson, member, 3533 New Hampshire Avenue, 20010.
Louis N. Nichols, member, 7219 Western Avenue, 20015.
William O. Woodson, chief inspector, 5348 East Capitol Street, 20019.
Dorothy L. Albert, executive secretary, 49 East Taylor Run Parkway, Alexandria, Va., 22314.

APPRENTICESHIP COUNCIL

1145 Nineteenth Street, Room 405.   Phone, 629-2842 (Code 137, extension 2842)

Chairman.—John R. Evans, labor member, representing the Greater Washington Labor Council (AFL–CIO) and the printing and publishing industries, 1003 K Street NW., 20001.
Vice Chairman.—Malcolm C. MacKinnon, management member, representing the Merchants and Manufacturers, Hotel, and Restaurant Associations, 3835 Fessenden Street, 20016.
  [Vacancy], labor member.
  Clarence E. Harlowe, management member, representing Metropolitan Washington Board of Trade and the Printing Industry of Washington, D.C., 9512 St. Andrews Way, Silver Spring, Md., 21001.
  Robert L. Wearring, labor member, Secretary-Treasurer, Laborers District Council of Washington, D.C., and vicinity (AFL–CIO), 1351 Wallach Place, 20009.
  [Vacancy], management member.
Executive Secretary.—Edward N. Thomas, Director of Apprenticeship, D.C., 10303 Folk Street, Silver Spring, Md., 20902.
Field Representative.—Archie B. Moore, 1414 Quebec Street, Langley Park, Hyattsville, Md., 20783.
Apprenticeship Statistician.—Hazel I. Abel, River House, 1111 Army-Navy Drive, Arlington, Va., 22202.

DEPARTMENT OF BUILDINGS AND GROUNDS

Director.—James A. Blaser, 656 Timber Branch Parkway, Alexandria, Va., 22302.
Deputy Director.—W. A. Curtis, 800 Fourth Street SW., 20024.
Office of Business Administration, Chief.—Arnold O. Olson, 604 Charles Drive, Fairfax, Va., 22030.
Office of Design and Engineering, Chief.—Richard C. Crutchfield, 2038 Edmondson Avenue, Catonsville, Md., 21228.
Buildings Management Division, Chief.—James C. Bailey, 145 Upsal Street SE., 20032.
Construction Management Division, Chief.—Samuel E. Neely, 2424 Evans Drive, Silver Spring, Md., 20902.
Repairs and Improvements Division, Chief.—Norman L. Biggs, 4927 Fourth Street, 20011.
Office of Program Planning, Chief.—George F. Koehler, 436 Northwest Drive, Silver Spring, Md., 20901.

OFFICE OF CIVIL DEFENSE

4820 Howard Street, 20016.   Phone, 629-4791 (Code 137, extension 791)

Director.—George R. Rodericks, 13 Woodlawn Lane, Alexandria, Va., 22306.
Deputy Director.—Melvin E. McBride, 3428 Oakhurst Drive, Burtonsville, Md., 20730.

OFFICE OF THE CORONER

Nineteenth and E Streets SE., 20003.   Phone, 629–4520 (Code 137, extension 520)

Coroner.—Dr. Richard L. Whelton, 1021 University Boulevard, East Langley Park, Md., 20787.
Deputy Coroners:
  Dr. Linwood L. Rayford, 35 Gallatin Street, 20011.
  Dr. Marion Mann, 2817 Brentwood Road NE., 20018.
Superintendent.—George E. Stone, 224 Waterway Drive, Falls Church, Va., 22044.

OFFICE OF THE CORPORATION COUNSEL

Corporation Counsel.—Chester H. Gray, 4000 Massachusetts Avenue, 20016.
  Secretary.—Eileen H. Hardesty, 7509 Granada Drive, Landon Woods, Bethesda, Md., 20034.
Principal Assistant Corporation Counsel.—Milton D. Korman, 3314 Stephenson Place, 20015.
  Secretary.—Lillian L. Withers, 4913 Monroe Street, Newton Village, Bladensburg, Md., 20710.
  Librarian and Research.—Ernest F. Williams, 4451 Albemarle Street, 20016.
Assistant Corporation Counsel assigned to divisions of the office:
  Appellate Division.—Hubert B. Pair, chief, 4301 18th Street, 20011; Richard W. Barton, assistant chief, South 2816 Buchanan Street, Arlington, Va., 22206; John R. Hess, 4A Fort Hill Drive, Alexandria, Va., 22313; Ted D. Kuemmerling, 1111 Army-Navy Drive, Arlington, Va., 22202; David P. Sutton, 3103 Teal Lane, Belair, Md., 20715.
  Civil Proceedings Division.—John A. Earnest, chief, 3250 Highland Place, 20008; Lyman J. Ulmstead, assistant chief, 2703 Valley Drive, Braddock Heights, Alexandria, Va., 22302; Robert D. Wise, 411 Valleybrook Drive, Silver Spring, Md., 20904; Andrew G. Conlyn, 531 Creek Crossing Road NE., Vienna, Va., 22180; William R. Kearney, 2610 Spencer Road, Chevy Chase, Md., 20015; William F. Patten, 4229 46th Street, 20016; Robert R. Redmon, 6706 Wilson Lane, Bethesda, Md., 20014; James M. Cashman, 939 26th Street, 20037; Bruce S. Mencher, 4418 Rosedale Avenue, Bethesda, Md., 20014; Gilbert Gimble, 6152 31st Street, 20015; John B. Middleton, 4507 Sangamore Road, Bethesda, Md., 20014; Morton N. Goldstein, 3522 Cumberland Street, 20008.
  Domestic Relations and Collections Division.—Una Rita Quenstedt, chief, 1212 La Ronde Court, Alexandria, Va., 22307; Earl R. Smith, 421 New Orleans Drive, Alexandria, Va., 22308; Albert S. Povich, 6105 Plainview Road, Bethesda, Md., 20015; P. James Underwood, 9 Maryland Avenue, Annapolis, Md., 21401; Nicholas S. Nunzio, 8201 Bryant Drive, Bethesda, Md., 20034; Robert M. Sandler, 321 Peabody Street NE., 20001; E. Newton Steely, Jr., 1912 Fox Street, Adelphi, Md., 20783; Semi Feuer, 8500 16th Street, Silver Spring, Md., 20904; Vincent E. Ferretti, Jr., 3063 South Woodrow Street, Arlington, Va., 22206; Robert W. Hillis, 2256 Cathedral Avenue, 20008; William N. Albus, 1524 Allison Street, 20011; Edmund L. Browning, Jr., 3145 N Street, 20007.
  Law Enforcement Division.—Clark F. King, chief, 26110 Ridge Road, Damascus, Md., 20750; Robert H. Campbell, assistant chief, 6500 Seventh Place, 20012; James Weldon Hill, 5423 Bass Place SE., 20019; Robert P. Murphy, M–739 Arlington Towers, Arlington, Va., 22206; George A. Kramer, 4970 Battery Lane, Bethesda, Md., 20014; Robert M. Werdig, 7725 Walters Lane, Forestville, Md., 20002; Stephen Miller, Potomac Towers, 2001 North Adams Street, Arlington, Va., 22201; Thomas C. Bell, 4818 Chevy Chase Drive, 20015.
  Legislation and Opinions Division.—Irving Bryan, chief, 4501 Connecticut Avenue, 20008; Robert F. Kneipp, assistant chief, 2800 Quebec Street, 20008; Thomas F. Moyer, 1333 Peabody Street, 20011; William A. Robinson, 3734 Hayes Street NE., 20019; Lawrence S. Margolis, 107 Carlisle Drive, Silver Spring, Md., 20904; Richard S. Ehrlich, 10619 Weymouth Street, Bethesda, Md., 20014.

Assistant Corporation Counsel Assigned to Divisions of the Office—Continued
  Public Utilities Division.—George F. Donnella, 3726 Camden Street SE., 20020;
    C. Belden White II, 3905 Thornapple Street, Chevy Chase, Md., 20015.
  Special Assignments Division.—Oscar P. Mast, chief, 924 Upshur Street NE.,
    20017; C. Francis Murphy, assistant chief, 5055 Sargent Road NE., 20017;
    Louis P. Robbins, 328 Sixth Street SE., 20003; John F. Middleton, 113
    Tuckerman Street NE., 20011; James E. Lemert, 3408 Morrison Street,
    20015.
  Taxation Division.—Henry E. Wixon, chief, 9621 Old Spring Road, Kensington,
    Md., 20795; Robert E. McCally, 9705 Byeford Road, Kensington, Md.,
    20795; Gordon M. Van Sanford, 1710 Lamont Street, 20010; Peter H. Wolf,
    3111 Cathedral Avenue, 20008; Ronald L. Lenkin, 1900 Erie Street, Hyatts-
    ville, Md., 20783.
  Contract Appeals Board.—Lee F. Dante, chairman, 5821 Nevada Avenue, 20015.
  Administrative Division.—Adam A. Giebel, administrative officer, 4710 Jones
    Bridge Road, Bethesda, Md., 20014.

DEPARTMENT OF CORRECTIONS

Director.—Donald Clemmer, 5302 Neptune Drive, Alexandria, Va., 22309.
Assistant Director.—Thomas R. Sard, 6700 Belcrest Road, Hyattsville, Md.,
  20782.
Deputy Director.—Kenneth L. Hardy, Box 154–A, Lorton, Va., 22079.
Superintendent, District of Columbia Jail.—Sam A. Anderson, Shirlington House,
  Arlington, Va., 22206.
Superintendent, District of Columbia Reformatory.—Kermit A. Weakley, Lorton,
  Va., 22079.
Superintendent, District of Columbia Workhouse.—Marcel Pfalzgraf, Lorton, Va.,
  22079.
Superintendent, District of Columbia Reformatory for Women.—[Vacant.]
Superintendent, Industries Division.—Henry M. Lindsay, Lorton, Va., 22079.
Superintendent, Youth Center.—Joseph H. Havener, Lorton, Va., 22079.

BOARD OF EDUCATION

Thirteenth and K Streets, 20008.   Phone, STerling 3–6111 (Code 219)

Wesley S. Williams, president, 620 Fifth Street, 20001.
Carl C. Smuck, vice president, 1340 Good Hope Road SE., 20020.
Col. West A. Hamilton, 1353 U Street, 20009.
Dr. Euphemia L. Haynes, 1601 Holly Street, 20012.
Dr. Mordecai W. Johnson, 1610 Buchanan Street, 20011.
Dr. Preston A. McLendon, 4607 Western Avenue, 20016.
Mrs. Gloria K. Roberts, 4212 Ingomar Street, 20016.
Mrs. Louise S. Steele, 3100 Newark Street, 20008.
Irving B. Yochelson, 1707 H Street, 20006.
Mrs Gertrude L. Williamson, executive secretary, 1951 S Street SE., 20020.
Dr. Carl F. Hansen, superintendent of schools, 6946 Greenvale Street, 20016.
John M. Riecks, deputy superintendent, 204 Emerald Hill Drive, 20022.
Dr. Rufus C. Browning, assistant superintendent, 2213 Parker Avenue, Silver
  Spring, Md.
Dr. Joseph M. Carroll, assistant superintendent, 1911 Sudbury Road, 20012.
Harold A. Clark, assistant superintendent, 4815 Ruatan Street, College Park, Md.
Mrs. Aileen H. Davis, assistant superintendent, 2847 University Terrace, 20016.
Benjamin J. Henley, assistant superintendent, 237 Rock Creek Church Road,
  20011.
John D. Koontz, assistant superintendent, 6113 Lombard Street, Cheverly, Md.
Miss Edith A. Lyons, assistant superintendent, 1833 S Street, 20009.
Norman W. Nickens, assistant superintendent, 4228 19th Street, NE., 20018.
George E. S. Reynolds, assistant superintendent, Woodbridge, Va., 22291.
Granville W. Woodson, assistant superintendent, 1311 Delaware Avenue SE.,
  20024.
Charles S. Lofton, executive assistant to the superintendent of schools, 4825
  Blagden Avenue, 20011.

BOARD OF ELECTIONS

[Vacancy], Chairman.
Ernest Schein, 1025 Connecticut Avenue, 20006.
Robert Earl Martin, 1020 Irving Street NE., 20012.

FIRE DEPARTMENT

Headquarters (McMillan Park), 300 McMillan Drive. Phone, HObart 2-1762 (Code 137)

Fire Chief.—Henry A. Galotta, 3145 Birch Street, 20015.
Assistant Fire Chief.—William C. Weitzel, 3235 Highwood Drive SE., 20020.
Administrative Officer.—Alexander J. Patrick, 5005 Rodman Road, Westgate, Md., 20016.
Assistant Administrative Officer.—Raymond F. Henry, 5035 55th Avenue, Hyattsville, Md., 20781.
Deputy Fire Chiefs:
   Everett T. Haas, 3419 Nichols Avenue SE., 20032.
   Robert T. Huntington, 7419 Harwood Road, District Heights, Md., 20028.
   Edward O. Moeller, 2348 High Street SE., 20020.
Battalion Fire Chiefs:
   Ressie L. Attaway, 10022 Menlo Avenue, Silver Spring, Md., 20910.
   Loyde N. Balcom, 6708 41st Avenue, Hyattsville, Md., 20782.
   Dexter A. Beacham, 1510 White Place SE., 20020.
   Frank A. Berry, 1601 North Lexington, Arlington, Va., 22205.
   Raymond L. Boatman, 6005 85th Avenue, Carrollton, Md., 20784.
   Sydney G. Carter, 6637 Washington Drive, Falls Church, Va., 20041.
   Harry M. Carver, 4934 North 35th Street, Arlington, Va., 22207.
   John K. Cronin, 607 Ray Drive, Silver Spring, Md., 20910.
   George E. Deaner, 4729 North 20th Street, Arlington, Va., 22207.
   Bernard A. Essex, 4215 Woodbery Street, University Park, Md., 20782.
   Meade C. Fairall, 4212 Glenridge Street, Kensington, Md., 20795.
   Doyle E. Harpster, 3620 Nash Place S.E., 20019.
   Hugh C. Hoy, 207 Southwick Street, Fairfax, Va., 22030.
   John F. Lieb, 3822 Carpenter Street SE., 20020.
   Willard H. Maier, 4501 Brooks Drive, Suitland, Md., 20023.
   Joseph H. Mattare, 490 M Street SW., 20024.
   Edward O. Moeller, 2348 High Street SE., 20020.
   Sidney C. Morey, 2027 Glen Ross Road, Silver Spring, Md., 20910.
   John R. Mowatt, 5318 Taylor Street, Bladensburg, Md., 20710.
   Adloph M. Peel, 319 Elm Avenue, Takoma Park, Md., 20012.
   Norris P. Peterson, 13917 Vista Drive, Rockville, Md., 20853.
   Charles G. Raymond, Jr., 3607 Highwood Drive SE., 20020.
   Stewart H. Ritnour, 3181 Westover Drive SE., 20020.
   Elmer F. Stein, 9142 Piney Branch Road, Silver Spring, Md., 20903.
   Carl B. Sugg, 10226 Green Forest Drive, Silver Spring, Md., 20903.
   Wayne L. Summerville, 1513 North Utah Street, Arlington, Va., 22207.
   Hugh W. Swanner, 9333 East Parkhill Drive, Bethesda, Md., 20014.
   George E. Tacey, Box 61, Great Falls, Va., 22066.
   James C. Varah, 5409 Fisher Road SE., Temple Hills, Md., 20031.
Chief Instructor.—William R. Sweeney, Route 1, Box 190–B, Vienna, Va., 22180.
Fire Marshal.—Hugh A. Groves, 5113 Westridge Road, Westgate, Md., 20016.
First Deputy Fire Marshal:
   Warren C. Kelly, 1416 W Street SE., 20020.
   Anthony B. Mileo, 7316 Oakcrest Drive, Lanham, Md., 20021.
Property Officer.—Morris H. Clarke, 1608 23d Street SE., 20020.
Procurement Officer.—Hugh A. Gallagher, 7404 Gateway Boulevard, District Heights, Md., 20028.
Superintendent of Machinery.—Henry B. McDonald, 805 Sligo Creek Parkway, Takoma Park, Mk., 20012.
Assistant Superintendent of Machinery.—Vance T. Bartley, 5601 Kalmia Street, Springfield, Va., 22150.

District of Columbia 691

BOARD OF POLICE AND FIRE SURGEONS

Dr. Benjamin F. Dean, Jr., chairman, 3730 Manor Road, Chevy Chase, Md., 20015.
Dr. Joseph F. Dyer, 2505 13th Street, 20009.
Dr. Robert F. Dyer, 3813 Garrison Street, 20016.
Dr. Victor H. Esch, 3409 Wisconsin Avenue, 20016.
Dr. Jerome B. Harrell, 5213 Falmouth Road, Westmoreland, Md., 20016.
Dr. Hugh O. House, 4500 Edmunds Street, 20007.
Dr. Maurice Mensh, 4701 32d Street, 20008.
Dr. Wilder P. Montgomery, 1728 Shepherd Street, 20011.
Dr. Hyman D. Shapiro, 4000 Massachusetts Avenue, 20016.
Dr. William H. Yeager, 4206 Oakridge Lane, Chevy Chase, Md., 20015.

DEPARTMENT OF HIGHWAYS AND TRAFFIC

Director.—Thomas F. Airis, 10119 Gary Road, Potomac, Md., 20854.
Deputy Director.—Richard D. Wallace, 205 Guilford Court, McLean, Va., 22101.
Chief, Office of Business Administration.—William Lissek, 504 Gatewood Drive, Alexandria, Va., 22307.
Chief, Office of Planning and Programming.—Albert A. Grant, 2208 Quinton Road, Silver Spring, Md., 20910.
Deputy Director, Bureau of Design, Engineering and Research.—G. I. Sawyer, 4020 17th Street, 20011.
Deputy Director, Bureau of Traffic Engineering and Operations.—[Vacant.]
Deputy Director, Bureau of Construction and Maintenance.—Bernard J. O'Donnell, 3613 Farragut Street, Hyattsville, Md., 20782.
Special Assistant to the Director.—T. V. Bohner, 511 Adelman Circle SW., Vienna, Va., 22180.
Special Assistant to the Director (Administration).—Lynn J. Heath, 1111 Army-Navy Drive, Arlington, Va., 22202.

DEPARTMENT OF INSURANCE

1145 Nineteenth Street, 20036   Phone, NAtional 8-6000 (Code 137, extension 514)

Superintendent.—Albert F. Jordan, 32 Morningside Drive, Alexandria, Va., 22308.
Deputy Superintendents.—George F. Hughes, 9119 Manchester Road, Silver Spring, Md., 30901; Edward P. Lombard, 4912 Flint Drive, 20016.
Actuaries.—Life, Maximilian Wallach, 8305 Melody Court, Bethesda, Md., 20034; Casualty, James R. Montgomery III, Route 1, Box 176, Great Falls, Va., 222066.
Chief Examiner.—Kenneth L. Schrader, 5914 24th Avenue, Hillcrest Heights, 20031.

DEPARTMENT OF LICENSES AND INSPECTIONS
OFFICE OF ADMINISTRATION

Director of Licenses and Inspections.—Joseph J. Ilgenfritz, 401 West Montgomery Avenue, Rockville, Md., 20850.
Deputy Director of Licenses and Inspections.—R. Donald Kinney, 3812 Beecher Street, 20007.
Research Engineer.—Bertram M. Vogel, 8511 Ewing Drive, Bethesda, Md., 20034.
Research Engineer.—John M. Lake 4604 Hartwick Road, College Park, Md., 20740.
Superintendent, Inspection Division.—William N. Dripps, 3903 Ryegate Lane, Alexandria, Va., 22308.
Deputy Superintendent, Inspection Division.—George J. Long, 146 Wesmond Drive, Alexandria, Va., 22305.

Chief, Engineering Branch.—Paul O. Smeltzer, 7206 Elmhurst Street, District Heights, Md., 20028.
Chief, Weights, Measures and Markets Branch.—J. Thomas Kennedy, 4519 19th Road North, Arlington, Va., 22207.
Superintendent, License and Permit Division.—C. T. Nottingham, 12916 Deane Road, Silver Spring, Md., 20906.
Assistant Superintendent, License and Permit Division.—Julian P. Green, Jr., 2120 14th Street SE., 20020.
Chief, License Branch.—Mrs. Agnes E. McKee, 4333 Montgomery Avenue, Bethesda, Md., 20014.
Chief, Permit Branch.—John R. Beemer, 3803 Kayson Street, Silver Spring, Md., 20906.
Chief, Enforcement Branch.—Frederick L. Vitiello, 6916 Barton Road, Radiant Valley, Hyattsville, Md., 20784.
Superintendent, Housing Division.—Frederick W. Mallon, 7211 Atlee Place North, Springfield, Va., 22151.
Deputy Superintendent, Housing Division.—S. Tudor Strang, 5708 Inzer Street, Springfield, Va., 22151.
Chief, Office of Administration.—Lillia B. Robbins, 811 East Capitol Street, 20003.
Assistant Chief, Office of Administration.—Conrad N. Cardano, 2020 Evansdale Drive, Adelphi, Md., 20783.
Administrator, Zoning Division.—H. Warren Stewart, 1100 Dale Drive, Silver Spring, Md., 20910.
Assistant to the Zoning Administrator.—Thomas H. Dudley, 4731 Kirby Road, McLean, Va., 22101.
Chief, Engineering Review Branch.—James J. Fahey, 2416 Evans Drive, Silver Spring, Md., 20902.
Chief, Zoning and Occupancy Inspection Branch.—Leland D. Walker, 5271 North Old Dominion Drive, Arlington, Va., 22207.
Executive Secretary, Board for the Condemnation of Insanitary Buildings.—Richard L. Mattingly, 4413 17th Street North, Arlington, Va., 22207.

METROPOLITAN POLICE DEPARTMENT

Phone, NAtional 8-4000 (Code 137)

Chief of Police.—John B. Layton, 1717 Elton Road, Silver Spring, Md., 20903.
Deputy Chief of Police, Executive Officer.—Howard V. Covell, 3342 Erie Street SE., 20020.

INTERNAL INVESTIGATIONS UNIT

Deputy Chief.—Loraine T. Johnson, 308 Aspen Street, 20012.
Inspector.—John J. Boyd, 4211 Chain Bridge Road, McLean, Va., 22101.

UNIFORMS AND EQUIPMENT SECTION

Deputy Chief.—Henry H. Heflin, 833 Cox Avenue, Chillum, Md., 20783.

CHIEF CLERK'S SECTION

Deputy Chief.—Ashley A. Aderholdt, 7402 Halleck Street, District Heights, Md., 20028.
Inspector.—Jerry V. Wilson, 4518 Garrison Street, 20016.

COMMUNICATIONS AND RECORDS BUREAU

Inspector.—James J. McAuliffe, 323 Branch Drive, Silver Spring, Md., 20901.

POLICE COMMUNITY RELATIONS UNIT

Inspector.—George E. Causey, 5528 Helmont Drive SE., 20021.

MORALS DIVISION

Inspector.—Scott E. Moyer, 2800 Jennings Road, Kensington, Md., 20795.

DETECTIVE DIVISION

Deputy Chief, Chief of Detectives.—Lawrence A. Hartnett, 4436 Windom Place, 20016.
Inspector, Assistant Chief of Detectives.—David A. Higgins, 2615 Afton Street, Hillcrest Heights, Md., 20031.
Inspectors:
Nunzio Bonaccorsy, 3615 Carpenter Street SE., 20020.
Charles Burns, 208 Midvale Street, Falls Church, Va., 22046.
John L. Sullivan, 2242 Observatory Place, 20007.
John G. Williams, 6518 Eighth Place, Ray Park, West Hyattsville, Md., 20783.

PATROL DIVISION

Deputy Chiefs:
Albert L. Embrey, 4000 Massachusetts Avenue, 20016.
Thomas Rasmusen, 1514 Madison Street, Chillum Heights, Md., 20783.
George R. Wallrodt, 5101 Sargent Road NE., 20017.
Inspectors:
Otto P. Fuss, 3822 Beecher Street, 20007.
John S. Hughes, 5111 24th Street North, Arlington, Va., 22207.
Howard F. Mowry, 4431 Wheeler Road SE., 20021.
Karol L. Kratochvil, 1100 Haverford Road, Tokoma Park, Md., 20012.
James E. Stargel, 10625 Greenacres Drive, Silver Spring, Md., 20903.
John W. Trotter, 3142 M Place SE., 20019.

TRAFFIC DIVISION

Deputy Chief in Charge of Traffic.—Charles L. Wright, 3932 Madison Street, Hyattsville, Md., 20781.
Inspector.—Joseph V. Osterman, 4004 52d Street, Bladensburg, Md., 20710.

YOUTH AID DIVISION

Deputy Chief.—John E. Winters, 5404 Spring Road, Bladensburg, Md., 20710.
Inspector.—John F. Ryan, 2412 Davis Avenue, Alexandria, Va., 22302.

DEPARTMENT OF OCCUPATIONS AND PROFESSIONS

1145 Nineteenth Street, 20006. Phone, Code 137, extension 543

OFFICE OF THE DIRECTOR

Director.—Lawrence E. Duvall, 4627 Warren Street, 20016.
Deputy Director.—Samuel J. Fusco, Route 1, Box 281, Accokeek, Md., 20607.
Executive Assistant to the Director.—Paul Foley, 3 Derbyshire Court, Bethesda, Md., 20034.
Secretary.—Jean F. Frederickson, 1 Washington Circle, 20037.
Board of Accountancy.—Herman O. Corder, president, 3021 North Florida Street, Arlington, Va., 22207; Charles Kershenbaum, secretary, 5925 16th Street, 20011; William L. Porter, 1820 Irving Street, 20018.
Board of Examiners and Registrars of Architects.—Paul August Goettelmann, president, 201 Vierling Drive, Colesville, Md., 20904; Leon Brown, secretary, 4158 Linnean Avenue, 20008; John W. McLeod, 2 Admirals Way, Potomac, Rockville, Md., 20850; Frank J. Duane, 710 Bennington Drive, Silver Spring, Md., 20910; Louis Edwin Fry, 19 40th Street, 20019.
Board of Barber Examiners.—Benedict L. Lombardi, president, 3112 Massachusetts Avenue, 20019; Frank P. Suraci, secretary, 7605 Little River Turnpike, Annandale, Va., 22003; John A. Wells, 1358 Jackson Street, 20017.
Boxing Commission.—Norvel L. R. Lee, president, 5808 Eighth Street, 20011; Inspector Nunzio Bonaccorsy, 3615 Carpenter Street, 20020; Ben Alperstein, 3636 16th Street, 20010.
Board of Cosmetology.—Marcel Cadeaux, president, 1705 Tamarack Street, 20012; Dorothy S. Atkinson, 1366 Meridian Place, 20010; Bettye Grinder, 2820 Connecticut Avenue, 20008; Elizabeth Cardozo Barker, 1350 Jackson Street, 20017; Odelle M. Roper, 39 54th Street, 20019.

Board of Dental Examiners.—Dr. Howard R. Lady, president, 2415 Fort Scott Drive, Arlington, Va., 22202; Dr. Clement C. Alpert, secretary, 4530 Linnean Avenue, 20008; Dr. John A. O'Keefe, 1660 Foxhall Road, 20007; Dr. William K. Collins, 117 49th Street, 20019; Dr. Samuel A. Leishear, 2500 Minnesota Avenue, 20020.

Electrical Board.—Saylor L. Garbrick, chairman, 3714 Appleton Street, 20016; James J. Kirchner, vice chairman, 5409 North 37th Street, Arlington, Va., 22207; Oliver S. Kern, secretary, 6601 Sixth Street, 20012; Richard M. Spicer, 6606 Newport Road, Hyattsville, Md., 20784; Malcolm E. Cox, 11500 Nairn Road, Wheaton, Md., 20902; Milton L. Klein, 2724 26th Street, 20015; Frederick Kern, 2014 Powhatan Road, Brooksdale Manor, Hyattsville, Md., 20782; William E. Ruffin, Jr., 5357 Astor Place, 20019; Irving T. Jones, 6400 Lynhaven Drive, 20022; Elgin Miller Noack, 4017 Tennyson Road, University Park, Md., 20015.

Commission on Licensure to Practice the Healing Art.—President, Board of Commissioners, District of Columbia; United States Commissioner of Education; Corporation Counsel for the District of Columbia; Director of Public Health District of Columbia.

Nurses' Examining Board.—Shirley Wilson, R.N., president, 4302 North Fourth Street, Arlington, Va., 22203; Anna Louise Bailey Coles, R.N., vice president 2705 13th Street, 20018; Gladys Jorgenson, R.N., 2306 Colston Drive, Apt. 102, Silver Spring, Md., 20015; Ida C. Robinson, R.N., 325 Anacostia Avenue, 20019; Charlotte C. Young, R.N., 4513 Amherst Road, College Park, Md., 20740.

Board of Optometry.—Dr. John K. Shelton, president, 1610 Bent Branch Road, Falls Church, Va., 22041; Dr. Shew Kuhn Lee, vice president, 6301 Ninth Street, 20011; Dr. Evart F. Warren, secretary, 4101 North Richmond Street, Arlington, Va., 22207; Dr. Zachary N. Ephraim, 8600 Bradmoor Drive, Bethesda, Md., 20034; Robert H. Teunis, 817 South Frederick Avenue, Gaithersburg, Md., 20760.

Board of Pharmacy.—Roderick H. Tarrer, Jr., president, 4409 Colorado Avenue, 20011; Henry R. Peters, secretary, 4214 Argyle Terrace, 20011; Elmer Charles Hillman, Jr., 5101 South 10th Street, Arlington, Va., Apt. 4, 22204; Frederick C. Schultz, 3235 North Abingdon Street, Arlington, Va., 22207; Harold M. Elwyn, 5809 Tanglewood Drive, Bethesda, Md., 20034.

Physical Therapists Examining Board.—Clara M. Arrington, chairman, 6817 Prince Georges Avenue, Takoma Park, Md., 20012; Florence G. Presley, 617 Gist Avenue, Silver Spring, Md., 20910; Margaret L. Sexton, 3014 South Abingdon Street, Arlington, Va., 22206.

Plumbing Board.—Thomas E. Clark, chairman, 4434 Connecticut Avenue, 20008; Henry J. Samaha, secretary, 5955 North Eighth Road, Arlington, Va., 22205; James L. DeChard, 1664 Michigan Avenue, 20017.

Board of Podiatry Examiners.—Dr. Muriel E. Osborne, president, 153 Rhode Island Avenue, 20001; Dr. Charles W. Shuffle, secretary, 6105 28th Street North, Arlington, Va., 22207; Dr. William Robert Walp, 4103 Whispering Lane, Annandale, Va., 22003.

Practical Nurses' Examining Board.—Lucille Kinlein, R.N., president, 7702 Colesville Road, Adelphi, Md., 20783; Bertha H. Bolden, R.N., vice president, 4814 Blagden Avenue, 20011; Idie Rudney, L.P.N., 2223 H Street, 20037; Katherine T. Seward, L.P.N., 3359 Baker Street, 20019; Ida M. Trump, L.P.N., 711 Main Street, Flint Hill, Va., 22627; Dorothea Orem, R.N., 2700 Connecticut Avenue, 20008; Grace C. Robinson, R.N., 1229 Jackson Street, 20017.

Board of Registration for Professional Engineers.—Donald E. Marlowe, chairman, 9332 Wilmer Street, Silver Spring, Md., 20901; Daniel C. Vaughan, vice chairman, 4610 47th Street, 20016; James H. Carr, Jr., secretary, 3121 Beech Street, 20015; Lewis K, Downing, 1323 Girard Street, 20009; J. Howard Flint, Round Hill, Va., 22141.

Real Estate Commission.—Kenneth Back, chairman, 4620 Brandywine Street, 20016; Irving B. Yochelson, 2005 Branch Avenue, 20020; Eugene Davidson, 1333 R Street, 20009; Ernest T. Eiland, 2426 Otis Street, 20018; William Calomiris, 5150 Rockwood Parkway, 20016.

Refrigeration and Air Conditioning Board.—Kent D. Boucher, chairman, 2044 Trumbull Terrace, 20011; Alfred M. Hansch, secretary, Beulah Road, Vienna, Va., 22180; William A. Mastin, 240 Tenth Street, 20003; Dwight E. Shytle,

5604 Pioneer Lane, Sumner, Md., 20016; Harold W. Sadler, 520 North Emerson Street, Arlington, Va., 22207; V. Lee Saunders, Jr., 5300 West Bard Avenue, 20016.

Steam and Other Operating Engineers' Board.—Richard T. Clark, Jr., chairman, 724 Barnum Lane, Alexandria, Va., 22312; Wilford J. Robinson, 4737 North 34th Street, Arlington, Va., 22207; Milton L. Becker, 2047 South Kings Highway, Alexandria, Va., 22306; Charles H. Evans, 3203 Cheverly Avenue, Cheverly, Md., 20785; John E. Sawyer, 3409 Fairhill Drive, 20023; Robert A. Radcliffe, 126 Lawrence Drive, Falls Church, Va., 22042.

Undertakers' Committee.—Harry Donald DeVol, chairman, 2224 Wisconsin Avenue, 20007; Thomas M. Hysong, 6510 16th Street, 20012; Robert G. McGuire, Jr., 1820 Ninth Street, 20001; Bernard F. vonAhn, 603 West Joppa Road, Towson, Md., 21204; Macy G. Hall, Sr., 3918 18th Street, 20018.

Board of Examiners of Veterinary Medicine.—Dr. J. Raymond Currey, president, 6620 Bradley Boulevard, Bethesda, Md., 20014; Dr. Jean S. Goudy, secretary, 2922 Garfield Street, 20008; Dr. Bernard J. Berliner, 5401 Georgia Avenue, 20011; Dr. William C. Ready, 5100 Dorset Avenue, Chevy Chase, Md., 20015; Dr. Lanxter D. Webber, 1438 G Street, 20003.

MINIMUM WAGE AND INDUSTRIAL SAFETY BOARD

499 Pennsylvania Avenue, 20001. Phone, 629-4566 (Code 137, extension 566)

Charles W. Putnam, chairman and public member, 2228 Cathedral Avenue, 20008.

Edward J. Austin, employer member, 326 N Street SW., 20024.

Richard D. Bailey, employee member, 4114 Davis Place, 20007.

Miss Carrie L. Allgood, executive secretary and director of wage and hour division, 4807 Dover Road, 20016.

Charles T. Greene, director of industrial safety division, 3229 Chestnut Street NE., 20018.

BOARD OF PAROLE

Chairman.—Joseph H. DeWitt, 6005 32d Street, 20015.
Member.—Maj. Philip Ershler, 4000 Cathedral Avenue, 20016.
Member.—George G. Jefferson, 1605 Kearney Street, 20018.
Member.—Rev. H. Albion Ferrell, 2333 First Street, 20001.
Member and Parole Executive.—Hugh F. Rivers, 524 Ashford Road, Silver Spring, Md.

DEPARTMENT OF PUBLIC HEALTH

Director of Public Health.—Murray Grant, M.D., D.P.H., 7105 Lock Lomond Drive, Bethesda, Md., 20034.
Deputy Director of Public Health.—Frederick C. Heath, M.D., M.P.H., 111 Lee Avenue, Takoma Park, Md., 20012.
Associate Director for Administration.—Charles L. Harper, 4095 Dodson Drive, Annandale, Va., 22003.
Associate Director for Environmental Health.—William H. Cary, 9607 Glencrest Lane, Kensington, Md., 20795.
Associate Director for Preventive Services.—Charles R. Hyman, M.D., M.P.H., 2 Woodridge Circle, Alexandria, Va., 22308.
Associate Director for Mental Health and Retardation.—John D. Schultz, M.D., 1206 Woodside Parkway, Silver Spring, Md., 20910.
Associate Director for Medical Care and Hospitals.—Herbert McC. Wortman, M.D., Southern Towers, The Stratford, Apt. 1130, 4901 Seminary Road, Alexandria, Va., 22311.
D.C. General Hospital, Medical Director.—John P. Nasou, M.D., 725 Dartmouth Avenue, Silver Spring, Md., 20910.
Glenn Dale Hospital, Medical Director.—Moe Weiss, M.D., Glenn Dale Hospital, Glenn Dale, Md., 20769.

PUBLIC LIBRARY

Eighth and K Streets, 20001.   Phone, NAtional 8-6000 (Code 137, extension 867)

BOARD OF TRUSTEES

President.—Dr. Albert W. Atwood, Sheraton Park Hotel, 20008.
Vice President.—Nelson T. Hartson, 2029 Connecticut Avenue, 20008.
  Clark G. Diamond, 4619 Charleston Terrace, 20007.
  John W. Heckinger, 2838 Chain Bridge Road, 20016.
  B. M. McKelway, 4920 Palisade Lane, 20016.
  Mrs. James M. Newmyer, 2829 Tilden Street, 20008.
  J. C. Turner, 6961 32d Street, 20015.
  Mrs. Wallace M. Yater, 4907 Indian Lane, 20016.

LIBRARY OFFICIALS

Director.—Harry N. Peterson, 2000 Connecticut Avenue, 20008.
Associate Director.—Catherine M. Houck, 2732 Rittenhouse Street, 20015.
Assistant Director in Charge of Personnel.—John T. Cheney, 1728 Q Street, 20009.
Coordinator, Adult Service.—M. Clare Ruppert, 2924 Cortland Place, 20008.
Coordinator, Children's Service.—Maxine LaBounty, 4520 Fessenden Street, 20016.
Head, Budget and Fiscal Department.—Miss Frances W. Shibley, 1300 35th Street, Apt. 3, 20007.
Head, Technical Processes.—Francis X. Doherty, 816 E Street, 20002.
Head, Editorial, Exhibits, and Public Information Department.—Dorothy D. Mason, 4750 Chevy Chase Drive, Apt. 403, Chevy Chase, Md., 20015.
Head, Department of Planning and Operations.—Alvan C. Chaney, 9110 Glenridge Road, Silver Spring, Md., 20910.
Central Librarian.—Beatrice E. Tear, 720 Kennebec Avenue, Takoma Park, Md., 20012.
Coordinator, Central Library Reference Service.—Helen R. Thompson, 4501 Connecticut Avenue, 20008.
Consultant in Adult Education.—Emily W. Reed, 2319 40th Place, 20007.

PUBLIC SERVICE COMMISSION

1625 I Street, Room 204, 20006.   Phone, 629-2301 (Code 137, extension 2301)

Commissioners:
  James A. Washington, Jr., chairman, 4302 13th Street NE., 20017.
    Private Secretary.—Catherine C. Purnell, 1799 Verbena Street, 20012.
  Edgar H. Bernstein, vice chairman, 2120 Yorktown Road, 20012.
    Private Secretary.—Josephine C. Beckham, 5913 Southern Avenue SE., 20019.
  Brig. Gen. C. M. Duke, 5712 26th Street, 20015.
Executive Secretary.—Joseph S. Greco, 3040 Oliver Street, 20015.
General Counsel.—Chester H. Gray, 4000 Massachusetts Avenue, 20016.
Assistant General Counsel.—George F. Donnella, 3736 Camden Street SE., 20020.
Chief Accountant.—E. Edward McLean, 3700 Cedar Drive, Baltimore, Md., 21207.
Chief Engineer.—Norman B. Belt, 4508 Burlington Road, Hyattsville, Md., 20781.
Mechanical Engineer, Gas and Meters.—Elwin A. Potter, 4425 Yuma Street, 20016.
Assistant Executive Secretary.—Jessie W. Barron, 5606 Hamilton Manor Drive, West Hyattsville, Md., 20782.
Securities Administrator.—Stanley H. Ragle, 637 Dahlia Street, 20012.

DEPARTMENT OF PUBLIC WELFARE

Director.—Donald D. Brewer, 2901 Park Drive SE., 20020.
Controller and Deputy Director for Administration.—Alvin R. Rosin, 5329 Pooks Hill Road, Bethesda, Md., 20014.
Deputy Director for Institutional Services.—Winifred G. Thompson, 6006 Inwood Street, Cheverly, Md., 20785.
Deputy Director for Family and Children Services.—Albert P. Russo, D.C. Village, Blue Plains, D.C., 20024.

Finance and Business Manager.—Shepard Cohen, 10604 Cavalier Drive, Silver Spring, Md., 20901.
Personnel Officer.—Willard Sidlick, 8600 16th Street, Silver Spring, Md., 20910.
Chief, Public Assistance Division.—Donald Gray, 6902 Alpine Drive, Annandale, Va., 22003.
Chief, Child Welfare Division.—Alice R. Smith, 3420 38th Street, 20016.
Administrator, District of Columbia Welfare Institutions.—Gerard M. Shea, 6614 31st Street, 20015.
Administrator, D.C. Village.—David B. Schwartz, 525 Thayer Avenue, Apt. 210, Silver Spring, Md., 20910.
Administrator, Receiving Home for Children.—William J. Stone, 4236 Powder Mill Road, Beltsville, Md., 20783.
Administrator, Junior Village.—Joseph S. Kosisky, 8 Crest Park Court, Silver Spring, Md., 20903.
Superintendent, Municipal Lodging House.—Henry A. Koch, 458 C Street, 20001.
Administrator, Children's Center.—Billie G. Meese, D.C. Children's Center, Laurel, Md., 20810.
Administrator, District Training School.—Guy W. Puntch, D.C. Children's Center, Laurel, Md., 20810.
Administrator, Maple Glen School.—Carl A. Oliver, D.C. Children's Center, Laurel, Md., 20810.
Administrator, Cedar Knoll School.—William Barr, 617 Jefferson Street, 20011.
Investigations and Collections Officer.—William R. Galvin, 5308 Pender Court, Alexandria, Va., 20304.
Administrator, Public Welfare Training Center.—Elsie M. Warren, 1221 Jefferson Street, 20011.

RECREATION BOARD AND DEPARTMENT

3149 Sixteenth Street, 20010.   Phone, 629-1214 (Code 137, extension 1214)

William H. Waters, Jr., chairman, 4507 MacArthur Boulevard, 20007.
Gerson Nordlinger, Jr., vice chairman, 2737 Devonshire Place, 20008.
Jane M. Lucas, secretary, 1605 Buchanan Street, 20011.
William Beasley Harris, member, 2804 13th Street NE., 20017.
F. E. Ropshaw, representative for the Commissioners, 7816 Libeau Lane, Annandale, Va., 22003.
Carl D. Coleman, alternate for the Commissioners, 2 Elwyn Court, Silver Spring, Md., 20910.
West A. Hamilton, representative for the Board of Education, 4362 Argyle Terrace, 20011.
Mrs. Louise S. Steele, alternate for the Board of Education, 3100 Newark Street, 20008.
T. Sutton Jett, representative, National Park Service, 121 Hilltop Road, Silver Spring, Md., 20910.
Robert C. Horne, alternate for the National Park Service, 9432 Rosehill Drive, Bethesda, Md., 20014.
Margaret S. Chase, clerk to the board, 1905 Ingraham Street, Avondale Terrace, Hyattsville, Md., 20782.
Milo F. Christiansen, superintendent, 5100 Dorset Avenue, Chevy Chase, Md., 20015.
Joseph H. Cole, assistant superintendent, 2827 Myrtle Avenue NE., 20018.
Richard B. Leech, administrative officer, 5432 Connecticut Avenue, 20015.
Arthur Kriemelmeyer, administrative recreation assistant, 7500 Holiday Terrace, Bethesda, Md., 20034.
Katherine Caul, director, Neighborhood Centers, 135 Churchill Road, McLean, Va., 22101.
C. Clinton Price, director, City-Wide Division, 1789 Lanier Place, 20009.
Lawrence C. Lemmon, director, Planning and Development, 2514 Fourth Street South, Arlington, Va., 22206.
Edward H. Thacker, recreation analyst, 3588 South Stafford Street, Arlington, Va., 22206.
Benjamin A. Orringer, deputy administrative officer, 5502 Avon Court, Springfield, Va.

DEPARTMENT OF SANITARY ENGINEERING

Director of Sanitary Engineering.—Roy L. Orndorff, 4624 23d Road North, Arlington, Va., 22207.
Deputy Director of Sanitary Engineering.—[Vacant.]
Superintendent, Office of Planning, Design and Engineering.—Emil A. Press, 1423 34th Street, 20007.
Deputy Superintendent, Office of Planning, Design and Engineering.—Jean B. Levesque, 6705 Eldridge Street, Hyattsville, Md., 20784.
Superintendent, Office of Suburban Operations.—Norman E. Jackson, 3011 Porter Street, 20008.
Superintendent, Sanitation and Equipment Divisions.—William F. Roeder, 6914 Greentree Drive, Falls Church, Va., 22041.
Deputy Superintendent, Sanitation and Equipment Divisions.—Robert R. Perry, 709 East Broad Street, Falls Church, Va., 22046.
Superintendent, Construction and Repair Division.—James C. Robertson, 4003 North Glebe Road, Arlington, Va., 22207.
Deputy Superintendent, Construction and Repair Division.—Ray M. Dowe, Old Chapel Road, Bowie, Md., 20715.
Superintendent, Sewer Operations Division.—Allen B. Fay, 6116 Overlea Road, 20016.
Deputy Superintendent, Sewer Operations Division.—Paul V. Freese, 5225 Janice Lane SE., 20031.
Superintendent, Water Operations Division.—James W. Head, Jr., 1931 38th Street, 20007.
Deputy Superintendent, Water Operations Division.—Thomas M. Latimer, 504 Wayne Avenue, Silver Spring, Md., 20910.
Administrative Officer.—Raymond B. Ward, 5711 Jamestown Road, Hyattsville, Md., 20782.
Deputy Administrative Officer.—Daniel H. Hudson, 3601 Kayson Street, Silver Spring, Md., 20296.
Water Register.—William H. Brown, 6218 Dunrobbin Drive, 20016.

OFFICE OF THE SURVEYOR

Surveyor.—Roy C. Hoyle, 8611 Springvale Road, Silver Spring, Md., 20910.
Assistant Surveyor.—Francis B. Werle, 1635 Webster Street NE., 20017.

DISTRICT OF COLUMBIA TAX COURT

Fifth and E Streets, 20001.   Phone, 629-2284 (Code 137, extension 2284)

Judge.—Jo. V. Morgan, 5420 Moorland Lane, Bethesda, Md., 20014.
  Clerk.—Phyllis R. Liberti, 3920 McKinley Street, 20015.
  Deputy Clerk.—Mae W. Thomas, 3141 North Quincy Street, Arlington, Va., 22207.

DISTRICT UNEMPLOYMENT COMPENSATION BOARD

451 Pennsylvania Avenue, 20001.   Phone, 629-1243 (Code 137, extension 1243)

Commissioners of the District of Columbia, ex-officio members.
Harry L. Grubbs, Jr., 61 Pierce Street NE., 20002.
J. C. Turner, 1311 L. Street, 20005.
Edgar L. Lickey, director, 4900 Sherrier Place, 20016.
Frank G. Preston, assistant director, 535 Mellon Street SE., 20032.

DEPARTMENT OF MOTOR VEHICLES

Director of Motor Vehicles.—George A. England, 2416 Darrow Street, Silver Spring, Md., 20902.
Deputy Director.—Herman S. Cole, 1219 Clement Place, Silver Spring, Md., 20910.
Executive Officer.—William J. Quinn, 3413 Tulane Drive, West Hyattsville, Md., 20783.

Chief, Office of Traffic Safety Education.—Anthony L. Ellison, 7606 Nancemond Street, Springfield, Va., 22150.
Chief, Permit Control Division.—Mary A. Silver, 858 North Abingdon Street, Arlington, Va., 22203.
Chief, Vehicle Control Division.—Charles W. Reed, 1620 Fuller Street, 20009.
Chief, Safety Responsibility Division.—Joseph P. Murphy, 2410 26th Street South, Arlington, Va., 22206.

MOTOR VEHICLE PARKING AGENCY

Chairman.—Edward C. Baltz, 8007 Glendale Road, Chevy Chase, Md., 20015.
Vice Chairman.—Douglas R. Smith, Ridgelea, Warrenton, Va., 22186.
Thomas F. Airis, 10119 Gary Road, Potomac, Md., 20854.
W. Bruce Alexander, 1559 Mt. Eagle Place, Alexandria, Va., 22302.
Lewis T. Breuninger, 2701 Foxall Road, 20007.
David R. Byrd, 1830 Varnum Street, 20011.
Frank Coleman, 1232 Girard Street NE., 20017.
Edward H. Holmes, 4814 De Russey Parkway, Chevy Chase, Md., 20015.
T. Sutton Jett, 121 Hilltop Road, Silver Spring, Md., 20910.
Arthur T. Lyon, 4111 Bradley Lane, Chevy Chase, Md., 20015.
John W. Lyon, 11012 Picasso Lane, Potomac, Md., 20854.
J. A. Weinberg, Jr., 3126 Arizona Avenue, 20016.
Executive Director.—William D. Heath, 1111 Army-Navy Drive, Arlington, Va., 22202.

DEPARTMENT OF VETERANS' AFFAIRS

Twelfth Street and Pennsylvania Avenue (Old Post Office Building), 20004.
Phone, 629-1211 (Code 137, extension 1211)

Director.—Col. Waldron E. Leonard, 114 East Fairview Avenue, Groveton Station, Alexandria, Va., 22306.
Assistant Director.—A. Leo Anderson, 13500 Justice Road, Rockville, Md., 20853.

BOARD OF ZONING ADJUSTMENT

Chairman.—Samuel Scrivener, Jr., 2543 Waterside Drive, 20037.
Arthur P. Davis, 1726 M Street, 20036
William F. McIntosh, 1701 Pennsylvania Avenue, 20576.
William S. Harps, 1614 Allison Street, 20011.
Robert O. Clouser, 2357 24th Street SE., 20020.

ZONING COMMISSION

Members
Commissioners of the District of Columbia.
Architect of the Capitol.
Director of the National Park Service.
Planning Officer.—Robert O. Clouser.
Executive Officer.—William E. Chase.

RECORDER OF DEEDS

Sixth and D Streets, 20001.   Phone, DIstrict 7-0671

Recorder of Deeds.—Peter S. Ridley, 3816 17th Street NE., 20018.
Private Secretary.—Thelma L. Howard, 1712 16th Street, 20009.
First Deputy Recorder of Deeds.—Eleanore Dague Williams, 7200 Euclid Street, Hyattsville, Md., 20785.
Second Deputy Recorder of Deeds.—Columbus W. Kelley, 3613 28th Street NE., 20018.

Superintendent of Corporations—Alfred Goldstein, 4201 Cathedral Avenue, 20008.
  Assistant Superintendent of Corporations.—Nathaniel Grosman, 7519 Eighth Street, 20012.
Auditing and Budget Analyst.—John W. Fenwick, 711 Longfellow Street, 20011.
Procurement and Record Custody Officer.—John Herbert, 3401 R Street, 20007.
Personnel Management Assistant.—Willie J. Fudge, 1227 Savannah Place SE., 20032.
Accountant.—John A. Harris, 1425 Taylor Street, 20011.

DEPARTMENT OF VOCATIONAL REHABILITATION

1331 H Street NW.   Phone, 393-5268 (Code 137, extension 1267)

Director.—Norman W. Pierson, 3682 Camden Street SE., 20020.
Deputy Director.—Leonard M. Hill, 1338 Leegate Road, 20012.
Executive Assistant.—Joseph E. Gangi, 12 Tunlaw Court, Alexandria, Va., 22312.
Chief Counselor.—Edith R. Henry, 5425 Connecticut Avenue, 20015.
Chief Counselor.—Mildred M. Vernon, 654 Girard Street, 20001.
Chief Counselor.—E. Susan Hendricks, 6319 Kilmer Street, Hyattsville, Md., 20705.
Chief Counselor.—Ruth M. O'Neil, 3426 Brown Street, 20010.
Chief, Services to Mentally Ill.—Gertrude T. Bigman, 3302 Camalier Drive, Chevy Chase, Md., 20015.
Chief, Services to Mentally Retarded.—Arlene Blaha, 508 North Kenmore Street, Arlington, Va., 22201.
Chief, Services to Visually Impaired.—Stephen A. Gambaro, 3005 University Boulevard West, Kensington, Md., 20795.
Chief, Industrial Operations.—Leslie B. Cole, 5910 LeMay Road, Rockville, Md., 20851.
Chief Disability Determinations Units, Old Age and Survivors Insurance.—Murray Rottenberg, 3215 McKinley Street, 20015.

OFFICE OF URBAN RENEWAL

Room 510, District Building, Pennsylvania Avenue and 14th Street.   Phone, Code 137, extension 3331

Executive Director.—John S. Crocker, 1963 39th Street, 20007.

WASHINGTON CITY POST OFFICE

Corner Massachusetts Avenue and North Capitol Street.   Phone, STerling 3-5100 (Code 177)

Postmaster.—Carlton G. Beall, 4782 West Avenue SE., 20028.

Assistant Postmaster.—Herbert E. Waddy, 2 Adams Street, 20001.

Chief Personnel Officer.—Vincent J. Mastrovito, 4801 Kenmore Avenue, Apt. 505, Alexandria, Va., 22304.

Chief Accountant.—William E. Cooper, 4820 16th Road North, Arlington, Va., 22207.

Chief, Cost Control.—Hiram Hodges, 1509 Jefferson Street, Hyattsville, Md., 20782.

Chief, General Accounting Section.—Elmer C. Ray, 5914 Enterprise Avenue, McLean, Va., 22101.

Superintendent, Accountable Paper.—Frederick G. Belz, 3310 28th Street South, Apt. 302, Alexandria, Va., 22302.

Superintendent, Main Office Windows.—Louis H. Aikens, 4011 19th Place NE., 20018.

Chief Station Examiner.—Harold M. Cole, 3706 Jefferson Street, Hyattsville, Md., 20782.

General Superintendent of Mails.—Harvey R. McConnell, 12417 Melling Lane, Bowie, Md., 20715.

Assistant General Superintendent of Mails, Designated Services.—Lawrence J. Carrico, 1117 North Kentucky Street, Arlington, Va., 22205.

Assistant General Superintendent of Mails, Distribution.—Burder S. Athey, 23 East Oak Street, Alexandria, Va., 22301.

Superintendent, Delivery and Collection.—Robert E. Heflin, 219 Van Buren Street, Falls Church, Va., 22046.

Assistant Superintendent, Delivery and Collection.—William C. Massie, Jr., 1609 Fairwood Lane, Falls Church, Va., 22046.

Superintendent, Registry.—Richard E. Connor, 10621 Loraine Avenue, Silver Spring, Md., 20901.

Assistant Superintendent, Registry.—John W. L'Hommedieu, 9203 Second Avenue, Silver Spring, Md., 20910.

Tour Superintendents, Mails.—Roland J. Brill, 1801 Shepherd Street, 20011; Lawrence V. Bateman, Jr., 4640 Fourth Street South, Arlington, Va., 22204; Edwin E. Estes, 1701 52d Avenue SE., 20027.

Administrative Officer, Stations.—James F. Wafle, 1801 21st Road North, Arlington, Va., 22209.

Chief, Administrative Services.—Henry S. Halley, 5022 Leland Drive SE., 20021.

Superintendent, Mailing Requirements and Patron Relations.—[Vacant.]

Superintendent, Official Mail.—James E. Cloer, 3622 Horner Place SE., 20020.

Superintendent, Detached Mailing Unit.—Jack I. Resnicoff, 2214 Banning Place, Hyattsville, Md., 20783.

Superintendent, Claims and Inquiry.—Carl C. Malone, 3517 Toledo Terrace, Hyattsville, Md., 20782.

Superintendent, Special Delivery Service.—Robert G. Burkley, 2206 Banning Place, Hyattsville, Md., 20783.

Medical Officer.—Dr. Allan S. Cross, 3301 Nebraska Avenue, 20016.

CLASSIFIED STATIONS

Station or branch	Zip code	Superintendent	Location
Anacostia	20020	E. Duffel	1217 Good Hope Rd., SE.
Andrews Field Branch	20331	F. J. Healy	Andrews Air Force Base.
Apex	20004	W. H. Andrews (acting)	316 9th St.
Benjamin Franklin	20004	H. T. Barnett	Post Office Dept. Bldg.
Benning	20019	W. B. McDonald	3962 Minnesota Ave. NE.
Bethesda Branch	20014	C. A. Manoff	7400 Wisconsin Ave.
Bolling Air Force Base	20332	J. F. Sherman	Bolling Air Force Base.
Brightwood	20011	F. I. Wood	5921 Georgia Ave.
Brookland	20017	W. J. Kirby	3309 12th St. NE.
Capitol Heights Branch	20027	M. P. Carroll	6201 Central Ave. SE.
Central	20005	T. J. McCawley (acting)	819 14th St.
Chevy Chase Branch	20015	J. L. Menefee	5910 Connecticut Ave.
Cleveland Park	20008	T. J. Bayliss	3430 Connecticut Ave.
Columbia Heights	20010	L. F. Holmberg	1423 Irving St.
Congress Heights	20032	T. S. McConnell	3703 Nichols Ave. SE.
Dulles International Airport Branch.	20041	W. M. Hoffer (acting)	Dulles International Airport.
F Street	20004	A. L. Maus	Tariff Commission Bldg.
Fort Davis	20020	K. Ledbetter	3843 Pennsylvania Ave. SE.
Fort McNair	20315	J. D. Day	Fort L. J. McNair.
Friendship	20016	L. M. Thompson	4005 Wisconsin Ave.
Georgetown	20007	O. H. Reed	1215 31st St.
Kalorama	20009	A. L. Smith	2434 18th St.
Mid City	20005	C. G. Dern, Jr	1408 14th St.
National Airport	20001	J. M. Higgins	Gravelly Point.
National Naval Medical Center Branch.	20014	R. D. McElroy	Bethesda, Md.
Naval Air Facility Branch	20390	C. E. Jorgensen	Andrews Air Force Base.
Naval Research Laboratory	20390	D. E. Alt	Bellevue, D.C.
Navy Annex Branch	20370	G. E. Beard	Navy Annex Bldg.
Navy Department	20360	M. J. Hough	Navy Department Bldg.
Naval, U.S	20390	S. G. Kent	Anacostia.
Northeast	20002	E. V. Edmead	1016 H St. NE.
Northwest	20015	W. W. Basil	5632 Connecticut Ave.
Oxon Hill Branch	20021	J. T. Mulcare	5616 Oxon Hill Road SE.
Pentagon Branch	20301	S. E. Stoddard	Pentagon Bldg.
Petworth	20011	F. J. Ging, Jr	4211 9th St.
Randle	20020	W. B. Blagman	2306 Prout St. SE.
Southeast	20003	E. C. Mobray	327 7th St. SE.
Southwest	20024	R. T. Harris	1004 4th St. SW.
State Department	20520	D. O. Coon	State Dept. Bldg.
Suitland Branch	20023	J. E. Clark	4520 Suitland Rd. SE.
T Street	20009	D. E. Stewart	1409 T St.
Takoma Park Branch	20012	B. I. Wade	7117 Maple Ave.
Temple Heights	20009	A. P. Hall	1921 Florida Ave.
Treasury	20220	C. L. Gardner (acting)	Treasury Department Bldg.
Truxton Circle	20002	B. M. Grant	17 Florida Ave. NE.
Twentieth Street	20036		1216 20th St.
Walter Reed	20012	M. A. Huhn	Army Medical Center.
West End	20006	W. S. Omohundro	1751 Pennsylvania Ave.
Woodridge	20018	L. P. Thorton	2211 Rhode Island Ave. NE.

INTERNATIONAL
ORGANIZATIONS

INTERNATIONAL ORGANIZATIONS

CARIBBEAN ORGANIZATION

**Headquarters: Central Secretariat, 452 Avenida Ponce de Leon, Hato Rey, Puerto Rico, 00919
Phone, 767-0250**

TERMINATION OF AGREEMENT ESTABLISHING CARIBBEAN ORGANIZATION

The Caribbean Organization was created under the terms of an Agreement entered into by the Governments of the Republic of France, The Kingdom of the Netherlands, the United Kingdom of Great Britain and Northern Ireland and the United States of America. This Agreement was brought into force on September 6th, 1961, at which time the Caribbean Council, governing body of the Organization, held its first meeting in San Juan, Puerto Rico.

The Caribbean Organization succeeded the Caribbean Commission which was created in 1946 and continued to serve the area until 1961.

The Members of the Organization were France (for the Department of French Guiana, Guadeloupe and Martinique), the Netherlands Antilles, Surinam, British Guiana, the British Virgin Islands, The West Indies, the Commonwealth of Puerto Rico and the Virgin Islands of the United States.

In May 1962, the Federation of The West Indies was dissolved and thus ceased to be a Member of the Organization. In December 1963, the Government of British Guiana served notice of withdrawal from the Organization and this was followed by Surinam in April 1964 and the Commonwealth of Puerto Rico in November 1964. Withdrawal takes effect one year after date of receipt of notification.

Faced with this situation, the Caribbean Council, at its meeting held in Curacao from November 30 to December 4, 1964, decided to cease the operations of its Secretariat by June 30, 1965, and to request the Signatory Governments to terminate the Agreement establishing the Organization by December 31, 1965.

The technical services and the publications of the Organization will cease early in 1965. A small administrative staff will remain on duty until June 30, 1965, to wind up the affairs of the Organization.

FOOD AND AGRICULTURE ORGANIZATION OF THE UNITED NATIONS

**Headquarters: Rome, Italy; North American Regional Office: 1325 C Street SW., Washington D.C., 20437
Phone, REpublic 7-7614 (Code 111, extension 6121)**

Headquarters:
  Director General.—B. R. Sen (Via S. Alessio 19, Rome, Italy).
North American Regional Office:
  Regional Representative.—Harold A. Vogel, 4862 29th Street North, Arlington, Va., 22207.
  Assistant to Regional Representative.—Stefan F. Gavell, 3140 North Thomas Street, Arlington, Va., 22207.
  Administrative Officer.—Edwin M. Duerbeck, 6329 22d Street North, Arlington, Va., 22205.
  Agricultural Officer.—Roy C. Dawson, 4019 Beechwood Road, University Park, Md., 20782.
  Information Adviser.—Robert T. Hartmann, 5001 Baltimore Avenue, Westgate, Md. 20016.
  Nutrition Officer.—Mary A. Ross, 1201 South Courthouse Road, Arlington, Va., 22204.
  Regional Economist.—Charles W. McLean, 9724 Kensington Parkway, Kensington, Md., 20795.
  Fellowships Officer.—Robert E. Osterbur, 1111 Army-Navy Drive, Arlington, Va., 22202.

INTER-AMERICAN DEFENSE BOARD

2600 Sixteenth Street. Phone, DUpont 7-7860

Chairman.—Vice Adm. B. L. Austin, USN, 11201 Stephalee Lane, Luxmanor, Rockville, Md.
Vice Chairman.—Col. Doroteo Reyes, Army of Guatemala, 4014 Reckover Road, Silver Spring, Md.
Secretary.—Col. Louis G. Mendez, Jr., USA, 1319 Stoneybrae Drive, Falls Church, Va.
Vice Secretary.—Col. Gentil Marcondes Filho, Army of Brazil, 4500 Connecticut Avenue.
Deputy Secretary for Conferences—Documents.—Lt. Col. Michael Alba, USAF, 829 Loxford Terrace, Silver Spring, Md.
Deputy Secretary for Finance.—Lt. Col. Haywood O. Kilby, USA, 7502 Gresham Street, North Springfield, Va.
Deputy Secretary for Administration.—Lt. Comdr. Robert L. Kirkhorn, USN, 7112 Lanier Street, Annandale, Va.
Deputy Secretary for Liaison.—Lt. Col. Raoul C. Ramos, USAF, 4806 Pomponio Place, Annandale, Va.
Director of the Staff.—Brig. Gen. Wilbur W. Aring, USAF, 7547 Spring Lake Drive, Bethesda, Md., 20014.
Vice Director.—Col. José A. Ponciano S., Army of Guatemala, 2220 R Street.

CHIEF OF DELEGATIONS

Argentina.—Maj. Gen. Adolfo T. Alvarez, 3703 Taylor Street, Chevy Chase, Md.
Bolivia.—[Not represented at this time.]
Brazil.—Vicealmirante Antonio Junqueira Giovannini, 6106 Massachusetts Avenue.
Chile.—Rear Adm. José Costa F., 3009 34th Street.
Colombia.—Maj. Gen. César A. Cabrera, 3123 Rittenhouse Street.
Costa Rica.—Col. Rodolfo Herrera, 2112 S. Street.
Dominican Republic.—Col. Angel Ramos-Usera, 4505 Saul Road, Kensington, Md.
Ecuador.—Brig. Gen. Telmo O. Vargas, 7903 Woodbury Drive, Silver Spring, Md.
El Salvador.—Col. Carlos Urrutia, 1481 Monroe Street.
Guatemala.—Col. Doroteo Reyes, 4014 Reckover Road, Silver Spring, Md.
Haiti.—Col. Nerva Staco, 806 Rittenhouse Street.
Honduras.—Lt. Col. Cecilio Castro, 2112 Forest Glen Road, Silver Spring, Md.
Mexico.—[Not represented at this time.]
Nicaragua.—Brig. Gen. Julio C. Morales (Army), 4201 Massachusetts Avenue.
Panama.—Lt. Col. Francisco Aued, 6402 Wilson Lane, Bethesda, Md.
Paraguay.—Rear Adm. Guillermo Haywood, 3417 Manor Place.
Peru.—Lt. Gen. Pedro Vargas P., 2903 Ellicott Street, 20008.
United States.—Rear Adm. Hazlett P. Weatherwax, USN, 3745 Orange Court Alexandria, Va.
Uruguay.—Rear Adm. Victor M. Dodino, 2320 20th Street, 20009.
Venezuela.—Maj. Gen. Antonio Briceño Linares, 5908 16th Street.

INTER-AMERICAN DEFENSE COLLEGE, FORT McNAIR

Director.—Maj. Gen. Roland H. del Mar, USA, Quarters 4, Fort McNair.
Assistant Director.—Gen. Juan E. Aguirre, Army of Paraguay, 3836 McKinley Street.
Chief of Studies.—Brig. Gen. Manuel Iricibar, Army of Argentina, 4201 Warren Street, 20016.

INTER-AMERICAN DEVELOPMENT BANK

808 Seventeenth Street, Washington, D.C., 20577.   Phone EXecutive 3-4171 (Code 128, extension 5860)

OFFICERS

President.—Felipe Herrera (Chile), 3041 Normanstone Terrace, 20008.
Executive Vice President.—T. Graydon Upton (United States), Box 347, Old Georgetown Pike, McLean, Va., 22101.
  Financial Advisor.—Robert B. Menapace (United States), 2300 Connecticut Avenue, 20009.

Executive Vice President—Continued
   Program Advisor.—Alfred C. Wolf (United States), Rocky Run Road, McLean,
      Va., 22101.
Manager, Financial-Administrative Department.—Ignacio Copete-Lizarralde
   (Colombia), 4815 V Street, 20007.
   Acting Treasurer.—Lambert E. Jones (United States), 3245 Klingle Road,
      20008.
   Secretary.—Jorge Hazera (Costa Rica), 4005 Albermarle Street, McLean Va.,
      22101.
   Director, Division of Administration.—Fausto Ruggiero (Brazil), 5045 Overlook
      Road, 20016.
   Director, Division of Information.—Joaquín E. Meyer (Cuba), 4602 Massa-
      chusetts Avenue, 20016.
   Deputy Director, Division of Information.—Joseph U. Hinshaw (United States),
      1302 Stoneybrae Drive, Falls Church, Va., 22044.
Manager, Operations Department.—Ewaldo Correia Lima (Brazil), 5301 Mohican
   Road, Bethesda, Md., 20016.
   Director, Loan Division North.—Guillermo Moore (Chile), 4101 Cathedral
      Avenue, 20016.
   Director, Loan Division South.—G. Lincoln Sandelin (United States), 4000
      Cathedral Avenue, 20016.
   Director, Project Analysis Division.—Alfredo E. Hernández (Costa Rica), 511
      Crestwood Drive, Alexandria, Va., 22302.
   Director, Operations Control Division.—Hawthorne Arey (United States), 4224
      Franklin Street, Kensington, Md., 20795.
Manager, Technical Department.—Alfonso Rochac (El Salvador), 2904 Cameron
   Mills Road, Alexandria, Va., 22302.
   Director, Economic and Social Development Division.—Pedro Irañeta (Chile),
      4011 Nellie Custis Drive, Arlington, Va., 22207.
   Coordinator of Technical Assistance.—Milton Messina (Dominican Republic),
      6101 Durbin Road, Bethesda, Md., 20034.
General Counsel.—Elting Arnold (United States), 4914 Dorset Avenue, Chevy
   Chase, Md., 20015.
   Deputy General Counsel.—Rodrigo Llorente (Colombia), 5219 Ridgefield Road,
      20016.

BOARD OF EXECUTIVE DIRECTORS

Manuel Barros Sierra (Mexico), casting votes of the Dominican Republic, El
   Salvador, Guatemala, Honduras, Mexico, Panama, and Uruguay, 6851
   Tulip Hill Terrace, Bethesda, Md., 20016.
   Alternate: Arturo Calventi (Dominican Republic), 6100 Overlea Road,
      Bethesda, Md., 20016.
Francisco Norberto Castro (Argentina), casting votes of Argentina and Peru,
   5009 Hawthorne Place, 20016.
   Alternate: Juan Ramírez Valdeavellano (Peru), 808 17th Street, 20577.
Raúl Hess (Costa Rica), casting votes of Costa Rica and Nicaragua, 3812 North
   Wakefield Street, Arlington, Va., 22207.
   Alternate: José María Castillo (Nicaragua), 5511 Westbard Avenue, Bethesda,
      Md., 20016.
Tom Killefer (United States), casting votes of United States, 4201 Kirby Road,
   McClean, Va., 22101.
   Alternate: Alexander M. Rosenson (United States), 6301 Dahlonega Road,
      20016.
Oscar Niemtschik (Venezuela), casting votes of Chile, Colombia, and Venezuela,
   5005 Balton Road, 20016.
   Alternate: Luis Fernando Echavarría Vélez (Colombia), 5214 Wapakoneta
      Road, Glen Echo Heights, Md., 20016.
Victor da Silva Alves Filho (Brazil), casting votes of Brazil, Ecuador, and Haiti,
   2401 Calvert Street.
   Alternate: Federico Intriago Arrata (Ecuador), 808 17th Street, 20577.
Julio Solsona Flores (Uruguay), casting votes of Bolivia and Paraguay, 4201
   Cathedral Avenue, 20016.
   Alternate: Julio C. Gutiérrez (Paraguay), 4000 Tunlaw Road, 20007.

INTER-AMERICAN TROPICAL TUNA COMMISSION

Headquarters office, Scripps Institution of Oceanography, La Jolla, Calif, 92038
Phone, 453-2820 (Area Code 714)

United States Members:
Eugene D. Bennett, Standard Oil Building, San Francisco, Calif.
Dr. J. Laurence McHugh, Chief, Division of Biological Research, Bureau of Commercial Fisheries, Washington, D.C.
Robert L. Jones, Box 517, Gearhart, Oreg.
John G. Driscoll, Jr., San Diego Trust & Savings Building, San Diego, Calif.

Costa Rican Members:
Virgilio Aguiluz, Apartado 1110, San José, Costa Rica.
José Luis Cardona-Cooper, Apartado 1583, San José, Costa Rica.
Col. Fernando Flores, 705 North Windsor Boulevard, Hollywood, Calif.
Victor Nigro, 1140 North Harbor Drive, San Diego, Calif.

Panamanian Members:
Juan L. Obarrio, Jefe de la Sección de Pescas, Ministerio de Agricultura, Comercio e Industrias, Panamá, Republic de Panamá.
Dr. Carlos A. López-Guevara, Secretary, Apartado 4493, Panamá, Republic de Panamá.
Mrs. Dora Lanzner, Consul of Panama, 204 South Arnaz Drive, Beverly Hills, Calif.
Sr. Camilo Quintero Casamar, Apartado 8448, Panama, Republic of Panama.

Ecuadoran Members:
Dr. Eduardo Burneo Ojeda, Capt. de Corbeta, Ministerio de la Marina, Quito, Ecuador.
Dr. Enrique Ponce y Carbo, Asesor Técnico Jurídico, Ministerio de Relaciones Exteriores, Quito, Ecuador.
Capt. Héctor A. Chiriboga, Ministerio de Fomento, Casilla 5386, Guayaquil, Ecuador.

Mexican Members:
Dr. Mauro Cardenas F., chairman, Direccion General de Pesca, Av. Cuauhtemoc No. 80, 6° Piso, Mexico 7, D.F., Mexico.
Dr. Hector Chapa-Saldana, Direccion General de Pesca, Av. Cuauhtemoc No. 80, 6° Piso, Mexico 7, D.F., Mexico.
Dr. Rodolfo Ramirez G., Sub-Director General de Pesca, Av. Cuauhtemoc No. 80, 6° Piso, Mexico 7, D.F., Mexico.
Lic. Maria Emilia Tellez B., Sub-Directora de Organismos Internacionales, de la Secretaria de Relaciones Exteriores, Mexico, D.F., Mexico.

Director of Investigations.—Dr. John Laurence Kask.

INTERGOVERNMENTAL COMMITTEE FOR EUROPEAN MIGRATION

Headquarters: Geneva, Switzerland: 9 Rue Du Valais
Washington Liaison Mission: 1346 Connecticut Avenue, Washington, D.C., 20036; Phone, ADams 2-8000
New York Liaison Office: 370 Lexington Avenue, New York, N.Y., 10017. Phone: Murray Hill 9-8930

HEADQUARTERS

Director.—B. W. Haveman (Netherlands).
Deputy Director.—W. M. Besterman (U.S.A.)

MEMBER GOVERNMENTS

Argentina
Australia
Austria
Belgium
Bolivia
Brazil
Chile
Colombia
Costa Rica
Denmark
Ecuador
France
Germany
Greece
Israel

Italy
Luxembourg
Malta
Netherlands
New Zealand
Norway
Panama
Paraguay
Republic of South Africa
Spain
Switzerland
United Kingdom
United States of America
Venezuela

ICEM FIELD LIAISON MISSIONS

Buenos Aires, Argentina
Canberra, Australia
Vienna, Austria
Rio de Janeiro, Brazil
Santiago, Chile
Bogota, Colombia

Bonn, Germany
Athens, Greece
Rome, Italy
Madrid, Spain
Caracas, Venezuela

INTERNATIONAL BANK FOR RECONSTRUCTION AND DEVELOPMENT

1818 H Street NW., Washington, D.C., 20433. Phone, EXecutive 3-6360 (Code 181)

OFFICERS

President.—George D. Woods (United States), Sheraton Park Hotel, 2660 Woodley Road.
Vice President.—J. Burke Knapp (United States), 3701 Curtis Court, Chevy Chase, Md.
Vice President.—Geoffrey M. Wilson (United Kingdom), 3435 34th Place.
Director of Projects Department.—Simon Aldewereld (Netherlands), 4000 Massachusetts Avenue.
General Counsel.—Aron Broches (Netherlands), 2600 Tilden Place.
Director of Development Services Department.—Richard H. Demuth (United States), 5404 Bradley Boulevard, Bethesda, Md.
The Economic Adviser to the President.—Irving S. Friedman (United States), 6620 Fernwood Court, Bethesda, Md.
Director of the Economic Development Institute.—John H. Adler (United States), 5620 Western Avenue, Chevy Chase, Md.
Director of Western Hemisphere Department.—Gerald M. Alter (United States), 5124 Linnean Terrace.
Director of Special Economic Studies.—Dragoslav Avramovic (Yugoslavia), 2705 Ross Drive, Chevy Chase, Md.
Director of Far East Department.—I. P. M. Cargill (United Kingdom), Apartment 408 750 South Dickerson Street, Arlington, Va.
Treasurer.—Robert W. Cavanaugh (United States), 5215 Norway Drive, Chevy Chase, Md.
Associate Director of Projects Department.—Bernard Chadenet (France), 4759 Berkeley Terrace.
Special Representative for United Nations Organization.—Frederico Consolo (Italy), 2500 Q Street.
Director of Europe and Middle East Department.—S. R. Cope (United Kingdom), 3413 R Street.
Director of Africa Department.—Abdel G. El Emary (United Arab Republic), Apartment B4A, 3900 Watson Place.
Director of Information.—Harold N. Graves, Jr. (United States), 4816 Grantham Avenue, Chevy Chase, Md.
Director of New York Office.—Howard C. Johnson (United States), 5 Beekman Place, New York, N.Y.
Director of Economics Department.—Andrew M. Kamarck (United States), 7013 Meadow Lane, Chevy Chase, Md.
Director of Administration.—Michael L. Lejeune (United States), 4419 Chain Bridge Road, McLean, Va.
Secretary.—M. M. Mendels (Canada), 3400 Garrison Street.
Director of European Office.—John D. Miller (United Kingdom), 57 Boulevard de Beausejour, Paris 16, France.
Special Adviser to the President.—Leonard B. Rist (France), 3130 Ordway Street.
Special Adviser to the President.—Orvis A. Schmidt (United States), 3414 Cummings Lane, Chevy Chase, Md.
Director of South Asia Department.—Alexander Stevenson (United States), 6817 Laverock Court, Bethesda, Md.

EXECUTIVE DIRECTORS AND ALTERNATES

John C. Bullitt (United States), R.F.D. 1, Princeton, N.J.; alternate [Vacant].
J. M. Stevens (United Kingdom), 76 Kalorama Circle; alternate, N. M. P. Reilly (United Kingdom), 3101 34th Street.

Rene Larre (France), 2919 Woodland Drive; alternate, Jean Malaplate (France), 1436 Foxhall Road.

Otto Donner (Germany), 10011 Connecticut Avenue, Kensington, Md.; alternate, Helmut Abramowski (Germany), 4647 Kenmore Drive.

K. S. Sundara Rajan (India), 5302 Reno Road; alternate, S. Guhan (India), 3908 Jocelyn Street.

John M. Garland (Australia), 5142 Worthington Drive, Westgate; alternate, A. J. J. van Vuuren (South Africa), 4318 Crestwood Lane, McLean, Va.; represents Australia, South Africa, New Zealand, and Viet-Nam.

Gengo Suzuki (Japan), The Rittenhouse, 6101 16th Street; alternate, Eiji Ozaki (Japan), 7307 Broxburn Court, Bethesda, Md.; represents Japan, Ceylon, Thailand, Burma, and Nepal.

A. F. W. Plumptre (Canada), 85 Lakeway Drive, Rockcliffe Park, Ottawa, Ontario, Canada; alternate, S. J. Handfield-Jones (Canada), 3508 Rodman Street; represents Canada, Ireland, and Jamaica.

Mumtaz Mirza (Pakistan), 5442 31st Street; alternate, Ali Akbar Khosropur (Iran), 3818 Military Road; represents Pakistan, United Arab Republic, Iran, Saudi Arabia, Kuwait, Syrian Arab Republic, Iraq, Jordan, and Lebanon.

Pieter Lieftinck (Netherlands), 3229 Idaho Avenue; alternate, Aleksandar Bogoev (Yugsolavia), 5300 Westbard Avenue, Bethesda, Md.; represents Netherlands, Yugoslavia, Israel, and Cyprus.

Andre van Campenhout (Belgium), 2527 P Street; alternate, Othmar Haushofer (Austria), 3 Bermuda Court, Chesterbrook Estates, McLean, Va.; represents Belgium, Turkey, Austria, Korea, and Luxembourg.

Joaquin Gutierrez Cano (Spain), 5132 Baltan Road, Sumner, Md.; alternate, Sergio Siglienti (Italy), 4201 Cathedral Avenue; represents Italy, Spain, Portugal, and Greece.

Abderrahman Tazi (Morocco), 3026 44th Place; alternate, Chedly Ayari (Tunisia), 2322 20th Street; represents Indoneisa, Algeria, Morocco, Malaysia, Ghana, Afghanistan, Tunisia, Libya, and Laos.

Reignson C. Chen (China), 5604 Durbin Road, Bethesda, Md.

Vilhjalmur Thor (Iceland), 2401 Calvert Street; alternate, Odd Høkedal (Norway), 3725 Nellie Custis Drive, Arlington, Va.; represents Sweden, Finland, Denmark, Iceland, and Norway.

Jorge Mejia-Palacio (Colombia), 4201 Cathedral Avenue; alternate, Jose Camacho (Colombia), 4101 Cathedral Avenue; represents Brazil, Philippines, Colombia, Ecuador, and Dominican Republic.

John Mamman Garba (Nigeria), 6402 West Halbert Road, Bethesda, Md.; alternate, S. Othello Coleman (Liberia), 203 G Street SW.; represents Nigeria, Guinea, Democratic Republic of Congo, Kenya, Uganda, United Republic of Tanzania, Trinidad and Tobago, Sudan, Mali, Burundi, Liberia, Sierra Leone, and Ethiopia.

Luis Machado (Cuba), 6832 Tulip Hill Terrace; alternate, Rufino Gil (Costa Rica), 4909 Elsmere Avenue, Bethesda, Md.; represents Mexico, Costa Rica, Venezuela, Peru, Guatemala, Honduras, Haiti, Nicaragua, El Salvador, and Panama.

Manuel San Miguel (Argentina), Dupont East, 1545 18th Street; alternate, Juan Haus-Solis (Bolivia), 4530 Connecticut Avenue; represents Argentina, Chile, Bolivia, Uruguay, and Paraguay.

Mohamed Nassim Kochman (Mauritania), 4201 Cathedral Avenue; alternate, Said Mohamed Ali (Somalia), 1545 18th Street; represents Senegal, Cameroon, Ivory Coast, Malagasy Republic, Rwanda, Somalia, Togo, Chad, Dahomey, Gabon, Niger, Mauritania, Upper Volta, Congo (Brazzaville), and Central African Republic.

INTERNATIONAL BOUNDARY AND WATER COMMISSION, UNITED STATES AND MEXICO

UNITED STATES SECTION

Offices, Fourth Floor, Mart Building, 206 San Francisco, El Paso, Tex. Phone, 532–5476

Commissioner.—Joseph F. Friedkin, 2618 Frankfort, El Paso, Tex., 79930.
Principal Engineer.—Lyle H. Henderson, Residence No. 4, Amistad Dam, Del Rio, Tex., 78840.

Principal Engineer.—William E. Walker, 8302 Solar Place, El Paso, Tex., 79904.
Counsel.—Marvin E. Whittington, 304 Benedict Road, El Paso, Tex., 79922.
Secretary.—Louis F. Blanchard, 607 Linda Way, El Paso, Tex., 79922.
Comptroller.—John B. Moore, 248 Northwind, El Paso, Tex., 79912.

MEXICAN SECTION
Offices, Avenida Lerdo 232 Norte, Ciudad Juárez, Chihuahua, Mexico
Phone, Juárez 2-24-40 and 41, Post Office address, Box 14, El Paso, Tex.

Commissioner.—David Herrera Jordán.
Assistant to Commissioner.—Joaquin C. Bustamante.
Acting Principal Engineer.—Jenaro Paz Reyes.
Principal Engineer.—Norberto Sánchez Gómez.
Secretary.—Fernando Rivas S.
Assistant Secretary.—Mrs. Luz H. G. de Partearroyo.

INTERNATIONAL BOUNDARY COMMISSION, UNITED STATES AND CANADA

(For defining, marking, and maintaining the boundary between the United States and Canada). Office, room 3810, General Accounting Office Building, 441 G Street. Phone, STerling 3-9151

United States Section:
  Commissioner.—Edward J. King, room 3810 General Accounting Office Building, 20548.
Engineer to the Commission.—Nelson W. Smith, 5607 Second Street, 20011.
  Administrative Officer.—Mrs. Marie A. Sheehy, 2205 Beechwood Road, Lewisdale-Adelphi, Md., 20783.
Canadian Section:
  Commissioner.—A. F. Lambert, 227 Latchford Road, Ottawa 3, Canada.
  Engineer to the Commission.—[Vacant.]

INTERNATIONAL DEVELOPMENT ASSOCIATION

1818 H Street, Washington, D.C.

[The Officers, Executive Directors, and Alternates are the same as those of the International Bank for Reconstruction and Development.]

INTERNATIONAL FINANCE CORPORATION

1818 H Street, 20433. Phone, EXecutive 3-6360 (Code 181)

PRINCIPAL OFFICERS

President.—George D. Woods (United States), Sheraton-Park Hotel.
Executive Vice President.—Martin M. Rosen (United States), 410 Paul Spring Road, Alexandria, Va.
Treasurer.—Robert W. Cavanaugh (United States), 5215 Norway Drive, Chevy Chase, Md.
Director, Department of Operations, Development Finance Companies.—William Diamond (United States), 8201 Larry Place, Chevy Chase, Md.
Director of Engineering Department.—J. David Dodd (United Kingdom), R.F.D. 2, Leesburg, Va.
Director of Information.—Harold N. Graves, Jr. (United States), 4816 Grantham Avenue, Chevy Chase, Md., 20015.
Director of Investments, Africa, Asia and Middle East.—Ladislaus von Hoffman (Germany), 4741 Fulton Street.
Director of New York Office.—Howard C. Johnson (United States), 5 Beekman Place, New York, N.Y.
Director of Administration.—Michael L. Lejeune (United States), 4419 Chain Bridge Road, McLean, Va.
Secretary.—M. M. Mendels (Canada), 3400 Garrison Street, 20008.

Director of European Office.—John D. Miller (United Kingdom), 57 Boulevard de Beausejour, Paris 16e, France.

Director of Investments, Latin America, Europe and Australasia.—Neil J. Paterson (Australia), 3 Bermuda Court, Chesterbrook Estates, McLean, Va.

General Counsel.—R. B. J. Richards (United Kingdom), 2122 Massachusetts Avenue.

Accounting Adviser.—H. J. Williams (United States), 4101 Cathedral Avenue, Apt. 511, 20016.

DIRECTORS AND ALTERNATES

John C. Bullitt (United States), R.F.D. 1, Princeton, N.J.

J. M. Stevens (United Kingdom), 76 Kalorama Circle; alternate, N. M. P. Reilly (United Kingdom), 3101 34th Street.

Rene Larre (France), 2919 Woodland Drive; alternate, Jean Malaplate (France), 1436 Foxhall Road.

K. S. Sundara Rajan (India), 5302 Reno Road, 20015; alternate, S. Guhan (India), 3908 Jocelyn Street.

Otto Donner (Germany), 10011 Connecticut Avenue, Kensington, Md.; alternate, Helmut Abramowski (Germany), 4647 Kenmore Drive, 20007.

Mumtaz Mirza (Pakistan), 5442 31st Street; alternate, Ali Akbar Khosropur (Iran), 3818 Military Road; represents Pakistan, United Arab Republic, Iran, Kuwait, Saudi Arabia, Syrian Arab Republic, Iraq, Lebanon, and Jordan.

Andre van Campenhout (Belgium), 2527 P Street; alternate, Othmar Haushofer (Austria), 3 Bermuda Court, Chesterbrook Estates, McLean, Va.; represents Belgium, Austria, Turkey, Korea, and Luxembourg.

John M. Garland (Australia), 5142 Worthington Drive, Westgate, 20016; alternate, A. J. J. van Vuuren (South Africa), 4318 Crestwood Lane, McLean, Va.; represents Australia, South Africa, and New Zealand.

A. F. W. Plumptre (Canada), 85 Lakeway Drive, Rockcliff Park, Ottawa, Ontario, Canada; alternate, S. J. Handfield-Jones (Canada), 3508 Rodman Street; represents Canada, Ireland, and Jamaica.

Gengo Suzuki (Japan), The Rittenhouse, 6101 16th Street, 20011; alternate, Eiji Ozaki (Japan), 7307 Broxburn Court, Bethesda, Md.; represents Japan, Burma, Ceylon, and Thailand.

Joaquin Gutierrez Cano (Spain), 5132 Baltan Road, Sumner, Md.; alternate, Sergio Siglienti (Italy), 4201 Cathedral Avenue; represents Italy, Spain, and Greece.

Vilhjalmur Thor (Iceland), 2401 Calvert Street, 20008; alternate, Odd Høkedal (Norway), 3725 Nellie Custis Drive, Arlington, Va.; represents Sweden, Denmark, Norway, Finland, and Iceland.

Pieter Lieftinck (Netherlands), 3229 Idaho Avenue; alternate, Aleksandar Bogoev (Yugoslavia), 5300 Westbard Avenue, Bethesda, Md.; represents Netherlands, Cyprus, and Israel.

Luis Machada (Cuba), 6832 Tulip Hill Terrace, 20016; alternate, Rufino Gil (Costa Rica), 4909 Elsmere Avenue, Bethesda, Md.; represents Mexico, Peru, Venezuela, Costa Rica, Guatemala, Haiti, El Salvador, Honduras, Nicaragua, and Panama.

John Mamman Garba (Nigeria), 6402 West Halbert Road, Bethesda, Md.; alternate, S. Othello Coleman (Liberia), 203 G Street SW.; represents Nigeria, Kenya, Uganda, United Republic of Tanzania, Sudan, Liberia, Sierra Leone, and Ethiopia.

Manuel San Miguel (Argentina), Dupont East, 1545 18th Street; alternate, Juan Haus-Solis (Bolivia), 4530 Connecticut Avenue; represents Argentina, Chile, Bolivia, and Paraguay.

Jorge Mejia-Palacio (Colombia), 4201 Cathedral Avenue; alternate, Jose Camacho (Colombia), 4101 Cathedral Avenue; represents Brazil, Colombia, Philippines, Ecuador, and Dominican Republic.

Abderrahman Tazi (Morocco), 3026 44th Place; alternate, Chedly Ayari (Tunisia), 2322 20th Street; represents Morocco, Malaysia, Ghana, Tunisia, Afghanistan, and Libya.

Mohamed Nassim Kochman (Mauritania), 4201 Cathedral Avenue; alternate, Said Mohamed Ali (Somalia), 1545 18th Street; represents Senegal, Ivory Coast, Malagasy Republic, Somalia, and Togo.

INTERNATIONAL JOINT COMMISSION

1711 New York Avenue, Room B–208, Washington, D.C., 20440 (Stop 86). Phone, 347–3733

United States Section:
  Chairman.—[Vacant.]
    Eugene W. Weber, 5407 Harwood Road, Bethesda, Md., 20014.
    Charles R. Ross, 10814 Alloway Drive, Bethesda, Md., 20854.
  Secretary.—William A. Bullard, 388 Trenton Drive, Alexandria, Va., 22308.
Canadian Section:
  Chairman.—A. D. P. Heeney, Ottawa, Ontario.
    D. M. Stephens, Winnipeg, Manitoba.
    Rene Dupuis, Montreal, Quebec.
  Secretary.—David G. Chance, Ottawa, Ontario.

INTERNATIONAL LABOR ORGANIZATION

Headquarters: Geneva, Switzerland

Washington Branch Office: 917 Fifteenth Street, Washington, D.C., 20005. Phone, DIstrict 7–9120

Liaison Office with the United Nations, 345 East 46th Street, New York, N.Y., 10017

International Labor Office (Permanent Secretariat of the Organization):
  Headquarters (Geneva):
    Director General.—David A. Morse (U.S.A.).
    Principal Deputy Director General.—Jef Rens (Belgium).
    Deputy Directors General:
      C. Wilfred Jenks (United Kingdom).
      Abbas Moustapha Ammar (United Arab Republic).
    Assistant Directors General:
      William Yalden-Thomson (Canada).
      Francis Blanchard (France).
      Ana Figueroa (Chile).
      H. A. Majid (Pakistan).
      E. J. Riches, Treasurer-Comptroller (New Zealand).
  Washington Branch:
    Director.—Ralph Wright.
  Other Branch Offices:
    Bonn, London, New Delhi, Ottawa, Paris, Rome, Tokyo, Rio de Janeiro, Moscow, Cairo, Buenos Aires.

INTERNATIONAL MONETARY FUND

Nineteenth and H Streets, Washington, D.C., 20431. Phone, EXecutive 3–6360 (Code 181)

BOARD OF EXECUTIVE DIRECTORS

J. J. Anjaria (India), 4600 Connecticut Avenue, Apt. 306; alternate, Arun K. Ghosh (India), 3701 Massachusetts Avenue, Apt. 505.
Ulrich Beelitz (Federal Republic of Germany), 4301 Massachusetts Avenue, Apt. 7003; alternate, Walter O. Habermeier (Federal Republic of Germany), 4720 45th Street.
Maurício C. Bicalho (Brazil), 4545 Connecticut Avenue, Apt. 917; alternate, Antonio de Abreu Coutinho (Brazil), 5441 Chevy Chase Parkway.
William B. Dale (United States), 6008 Landon Lane, Bethesda, Md.; alternate, John S. Hooker (United States), 7403 Connecticut Avenue, Chevy Chase, Md.
Kurt Eklöf (Sweden), 5205 Falmouth Road, Westmoreland, Washington, D.C.; alternate, Otto Schelin (Denmark), 5005 Elsmere Place, Bethesda, Md.
Luis Escobar (Chile), 6800 Millwood Road, Kenwood Park, Md.; alternate, Enrique Domenech (Argentina), 3737 Legation Street, Apt. 107.
Alfonso Espinosa (Venezuela), Room 1309, International Monetary Fund; alternate, Jorge González del Valle (Guatemala), 5841 Marbury Road, Kenwood Park, Bethesda, Md.
John M. Garland (Australia), 5142 Worthington Drive, Westgate, Washington, D.C.; alternate Roy Daniel (Australia), 3012 Oliver Street.

Louis Kandé (Senegal), 2931 Tilden Street; alternate, Antoine W. Yaméogo (Upper Volta), 1614 Tuckerman Street.

Semyano Kiingi (Uganda), 5455 30th Street; alternate, Paul L. Faber (Guinea), 6401 16th Street.

René Larre (France), 2919 Woodland Drive; alternate, Gérard M. Teyssier (France), 4701 Berkley Terrace.

Pieter Lieftinck (Netherlands), 3229 Idaho Avenue; alternate, H.M.H.A. van der Valk (Netherlands), 3113 Macomb Street.

A. F. W. Plumptre (Canada), Room 1005, International Bank for Reconstruction and Development; alternate, S. J. Handfield-Jones (Canada), 3508 Rodman Street.

A. Z. Saad (United Arab Republic), 3132 16th Street; alternate, Albert Mansour (United Arab Republic), 4000 Cathedral Avenue.

Sergio Siglienti (Italy), 4201 Cathedral Avenue; alternate, Costa P. Caranicas (Greece), 5605 Center Street, Chevy Chase, Md.

J. M. Stevens (United Kingdom), 76 Kalorama Circle; alternate, John A. Kirbyshire (United Kingdom), 3229 R Street.

Sumanang (Indonesia), 3212 Chestnut Street; alternate, Amon Nikoi (Ghana), 1748 Taylor Street.

Gengo Suzuki (Japan), 6101 16th Street; alternate, Chalong Pungtrakul (Thailand), 5701 English Court, Bethesda, Md.

Beue Tann (China), 5406 Greystone Street, Chevy Chase, Md.; alternate, I-Shuan Sun (China), 11310 Cloverhill Drive, Silver Spring, Md.

André van Campenhout (Belgium), 2100 Massachusetts Avenue; alternate, Maurice Toussaint (Belgium), 5329 Massachusetts Avenue.

OFFICERS

Managing Director.—Pierre-Paul Schweitzer, 1717 Foxhall Road, 20007.
Deputy Managing Director.—Frank A. Southard, Jr., 4328 Van Ness Street, 20016.
Administration Department, Director.—Phillip Thorson, 7001 MacArthur Boulevard, 20016.
African Department, Director.—Hamzah Merghani, 2816 Ellicott Street.
Asian Department, Director.—D. S. Savkar, 6116 32d Place.
European Department, Director.—L. A. Whittome, 2816 Arizona Terrace.
Exchange Restrictions Department.—Ernest Sturc, 7200 Orkney Parkway, Bannockburn Heights, Bethesda, Md., 20034.
Fiscal Affairs Department, Director.—Richard B. Goode, 1623 45th Street.
International Monetary Fund Institute, Director.—F. A. G. Keesing, 7809 Greentwig Road, Bethesda, Md., 20034.
Legal Department, General Counsel.—Joseph Gold, 7020 Braeburn Place, Bethesda, Md.
Middle Eastern Department, Director.—Anwar Ali, International Monetary Fund, 19th and H Streets.
Research and Statistics Department, Director.—J. J. Polak, 3420 Porter Street, 20016.
Secretary's Department, Secretary.—Roman L. Horne, Box 370, Route 2, McLean, Va.
Treasurer's Department, Treasurer.—Y. C. Koo, 4013 Cleveland Street, Kensington, Md., 20015.
Western Hemisphere Department, Director.—Jorge Del Canto, 5412 Christy Drive, Springfield, Md., 20016.

OFFICE OF MANAGING DIRECTOR

Central Banking Service, Director.—J. V. Mládek 1320 30th Street.
Office in Europe (Paris), Director.—Jean-Paul Sallé.
Chief Editor.—J. Keith Horsefield, 3701 Massachusetts Avenue, Apt. 609.
Chief Information Officer.—Jay Reid, 7208 Blacklock Road, Bethesda, Md.
Historian.—Oscar L. Altman, 922 24th Street, 20037.
Internal Auditor.—J. William Lowe, 5435 19th Street North, Arlington, Va.
Special Representative to the United Nations.—Gordon Williams, 1611 35th Street, 20007.

INTERNATIONAL PACIFIC HALIBUT COMMISSION, UNITED STATES AND CANADA

Headquarters office, University of Washington, Seattle, Wash. Phone, LAkeview 5-5323

American Members—
  H. E. Crowther, vice chairman, Bureau of Commercial Fisheries, Washington, D.C., 20240; residence, 7105 Claymore Avenue, West Hyattsville, Md.
  Haakon M. Selvar, Box 1087, Bainbridge Island, Wash.
  [Vacancy.]
Canadian Members—
  William M. Sprules, chairman, Department of Fisheries, Ottawa, Ontario; residence, 2248 McQuaig Street, Ottawa, Ontario.
  Martin K. Eriksen, 308 Fourth Avenue East, Prince Rupert, B.C.
  Francis W. Millerd, 4155 Woodland Avenue, West Vancouver, B.C.
Director of Investigations and Secretary (ex officio).—F. Heward Bell, University of Washington, Fisheries Hall No. 2, Seattle, Wash.

INTERNATIONAL PACIFIC SALMON FISHERIES COMMISSION

Headquarters office, Federal Building, New Westminister, British Columbia

American Members—
  DeWitt Gilbert, chairman, 71 Columbia Street, Seattle, Wash.
  Clarence F. Pautzke, member, United States Fish and Wildlife Service, Washington, D.C., 20240.
  George C. Starlund, Washington State Department of Fisheries, Room 115, General Administration Building, Olympia, Wash.
Canadian Members—
  Senator Thomas Reid, vice chairman, 6115 Bergstrom Road, North Surrey, B.C.
  A. J. Whitmore, 4093 Norland Avenue, North Burnaby, B.C.
  W. R. Hourston, Department of Fisheries, Vancouver, B.C.

JOINT BRAZIL-UNITED STATES DEFENSE COMMISSION

UNITED STATES DELEGATION

Room 2A-882, The Pentagon, 20301. Phone, OXford 7-5125 or 5-5218 (Code 11)

MEMBERS

Rear Adm. H. P. Weatherwax, USN, chairman and Navy member, 3745 Orange Court, Alexandria, Va.
Maj. Gen. William R. Peers, USA, Army member, 1512 South 22d Street, Arlington, Va.
Brig. Gen. Richard A. Yudkin, USAF, Air Force member, 1400 South Joyce Street, Apt. A-313, Arlington, Va.

ADVISORS

Col. William F. Kernan, USA, Army advisor.
Capt. James C. Houghton, USN, Navy advisor.
Col. George M. Johnson, Jr., USAF, Air Force advisor.
Col. Ted Brown, USAF, Air Force advisor.
Col. Edwin H. Simmons, USMC, Navy advisor.
Lt. Col. Henry F. Prysi, USA, Army advisor.
Lt. Col. John A. Seddon, USA, Army advisor and secretary.
Cdr. Bruce E. Prum, USN, Navy advisor and secretary.
Lt. Cdr. Raymond D. Donnelly, USN, Navy advisor.
Maj. Alfred L. Thieme, USA, Army advisor.

BRAZILIAN DELEGATION

MEMBERS

Vice Adm. Antonio Junqueira Giovannini, chairman and Navy member, 6106 Massachusetts Avenue NW., 20016.
Brig. Gen. Emilio Garrastazu Medici, Army member, 4600 Connecticut Avenue NW., Apt. 429, 20008.
Brig. Gen. Ary Presser Bello, Air Force member, 4600 Connecticut Avenue NW., Apt. 824, 20008.

ADVISORS

Col. Omar Diogenes de Carvalho, Army advisor.
Col. Carlos Julio Amaral da Cunha, Air Force advisor.
Capt. Herbert Lima Caspary, Navy advisor.
Col. Newton Correa de Andrade Mello, Army advisor and secretary.
Lt. Col. Gladstone Maia, Army advisor.
Lt. Col. Aecio Morrot Coelho, Army advisor.
Lt. Col. Aldo da Costa Dantas, Army advisor.
Cdr. Athos Monteiro da Silveira, Navy advisor.
Maj. Luis A. S. Araujo, Army advisor.

JOINT MEXICAN-UNITED STATES DEFENSE COMMISSION

UNITED STATES SECTION

Room 2A-882, The Pentagon, 20301.   Phone, OXford 7-5125 or 4-4218 (Code 11)

MEMBERS

Rear Adm. H. P. Weatherwax, USN, chairman and Navy member, 3745 Orange Court, Alexandria, Va.
Maj. Gen. William R. Peers, USA, Army member, 1512 South 22d Street, Arlington, Va.
Brig. Gen. Richard A. Yudkin, USAF, Air Force member, 1400 South Joyce Street, Apt. A-313, Arlington, Va.

ADVISORS

Terrance Leonhardy, Department of State representative.
Col. William F. Kernan, USA, Army advisor.
Capt. James C. Houghton, USN, Navy advisor.
Col. George M. Johnson, Jr., USAF, Air Force advisor.
Col. Ted Brown, USAF, Air Force advisor.
Col. Edwin H. Simmons, USMC, Navy advisor.
Lt. Col. Maurice W. Gouchoe, USAF, Air Force advisor.
Lt. Col. Henry F. Prysi, USA, Army advisor.
Lt. Col. John A. Seddon, USA, Army advisor and secretary
Cdr. Bruce E. Prum, USN, Navy advisor and secretary.
Lt. Cdr. Raymond D. Donnelly, USN, Navy advisor.
Maj. Alfred L. Thieme, USA, Army advisor.

MEXICAN SECTION

Vice Adm. Alvaro Sandovar, Navy member.

ADVISORS

Ambassador Vicente Sanchez Gavito, Mexican Embassy representative.
Col. Angel Rodriguez Garcia, acting chairman and Army advisor.
Col. Raúl Flores Romero, Army advisor.
Col. Miguel Rodriguez Iturralde, Army advisor.
Col. Roberto Sanchez Coronel, Army advisor and secretary.
Maj. Vicente Loyola Gonzalez, Army advisor.
Capt. Antonio Oropeza Rendón, Army stenographer.

ORGANIZATION OF AMERICAN STATES

HEADQUARTERS, PAN AMERICAN UNION

Seventeenth Street, Between Constitution Avenue and C.   Phone, EXecutive 3-8450 (Code 176)

THE COUNCIL

Chairman.—The Honorable Ellsworth Bunker (Ambassador, representative of the United States), Department of State, Room 6494, 20520.

Vice Chairman.—H. E. Dr. Juan Plate (Ambassador, representative of Paraguay), 3230 Broad Branch Terrace, 20008.

H. E. Dr. Ricardo M. Colombo (Ambassador, representative of Argentina), 2232 Massachusetts Avenue, 20008.

H. E. Dr. Raúl Diez de Medina (Ambassador, representative of Bolivia), 3012 Massachusetts Avenue, 20008.

H. E. Ilmar Penna Marinho (Ambassador, representative of Brazil), 3305 Cleveland Avenue, 20008.

H. E. Don Alejandro Magnet (Ambassador, representative of Chile), 1120 Connecticut Avenue, Suite 410, 20036.

H. E. Lic. Gonzalo J. Facio (Ambassador, representative of Costa Rica), 2112 S Street, 20008.

H. E. Dr. Rodrigo Jácome M. (Ambassador, representative of Ecuador), 2535 15th Street, 20009.

H. E. Don Ramón de Clairmont Dueñas (Ambassador, representative of El Salvador), 2308 California Street, 20008.

H. E. Don Alfredo Vázquez Carrizosa (Ambassador, representative of Colombia), 1609 22d Street.

H. E. Dr. José A. Bonilla Atiles (Ambassador, representative of the Dominican Republic), 4501 Nebraska Avenue.

H. E. Dr. Carlos García Bauer (Ambassador, representative of Guatemala), 2220 R Street.

H. E. Fern D. Baguidy (Ambassador, representative of Haiti), 4400 17th Street.

H. E. Dr. Ricardo A. Midence Soto (Ambassador, representative of Honduras), 4715 16th Street, 20011.

H. E. Don Rafael de la Colina (Ambassador, representative of Mexico), 2440 Massachusetts Avenue, 20008.

H. E. Dr. Guillermo Sevilla-Sacasa (Ambassador, representative of Nicaragua), 1627 New Hampshire Avenue.

H. E. Lic. Humberto G. Calamari (Ambassador, representative of Panama), 2862 McGill Terrace, 20008.

H. E. Dr. Juan Bautista de Lavalle (Ambassador, representative of Peru), 2401 Calvert Street, 20008.

Dr. Emilio N. Oribe (Minister Counselor, interim representative of Uruguay), 2362 Massachusetts Avenue, 20008.

H. E. Dr. Enrique Tejera Paris (Ambassador, representative of Venezuela), 2445 Massachusetts Avenue, 20008.

Secretary General.—H. E. Dr. José A. Mora, 201 18th Street.

Assistant Secretary General.—William Sanders, 2708 36th Street.

PAN AMERICAN UNION

General Secretariat

Office of the Secretary General, Protocol Officer.—Paul W. Murphy, 1909 Glenallan Avenue, Glenmont, Silver Spring, Md.

Assistant Secretary for Economic and Social Affairs.—Walter J. Sedwitz, 6704 Tulip Hill Terrace, Bethesda, Md.

  Special Assistant.—Jose M. Ribas, 3612 Albemarle Street.

Assistant Secretary for Cultural, Scientific, and Informational Affairs.—Jaime Posada, 4816 Cola Drive, Potomac Hills, McLean, Va.

Special Adviser.—Arturo Morales Carrión, 5520 Westbard Avenue, Bethesda, Md.

PAU Offices in the Member States, Chief.—Héctor Obes Polleri, 5317 Potomac Avenue.

Department of Administrative Affairs, Director.—Luis Raúl Betances, 4809 45th Street.
Budget Officer.—Hernán Banegas, 5936 Second Street, Arlington, Va.
General Services.—Frank W. Loops, 3506 North Ottawa Street, Arlington, Va.
Internal Audit Officer.—Abdon Alvarez, 727 Forest Grove Drive, Annandale, Va.
Organization and Methods Officer.—Charles Miller, 1005 Lincoln Avenue, Falls Church, Va.
Personnel Officer.—Juan A. Nimo, 761 Ivydale Drive, Annandale, Va.
Programming and Planning.—Carr L. Donald, 6112 Xavier Court, McLean, Va.
Department of Cultural Affairs, Director.—Rafael Squirru, 2707 P St.
Deputy Director.—Guillermo De Zendegui, 5205 Massachusetts Avenue.
Columbus Memorial Library.—Arthur E. Gropp, 5113 Western Avenue, 20016.
Music.—Guillermo Espinosa, 4201 Cathedral Avenue, 20016
Philosophy and Letters.—Armando C. Pacheco, 400 Valley Lane, Falls Church, Va.
Visual Arts.—Jose Gomez-Sicre, 1756 Lanier Place.
Department of Economic Affairs, Director.—Dr. Germanico Salgado, 6019 Neilwood Drive, Rockville, Md.
Deputy Director.—René Monserrat, 8600 16th Street, Silver Spring, Md.
Assistant Director.—Theodore Mesmer, 3810 Yuma Street.
Administrative Coordinator.—Ernesto F. Betancourt, 6151 30th Street.
Graphs and Computations.—Andres Aviles, 6934 North 27th Road, Arlington, Va.
Inter-American Committee for Agricultural Development.—José Irineu Cabral, 4600 Connecticut Avenue.
International Economics.—Alberto Fraguio, 4000 Tunlaw Road.
Planning and Programming.—[Vacant.]
Public Finance and Administration.—[Vacant.]
Publications and Documents.—Marc Yaffe, 3393 Stephenson Place.
Tourism.—Francisco Hernandez, 1500 Massachusetts Avenue.
Department of Educational Affairs, Director.—Francisco S. Cespedes, 1616 Brisbane Street, Silver Spring, Md.
Deputy Director.—Juan M. Campos, 2500 Q Street.
Special Assistant.—Hugo Albornoz, 904 Arrington Drive, Silver Spring, Md.
Special Assistant.—Estella Hart, 129 Devon Drive, Falls Church, Va.
Documentation.—Hugo Muñoz, 4531 North Henderson Road, Arlington, Va.
Exchange of Persons.—David Heft, 9330 Wilmer Street, Silver Spring, Md.
"La Educación", Editor.—Luis Reissig, 2020 F Street.
Student Locan (Rowe Fund).—Luis Ramirez Velarde, 1206 Oakview Drive, Silver Spring, Md.
Technical Operations.—Ovidio de Leon, 1733 N Street.
Transportation.—(Acting), Hugo Seifart, 4108 Oak Lane, McLean, Va.
Department of Legal Affairs, Director.—Francisco V. García-Amador, 5800 Marbury Road, Kenwood Park, Bethesda, Md.
Deputy Director.—Manuel Canyes, 3000 39th Street.
Codification.—Luis Reque, 6101 Berkshire Drive, Bethesda, Md.
General Legal.—Paul A. Colborn, 4600 38th Street North, Arlington, Va.
Inter-American Commission on Human Rights, Executive Secretary.—Luis Reque, 6101 Berkshire Drive, Bethesda, Md.
Inter-American Commission of Women, Chairman.—Carmen Natalia Martinez Bonilla, c/o Pan American Union.
Executive Secretary.—Esther N. de Calvo, 3700 Massachusetts Avenue.
Inter-American Peace Committee, Advisor.—Roberto Quiros, 4101 Calla Drive, McLean, Va.
Special Consultative Committee on Security, Advisor.—Roberto Quiros, 4101 Calla Drive, McLean, Va.
Department of Public Information, Interim Director.—Miguel Aranguren, 5505 North 33d Street, Arlington, Va.
Press.—Wilson Velloso, 9919 Pomona Drive.
Radio and Television.—Rene Olivares, 1415 North Taft Street, Arlington, Va.
Department of Scientific Affairs, Director.—Jesse D. Perkinson, Jr., 4510 Drummond Avenue, Chevy Chase, Md.
Deputy Director.—Marcelo Alonso, 7311 Broxburn Court, Bethesda, Md.
Natural Science.—Heitor de Souza, 10012 Montauk Avenue, Bethesda, Md.
Nuclear Science.—[Vacant.]
Radio Isotopes.—Jose Saiz del Rio, 10201 Farnham Drive, Bethesda, Md.
Science Information, Technology, and Productivity.—Maximo Halty Carrere, 3 Recard Lane, Alexandria, Va.

Department of Social Affairs.—
  *Director (acting).—*Theo R. Crevenna, 6720 Nevius Street, Falls Church, Va.
  *Community Development and Social Welfare.—*Gabriel Ospina Restrepo, 4105 Mason Ridge Drive, Annandale, Va.
  *Cooperatives.—*Fernando Chavez, 505 Pensa Drive, Falls Church, Va.
  *General Studies and Reports.—*Albert Frances, 1528 29th Street.
  *Housing and Planning, Principal Advisor.—*Walter D. Harris, 45 Killdeer Road, Hamden, Conn.
  *Labor Relations.—*Leo Suslow, 5920 Merritt Place, Falls Church, Va.
  *Agrarian Reform and Rural Development.—*Pier Giovanni Brunori, 5405 Brookeway Drive.
  *Social Security.—*Beryl Frank, 6009 Goldsboro Road, Bethesda, Md.
*Department of Statistics, Director.—*Tulo H. Montenegro, 9609 Singleton Drive, Bethesda, Md.
  *General Operations.—*Cecilia E. Washington, 3813 17th Place NE.
  Technical Operations.—
*Department of Technical Cooperation, Director.—*João Gonçalves de Souza, 6001 McKinley Street, Bethesda, Md.
  *Deputy Director.—*Jose A. Guerra, 8804 Second Avenue, Silver Spring, Md.
  *Advisory Services.—*Otto Howard Salzman, Jr., 515 Churchill Road, McLean, Va.
  *Fellowship and Professorship.—*Javier Malagón, 4840 43d Place.
  *Training Services.—*Earl J. Roueche, 218 Springvale Avenue, McLean, Va.
*Office of Council and Conference Secretariat Services, Director.—*Santiago Ortiz, 1913 Glenbrook Road, Fairfax, Va.
  *Deputy Director.—*Edward P. Davis, 407 North Livingston Street, Arlington, Va.
  *Council Secretariat Services.—*Samuel Echalar, 6405 Lee Highway, Arlington, Va.
  *Language Services.—*Maryjo Carlson, 1111 Marlan Drive, Alexandria, Va.
  *Official Records.—*Catharine Ryan, 3412 Prospect Street.
*Office of Financial Services, Director.—*Laurence W. Acker, 1619 Pepperdine Drive, Vienna, Va.
  *Deputy Director.—*John A. Balenger, 915 South Buchanan Street, Arlington, Va.
  *Fiscal Division.—*William W. Crowe, 5625 Ogden Road.
  *Technical Cooperation Unit.—*Carlos Graneros, 2115 Pennsylvania Avenue.
  *A.P. Accounting Division.—*Lester Frank, 500 New York Avenue, Takoma Park, Md.
*Office of Publication Services, Director.—*John McAdams, 5606 Forest Place, Bethesda, Md.
  *Assistant Director.—*Luis Rivera, Jr., 2520 North Stevens Street, Alexandria, Va.
  *Distribution.—*Anibal Zorrilla, 13009 Estelle Road, Silver Spring, Md.
  *Graphic Services.—*Jose I. Bermudez, Route 1, Box 279, Oakton, Va.
  *Production.—*Edward D. Fitzgerald, 1316 Beech Tree Lane, Falls Church, Va.
  *Sales and Promotion.—*Valentin A. Riva, 3635 Alton Place.
Panel of Experts:
  *Member.—*Rómulo de Almeida, c/o Pan American Union.
  *Member.—*Emilio Castañón Pasquel, c/o Pan American Union.
  *Member.—*Hollis B. Chenery, c/o Pan American Union.
  *Member.—*Ernesto Malaccorto, 608 Carper Street, McLean, Va.
  *Member.—*Jorge Méndez, c/o Pan American Union.
  *Member.—*Paul Rosenstein Rodan, 10 Emerson Place, Boston, Mass.
  *Coordinator.—*Raúl Hess, 3812 North Wakefield Street, Arlington, Va.
    *Secretary.—*Gerardo Canet, 5528 Westbard Avenue, Bethesda, Md.

ORGANIZATION FOR ECONOMIC CO-OPERATION AND DEVELOPMENT

Headquarters: Chateau de la Muette, 2 rue Andrè-Pascal, Paris, 16, France

*Member Countries.—*Austria, Belgium, Canada, Denmark, France, Germany, Greece, Iceland, Ireland, Italy, Japan, Luxemburg, Netherlands, Norway, Portugal, Spain, Sweden, Switzerland, Turkey, United Kingdom, United States; Observer: Yugoslavia.

The Commissions of the European Economic Community and of the European Atomic Energy Community, as well as the High Authority of the European Coal and Steel Community, take part in the work of the Organization.

The Council.—Chairman: Switzerland; Members: All Member countries voting by unanimity.

The Executive Committee.—Chairman: Belgium; Members: Canada, Denmark, France, Germany, Italy, Spain, Turkey, United Kingdom, United States.

The Economic Policy Committee.—Chairman: United Kingdom; Members: All Member countries.

The Trade Committee.—Chairman: Germany; Members: All Member countries.

The Development Assistance Committee.—Chairman: United States; Members: Belgium, Canada, Denmark, France, Germany, Italy, Japan, Netherlands, Norway, Portugal, United Kingdom, United States, European Economic Community.

The Council may establish subsidiary bodies as may be required to achieve the aims of the Organization.

THE SECRETARIAT

Chateau de la Muette, Paris (France).
Telephone: TRO. 7600/4610/7430.   Telegram: DEVELOPECONOMIE.

Secretary-General and Chairman of the Council at session of Permanent Representatives.—Thorkil Kristensen (Denmark).
Deputy Secretary-General.—Michael Harris (United States).
Deputy Secretary-General.—Jean Cottier (France).
Assistant Secretary-General (Economics).—Christopher Dow (United Kingdom).
Assistant Secretary-General (Development).—Luciano Giretti (Italy).
Assistant Secretary-General (Trade).—Wilhelm Hanemann (Germany).

WASHINGTON OFFICE

Suite 1223, 1346 Connecticut Avenue, 20036
Telephone: DUpont 7-4237.   Telegram: COPECON.

Head of Office.—Donald Mallett.

PAN AMERICAN HEALTH ORGANIZATION

Executive Organ: Pan American Sanitary Bureau (Regional Office for the Americas of the World Health Organization), 1501 New Hampshire Avenue, 20036.   Phone, HUdson 3-5280

PAN AMERICAN SANITARY BUREAU

Director.—Dr. Abraham Horwitz, 1501 New Hampshire Avenue.
Deputy Director.—Dr. John C. Cutler, 1501 New Hampshire Avenue.
Assistant Director.—Dr. Victor A. Sutter, 1501 New Hampshire Avenue.
Chief of Administration.—Dr. Stuart Portner, 1501 New Hampshire Avenue.
Zone I Representative, Caracas, Venezuela (Venezuela, Jamaica, Trinidad and Tobago, departments of France in the Americas, portions of the Kingdom of the Netherlands in the Americas, and members of the Commonwealth and territories of the United Kingdom in the Caribbean).—Dr. José L. García Gutiérrez, Avenida Los Jabillos 46, La Florida.
Zone II Representative, Mexico City, Mexico (Cuba, Dominican Republic, Haiti and Mexico).—Dr. Héctor Coll, Havre 30, Colonia Juárez.
Zone III Representative, Guatemala City, Guatemala (British Honduras, Costa Rica, El Salvador, Guatemala, Honduras, Nicaragua, Panama).—Dr. E. Ross Jenny, 7a. Avenida 8–92, Zone 9.
Zone IV Representative, Lima, Perú (Bolivia, Colombia, Ecuador and Perú).—Dr. Bogoslav Juricic, Ave. Salaverry 722.
Zone V Representative, Rio de Janeiro, Brazil (Brazil).—Dr. S. Renjifo Salcedo, Avenida General Justo 275–B.
Zone VI Representative, Buenos Aires, Argentina (Argentina, Chile, Paraguay, Uruguay).—Dr. Henrique Maia Penido, Marcelo T. de Alvear 684.
El Paso Field Office, El Paso, Texas.—Dr. Jorge Jimenez Gandica, Chief, 501 United States Court House.

PERMANENT JOINT BOARD ON DEFENSE, CANADA-UNITED STATES

Department of State Building. Phone, DUdley 3-4695

UNITED STATES SECTION

Chairman.—The Honorable H. Freeman Matthews, Rm 5511, Department of State.
Members:
  Maj. Gen. R. J. Clizbe, USAF, 7007 Eighth Street, Alexandria, Va.
  Rear Adm. Hazlett P. Weatherwax, USN, 3745 Orange Court, Alexandria, Va.
  Maj. Gen. William Peers, USA, 1512 South 22d Street, Arlington, Va.
  J. Harold Shullaw, Department of State, 3704 Leland Street, Chevy Chase, Md.
Secretary (Non-member).—Raymond J. Barrett, Department of State, 7505 Melvern Place, Alexandria, Va.

CANADIAN SECTION

Chairman.—The Honorable L. Dana Wilgress, Ottawa, Canada.
Members:
  Air Vice Marshal W. W. Bean, Canadian Defense Forces Member (Air).
  Commodore R. W. Murdoch, Canadian Defense Forces Member (Navy).
  Brigadier N. H. Ross, Canadian Defense Forces Member (Army).
  Arthur R. Menzies (Department of External Affairs).
Secretary (Non-member).—David H. W. Kirkwood (Department of External Affairs), Ottawa, Canada.

SOUTH PACIFIC COMMISSION

Department of State. Phone, DUdley 3-2839 (Code 182, extension 2839)

United States: (Department of State) Office of Southwest Pacific Affairs.
  Carlton Skinner, Senior Commissioner.
  Manuel Guerrero, Commissioner.
  Y. Baron Goto, Alternate Commissioner.
Australia: (Department of Territories, Canberra).
  R. Swift, Senior Commissioner.
  H. Max Loveday, Commissioner.
France: (Ministry of France Overseas, Paris).
  H. Nettre, Senior Commissioner.
  Bernard Hebert, Commissioner.
New Zealand: (Department of External Affairs, Wellington).
  J. B. Wright, Senior Commissioner.
  J. M. McEwen, Commissioner.
  G. Hensley, Alternate Commissioner.
United Kingdom: (Government House, Suva, Fiji).
  Sir Derek Jakeway, K.C.M.G., O.B.E., Senior Commissioner.
  T. R. Cowell, Commissioner.
  Sir Robert Foster, K.C.M.G., Alternate Commissioner.
Western Samoa: (Prime Minister's Department, Apia).
  The Hon. Laufili Time, Senior Commissioner.
  Lauofo Meti, Commissioner.

SECRETARIAT

Nouméa, New Caledonia

Secretary-General.—Mr. W. D. Forsyth.
Executive Officer for Health.—Dr. Guy Loison.
Executive Officer for Economic Development.—Mr. William Granger.
Executive Officer for Social Development.—Dr. R. E. Seddon.

UNITED NATIONS

GENERAL ASSEMBLY

Composed of all Member States of the United Nations. Each Member State has one vote.

Alex Quaison-Sackey of Ghana was elected President of the Nineteenth Session of the General Assembly. According to its Rules of Procedure, the General Assembly commences its regular session on the third Tuesday in September of each year. As of December 1, 1964, the following 115 countries were members of the United Nations:

Afghanistan
Albania
Algeria
*Argentina
*Australia
Austria
*Belgium
*Bolivia
*Brazil
Bulgaria
Burma
Burundi
*Byelorussian
Cambodia
Cameroon
*Canada
Central African Republic
Ceylon
Chad
*Chile
*China
*Colombia
Congo (Brazzaville)
Congo (Democratic
  Republic of)
*Costa Rica
*Cuba
Cyprus
*Czechoslovakia
Dahomey
*Denmark
*Dominican Republic
*Ecuador
*El Salvador
*Ethiopia
Finland
*France
Gabon
Ghana

*Greece
*Guatemala
Guinea
*Haiti
*Honduras
Hungary
Iceland
*India
Indonesia [4]
*Iran
*Iraq
Ireland
Israel
Italy
Ivory Coast
Jamaica
Japan
Jordan
Kenya
Kuwait
Laos
*Lebanon
*Liberia
Libya
*Luxembourg
Madagascar
Malawi
Malaysia
Mali
Malta
Mauritania
*Mexico
Mongolia
Morocco
Nepal
*Netherlands
*New Zealand
*Nicaragua
Niger

Nigeria
*Norway
Pakistan
*Panama
*Paraguay
*Peru
*Philippines
*Poland
Portugal
Romania
Rwanda
*Saudi Arabia
Senegal
Sierra Leone
Somalia
*South Africa
Spain
Sudan
Sweden
*Syria [1]
Thailand
Togo
Trinidad and Tobago
Tunisia
*Turkey
Uganda
*Ukraine
*USSR
*United Arab Republic [2]
*United Kingdom
United Republic of
  Tanzania [3]
*United States
Upper Volta
*Uruguay
*Venezuela
Yemen
*Yugoslavia
Zambia

*Original member.

[1] Syria was an original member of the United Nations from 24 October 1945. Following a plebiscite held on 21 February 1958, Syria and Egypt joined in establishing the United Arab Republic, which continued as a single member of the United Nations. On 13 October 1961 Syria, having resumed its status as an independent state, also resumed its separate membership in the Organization.

[2] Egypt was an original Member of the United Nations from 24 October 1945. Following a plebiscite held on 21 February 1958, the United Arab Republic was established by a union of Egypt and Syria and continued as a single Member of the United Nations. On 13 October 1961 Syria, having resumed its status as an independent State, resumed its separate membership.

[3] Tanganyika was a Member of the United Nations from 14 December 1961 and Zanzibar was a Member from 16 December 1963. Following the ratification, on 26 April 1964, of Articles of Union between Tanganyika and Zanzibar, the United Republic of Tanganyika and Zanzibar continued as a single Member of the United Nations, later changing its name to United Republic of Tanzania.

[4] On 21 January the Permanent Representative of Indonesia, Lambertus N. Palar, handed to the Secretary-General, U Thant, a letter dated 20 January 1965 from the First Deputy Prime Minister of Indonesia, Dr. Subandrio, stating that Indonesia had withdrawn from the United Nations and "from specialized agencies like the FAO, UNICEF and UNESCO". The letter stated: "While our actual withdrawal from the United Nations has already been carried out in New York as of 1 January 1965, I would suggest that, due to the technical winding up of the Indonesian Permanent Mission in New York and reciprocally your Office in Indonesia, officially our respective offices would be closed on 1 March 1965."

SECURITY COUNCIL

The Security Council is composed of five permanent members and six nonpermanent members, elected by the General Assembly for two-year terms. Nonpermanent members are not eligible for immediate reelection.

Permanent Members:	*Nonpermanent Members:*
China	Bolivia (through 1965)
France	Ivory Coast (through 1965)
U.S.S.R.	*Jordan (through 1965)
United Kingdom	**Malaysia (through 1965)
United States	Netherlands (through 1966)
	Uruguay (through 1966)

Presidency:

The Presidency of the Security Council, in accordance with its rules of procedure, rotates each month in the English alphabetical order of the names of the member States.

Military Staff Committee:

Composed of the Chiefs of Staff (or their representatives) of the five Permanent Members of the Security Council: China, France, U.S.S.R., United Kingdom and the United States. The chairmanship rotates in the same manner as the presidency of the Security Council.

Disarmament Commission:

Under the resolution adopted by the General Assembly at its thirteenth regular session on 4 November 1958, the Disarmament Commission is composed of all the members of the United Nations.

ECONOMIC AND SOCIAL COUNCIL

The Economic and Social Council is composed of eighteen members, six of which are elected each year by the General Assembly for a three-year term of office. Retiring members are eligible for immediate re-election.

Algeria (through 1966)	Iraq (through 1966)
Argentina (through 1965)	Japan (through 1965)
Austria (through 1965)	Luxembourg (through 1966)
Canada (through 1967)	Pakistan (through 1967)
Chile (through 1966)	Peru (through 1967)
Czechoslovakia (through 1965)	Romania (through 1967)
Ecuador (through 1966)	USSR (through 1965)
France (through 1966)	United Kingdom (through 1965)
Gabon (through 1967)	United States (through 1967)

TRUSTEESHIP COUNCIL

Composed of Member States administering Trust Territories, permanent members of the Security Council which do not administer Trust Territories, and enough other non-administering countries to provide a balance between countries administering Trust Territories and those that do not. The latter are elected by the General Assembly for a term of three years. Elected members of the Council are eligible, on the expiry of their terms of office, for immediate re-election.

Countries Administering Trust Territories:

Australia	United Kingdom
New Zealand	United States

Permanent Members of the Security Council not Administering Trust Territories:

China   France   Union of Soviet Socialist Republics

Country not Administering Trust Territories Elected by the General Assembly:

Liberia (until 1966)

---

*Regarding the two-year term 1965–66, it was agreed that Jordan would serve in 1965 and Mali in 1966.
**The two-year term 1964–65 was divided between Czechoslovakia and Malaysia, Czechoslovakia serving in 1964 and Malaysia in 1965.

INTERNATIONAL COURT OF JUSTICE

The International Court of Justice is the principal judicial organ of the United Nations. All Members of the United Nations are automatically parties to the Statute of the International Court of Justice. Other states can refer cases to the Court under conditions laid down by the Security Council. Except for judicial vacations, the Court is permanently in session at The Hague, Netherlands. Judges are elected by the General Assembly and the Security Council, voting independently, for a term of nine years and are eligible for reelection.

Name	*Nationality*
Abdel Hamid Badawi (1967)	United Arab Republic
Jose Luis Bustamante y Rivero (1970)	Peru
Sir Gerald Fitzmaurice (1973)	United Kingdom
Isaac Forster (1973)	Senegal
Andre Gros (1973)	France
Philip C. Jessup (1970)	United States
V. K. Wellington Koo (1967) Vice-President	China
Vladimir M. Koretsky (1970)	USSR
Gaetano Morelli (1970)	Italy
Luis Padilla Nervo (1973)	Mexico
Sir Percy Spender (1967) President	Australia
Jean Spiropoulous (1967)	Greece
Kotaro Tanaka (1970)	Japan
Bohdan Winiarski (1967)	Poland
Sir Muhammad Zafrulla Khan (1973)	Pakistan

Registrar: Jean Garnier-Coignet (France)

(All terms expire February 5 of the year designated.)

SECRETARIAT

United Nations, New York, N.Y. Phone, PLaza 4-1234

Secretary-General.—U Thant (Burma).

Officials of Under-Secretary Rank at Headquarters:

Ibrahim Helmi Abdel-Rahman (United Arab Republic), Commissioner for Industrial Development.

Godfrey K. J. Amachree (Nigeria), Under-Secretary for Trusteeship and Information from Non-Self-Governing Territories.

Ralph J. Bunche (United States), Under-Secretary for Special Political Affairs and in charge of UN Civilian Operation in the Congo.

Philippe de Seynes (France), Under-Secretary for Economic and Social Affairs.

Roberto Heurtematte (Panama), Associate Managing Director, UN Special Fund.

Paul G. Hoffman (United States), Managing Director, UN Special Fund.

Victor Hoo (China), Commissioner for Technical Assistance.

Sir Alexander MacFarquhar (United Kingdom), Director of Personnel.

C. V. Narasimhan (India), Under-Secretary for General Assembly Affairs and Chef de Cabinet of the Secretary-General.

Jiri Nosek (Czechoslovakia), Under-Secretary for Conference Services.

David Owen (United Kingdom), Executive Chairman, Technical Assistance Board.

E. J. R. Heyward (Australia), Acting Executive Director, UN Children's Fund.

Dragoslav Protitch (Yugoslavia), Director, United Nations Training Programme for Foreign Service Officers from Newly Independent Countries.

José Rolz-Bennett, Under-Secretary for Special Political Affairs.

Constantin A. Stavropoulos (Greece), Legal Counsel.

Vladimir Pavlovich Suslov (USSR), Under-Secretary for Political and Security Council Affairs.

Hernane Tavares de Sa (Brazil), Under-Secretary for Public Information.

Bruce Turner (New Zealand), Controller.

David B. Vaughan (United States), Director of General Services.

EUROPEAN OFFICE OF THE UNITED NATIONS

Palais des Nations, Geneva, Switzerland

Director of the European Office.—Pier Pasquale Spinelli (Italy).

Deputy Director.—Georges Palthey (France).

UNITED NATIONS ECONOMIC COMMISSION FOR EUROPE
Palais des Nations, Geneva, Switzerland

Executive Secretary.—Vladimir Velebit (Yugoslavia).

UNITED NATIONS ECONOMIC COMMISSION FOR ASIA AND THE FAR EAST
Sala Santitham, Rajadamnern Avenue, Bangkok, Thailand

Executive Secretary.—U Nyun (Burma).

UNITED NATIONS ECONOMIC COMMISSION FOR LATIN AMERICA
Avenida Providencia 871, Santiago, Chile

Mexico Office: Apartado Postal 20718, Mexico 6, D. F., Mexico

Executive Secretary.—José Antonio Mayobre (Venezuela).
Chief of Washington Group.—David H. Pollock (Canada), Room 905, 1028 Connecticut Avenue.   Phone, 296–0822.

UNITED NATIONS ECONOMIC COMMISSION FOR AFRICA
Africa Hall, Addis Ababa, Ethiopia

Executive Secretary.—Robert K. A. Gardiner (Ghana).

UNITED NATIONS WASHINGTON INFORMATION CENTER
1028 Connecticut Avenue.   Phone, 296–5370

Director.—Hernando Samper (Columbia), as of May 1965.

INTERGOVERNMENTAL AGENCIES RELATED TO THE UNITED NATIONS

FOOD AND AGRICULTURE ORGANIZATION
Headquarters: Viale delle Terme di Caracalla, Rome, Italy

Headquarters:
  Director-General.—B. R. Sen (India).
North American Regional Office.—1325 C Street SW., Washington, D.C.
  Director.—Harold A. Vogel.

INTERGOVERNMENTAL MARITIME CONSULTATIVE ORGANIZATION
Headquarters: Chancery House, Chancery Lane, London, W.C.2, England

Headquarters:
  Secretary-General.—Jean Roullier (France).

INTERIM COMMISSION FOR INTERNATIONAL TRADE ORGANIZATION
(Contracting Parties to General Agreement on Tariffs and Trade)

Headquarters: Villa le Bocage, Palais des Nations, Geneva, Switzerland

Headquarters:
  Executive Secretary of Interim Commission and GATT Parties.—Eric Wyndham White (United Kingdom).

INTERNATIONAL ATOMIC ENERGY AGENCY
Headquarters: Kaerntnerring, Vienna I, Austria

Headquarters:
  Director-General.—Dr. Sigvard Eklund (Sweden).
Representative of the Director-General to the United Nations, N.Y.—Evgueni V. Piskarev.

39–650°—65——48

INTERNATIONAL BANK FOR RECONSTRUCTION AND DEVELOPMENT

Headquarters: 1818 H Street, Washington, D.C.

Headquarters:
  President.—George D. Woods (United States).

INTERNATIONAL CIVIL AVIATION ORGANIZATION

Headquarters: International Aviation Building, Montreal, Canada

Headquarters:
  Secretary-General.—Ronald M. Macdonnell (Canada).

INTERNATIONAL DEVELOPMENT ASSOCIATION

(International Development Association is an affiliate of the International Bank)

Headquarters: 1818 H Street, Washington, D.C.

Headquarters:
  President.—George D. Woods (United States) (ex officio).

INTERNATIONAL FINANCE CORPORATION

(International Finance Corporation is an affiliate of the International Bank)

Headquarters: 1818 H Street, Washington, D.C.

Headquarters:
  President.—George D. Woods (United States) (ex officio).

INTERNATIONAL LABOR ORGANIZATION

Headquarters: 154 Rue de Lausanne, 1211 Geneva 22, Switzerland

Headquarters:
  Director-General.—David A. Morse (United States).
Washington Branch.—International Labor Office, 917 15th Street.
  Director.—Ralph Wright.

INTERNATIONAL MONETARY FUND

Headquarters: Nineteenth and H Streets, Washington, D.C.

Headquarters:
  Managing Director.—Pierre-Paul Schweitzer (France).

INTERNATIONAL TELECOMMUNICATION UNION

Headquarters: Place des Nations, Geneva, Switzerland

Headquarters:
  Secretary General.—Gerald C. Gross (United States of America).

UNITED NATIONS EDUCATIONAL, SCIENTIFIC AND CULTURAL ORGANIZATION

Headquarters: Place de Fontenoy, Paris 7e, France

Headquarters:
  Director-General.—Rene Maheu (France).
  Deputy Director-General.—Malcolm Adiseshiah (India).
New York Office (United Nations):
  Director.—Arthur F. Gagliotti.

UNIVERSAL POSTAL UNION

Headquarters: Case Postale 3000 Bern 15, Switzerland

Headquarters:
  Director of the International Bureau.—Dr. Edouard Weber (Switzerland).

WORLD HEALTH ORGANIZATION

Headquarters: Palais des Nations, Geneva, Switzerland

Headquarters:
  Director-General.—Dr. M. G. Candau (Brazil).
Regional Office for the Americas.—1501 New Hampshire Avenue, Washington, D.C.
  Director.—Dr. Abraham Horowitz.
  Public Information Office.—Roberto Rendueles.

WORLD METEOROLOGICAL ORGANIZATION

Headquarters: 41 Avenue Giuseppe Motta, Geneva, Switzerland

Headquarters:
  Secretary-General.—David A. Davies (United Kingdom).
New York Representative.—Louis Harmantas (Weather Bureau Airport Station, CAA Operations Building, Hangar 11, J. F. Kennedy International Airport).

VALIDATION BOARD FOR GERMAN DOLLAR BONDS

30 Broad Street, New York, N.Y.   Phone, BOwling Green 9-8070

United States Member.—Saul L. Sherman, 45 Christopher Street, New York, N.Y., 10014.
German Member.—Dr. Helmut Mueller-Dethard, 5820 Tanglewood Drive, Washington, D.C., 20034.
Chairman of the Board.—David A. Stretch (acts only to resolve differences between the United States and German members).

UNIVERSAL POSTAL UNION

Headquarters: Case Postale 3000 Bern 15, Switzerland

Headmaster:

Deputy of the Intternatiional Bureau of the Biblical of Webster (Switzerland)

WORLD HEALTH ORGANIZATION

Headquarters: Pavillon du Bureau, Geneva, Switzerland

Branches:

Regional Office, Dr. M. The Central Official,
Pan-American Sanitary Bureau, 1501 New Hampshire Avenue, Washington, D.C.
Director, Dr. Abraham Horwitz.
Field Coordination Officer—Chief—Dr. Horwitz.

WORLD METEOROLOGICAL ORGANIZATION

Headquarters: 41 Avenue Giuseppe Motta, Geneva, Switzerland

Headquarters:
Secretary-General—David A. Davies (United Kingdom).
New York Representative—John Dominika (World Weather Bureau service),
ICAA Operations Building, Hangar H, J.F. Kennedy International Airport.

VALIDATION BOARD FOR GERMAN DOLLAR BONDS

30 Broad Street, New York, N.Y., Pierre Michaelis, Chairman

Vice-Chairman—Werner Schell, Landmark, 25 Chestnut Street, New York,
N.Y., 10005.

Secretary-Member—Dr. Hellmut Mueller-Bernhard, 5420 Trenchwood Drive,
Washington, D.C. 20015.

(Chairman of the Board—David A. Black (arbitral, to resolve differences between
the United States and German nationals).

FOREIGN DIPLOMATIC REPRESENTATIVES AND FOREIGN CONSULAR OFFICES IN THE UNITED STATES

FOREIGN DIPLOMATIC REPRESENTATIVES AND FOREIGN CONSULAR OFFICES IN THE UNITED STATES

[For complete Diplomatic personnel consult Diplomatic List published quarterly by the Department of State. The * designates those whose wives or husbands accompany them. The † designates those whose unmarried daughters in society accompany them]

AFGHANISTAN

Office of the Embassy, 2341 Wyoming Avenue
Phone, ADams 4-3770

*Dr. Abdul Majid, Ambassador Extraordinary and Plenipotentiary

Consular Office: New York, New York City

ALGERIA

Office of the Embassy, 2200 R Street
Phone, 234-7246

Mr. Cherif Guellal, Ambassador Extraordinary and Plenipotentiary

ARGENTINA

Office of the Embassy, 1600 New Hampshire Avenue
Phone, DEcatur 2-7100

*Dr. Norbert M. Barrenechea, Ambassador Extraordinary and Plenipotentiary

Consular Offices:
California {Los Angeles / San Francisco
Florida, Miami
Illinois, Chicago
Louisiana, New Orleans
Maryland, Baltimore
Massachusetts, Boston
New York, New York City
Texas, Houston

AUSTRALIA

Office of the Embassy, 1700 Massachusetts Avenue
Phone, NOrth 7-6551

*††Mr. John Keith Waller, Ambassador Extraordinary and Plenipotentiary

Consular Offices:
California, San Francisco
District of Columbia, Washington
New York, New York City

AUSTRIA

Office of the Embassy, 2343 Massachusetts Avenue
Phone, DUpont 7-2477

*Dr. Wilfried Platzer, Ambassador Extraordinary and Plenipotentiary

Consular Offices:
California {Los Angeles / San Francisco
District of Columbia, Washington
Florida, Miami
Georgia, Atlanta
Illinois, Chicago
Louisiana, New Orleans
Massachusetts, Boston
Michigan, Detroit

AUSTRIA—Continued

Consular Offices—Continued
New York, New York City
Ohio, Cleveland
Oregon, Portland
Pennsylvania, Philadelphia
Texas, Dallas
Washington, Seattle

BELGIUM

Office of the Embassy, 3330 Garfield Street
Phone, FEderal 3-6900

*†Mr. Louis Scheyven, Ambassador Extraordinary and Plenipotentiary

Consular Offices:
Alabama, Mobile
Arizona, Phoenix
California {Los Angeles / San Francisco
Canal Zone, Colón, Panama
Colorado, Denver
Florida {Miami / Tampa
Georgia {Atlanta / Savannah
Hawaii, Honolulu
Illinois {Chicago / Moline
Indiana, South Bend
Iowa, Des Moines
Kentucky, Louisville
Louisiana, New Orleans
Maryland, Baltimore
Massachusetts, Boston
Michigan, Detroit
Minnesota, Minneapolis
Missouri {Kansas City / St. Louis
New York, New York City
Ohio {Cincinnati / Cleveland
Oregon, Portland
Pennsylvania, Pittsburgh
Puerto Rico, San Juan
Texas {Dallas / Galveston / Houston
Utah, Salt Lake City
Virgin Islands, Charlotte Amalie
Washington, Seattle
Wisconsin, Green Bay

BOLIVIA

Office of the Embassy, Suite B 1250, 3636 16th Street
Phone, 667-5712

Mr. Guillermo Scott-Murga, Charge d'Affaires a.i.

Consular Offices:
California {Los Angeles / San Francisco / San Leandro

BOLIVIA—Continued

Consular Offices—Continued

District of Columbia, Washington
Florida {Key West / Miami}
Illinois, Chicago
Iowa, West Des Moines
Louisiana, New Orleans
Massachusetts, Boston
Missouri, St. Louis
New York, New York City
Pennsylvania, Philadelphia
Puerto Rico, San Juan
Texas {Dallas / Galveston / Houston}
Virginia {Hampton Roads / Richmond}

BRAZIL

Office of the Embassy, 3007 Whitehaven Street
Phone, ADams 2-1164

*Mr. Juracy Magalhães, Ambassador Extraordinary and Plenipotentiary

Consular Offices:
California {Los Angeles / San Francisco}
District of Columbia, Washington
Florida {Miami / Tampa}
Georgia, Savannah
Illinois, Chicago
Louisiana, New Orleans
Maryland, Baltimore
Massachusetts {Boston / New Bedford}
New York, New York City
North Carolina, Wilmington
Pennsylvania {Chester / Philadelphia}
South Carolina, Charleston
Texas, Houston
Virginia, Norfolk
Washington, Seattle

BULGARIA

Office of the Legation, 2100 Sixteenth Street
Phone, DUpont 7-7969

*Mr. Lyubomir Popov, Envoy Extraordinary and Minister Plenipotentiary

BURMA

Office of the Embassy, 2300 S Street
Phone, DEcatur 2-9044

*U On Sein, Ambassador Extraordinary and Plenipotentiary
Consular Offices:
District of Columbia, Washington
New York, New York City

BURUNDI

Office of the Embassy, 2018 R Street
Phone, 387-4477

*Mr. Leon Ndenzako, Ambassador Extraordinary and Plenipotentiary

CAMBODIA

Office of the Embassy, 4500 Sixteenth Street
Phone, RAndolph 3-8500

CAMEROUN

Office of the Embassy, 5420 Colorado Avenue
Phone, RAndolph 3-8440

*Mr. Jacques Kuoh Moukouri, Ambassador Extraordinary and Plenipotentiary

CANADA

Office of the Embassy, 1746 Massachusetts Avenue
Phone, DEcatur 2-1011

*Mr. Charles S. A. Ritchie, Ambassador Extraordinary and Plenipotentiary

Consular Offices:
California {Los Angeles / San Francisco}
District of Columbia, Washington
Illinois, Chicago
Louisiana, New Orleans
Massachusetts, Boston
Michigan, Detroit
New York, New York City
Ohio, Cleveland
Pennsylvania, Philadelphia
Washington, Seattle

CENTRAL AFRICAN REPUBLIC

Office of the Embassy, 1618 22d Street
Phone, 265-5637

*Mr. Michel Gallin-Douathe, Ambassador Extraordinary and Plenipotentiary

CEYLON

Office of the Embassy, 2148 Wyoming Avenue
Phone, HUdson 3-4025

*Mr. M. F. de S. Jayaratne, Ambassador Extraordinary and Plenipotentiary
Consular Office: California, San Francisco

CHAD

Office of the Embassy, 1132 New Hampshire Avenue
Phone, 965-1696

*Mr. Boukar Abdoul, Ambassador Extraordinary and Plenipotentiary

CHILE

Office of the Embassy, 1736 Massachusetts Avenue
Phone, NOrth 7-0746

*Mr. Radomiro Tomic, Ambassador Extraordinary and Plenipotentiary

Consular Offices:
Alabama, Mobile
California {Long Beach / Los Angeles / Oakland / San Diego / San Francisco / Santa Monica}
Florida {Miami / West Palm Beach}
Hawaii, Honolulu
Illinois {Chicago / Evanston}
Louisiana, New Orleans
Maryland, Baltimore
Massachusetts, Boston
Michigan, Detroit
Minnesota, St. Paul
Missouri, Kansas City
New Jersey, Jersey City
New York {Ithaca / New York City}
Pennsylvania, Philadelphia
Puerto Rico, San Juan
Texas {Dallas / Fort Worth / Galveston}
Washington, Seattle
Wisconsin, Milwaukee

CHINA

Office of the Embassy, 2311 Massachusetts Avenue
Phone, NOrth 7-9000

*Dr. Tingfu F. Tsiang, Ambassador Extraordinary and Plenipotentiary
Consular Offices:
California {Los Angeles / San Francisco}

CHINA—Continued
Consular Offices—Continued
- Hawaii, Honolulu
- Illinois, Chicago
- New York, New York City
- Texas, Houston
- Washington, Seattle

COLOMBIA
Office of the Embassy, 2118 LeRoy Place
Phone, DUpont 7-5828

Dr. Eduardo Uribe, Ambassador Extraordinary and Plenipotentiary

Consular Offices:
- Alabama, Mobile
- California {Los Angeles, San Francisco}
- Canal Zone {Colón, Panama; Panamá, Panama}
- Florida {Jacksonville, Miami, Tampa}
- Illinois, Chicago
- Louisiana, New Orleans
- Maryland, Baltimore
- Massachusetts, Boston
- Michigan, Detroit
- Minnesota {Minneapolis, Rochester}
- Missouri, Kansas City
- New York, New York City
- Pennsylvania {Philadelphia, Pittsburgh}
- Puerto Rico {Mayagüez, San Juan}
- Texas {Dallas, Houston}
- Washington, Seattle

CONGO (BRAZZAVILLE)
Office of the Embassy, 4891 Colorado Avenue
Phone, 723-3440

*Mr. Jonas Mouanza, Ambassador Extraordinary and Plenipotentiary

CONGO (LÉOPOLDVILLE)
Office of the Embassy, 4800 Sixteenth Street
Phone, 829-0190

*Mr. Mario Cardoso, Minister Plenipotentiary, Chargé d'Affaires

COSTA RICA
Office of the Embassy, 2112 S Street
Phone, ADams 4-2945

*Mr. Gonzalo J. Facio, Ambassador Extraordinary and Plenipotentiary

Consular Offices:
- Alabama, Mobile
- California {Los Angeles, San Diego, San Francisco, South Pasadena}
- Canal Zone, Cristóbal
- Colorado, Denver
- Connecticut, Norwalk
- District of Columbia, Washington
- Florida {Coral Gables, Jacksonville, Miami, St. Petersburg, Tampa}
- Georgia {Atlanta, Savannah}
- Hawaii, Honolulu
- Illinois, Chicago
- Iowa, Garwin
- Kansas {Kansas City, Lawrence}
- Kentucky, Lexington
- Louisiana {Baton Rouge, New Orleans}
- Maryland, Baltimore
- Massachusetts {Boston, Springfield}
- Michigan {Detroit, Lansing}
- Minnesota {Minneapolis, Rochester}

COSTA RICA—Continued
Consular Offices—Continued
- Missouri, St. Louis
- New Jersey {Elizabeth, Plainfield}
- New York {New York City, Rochester}
- Ohio, Cleveland
- Oklahoma, Tulsa
- Oregon, Portland
- Pennsylvania {Philadelphia, Pittsburgh}
- Puerto Rico, San Juan
- Tennessee {Chattanooga, Memphis, Nashville}
- Texas {Corpus Christi, Dallas, El Paso, Houston, San Antonio}
- Virginia, Richmond
- Washington, Seattle
- Wisconsin, Milwaukee

CYPRUS
Office of the Embassy, 2211 R Street
Phone, 423-4920

*Mr. Zenon Rossides, Ambassador Extraordinary and Plenipotentiary

Consular Office:
- Massachusetts, Boston
- New York, New York City

CZECHOSLOVAKIA
Office of the Embassy, 2349 Massachusetts Avenue
Phone, NOrth 7-3301

*Dr. Karel Duda, Ambassador Extraordinary and Plenipotentiary

DAHOMEY
Office of the Embassy, 6600 16th Street
Phone, 829-9394

*Louis Ignacio Pinto, Ambassador Extraordinary and Plenipotentiary

DENMARK
Office of the Embassy, 3200 Whitehaven Street
Phone, ADams 4-4300

*†Count Kield Gustav Knuth-Winterfeldt, Ambassador Extraordinary and Plenipotentiary

Consular Offices:
- Alabama, Mobile
- Alaska, Anchorage
- California {Los Angeles, San Diego, San Francisco}
- Canal Zone {Colón, Panama; Panamá, Panama}
- Colorado, Denver
- District of Columbia, Washington
- Florida {Jacksonville, Miami, Tampa}
- Georgia, Savannah
- Hawaii, Honolulu
- Illinois, Chicago
- Iowa, Des Moines
- Louisiana, New Orleans
- Maryland, Baltimore
- Massachusetts, Boston
- Michigan, Detroit
- Minnesota, Minneapolis
- Missouri {Kansas City, St. Louis}
- Nebraska, Omaha
- New York, New York City
- Ohio, Cleveland
- Oregon, Portland
- Pennsylvania, Philadelphia
- Puerto Rico {Ponce, San Juan}
- South Carolina, Charleston

DENMARK—Continued

Consular Offices—Continued

Texas { Dallas / Galveston / Houston
Utah, Salt Lake City
Virginia { Newport News / Norfolk
Virgin Islands { Charlotte Amalie / Christiansted
Washington, Seattle

DOMINICAN REPUBLIC

Office of the Embassy, 1715 Twenty-second Street

Phone, DEcatur 2-6280

*Dr. Jose Antonio Bonilla Atiles, Ambassador Extraordinary and Plenipotentiary

Consular Offices:

Alabama, Mobile
California { Los Angeles / San Francisco / Santa Barbara
Canal Zone { Cristóbal / Panamá, Panama
Colorado, Denver
District of Columbia, Washington
Florida { Gainesville / Hollywood / Jacksonville / Miami / Panama City / Pensacola / Tallahassee / Tampa / West Palm Beach
Georgia { Atlanta / Savannah
Illinois, Chicago
Indiana, Fort Wayne
Louisiana { Lake Charles / New Orleans
Maryland, Baltimore
Massachusetts, Boston
Michigan, Detroit
Minnesota { Duluth / Minneapolis / Rochester
Mississippi, Biloxi
Montana, Great Falls
New Jersey, Orange
New Mexico, Albuquerque
New York { Buffalo / New York City
North Carolina { Charlotte / Raleigh
Ohio { Cincinnati / Cleveland / Dayton
Oregon, Portland
Pennsylvania, Philadelphia
Puerto Rico { Arecibo / Guanica / Mayagüez / Ponce / San Juan
Rhode Island, Providence
Tennessee { Knoxville / Memphis / Nashville
Texas { Dallas / Fort Worth / Galveston / Houston / Port Arthur
Virgin Islands { Charlotte Amalie / Christiansted
Virginia, Richmond
Washington, Seattle
Wisconsin, Milwaukee

ECUADOR

Office of the Embassy, 2535 15th Street

Phone, ADams 4-7200

*Mr. Gustavo Larrea, Ambassador Extraordinary and Plenipotentiary

ECUADOR—Continued

Consular Offices:

Alabama, Mobile
Arizona, Phoenix
California { Inglewood / Los Angeles / San Diego / San Francisco
Canal Zone { Colon / Panama
District of Columbia, Washington
Florida { Miami / Tampa
Georgia, Atlanta
Illinois, Chicago
Louisiana, New Orleans
Maryland, Baltimore
Massachusetts, Boston
Michigan, Detroit
Missouri { Kansas City / St. Louis
New York { Buffalo / New York City
Ohio { Cincinnati / Cleveland
Pennsylvania, Philadelphia
Puerto Rico, San Juan
Texas, Houston
Virginia { Norfolk / Richmond
Washington, Seattle
Wisconsin, Milwaukee

EL SALVADOR

Office of the Embassy, 2308 California Street

Phone, COlumbia 5-3480

*Mr. Ramon de Clairmont Duenas, Ambassador Extraordinary and Plenipotentiary

Consular Offices:

Alabama, Mobile
Arizona, Phoenix
California { Berkeley / Burlingame / Long Beach / Los Altos / Los Angeles / Richmond / San Francisco / San Mateo / Santa Barbara
Florida { Miami / Tampa
Georgia, Atlanta
Hawaii, Honolulu
Illinois, Chicago
Louisiana, New Orleans
Maryland, Baltimore
Massachusetts, Boston
Michigan, Detroit
Minnesota, Minneapolis
Missouri, St. Louis
Nevada, Reno
New York { New York City / Rochester
Oregon, Portland
Pennsylvania, Philadelphia
Puerto Rico, San Juan
Texas { Dallas / Houston / Laredo / San Antonio
Virgin Islands, Charlotte Amalie
Washington, Seattle
Wisconsin, Madison

ESTONIA

Office of the Consulate General, 9 Rockefeller Plaza

New York City

Phone, CIrcle 7-1450

*Mr. Johannes Kaiv, Acting Consul General of Estonia at New York City in charge of Legation

Consular Offices:

California, Los Angeles
New York, New York City

ETHIOPIA

Office of the Embassy, 2134 Kalorama Road
Phone, ADams 4-2281

Mr. Berhanou Dinke, Ambassador Extraordinary
and Plenipotentiary

Consular Office: California, San Francisco

FINLAND

Office of the Embassy, 1900 Twenty-fourth Street
Phone, HObart 2-0556

*Mr. Olavi Munkki, Ambassador Extraordinary
and Plenipotentiary

Consular Offices:
Alabama, Mobile
Alaska, Anchorage
Arizona, Phoenix
California {Los Angeles
San Diego
San Francisco
Canal Zone, Colón, Panama
Colorado, Denver
Connecticut, Danielson
Florida {Jacksonville
Lake Worth
Miami
Georgia, Savannah
Hawaii, Honolulu
Illinois, Chicago
Louisiana, New Orleans
Maine, Norway
Maryland, Baltimore
Massachusetts {Boston
Fitchburg
Michigan {Detroit
Hancock
Negaunee
Minnesota {Duluth
Minneapolis
Virginia
Missouri, Kansas City
Montana, Butte
New York, New York City
North Carolina, Wilmington
Ohio {Ashtabula
Cleveland
Astoria
Oregon, Portland
Pennsylvania, Philadelphia
Puerto Rico, San Juan
Texas {Dallas
Houston
Utah, Salt Lake City
Virginia, Newport News
Washington, Seattle

FRANCE

Office of the Embassy, 2535 Belmont Road
Phone, ADams 4-0990

*Mr. Hervé Alphand, Ambassador Extraordinary
and Plenipotentiary

Consular Offices:
Alabama {Birmingham
Montgomery
Alaska {Anchorage
Juneau
American Samoa, Pago Pago
Arizona, Phoenix
California {Los Angeles
San Francisco
Colorado, Denver
District of Columbia, Washington
Florida {Jacksonville
Miami
Georgia {Atlanta
Savannah
Hawaii, Honolulu
Illinois, Chicago
Indiana, Indianapolis
Kentucky, Louisville
Louisiana {Lafayette
New Orleans
Shreveport

FRANCE—Continued

Consular Offices—Continued
Maine, Portland
Maryland, Baltimore
Massachusetts, Boston
Michigan, Detroit
Minnesota {Minneapolis
St. Paul
Mississippi, Gulfport
Missouri {Kansas City
St. Louis
Nebraska, Omaha
Nevada, Reno
New York {Buffalo
New York City
North Dakota, Bismarck
Ohio {Cincinnati
Cleveland
Columbus
Oklahoma {Oklahoma City
Tulsa
Oregon, Portland
Pennsylvania, Philadelphia
Puerto Rico {Mayagüez
Ponce
San Juan
Rhode Island, Providence
South Carolina, Charleston
Texas {Dallas
Houston
San Antonio
Utah, Salt Lake City
Virginia, Norfolk
Virgin Islands, Charlotte Amalie
Washington, Seattle
West Virginia, Wheeling
Wyoming, Rock Springs

GABON

Office of the Embassy, 4900 16th Street
829-9070

Mr. Aristide Issembe, Ambassador Extraordinary
and Plenipotentiary

GERMANY

Office of the Embassy, 4645 Reservoir Road
Phone, 331-3000

*Mr. Heinrich Knappstein, Ambassador Extraordinary and Plenipotentiary

Consular Offices:
Alabama, Mobile
Alaska, Anchorage
Arizona, Phoenix
California {Los Angeles
San Diego
San Francisco
Canal Zone. Colón, Panama
Colorado, Denver
District of Columbia, Washington
Dominican Republic, Santo Domingo
(for Puerto Rico and the Virgin Islands)
Florida, Miami
Georgia {Atlanta
Savannah
Hawaii, Honolulu
Illinois, Chicago
Louisiana, New Orleans
Massachusetts, Boston
Michigan, Detroit
Minnesota, Minneapolis
Missouri, Kansas City
New York, New York City
Ohio, Cleveland
Oklahoma, Oklahoma City
Oregon, Portland
Pacific Islands {Manila
Philippines
Pennsylvania, Philadelphia
Puerto Rico, San Juan
Texas {Dallas
Houston
Utah, Salt Lake City
Virginia, Norfolk
Washington, Seattle

GHANA

Office of the Embassy, 2460 Sixteenth Street
Phone, 462-0761

*Mr. Miguel Augustus Ribeiro, Ambassador Extraordinary and Plenipotentiary
Consular Office: New York, New York City

GREAT BRITAIN

Office of the Embassy, 3100 Massachusetts Avenue
Phone, HObart 2-1340

*†The Right Honorable The Lord Harlech, K.C.M.G. Ambassador Extraordinary and Plenipotentiary

Consular Offices:
California{Los Angeles
{San Francisco
Colorado, Denver
District of Columbia, Washington
Florida, Miami
Georgia, Atlanta
Hawaii, Honolulu
Illinois, Chicago
Louisiana, New Orleans
Maryland, Baltimore
Massachusetts, Boston
Michigan, Detroit
Minnesota, Minneapolis and St. Paul
Missouri{Kansas City
{St. Louis
New York, New York City
Ohio, Cleveland
Oregon, Portland
Pacific Islands, Suva
Pennsylvania, Philadelphia
Puerto Rico, San Juan
Texas, Houston
Virginia, Norfolk
Virgin Islands, Charlotte Amalie
Washington, Seattle

GREECE

Office of the Embassy, 2221 Massachusetts Avenue
Phone, NOrth 7-3168

*†Mr. Alexander M. Matsas, Ambassador Extraordinary and Plenipotentiary

Consular Offices:
California, San Francisco
Canal Zone, Colón, Panama
District of Columbia, Washington
Illinois, Chicago
Louisiana, New Orleans
Massachusetts, Boston
New York, New York City

GUATEMALA

Office of the Embassy, 2220 R Street
Phone, DEcatur 2-2865

*Dr. Carlos Garcia-Bauer, Ambassador Extraordinary and Plenipotentiary

Consular Offices:
Alabama{Mobile
{Montgomery
California{Eureka
{Hillsborough
{Los Angeles
{San Diego
{San Francisco
{San Luis Obispo
{San Mateo
Colorado, Denver
Connecticut, Hartford
Florida{Daytona Beach
{Jacksonville
{Miami
{Pensacola
{St. Petersburg
{Tampa
Georgia, Atlanta
Hawaii, Honolulu
Illinois, Chicago

GUATEMALA—Continued

Consular Offices—Continued
Indiana{Fort Wayne
{Indianapolis
{South Bend
Iowa, Des Moines
Louisiana, New Orleans
Maryland{Annapolis
{Baltimore
{Gaithersburg
Massachusetts, Boston
Michigan, Detroit
Missouri{Kansas City
{St. Louis
Nebraska, Omaha
New Jersey{Newark
{Paterson
New York{Buffalo
{New York City
North Carolina, Durham
North Dakota, Bismarck
Ohio{Cincinnati
{Cleveland
{Dayton
Pennsylvania{Philadelphia
{Pittsburgh
Puerto Rico, San Juan
Rhode Island, Providence
Tennessee, Memphis
Texas{Abilene
{Brownsville
{Corpus Christi
{Dallas
{El Paso
{Fort Worth
{Galveston
{Houston
{Laredo
{San Antonio
{San Juan
Virginia, Richmond
Washington, Seattle
Wyoming{Casper
{Cheyenne

GUINEA

Office of the Embassy, 2112 Leroy Place
Phone, HUdson 3-9420

*Mr. Karim Bangoura, Ambassador Extraordinary and Plenipotentiary

HAITI

Office of the Embassy, 4400 Seventeenth Street
Phone, RAndolph 3-7000

*Mr. Andre Theard, Ambassador Extraordinary and Plenipotentiary

Consular Offices:
Alabama, Mobile
California{Los Angeles
{San Francisco
Canal Zone, Cristobal
Florida, Miami
Illinois, Chicago
Louisiana, New Orleans
Maryland, Baltimore
Massachusetts, Boston
Michigan, Detroit
New York, New York City
Ohio{Cleveland
{Easton
Pennsylvania, Philadelphia
Puerto Rico, San Juan
Texas{Galveston
{Houston
{San Antonio
Virgin Islands, Charlotte Amalie

HONDURAS

Office of the Embassy, 4715 Sixteenth Street
Phone, RAndolph 3-9318

*Mr. Ricardo Midence Soto, Ambassador Extraordinary and Plenipotentiary

HONDURAS—Continued

Consular Offices:
California {Los Angeles / San Francisco}
Canal Zone {Balboa / Cristóbal}
Connecticut, New Britain
Florida {Gainesville / Miami / Tampa}
Illinois, Chicago
Iowa, Des Moines
Louisiana, New Orleans
Maryland, Baltimore
Massachusetts, Boston
Michigan, Detroit
Missouri, St. Louis
New York, New York City
Ohio {Cincinnati / Cleveland}
Oregon, Portland
Pennsylvania, Philadelphia
Puerto Rico {Cayey / Ponce / San Juan}
Texas {Brownsville / Dallas / Fort Worth / Galveston / Houston / San Antonio}
Virginia, Norfolk
Washington, Seattle

HUNGARY

Office of the Legation, 2437 Fifteenth Street
Phone, DUpont 7-3800

*Mr. Janos Radvanyi, Chargé d'Affaires a.i.

Consular Office: District of Columbia, Washington

ICELAND

Office of the Embassy, 1906 Twenty-third Street
Phone, COlumbia 5-6653

*Mr. Ingvi S. Ingvarsson, Chargé d'Affaires a.i.
Consular Offices:
California {Berkeley / Los Angeles / San Francisco}
District of Columbia, Washington
Illinois, Chicago
Maryland, Baltimore
Massachusetts, Boston
Minnesota, Minneapolis
New York, New York City
North Dakota, Grand Forks
Oregon, Portland
Washington, Seattle

INDIA

Office of the Embassy, 2107 Massachusetts Avenue
Phone COlumbia 5-5050

*Mr. B. K. Nehru, Ambassador Extraordinary and Plenipotentiary
Consular Offices:
California, San Francisco
District of Columbia, Washington
Hawaii, Honolulu
New York, New York City
Ohio, Cleveland

INDONESIA

Office of the Embassy, 2020 Massachusetts Avenue
Phone HUdson 3-6600

Dr. Zairin Zain, Ambassador Extraordinary and Plenipotentiary
Consular Offices:
California, San Francisco
New York, New York City

IRAN

Office of the Embassy, 3005 Massachusetts Avenue
Phone, DEcatur 2-7000

*Mr. Mahmoud Foroughi, Ambassador Extraordinary and Plenipotentiary
Consular Offices:
California, San Francisco
New York, New York City

IRAQ

Office of the Embassy, 1801 P Street
Phone, HUdson 3-7500

*Mr. Nasir Hani, Ambassador Extraordinary and Plenipotentiary

Consular Office: New York, New York City

IRELAND

Office of the Embassy, 2234 Massachusetts Avenue
Phone, HUdson 3-7639

*Mr. William Fay, Ambassador Extraordinary and Plenipotentiary

Consular Offices:
California, San Francisco
Illinois, Chicago
Massachusetts, Boston
New York, New York City

ISRAEL

Office of the Embassy, 1621 Twenty-second Street
Phone, HUdson 3-4100

*Mr. Avraham Harman, Ambassador Extraordinary and Plenipotentiary

Consular Offices:
California {Los Angeles / San Francisco}
District of Columbia, Washington
Georgia, Atlanta
Illinois, Chicago
Massachusetts, Boston
New York, New York City
Pennsylvania, Philadelphia
Texas, Houston

ITALY

Office of the Embassy, 1601 Fuller Street
Phone, ADams 4-1935

*Mr. Sergio Fenoaltea, Ambassador Extraordinary and Plenipotentiary

Consular Offices:
Alabama, Mobile
Arizona {Phoenix / Tucson}
Arkansas, Little Rock
California {Los Angeles / Monterey / San Diego / San Francisco / Santa Barbara / Stockton}
Colorado, Denver
Connecticut, New Haven
District of Columbia, Washington
Florida {Jacksonville / Miami / Tampa}
Georgia {Atlanta / Savannah}
Hawaii, Honolulu
Illinois, Chicago
Indiana, Indianapolis
Louisiana, New Orleans
Maine, Portland
Maryland, Baltimore

ITALY—Continued

Consular Offices—Continued
Massachusetts { Boston / Springfield
Michigan, Detroit
Minnesota, St. Paul
Missouri { Kansas City / St. Louis
Nevada, Reno
New Jersey, Trenton
New Mexico, Albuquerque
New York { Albany / Buffalo / Newburgh / New York City / Suffern / Yonkers
Ohio { Cincinnati / Cleveland
Oregon, Portland
Pennsylvania, Philadelphia
Rhode Island, Providence
Tennessee, Memphis
Texas { Dallas / Galveston / Houston
Utah, Salt Lake City
Virginia, Norfolk
Washington, Seattle
West Virginia, Charleston

IVORY COAST

**Office of the Embassy, 2424 Massachusetts Avenue
Phone, DEcatur 2-3343**

*Mr. Konan Bédié, Ambassador Extraordinary and
Plenipotentiary

JAMAICA

**Office of the Embassy, 2129 Leroy Place
Phone, 232-1036**

*Sir Neville Noel Ashenheim, Ambassador Ex-
traordinary and Plenipotentiary
Consular Offices:
New York, New York City
District of Columbia, Washington

JAPAN

**Office of the Embassy, 2520 Massachusetts Avenue
Phone, ADams 4-2266**

*Mr. Ryuji Takeuchi, Ambassador Extraordinary
and Plenipotentiary

Consular Offices:
California { Los Angeles / San Francisco
Hawaii, Honolulu
Illinois, Chicago
Louisiana, New Orleans
Massachusetts, Boston
New York, New York City
Oregon, Portland
Pennsylvania, Philadelphia
Texas, Houston
Washington, Seattle

JORDAN

**Office of the Embassy, 2319 Wyoming Avenue
Phone, COlumbia 5-1606**

*Mr. Saad Juma, Ambassador Extraordinary and
Plenipotentiary
Consular Office:
California, San Francisco
Illinois, Chicago
Michigan, Detroit
New York, New York City

KENYA

**Office of the Embassy, 1875 Connecticut Avenue
Phone, 234-4350**

*Mr. Burudi Nabwera, Ambassador Extraordinary
and Plenipotentiary

KOREA

**Office of the Embassy, 2322 Massachusetts Avenue
Phone, 483-7383**

*Mr. Hyun Chul Kim, Ambassador Extraordinary
and Plenipotentiary
Consular Offices:
California { Los Angeles / San Francisco
District of Columbia, Washington
Hawaii, Honolulu
New York, New York City

KUWAIT

**Office of the Embassy, Suites C330-C333, Shoreham
Hotel. Phone, 265-3232**

*Mr. Talaat Al-Ghoussein, Ambassador Extraor-
dinary and Plenipotentiary
Consular Offices:
District of Columbia, Washington
New York, New York City

LAOS

**Office of the Embassy, 2222 S Street
Phone, DEcatur 2-6416**

*H. R. H. Prince Tiao Khampan, Ambassador
Extraordinary and Plenipotentiary

LATVIA

**Office of the Legation, 4325 Seventeenth Street
Phone, RAndolph 6-8213**

*Dr. Arnolds Spekke, Minister Plenipotentiary,
Chargé d'Affaires
Consular Offices:
California, Los Angeles
District of Columbia, Washington
Puerto Rico, San Juan

LEBANON

**Office of the Embassy, Suite 400A, Sheraton-Park
Hotel. Phone, COlumbia 5-4100**

*Mr. Ibrahim Husayn El-Ahdab, Ambassador
Extraordinary and Plenipotentiary
Consular Offices:
Alabama, Birmingham
California, Los Angeles
Illinois, Chicago
Massachusetts, Boston
Michigan, Detroit
New Jersey, Orange
New York, New York City
North Carolina, Goldsboro
Ohio, Cleveland
Oregon, Portland

LIBERIA

**Office of the Embassy, 5201 Sixteenth Street
Phone, Randolph 3-0437**

*Mr. Samuel Edward Peal, Ambassador Extraordi-
nary and Plenipotentiary
Consular Offices:
California, Los Angeles
District of Columbia, Washington
Florida, Miami
Illinois, Chicago
Louisiana, New Orleans
Michigan, Detroit
New York, New York City
Pennsylvania, Philadelphia
Texas { Houston / Port Arthur

LIBYA

**Office of the Embassy, 1611 Upshur Street,
Phone, 726-7606**

*Mr. Fathi Abidia, Ambassador Extraordinary and
Plenipotentiary

LITHUANIA

Office of the Legation, 2622 Sixteenth Street
Phone, ADams 4-5860

*Mr. Joseph Kajeckas, Counselor, Chargé d'Affaires ad interim

Consular Offices:
California, Los Angeles
Illinois, Chicago
Massachusetts, Boston
New York, New York City

LUXEMBOURG

Office of the Embassy, 2210 Massachusetts Avenue
Phone, 265-4171

*Mr. Maurice Steinmetz, Ambassador Extraordinary and Plenipotentiary

Consular Offices:
Arizona, Phoenix
California, Los Angeles
Colorado, Denver
Illinois, Chicago
Minnesota, St. Paul
New York, New York City

MALAGASY REPUBLIC

Office of the Embassy, 2374 Massachusetts Avenue
Phone, 265-5525

*Mr. Louis Rakotomalala, Ambassador Extraordinary and Plenipotentiary

Consular Offices:
California, San Francisco
Pennsylvania, Philadelphia

MALAWI

Office of Embassy, 2019 Q Street
Phone, 234-9313

*Mr. James David Rubadiri, Ambassador Extraordinary and Plenipotentiary

MALAYSIA

Office of the Embassy, 2401 Massachusetts Avenue
Phone, ADams 4-7600

*Dato Ong Yoke Lin, Ambassador Extraordinary and Plenipotentiary

MALI

Office of the Embassy, 2130 R Street
Phone, DEcatur 2-2249

*Mr. Oumar Sow, Ambassador Extraordinary and Plenipotentiary

MAURITANIA

Office of the Embassy, 2737 Cathedral Avenue
Phone, 232-0965

*Mr. Ahmed-Baba Miske, Ambassador Extraordinary and Plenipotentiary

MEXICO

Office of the Embassy, 2829 Sixteenth Street
Phone, ADams 4-6000

*Mr. Hugo B. Margain, Ambassador Extraordinary and Plenipotentiary

Consular Offices:
Alabama, Mobile
Arizona: Douglas, Nogales, Phoenix, Tucson
California: Calexico, Fresno, Los Angeles, Sacramento, San Bernardino, San Diego, San Francisco, San José
Colorado, Denver

MEXICO—Continued

Consular Offices—Continued
District of Columbia, Washington
Florida: Miami, Tampa
Georgia, Atlanta
Hawaii, Honolulu
Illinois, Chicago
Indiana, Indianapolis
Louisiana, New Orleans
Massachusetts, Boston
Michigan, Detroit
Minnesota: Rochester, St. Paul
Missouri: Kansas City, St. Louis
New Jersey, Newark
New Mexico, Albuquerque
New York: Buffalo, New York City
Ohio, Cincinnati
Oklahoma, Oklahoma City
Pennsylvania: Philadelphia, Pittsburgh
Puerto Rico, San Juan
Tennessee, Memphis
Texas: Austin, Brownsville, Corpus Christi, Dallas, Eagle Pass, El Paso, Fort Worth, Galveston, Houston, Laredo, McAllen, San Antonio
Utah, Salt Lake City
Washington: Seattle, Spokane
Wisconsin: Milwaukee, Neenah

MONACO

Consular Offices:
California: Los Angeles, San Francisco
District of Columbia, Washington
Hawaii, Honolulu
Illinois, Chicago
Louisiana, New Orleans
Massachusetts, Boston
New York, New York City
Utah, Salt Lake City

MOROCCO

Office of the Embassy, 1601 21st Street
Phone, HObart 2-7979

*Mr. Ali Bengelloun, Ambassador Extraordinary and Plenipotentiary

Consular Offices:
New York, New York City
Texas, Dallas

NEPAL

Office of the Embassy, 2131 Leroy Place
Phone, ADams 2-0211

*Major General Padma Bahadur Khatri, Ambassador Extraordinary and Plenipotentiary

Consular Offices:
New York, New York City

NETHERLANDS

Office of the Embassy, 4200 Linnean Avenue
Phone, 244-5300 to 5309

*Mr. Carl W. A. Schurmann, Ambassador Extraordinary and Plenipotentiary

Consular Offices:
Alabama, Mobile

NETHERLANDS—Continued

Consular Offices—Continued

California
- Los Angeles
- San Diego
- San Francisco

Canal Zone
- Colon, Panama
- Panamá, Panama

District of Columbia, Washington

Florida
- Jacksonville
- Miami
- Tampa

Georgia, Savannah
Hawaii, Honolulu
Illinois, Chicago
Iowa, Orange City
Louisiana, New Orleans
Maryland, Baltimore
Massachusetts, Boston

Michigan
- Detroit
- Grand Rapids

Minnesota, St. Paul

Missouri
- Kansas City
- St. Louis

New Jersey, Paterson

New York
- Buffalo
- New York City

Ohio, Cleveland
Oregon, Portland

Pennsylvania
- Philadelphia
- Pittsburgh

Puerto Rico
- Mayagüez
- Ponce
- San Juan

Texas
- Galveston
- Houston

Utah, Salt Lake City
Virginia, Norfolk
Virgin Islands, Charlotte Amalie
Washington, Seattle

NEW ZEALAND

Office of the Embassy, 19 Observatory Circle

Phone, COlumbia 5-1721

†Mr. G. R. Laking, Ambassador Extraordinary and Plenipotentiary

Consular Offices:

California
- Los Angeles
- San Francisco

District of Columbia, Washington
New York, New York City

NICARAGUA

Office of the Embassy, 1627 New Hampshire Avenue

Phone, DUpont 7-4371

*Dr. Guillermo Sevilla-Sacasa, Ambassador Extraordinary and Plenipotentiary

Consular Offices:

Airzona, Phoenix

California
- Long Beach
- Los Angeles
- Pasadena
- San Diego
- San Francisco

Canal Zone, Cristobal
Colorado, Denver
District of Columbia, Washington

Florida
- Miami
- Tallahassee
- Tampa

Hawaii, Honolulu
Illinois, Chicago

Louisiana
- Baton Rouge
- New Orleans

Massachusetts, Boston
Michigan, Lansing
Minnesota, Rochester
Missouri, St. Louis

New Jersey
- Englewood
- Fort Lee

New Mexico, Carlsbad
New York New York City
Oregon, Portland

NICARAGUA—Continued

Consular Offices—Continued
Pennsylvania, Philadelphia
Puerto Rico, San Juan

Texas
- Brownsville
- Corpus Christi
- Dallas
- El Paso
- Fort Worth
- Houston
- San Antonio

Virginia, Richmond
Washington, Seattle
Wisconsin, Milwaukee

NIGER

Office of the Embassy, 2013 Q Street

Phone, 483-4224

Mr. Ary Tanimoune, Ambassador Extraordinary and Plenipotentiary

NIGERIA

Office of the Embassy, 1333 16th Street

Phone, ADams 4-4800

*Mr. Julius Momo Udochi, Ambassador Extraordinary and Plenipotentiary

Consular Office: New York, New York City

NORWAY

Office of the Embassy, 3401 Massachusetts Avenue

Phone, FEderal 3-6000

*Mr. Hans Kristian Engen, Ambassador Extraordinary and Plenipotentiary

Consular Offices:
Alabama, Mobile

Alaska
- Anchorage
- Juneau

Arizona, Phoenix

California
- Los Angeles
- San Diego
- San Francisco

Canal Zone
- Balboa
- Cristobal

District of Columbia, Washington

Florida
- Jacksonville
- Miami
- Pensacola
- Tampa

Georgia, Savannah
Hawaii, Honolulu
Illinois, Chicago
Iowa, Decorah

Louisiana
- Baton Rouge
- New Orleans

Maine, Portland
Maryland, Baltimore
Massachusetts, Boston
Michigan, Detroit

Minnesota
- Duluth
- Minneapolis

Mississippi, Gulfport
Missouri, St. Louis
Montana, Lewistown
Nebraska, Omaha
New Mexico, Albuquerque
New York, New York
North Carolina, Wilmington
North Dakota, Fargo
Ohio, Cleveland
Oklahoma, Tulsa
Oregon, Portland
Pennsylvania, Philadelphia
Puerto Rico, San Juan
South Carolina, Charleston
South Dakota, Sioux Falls

Texas
- Brownsville
- Galveston
- Houston

Utah, Salt Lake City

Virginia
- Newport News
- Norfolk

Virgin Islands, Charlotte Amalie
Washington, Seattle
Wisconsin, Milwaukee

PAKISTAN

Office of the Embassy, 2315 Massachusetts Avenue
Phone, DEcatur 2-8330

*Mr. Ghulam Ahmed, Ambassador Extraordinary
and Plenipotentiary

Consular Offices:
California, San Francisco
New York, New York City
Wisconsin, Milwaukee

PANAMA

Office of the Embassy, 2601 29th Street
Phone, 387-7400

*Mr. Ricardo Arias Espinosa, Ambassador Extraordinary and Plenipotentiary

Consular Offices:
Alabama {Birmingham / Mobile}
Arizona, Tucson
California {Alameda / Berkeley / Beverly Hills / Burbank / Coronado / Glendale / Long Beach / Los Angeles / Monrovia / Oakland / Pasadena / Sacramento / San Diego / San Francisco / San Jose / Santa Barbara / Santa Monica / Vallejo}
Colorado, Colorado Springs
District of Columbia, Washington
Florida {Clearwater / Coral Gables / Fort Lauderdale / Jacksonville / Miami / Miami Beach / Palm Beach / Tallahassee / Tampa}
Georgia, Atlanta
Hawaii, Honolulu
Illinois, Chicago
Indiana {Albany / Indianapolis / South Bend}
Louisiana, New Orleans
Maine, Portland
Maryland, Baltimore
Massachusetts, Boston
Michigan {Detroit / Kalamazoo}
Minnesota, Minneapolis
Missouri {Kansas City / St. Louis}
Montana, Havre
Nebraska {Lincoln / Omaha}
New Jersey, Jersey City
New Mexico, Farmington
New York, New York City
North Carolina, Raleigh
Ohio, Cleveland
Oregon, Portland
Pennsylvania, Philadelphia
Puerto Rico {Arecibo / Mayagüez / Ponce / San Juan}
Rhode Island, Providence
South Carolina, Charleston
Tennessee {Knoxville / Memphis}

PANAMA—Continued

Consular Offices—Continued
Texas {Brownsville / Corpus Christi / Dallas / Galveston / Houston / Port Arthur / San Antonio}
Utah, Salt Lake City
Virginia {Annandale / Norfolk / Richmond}
Virgin Islands, Charlotte Amalie
Washington, Seattle
Wisconsin {Milwaukee / Waukesha}

PARAGUAY

Office of the Embassy, 1825 Connecticut Avenue
Phone, HUdson 3-6960

*†Dr. Juan Plate, Ambassador Extraordinary and Plenipotentiary

Consular Offices:
Alaska, Anchorage
California {Los Angeles / San Francisco}
District of Columbia, Washington
Florida {Fort Lauderdale / Miami}
Illinois, Chicago
Louisiana, New Orleans
New York, New York City
Texas {Dallas / Houston}
Washington, Seattle

PERSIA

(See Iran)

PERU

Office of the Embassy, 1320 Sixteenth Street
Phone, DUpont 7-5150

*Mr. Celso Pastor, Ambassador Extraordinary and Plenipotentiary

Consular Offices:
Alabama {Birmingham / Mobile}
Alaska, Anchorage
Arizona, Tucson
California {Los Angeles / San Diego / San Francisco / Santa Barbara}
Florida {Miami / Tampa}
Hawaii, Honolulu
Illinois, Chicago
Indiana, Indianapolis
Louisiana, New Orleans
Massachusetts, Boston
Minnesota, Rochester
Missouri {Kansas City / Rolla}
New York, New York City
Oregon, Portland
Pennsylvania, Philadelphia
Puerto Rico {Cahuas / Mayagüez / San Juan}
Tennessee, Nashville
Texas {Dallas / Houston}
Washington, Seattle

PHILIPPINES

Office of the Embassy, 1617 Massachusetts Avenue
Phone, HObart 2-1400

*Mr. Oscar Ledesma, Ambassador Extraordinary and Plenipotentiary

Consular Offices:
California {Los Angeles / San Francisco
District of Columbia, Washington
Guam, Agaña
Hawaii, Honolulu
Illinois, Chicago
Louisiana, New Orleans
New York, New York City
Puerto Rico, San Juan
Washington, Seattle

POLAND

Office of the Embassy, 2640 Sixteenth Street
Phone, ADams 4-3800

*Mr. Edward Drozniak, Ambassador Extraordinary and Plenipotentiary

Consular Offices:
District of Columbia, Washington
Illinois, Chicago

PORTUGAL

Office of the Embassy, 2125 Kalorama Road
Phone, COlumbia 5-1643

*Mr. Vasco Vieira Garin, Ambassdor Extraordinary and Plenipotentiary

Consular Offices:
California {Los Angeles / San Francisco
Connecticut, Waterbury
Hawaii, Honolulu
Louisiana, New Orleans
Massachusetts {Boston / Fall River / New Bedford
New York, New York City
Pennsylvania, Philadelphia
Rhode Island, Providence
Texas, Houston

RUMANIA

Office of Embassy, 1601 Twenty-third Street
Phone, ADams 2-4747

*Petre Balaceanu, Ambassador Extraordinary and Plenipotentiary

RWANDA

Office of Embassy, 5308 Colorado Avenue
Phone, 726-4350

*Mr. Celestin Kabanda, Ambassador Extraordinary and Plenipotentiary

SALVADOR

(See El Salvador)

SAN MARINO

Consular Offices:
District of Columbia, Washington
Michigan, Detroit
New York, New York City

SAUDI ARABIA

Office of the Embassy, 2233 Wisconsin Avenue
Phone, ADams 4-7000

*Mr. Ibrahim Al-Sowayel, Ambassador Extraordinary and Plenipotentiary

Consular Offices:
District of Columbia, Washington
New York, New York City

SENEGAL

Office of the Embassy, 2112 Wyoming Avenue
Phone, 234-0540

*Mr. Ousmane Socé Diop, Ambassador Extraordinary and Plenipotentiary

SIAM

(See Thailand)

SIERRA LEONE

Office of the Embassy, 1701 Nineteenth Street
Phone, NOrth 7-8300

Mr. Gershon B. O. Collier, Ambassador Extraordinary and Plenipotentiary

Consular Office: New York, New York City

SOMALIA

Office of the Embassy, 1806 New Hampshire Avenue
Phone, Adams 2-3261

*Dr. Omar Mohallim Mohamed, Ambassador Extraordinary and Plenipotentiary

Consular Office:
District of Columbia, Washington
New York, New York City

SOUTH AFRICA

Office of the Embassy, 3051 Massachusetts Avenue
Phone, 232-4400

*Mr. Harold L. T. Taswell, Ambassador Extraordinary and Plenipotentiary

Consular Offices:
California, San Francisco
Louisiana, New Orleans
New York City, N.Y.

SPAIN

Office of the Embassy, 2700 Fifteenth Street
Phone, COlumbia 5-0190

*The Marquis de Merry del Val, Ambassador Extraordinary and Plenipotentiary

Consular Offices:
California {Los Angeles / San Francisco
District of Columbia, Washington
Florida, Miami
Illinois, Chicago
Louisiana, New Orleans
Massachusetts, Boston
Missouri {Kansas City / St. Louis
New York, New York City
Pennsylvania, Philadelphia
Puerto Rico {Ponce / San Juan
Texas {Houston / Port Arthur
Washington, Seattle

SUDAN

Office of the Embassy, 3421 Massachusetts Avenue
Phone, FEderal 8-8565

*Mr. Tageldin Eltahir, Charge d'Affaires a.i.

Consular Office: New York, New York City

SWEDEN

Office of the Embassy, 2249 R Street
Phone, COlumbia 5-3600

*Mr. Hubert W. A. de Beshe, Ambassador Extraordinary and Plenipotentiary

Consular Offices:
Alabama, Mobile

SWEDEN—Continued

Consular Offices—Continued
Alaska, Anchorage
Arizona, Phoenix
California { Los Angeles
{ San Diego
{ San Francisco
Florida { Jacksonville
{ Miami
{ Tampa
Georgia { Atlanta
{ Savannah
Hawaii, Honolulu
Illinois, Chicago
Louisiana, New Orleans
Maryland, Baltimore
Massachusetts, Boston
Michigan, Detroit
Minnesota { Duluth
{ Minneapolis
Missouri, Kansas City
Nebraska, Omaha
New York { Buffalo
{ Jamestown
{ New York City
Ohio, Cleveland
Oregon, Portland
Pennsylvania { Philadelphia
{ Pittsburgh
Puerto Rico { Ponce
{ San Juan
Texas { Brownsville
{ Dallas
{ Galveston
{ Houston
Virginia, Norfolk
Virgin Islands, Charlotte Amalie
Washington, Seattle
Wisconsin, Milwaukee

SWITZERLAND

Office of the Embassy, 2900 Cathedral Avenue
Phone, HObart 2-1811

*Mr. Alfred Zehnder, Ambassador Extraordinary
and Plenipotentiary

Consular Offices:
California { Los Angeles
{ San Francisco
Canal Zone, Panamá, Panama
District of Columbia, Washington
Georgia, Atlanta
Illinois, Chicago
Louisiana, New Orleans
Maryland, Baltimore
Massachusetts, Boston
Minnesota, Minneapolis
Missouri, St. Louis
New York, New York City
Ohio, Cleveland
Pennsylvania { Philadelphia
{ Pittsburgh
Puerto Rico, San Juan
Washington, Seattle

SYRIAN ARAB REPUBLIC

Office of the Embassy, 2144 Wyoming Avenue
Phone, 387-6444

Dr. Jawdat Mufti, Minister, Charge d'Affaires ad
interim

Consular Office:
New York, New York City

TANGANYIKA

Consular Office:
New York, New York City.

TANZANIA

Office of the Embassy, 1818 Q Street
Phone, 483-4116

*Mr. Othman Shariff, Ambassador Extraordinary
and Plenipotentiary

THAILAND

Office of the Embassy, 2300 Kalorama Road
Phone, 667-1446

*Mr. Sukich Nimmanheminda, Ambassador Extraordinary and Plenipotentiary

Consular Offices:
California { Los Angeles
{ San Francisco
Florida, Miami
Hawaii, Honolulu
Illinois, Chicago
Massachusetts, Boston
Michigan, Detroit
Pennsylvania, Philadelphia
Virginia, Richmond

TOGO

Office of the Embassy, 2208 Massachusetts Avenue
Phone, 234-4212

Dr. Robert Ajavon, Ambassador Extraordinary and
Plenipotentiary

TRINIDAD AND TOBAGO

Office of the Embassy, 2209 Massachusetts Avenue
Phone, 232-3134

*Mr. E. E. I. Clarke, C.M.G., Ambassador Extraordinary and Plenipotentiary

TUNISIA

Office of the Embassy, 2408 Massachusetts Avenue
Phone, ADams 4-6644

*Mr. Rachid Driss, Ambassador Extraordinary and
Plenipotentiary

Consular Offices:
District of Columbia, Washington
New York, New York City

TURKEY

Office of the Embassy, 1606 Twenty-third Street
Phone, NOrth 7-6400

*Mr. Turgut Menemencioglu, Ambassador Extraordinary and Plenipotentiary

Consular Offices:
California, San Francisco
Illinois, Chicago
New York, New York City

UGANDA

Office of the Embassy, 5909 16th Street
Phone, 726-7100

*Mr. Solomon Asea, Ambassador Extraordinary and
Plenipotentiary

Consular Office: New York, New York City

UNION OF SOVIET SOCIALIST REPUBLICS

Office of the Embassy, 1125 Sixteenth Street
Phone, NAtional 8-7550

*Mr. Anatoly F. Dobrynin, Ambassador Extraordinary and Plenipotentiary

UNITED ARAB REPUBLIC

Office of the Embassy, 2310 Decatur Place
Phone: ADams 2-5400

Dr. Mostafa Kamel, Ambassador Extraordinary and
Plenipotentiary

Consular Offices:
District of Columbia, Washington
California, San Francisco
Illinois, Chicago
New York, New York City

UPPER VOLTA

Office of the Embassy, 5500 Sixteenth Street
Phone, 726–0992

Mr. Boureima John Kabore, Ambassador Extraordinary and Plenipotentiary

URUGUAY

Office of the Embassy, 2362 Massachusetts Avenue
Phone, HUdson 3–7266

*Mr. Juan Felipe Yriart, Ambassador Extraordinary and Plenipotentiary

Consular Offices:
California {Los Angeles
San Francisco
Santa Monica}
Florida {Jacksonville
Miami}
Georgia, Atlanta
Illinois, Chicago
Louisiana, New Orleans
Massachusetts, Boston
New York {Buffalo
New York City}
Oregon, Portland
Pennsylvania, Philadelphia
Puerto Rico, San Juan
Utah, Salt Lake City
Washington, Seattle

VENEZUELA

Office of the Embassy, 2445 Massachusetts Avenue
Phone, 256–9600

*Mr. Enrique Tejera-Paris, Ambassador Extraordinary and Plenipotentiary

Consular Offices:
Alabama, Mobile
California {Los Angeles
San Francisco}
Canal Zone, Colón, Panama
District of Columbia, Washington
Florida {Jacksonville
Miami}
Georgia, Savannah
Illinois, Chicago
Louisiana, New Orleans
Maryland, Baltimore
Massachusetts, Boston

VENEZUELA—Continued

Consular Offices—Continued
Missouri {Bolivar
St. Louis}
New York {Albany
New York}
Oregon, Portland
Pennsylvania, Philadelphia
Puerto Rico {Ponce
San Juan}
Texas {Galveston
Houston
San Antonio}

VIET-NAM

Office of the Embassy, 2251 R Street
Phone, ADams 4–3301

*Lieutenant General Tranh Thien Khiem, Ambassador Extraordinary and Plenipotentiary

YEMEN

Office of the Embassy, Universal Bldg., Suite 1115
1875 Connecticut Avenue
Phone, 667–0600

*Mr. Mohsin A. Alaini, Ambassador Extraordinary and Plenipotentiary

YUGOSLAVIA

Office of the Embassy, 2410 California Street
Phone, HObart 2–6566

*Mr. Veljko Micunovic, Ambassador Extraordinary and Plenipotentiary

Consular Offices:
California, San Francisco
District of Columbia, Washington
Illinois, Chicago
New York, New York City
Pennsylvania, Pittsburgh

ZAMBIA

Office of the Embassy, 1875 Connecticut Avenue
Phone, 265–9717

*Mr. Hosea Josias Soko, Ambassador Extraordinary and Plenipotentiary

UNITED STATES DIPLOMATIC AND CONSULAR OFFICES

UNITED STATES DIPLOMATIC AND CONSULAR OFFICES

AFGHANISTAN

Embassy: Kabul

John M. Steeves, Ambassador Extraordinary and Plenipotentiary

ALGERIA

Embassy: Algiers

William J. Porter, Ambassador Extraordinary and Plenipotentiary

Consular Offices:
Constantine
Oran

ARGENTINA

Embassy: Buenos Aires

Edwin M. Martin, Ambassador Extraordinary and Plenipotentiary

Consular Office: Cordoba

AUSTRALIA

Embassy: Canberra

—— ——, Ambassador Extraordinary and Plenipotentiary

Consular Offices:
Adelaide, South Australia
Brisbane, Queensland
Melbourne, Victoria
Perth, Western Australia
Sydney, New South Wales

AUSTRIA

Embassy: Vienna

James W. Riddleberger, Ambassador Extraordinary and Plenipotentiary

BELGIUM

Embassy: Brussels

—— ——, Ambassador Extraordinary and Plenipotentiary

Consular Office: Antwerp

BOLIVIA

Embassy: La Paz

Douglas Henderson, Ambassador Extraordinary and Plenipotentiary

Consular Office: Cochabamba

BRAZIL

Embassy: Rio de Janeiro

Lincoln Gordon, Ambassador Extraordinary and Plenipotentiary

Office: Brasilia

Consular Offices:
Belém, Pará
Belo Horizonte
Curitiba, Paraná
Pôrto Alegre, Rio Grande do Sul
Recife, Pernambuco
Salvador, Bahia
São Paulo, Sao Paulo

BULGARIA

Legation: Sofia

—— ——, Envoy Extraordinary and Minister Plenipotentiary

BURMA, UNION OF

Embassy: Rangoon

Henry A. Byroade, Ambassador Extraordinary and Plenipotentiary

Consular Office: Mandalay

BURUNDI

Embassy: Bujumbura

Donald A. Dumont, Ambassador Extraordinary and Plenipotentiary

CAMBODIA

Embassy: Phnom Penh

Randolph A. Kidder, Ambassador Extraordinary and Plenipotentiary

CAMEROON

Embassy: Yaoundé

Leland Barrows, Ambassador Extraordinary and Plenipotentiary

Consular Office: Douala

CANADA

Embassy: Ottawa, Ontario

W. Walton Butterworth, Ambassador Extraordinary and Plenipotentiary

Consular Offices:
Calgary, Alberta
Halifax, Nova Scotia
Montreal, Quebec
Quebec, Quebec
Saint John, New Brunswick
St. John's, Newfoundland
Toronto, Ontario
Vancouver, British Columbia
Windsor, Ontario
Winnipeg, Manitoba

CENTRAL AFRICAN REPUBLIC

Embassy: Bangui

Claude G. Ross, Ambassador Extraordinary and Plenipotentiary

CEYLON

Embassy: Colombo

Cecil B. Lyon, Ambassador Extraordinary and Plenipotentiary

CHAD

Embassy: Fort Lamy

Brewster H. Morris, Ambassador Extraordinary and Plenipotentiary

747

CHILE

Embassy: Santiago

Ralph A. Dungan, Ambassador Extraordinary and Plenipotentiary

Consular Office: Antofagasta

CHINA

Embassy: Taipei, Taiwan (Formosa)

Jerauld Wright, Ambassador Extraordinary and Plenipotentiary

COLOMBIA

Embassy: Bogotá

Covey T. Oliver, Ambassador Extraordinary and Plenipotentiary

Consular Offices:
Barranquilla
Cali
Medellín

CONGO, REPUBLIC OF

Embassy: Brazzaville

Henry L. T. Koren, Ambassador Extraordinary and Plenipotentiary

CONGO, DEMOCRATIC REPUBLIC OF THE

Embassy: Léopoldville

G. McMurtrie Godley, Ambassador Extraordinary and Plenipotentiary

Consular Offices:
Bukavu
Elisabethville
Stanleyville

COSTA RICA

Embassy: San José

Raymond Telles, Ambassador Extraordinary and Plenipotentiary

CYPRUS

Embassy: Nicosia

Taylor G. Belcher, Ambassador Extraordinary and Plenipotentiary

CZECHOSLOVAKIA

Embassy: Prague

Outerbridge Horsey, Ambassador Extraordinary and Plenipotentiary

DAHOMEY

Embassy: Cotonou

Clinton E. Knox, Ambassador Extraordinary and Plenipotentiary

DENMARK

Embassy: Copenhagen

Katharine E. White, Ambassador Extraordinary and Plenipotentiary

DOMINICAN REPUBLIC

Embassy: Santo Domingo

W. Tapley Bennett, Jr., Ambassador Extraordinary and Plenipotentiary

Consular Office: Santiago de los Caballeros

ECUADOR

Embassy: Quito

Wymberley DeR. Coerr, Ambassador Extraordinary and Plenipotentiary

Consular Office: Guayaquil

EL SALVADOR

Embassy: San Salvador

Paul H. Castro, Ambassador Extraodinary and Plenipotentiary

ETHIOPIA

Embassy: Addis Ababa

Edward M. Korry, Ambassador Extraordinary and Plenipotentiary

Consular Office: Asmara, Eritrea

FINLAND

Embassy: Helsinki

Tyler Thompson, Ambassador Extraordinary and Plenipotentiary

FRANCE

Embassy: Paris

Charles E. Bohlen, Ambassador Extraordinary and Plenipotentiary

Consular Offices:
Bordeaux
Lyon
Marseille
Nice
Strasbourg
Overseas Departments:
Martinique, French West Indies
Papeete, Tahiti

GABON

Embassy: Libreville

Charles F. Darlington, Ambassador Extraordinary and Plenipotentiary

GERMANY

Embassy: Bonn

George C. McGhee, Ambassador Extraordinary and Plenipotentiary

Consular Offices:
Berlin (U. S. Mission)
Bremen
Düsseldorf
Frankfurt am Main
Hamburg
Munich
Stuttgart

GHANA

Embassy: Accra

William P. Mahoney, Jr., Ambassador Extraordinary and Plenipotentiary

GREAT BRITAIN AND NORTHERN IRELAND

Embassy: London

David K. E. Bruce, Ambassador Extraordinary and Plenipotentiary

Consular Offices:
Belfast, Northern Ireland
Birmingham, England
Edinburgh, Scotland
Glasgow, Scotland
Liverpool, England
Southampton, England
Asia:
Aden
Hong Kong
Suva, Fiji Islands

GREAT BRITAIN AND NORTHERN IRELAND—Continued

Consular Offices—Continued
Africa:
  Southern
  Salisbury, Southern Rhodesia
Zanzibar, Zanzibar
America:
  Barbados, The West Indies
  Belize, British Honduras
  Georgetown, British Guiana
  Hamilton, Bermuda
  Nassau, N. P., Bahamas

GREECE

Embassy: Athens

Henry R. Labouisse, Ambassador Extraordinary and Plenipotentiary

Consular Office: Thessaloniki

GUATEMALA

Embassy: Guatemala

John O. Bell, Ambassador Extraordinary and Plenipotentiary

GUINEA

Embassy: Conakry

James I. Loeb, Ambassador Extraordinary and Plenipotentiary

HAITI

Embassy: Port-au-Prince

Benson E. L. Timmons 3d, Ambassador Extraordinary and Plenipotentiary

HONDURAS

Embassy: Tegucigalpa

Charles R. Burrows, Ambassador Extraordinary and Plenipotentiary

Consular Office: San Pedro Sula

HUNGARY

Legation: Budapest

—— ——, Envoy Extraordinary and Minister Plenipotentiary

ICELAND

Embassy: Reykjavik

James K. Penfield, Ambassador Extraordinary and Plenipotentiary

INDIA

Embassy: New Delhi

Chester Bowles, Ambassador Extraordinary and Plenipotentiary

Consular Offices:
  Bombay
  Calcutta
  Madras

INDONESIA

Embassy: Djakarta

Howard P. Jones, Ambassador Extraordinary and Plenipotentiary

Consular Offices:
  Medan
  Surabaya

IRAN

Embassy: Tehran

Armin J. Meyer, Ambassador Extraordinary and Plenipotentiary

Consular Offices:
  Isfahan
  Khorramshahr
  Meshed
  Tabriz

IRAQ

Embassy: Baghdad

Robert C. Strong, Ambassador Extraordinary and Plenipotentiary

Consular Office: Basra

IRELAND

Embassy: Dublin

Raymond R. Guest, Ambassador Extraordinary and Plenipotentiary

ISRAEL

Embassy: Tel Aviv

Walworth Barbour, Ambassador Extraordinary and Plenipotentiary

ITALY

Embassy: Rome

G. Frederick Reinhardt, Ambassador Extraordinary and Plenipotentiary

Consular Offices:
  Florence
  Genoa
  Milan
  Naples
  Palermo
  Trieste
  Turin

IVORY COAST

Embassy: Abidjan

James Wine, Ambassador Extraordinary and Plenipotentiary

JAMAICA

Embassy: Kingston

—— ——, Ambassador Extraordinary and Plenipotentiary

JAPAN

Embassy: Tokyo

Edwin O. Reischauer, Ambassador Extraordinary and Plenipotentiary

Consular Offices:
  Fukuoka
  Kobe—Osaka
  Nagoya
  Naha, Okinawa (Consular Unit)
  Sapporo

JERUSALEM

Consular Office: Jerusalem

Evan M. Wilson, Consul General

JORDAN

Embassy: Amman

Robert G. Barnes, Ambassador Extraordinary and Plenipotentiary

KENYA

Embassy: Nairobi

William Attwood, Ambassador Extraordinary and Plenipotentiary

KOREA

Embassy: Seoul

Winthrop G. Brown, Ambassador Extraordinary and Plenipotentiary

KUWAIT

Embassy: Kuwait

Howard Rex Cottam, Ambassador Extraordinary and Plenipotentiary

LAOS

Embassy: Vientiane

William H. Sullivan, Ambassador Extraordinary and Plenipotentiary

LEBANON

Embassy: Beirut

Dwight J. Porter, Ambassador Extraordinary and Plenipotentiary

LIBERIA

Embassy: Monrovia

Ben H. Brown, Jr., Ambassador Extraordinary and Plenipotentirary

LIBYA

Embassy: Tripoli/Baida

E. Allan Lightner, Jr., Ambassador Extraordinary and Plenipotentiary

Consular Office: Benghazi

LIECHTENSTEIN

Consular Office: Vaduz (no office maintained)

†Howard Elting, Jr., Consul General

†Assigned also to and resident in Zürich.

LUXEMBOURG

Embassy: Luxembourg

William R. Rivkin, Ambassador Extraordinary and Plenipotentiary

MALAGASY REPUBLIC

Embassy: Tananarive

C. Vaughan Ferguson, Jr., Ambassador Extraordinary and Plenipotentiary

MALAWI

Embassy; Zomba
(address correspondence to Blantyre)

Sam P. Gilstrap, Ambassador Extraordinary and Plenipotentiary

MALAYSIA

Embassy: Kuala Lumpur

James D. Bell, Ambassador Extraordinary and Plenipotentiary

Consular Offices:
Kuching
Singapore

MALI, REPUBLIC OF

Embassy: Bamako

C. Robert Moore, Ambassador Extraordinary and Plenipotentiary

MALTA

Embassy; Valletta
———— ————, Ambassador Extraordinary and Plenipotentiary

MAURITANIA

Embassy: Nouakchott

Geoffrey W. Lewis, Ambassador Extraordinary and Plenipotentiary

MEXICO

Embassy: México, D.F.

Fulton Freeman, Ambassador Extraordinary and Plenipotentiary

Consular Offices:
Ciudad Juárez, Chihuahua
Guadalajara, Jalisco
Matamoros, Tamaulipas
Mazatlán, Sinaloa
Mérida, Yucatán
Mexicali, Baja California
Monterrey, Nuevo León
Nogales, Sonora
Nuevo Laredo, Tamaulipas
Piedras Negras, Coahuila
Tampico, Tamaulipas
Tijuana, Baja California
Veracruz, Veracruz

MONACO

Consular Office: Monte Carlo (no office maintained)

† Paul F. DuVivier, Consul

†Resident in Nice.

MOROCCO

Embassy: Rabat
———— ————, Ambassador Extraordinary and Plenipotentiary

Office: Tangier
Consular Office: Casablanca

THE SULTANATE OF MUSCAT AND OMAN

Consular Office: Muscat (no office maintained)

† John T. Wheelock, Consul

†Resident in Aden.

NEPAL

Embassy: Katmandu

Henry E. Stebbins, Ambassador Extraordinary and Plenipotentiary

NETHERLANDS

Embassy: The Hague
———— ————, Ambassador Extraordinary and Plenipotentiary

Consular Offices:
Amsterdam
Rotterdam
Curaçao, Netherlands Antilles
Paramaribo, Surinam

NEW ZEALAND

Embassy: Wellington

Herbert B. Powell, Ambassador Extraordinary and Plenipotentiary

Consular Office: Auckland

NICARAGUA

Embassy: Managua

Aaron S. Brown, Ambassador Extraordinary and Plenipotentiary

NIGER, REPUBLIC OF
Embassy: Niamey
Robert J. Ryan, Ambassador Extraordinary and Plenipotentiary

NIGERIA, FEDERATION OF
Embassy: Lagos
Elbert G. Mathews, Ambassador Extraordinary and Plenipotentiary

Consular Offices:
Enugu
Ibadan
Kaduna

NORWAY
Embassy: Oslo
Margaret Joy Tibbetts, Ambassador Extraordinary and Plenipotentiary

PAKISTAN
Embassy: Karachi
Walter P. McConaughy, Ambassador Extraordinary and Plenipotentiary

Office: Rawalpindi

Consular Offices:
Dacca
Lahore
Peshawar

PALESTINE
Consular Office: Jerusalem
William L. Hamilton, Jr., Consul General

PANAMA
Embassy: Panamá
Jack H. Vaughn, Ambassador Extraordinary and Plenipotentiary

Consular Office: David

PARAGUAY
Embassy: Asunción
William P. Snow, Ambassador Extraordinary and Plenipotentiary

PERU
Embassy: Lima
J. Wesley Jones, Ambassador Extraordinary and Plenipotentiary

Consular Office: Arequipa

PHILIPPINES
Embassy: Manila
William McC. Blair, Jr., Ambassador Extraordinary and Plenipotentiary

Consular Office: Cebu

POLAND
Embassy: Warsaw
John M. Cabot, Ambassador Extraordinary and Plenipotentiary

Consular Office: Poznan

PORTUGAL AND POSSESSIONS
Embassy: Lisbon
George W. Anderson, Jr., Ambassador Extraordinary and Plenipotentiary

Consular Offices:
Oporto
Ponta Delgada, São Miguel, Azores
Lourenço Marques, Mozambique, Africa
Luanda, Angola, Africa

RUMANIA
Legation: Bucharest
William A. Crawford, Envoy Extraordinary and Minister Plenipotentiary

RWANDA
Embassy: Kigali
Charles D. Withers, Ambassador Extraordinary and Plenipotentiary

SAN MARINO
Consular Office: San Marino (no office maintained)
†Merritt N. Cootes, Consul General
†Resident in Florence.

SAUDI ARABIA
Embassy: Jidda
Parker Thompson Hart, Ambassador Extraordinary and Plenipotentiary

Consular Office: Dhahran

SENEGAL
Embassy: Dakar
Mercer Cook, Ambassador Extraordinary and Plenipotentiary

SIERRA LEONE
Embassy: Freetown
Andrew V. Corry, Ambassador Extraordinary and Plenipotentiary

SOMALI REPUBLIC
Embassy: Mogadiscio
Horace G. Torbert, Jr., Ambassador Extraordinary and Plenipotentiary

SOUTH AFRICA, REPUBLIC OF
Embassy: Pretoria, Transvaal
Joseph C. Satterthwaite, Ambassador Extraordinary and Plenipotentiary

Consular Offices:
Cape Town, Cape Province
Durban, Natal
Johannesburg, Transvaal
Port Elizabeth, Cape Province

SPAIN
Embassy: Madrid
Angier Biddle Duke, Ambassador Extraordinary and Plenipotentiary

Consular Offices:
Barcelona
Bilbao
Seville
Valencia
Vigo

SUDAN
Embassy: Khartoum
William M. Rountree, Ambassador Extraordinary and Plenipotentiary

SWEDEN
Embassy: Stockholm
J. Graham Parsons, Ambassador Extraordinary and Plenipotentiary

Consular Office: Göteborg

SWITZERLAND
Embassy: Bern
W. True Davis, Jr., (nominated), Ambassador Extraordinary and Plenipotentiary
Consular Office:
Zürich

SYRIAN ARAB REPUBLIC
Embassy, Damascus
Ridgway B. Knight, Ambassador Extraordinary and Plenipotentiary
Consular Office: Aleppo

TANZANIA, UNITED REPUBLIC OF
Embassy: Dar-es-Salaam
William Leonhart, Ambassador Extraordinary and Plenipotentiary
Consular Office: Zanzibar

THAILAND
Embassy: Bangkok
Graham A. Martin, Ambassador Extraordinary and Plenipotentiary
Consular Offices:
Chiengmai
Udorn

TOGO, REPUBLIC OF
Embassy: Lomé
William Witman II, Ambassador Extraordinary and Plenipotentiary

TRINIDAD AND TOBAGO
Embassy: Port-of-Spain
Robert G. Miner, Ambassador Extraordinary and Plenipotentiary

TUNISIA
Embassy: Tunis
Francis H. Russell, Ambassador Extraordinary and Plenipotentiary

TURKEY
Embassy: Ankara
Raymond A. Hare, Ambassador Extraordinary and Plenipotentiary
Consular Offices:
Adana
Istanbul
Izmir

UGANDA
Embassy: Kampala
Olcott H. Deming, Ambassador Extraordinary and Plenipotentiary

UNION OF SOVIET SOCIALIST REPUBLICS
Embassy: Moscow
Foy D. Kohler, Ambassador Extraordinary and Plenipotentiary

UNITED ARAB REPUBLIC
Embassy: Cairo
Lucius D. Battle, Ambassador Extraordinary and Plenipotentiary
Consular Offices:
Alexandria
Port Said

UPPER VOLTA
Embassy: Ouagadougou
Thomas S. Estes, Ambassador Extraordinary and Plenipotentiary

URUGUAY
Embassy: Montevideo
—— ——, Ambassador Extraordinary and Plenipotentiary

VENEZUELA
Embassy: Caracas
Maurice M. Bernbaum, Ambassador Extraordinary and Plenipotentiary
Consular Offices:
Maracaibo
Puerto la Cruz, Anzoátegui

VIET-NAM, REPUBLIC OF
Embassy: Saigon
Maxwell D. Taylor, Ambassador Extraordinary and Plenipotentiary
Consular Office: Hué

YEMEN
Embassy: Taiz
—— ——, Ambassador Extraordinary and Plenipotentiary
Office: Sana'a

YUGOSLAVIA
Embassy: Belgrade
C. Burke Elbrick, Ambassador Extraordinary and Plenipotentiary
Consular Offices:
Zagreb

ZAMBIA
Embassy: Lusaka
Robert C. Good, Ambassador Extraordinary and Plenipotentiary

SPECIAL MISSIONS
USRO (U. S. Mission to the North Atlantic Treaty Organization and European Regional Organizations), Paris:
Thomas K. Finletter, U.S. Permanent Representative with the rank and status of Ambassador Extraordinary and Plenipotentiary.

USEC (U. S. Mission to the European Communities), Brussels and Luxembourg:
John W. Tuthill, U.S. Representative with the rank and status of Ambassador Extraordinary and Plenipotentiary.

U. S. Mission to the United Nations, New York:
Adlai E. Stevenson, U.S. Representative to the United Nations and U.S. Representative in the Security Council with the rank and status of Ambassador Extraordinary and Plenipotentiary.

U. S. Mission to the European Office of the United Nations and Other International Organizations, Geneva:
Roger W. Tubby, U.S. Representative with the personal rank of Ambassador.

IAEA (U. S. Mission to the International Atomic Energy Agency), Vienna:
Henry D. Smyth, U.S. Representative with the personal rank of Ambassador.

OAS (U.S. Mission to the Organization of American States), Washington, D.C.:
Ellsworth Bunker, U.S. Representative with the personal rank of Ambassador.

ICAO (U.S. Mission to the International Civil Aviation Organization), Montreal:
Nelson B. David, U.S. Representative with the personal rank of Minister.

PRESS GALLERIES

PRESS PHOTOGRAPHERS GALLERY

WHITE HOUSE NEWS PHOTOGRAPHERS' ASSOCIATION

RADIO AND TELEVISION CORRESPONDENTS' GALLERIES

PERIODICAL PRESS GALLERIES

PRESS GALLERIES

SENATE PRESS GALLERY

Phone, CApitol 4–3121, extension 4551 (Code 180)

Superintendent.—Joseph E. Wills, 2907 John Marshall Drive, Arlington, Va.
Assistant Superintendents:
   Don C. Womack, 5818 26th Street North, Arlington, Va.
   Howard C. Dawes, 1509 T Street SE.
   Don C. Ferguson, 6304 Frontier Drive, Springfield, Va.
   Herbert L. Hall, 5930 North Kings Highway, Alexandria, Va.
Secretary.—Joan L. Galvin, 1543 Richmond Highway, Alexandria, Va.

HOUSE PRESS GALLERY

Phones, CApitol 4–3121, extensions 3945, 3969, 4350, 4235 (Code 180)

Superintendent.—Richard L. Embly, 314 East Capitol Street.
Assistant Superintendents:
   Benjamin C. West, 3612 Gramby Street, Radiant Valley, Hyattsville, Md.
   Thayer V. Illsley, 5505 Sheldon Drive, Brenmar Park, Alexandria, Va.
   Charles F. Marston, 2406 Lackawanna Street, Adelphi, Md.
   Wilbur G. De Perini, R.F.D. 227, Pomfret, Md.
Special Assistant Superintendent.—William J. Donaldson, Jr., 3730 Brandywine
   Street.

STANDING COMMITTEE OF CORRESPONDENTS

Robert N. Branson, Chairman
Barnet Nover, Secretary
Milton R. Berliner
Benjamin R. Cole
Frank Eleazer

RULES GOVERNING PRESS GALLERIES

1. Administration of the press galleries shall be vested in a Standing Committee of Correspondents elected by accredited members of the galleries. The Committee shall consist of five persons elected to serve for terms of 2 years. Provided, however, that at the election in January 1951, the three candidates receiving the highest number of votes shall serve for 2 years and the remaining two for 1 year. Thereafter, three members shall be elected in odd-numbered years and two in even-numbered years. Elections shall be held in January. The Committee shall elect its own chairman and secretary. Vacancies on the Committee shall be filled by special election to be called by the Standing Committee.

2. Persons desiring admission to the press galleries of Congress shall make application in accordance with Rule 34 of the House of Representatives, subject to the direction and control of the Speaker and Rule 34 of the Senate, which rules shall be interpreted and administered by the Standing Committee of Correspondents, subject to the review and approval by the Senate Committee on Rules and Administration.

3. The Standing Committee of Correspondents shall limit membership in the press galleries to bona fide correspondents of repute in their profession, under such rules as the Standing Committee of Correspondents shall prescribe.

4. Provided, however, that the Standing Committee of Correspondents shall admit to the galleries no person who does not establish to the satisfaction of the Standing Committee all of the following:

(*a*) That his or her principal income is obtained from news correspondence intended for publication in newspapers entitled to second-class mailing privileges.

(*b*) That he or she is not engaged in paid publicity or promotion work or in prosecuting any claim before Congress or before any department of the government, and will not become so engaged while a member of the galleries.

(*c*) That he or she is not engaged in any lobbying activity and will not become so engaged while a member of the galleries.

5. Members of the families of correspondents are not entitled to the privileges of the galleries.

6. The Standing Committee of Correspondents shall propose no change or changes in these rules except upon petition in writing signed by not less than 100 accredited members of the galleries.

JOHN W. McCORMACK,
Speaker of the House of Representatives.

Approved by the Committee on Rules and Administration of the Senate.
B. EVERETT JORDAN, *Chairman.*

PRESS GALLERIES

MEMBERS OF THE PRESS ENTITLED TO ADMISSION

[The * designates those whose wives or husbands accompany them; the † designates those whose unmarried daughters in society accompany them; the ‖ designates those having other ladies or gentlemen with them]

Name	Paper represented	Residence
*Adams, Maurice	Sydney (Australia) Sun and Sun-Herald	1301 15th St.
Agnew, Bruce A	New York Post	301 G St.
Albergo, Lilia Sanchez	La Republica (Bogota)	1750 16th St.
*Albright, Robert C	Washington Post	5509 Glenwood Rd., Bethesda, Md.
*Alexander, Holmes	McNaught Syndicate	922 25th St.
*Allen, Robert S	The Hall Syndicate, Philadelphia Daily News, Northern Virginia Sun, Santa Barbara (Calif.) News Press, Monterey (Calif.) Peninsula-Herald.	1525 28th St.
*Allen, Will	Lithuanian Daily News of Chicago	5606 Madison St., Bethesda, Md.
Alsop, Joseph W	Washington Post & Syndicate	2720 Dumbarton Ave.
*Altman, Henry	Washington Daily News	5340 37th St., North Arlington, Va.
*Amick, George E., Jr	Trenton Times Newspapers	205 Skyhill Rd., Alexandria, Va.
*Anderson, Floyd	NCWC News Service	3918 Childs La., Alexandria, Va.
*Anderson, J. W	Washington Post	514 Prince St., Alexandria, Va.
*Anderson, Jack N	Bell-McClure Syndicate	9801 Singleton Dr., Bethesda, Md.
Anderson, William F	Chicago Tribune Press Service	1200 North Nash St., Arlington, Va.
*Andrews, Robert M	United Press International	5741 Sanger Ave., Alexandria, Va.
*Angelo, Bonnie	Newhouse National News Service	1529 33d St.
*Aragón, Leopoldo	La Estrella (Panama City), Correo de la Tarde (Buenos Aires), Expreso (Lima, Peru).	2012 N. Daniel St., Arlington, Va.
*Arbogast, W. F	Associated Press	205 Summers Dr., Alexandria, Va.
*Arkus, Istvan	Nepszabadsag (Budapest, Hungary)	4500 Connecticut Ave.
*Arrowsmith, Marvin L	Associated Press	9605 Bellevue Dr., Bethesda, Md.
*Artigiani, Susan	Fairchild Publications	3420 16th St.
*Atwood, Marilyn	Anchorage Daily Times	2534 Queen Anne's La.
*Averill, John H	Los Angeles Times, L.A. Times-Washington Post News Service.	1325 Hemlock St.
*Aycock, Marlyn E	United Press International	5771-232 Sanger Ave., Alexandria, Va.
*Bacon, Don	Newhouse National News Service	6307 33d St.
*Bailey, Charles W., 2d	Minneapolis Star and Tribune, Des Moines Register and Tribune.	3001 Albemarle St.
*Baker, Robert E. L	Washington Post	5409 Fremont St., Springfield, Va.
*Baker, Russell	New York Times	5211 39th St.
Ball, Cornelia M	Washington Daily News	1101 New Hampshire Ave.
*Bandy, Leland Allen	Atlanta (Ga.) Times, Greenville (S.C.) News, Jackson (Miss.) Daily News, Nashville (Tenn.) Banner, Shreveport (La). Journal, Dayton (Ohio) Journal-Herald.	1104 S. Cleveland St., Arlington, Va.
Banos, Alicia	Windsor Daily Star	3752 Jocelyn St.
*Barber, Stephen Guy	London Sunday Telegraph	739 Delaware Ave. SW.
*Barkdoll, Robert S	Los Angeles Times	11307 Mitanher St., Kensington, Md.
*Barnes, Patricia M	Fairchild Publications, New York	2220 Virginia Ave.
Barnes, Peter F	Lowell (Mass.) Sun	4105 Fessendon St.
*Barnett, David L	North American Newspaper Alliance	306 Beechwood Rd., Alexandria, Va.
*Barr, Robert A	Fairchild Publications, New York	7317 Leesville Blvd., Springfield, Va.
*Barrett, Colin	Traffic World	4840 Eastern La., Suitland, Md.

MEMBERS OF THE PRESS ENTITLED TO ADMISSION—Continued

Name	Paper represented	Residence
*Barrett, Laurence	New York Herald Tribune	5708 Nebraska Ave.
*Barron, John	Washington Star	2406 Surrey Lane, Falls Church, Va.
*Barth, Alan	Washington Post	3520 Rodman St.
*Bartlett, Charles L	Chicago Sun-Times	4615 W St.
*Baskin, Robert E	Dallas Morning News	7420 Hamlet St., Springfield, Va.
*Basset, Gene	Scripps-Howard Newspaper Alliance	5810 Weaver Ave., McLean, Va.
Bassett, Grace	Washington Evening Star	2704 N St.
*Baulch, Jerry T	Associated Press	1931 Kimberly Rd., Silver Spring, Md.
*Bauman, Karl	Associated Press	2124 Key Blvd., Arlington, Va.
Beale, Betty	Hall Syndicate, Washington Star	2324 Tracy Pl.
*‖Beale, W. L., Jr	Associated Press	4040 51st St.
*Beckler, John W	Associated Press	3514 Cummings Lane, Chevy Chase, Md.
*Beecher, William M	Wall Street Journal	5908 9th St. North, Arlington, Va.
*Behr, Edward A	Wall Street Journal	3418 Bradley Lane, Chevy Chase, Md.
*Belair, Felix, Jr	New York Times	118 S. Fairfax St., Alexandria, Va.
*Bell, Jack L	Associated Press	4000 Cathedral Ave.
*Bell, Lester M	Copley News Service, Alhambra (Calif.) Post-Advocate, Aurora (Ill.) Beacon-News, Burbank (Calif.) Review, Culver City (Calif.) Star-News, Elgin (Ill.) Courier-News, Glendale (Calif.) News-Press, Joliet (Ill.) Herald-News, Monrovia (Calif.) News-Post, Redondo (Calif.) Daily Breeze, San Diego Tribune, San Diego Union, San Pedro (Calif.) News Pilot, Springfield (Ill.) State Journal, Springfield (Ill.) State Register, Venice (Calif.) Vanguard.	904 Bluedale St., Alexandria, Va.
*Benedi, Dr. Claudio	Continental Press, Inc	3929 Vacation La., Arlington, Va.
*Benesch, Aaron G	Newhouse National News Service	8600 16th St., Silver Spring, Md.
Benson, Michael	American Banker	1330 New Hampshire Ave.
*Bentley, Helen DeLich	Baltimore Sun	1008 E. Belvedere Ave., Baltimore, Md.
*Bergheim, Mel	India News & Feature Alliance	5535 Dawes Ave., Alexandria, Va.
*Bergman, Vonda	Burlington (Vt.) Free Press, Rutland (Vt.) Herald, Brattle Boro (Vt.) Reformer.	513 Constitution Ave. NE.
*Berliner, Milton R	Washington Daily News	602 Forest Glen Rd., Silver Spring, Md.
*Betts, Charles A	Science Service	4378 North Pershing Dr., Arlington, Va.
*Beveridge, George D., Jr	Washington Evening Star	9302 Kingsley Ave., Bethesda, Md.
*Bhattacharjea, Ajit K	Hindustan Times (New Delhi, India)	6613 32d St.
*Biossat, Bruce	Newspaper Enterprise Association	202 G St.
*Bishop, Freeman C	American Metal Market	1322 28th St.
*Blair, William M	New York Times	5602 Namakagan Rd., Mass. Ave. Hills, Md.
*Blatchford, Nicholas	Washington Daily News	231 Cedar Lane, Fairfax, Va.
*Blizin, Jerald	St. Petersburg Times & Independent	5335 43rd St.
Block, Herbert L	Washington Post	1417 N St.
*Block, Victor I	Congressional Quarterly	8021 Aberdeen Rd., Bethesda, Md.
*Boeckel, Richard M	Editorial Research Reports	2137 LeRoy Pl.
*Bolle, Maarten C	Het Vrije Volk (The Netherlands); Het Volk (Ghent, Belgium)	8314 Still Spring Ct., Bethesda, Md.
*Bonafede, Dom	New York Herald Tribune	5110 Brookway Dr., Sumner, Md.
Bowles, Edna	Diario Las Americas (The Americas Daily)	3636 16th St.
*Bowman, Lowery	United Press International	8824 Lanier Dr., Silver Spring, Md.
*Boyce, Richard H	Scripps-Howard Newspaper Alliance	4631 Hunt Ave., Chevy Chase, Md.
*Boyd, Robert S	Knight Newspapers, Akron Beacon Journal, Charlotte Observer, Detroit Free Press, Miami Herald.	3909 Morrell Ct., Kensington, Md.
*Braaten, David G	Washington Star	1501 N. Greenbrier St., Arlington, Va.
*Bradley, Frank E	Congressional Quarterly	1943 Biltmore St.
Brandon, Henry	London Sunday Times, Thomson Newspapers (England)	3501 Rodman St.
*Brandt, Raymond P	St. Louis Post-Dispatch	4955 Quebec St.

MEMBERS OF THE PRESS ENTITLED TO ADMISSION—Continued

Name	Paper represented	Residence
Branson, Robert N.	Federated Publications, Inc., Lansing (Mich.) State Journal, Marion (Ind.) Chronicle and Leader Tribune, Battle Creek (Mich.) Enquirer and News, Lafayette (Ind.) Journal and Courier, Boise (Idaho) Daily & Evening Statesman.	2005 Belmont Rd.
*Brazda, Jerome F.	United Press International	605 Glenbrook Rd., Fairfax, Va.
Breasted, David C.	Newhouse National News Service	2146 I St.
*Breitenstein, Rolf	United Press International	4522 Davis Ave., Suitland, Md.
*Bridge, Gardner	Associated Press	2325 North Jackson St., Arlington, Va.
*Brines, Russell	Continental Press, Inc.	2920 McKinley St.
*Britten, Milton	Scripps-Howard Newspaper Alliance	67A G St. SW.
*Britton, Lewis W.	Traffic World	6132 30th St.
*Broder, David S.	Washington Evening Star	4207 N. 23d St., Arlington, Va.
*Broniarek, Zygmunt	Trybuna Ludu (Poland)	4201 Massachusetts Ave.
*Brooks, Jack	Vancouver Sun	6511 Winnepeg Rd., Bethesda, Md.
*Brooks, Rosemarie Tyler	Chicago Defender	67A G St., SW.
*Broom, William W.	Ridder Publications, St. Paul Pioneer Press & Dispatch, Duluth Herald & News-Tribune, Long Beach Independent & Press-Telegram, San Jose Mercury & News, Pasadena Independent & Star-News, Aberdeen (S. Dak.) American-News, Grand Forks (N. Dak.) Herald, Garden Grove (Calif.) News.	4609 30th St.
Brophy, Donald F.	N.C.W.C. News Service	1305 22d St.
*Brown, Nona Baldwin	New York Times	3801 Kanawha St.
*Brown, R. Gordon	Associated Press	207 Miles Dr., Forest Heights, Md.
*Brunn, Robert R.	Christian Science Monitor	7215 Arrowwood Dr., Bethesda, Md.
*Buchwald, Art	New York Herald Tribune Syndicate	3102 Cleveland Ave.
*Buckhorn, Robert F.	United Press International	236 Pine Springs Rd., Falls Church, Va.
*Burch, John T.	Washington Daily News	5015 46th St.
*Burd, Laurence H.	Los Angeles Times	5721 Bradley Blvd., Bethesda, Md.
*Burnett, Leon R.	United Press International	4415 N. Pershing Dr., Arlington, Va.
Burns, Ronald G.	N.Y. Journal of Commerce	2126 R St.
*Buscher, Jessie Stearns	Columbus (Ohio) Dispatch	100 5th St., SE.
*Butler, Robert M.	Traffic World	930 North Danville St., Arlington, Va.
*Bylinsky, Gene	Newhouse National News Service, Progress Report (Science Service of Advance).	8222 Larry Pl., Chevy Chase, Md.
Byrnes, Dorothy Seymour	Hartford Courant	428 North Nelson St., Arlington, Va.
*Byrnes, Robert D.	Hartford Courant	428 North Nelson St., Arlington, Va.
*Cahill, Jerome S.	Philadelphia Inquirer	8948 Victoria Rd. West, Springfield, Va.
*Cahn, Robert	Christian Science Monitor	3315 Wisconsin Ave.
*Canan, James William	Gannett News Service, Hartford (Conn.) Times, Danville (Ill.) Commercial-News, Plainfield (N.J.) Courier-News, Binghamton (N.Y.) Press, Elmira (N.Y.) Star Gazette, Ithaca (N.Y.) Journal, Malone (N.Y.) Evening Telegram, Newburgh-Beacon (N.Y.) News, Niagara Falls (N.Y.) Gazette, Rochester (N.Y.) Democrat and Chronicle, Rochester (N.Y.) Times Union, Saratoga Springs (N.Y.) Saratogian, Utica (N.Y.) Daily Press, Utica (N.Y.) Observer-Dispatch, Camden (N.J.) Courier-Post, Mamaroneck Daily Times, Mt. Vernon Daily Argus, New Rochelle Standard-Star, Ossining Citizen Register, Port Chester Daily Item, Rockland County Journal-News, Tarrytown Daily News, White Plains Reporter Dispatch, Yonkers Herald Statesman, Peekskill Evening Star.	212 North Greenbrier St., Arlington, Va.
Canessa, Guiseppe	ANSA News Agency	2475 Virginia Ave.
*Carey, Francis E.	Associated Press	12 North Edison St., Arlington, Va.
*Carlson, Herbert P.	Fairchild Publications	820 Philadelphia Ave., Silver Spring, Md.
*Carmack, George	Scripps-Howard Newspaper Alliance	1239 Vermont Ave.

MEMBERS OF THE PRESS ENTITLED TO ADMISSION—Continued

Name	Paper represented	Residence
*Carpenter, Leslie E_____	Boston Herald and Traveler, Arkansas Gazette, Variety Daily, Beaumont (Tex.) Enterprise, Beaumont (Tex.) Journal, Corpus Christi (Tex.) Caller-Times, San Angelo (Tex.) Standard-Times, San Antonio (Tex.) Express & Evening News, Abilene (Tex.) Reporter-News, Lubbock (Tex.) Avalanche-Journal, Honolulu Advertiser, Springfield (Mass.) Daily News, Austin American-Statesman, Waco News-Tribune & Times-Herald, Dallas Times Herald, Wichita Falls (Tex.) Record-News & Times, Amarillo (Tex.) News-Globe, Hall Syndicate.	4701 Woodway Lane.
Carper, Elsie_____	Washington Post_____	4421 Windom Pl.
Carroll, Margaret_____	Congressional Quarterly_____	2912 Olive Ave.
Carter, J. Stanley_____	New York Daily News_____	1272 National Press Bldg.
*Carter, Luther J_____	Norfolk Virginian Pilot_____	4522 Lowell St.
*Cary, James D_____	Associated Press_____	10400 Crestmoor Dr., Silver Spring, Md.
*Cassady, John H_____	Washington Star_____	4125 S. 36th St. Arlington, Va.
*Cassels, Louis_____	United Press International_____	6815 Melody Lane, Bethesda, Md.
Cauley, John R_____	Kansas City Star and Times_____	1727 Massachusetts Ave.
*Cazalas, David P_____	New York Journal of Commerce_____	1112 Marshall St., Falls Church, Va.
*Chadwick, John_____	Associated Press_____	5004 Fort Sumner Dr., Sumner, Md.
Chapman, R. Stanley_____	Traffic World_____	5606 36th St. North, Arlington, Va.
*Cho, Dong-won_____	Donghwa News Agency_____	6312 N. 27th St., Arlington, Va.
*Childs, Marquis W_____	St. Louis Post-Dispatch_____	3554 Edmunds St.
Choumenkovitch, Milena_____	United Feature Syndicate_____	3630 Patterson St.
Christmas, Anne H_____	Washington Star_____	Sugarland Farm, Poolesville, Md.
*Claiborne, Jack E_____	Knight Newspapers, Charlotte Observer, Akron Beacon Journal, Detroit Free Press, Miami Herald.	210 N. Alfred St., Alexandria, Va.
*Clark, Evert B_____	New York Times_____	5601 Lambeth Rd., Bethesda, Md.
Clark, Martha Ann_____	Nashville Tennessean_____	2020 F St.
Clark, Timothy B_____	Lincoln Journal, El Mundo (San Juan)_____	1753 Church St.
*Clayton, James E_____	Washington Post_____	2847 Lorcom La., Arlington, Va.
*Cleland, John A_____	Houston Chronicle, Ft. Worth Star-Telegram.	3681 Upton St.
*Clément, Alain_____	Le Monde (Paris)_____	2327 49th St.
*Clifford, George_____	Washington Daily News_____	2926 Kanawha St.
*Cline, John H_____	Washington Evening Star_____	351 North Washington St., Falls Church, Va.
*Clopton, Willard C., Jr_____	Washington Post_____	12427 Seabury La., Bowie, Md.
*Clymer, Adam_____	Baltimore Sun_____	1214 National Press Bldg.
*Cohn, Leon N_____	Washington Evening Star_____	3391 Stephenson Pl.
*Cole, Benjamin R_____	Indianapolis Star, Muncie Star, Arizona Republic.	6529 Beverly Ave., McLean, Va.
Cole, Martha_____	Associated Press_____	3420 R St.
*Collier, Barnard L_____	New York Herald Tribune_____	3418 R St.
*Collins, Frederic W_____	Ridder Publications_____	3929 Jenifer St.
*Collins, James M_____	Oil Daily_____	905 Chalfonte Dr., Alexandria, Va.
Collins, Thomas_____	Newsday_____	2816 Connecticut Ave.
*Conn, Harry F_____	Press Associates, Inc_____	3245 Livingston St.
*Connors, Thomas J., Jr_____	New York Journal of Commerce_____	707 Barrett Rd., Falls Church, Va.
Constantine, Gus_____	N.Y. Journal of Commerce_____	5601 Cromwell Dr., Bethesda, Md.
*Cooper, Adren_____	Associated Press_____	2511 St. John Pl., Alexandria, Va.
*Coopersmith, Esther L_____	The Hall Syndicate_____	3219 Park View Rd., Silver Spring, Md.
*Corddry, Charles W., Jr_____	United Press International_____	4304 Glen Ridge St., Kensington, Md.
*Cordtz, Howard Dan_____	Wall Street Journal_____	6312 Kenhowe Dr., Bethesda, Md.
*Cormier, Frank_____	Associated Press_____	1710 Coronado Ter., Fairfax, Va.

MEMBERS OF THE PRESS ENTITLED TO ADMISSION—Continued

Name	Paper represented	Residence
*Corlett, Cleve Edward	Federated Publications, Inc., Lansing (Mich.) State Journal, Marion (Ind.) Chronicle & Leader Tribune, Battle Creek (Mich.) Enquirer & News, Lafayette (Ind.) Journal & Courier, Boise (Idaho) Daily & Evening Statesman.	5111 8th Road South, Arlington, Va.
*Cornell, Douglas B	Associated Press	2500 Q St.
Coyne, Joseph R	Associated Press	7719 Rowan Ct., Annandale, Va.
*Craig, Hugh	Wall Street Journal	1441 N. Inglewood St., Arlington, Va.
Craig, May	Portland Press Herald, Portland (Maine) Evening Express, Kennebec (Maine) Journal, Waterville (Maine) Sentinel, Portland (Maine) Sunday Telegram.	717 North Carolina Ave. SE.
*Craig, William O	Traffic World	6125 9th Rd., North, Arlington, Va.
*Cramer, John F	Washington Daily News	Cape St. John, Rt. 1, Annapolis, Md.
*Crater, Robert W	Cincinnati Post and Times Star, Cleveland Press, Columbus Citizen-Journal, Kentucky Post and Times-Star.	7000 40th Ave., University Park, Md.
*Crawford, Clare W	Washington Daily News	4204 Southend Rd., Rockville, Md.
*Cromley, Allan W	Daily Oklahoman. Oklahoma City Times	1305 Stoneybrae Dr., Falls Church, Va.
*Cromley, Ray	Newspaper Enterprise Association	108 Martha's Rd., Alexandria, Va.
*Cronan, Carey	Bridgeport Post, Bridgeport Telegram, Stamford Advocate, Waterbury (Conn.) Republican, Waterbury American.	2 Fairfax Ct., Chevy Chase, Md.
*Crowley, Raymond J	Associated Press	3620 S St.
*Crowther, Rodney	Baltimore Sun	4411 Bradley Lane, Chevy Chase, Md.
Culhane, Charles P	Houston Post, Galveston News, Galveston Tribune, Texas City Sun.	1600 16th St.
*Culic, Davor	Tanjug News Agency (Yugoslavia)	2727 29th St.
*Cunningham, Morris	Memphis Commercial Appeal	6002 Woodacres Dr.
*Curran, Ned	Boston Herald and Traveler, Arkansas Gazette, Variety Daily, Beaumont (Tex.) Enterprise, Beaumont (Tex.) Journal, Corpus Christi (Tex.) Caller-Times, San Angelo (Tex.) Standard-Times, San Antonio (Tex.) Express & Evening News, Abilene (Tex.) Reporter-News, Lubbock (Tex.) Avalanche-Journal, Honolulu Advertiser, Springfield (Mass.) Daily News, Austin American-Statesman, Wichita Falls (Tex.) Record-News & Times, Amarillo (Tex.) News-Globe.	608 Birch St. SW., Vienna, Va.
*Dale, Edwin L., Jr	New York Times	4526 Lowell St.
*Daly, John Joseph, Jr	N.C.W.C. News Service	1017 Upshur St. NE.
*Davis, J. W	Associated Press	1202 North Columbus St., Arlington, Va.
Davis, Marguerite	United Press International	2475 Virginia Ave.
*Davis, Saville	Christian Science Monitor	3038 O St.
*Davis, Spencer	Associated Press	3907 Huntington St.
*†Davis, Watson	Science Service	3620 Garfield St.
*Day, Anthony	Philadelphia Bulletin	3241 Livingston St.
*Day, Daniel E	Atlanta Daily World, National Negro Press Association.	4011 Ames St. NE.
*Deakin, James	St. Louis Post-Dispatch	2500 Q St.
Dear, Cyrene	Dear Publications, Elizabeth City (N.C.) Advance, Wheaton (Ill.) Journal, Sedalia (Mo.) Democrat, Henderson (Ky.) Gleaner and Journal.	7308 Broxburn Ct., Bethesda, Md.
*Dear, Joseph A	Dear Publications, Elizabeth City (N.C.) Advance, Wheaton (Ill.) Journal, Sedalia (Mo.) Democrat, Henderson (Ky.) Gleaner and Journal.	7308 Broxburn Ct., Bethesda, Md.
*DeBloom, Carl	Columbus (Ohio) Dispatch	7725 Walters La., Forestville, Md.
*de Medici, Marino	Il Tempo (Rome)	2727 29th St.
de Saint-Pol, Michel	Agence France Presse	2500 Q St.
*de Thier, Guenter	Deutsche Presse Agentur	1301 S. Scott St., Arlington, Va.
*Denniston, Lyle W	Washington Evening Star	2104 Windham La., Silver Spring, Md.
*Denny, Ludwell	Scripps-Howard Newspaper Alliance	1661 Crescent Pl.
*Deroche, Louis	Agence France Presse	2957 Tilden St.
*de Segonzac, Adalbert	France-Soir	4959 Hillbrook Lane.
*de Toledano, Ralph	King Features Syndicate	2900 Connecticut Ave.

MEMBERS OF THE PRESS ENTITLED TO ADMISSION—Continued

Name	Paper represented	Residence
*Dickinson, William Boyd, III.	Editorial Research Reports	5348 Ravensworth Rd., Springfield, Va.
*Dickson, Edward H	Sacramento (Calif.) Bee, Fresno (Calif.) Bee, Modesto (Calif.) Bee.	7002 Sycamore Ave., Takoma Park, Md.
*Dietsch, Robert W	Scripps-Howard Newspaper Alliance	5303 Elliott Rd.
*Dillman, Grant	United Press International	5161 N. 38th St., Arlington, Va.
*Dixon, George	King Features Syndicate	2523 P St.
Dobbin, Muriel	Baltimore Sun	104 E. Madison St., Baltimore, Md.
*Dobbyn, Alan R	Sydney Morning Herald	1301 15th St.
*Dodd, Philip W	Chicago Tribune Press Service	1602 Pinecastle Rd., Falls Church, Va.
*Donaldson, Gordon	Toronto Telegram	5470 30th St.
Donnelly, Tom	Washington Daily News	12 4th St. NE.
*Donovan, Robert J	Los Angeles Times	7309 Delfield St., Chevy Chase, Md.
Doss, Gretchen R	Dear Publications, Elizabeth City (N.C.) Advance, Wheaton (Ill.) Journal, Sedalia (Mo.) Democrat, Henderson (Ky.) Gleaner and Journal.	5200 Oakcrest Dr., Oxon Hill, Md.
Dougherty, Richard	New York Herald Tribune	3228 Prospect St.
Drummond, Geoffrey	New York Herald Tribune	3029 Cambridge Place.
*Drummond, Roscoe	New York Herald Tribune Syndicate	3029 Cambridge Place.
Dubivsky, Barbara I	New York Times	2710 Macomb St.
*Dudman, Richard	St. Louis Post-Dispatch	3409 Newark St.
Duffee, Warren S	United Press International	601 19th St.
*Duscha, Julius	Washington Post	4309 Stanford St., Chevy Chase, Md.
*Easley, L. T., Jr	Associated Press	1406 Crestwood Dr., Alexandria, Va.
*Eastman, Sam	Washington Evening Star	2413 Cypress Dr., Falls Church, Va.
*Eaton, William J	United Press International	1106 Trinity Dr., Alexandria, Va.
Eberhart, Jonathan	Science Service	7935 Deepwell Dr., Bethesda, Md.
Eddinger, Lucille	Copley News Service, Springfield (Ill.) Illinois State Journal, Springfield (Ill.) Illinois State Register, Aurora (Ill.) Beacon-News, Joliet (Ill.) Herald-News, Elgin (Ill.) Courier-News, San Diego (Calif.) Tribune, San Diego (Calif.) Union, Alhambra (Calif.) Post-Advocate, Monrovia (Calif.) News-Post, Redondo (Calif.) Daily Breeze, San Pedro (Calif.) News-Pilot, Glendale (Calif.) News-Press, Culver City (Calif.) Star-News, Venice (Calif.) Vanguard, Burbank (Calif.) Review.	2120 16th St.
*Edson, Arthur L	Associated Press	512 Benson Dr., Alexandria, Va.
*Edstrom, Eve	Washington Post	4201 Cathedral Ave.
*Edwards, Willard	Chicago Tribune Press Service	101 4th Street SE.
*Egger, Charles	Scripps-Howard Newspaper Alliance	418 Hillmoor Drive, Silver Spring, Md.
*Eisen, Jack E	Washington Post	1507 Ridgecrest Dr., Alexandria, Va.
*Eklund, Laurence C	Milwaukee Journal, Milwaukee Sentinel	5602 York Lane, Bethesda, Md.
Elder, Shirlsy	Washington Daily News	5330-A Sanger Ave., Alexandria, Va.
*Eleazer, Frank	United Press International	7211 Beechwood Rd., Alexandria, Va.
*Emory, Alan S	Watertown (N. Y.) Daily Times, Oswego (N. Y.) Palladium-Times, Schenectady (N.Y.) Gazette.	6302 Crossroads Circle, Falls Church, Va.
*Engle, J. B	Associated Press	7105 Orkney Parkway, Bethesda, Md.
*Epstein, Sidney	Washington Evening Star	2800 Woodley Ave.
*Erice, Michael A	El Diario la Prensa (N.Y.)	4317 N. 4th St., Arlington, Va.
*Ernst, Harry W	Charleston (W. Va.) Gazette	317 Whittier St.
*Evans, Rowland, Jr	New York Herald Tribune Syndicate	3125 O St.
*Everett, Glenn D	Bowling Green (Ohio) Sentinel-Tribune, Tiffin (Ohio) Advertiser-Tribune, Bellevue (Ohio) Gazette, Bryan (Ohio) Times.	11110 South Glen Rd., Potomac, Md.
Ewing, Ann	Science Service	5927 Old Dominion Dr., McLean, Va.
Fagg, Mrs. Nancy M	El Paso Times, Sherman Democrat	4600 Langdrum La., Chevy Chase, Md.
*Farmer, Elizabeth Fairchild	Washington Post and Syndicate	3456 Macomb St.

MEMBERS OF THE PRESS ENTITLED TO ADMISSION—Continued

Name	Paper represented	Residence
*Faron, Hamilton	Associated Press	10213 Edgewood Ave., Silver Spring, Md.
*Farris, Frederick J	New York Herald Tribune	2830 Rittenhouse St.
*Fay, Elton C	Associated Press	1201 Noyes Dr., Silver Spring, Md.
*Felder, Stanford	Washington Daily News	1106 Ware St., SW., Vienna, Va.
*Ferguson, Harry	United Press International	4600 Connecticut Ave.
*Fernsworth, Lawrence	Johnson City (Tenn.) Press-Chronicle, Maryville-Alcoa (Tenn.) Daily Times.	329 C St. SE.
*Ferris, Frederick L	United Press International	7210 Gallows Rd., Annandale, Va.
*Fine, Francis	Central News Agency of China	2121 H St.
*Finney, John Warren	New York Times	3025 Dent Pl.
*Finney, Nat S	Buffalo Evening News	9131 Aldershot Drive, Bethesda, Md.
*Finney, Ruth	Albuquerque (N. Mex.) Tribune	1525 28th St.
Fisher, Diane	Congressional Quarterly	1237 34th St.
*Fisher, Joseph A	Rockford (Ill.) Morning Star, Rockford (Ill.) Register-Republic.	1912 Cedardale Dr., Alexandria, Va.
*Flaherty, Hugh E	Philadelphia Bulletin	Box 211M, Vienna, Va.
*Fleeson, Doris	United Feature Syndicate	2120 S St.
*Fogg, Sam	United Press International	5425 20th St. North, Arlington, Va.
*Foley, Thomas J	Los Angeles Times	5013 34th Rd. N., Arlington, Va.
*Follard, Edward T	Washington Post	3200 44th St.
*Forrester, Leland S	Chicago Tribune Press Service	810 10th St., Alexandria, Va.
*Fortune, Francis C	Buffalo Evening News	2712 Wisconsin Ave.
*Frandsen, Julius	United Press International	5134 Worthington Dr.
*Frank, Murray	The Day-Jewish Journal, London Jewish Chronicle.	7810 16th St.
*Frankel, Max	New York Times	5607 Montgomery St., Chevy Chase, Md.
*Franklin, Benjamin A	New York Times	11404 Rokeby Ave., Garrett Park, Md.
Free, Ann Cottrell	Birmingham News, North American Newspaper Alliance.	4500 Q Lane.
*Free, James	Birmingham News, Newhouse National News Service.	4500 Q Lane.
*Freeburg, Russell W	Chicago Tribune Press Service	3916 Ryegate Lane, Alexandria, Va.
*Freedman, Max	Chicago Daily News	1642 29th St.
Friedenberg, Walter	Scripps-Howard Newspaper Alliance	1013 13th St.
*Friedman, Milton	Jewish Telegraphic Agency	1600 S. Joyce St. Arlington, Va.
*Friendly, Alfred	Washington Post	1645 31st St.
*Fruth, Helen-Marie	St. Louis Post Dispatch	925 25th St.
*Fryklund, Richard	Washington Evening Star	4403 Westmoreland St., McLean, Va.
*Furgurson, Ernest B	Baltimore Sun	3706 Williams La., Chevy Chase. Md.
*Gale, Richardson (Dick)	Gannet News Service, Binghamtom (N.Y.) Press, Camden (N.J.) Courier-Post, Danville (Ill.) Commercial-News, Elmira (N.Y.) Star-Gazette, Hartford (Conn.) Times, Ithaca (N.Y.) Journal, Malone (N.Y.) Evening Telegram, Newburgh-Beacon (N.Y.) News, Niagara Falls (N.Y.) Gazette, Plainfield (N.J.) Courier-News, Rochester (N.Y.) Democrat & Chronicle, Rochester (N.Y.) Times-Union, Saratoga Springs (N.Y.) Saratogian, Utica (N.Y.) Daily Press, Utica (N.Y.) Observer-Dispatch, Mamaroneck Daily Times, Mt. Vernon Daily Argus, New Rochelle Standard-Star, Ossining Citizen Register, Port Chester Daily Item, Rockland County Journal-News, Tarrytown Daily News, White Plains Reporter Dispatch, Yonkers Herald Statesman, Peekskill Evening Star.	4727 Arlington Boulevard, Arlington, Va.
*Gallagher, Mary	Cincinnati Enquirer	4421 31st St. South, Arlington, Va.
*Garel, Arthur	Fairchild Publications, New York	4823 Cumberland Ave., Chevy Chase, Md.
*Garrett, H. Lee	Associated Press	7909 Sleaford Pl., Bethesda, Md.
*Garrett, W. Barry	Baptist Press	9805 Cedar Lane, Bethesda, Md.

MEMBERS OF THE PRESS ENTITLED TO ADMISSION—Continued

Name	Paper represented	Residence
*Garrett, William A	Gannett News Service, Hartford (Conn.) Times, Danville (Ill.) Commercial-News, Plainfield (N.J.) Courier-News, Binghamton (N.Y.) Press, Elmira (N.Y.) Star-Gazette, Ithaca (N.Y.) Journal, Malone (N.Y.) Evening Telegram, Newburgh-Beacon (N.Y.) News, Niagara Falls (N.Y.) Gazette, Rochester (N.Y.) Democrat and Chronicle, Rochester (N.Y.) Times-Union, Saratoga Springs (N.Y.) Saratogian, Utica (N.Y.) Daily Press, Utica (N.Y.) Observer-Dispatch, Camden (N.J.) Courier-Post, Mamaroneck Daily Times, Mt. Vernon Daily Argus, New Rochelle Standard-Star, Ossining Citizen Register, Port Chester Daily Item, Rockland County Journal-News, Tarrytown Daily News, White Plains Reporter Dispatch, Yonkers Herald Statesman, Peekskill Evening Star.	11310 Galt Ave., Wheaton Md.
*Garwood, Darrell	United Press International	6204 Wilson Lane, Bethesda Md.
*Gemmill, Henry	Wall Street Journal	4108 Aspen St., Chevy Chase, Md.
*Georg, Anders	Berlingske Tidende (Denmark)	1014 Madison Bldg., Arlington Towers, Arlington, Va
*Germond, Jack W	Gannett News Service, Binghamton (N.Y.) Press, Camden (N.J.) Courier-Post, Danville (Ill.), Commercial-News, Elmira (N.Y.) Star-Gazette, Hartford (Conn.) Times, Ithaca (N.Y.) Journal, Malone (N.Y.) Evening Telegram, Newburgh-Beacon (N.Y.) News, Niagara Falls (N.Y.) Gazette, Plainfield (N.J.) Courier-News, Rochester (N.Y.) Democrat & Chronicle, Rochester (N.Y.) Times-Union, Saratoga Springs (N.Y.) Saratogian, Utica (N.Y.) Daily Press, Utica (N.Y.) Observer-Dispatch, Mamaroneck Daily Times, Mt. Vernon Daily Argus, New Rochelle Standard-Star, Ossining Citizen Register, Port Chester Daily Item, Rockland County Journal-News, Tarrytown Daily News, White Plains Reporter Dispatch, Yonkers Herald Statesman, Peekskill Evening Star.	7912 West Beach Dr.
*Gerrity, John	Daily Bond Buyer (N.Y.)	Bx. 423, Route 4, Old Courthouse Rd., Vienna, Va.
*Gerson, Walter	World Markets Publications	3714 Washington St., Kensington, Md.
Gerstel, Steven V	United Press International	1325 New Hampshire Ave.
*Geyelin, Philip L	Wall Street Journal	4511 Cathedral Ave.
*Gilbert, Ben W	Washington Post	4537 Grant Rd.
*Gilbride, Neil	Associated Press	Rte. 2, Box 151, Hidden La. Vienna, Va.
*Gilmour, Miriam G	Fairchild Publications	5001 Seminary Rd., Alexandria, Va.
*Gimlin, Hoyt L	Newhouse National News Service	2626 N. Quantico St., Arlington, Va.
Gingras, Angele de T	Bell-McClure Newspaper Syndicate	316 North Carolina Ave SE.
*Glaser, Vera R	Norfolk (Neb.) Daily News, North American Newspaper Alliance, Womens News Service.	5000 Cathedral Ave.
*Glass, Andrew J	New York Herald Tribune	606 Independence Ave. SE.
Godofsky, Laura	Collegiate Press Service	1707 Irving St.
*Godwin, Gaylord P	United Press International	4529 Peacock Ave., Alexandria, Va.
Goethals, Henry W	Copley News Service, Alhambra (Calif.) Post-Advocate, Aurora (Ill.) Beacon-News, Burbank (Calif.) Review, Culver City (Calif.) Star-News, Elgin (Ill.) Courier-News, Glendale (Calif.) News-Press, Joliet (Ill.) Herald-News, Monrovia (Calif.) News-Post, Redondo (Calif.) Daily Breeze, San Diego Tribune, San Diego Union, San Pedro (Calif.) News Pilot, Springfield (Ill.) State Journal, Springfield (Ill.) State Register, Venice (Calif.) Vanguard.	1801 Clydesdale Pl.
*Goins, Craddock	Jackson (Miss.) State Times	517 E. Capitol St.
Gold, Walter L	Washington Star	101 G St. SW.

MEMBERS OF THE PRESS ENTITLED TO ADMISSION—Continued

Name	Paper represented	Residence
*Gold, William E	Washington Post	7036 Wilson Lane, Bethesda, Md.
*Goldsmith, John A	United Press International	4605 Franconia Rd., Alexandria, Va.
*Goodman, Martin W	Toronto Daily Star	3134 Q St.
*Goshko, John M	Washington Post	2725 39th St.
*Gottlieb, Daniel W	Reuters	3311 Carpenter St. SE.
*Gould, Geoffrey S	Associated Press	6417 Dahlomega Rd., Bethesda, Md.
*Goulding, Phil G	Cleveland Plain Dealer	7210 Glenbrook Rd., Bethesda, Md.
*Graham, Dillon	Associated Press	412 New Jersey Ave. SE.
*Graham, Fred P	New York Times	1043 Cecil Pl.
*Graham, Katharine	Washington Post	2920 R St.
*Grant, Bruce A	Melbourne Age (Australia)	6640 32d St.
*Grant, Gerald P	Washington Post	2850 28th St.
*Graves, Aubrey A	Washington Post	RFD 1, Centerville, Va.
*Gray, Annette L	St. Thomas (Virgin Islands) Daily News, Agana (Guam) Daily News.	1817 16th St.
*Green, Sterling F	Associated Press	5337 MacArthur Blvd.
*Greene, Charles J., Jr	New York Daily News	3427 O St.
*†Griffin, Bulkley	Springfield Union, Bangor Daily News, Worcester Telegram-Gazette, Pawtucket Times, Fall River Herald News, Lynn Item, Holyoke Transcript-Telegram, Northampton Gazette, New Bedford Standard-Times, Newport (R.I.) Daily News, Quincy (Mass.) Patriot-Ledger, Waterloo (Iowa) Courier, Brockton (Mass.) E nterprise, Lowell (Mass.) Sun, Sioux City (Iowa) Journal.	4817 Woodway Lane.
Griffin, Isabel Kinnear	Worcester Telegram-Gazette Bangor Daily News, New Bedford Standard-Times, Fall River Herald News, Lynn Item, Springfield Union, Holyoke Transcript-Telegram, Pawtucket Times, Northampton Gazette, Newport (R. I.) Daily News, Quincy (Mass.) Patriot-Ledger, Waterloo (Iowa) Courier, Brockton (Mass.) Enterprise, Lowell (Mass.) Sun, Sioux City (Iowa) Journal.	4817 Woodway Lane.
*Grimes, John A	Wall Street Journal	3507 Inverness Dr., No. Chevy Chase, Md.
*Gritz, Edwin D	Washington Post	3080 North Pollard St., Arlington, Va.
*Gruenberg, Robert	Chicago's American	2560 Holman Ave., Silver Spring, Md.
Gulick, Lewis	Associated Press	1415 N. Nash St., Arlington, Va.
Gwertzman, Bernard M	Washington Evening Star	2307 Pennsylvania Ave.
*Haakinson, Edwin B	Associated Press	2765 North Quincy St., Arlington, Va.
*Hadley, Edmund E	North American Newspaper Alliance	217 Wellesley Ave., Glen Echo, Md.
Haggett, Alice B	New Orleans Times-Picayune	3016 Tilden St.
*Hall, Frank A	N. C. W. C. News Service	3619 Fordham Rd.
*Hall, Joseph W., Jr	Associated Press	6009 Avon Dr., Bethesda, Md.
*Halpern, Jessie	Jewish Telegraphic Agency	5755-A Sanger Ave., Alexandria, Va.
Halsband, Donald	Wall Street Journal	2724 Porter St.
Halsell, Grace	Houston Post, Galveston News & Tribune, Texas City Sun.	1464 Rhode Island Ave.
Hamil, Mary K	Congressional Quarterly	2823 27th St.
*Hamilton, John Andrew, Jr.	Congressional Quarterly	1757 Church St.
*Hamilton, Stanley	Traffic World	3924 Arcadia Rd., Alexandria, Va.
*Hanna, Sam	New Orleans (La.) States Item, Shreveport (La.) Times, Baton Rouge (La.) State Times and Morning Advocate, Monroe (La.) World, Jackson (Miss.) Clarion-Ledger, Wilmington (Del.) Evening Journal, Wilmington (Del.) Morning News, Youngstown (Ohio) Vindicator, Rock Island Argus.	610 Melrose, Alexandria, Va.
*Hannan, Mark C	Congressional Quarterly	5215 Acacia Ave., Bethesda, Md.
*Harris, Eugene D	King Features Syndicate	4858 Battery La., Bethesda, Md.
*Harris, Ralph	Reuters, Australian Associated Press	6312 Alcott Rd., Bethesda, Md.
*Harrison, William H	Washington Evening Star	2029 Connecticut Ave.
*Harter, Kenneth W	Washington Post	5906 Ramsgate Rd.

MEMBERS OF THE PRESS ENTITLED TO ADMISSION—Continued

Name	Paper represented	Residence
*Harwood, James	Wall Street Journal	2205 N. Kensington St., Arlington, Va.
*Harwood, Richard	Louisville (Ky.) Courier Journal & Times	4521 Drummond Ave., Chevy Chase, Md.
*Haseltine, Nathan S	Washington Post	4916 35th St. North, Arlington, Va.
*Hashimoto, Masakuni	Kyodo News Service (Tokyo, Japan)	5437 33d St.
*Haslet, Charles C	Associated Press	4610 3d St. North, Arlington, Va.
*Haugland, Vern	Associated Press	219 Holmes Run Rd., Falls Church, Va.
*Hawkins, Lewis E	Associated Press	8713 Seven Locks Rd., Bethesda, Md.
Haworth, Mary	King Features Syndicate	2219 California St.
*Hayden, Jay G	Detroit News, North American Newspaper Alliance.	9605 East Bexhill Dr., Kensington, Md.
*Hayden, Wesley F	Jacksonville (N.C.) Daily News, Columbia (S.C.) State & Record, Anderson (S.C.) Independent, Marietta (Ga.) Journal, Augusta (Ga.) Chronicle-Herald, Clearwater (Fla.) Sun, Tampa (Fla.) Tribune, Tampa (Fla.) Times, Florida Times-Union (Jacksonville).	1009 Cherokee Ave., Alexandria, Va.
*Healy, Paul F	New York Daily News	10638 Weymouth Ave., Bethesda, Md.
*Heard, Raymond E	Montreal Star	9415 Woodland Dr., Silver Spring, Md.
*Hearin, Glen M	Northern Virginia Sun	Crosstree Farm, Delaplane, Va.
*Hearst, Joseph F	Chicago Tribune Press Service	4301 Columbia Pike, Arlington, Va.
*Heffernan, John W	Reuters-Australian Associated Press	2852 Arizona Ave.
*Heimar, Björn	Aftenposten (Oslo, Norway)	8316 Fenway Rd., Bethesda, Md.
*Hennessee, Robert E	Dear Publications, Elizabeth City (N.C.) Advance, Wheaton (Ill.) Journal, Henderson (Ky.) Gleaner & Journal, Sedalia (Mo.) Democrat.	Route #1, Box 123A, Vienna, Va.
*†Henning, Arthur S	Chicago Tribune Press Service	2728 32d St.
*Henry, John C	Washington Evening Star	5246 Loughboro Rd.
*Henry, Thomas Robert	North American Newspaper Alliance	3816 Albemarle St.
*Hensley, M. Stewart	United Press International	3914 Leland St., Chevy Chase, Md.
*Herbers, John	New York Times	1701 K St.
*Herbert, Dennis Nicholas	London Times	4849 Brandywine St.
*Heren, Louis	London Times	4016 48th St.
*Herling, John	National Newspaper Syndicate	6504 East Halbert Rd., Bethesda, Md.
*Hewlett, Frank	Salt Lake Tribune, Honolulu Star-Bulletin, Spokane Spokesman-Review.	3412 North Thomas St., Arlington, Va.
Heymanson, S. Randal	Australian Newspaper Service	Shoreham Hotel.
Hickman, William D., Jr	Fairchild Publications	4207 Eastern Ave., Mt. Rainier, Md.
*Higgins, Marguerite	Newsday	1832 24th St.
*Higgs, Edward H	Associated Press	3046 South Buchanan St., Arlington, Va.
*Highsmith, David A	Traffic World	2901 Sheraton St., Wheaton, Md.
*Hightower, John M	Associated Press	6415 Bradley Blvd., Bethesda, Md.
*Hilburn, Robert E	Fort Worth Star-Telegram, Houston Chronicle.	8018 Glendale Rd., Chevy Chase, Md.
*Hildebrand, W. A	Greensboro Daily News	2805 35th St.
*Hill, I. William	Washington Star	3203 Leland St., Chevy Chase, Md.
*Himes, Dale	Donrey Media Group, Bartlesville Okla.) Examiner-Enterprise, Blackwell (Okla.) Journal-Tribune, Guthrie (Okla.) Leader, Chickasha (Okla.) Express, Okmulgee (Okla.) Times, Rogers (Ark.) News, Fort Smith (Ark.) Southwest American, Fort Smith (Ark.) Times-Record, Las Vegas (Nev.) Review-Journal, Carson City (Nev.) Nevada-Appeal, Ely (Nev.) Times, Hilo (Hawaii) Herald-Tribune, Juneau (Alaska) Alaskan Empire, Levelland (Tex.) Sun-News.	3960 Suitland Rd.
*Hiner, Louis O	Indianapolis News, Muncie Press, Phoenix Gazette.	1405 Farm Hill Circle, Falls Church, Va.
*Hinson, Daniel	Wall Street Journal	3634 Dean Dr., Apt. E, Hyattsville, Md.
*Hines, William M., Jr	Washington Evening Star	8509 Cherry Valley La., Alexandria, Va.

MEMBERS OF THE PRESS ENTITLED TO ADMISSION—Continued

Name	Paper represented	Residence
Hochman, Jiri	Rude Pravo (Prague)	1629 Columbia Rd.
Hochstein, Joseph M	Newhouse National News Service	133 North Carolina Ave. SE.
Hochstein, Philip	Newhouse National News Service	133 North Carolina Ave. SE.
Hodenfield, G. K	Associated Press	19 E. Ridge Rd., Greenbelt, Md.
Hodgson, Godfrey M. T	London Observer	3306 Porter St.
Hoeffer, Hans Juergen	Deutsche Presse Agentur	4343 Lee Hwy., Arlington, Va.
Hoffman, Burton	Washington Star	7104 44th St., Chevy Chase, Md.
Hoffman, David H	New York Herald Tribune	1 Washington Circle.
Hoffman, Fred S	Associated Press	1705 Preston Rd., Alexandria, Va.
Hoik, Daniel B	Washington Daily News	3700 Shepherd St., Chevy Chase, Md.
Holland, Cecil	Washington Evening Star	14 West Lenox St., Chevy Chase, Md.
Holland, Iva	David Lawrence Associates	403 Jackson St., Falls Church, Va.
Hollander, Richard	Washington Daily News	3502 Macomb St.
Hollingsworth, Robert E	Dallas Times Herald	6013 Melvern St., Bethesda, Md.
Holmes, Peter E	Congressional Quarterly	1823 Riggs Pl.
Hoover, John R	Washington Daily News	3706 Thornapple St., Chevy Chase, Md.
Hope, Paul B	Washington Evening Star	6808 Cabin John Rd., Springfield, Va.
Horne, Richard L	Continental Press	1230 13th St.
Horner, Garnett D	Washington Evening Star	4811 Albemarle St.
Howard, William E	Newhouse National News Service Progress Report (Science Service of Advance).	4006 Virgilia St., Chevy Chase, Md.
Hoyle, Leonard H., Jr	Wall Street Journal	24 Maryland Ave., Gaithersburg, Md.
Humphries, Harrison B	Associated Press	411 Deerfield Ave., Silver Spring, Md.
Hunt, Robert A	Associated Press	4612 2d St. South, Arlington, Va.
Hunter, Clarence H	Washington Star	453 Park Rd.
Hunter, Marjorie	New York Times	1711 Massachusetts Ave.
Husain, Ejaz	Dawn (Karachi, Pakistan)	3652 Alton Pl.
Hussey, Ruth	Congressional Quarterly	412 Tennessee Ave., Alexandria, Va.
Hutnyan, Joseph D	United Press International	8717 Ridge Rd., Bethesda, Md.
Iguchi, Norio	JiJi Press (Tokyo)	3636 16th St.
Imhoof, Werner	Neue Zuercher Zeitung	1601 30th St.
Irelan, Robert W	Wall Street Journal	10805 Tenbrook Rd., Silver Spring, Md.
Irwin, Don	Los Angeles Times	3904 Blackthorn St., Chevy Chase, Md.
Ishihara, Hiroshi	Yomiuri Shimbun (Tokyo)	1845 Summit Pl.
Ishimaru, Kazuto	Mainichi Newspapers (Tokyo)	6666 Georgia Ave.
Itskov, Andrei	Izvestia (Moscow, Russia)	1401 Blair Mill Rd., Silver Spring Md.
Jackman, Francis P	United Press International	501 Schley Rd., Annapolis, Md.
Janssen, Richard F	Wall Street Journal	2030 Lanier Dr., Silver Spring, Md.
Jaques, Milton G	Newhouse National News Service	Route 2, Box 15G, Edgewater, Md.
Jarrell, John W	Omaha World-Herald	4301 Massachusetts Ave.
Jenks, George F	Toledo Blade, Pittsburgh Post-Gazette	5315 Carvel Rd.
Jewell, Ingrid M	Pittsburgh Post-Gazette	2141 I St.
Johnson, Alice Frein	Seattle Times	5900 Bradley Blvd., Bethesda, Md.
Johnson, Haynes B	Washington Evening Star	2402 Cameron Mills Rd., Alexandria, Va.
Johnson, Walter	Fairchild Publications, New York	5807 Deal Pl., Chevy Chase, Md.
Jolly, Bruce O	Greensboro (N. C.) Daily News, Greensboro (N. C.) Record.	6213 11th Rd. North, Arlington, Va.
Joyce, Tom	Detroit News	504 Deerfield Ave., Silver Spring, Md.
Jun, Wan Soo	Chosun Ilbo (Seoul)	6312 N. 27th St., Arlington, Va.
Kamps, John H	Associated Press	3008 North Underwood St., Arlington, Va.
Kane, Joseph F	Associated Press	2500 Wisconsin Ave.
Kantor, Seth	El Paso Herald-Post, Fort Worth Press	4325 Maple Ave., Bethesda, Md.

MEMBERS OF THE PRESS ENTITLED TO ADMISSION—Continued

Name	Paper represented	Residence
*Kaplan, Milton L	Hearst Newspapers, Albany Times-Union, Albany Knickerbocker News, Baltimore News-American, Boston Record American & Sunday Advertiser, Los Angeles Herald-Examiner, New York Journal-American, San Antonio Light, San Francisco Examiner, San Francisco News Call Bulletin, Seattle Post-Intelligence.	3408 Macomb St.
*Karmin, Monroe W	Wall Street Journal	8 Teton Pl., Alexandria, Va
*Kato, Shunpei	Sankei Shimbun	5507 Broad Branch Rd.
*Kawanago, Makoto	Sankei Shimbun	3636 16th St.
Kelly, Daniel F	United Press International	1209A 35th St.
*Kelly, G. M	Associated Press	13104 Matey Rd., Silve Spring, Md.
*Kelly, Harry C	Washington Daily News	3515 R St.
*Kelly, Harry J	Associated Press	2212 S. Columbus St., Ar lington, Va.
*Kelly, Thomas V	Washington Daily News	404 Constitution Ave. NE
Kelly, Virginia W	Long Beach (Calif.) Independent and Press-Telegram, St. Paul (Minn.) Pioneer Press-Dispatch, Pasadena (Calif.) Independent and Star News.	3930 Connecticut Ave.
*Kent, Carleton	Chicago Sun-Times	4609 34th St. S., Arlington Va.
*Kentera, George R	Newark (N. J.) Evening News	1004 North Potomac St Arlington, Va.
*Kenworthy, Carroll H	United Press International	1425 44th St.
*Kenworthy, E. W	New York Times	3062 Porter St.
*Kernan, Edward	Cleveland Plain Dealer	8600 16th St., Silver Spring Md.
*Kernodle, Margaret	Associated Press	Duchess Gardens, Alex andria, Va.
*Keys, Henry	United Press International	2718 Arizona Ave.
*Kidel, Boris	London Daily Mail	3540 Springland La.
*Kiker, Douglas	New York Herald Tribune	4121 Leland St., Chev Chase, Md.
Kilgore, Margaret A	United Press International	301 G St. SW.
*Kilpatrick, Carroll	Washington Post	4238 43d St.
*Kim, Seong Jin	Orient Press Agency	3917 Military Rd.
*King, Quentin Scott	Reuters	4214 37th St.
Kirkpatrick, Richard B	Cincinnati Enquirer	5006 Westport Rd., Chev Chase. Md.
*Kis, Csaba	Hungarian News Agency	8510 16th St., Silver Spring Md.
Kissling, Thomas E	N.C.W.C. News Service	1711 Massachusetts Ave.
Klinefelter, Karen	Dallas Morning News	4245 S. 16th St., Arlington Va.
*Kluttz, Jerry	Washington Post	3705 North Lorcom Lane Arlington, Va.
*Knap, Ted	New York World Telegram & Sun	1429 Woodacre Dr., McLear Va.
*Knoll, Erwin	Newhouse National News Service	314 N St. SW.
Kober, Barbara	Boston Herald & Traveler, A ansas Gazette, Austin American-Statesman, Beaumont (Tex.) Enterprise, Beaumont Journal, Corpus Christi (Tex.) Caller-Times, Abilene (Tex.) Reporter-News, Honolulu Advertiser, Lubbock (Tex.) Avalanche-Journal, San Angelo (Tex.) Standard-Times, San Antonio (Tex.) Express & News, Springfield (Mass.) Daily News, Variety Daily, Waco News-Tribune & Times-Herald, Amarillo (Tex.) News-Globe, Wichita Falls (Tex.) Record-News & Times.	2828 Connecticut Ave.
Koenig, John, Jr	Associated Press	1305 30th St.
*Kohlmeir, Louis M	Wall Street Journal	5902 Madawaska Rd.
*Kole, John W	Milwaukee Journal, Milwaukee Sentinel	5604 Seminary Rd., Ale: andria, Va.
*Kopytin, Viktor V	TASS	3636 16th St.
*Korns, William A	Congressional Quarterly	4211 River Rd.
*Kotz, Nathan K. (Nick)	Minneapolis Star & Tribune, Des Moines Register & Tribune.	5413 Center St., Chev Chase, Md.
*Kraslow, David J	Los Angeles Times	1120 Caddington Ave Silver Spring, Md.
Krause, Joanne	Washington Post Syndicate	2455 Tunlaw Rd.
*Krivickas, Grazina E	Draugas (Lithuanian Daily of Chicago)	50 Nicholson St.
*Krock, Arthur	New York Times	1825 24th St.
Kuebler, Jeanne	Editorial Research Reports	1508 21st St.
*Kuh, Frederick	Chicago Sun-Times	4415 Davenport St.
*Kumpa, Peter J	Baltimore Sun	3752 McKinley St.
Kurzman, Dan	Washington Post	1400 S. Joyce St., Arlingto Va.

MEMBERS OF THE PRESS ENTITLED TO ADMISSION—Continued

Name	Paper represented	Residence
*LaGrange, J. E	Agence France Presse	1319 33d St.
LaHay, Wauhillau	Washington Daily News	630 East Capitol St.
*Lahey, Edwin A	Knight Newspapers, Akron Beacon Journal, Charlotte Observer, Detroit Free-Press, Miami Herald.	5863 Chevy Chase Parkway.
*Lahr, Raymond M	United Press International	3321 Laurel Court, Falls Church, Va.
*Lambert, Tom	New York Herald Tribune	3271 Prospect St.
*Lambeth, Edmund Barry	Gannett Newspapers, Binghamton (N.Y.) Press, Camden (N.J.) Courier-Post, Danville (Ill.) Commercial-News, Elmira (N.Y.) Star-Gazette, Ithaca (N.Y.) Journal, Hartford (Conn.) Times, Malone (N.Y.) Evening Telegram, Newburgh-Beacon (N.Y.) News, Niagara Falls (N.Y.) Gazette, Plainfield (N.J.) Courier-News, Rochester (N.Y.) Democrat & Chronicle, Rochester (N.Y.) Times-Union, Saratoga Springs (N.Y.) Saratogian, Utica (N.Y.) Daily Press, Utica (N.Y.) Observer-Dispatch, Mamaroneck Daily Times, Mt. Vernon Daily Argus, New Rochelle Standard-Star, Ossining Citizen Register, Port Chester Daily Item, Rockland County Journal-News, Tarrytown Daily News, White Plains Reporter Dispatch, Yonkers Herald Statesman, Peekskill Evening Star.	4407 S. 36th St., Arlington, Va.
Lammi, Elmer W	United Press International	311 A St. NE.
Landauer, Jerry G	Wall Street Journal	1503 30th St.
*Lando, Harry	Radio-TV Daily, New York Film Daily, Mason City (Iowa) Globe-Gazette.	4423 Stanford St., Chevy Chase, Md.
Lara de Chaban, Francis R	Agence France Presse	3105 Cathedral Ave.
*Larder, George E., Jr	Washington Post	1607 Lee Park Ct., Falls Church, Va.
Large, Arlen J	Wall Street Journal	120½ Rumsey Ct., SE.
*Larrabee, Donald R	Worcester Telegram-Gazette, Bangor Daily News, New Bedford Standard-Times, Fall River Herald News, Lynn Item, Springfield Union, Holyoke Transcript-Telegram, Pawtucket Times, Northampton Gazette, Newport (R.I.) Daily News, Quincy (Mass.) Patriot-Ledger, Waterloo (Iowa) Courier, Brockton (Mass.) Enterprise, Lowell (Mass.) Sun, Sioux City (Iowa) Journal.	4704 Jamestown Rd.
Lastelic, Joseph Anthony	Kansas City Star and Times	4921 Seminary Rd., Alexandria, Va.
*Laurent, Lawrence B	Washington Post	215 Jefferson St., Alexandria, Va.
*Lawrence, David	David Lawrence Associates	1241 24th St.
Lawrence, Richard A	New York Journal of Commerce	1545 18th St.
*Laycook, L. G	Nashville Tennessean	5023 Mineola Rd., College Park, Md.
*Leacacos, John Peter	Cleveland Plain Dealer	1600 S. Joyce St., Arlington, Va.
*Le Breton, Edmond	Associated Press	5302 Wakefield Rd.
*Lebkicher, John V. R	NCWC News Service	321 Forest Dr., Falls Church, Va.
Lederer, Edith	Science Service	1426 21st St.
*Lee, Charles C	Wall Street Journal	9304 Glenville Rd., Silver Spring, Md.
*Leissler, Kurt T	Springer Foreign News Service (Hamburg, Germany).	1200 S. Courthouse Rd., Arlington, Va.
*Lepkowski, Will	Newhouse National News Service, Progress Reports (Science Service of Advance).	10402 46th Ave., Beltsville, Md.
*Leubsdorf, Carl P	Associated Press	4449 Sedgwick St.
Lewine, Frances L	Associated Press	1702 37th St.
*Lewis, Edward W	New York Daily News	1515 28th St.
*Li, Chiang-Kwang	Central News Agency of China	4907 Battery La., Bethesda, Md.
*Lincoln, G. Gould	Washington Evening Star	4000 Cathedral Ave.
*Lippman, Theo, Jr	Atlanta Constitution	810 S. Overlook Dr., Alexandria, Va.
*Lippmann, Walter	Washington Post Syndicate	3525 Woodley Rd.
*Lisagor, Peter	Chicago Daily News	1528 N. Ivanhoe St., Arlington, Va.
*Littlewood, Thomas B	Chicago Sun-Times	1509 Rice St., Falls Church, Va.
*Loftus, Joseph A	New York Times	3327 Legation St.
Lucas, J. Bob	Tulsa Tribune	600 G St. SE.
*Lucas, Jim G	Scripps-Howard Newspaper Alliance	1008 North Carolina Ave., SE.

MEMBERS OF THE PRESS ENTITLED TO ADMISSION—Continued

Name	Paper represented	Residence
*Lyons, Richard L	Washington Post	4435 Garfield St.
*MacDonald, Bruce	Toronto Globe & Mail	5410 Newington Rd., Westwood, Md.
*Macfarlan, W. Joynes	Associated Press	3120 4th St. North, Arlington, Va.
*MacKaye, William Ross	Houston (Tex.) Chronicle, Ft. Worth Star Telegram.	3819 Beecher St.
*MacKenzie, Arch	Canadian Press	4914 Cumberland Ave., Chevy Chase, Md.
*MacKenzie, John P	Washington Post	5208 38th St.
Mackin, Catherine	Hearst Newspapers, Albany Times Union, Albany Knickerbocker News, Baltimore News-American, Boston Record American & Advertiser, L.A. Herald Examiner, New York Journal American, San Antonio Light, San Francisco Examiner, San Francisco News Call Bulletin, Seattle Post-Intelligencer.	1504 44th St.
MacLean, Don	Washington Daily News	1800 Park Rd.
*MacNees, James B	Baltimore Evening Sun	3903 Nicholson St., Hyattsville, Md.
Mahoney, Florence S	Miami Daily News	3600 Prospect Ave.
*Maloy, Richard J	Washington Post	7723 Old Chester Rd., Bethesda, Md.
*Manthey, Marlene	Die Presse	3019 Cambridge Pl.
*Manthey, Wilhelm M	Rhein Zeitung (Germany)	3019 Cambridge Pl.
*Marder, Murray	Washington Post	5013 Forest Haven Dr., Alexandria, Va.
*Margolis, Howard	Washington Post	715 3d St. SW.
*Mark, Ross F	London Daily Express	3218 Cleveland Ave.
*Marks, Dorothy H	Sioux Falls (S.D.) Argus-Leader	2914 P St.
Marley, Faye	Science Service	215 North Piedmont St., Arlington, Va.
*Marlow, James	Associated Press	6707 Glen Carlyn Dr., Falls Church, Va.
*Marshall, Clarence G	Newport News Daily Press, Newport News Times Herald.	5713 Overlea Rd.
*Martin, Edwin G	Copley News Service, Alhambra (Calif.) Post-Advocate, Aurora (Ill.) Beacon-News, Burbank (Calif.) Review, Culver City (Calif.) Star-News, Elgin (Ill.) Courier-News, Glendale (Calif.) News-Press, Joliet (Ill.) Herald-News, Monrovia (Calif.) News-Post, Redondo (Calif.) Daily Breeze, San Diego Tribune, San Diego Union, San Pedro (Calif.) News-Pilot, Springfield (Ill.) State Register, Springfield (Ill.) State Journal, Venice (Calif.) Vanguard.	402 Karl Rd., Alexandria, Va.
*Martin, Neil A	United Press International	5363 Sanger Ave., Alexandria, Va.
*Martin, Ovid	Associated Press	Rt. #2, 358A, McLean, Va.
*Martin, Paul L	Gannett News Service, Hartford (Conn.) Times, Danville (Ill.) Commercial-News, Plainfield (N. J.) Courier-News, Binghamton (N.Y.) Press, Elmira (N.Y.) Star-Gazette, Ithaca (N.Y.) Journal, Malone (N.Y.) Evening Telegram, Newburgh-Beacon (N.Y.) News, Niagara Falls (N.Y.) Gazette, Rochester (N.Y.) Democrat and Chronicle, Rochester (N.Y.) Times-Union, Saratoga Springs (N.Y.) Saratogian, Utica (N.Y.) Daily Press, Utica (N.Y.) Observer-Dispatch, Camden (N.J.) Courier-Post, Mamaroneck Daily Times, Mt. Vernon Daily Argus, New Rochelle Standard-Star, Ossining Citizen Register, Port Chester Daily Item, Rockland County Journal-News, Tarrytown Daily News, White Plains Reporter Dispatch, Yonkers Herald Statesman, Peekskill Evening Star.	3615 North Glebe Rd., Arlington, Va.
*Martin, Wilbur F	Associated Press	1509 Sheldon Dr., Alexdria, Va.
*Marton, Endre	Associated Press	4213 Leland St., Chevy Chase, Md.
*Mathew, David J	Reuters-Australian Associated Press	6101 Wiscasset Rd., Mohican Hills, Md.
*Matsuyama, Yukio	Asahi Shimbun (Tokyo)	1301 South Scott St., Arlington, Va.
*Maxwell, J. W	Washington Daily News	Clarksville, Md.
*May, Donald H	United Press International	609 South Lee St., Alexandria, Va.
May, William	Newark News	800 4th St., SW.

MEMBERS OF THE PRESS ENTITLED TO ADMISSION—Continued

Name	Paper represented	Residence
McCamey, Charles Dennis___	Congressional Quarterly_____	5706 42d Ave., Hyattsville, Md.
McCann, William_____	Science Service_____	1717 N St.
McCardle, Dorothy Bartlett_	Washington Post_____	4422 Ramshorn Pl., McLean, Va.
McCartney, James H_____	Chicago Daily News_____	3703 Bradley La., Chevy Chase, Md.
McCash, Lewis S_____	Jacksonville (N.C.) Daily News, Columbia (S.C.) State & Record, Anderson (S.C.) Independent, Marietta (Ga.) Journal, Augusta (Ga.) Chronicle-Herald, Clearwater (Fla.) Sun, Tampa (Fla.) Tribune, Tampa (Fla.) Times, Florida Times-Union (Jacksonville).	130 3d St., SE.
McClendon, Sarah_____	El Paso Times, Sherman (Tex.) Democrat, San Antonio Light, Port Arthur News, Lufkin (Tex.) Daily News, Santa Fe New Mexican.	2933 28th St.
McCloskey, Paul W_____	NCWC News Service_____	3405 Cummings Lane, Chevy Chase, Md.
McCord, Merrill T_____	Congressional Quarterly_____	10208 Fleming Ave., Bethesda, Md.
McDaniel, C. Yates_____	Associated Press_____	1416 Turkey Run Rd., McLean, Va.
McFarland, Kermit_____	Scripps-Howard Newspaper Alliance_____	2480 16th St.
McGaffin, William_____	Chicago Daily News_____	6208 Beachway Dr., Falls Church, Va.
McGahan, Paul J_____	Philadelphia Inquirer_____	Army and Navy Club.
McGhee, Roy L_____	United Press International_____	4201 Cathedral Ave.
McGowan, Richard Joseph__	New York Daily News_____	8811 Montgomery Ave., Chevy Chase, Md.
McGrain, John J_____	Reuters-Australian Associated Press_____	1900 S. Eads St., Arlington, Va.
McGrory, Mary_____	Washington Evening Star, United Features Syndicate.	2710 Macomb St.
McHugh, Raymond J_____	Copley News Service, Alhambra (Calif.) Post-Advocate, Aurora (Ill.) Beacon-News, Burbank (Calif.), Review, Culver City (Calif.) Star-News, Elgin (Ill.) Courier-News, Glendale (Calif.) News-Press, Joliet (Ill.) Herald-News, Monrovia (Calif.) News-Post, Redondo (Calif.) Daily Breeze, San Diego Tribune, San Diego Union, San Pedro (Calif.) News Pilot, Springfield (Ill.) State Journal, Springfield (Ill.) State Register, Venice (Calif.) Vanguard.	5902 Enterprise Ave., McLean, Va.
McKelway, Benjamin M____	Washington Evening Star_____	4920 Palisade Lane.
McKelway, John M_____	Washington Evening Star_____	9816 Culver St., Kensington, Md.
McLaren, John H_____	Copley News Service, Springfield (Ill.) State Journal, Springfield (Ill.) State Register, Aurora (Ill.) Beacon-News, Joliet (Ill.) Herald-News, Elgin (Ill.) Courier-News, San Diego (Calif.) Tribune, San Diego (Calif.) Union, Alhambra (Calif.) Post-Advocate, Monrovia (Calif.) News-Post, Redondo (Calif.) Daily Breeze, San Pedro (Calif.) News-Pilot, Glendale (Calif.) News-Press, Culver City (Calif.) Star-News, Venice (Calif.) Vanguard, Burbank (Calif.) Review.	1101 Third St. SW.
McMasters, Theresa_____	Boston Herald-Traveler, Springfield (Mass.) News, Arkansas Gazette, Amarillo (Tex.) News-Globe, Austin American-Statesman, Beaumont (Tex.) Enterprise, Beaumont Journal, Corpus Christi (Tex.) Caller-Times, Abilene (Tex.) Reporter-News, Honolulu Advertiser, Lubbock (Tex.) Avalanche-Journal, San Angelo (Tex.) Standard-Times, San Antonio (Tex.) Express & News, Variety Daily, Waco News-Tribune & Times-Herald, Wichita Falls (Tex.) Record-News & Times.	3509 M St.
McMullan, John E_____	Knight Newspapers, Akron Beacon Journal, Charlotte Observer, Detroit Free Press, Miami Herald.	4105 Pine Tree Rd., McLean, Va.
McNamara, Tom_____	Bell-McClure Syndicate_____	40 North Irving St., Arlington, Va.
McNeil, Marshall_____	Scripps-Howard Newspaper Alliance_____	2845 29th Pl.

MEMBERS OF THE PRESS ENTITLED TO ADMISSION—Continued

Name	Paper represented	Residence
*McNeill, Robert S	United Press International	2919 Tallow La., Bowie Md.
Means, Marianne	Hearst Newspapers, New York Journal-American, Los Angeles Herald-Examiner, Baltimore News-American, Boston Record-American, Boston Advertiser, San Francisco Examiner, Seattle Post-Intelligencer, San Antonio Light, Albany Times-Union, Albany Knickerbocker News, San Francisco News-Call Bulletin.	3257 O St.
Mears, Walter R	Associated Press	320 Marcy Dr., Oxon Hill, Md.
*Mendez, Don Luis	"YA" Madrid. Spain	4545 Connecticut Ave.
Metcalfe, John H	New York Daily News	8805 Walnut Hill Rd. Chevy Chase, Md.
*Meyer, Ben F	Associated Press	2632 South Grant St., Arlington, Va.
*Meyer, Hans B	Koelnische Rundschau (Germany)	2246 49th St.
Meyer, Karl E	Washington Post	3617 Ordway St.
*Meyer, Philip E	Knight Newspapers, Akron Beacon Journal, Charlotte Observer, Detroit Free Press, Miami Herald.	1371 Kalmia Rd.
Meyers, Kathleen M	London Daily Express	2507 20th Rd., North Arlington, Va.
*Michael, Mary N	Fairchild Publications, New York	2730 Wisconsin Ave.
*Michelson, Edward J	Pittsfield (Mass.) Berkshire Evening Eagle, Malden (Mass.) Evening News, Medford (Mass.) Mercury, Bennington (Vt.) Banner.	2153 Florida Ave.
*Mickel, Ernest P	Chicago Construction News (m), Denver Daily Journal (m), San Francisco Daily Pacific Builder (n).	6209 Poe Rd., Bethesda, Md.
*Millar, Geraldine	Buffalo Courier-Express	5912 Halsey Rd., Rockville Md.
Miller, Michael V	Knoxville News-Sentinel, Memphis Press-Scimitar, Birmingham Post-Herald.	911 Hughes Mews.
Miller, O. C	Springfield (Mo.) Leader and Press, Springfield (Mo.) Daily News, Kennett (Mo.) Democrat, Poplar Bluff (Mo.) American-Republic.	6904 22d Pl., Hyattsville Md.
*Millstone, James C	St. Louis Post Dispatch	5432 32d St.
*Miltich, Paul A	Booth Newspapers of Michigan, Grand Rapids Press, Flint Journal, Kalamazoo Gazette, Saginaw News, Jackson Citizen Patriot, Muskegon Chronicle. Bay City Times, Ann Arbor News, Ypsilanti Daily Press.	11104 Inwood Ave., Silver Spring, Md.
Mintz, Morton	Washington Post	3022 Macomb St.
*Miyazaki, Kozo	The Nishi-Nippon Press	3829 Veazey St.
*Mobley, Willard H	Associated Press	302 Leesburg Pike, Fall Church, Va.
*Modesti, Girolamo	LaNazione (Florence), Il Resto del Carlino (Bologna).	4101 Cathedral Ave.
*Mohbat, Joseph E	Associated Press	24 Wellesley Circle, Glen Echo, Md.
*Mohr, Charles H	New York Times	22 Grafton St., Chevy Chase, Md.
*Moisy, Claude M. P	Agence France Presse	2929 28th St.
*Moleon, Ary	Associated Press	46–04 Bayard Blvd.
*Mollenhoff, Clark R	Des Moines Register and Tribune, Minneapolis Star and Tribune.	5704 32d St.
Monberg, Helene C	Pueblo (Colo.) Chieftain and Star-Journal, Grand Junction (Colo.) Sentinel, Durango (Colo.) Herald, Farmington (N. Mex.) Times, Gallup (N. Mex.) Independent, Leadville (Colo.) Herald-Democrat.	1618 17th St.
*Montgomery, Hale	United Press International	1675 Preston Rd., Alexandria, Va.
Montgomery, Ruth S	Hearst Newspapers, Albany Times-Union, Albany Knickerbocker News, Baltimore News-American, Boston Record American & Sunday Advertiser, Los Angeles Herald-Examiner, New York Journal-American, San Antonio Light, San Francisco Examiner, San Francisco News Call Bulletin, Seattle Post-Intelligencer.	2236 Massachusetts Ave.
*Moon, Meung Ja	Chosun Ilbo (Seoul, Korea)	1817 N. Quinn St., Arlington, Va.
Moon, Toh Sang	Seoul Orient Press (Korea)	3917 Military Rd.

MEMBERS OF THE PRESS ENTITLED TO ADMISSION—Continued

Name	Paper represented	Residence
*Moore, William T	Chicago Tribune Press Service	3626 Prospect St.
*Morison, Robert F	New York Journal of Commerce	431 Bainbridge Rd., Alexandria, Va.
Morris, Betty	New York Journal of Commerce	399 National Press Bldg.
*Morris, John D	New York Times	4003 Rosemary St., Chevy Chase, Md.
*Morrison, Julian K	Washington Daily News	1420 Claremont Dr., Falls Church, Va.
*Mort, John	Ft. Worth Star-Telegram, Houston Chronicle.	5407 Wilson La., Bethesda, Md.
Mosettig, Michael D	Boston Herald-Traveler, Arkansas Gazette, Variety Daily, Beaumont (Tex.) Enterprise, Beaumont (Tex.) Journal, Corpus Christi (Tex.) Caller-Times, San Angelo (Tex.) Standard-Times, San Antonio (Tex.) Express & Evening News, Abilene (Tex.) Reporter-News, Lubbock (Tex.) Avalanche-Journal, Honolulu Advertiser, Springfield (Mass.) Daily News, Austin American-Statesman, Waco News-Tribune & Times-Herald, Amarillo (Tex.) News-Globe, Wichita Falls (Tex.) Record-News & Times.	6615 First St.
Moulton, Charlotte G	United Press International	6806 Orland St., Falls Church, Va.
*Mowery, Edward J	Newhouse National News Service	711 14th St.
*Mowrer, Edgar Ansel	Bell-McClure Newspaper Syndicate	3301 Garfield St.
*Munn, James C	Associated Press	209 Elmira St. SW.
*Munroe, Mary Norris	Lincoln (Nebr.) Journal, El Mundo (San Juan, P.R.).	9025 Bronson Dr., Potomac, Md.
*Munroe, Pat	Lincoln (Nebr.) Journal, El Mundo (San Juan, P.R.).	9025 Bronson Dr., Potomac, Md.
*Myler, Joseph L	United Press International	3201 Wisconsin Ave.
Naff, Carolyn S	Congressional Quarterly	3144 N St.
*Nakamura, Mitsugu	Asahi Shimbun (Tokyo)	6301 N. 23d St., Arlington, Va.
Nannes, Casper	Washington Star	3800 Porter St.
*Naumann, Oscar E	New York Journal of Commerce	3130 Tennyson St.
*Neal, Jack Charles	Hall Syndicate	4405 Puller Dr., Kensington, Md.
*Nicodemus, Charles E., Jr	Chicago Daily News	4907 Chevy Chase Blvd., Chevy Chase, Md.
*Noelter, Wolfgang	Deutsche Presse Agentur	2413 North Vernon St., Arlington, Va.
*Nofziger, Franklyn C	Copley Newspapers, Springfield (Ill.) State Journal, Springfield (Ill.) State Register, Aurora (Ill.) Beacon-News, Joliet (Ill.) Herald-News, Elgin (Ill.) Courier-News, San Diego (Calif.) Tribune, San Diego (Calif.) Union, Alhambra (Calif.) Post-Advocate, Monrovia (Calif.) News-Post, Redondo Beach (Calif.) Daily Breeze, San Pedro (Calif.) News-Pilot, Glendale (Calif.) News Press, Culver City (Calif.) Star-News, Venice (Calif.) Vanguard, Burbank (Calif.) Review.	6026 Illinois Ave., McLean, Va.
*Nolan, Thomas B., Jr	Newspaper Enterprise Association	1627 26th St. South, Arlington, Va.
‖Norman, John T	Fairchild Publications, New York	9420 Columbia Blvd., Silver Spring, Md.
*Norris, John G	Washington Post	516 A St. SE.
*Novak, Robert D	New York Herald Tribune Syndicate	1001 Mass. Ave. NE.
*Nover, Barnet	Denver Post	4545 Connecticut Ave.
*Nover, Naomi	Denver Post	4545 Connecticut Ave.
*Noyes, Newbold, Jr	Washington Evening Star	10600 River Rd., Potomac, Md.
*Noyes, Thomas E	Washington Evening Star	2811 Chesterfield Pl.
*O'Brien, Cyril J	Trenton Trentonian, Vineland Times-Journal, Billings (Mont.) Gazette	10004 Reddick Dr., Silver Spring, Md.
*O'Brien, Edward W	St. Louis Globe-Democrat, Newhouse National News Service.	Route 2, Box 358, McLean, Va.
*O'Brien, John C	Philadelphia Inquirer	3903 West Underwood St., Chevy Chase, Md.
O'Brien, Sally	El Paso Times	2933 28th St.
Odell, Rice	Washington Daily News	5232 Sherrier Pl.
Oehlschlaeger, Lorelies	Reuters	1305 Potomac St.
*Ogawa, Takeshi	Yomiuri Shimbun	3636 16th St.
*Ohara, Susumu	Japan Economic Journal	5601 Cromwell Dr., Bethesda, Md.

MEMBERS OF THE PRESS ENTITLED TO ADMISSION—Continued

Name	Paper represented	Residence
Ohliger, Gloria A	Washington Daily News	1330 New Hampshire Ave.
*Olofson, Darwin R	Omaha World-Herald	10828 Admiral's Way, Potomac, Md.
*Omohundro, Baxter	Ridder Publications, Aberdeen (S.D.) American News, Duluth (Minn.) News Tribune & Herald, Garden Grove (Calif.) News, Grand Forks (N.D.) Herald, Long Beach Independent & Press-Telegram, Pasadena Independent & Star News, St. Paul Pioneer Press & Dispatch, San Jose Mercury & News.	2415 Military Rd., Arlington, Va.
O'Neil, Dorothy	Chicago Daily News	2000 Connecticut Ave.
*O'Neill, Michael J	New York Daily News	7116 Armat Dr., Bethesda, Md.
*O'Neill, Thomas	Baltimore Sun	4209 Tuscany Ct., Baltimore, Md.
*O'Rourke, John	Washington Daily News	10424 Windsor View Dr., Potomac, Md.
O'Rourke, Lawrence M	Philadelphia Bulletin	4900 Fort Totten Dr. NE.
*Osius, Larry C	Copley News Service, Alhambra (Calif.) Post-Advocate, Aurora (Ill.) Beacon-News, Burbank (Calif.) Review, Culver City (Calif.) Star-News, Elgin (Ill.) Courier-News, Glendale (Calif.) News-Press, Joliet (Ill.) Herald-News, Monrovia (Calif.) News-Post, Redondo (Calif.) Daily Breeze, San Diego Tribune, San Diego Union, San Pedro (Calif.) News Pilot, Springfield (Ill.) State Journal, Springfield (Ill.) State Register, Venice (Calif.) Vanguard.	6000 Grayson St., Springfield, Va.
*Öste, Sven Rudolf	Dagens Nyheter (Stockholm)	131 D St. SE.
*Otsuka, Takashige	Kyodo News Service	11508 Elkin St., Wheaton, Md.
*Otten, Alan L	Wall Street Journal	6601 Rivercrest Ct.
*Ottenad, Thomas W	St. Louis Post-Dispatch	4021 Everett St., Kensington, Md.
Ottenberg, Miriam	Washington Evening Star	3701 Connecticut Ave.
*Ozeki, Tetsuya	Ji Ji Press	3823 Hamilton St., Hyattsville, Md.
*Padev, Michael A	Indianapolis Star, Muncie, Star, Arizona Republic, Phoenix Gazette.	1101 New Hampshire Ave.
*Padilla-Vidaurre, Oscar	La Hora (Guatemala)	3823 Legation St.
Page, Samuel A	Congressional Quarterly	3627 New Hampshire Ave.
*Pakenham, Mary C	Chicago Tribune Press Service	126 11th St. SE.
*Pakenham, Michael	Chicago Tribune Press Service	126 11th St. SE.
*Parasuram, Tattamangalam V.I.	Indian Express Newspapers	5442 Broad Branch Rd.
Pardue, Mary Ann	Arkansas Democrat, Chattanooga News Free Press, Jackson Clarion Ledger.	2022 Columbia Rd.
*Parker, Roy, Jr	Raleigh (N.C.) News & Observer, Winston-Salem Journal & Sentinel.	3548 Whitehaven Pky.
*Patch, Buel W	Editorial Research Reports	3016 Tilden St.
*Pattie, J. Delton	Traffic World	819 Copley Lane, Silver Spring, Md.
*Paull, Joseph	Washington Post	4827 Nebraska Ave.
*Peacock, W. T	Associated Press	810 Timber Branch Parkway, Alexandria, Va.
*Pearson, Drew	Bell-McClure Syndicate	2820 Dumbarton Ave.
*Peirce, Neal R	Congressional Quarterly	835 3d St. SW.
Perrin, Gail	Washington Daily News	5804 Connecticut Ave.
*Petroussenko, Vitaly V	Tass (Telegraph Agency of the U.S.S.R.)	3636 16th St.
*Petty, Milburn	Oil Daily	Route 1, Gainsville, Va.
*Phillips, Cabell	New York Times	3910 Garrison St.
Phillips, James G	Congressional Quarterly	M–518 Arlington Towers, Arlington, Va.
*Pierce, Charles D	Washington Evening Star	403 North Fillmore St., Arlington, Va.
*Pierpoint, Paul V	Daily Bond Buyer	3438 Terrace Ct., Alexandria, Va.
Pierson, John	United Press International	1730 Conn. Ave.
Pincus, Walter H	Washington Star	924 25th St.
*Poe, Delores N	Motion Picture Daily	9907 Montauk Ave., Bethesda, Md.
*Poe, Edgar	New Orleans Times-Picayune, Newhouse National News Service.	2615 South Lynn St., Arlington, Va.
*Pomfret, John D	New York Times	7524 Morningside Dr.
*Porter, Frank C	Washington Post	3702 Morrison St.
Posner, Michael L	United Press International	1567 Colonial Terrace, Arlington, Va.
*Potter, Philip	Baltimore Sun	1011 Copley Lane, Silver Spring, Md.
*Powell, Roland A	Buffalo Evening News	13025 Bluhill Rd., Silver Spring, Md.

MEMBERS OF THE PRESS ENTITLED TO ADMISSION—Continued

Name	Paper represented	Residence
*Powers, Richard P	Associated Press	8610 Melwood Rd., Bethesda, Md.
*Poynter, Henrietta M	Congressional Quarterly	1156 19th St.
*Poynter, Nelson P	St. Petersburg Times	1156 19th St.
*Preston, Alexander R	Washington Evening Star	2614 N. Rockingham St., Arlington, Va.
*Preston, Dickson J	Scripps-Howard Newspaper Alliance	Bx. 466, Rt. No. 2, McLean, Va.
*Price, Bem	Associated Press	3916 Mackall Ave., McLean, Va.
*Priest, Walter S., Jr	San Juan (Puerto Rico) Star	522 6th St. SE.
*Prina, L. Edgar	Washington Evening Star	4813 Quebec St.
*Prochnau, William W	Seattle Times	200 Maple Ave., Falls Church, Va.
*Pusey, Merlo J	Washington Post	Rt. 2, Dickerson, Md.
*Pyper, William F	Booth Newspapers of Michigan, Grand Rapids Press, Flint Journal, Kalamazoo Gazette, Saginaw News, Jackson Citizen Patriot, Muskegon Chronicle, Bay City Times, Ann Arbor News, Ypsilanti Press.	47 Northdown Rd., Wellington Villa, Alexandria, Va.
*Quinn, John M	Dallas Morning News	1013 N. Quantico St., Arlington, Va.
*Ragsdale, Warner B., Jr	Associated Press	4111 Byrd Ct., Kensington, Md.
*Rannells, A. K	American Metal Market	8520 60th Ave., Berwyn Heights, Md.
*Rapoport, Daniel	United Press International	3737 Legation St.
*Rathburn, Georgianna	Congressional Quarterly	3711 Upton St.
*Raymond, Jack	New York Times	2316 Ashmead Pl.
†Reardon, Edward J	Passaic (N. J.) Herald-News	2500 Wisconsin Ave.
*Reed, T. Dean	Newhouse National News Service	5018 North 27th St., Arlington, Va.
*Reichek, Morton A	Newhouse National News Service	606 Lamberton Dr., Silver Spring, Md.
*Reichmann, John A	Alexandria (Va.) Gazette	226 N. Royal St., Alexandria, Va.
*Reifenberg, Jan G	Frankfurter Allgemeine Zeitung (Frankfurt, Germany).	5117 Watson St.
Rengkoe, Marius L	ANTARA News Agency (Indonesia)	1914 Connecticut Ave.
*Reston, James B	New York Times	3124 Woodley Rd.
Reston, Richard F	Los Angeles Times	1851 Columbia Rd.
*Rhodes, Robert E	Newsday	6700 Selkirk Dr., Bethesda, Md.
*Rich, Spencer Alan	Congressional Quarterly	3428 Porter St.
Richards, Douglas D	United Press International	1825 T St.
*Richert, Earl H	Scripps-Howard Newspaper Alliance	5214 Farrington Rd.
*Ridder, Marie	Ridder Publications, St. Paul Pioneer Press and Dispatch, Duluth Herald News-Tribune, Long Beach Independent and Press Telegram, San Jose Mercury News, Aberdeen (S. Dak.) American News, Grand Forks (N. Dak.) Herald, Pasadena (Calif.) Independent and Star-News, Garden Grove (Calif.) News, N.Y. Journal of Commerce.	4509 Crest Lane, McLean, Va.
*Ridder, Walter T	Ridder Publications, St. Paul Pioneer Press and Dispatch, Duluth Herald News-Tribune, Long Beach Independent and Press Telegram, San Jose Mercury News, Aberdeen (S. Dak.) American News, Grand Forks (N. Dak.) Herald, Pasadena (Calif.) Independent and Star-News, Garden Grove (Calif.) News, N.Y. Journal of Commerce.	4509 Crest Lane, McLean, Va.
*Riggs, Robert L	Louisville Courier-Journal and Times	5412 Duvall Dr.
*Riley, Patrick G. D	N. C. W. C. News Service	1312 Massachusetts Ave.
*Ring, William E	N. C. W. C. News Service	6204 32d St.
Ripley, Josephine B	Christian Science Monitor	730 24th St.
*Riseling, John J. W	Washington Post	3608 Park Pl.
*Rivers, Caryl	El Mundo (San Juan, P.R.), Lincoln (Neb.) Journal.	806 8th St., Laurel, Md.
*Roberts, Arthur S	Associated Press	11515 College View Dr., Silver Spring, Md.
*Roberts, Chalmers M	Washington Post	6699 MacArthur Blvd.
Roberts, Steven V	New York Times	1701 Rhode Island Ave.
*Robertson, Nan	New York Times	3701 Massachusetts Ave.
*Robinson, James L	Knight Newspapers, Detroit Free Press, Akron Beacon-Journal, Charlotte Observer, Miami Herald.	4511 Davenport St.
*Rodgers, Wilfrid C	Boston Globe	9601 Pinkney Ct., Potomac, Md.

MEMBERS OF THE PRESS ENTITLED TO ADMISSION—Continued

Name	Paper represented	Residence
*Rogers, Warren, Jr	Hearst Newspapers, Albany Times-Union, Albany Knickerbocker News, Baltimore News American, Boston Advertiser, Boston Record-American, Los Angeles Herald-Examiner, New York Journal-American, San Antonio Light, San Francisco Examiner, San Francisco News Call Bulletin, Seattle Post-Intelligencer.	715 Dennis Ave., Silver Spring, Md.
Roosevelt, Edith Kermit	Edith Kermit Roosevelt Syndicate	800 4th St. SW.
Ross, Thomas B	Chicago Sun-Times	1318 29th St.
*Roth, Robert	Philadelphia Bulletin	2500 Q St.
*Rothman, A. D	Sydney (Australia) Morning Herald	1137 National Press Bldg.
Ruffin, Cordelia	Washington Daily News	1410 33d St.
*Runnion, Norman R	United Press International	2316 N. Monroe St., Arlington, Va.
*Russell, Oland D	Scripps-Howard Newspaper Alliance	2251 N. Quincy St., Arlington, Va.
*Rybeck, Walter	Dayton Daily News	10615 Brunswick Ave., Kensington, Md.
Ryder, Vincent	London Daily Telegraph	1240 27th St.
Safford, Edwin J	Newhouse National News Service	22 7th St. SE.
*Sagar, Easwar	The Hindu (Madras, India)	3228 Rittenhouse St.
*Saito, Yasaburo	Yomiuri Shimbun	1201 S. Court House Rd., Arlington, Va.
*Sakai, Yoneo	Sankei Shimbun	1915 Kalorama Rd.
*Salpeter, Eliahu A	"Haaretz" Daily (Tel Aviv, Israel)	1705 East West Highway Silver Spring, Md.
*Sanders, Donald	Associated Press	5616 Gary Ave., Alexandria Va.
*Sasagawa, Masahiro	Asahi Shimbun (Tokyo)	1475 Euclid St.
*Sato, Tatsuro	JiJi Press (Tokyo)	1825 T St.
Saturday, Winona	Baptist Press	3055 16th St.
Sauer, Marie Frances	Washington Post	2122 Massachusetts Ave.
Sawicki, John P	Northern Virginia Sun	2121 H St.
*Sawislak, Arnold B	United Press International	7203 16th Ave., Takoma Park, Md.
*Schaeffer, Charles	Newhouse National News Service Progress Report (Science Service of Advance)	2116 Seminary Rd., Silver Spring, Md.
*Scheibel, Kenneth M	Donrey Media Group, Bartlesville (Okla.) Examiner-Enterprise, Blackwell (Okla.) Journal-Tribune, Carson City (Nev.) Appeal, Chickasha (Okla.) Express, Ely (Nev.) Times, Guthrie (Okla.) Leader, Hilo (Hawaii) Tribune-Herald, Ft. Smith (Ark.) Southwest American, Ft. Smith (Ark.) Times-Record, Juneau (Alaska) Empire, Levelland (Tex.) Sun News, Okmulgee (Okla.) Times, Las Vegas (Nev.) Review-Journal, Missoula (Mont.) Missoulian-Sentinel, La Crosse (Wis.) Tribune, Madison (Wis.) State Journal.	2 Winterberry Ct., Bethesda, Md.
*Scheleen, Joseph C	Traffic World	3211 Old Dominion Blvd., Alexandria, Va.
Schlitz, William P	Wall Street Journal	1412 Montague St.
*Schlossberg, Kenneth	Washington Daily News	1305 22d St.
Schoellkopf, John L	Dallas Times Herald	1402A 30th St.
*Schriver, Dorothy	Science Service	4510 Highland Ave., Bethesda, Md.
*Schroth, Thomas N	Congressional Quarterly, Editorial Research Reports.	2123 Leroy Pl.
*Schuette, Paul A	Washington Post	738 Van Buren St.
*Schwartz, Lloyd M	Fairchild Publications, New York	348 Courtland Rd., Alexandria, Va.
Schweid, Barry	Associated Press	1272 New Hampshire Ave.
*Schwelien, Joachim H	Stuttgarter Zeitung (Germany)	2553 N. Utah St., Arlington 7, Va.
*Scott, Paul	The Hall Syndicate, Philadelphia Daily News, Northern Virginia Sun, Santa Barbara (Calif.) News-Press, Monterey (Calif.) Peninsula-Herald.	7508 Elmhurst St., District Heights, Md.
Scott, Richard F	Manchester Guardian	1524 31st St.
*Segal, Harvey H	Washington Post	2843 Allendale Pl.
Sehlstedt, Albert, Jr	Baltimore Sun	4405 East West Hwy., Bethesda, Md.
*Seib, Charles B	Washington Evening Star	3750 Oliver St.
*Sell, Ted	Los Angeles Times	5831 Quantrell, Alexandria, Va
*Semple, Robert B., Jr	New York Times	6001 Utah Ave.
Sentner, David P	Hearst Newspapers, Albany Times-Union, Baltimore News-American, Boston Advertiser, Boston Record-American, Los Angeles Herald-Examiner, New York Journal-American, San Antonio Light, San Francisco Examiner, Seattle Post-Intelligencer, Albany Knickerbocker News, San Francisco News-Call Bulletin.	2601 Woodley Pl.

MEMBERS OF THE PRESS ENTITLED TO ADMISSION—Continued

Name	Paper represented	Office
Serling, Robert J	United Press International	6016 Berkshire Dr., Bethesda, Md.
*Sessions, Cliff	United Press International	1601 N. Springwood Dr., Silver Spring, Md.
*Shackford, R. H	Scripps Howard Newspaper Alliance	7201 46th St., Chevy Chase, Md.
*Shaffer, Helen B	Editorial Research Reports	3750 Kanawha St.
*Shafir, Shlomo	Davar (Tel-Aviv)	4500 Connecticut Ave.
*Shanahan, Eileen	New York Times	3608 Van Ness St.
Shannon, Margaret R	Atlanta Journal	2829 Connecticut Ave.
*Sharpe, Harry W	United Press International	2000 S. Eads St., Arlington, Va.
*Shaw, Bynum G	Baltimore Sun	316 Taplow Rd., Baltimore, Md.
*Shaw, Russell B	N. C. W. C. News Service	2455 39th Pl.
*Shelton, Isabelle	Washington Evening Star	4519 43d St.
Shumate, Eugene C	Washington Daily News	12704 Hathaway Dr., Silver Spring, Md.
*Shuster, Alvin	New York Times	11711 Stonington Pl., Silver Spring, Md.
*Silverman, Alvin	Cleveland Plain Dealer	4740 Connecticut Ave.
*Simons, Howard	Washington Post	3604 Gunston Rd., Alexandria, Va.
Sizemore, Richard C	Fairchild Publications, New York	2801 Quebec St.
*Slaughter, Adolph James	Associated Negro Press	417 Quincy St.
*Slevin, Joseph R	New York Herald Tribune	16 East Melrose St., Chevy Chase, Md.
*Sloyan, Patrick J	United Press International	7815 Chicago Ave., Silver Spring, Md.
*Smith, A. Robert	Portland Oregonian, Eugene (Oreg.) Register-Guard, Oregon Statesman, Pendleton (Oreg.) East Oregonian, Medford (Oreg.) Mail Tribune, Corvallis (Oreg.) Gazette Times, Tacoma (Wash.) News Tribune, Bend (Oreg.) Bulletin.	3439 Oliver St.
*Smith, Donald Lloyd	Newsday	2506 Clay Rd., Alexandria, Va.
*Smith, Douglas	Pittsburgh Press	3326 South Wakefield St., Arlington, Va.
*Smith, Marie D	Washington Post	46 Laurel Dr., Fairfax, Va.
*Smith, McLellan	Delaware State News, York (Pa.) Dispatch	2310 Ashmead Pl.
Smith, Merriman	United Press International	5323 Connecticut Ave.
*Smith, Yvonne Franklin	Portland Oregonian, Eugene (Oreg.) Register-Guard, Oregon Statesman, Pendleton (Oreg.) East Oregonian, Medford (Oreg.) Mail-Tribune, Corvallis (Oreg.) Gazette Times, Tacoma (Wash.) News Tribune. Bend (Oreg.) Bulletin.	3439 Oliver St.
*Soresi, C. D	World Press	490 Ingleside Ave., McLean, Va.
*Sparks, John S., Jr	Lawton (Okla.) Constitution, Wichita Eagle & Beacon.	820 S. Washington St., Alexandria, Va.
Spencer, George Adams	St. Thomas Daily News (Virgin Islands), Agana (Guam) Daily News, El Imparcial (P.R.).	1817 16th St.
*Spivack, Robert G	New York Herald Tribune Syndicate, Potomac News Associates.	408 Paul Spring Rd., Hollin Hills, Alexandria, Va.
Spivak, Alvin A	United Press International	1021 Arlington Blvd., Arlington, Va.
*Spivak, Jonathan M	Wall Street Journal	3222 Oliver St.
*Spong, Richard	Editorial Research Reports	5120 Duvall Dr.
*Spoor, André Simon	Grote Provinciale Dagbladen (Netherlands).	4411 Ridge St., Chevy Chase, Md.
*Stackelberg, Garnett	Baltimore News-Post	1673 Columbia Rd.
*Stafford, Samuel A	Washington Daily News	8513 Irvington Ave., Bethesda, Md.
*Stanford, Neal A	Christian Science Monitor	Montresor, Leesburg, Va.
*Starnes, Richard	Scripps-Howard Newspaper Alliance, United Features Syndicate.	6215 22nd Rd. North, Arlington, Va.
*Stearns, Jessie	Topeka (Kansas) Capital-Journal	100 5th St. SE.
*Steele, Jack	Scripps-Howard Newspaper Alliance	5824 Osceola Rd.
*Steele, Sally	Enid (Okla.) News & Eagle	5004 Jamestown Rd.
*Steen, John M	Nashville Banner, Greenville (S.C.) News, Jackson (Miss.) News, Shreveport (La.) Journal, Dayton (Ohio) Journal Herald, Atlanta (Ga.) Times.	7619 Elgar St., N. Springfield, Va.
*Steers, Nina	Chattanooga Times	6601 River Rd., Bethesda, Md.
*Steif, William	Scripps-Howard Newspaper Alliance	7103 Lenhart Dr., Chevy Chase, Md.
Stephenson, Malvina	Tulsa World	330 A St. SE.
*Stern, Laurence	Washington Post	7616 14th St.

MEMBERS OF THE PRESS ENTITLED TO ADMISSION—Continued

Name	Paper represented	Office
*Sterne, Joseph R. L.	Baltimore Sun	3702 Raymond St., Chevy Chase, Md.
*Stevenson, Robert L.	Associated Press	3231 Ravensworth Place, Alexandria, Va.
*Stichman, Ellen	Bell-McClure Syndicate	3850 Tunlaw Rd.
Stimmel, Thomas S.	Newhouse National News Service	612 Independence Ave. SE.
*Stokes, Dillard	Council Bluffs (Iowa) Nonpareil, The Public Business Associates.	207 North Columbus St., Alexandria, Va.
*Stone, Walker	Scripps-Howard Newspaper Alliance	2030 Hillyer Pl.
Strom, Else	Aftonbladet (Sweden)	1555 Colonial Ter., Arlington, Va.
*Strout, Richard L.	Christian Science Monitor	4517 Garfield St.
*Sugiura, Hideo	Chubu Nippon Shimbun	4306 37th St.
Sul, Kuk-Whan	The Korea Times	7115 Brookville Rd., Chevy Chase, Md.
*Sullivan, Joseph W. III	Wall Street Journal	8809 Ridge Rd., Bethesda, Md.
*Swift, Ivan	Louisville (Ky.) Courier-Journal & Times	3022 Homewood Pky., Kensington, Md.
*Szulc, Tad	New York Times	3218 Woodley Rd.
Taishoff, Albert Edward	American Metal Market	9708 Admiralty Dr., Silver Spring, Md.
*Talburt, Thomas M.	Cleveland Press & News, Cincinnati Post and Times Star, Columbus Citizen-Journal, Kentucky Post and Times-Star.	1604 Byrnes Dr., McLean, Va.
*Tankersley, Bazy McCormick.	Chicago Tribune Press Service	7500 River Rd.
*Tarr, David R.	Congressional Quarterly	603 Sligo Ave., Silver Spring, Md.
*Taylor, George F.	Wall Street Journal	3607 McKinley St.
Taylor, Robert J.	Washington Capital News Service	1859 Mintwood Pl.
*Temple, Truman P.	Washington Evening Star	4501 Chase Ave., Bethesda, Md.
Ten Eyck, Charles R.	Oil Daily	1228 I St.
*Ter Horst, J. F.	Detroit News	1416 Evening Lane, Hollinbrook Park, Alexandria, Va.
Terry, Ann	Ridder Publications, Aberdeen (S.Dak.) American News, Duluth Herald News-Tribune, Garden Grove (Calif.) News, Grand Forks (N.Dak.) Herald, Long Beach (Calif.) Independent & Press Telegram, Pasadena (Calif.) Independent & Star-News, St. Paul Pioneer Press & Dispatch, San Jose Mercury News, N.Y. Journal of Commerce.	912½ 25th St.
*Teter, Daniel P.	Congressional Quarterly	1765 P St.
*Theis, J. William	United Press International	10 Granville Dr., Silver Spring, Md.
Thomas, Helen	United Press International	1711 Massachusetts Ave.
*Thomasson, Dan K.	Rocky Mountain (Colo.) News	5405 Duke St., Alexandria, Va.
Thompson, Robert E.	Los Angeles Times, Los Angeles Times-Washington Post News Service.	4626 Tomkins Dr., McLean, Va.
*Thornburgh, Richard A.	Washington Post	1701 16th St.
*Till, Vladimir	Czechoslovak News Agency	1444 Rhode Island Ave.
*Tillman, Steve	El Paso Times, Leavenworth (Kans.) Times, Newport News (Va.) Daily Press, Okinawa Star, San Antonio Express, Colorado Springs Gazette-Telegraph.	3212 Cummings La., Chevy Chase, Md.
Timlin, Eileen C.	Gannett News Service, Hartford (Conn.) Times, Danville (Ill.) Commercial-News, Plainfield (N.J.) Courier-News, Binghamton (N.Y.) Press, Elmira (N.Y.) Star Gazette, Ithica (N.Y.) Journal, Malone (N.Y.) Evening-Telegram, Newburgh-Beacon (N.Y.) News, Niagara Falls (N.Y.) Gazette, Rochester (N.Y.) Democrat and Chronicle, Rochester (N.Y.) Times-Union, Saratoga Springs (N.Y.) Saratogian, Utica (N.Y.) Daily Press, Utica (N.Y.) Observer-Dispatch, Camden (N.J.) Courier-Post, Mamaroneck Daily Times, Mt. Vernon Daily Argus, New Rochelle Standard-Star, Ossining Citizen Register, Port Chester Daily Item, Rockland County Journal-News, Tarrytown Daily News, White Plains Reporter Dispatch, Yonkers Herald Statesman, Peekskill Evening Star.	1722 19th St.

MEMBERS OF THE PRESS ENTITLED TO ADMISSION—Continued

Name	Paper represented	Office
*Timmons, Bascom N.	Houston Chronicle, Fort Worth Star Telegram, Tulsa World, New Orleans States Item, Shreveport Times, Nashville Tennessean, Youngstown Vindicator, Arkansas Democrat, Raleigh News and Observer, Wilmington (Del.) Evening Journal, Wilmington (Del.) News, Baton Rouge State Times, Baton Rouge Morning Advocate, Jackson (Miss.) Clarion-Ledger, Chattanooga News Free-Press, Wichita (Kans.) Eagle, Wichita Beacon, Twin City Sentinel (Winston-Salem), Winston-Salem (N.C.) Journal.	1316 30th St.
*Torrey, Reginald F.	Gannett News Service, Hartford (Conn.) Times, Danville (Ill.) Commercial-News, Plainfield (N.J.) Courier-News, Binghamton (N.Y.) Press, Elmira (N.Y.) Star-Gazette, Ithaca (N.Y.) Journal, Malone (N.Y.) Evening Telegram, Newburgh-Beacon (N.Y.) News, Niagara Falls (N.Y.) Gazette, Rochester (N.Y.) Democrat and Chronicle, Rochester (N.Y.) Times-Union, Saratoga Springs (N.Y.) Saratogian, Utica (N.Y.) Daily Press, Utica (N.Y.) Observer-Dispatch, Camden (N.J.) Courier-Post, Mamaroneck Daily Times, Mt. Vernon Daily Argus, New Rochelle Standard-Star, Ossining Citizen Register, Port Chester Daily Item, Rockland County Journal-News, Tarrytown Daily News, White Plains Reporter Dispatch, Yonkers Herald Statesman, Peekskill Evening Star.	9030 49th Ave., College Park, Md.
*Toth, Robert C.	Los Angeles Times	2400 41st St.
*Tragle, J. Frank	Associated Press	606 Dale Dr., Silver Spring, Md.
*Tribble, Edwin	Washington Evening Star	3115 Foxhall Rd.
Triveri, Edgar A.	La Nueva Prensa (Bogotá, Colombia)	26 West Bldg., Hunting-Towers, Mount Vernon Blvd., Alexandria, Va.
*Troan, John	Scripps-Howard Newspaper Alliance	3500 Kent St., Kensington, Md.
*Trohan, Walter	Chicago Tribune Press Service	2135 R St.
*Trupp, Philip	Fairchild Publications	5411 56th Pl., E. Riverdale, Md.
*Trussell, Charles P.	New York Times	4900 Western Ave.
*Tsompanas, Paul L.	Copley News Service, Alhambra (Calif.) Post-Advocate, Aurora (Ill.) Beacon-News, Burbank (Calif.) Review, Culver City (Calif.) Star-News, Elgin (Ill.) Courier-News, Glendale (Calif.) News-Press, Joliet (Ill.) Herald-News, Monrovia (Calif.) News-Post, Redondo (Calif.) Daily Breeze, San Diego Tribune, San Diego Union, San Pedro (Calif.) News Pilot, Springfield (Ill.) State Journal, Springfield (Ill.) State Register, Venice (Calif.) Vanguard.	4602 Marley Rd., Fairfax, Va.
*Tufty, Barbara Jean	Science Service	3812 Livingston St.
Tufty, Esther Van Wagoner	Tufty News Service, Michigan League of Home Dailies, Central Press Association, Midland (Mich.) Daily News, Owosso (Mich.) Argus Press, Three Rivers (Mich.) Commercial, Holland (Mich.) Sentinel, Port Huron (Mich.) Times Herald, Cadillac (Mich.) News, Ogdensburg (N.Y.) Journal.	508 Arcturus Lane, Alexandria, Va.
*Tully, Andrew	Bell-McClure Newspaper Syndicate	1330 New Hampshire Ave.
*Uhl, Alexander H.	Press Associates, Inc.	Cattail Rd., Poolesville, Md.
*Umstead, William L.	United Press International	2437 Cypress Dr., Falls Church, Va.
Unna, Warren W.	Washington Post	121 Sixth Street NE.
*Vaccaro, Ernest B.	Associated Press	4200 Cathedral Ave.
*Valencia, A. L.	Manila Chronicle	4009 Van Ness St.
*Vandenberg, Jack C.	United Press International	5481 Sanger Ave., Alexandria, Va.
Van der Heuvel, Gerry	New York Daily News	1019 Beechwood La., Falls Church, Va.
*van der Linden, Frank	Nashville Banner, Greenville (S.C.) News, Jackson (Miss.) Daily News, Shreveport (La.) Journal, Dayton (Ohio) Journal-Herald, Atlanta (Ga.) Times.	5312 Blackistone Rd., Westmoreland Hills, Md.

MEMBERS OF THE PRESS ENTITLED TO ADMISSION—Continued

Name	Paper represented	Office
*Van Wagoner, Lou G	Tufty News Service, Michigan League of Home Dailies, Central Press Association, Midland (Mich.) Daily News, Owosso (Mich.) Argus Press, Three Rivers (Mich.) Commercial, Holland (Mich.) Sentinel, Port Huron (Mich.) Times Herald, Cadillac (Mich.) News, Ogdensburg (N.Y.) Journal.	3900 16th St.
*Vashedchenko, Vladimir V	Tass, Telegraph Agency of the U.S.S.R	1515 Ogden St.
*Vichnevski, Serguei	Pravda (Moscow)	3020 Dent Pl.
*Viglietta, Andrew	Long Island Press, Long Island Star-Journal, Newhouse National News Service.	Congressional Hotel.
*Villar-Borda, Carlos J	United Press International	5707 Surrey St., Chevy Chase, Md.
*Viorst, Judith	Science Service	1725 Q St.
Vogel, Mary	Fairchild Publications	711 14th St.
*Vogt, John McFarland	Washington Capital New Service	2355 North Quincy St., Arlington, Va.
*Vohra, Hans Raj	The Times of India	2823 Cortland Pl.
*von Borch, Dr. Herbert	Die Welt (Hamburg)	1938 35th St.
*Von Eckardt, Wolf	Washington Post	2014 Hillyer Pl.
*Von Feldt, Elmer	N. C. W. C. News Service	418 Janmar Dr., Falls Church, Va.
von Herberg, Mary Philomene.	Bell-McClure Syndicate	1245 4th St. SW. #E211.
von Kahler, Anita	Agence France Presse	2828 Connecticut Ave.
Walker, Emily	Tacoma (Wash.) News Tribune	3863 Rodman St.
Walker, P. Wayne	Congressional Quarterly	1115 North Pitt St. Alexandria, Va.
*Wall, Alfred E	Associated Press	3628 Van Ness St.
*Walsh, Burke	N. C. W. C. News Service	1 Scott Circle.
*Walsh, Robert K	Washington Evening Star	2222 Q St.
*Ward, Paul W	Baltimore Sun	4711 Hunt Ave., Chevy Chase, Md.
Ward, Peggy	London Daily Mail	32 Wellesley Circle, NW., Glen Echo, Md.
*Warden, Philip L	Chicago Tribune Press Service	1104 Park Terrace Drive, Alexandria, Va.
*†Warren, Ernest G	Associated Press	4550 Connecticut Ave.
*Warren, Lucian C	Buffalo Courier-Express	5505 Sonoma Rd., Bethesda, Md.
*Watanabe, Bin	Asahi Shimbun	4812 S. 28th St., Arlington, Va.
*Watson, Mark S	Baltimore Sun	1 Merryman Ct., Baltimore, Md.
Watt, John David	London Financial Times	2615 P St.
*Weaver, Warren, Jr	New York Times	Rt. 2, Bx. 22, Lorton, Va.
*Weeks, George C	United Press International	219 North Piedmont St., Arlington, Va.
*Wentworth, Eric	Wall Street Journal	3509 Lowell St.
*West, Dick S	United Press International	3039 Crane Dr., Falls Church, Va.
*West, Felton	Houston (Tex.) Post, Galveston News, Galveston Tribune, Texas City Sun.	2605 N. Quantico St., Arlington, Va.
Wharton, Elizabeth	United Press International	5 Snows Court.
*White, Gordon Eliot	Salt Lake City Deseret News & Telegram	516 N. King's Hwy., Alexandria, Va.
White, Jean M	Washington Post	2512 Q St.
*White, Mary J	Salt Lake City Deseret News	516 N. King's Hwy., Alexandria, Va.
*White, William S	United Feature Syndicate	5223 Reno Rd.
*Whitney, Robert F	New York Times	Box 205, Rt. 2, Vienna, Va.
*Whitten, Leslie H	Hearst Newspapers, Albany Times-Union, Albany Knickerbocker News, Baltimore News-American, Boston Record American & Sunday Advertiser, Los Angeles Herald-Examiner, New York Journal-American, San Antonio Light, San Francisco Examiner, San Francisco News Call Bulletin, Seattle Post-Intelligencer.	114 Eastmoor Dr., Silver Spring, Md.
*Wick, Dodee	Roanoke Rapids (N.C.) Daily Herald, Bogalusa (La.) Daily News, Daily Iberian (New Iberia, La.), New Ulm (Minn.) Daily Journal, Fairmont (Minn.) Daily Sentinel, Williston (N.D.) Daily Herald.	135 D St., SE.
*Wicker, Thomas G	New York Times	3333 Cleveland Ave.
Wieck, Paul R	Albuquerque Journal	4901 Seminary Rd., Alexandria, Va.
*Wiggins, J. R	Washington Post	2218 Wyoming Ave.
Wightman, Richard	Fairchild Publications	711 14th St.

MEMBERS OF THE PRESS ENTITLED TO ADMISSION—Continued

Name	Paper represented	Office
Williams, Dorothy E_____	St. Joseph News-Press, St. Joseph Gazette, Decatur (Ill.) Herald, Decatur (Ill.) Review, Champaign-Urbana (Ill.) Courier, East St. Louis (Ill.) Journal, Southern Illinoisan, Davenport (Iowa) Times-Democrat, Cedar Rapids Gazette.	19 5th St. SE.
*Williams, Gladstone_____	Fresno (Calif.) Bee, Modesto (Calif.) Bee, Sacramento Bee.	2132 R St.
*Williams, Leonard_____	David Lawrence Associates _____	RFD 1, Bx. 73, Brookeville, Md.
*Willis, David K_____	Christian Science Monitor_____	2401 Calvert St.
*Willoughby, William Francis.	Religious News Service_____	1105 Ashby Rd., Fairfax Va.
*Wilson, Joann_____	Los Angeles Times_____	2108 16th St.
*Wilson, John B_____	Minneapolis Star and Tribune, Des Moines Register and Tribune.	4910 Klingle St.
*Wilson, John V_____	Indianapolis Times, Evansville Press_____	907 Caddington Ave., Silver Spring, Md.
Wilson, Madelaine_____	Daily Oklahoman, Oklahoma City Times__	1604 Barbour Rd., Falls Church, Va.
*Wilson, Richard L_____	Des Moines Register and Tribune, Minneapolis Star and Tribune.	2918 Garfield St.
Wilson, Stanley Eugene_____	New York Journal of Commerce_____	2430 Pennsylvania Ave.
Wilson, Victor_____	New York Herald Tribune_____	Willard Hotel.
*Winfrey, Lee_____	Knight Newspapers, Miami Herald, Akron Beacon-Journal, Charlotte Observer, Detroit Free Press.	527 5th St. SE.
*Wise, David_____	New York Herald Tribune_____	2700 O St.
*Witcover, Jules J_____	Newhouse National News Service_____	2 Ellenwood Lane, Fairfax, Va.
*Wolfe, Bennett_____	Associated Press_____	5415 Connecticut Ave.
*Wolfe, Medora Mason_____	Alexandria Gazette_____	1500 Arlington Blvd., Arlington, Va.
*Wolfenden, Jeremy J_____	London Telegraph_____	1200 National Press Bldg.
Wolfson, Lewis_____	Providence (R.I.) Journal-Bulletin_____	1060 30th St.
Worsnop, Richard Laidlaw___	Editorial Research Reports_____	1332 19th St.
*Wyant, William K., Jr_____	St. Louis Post Dispatch_____	7109 Braeburn Pl., Bethesda, Md.
*Yamada, Mitsuhiko_____	Kyodo News Service_____	8826 Lanier Dr., Silver Spring, Md.
*Yerxa, Fendall_____	New York Times_____	3916 Morrison St.
Yoshioka, Ruby M_____	Science Service_____	6016 Conway Rd., Bethesda, Md.
*Yost, Paul M_____	Associated Press_____	4608 Drexel Rd., College Park, Md.
*Young, Joseph_____	Washington Evening Star_____	415 Tulane Dr., Alexandria, Va.
Young, Peter A_____	Baltimore Evening Sun_____	12 West Mount Vernon Pl., Baltimore, Md.
*Young, Robert C_____	Chicago Tribune Press Service_____	3601 Porter St.
Young, William H_____	Providence (R.I.) Journal-Bulletin_____	2013 Kalorama Rd.
*†Zielke, George R_____	Toledo Blade, Pittsburgh Post-Gazette_____	503 N. Pickett St., Alexandria, Va.
Zusy, Fred J_____	Continental Press, Inc._____	10009 Frederick Ave., Kensington, Md.
*Zwiren, Henryk_____	Polish Press Agency (Warsaw)_____	2144 California St.

Paper represented and telephone number	Name	Office
Abilene (Tex.) Reporter News (m., e., S.)_ 393-4488, ST 3-5445.	Leslie E. Carpenter_____	784 National Press Bldg.
	Ned Curran_____	784 National Press Bldg.
	Michael D. Mosettig_____	784 National Press Bldg.
	Barbara Kober_____	784 National Press Bldg.
	Theresa McMasters_____	748 National Press Bldg.
Aberdeen (S. Dak.) American-News (m., e., S.)—737-8627.	Walter T. Ridder_____	1325 E St.
	William W. Broom_____	1325 E St.
	Marie Ridder_____	1325 E St.
	Baxter Omohundro_____	1325 E. St.
	Ann Terry_____	1325 E St.
DI 7-5123_____	Fred W. Collins_____	1299 National Press Bldg.
Advance News Service, Inc.—ST 3-1053__	(See Newhouse National News Service.)	
Aftenposten—638-4669_____	Bjorn Heimar_____	1140 National Press Bldg.
Aftonbladet (Sweden) (m., e., S.)_____ JA 2-0937.	Else Strom_____	1555 Colonial Terrace, Arlington, Va.
Agana (Guam) Daily News—387-3309_____	George A. Spencer_____	1817 16th St.
	Annette L. Gray_____	1817 16th St.
Agence France Presse—NA 8-8570_____	Jean Lagrange_____	914 National Press Bldg.
	Francis Lara_____	914 National Press Bldg.
	Louis Déroche_____	914 National Press Bldg.
	Claude Moisy_____	914 National Press Bldg.
	Michel de StPol_____	914 National Press Bldg.
	Anita Von Kahler_____	914 National Press Bldg.
Akron (Ohio) Beacon Journal (e., S.)_____ ME 8-2844.	Philip E. Meyer_____	1290 National Press Bldg.
	(See Knight Newspapers.)__	
Albany (N.Y.) Knickerbocker News (e.)____	Milton L. Kaplan_____	301 Pennsylvania Bldg.
	Warren Rogers_____	301 Pennsylvania Bldg.
	Catherine Mackin_____	301 Pennsylvania Bldg.
	Marianne Means_____	301 Pennsylvania Bldg.
	Ruth S. Montgomery_____	301 Pennsylvania Bldg.
	David Sentner_____	301 Pennsylvania Bldg.
	Leslie H. Whitten, Jr_____	301 Pennsylvania Bldg.
Albany (N.Y.) Times-Union (m. S.)_____ EX 3-8322.	Milton L. Kaplan_____	301 Pennsylvania Bldg.
	Warren Rogers_____	301 Pennsylvania Bldg.
	Catherine Mackin_____	301 Pennsylvania Bldg.
	Marianne Means_____	301 Pennsylvania Bldg.
	Ruth S. Montgomery_____	301 Pennsylvania Bldg.
	David Sentner_____	301 Pennsylvania Bldg.
	Leslie H. Whitten, Jr_____	301 Pennsylvania Bldg.
Albuquerque Journal (m., S.)_____ 931-3375.	Paul R. Wieck_____	4901 Seminary Rd., Alexandria, Va.
Albuquerque (N. Mex.) Tribune (e.)_____ DI 7-7750.	Ruth Finney_____	1013 13th St.
Alexandria (Va.) Gazette (e.)—KI 9-7185__	Medora Mason Wolfe_____	317 King St., Alexandria, Va.
	John A. Reichmann_____	317 King St., Alexandria, Va.
Alhambra (Calif.) Post-Advocate (e.)_____ 296-8565.	Raymond J. McHugh_____	1629 K St.
	Franklyn C. Nofziger_____	1629 K St.
	Lucille Eddinger_____	1629 K St.
	Edwin G. Martin_____	1629 K St.
	John H. McLaren_____	1629 K St.
	Lester M. Beir_____	1629 K St.
	Paul L. Tsompanas_____	1629 K St.
	Henry Goethals_____	1629 K St.
	Larry C. Osius_____	1629 K St.
Amarillo News & Globe Times (m., e., S.)_ 393-4488, ST 3-5445.	Leslie E. Carpenter_____	784 National Press Bldg.
	Ned Curran_____	784 National Press Bldg.
	Michael D. Mosettig_____	784 National Press Bldg.
	Barbara Kober_____	784 National Press Bldg.
	Theresa McMasters_____	784 National Press Bldg.
American Banker Daily (m.)—347-5529___	Michael Benson_____	769 National Press Bldg.
American Metal Market (m.)—RE 7-3230.	Freeman C. Bishop_____	1118 National Press Bldg.
	A. K. Rannells_____	1118 National Press Bldg.
	Albert Edward Taishoff____	1118 National Press Bldg.
A.N.S.A. Italian National News Agency__ DU 3-6887.	Guiseppe Canessa_____	State Dept. Press Rm.
Anchorage (Alaska) Daily Times (e.)_____ FE 8-9599.	Marilyn Atwood_____	2534 Queen Anne's La.
Anderson (S.C.) Independent (m., S.)_____ LI 7-2616.	Wesley F. Hayden_____	130 3d St. SE.
	Lewis S. McCash_____	130 3d St. SE.
Ann Arbor (Mich.) News (e.)—737-7770___	William F. Pyper_____	515 National Press Bldg.
	Paul A. Miltich_____	515 National Press Bldg.
Antara News Agency (Indonesia)_____ CO 5-9632.	Marius Rengkoe_____	1914 Connecticut Ave.

NEWSPAPERS REPRESENTED—Continued

Paper represented and telephone number	Name	Office
Arizona Republic (m., S.)—NA 8-4140	Benjamin R. Cole	408 Albee Bldg.
	Michael A. Padev	408 Albee Bldg.
Arkansas Democrat (e., S.)—EX 3-0146	Bascom N. Timmons	1253 National Press Bldg.
	Mary Ann Pardue	1253 National Press Bldg.
Arkansas Gazette (Little Rock) (m., S.)—393-4488, ST 3-5445.	Leslie E. Carpenter	784 National Press Bldg.
	Ned Curran	784 National Press Bldg.
	Michael D. Mosettig	784 National Press Bldg.
	Barbara Kober	784 National Press Bldg.
	Theresa McMasters	784 National Press B'dg.
Asahi Shimbun (m., e.)—ST 3-0523	Mitsugu Nakamura	794 National Press Bldg.
	Yukio Matsuyama	794 National Press Bldg.
	Masahiro Sasagawa	794 National Press Bldg.
	Bin Watanabe	794 National Press Bldg.
Associated Negro Press—638-5332	Adolph James Slaughter	918 F St., Rm. 300.
Associated Press—AD 4-5400	W. L. Beale, Jr	1300 Connecticut Ave.
	Elton C. Fay	1300 Connecticut Ave.
	J. B. Engle	1300 Connecticut Ave.
	Ernest G. Warren	1300 Connecticut Ave.
	Raymond J. Crowley	1300 Connecticut Ave.
	Edwin B. Haakinson	1300 Connecticut Ave.
	Karl Bauman	1300 Connecticut Ave.
	John M. Hightower	1300 Connecticut Ave.
	W. T. Peacock	1300 Connecticut Ave.
	Ovid A. Martin	1300 Connecticut Ave.
	J. W. Davis	1300 Connecticut Ave.
	Hamilton Faron	1300 Connecticut Ave.
	L. T. Easley, Jr	1300 Connecticut Ave.
	Paul M. Yost	1300 Connecticut Ave.
	Charles C. Haslet	1300 Connecticut Ave.
	Jack L. Bell	1300 Connecticut Ave.
	W. F. Arbogast	1300 Connecticut Ave.
	Sterling F. Green	1300 Connecticut Ave.
	Gardner Bridge	1300 Connecticut Ave.
	Joseph R. Coyne	1300 Connecticut Ave.
	Margaret Kernodle	1300 Connecticut Ave.
	Arthur S. Roberts	1300 Connecticut Ave.
	Richard P. Powers	1300 Connecticut Ave.
	Edward H. Higgs	1300 Connecticut Ave.
	J. Frank Tragle	1300 Connecticut Ave.
	James Marlow	1300 Connecticut Ave.
	Willard H. Mobley	1300 Connecticut Ave.
	Marvin L. Arrowsmith	1300 Connecticut Ave.
	Bennett Wolfe	1300 Connecticut Ave.
	Harrison B. Humphries	1300 Connecticut Ave.
	James C. Munn	1300 Connecticut Ave.
	Donald Sanders	1300 Connecticut Ave.
	Arthur L. Edson	1300 Connecticut Ave.
	John Chadwick	1300 Connecticut Ave.
	Alfred E. Wall	1300 Connecticut Ave.
	R. Gordon Brown	1300 Connecticut Ave.
	W. Joynes Macfarlan	1300 Connecticut Ave.
	Vern Haugland	1300 Connecticut Ave.
	Dillon Graham	1300 Connecticut Ave.
	Francis E. Carey	1300 Connecticut Ave.
	C. Yates McDaniel	1300 Connecticut Ave.
	G. M. Kelly	1300 Connecticut Ave.
	Joseph W. Hall, Jr	1300 Connecticut Ave.
	Fred S. Hoffman	1300 Connecticut Ave.
	John H. Kamps	1300 Connecticut Ave.
	H. Lee Garrett	1300 Connecticut Ave.
	Jerry T. Baulch	1300 Connecticut Ave.
	Lewis Gulick	1300 Connecticut Ave.
	Edmond Le Breton	1300 Connecticut Ave.
	Douglas B. Cornell	1300 Connecticut Ave.
	Bem Price	1300 Connecticut Ave.
	Ben Meyer	1300 Connecticut Ave.
	Spencer Davis	1300 Connecticut Ave.
	Frank Cormier	1300 Connecticut Ave.
	Martha Cole	1300 Connecticut Ave.
	Ernest B. Vaccaro	1300 Connecticut Ave
	John Koenig, Jr	1300 Connecticut Ave.
	Frances L. Lewine	1300 Connecticut Ave.
	Robert A. Hunt	1300 Connecticut Ave.
	Adren Cooper	1300 Connecticut Ave.
	Neil Gilbride	1300 Connecticut Ave.
	Harry J. Kelly	1300 Connecticut Ave.
	Joseph E. Mohbat	1300 Connecticut Ave.
	Robert L. Stevenson	1300 Connecticut Ave.
	Endre Marton	1300 Connecticut Ave.
	Joseph F. Kane	1300 Connecticut Ave.
	G. K. Hodenfield	1300 Connecticut Ave.
	Geoffrey S. Gould	1300 Connecticut Ave.
	John W. Beckler	1300 Connecticut Ave.
	Warner B. Ragsdale	1300 Connecticut Ave.

NEWSPAPERS REPRESENTED—Continued

Paper represented and telephone number	Name	Office
Associated Press—Continued	Lewis E. Hawkins	1300 Connecticut Ave.
	James D. Cary	1300 Connecticut Ave.
	Walter R. Mears	1300 Connecticut Ave.
	Barry Schweid	1300 Connecticut Ave.
	Ary Moleon	1300 Connecticut Ave.
	Carl P. Leubsdorf	1300 Connecticut Ave.
	Wilbur F. Martin	1300 Connecticut Ave.
Atlanta (Ga.) Constitution (m.) 628–5962	Theo Lippman	614 Albee Bldg.
Atlanta Daily World (m.)—582–8565	Daniel E. Day	P.O. Bx. 5105
Atlanta (Ga.) Journal (e., S.)—628–5962	Margaret R. Shannon	614 Albee Bldg.
Atlanta (Ga.) Times—LI 4–8238	Frank Van der Linden	132 3d St. SE.
	John M. Steen, Jr	132 3d St. SE.
	Leland A. Bandy	132 3d St. SE.
Augusta (Ga.) Chronicle Herald	Wesley F. Hayden	130 3d St. SE.
LI 7–2616.	Lewis S. McCash	130 3d St. SE.
Aurora (Ill.) Beacon-News (e., S.)	Raymond J. McHugh	1629 K St.
296–8565.	Franklyn C. Nofziger	1629 K St.
	Lucille Eddinger	1629 K St.
	Edwin G. Martin	1629 K St.
	John H. McLaren	1629 K St.
	Lester M. Bell	1629 K St.
	Paul L. Tsompanas	1629 K St.
	Henry Goethals	1629 K St.
	Larry C. Osius	1629 K St.
Austin-American (m.)—393–4488	Leslie E. Carpenter	784 National Press Bldg.
	Ned Curran	784 National Press Bldg.
	Michael D. Mosettig	784 National Press Bldg.
	Barbara Kober	784 National Press Bldg.
	Theresa McMasters	784 National Press Bldg.
Austin Statesman (S.)—393–4488	Leslie E. Carpenter	784 National Press Bldg.
	Ned Curran	784 National Press Bldg.
	Michael E. Mosettig	784 National Press Bldg.
	Barbara Kober	784 National Press Bldg.
	Theresa McMasters	784 National Press Bldg.
Australian Newspaper Service—NA 8–7127	S. Randal Heymanson	1196 National Press Bldg.
Baltimore American (S.)—EX 3–8322	Milton L. Kaplan	301 Pennsylvania Bldg.
	Warren Rogers	301 Pennsylvania Bldg.
	Catherine Mackin	301 Pennsylvania Bldg.
	Marianne Means	301 Pennsylbania Bldg.
	Ruth S. Montgomery	301 Pennsylvania Bldg.
	David Sentner	301 Pennsylvania Bldg.
	Leslie H. Whitten, Jr	301 Pennsylvania Bldg.
NO 7–6520 or CO 5–8806	Garnett Stackelberg	1617 Columbia Rd.
Baltimore (Md.) Evening Sun	James MacNees	1214 National Press Bldg.
DI 7–1234.	Peter A. Young	1214 National Press Bldg.
Baltimore (Md.) News-American (e.)	Milton L. Kaplan	301 Pennsylvania Bldg.
EX 3–8322.	Warren Rogers	301 Pennsylvania Bldg.
	Catherine Mackin	301 Pennsylvania Bldg.
	Marianne Means	301 Pennsylvania Bldg.
	Ruth S. Montgomery	301 Pennsylvania Bldg.
	David Sentner	301 Pennsylvania Bldg.
	Leslie H. Whitten, Jr	301 Pennsylvania Bldg.
NO 7–6520 or CO 5–8806	Garnett Stackelberg	1617 Columbia Rd.
Baltimore (Md.) Sun (m., S.)—DI 7–1234	Philip Potter	1214 National Press Bldg.
	Paul W. Ward	1214 National Press Bldg.
	Thomas O'Neill	1214 National Press Bldg.
	Rodney Crowther	1214 National Press Bldg.
	Mark S. Watson	1214 National Press Bldg.
	Helen Delich Bentley	1214 National Press Bldg.
	Joseph R. L. Sterne	1214 National Press Bldg.
	Peter J. Kumpa	1214 National Press Bldg.
	Albert Sehlstedt, Jr	1214 National Press Bldg.
	Muriel Dobbin	1214 National Press Bldg.
	Ernest B. Furgurson	1214 National Press Bldg.
	Bynum G. Shaw	1214 National Press Bldg.
	Adam Clymer	1214 National Press Bldg.
Bangor Daily News (m.)—NA 8–7350	Bulkley Griffin	1237 National Press Bldg.
	Isabel Kinnear Griffin	1237 National Press Bldg.
	Donald R. Larrabee	1237 National Press Bldg.
Baptist Press—232–3087	W. Barry Garrett	1628 16th St.
	Winona Saturday	1628 16th St.
Bartlesville (Okla.) Examiner-Enterprise	Kenneth M. Scheibel	1251 National Press Bldg.
(m., e.)—NA 8–7227.	Dale Himes	1251 National Press Bldg.
Baton Rouge Morning Advocate (m., S.)	Bascom N. Timmons	1253 National Press Bldg.
EX 3–0146.	Sam Hanna	1253 National Press Bldg.
Baton Rouge State-Times (e.)—EX 3–0146	Bascom N. Timmons	1253 National Press Bldg.
	Sam Hanna	1253 National Press Bldg.
Battle Creek (Mich.) Enquirer-News (e.,	Robert N. Branson	1134 National Press Bldg.
S.)—RE 7–2901.	Cleve Corlett	1134 National Press Bldg.
Bay City (Mich.) Times (e., S.)	William F. Pyper	515 National Press Bldg.
737–7770.	Paul A. Miltich	515 National Press Bldg.

NEWSPAPERS REPRESENTED—Continued

Paper represented and telephone number	Name	Office
Beaumont (Tex.) Enterprise (m., S.)_____ 393-4488, ST 3-5445.	Leslie E. Carpenter_____	784 National Press Bldg.
	Ned Curran_____	784 National Press Bldg.
	Michael D. Mosettig_____	784 National Press Bldg.
	Barbara Kober_____	784 National Press Bldg.
	Theresa McMasters_____	784 National Press Bldg.
Beaumont (Tex.) Journal (e.)_____ 393-4488, ST 3-5445.	Leslie E. Carpenter____	784 National Press Bldg.
	Ned Curran_____	784 National Press Bldg.
	Michael D. Mosettig_____	784 National Press Bldg.
	Barbara Kober_____	784 National Press Bldg.
	Theresa McMasters_____	784 National Press Bldg.
Bellevue (Ohio) Gazette (e.)—DI 7-1856____	Glenn D. Everett_____	926 National Press Bldg.
Bell-McClure Syndicate—AD 2-4321_____	Drew Pearson_____	1313 29th St.
347-4325_____	Jack Anderson_____	1612 K St.
	Ellen Stichman_____	1612 K St.
AD 2-4321_____	Tom McNamara_____	1313 29th St.
543-1166_____	Mary Philomene von Herberg.	1245 4th St. SW. #E211.
296-6777_____	Andrew Tully_____	1330 New Hampshire Ave.
FE 3-4166_____	Edgar A. Mowrer_____	3301 Garfield St.
LI 3-1109_____	Angele deT. Gingras_____	316 N. Carolina Ave. SE.
Bend (Ore.) Bulletin (e.)_____ LI 4-5100.	A. Robert Smith_____	328 Pennsylvania Ave. SE.
	Yvonne F. Smith_____	3439 Oliver St.
Bennington (Vt.) Banner (e.)_____ ME 8-4523.	Edward J. Michelson_____	1014 National Press Bldg.
Berlingske Tidende (Denmark) (m.)_____ EX 3-5794.	Anders Georg_____	1130 National Press Bldg.
Biddeford-Saco (Maine) Journal (e.)_____ NA 8-3335.	Esther van Wagoner Tufty__	997 National Press Bldg.
	Lou G. van Wagoner_____	997 National Press Bldg.
Billings (Mont.) Gazette (m., e., S.)_____ JU 8-4904.	Cyril J. O'Brien_____	10004 Reddick Dr., Silver Spring, Md.
Binghamton (N.Y.) Press (e., S.)_____ EX 3-3460.	Paul L. Martin_____	795 National Press Bldg.
	Reginald F. Torrey_____	795 National Press Bldg.
	William A. Garrett_____	795 National Press Bldg.
	Eileen C. Timlin_____	795 National Press Bldg.
	James W. Canan_____	795 National Press Bldg.
	Jack W. Germond_____	795 National Press Bldg.
	Edmund B. Lambeth_____	795 National Press Bldg.
	Richardson Gale_____	795 National Press Bldg.
Birmingham(Ala.)News (e., S.)—ST 3-1053.	James Free_____	4500 Q Lane.
	Ann Cottrell Free_____	4500 Q Lane.
Birmingham (Ala.) Post-Herald (m.)_____ DI 7-7750.	Michael V. Miller_____	1013 13th St.
Blackwell (Okla.) Journal-Tribune (e., S.) NA 8-7227.	Kenneth M. Scheibel_____	1251 National Press Bldg.
	Dale Himes_____	1251 National Press Bldg.
Bogalusa (La.) Daily News (e., S.)_____ LI 3-2978.	Dodee Wick_____	135 D St. SE.
Boise (Idaho) Daily & Evening Statesman (m., e.) RE 7-2901.	Robert N. Branson_____	1134 National Press Bldg.
	Cleve Corlett_____	1134 National Press Bldg.
Booth Newspapers of Michigan_____ 737-7770.	William F. Pyper_____	515 National Press Bldg.
	Paul A. Miltich_____	515 National Press Bldg.
Boston Advertiser (S.)—EX 3-8322_____	Milton L. Kaplan_____	301 Pennsylvania Bldg.
	Warren Rogers_____	301 Pennsylvania Bldg.
	Catherine Mackin_____	301 Pennsylvania Bldg.
	Marianne Means_____	301 Pennsylvania Bldg.
	Ruth S. Montgomery_____	301 Pennsylvania Bldg.
	David Sentner_____	301 Pennsylvania Bldg.
	Leslie H. Whitten, Jr_____	301 Pennsylvania Bldg.
Boston Globe (m., e., S.)—NA 8-8869_____	Wilfrid C. Rodgers_____	856 National Press Bldg.
Boston Herald and Traveler (m., e., S.)_____ 393-4488, ST 3-5445.	Leslie E. Carpenter_____	784 National Press Bldg.
	Ned Curran_____	784 National Press Bldg.
	Michael D. Mosettig_____	784 National Press Bldg.
	Barbara Kober_____	784 National Press Bldg.
	Theresa McMasters_____	784 National Press Bldg.
Boston Record American (m.)—EX 3-8322_	Milton L. Kaplan_____	301 Pennsylvania Bldg.
	Warren Rogers_____	301 Pennsylvania Bldg.
	Catherine Mackin_____	301 Pennsylvania Bldg.
	Marianne Means_____	301 Pennsylvania Bldg.
	Ruth S. Montgomery_____	301 Pennsylvania Bldg.
	David Sentner_____	301 Pennsylvania Bldg.
	Leslie H. Whitten, Jr_____	301 Pennsylvania Bldg.
Bowling Green (Ohio) Sentinel-Tribune (e)_ DI 7-1856.	Glenn D. Everett_____	926 National Press Bldg.
Brattleboro (Vt.) Reformer (e.)_____ LI 7-4404.	Vonda Bergman_____	513 Constitution Ave. NE.
Bridgeport (Conn.) Post and Bridgeport Telegram (m., e., S.)—ST 3-1070.	Carey Cronan_____	1205 National Press Bldg.
Brockton (Mass.) Enterprise (e.)_____ NA 8-7350.	Bulkley Griffin_____	1237 National Press Bldg.
	Isabel Kinnear Griffin_____	1237 National Press Bldg.
	Donald R. Larrabee_____	1237 National Press Bldg.
Bryan (Ohio) Times (e.)—DI 7-1856_____	Glenn D. Everett_____	926 National Press Bldg.
Buffalo (N.Y.) Courier-Express (m.)_____ NA 8-2906.	Lucian C. Warren_____	1389 National Press Bldg.
	Geraldine Millar_____	1389 National Press Bldg.

NEWSPAPERS REPRESENTED—Continued

Paper represented and telephone number	Name	Office
Buffalo Evening News (e.)—RE 7-3188____	Nat S. Finney_____	1207 National Press Bldg.
	Francis C. Fortune_____	1207 National Press Bldg.
	Roland A. Powell_____	1207 National Press Bldg.
Burbank (Calif.) Review (e).) 296-8565____	Raymond J. McHugh_____	1629 K St.
	Franklyn C. Nofziger_____	1629 K St.
	Lucille Eddinger_____	1629 K St.
	Edwin G. Martin_____	1629 K St.
	John H. McLaren_____	1629 K St.
	Lester M. Bell_____	1629 K St.
	Paul L. Tsompanas_____	1629 K St.
	Henry Goethals_____	1629 K St.
	Larry C. Osius_____	1629 K St.
Burlington (Vt.) Free Press (m.)_____ LI 7-4404.	Vonda Bergman_____	513 Constitution Ave. NE.
Cadillac (Mich.) News (e)_____ NA 8-3335.	Esther van Wagoner Tufty__	997 National Press Bldg.
	Lou G. van Wagoner_____	997 National Press Bldg.
Camden Courier-Post (e.)—EX 3-3460____	Paul Martin_____	795 National Press Bldg.
	Reginald F. Torrey_____	795 National Press Bldg.
	William A. Garrett_____	795 National Press Bldg.
	Eileen C. Timlin_____	795 National Press Bldg.
	James William Canan_____	795 National Press Bldg.
	Jack W. Germond_____	795 National Press Bldg.
	Edmund B. Lambeth_____	795 National Press Bldg.
	Richardson Gale_____	795 National Press Bldg.
Canadian Press—AD 4-5400_____	Arch MacKenzie_____	1300 Connecticut Ave.
Carson City (Nev.) Nevada-Appeal (e., S.)—NA 8-7227.	Kenneth M. Scheibel_____	1251 National Press Bldg.
	Dale Himes_____	1251 National Press Bldg.
Cedar Rapids Gazette (e., S.)_____ LI 7-3554.	Dorothy Williams_____	19 5th St. SE.
Central News Agency of China_____ NA 8-2738.	Chiang-Kwang Li_____	1046 National Press Bldg.
	Francis Fine_____	1046 National Press Bldg.
Central Press—NA 8-3335_____	Esther van Wagoner Tufty__	997 National Press Bldg.
	Lou G. van Wagoner_____	997 National Press Bldg.
Champaign-Urbana Courier (e., S.)_____ LI 7-3554.	Dorothy Williams_____	19 5th St. SE.
Charleston (W. Va.) Gazette (m.)_____ 882-1386.	Harry W. Ernst_____	317 Whittier St.
Chattanooga News Free-Press (e.)_____ EX 3-0146.	Bascom Timmons_____	1253 National Press Bldg.
	Mary Ann Pardue_____	1253 National Press Bldg.
Chattanooga Times (m., S.) 347-6742____	Nina Steers_____	1029 National Press Bldg.
Charlotte (N.C.) Observer (m., S.)_____ ME 8-2844.	Jack E. Claiborne_____	1290 National Press Bldg.
	(See Knight Newspapers.)	
Chicago Construction News (m.)_____ 296-2160.	Ernest P. Mickel_____	1030 15th St.
Chicago (Ill.) Daily News (e.)_____ DI 7-9828.	Peter Lisagor_____	1229 National Press Bldg.
	William McGaffin_____	1229 National Press Bldg.
	James H. McCartney_____	1229 National Press Bldg.
	Charles E. Nicodemus, Jr___	1229 National Press Bldg.
	Dorothy (Peggy) O'Neil___	1229 National Press Bldg.
DI 7-9832_____	Max Freedman_____	1256 National Press Bldg.
Chicago Defender (m.)—347-4739_____	Rosemarie Tyler Brooks____	67A G St. SW.
Chicago's American (e., S.)—DI 7-8283____	Robert Gruenberg_____	1272 National Press Bldg.
Chicago Sun-Times (m., S.)—EX 3-0151__	Carleton Kent_____	1245 National Press Bldg.
	Frederick Kuh_____	1245 National Press Bldg.
	Thomas B. Ross_____	1245 National Press Bldg.
	Charles L. Bartlett_____	1245 National Press Bldg.
	Thomas B. Littlewood_____	1245 National Press Bldg.
Chicago (Ill.) Tribune Press Service_____ 298-5959.	Walter Trohan_____	1750 Pennsylvania Ave.
	Willard Edwards_____	1750 Pennsylvania Ave.
	Leland S. Forrester_____	1750 Pennsylvania Ave.
	William T. Moore_____	1750 Pennsylvania Ave.
	Philip L. Warden_____	1750 Pennsylvania Ave.
	Robert C. Young_____	1750 Pennsylvania Ave.
	Philip W. Dodd_____	1750 Pennyslvania Ave.
	Joseph F. Hearst_____	1750 Pennsylvania Ave.
	Russell W. Freeburg_____	1750 Pennsylvania Ave.
	William F. Anderson_____	1750 Pennsylvania Ave.
	Michael Pakenham_____	1750 Pennsylvania Ave.
	Mary C. Pakenham_____	1750 Pennsylvania Ave.
	Arthur Sears Henning_____	1750 Pennsylvania Ave.
	Bazy McCormick Tankersley.	1750 Pennsylvania Ave.
Chickasha (Okla.) Daily Express (e., S.)___ NA 8-7227.	Kenneth M. Scheibel_____	1251 National Press Bldg.
	Dale Himes_____	1251 National Press Bldg.
Chosun Ilbo (Seoul, Korea)—525-5164____	Meung Ja Moon_____	1817 N. Quinn St., Arlington, Va.
DU 3-2522____	Wan Soo Jun_____	Press Rm., State Dept.
Christian Science Monitor (Boston) (e)____ NA 8-2142.	Saville R. Davis_____	1293 National Press Bldg.
	Richard L. Strout_____	1293 National Press Bldg.
	Neal A. Stanford_____	1293 National Press Bldg.
	Josephine B. Ripley_____	1293 National Press Bldg.
	Robert R. Brunn_____	1293 National Press Bldg.
	Robert Cahn_____	1293 National Press Bldg.
	David K. Willis_____	1293 National Press Bldg.

NEWSPAPERS REPRESENTED—Continued

Paper represented and telephone number	Name	Office
Chubu Nippon Shimbun (m., e.)_____ ST 3-9479.	Hideo Sugiura_____	1124 National Press Bldg.
Cincinnati (Ohio) Enquirer (rr.)_____ 628-0299.	Richard B. Kirkpatrick____	1387 National Press Bldg.
	Mary Gallagher_____	1387 National Press Bldg.
Cincinnati (Ohio) Post and Times Star (e.)_ DI 7-7750.	Robert W. Crater_____	1013 13th St.
	Thomas M. Talburt_____	1013 13th St.
Clearwater (Fla.) Sun (e., S.)—LI 7-2616__	Wesley F. Hayden_____	130 3d St. SE.
	Lewis S. McCash_____	130 3d St. SE.
Cleveland (Ohio) Plain Dealer (m.)_____ ME 8-1366.	Alvin Silverman_____	609 Albee Bldg.
	Edward Kernan_____	609 Albee Bldg.
	Phil G. Goulding_____	609 Albee Bldg.
	John Peter Leacacos_____	609 Albee Bldg.
Cleveland (Ohio) Press & News (e.)_____ DI 7-7750.	Robert W. Crater_____	1013 13th St.
	Thomas M. Talburt_____	1013 13th St.
Collegiate Press Service_____ 387-7952.	Laura Godofsky_____	1707 Irving St.
Collins Special Correspondence Service____ DI 7-5123.	Frederic W. Collins_____	1299 National Press Bldg.
Colorado Springs Gazette-Telegraph (e., S.)—OL 2-1803.	Steve Tillman_____	3212 Cummings La., Chevy Chase, Md.
Columbia (S.C.) State and Record (m., e., S.)—LI 7-2616.	Wesley F. Hayden_____	130 3d St. SE.
	Lewis S. McCash_____	130 3d St. SE.
Columbus (Ohio) Citizen Journal (m.)____ DI 7-7750.	Robert W. Crater_____	1013 13th St.
	Thomas M. Talburt_____	1013 13th St.
Columbus (Ohio) Dispatch (e., S.)_____ DI 7-3144.	Carl DeBloom_____	809 National Press Bldg.
	Jessie Stearns Buscher____	809 National Press Bldg.
Congressional Quarterly—296-6800_____	Thomas N. Schroth_____	1735 K St.
	Henrietta M. Poynter_____	1735 K St.
	William A. Korns_____	1735 K St.
	David R. Tarr_____	1735 K St.
	Georgianna F. Rathbun____	1735 K St.
	Ruth Hussey_____	1735 K St.
	P. Wayne Walker_____	1735 K St.
	Neal R. Peirce_____	1735 K St.
	Charles Dennis McCamey__	1735 K St.
	Margaret Carroll_____	1735 K St.
	Spencer Alan Rich_____	1735 K St.
	John Andrew Hamilton, Jr._	1735 K St.
	Daniel P. Teter_____	1735 K St.
	Mark C. Hannan_____	1735 K St.
	Peter E. Holmes_____	1735 K St.
	Victor I. Block_____	1735 K St.
	Frank E. Bradley_____	1735 K St.
	Mary K. Hamil_____	1735 K St.
	Samuel A. Page_____	1735 K St.
	Diane Fisher_____	1735 K St.
	Merrill T. McCord_____	1735 K St.
	Carolyn S. Naff_____	1735 K St.
	James G. Phillips_____	1735 K St.
Continental Press, Inc.—ME 8-5633_____	Fred Zusy_____	765 National Press Bldg.
	Russell Brines_____	765 National Press Bldg.
	Dr. Claudio Benedi_____	765 National Press Bldg.
	Richard L. Horne_____	765 National Press Bldg.
Copley News Service—296-8565_____	Raymond J. McHugh_____	1629 K St.
	Lucille Eddinger_____	1629 K St.
	Edwin G. Martin_____	1629 K St.
	John H. McLaren_____	1629 K St.
	Lester M. Bell_____	1629 K St.
	Paul L. Tsompanos_____	1629 K St.
	Henry Goethals_____	1629 K St.
	Larry C. Osius_____	1629 K St.
Copley Newspapers_____ 638-0934.	Franklyn C. Nofziger_____	1218 National Press Bldg.
Corpus Christi (Tex.) Caller-Times (m., e., S.)—393-4488, ST 3-5445.	Leslie E. Carpenter_____	784 National Press Bldg.
	Ned Curran_____	784 National Press Bldg.
	Michael D. Mosettig_____	784 National Press Bldg.
	Barbara Kober_____	784 National Press Bldg.
	Theresa McMasters_____	784 National Press Bldg.
Correo de la Tarde (Buenos Aires)_____ DU 3-6836.	Leopoldo Aragón_____	2012 N. Daniel St., Arlington, Va.
Corvallis (Oreg.) Gazette Times (e.)_____ LI 4-5100.	A. Robert Smith_____	328 Pennsylvania Ave. SE.
	Yvonne Franklin Smith____	3439 Oliver St.
Council Bluffs (Iowa) Nonpareil (e., S.)___ LI 7-4285.	Dillard Stokes_____	207 N. Columbus St., Alexandria, Va.
Culver City (Calif.) Star-News (e.)_____ 296-8565.	Raymond J. McHugh_____	1629 K St.
	Franklyn C. Nofziger_____	1629 K St.
	Lucille Eddinger_____	1629 K St.
	Edwin G. Martin_____	1629 K St.
	John H. McLaren_____	1629 K St.
	Lester M. Bell_____	1629 K St.
	Paul L. Tsompanos_____	1629 K St.
	Henry Goethals_____	1629 K St.
	Larry C. Osius_____	1629 K St.

NEWSPAPERS REPRESENTED—Continued

Paper represented and telephone number	Name	Office
Czechoslovak News Agency (Prague)_____ 462–5720.	Vladimir Till_____	1444 Rhode Island Ave.
Dagens Nyheter (Sweden) (m., e., S.)_____ 543–7638.	Sven Oste_____	131 D St. SE.
Daily Bond Buyer (N.Y.) (m.)_____ 638–3291.	John Gerrity_____	229 Transportation Bldg.
	Paul V. Pierpoint_____	229 Transportation Bldg.
Daily Iberian (New Iberia, La.) (e.)_____ LI 3–2978.	Dodee Wick_____	135 D St. SE.
Daily Oklahoman (m., S.)—628–0335_____	Allan W. Cromley_____	905 National Press Bldg.
	Madelaine Wilson_____	905 National Press Bldg.
Dallas (Tex.) Morning News (m.)_____ NA 8–5030.	Robert E. Baskin_____	620 Albee Bldg.
	Karen Klinefelter_____	620 Albee Bldg.
	John M. Quinn, Jr_____	620 Albee Bldg.
Dallas (Tex.) Times Herald (e., S.)_____ 393–4488, ST 3–5445.	Robert E. Hollingsworth____	788 National Press Bldg.
	John L. Schoellkopf_____	788 National Press Bldg.
	Leslie E. Carpenter_____	784 National Press Bldg.
Davar (Tel Aviv, Isreal) (m.)—393–5990___	Shlomo Shafir_____	4500 Connecticut Ave.
David Lawrence Associates—FE 3–7400____	David Lawrence_____	1241 24th St.
	Leonard Williams_____	1241 24th St.
	Iva Holland_____	1241 24th St.
Danville (Ill.) Commercial News (e., S.)__ EX 3–3460.	Paul L. Martin_____	795 National Press Bldg.
	Reginald F. Torrey_____	795 National Press Bldg.
	William A. Garrett_____	795 National Press Bldg.
	Eileen C. Timlin_____	795 National Press Bldg.
	James William Canan_____	795 National Press Bldg.
	Jack W. Germond_____	795 National Press Bldg.
	Edmund B. Lambeth_____	795 National Press Bldg.
	Richardson Gale_____	795 National Press Bldg.
Davenport (Iowa) Times—Democrat (m., e., S.)—LI 7–3554.	Dorothy E. Williams_____	19 5th St. SE.
Dawn (Karachi, Pakistan)—362–2383_____	Ejaz Husain_____	3652 Alton Pl.
Day-Jewish Journal (m.)—TU 2–3947_____	Murray Frank_____	7810 16th St.
Dayton Daily News (e., S.)—NA 8–5962___	Walter Rybeck_____	614 Albee Bldg.
Dayton Journal Herald (m.)—LI 4–8238___	Frank van der Linden_____	132 3d St. SE.
	John M. Steen, Jr_____	132 3d St. SE.
	Leland A. Bandy_____	132 3d St. SE.
Dear Publications—393–0979_____	Joseph A. Dear_____	1011 National Press Bldg.
	Cyrene Dear_____	1011 National Press Bldg.
	Gretchen R. Doss_____	1011 National Press Bldg.
	Robert E. Hennessee_____	1011 National Press Bldg.
Decatur (Ill.) Herald & Review (m., e., S.)_ LI 7–3554.	Dorothy Williams_____	19 5th St. SE.
Delaware State News (e.)—ME 8–0823_____	McLellan Smith_____	1131 National Press Bldg.
Denver Daily Journal (m.)—296–2160_____	Ernest P. Mickel_____	1030 15th St.
Denver Post (e.)—RE 7–1381_____	Barnet Nover_____	993 National Press Bldg.
	Naomi Nover_____	993 National Press Bldg.
Des Moines (Iowa) Register and Tribune (m., e., S.)—DI 7–9111.	Richard L. Wilson_____	852 National Press Bldg.
	John B. Wilson_____	852 National Press Bldg
	Clark R. Mollenhoff_____	852 National Press Bldg.
	Charles W. Bailey 2d_____	852 National Press Bldg.
	Nathan K. Kotz_____	852 National Press Bldg.
Detroit (Mich.) Free Press (m.)_____ ME 8–2844.	James L. Robinson_____ (See Knight Newspapers).__	1290 National Press Bldg.
Detroit (Mich.) News (e., S.)_____ NA 8–4566.	J. F. Ter Horst_____	511 National Press Bldg.
	Jay G. Hayden_____	511 National Press Bldg.
	Tom Joyce_____	511 National Press Bldg.
Deutsche Presse Agentur—ST 3–5097_____	Wolfgang Noelter_____	1075 National Press Bldg.
	Hans-Juergen Hoefer_____	1075 National Press Bldg.
	Guenter de Thier_____	1075 National Press Bldg.
Diario Las Americas—WO 6–5960_____	Edna Bowles_____	4951 Rockwood Pkwy.
Die Presse (Austrian) (m., e., S.)_____ 462–1978.	Marlene Manthey_____	3019 Cambridge Pl.
Die Welt (Hamburg) (m., e., S.)_____ FE 3–2988.	Dr. Herbert von Borch_____	1938 35th St.
Donghwa News Agency—DU 3–2522_____	Dong-Won Cho_____	6312 N. 27th St., Arlington, Va.
Donrey Media Group_____ NA 8–7227.	Kenneth M. Scheibel_____	1251 National Press Bldg.
	Dale Himes_____	1251 National Press Bldg.
Draugas (Lithuanian Daily of Chicago) (m.)—RA 3–9375.	Grazina E. Krivickas_____	50 Nicholson St.
Duluth Herald and News Tribune (m., e., S.)—737–8627.	Walter T. Ridder_____	1325 E St.
	William W. Broom_____	1325 E St.
	Marie Ridder_____	1325 E St.
	Baxter Omohundro_____	1325 E St.
	Ann Terry_____	1325 E St.
DI 7–5123_____	Fred W. Collins_____	1299 National Press Bldg.
Durango (Colo.) Herald (e., S.)_____ FE 8–4660.	Helene C. Monberg_____	1618 17th St.
East St. Louis (Ill.) Journal (e., S.)_____ LI 7–3554.	Dorothy Williams_____	19 5th St. SE.
Edith Kermit Roosevelt Syndicate_____ 638–5747.	Edith Kermit Roosevelt____	800 4th St. SW.

NEWSPAPERS REPRESENTED—Continued

Paper represented and telephone number	Name	Office
Editorial Research Reports—296–4880	Richard M. Boeckel	1735 K St.
	Richard Spong	1735 K St.
	Jeanne Kuebler	1735 K St.
	Helen B. Shaffer	1735 K St.
	William B. Dickinson III	1735 K St.
	Buel W. Patch	1735 K St.
	Richard Laidlaw Worsnop	1735 K St.
	Thomas N. Schroth	1725 K St.
El Diario la Prensa (N.Y.) JA 5-5707.	Michael A. Erice	4317 N. 4th St., Arlington, Va.
El Imparcial—387–3309	George A. Spencer	1817 16th St.
El Mundo (San Juan, P.R.)—ST 3-6756	Pat Munroe	1249 National Press Bldg.
	Mary Norris Munroe	1249 National Press Bldg.
	Caryl Rivers	1249 National Press Bldg.
	Timothy B. Clarky	1249 National Press Bldg.
Elgin (Ill.) Courier-News (e.) 296-8565.	Raymond J. McHugh	1629 K St.
	Franklyn C. Nofziger	1629 K St.
	Lucille Eddinger	1629 K St.
	Edwin G. Martin	1629 K St.
	John H. McLaren	1629 K St.
	Lester M. Bell	1629 K St.
	Paul L. Tsompanas	1629 K St.
	Henry Goethals	1629 K St.
	Larry C. Osius	1629 K St.
Elizabeth City (N.C.) Advance (e.) 393-0979.	Joseph A. Dear	1011 National Press Bldg.
	Cyrene Dear	1011 National Press Bldg.
	Gretchen R. Doss	1011 National Press Bldg.
	Robert E. Hennessee	1011 National Press Bldg.
Elmira (N.Y.) Star-Gazette (e.) EX 3-3460.	Paul L. Martin	795 National Press Bldg.
	Reginald F. Torrey	795 National Press Bldg.
	William A. Garrett	795 National Press Bldg.
	Eileen C. Timlin	795 National Press Bldg.
	James W. Canan	795 National Press Bldg.
	Richardson Gale	795 National Press Bldg.
	Jack W. Germond	795 National Press Bldg.
	Edmund B. Lambeth	795 National Press Bldg.
Ely (Nev.) Daily Times (e., S.) NA 8-7227.	Kenneth M. Scheibel	1251 National Press Bldg.
	Dale Himes	1251 National Press Bldg.
El Paso Herald—Post DI 7-7750(e.)	Seth Kantor	1013 13th St.
El Paso (Tex.) Times (m., S.) 483-3791, 483-7918.	Sarah McClendon	2933 28th St.
483-3791, 483-7918.	Nancy M. Fagg	2933 28th St.
OL 2-1803	Sally O'Brien	2933 28th St.
	Steve Tillman	3212 Cummings La., Chevy Chase, Md.
Enid (Okla.) Daily News & Eagle (m., e.) OL 6-2276.	Sally Steele	5004 Jamestown Rd.
Eugene (Oreg.) Register Guard (e., S.) LI 4-5100.	A. Robert Smith	328 Pennsylvania Ave., SE.
	Yvonne Franklin Smith	3439 Oliver St.
Evansville (Ind.) Press (e., S.) DI 7-7750.	John V. Wilson	1013 13th St.
Expreso (Lima, Peru)—DU 3-6836	Leopoldo Aragón	2012 N. Daniel St., Arlington, Va.
Fairchild Publications (N.Y.) (Daily News Record, Women's Wear Daily, Home Furnishings Daily)—RE 7-7090.	John T. Norman	399 National Press Bldg.
	Lloyd M. Schwartz	399 National Press Bldg.
	Walter Johnson	399 National Press Bldg.
	Robert A. Barr	399 National Press Bldg.
	Mary N. Michael	399 National Press Bldg.
	Arthur Garel	399 National Press Bldg.
	Susan Artigiani	399 National Press Bldg.
	Particia Barnes	399 National Press Bldg.
	Betty Morris	399 National Press Bldg.
	Richard C. Sizemore	399 National Press Bldg.
	Philip Trupp	399 National Press Bldg.
	Mary Vogel	399 National Press Bldg.
	Richard Wightman	399 National Press Bldg.
	Miriam G. Gilmour	399 National Press Bldg.
	William D. Hickman, Jr	399 National Press Bldg.
Fairmont (Minn.) Daily Sentinel (e.) LI 3-2978.	Dodee Wick	135 D St. SE.
Fall River (Mass.) Herald News (e.) NA 8-7350.	Bulkley Griffin	1237 National Press Bldg.
	Isabel Kinnear Griffin	1237 National Press Bldg.
	Donald R. Larrabee	1237 National Press Bldg.
Farmington (N. Mex.) Times (e., S.) FE 8-4660.	Helene C. Monberg	1618 17th St.
Federated Publications, Inc. RE 7-2901.	Robert N. Branson	1134 National Press Bldg.
	Cleve Corlett	1134 National Press Bldg.
Flint (Mich.) Journal (e., S.) 737-7770.	William F. Pyper	515 National Press Bldg.
	Paul A. Miltich	515 National Press Bldg.
Florida Times-Union (Jacksonville) LI 7-2616.	Wesley F. Hayden	130 3d St. SE.
	Lewis S. McCash	130 3d St. SE.
Fort Smith (Ark.) Southwest American (m.) NA 8-7227.	Kenneth M. Scheibel	1251 National Press Bldg.
	Dale Himes	1251 National Press Bldg.

NEWSPAPERS REPRESENTED—Continued

Paper represented and telephone number	Name	Office
Fort Smith (Ark.) Times-Record (e.) NA 8-7227.	Kenneth M. Scheibel	1251 National Press Bldg.
	Dale Himes	1251 National Press Bldg.
Fort Worth Press (e., S.)—DI 7-7750	Seth Kantor	1013 13th St.
Fort Worth (Tex.) Star Telegram (m., e.) EX 3-0146.	Bascom N. Timmons	1253 National Press Bldg.
	William R. MacKaye	1253 National Press Bldg.
	Robert E. Hilburn	1253 National Press Bldg.
	John Mort	1253 National Press Bldg.
	Jack Cleland	1253 National Press Bldg.
France-Soir (e.)—ME 8-0104	Adalbert de Segonzac	615 National Press Bldg.
Frankfurter Allgemeine Zeitung (m.,e.,S.) EM 2-4350.	Jan G. Reifenberg	5117 Watson St.
Fresno (Calif.) Bee (e.)—NA 8-6590	Gladstone Williams	1295 National Press Bldg.
JU 9-0459	Edward H. Dickson	7002 Sycamore Ave., Takoma Park, Md.
Gallup (N. Mex.) Independent (e., S.) FE 8-4660.	Helene C. Monberg	1618 17th St.
Galveston News (m., S.)—638-4332	Felton West, Jr	1276 National Press Bldg.
	Charles P. Culhane	1276 National Press Bldg.
	Grace Halsell	1276 National Press Bldg.
Galveston Tribune (e.)—638-4332	Felton West, Jr	1276 National Press Bldg.
	Charles P. Culhane	1276 National Press Bldg.
	Grace Halsell	1276 National Press Bldg.
Gannett News Service—EX 3-3460	Paul Martin	795 National Press Bldg.
	Reginald F. Torrey	795 National Press Bldg.
	William A. Garrett	795 National Press Bldg.
	Eileen C. Timlin	795 National Press Bldg.
	James William Canan	795 National Press Bldg.
	Edmund Barry Lambeth	795 National Press Bldg.
	Jack W. Germond	795 National Press Bldg.
	Richardson Gale	795 National Press Bldg.
Garden Grove (Calif.) News—737-8627	Walter T. Ridder	1325 E St.
	Marie Ridder	1325 E St.
	Baxter Omohundro	1325 E St.
	William W. Broom	1325 E St.
	Ann Terry	1325 E St.
DI 7-5123	Fred W. Collins	1299 National Press Bldg.
Glendale (Calif.) News-Press (e.) 296-8565.	Raymond J. McHugh	1629 K St.
	Franklyn C. Nofziger	1629 K St.
	Lucille Eddinger	1629 K St.
	Edwin G. Martin	1629 K St.
	John H. McLaren	1629 K St.
	Lester M. Bell	1629 K St.
	Paul L. Tsompanas	1629 K St.
	Henry Goethals	1629 K St.
	Larry C. Osius	1699 K St.
Grand Forks (N. Dak.) Herald (m., e., S.) 737-8627.	Walter T. Ridder	1325 E St.
	William W. Brown	1325 E St.
	Marie Ridder	1325 E St.
	Baxter Omohundro	1325 E St.
	Ann Terry	1325 E St.
Grand Junction (Colo.) Sentinel (e., S.) FE 8-4660.	Helene C. Monberg	1618 17th St.
Grand Rapids (Mich.) Press (e.) 737-7770.	William F. Pyper	515 National Press Bldg.
	Paul A. Miltich	515 National Press Bldg.
Greensboro (N.C.) Daily News (m.) JE 3-8630.	W. A. Hildebrand	2805 35th St.
	Bruce O. Jolly	6213 11th Rd. North, Arlington, Va.
Greensboro (N.C.) Record—JE 3-8630	Bruce O. Jolly	6123 11th Rd. North, Arlington, Va.
Greenville (S.C.) News (m.)—LI 4-8238	Frank van der Linden	132 3d St. SE.
	John M. Steen, Jr	132 3d St. SE.
	Leland A. Bandy	132 3d St. SE.
Grote Provinciale Dagbladen (Netherlands)—656-9286.	Andre Simon Spoor	4411 Ridge St., Chevy Chase, Md.
Guthrie (Okla.) Daily Leader (e., S.) NA 8-7227.	Kenneth M. Scheibel	1251 National Press Bldg.
	Dale Himes	1251 National Press Bldg.
"Haaretz" Daily (Tel Aviv, Israel) ME 8-1466.	Eliahu A. Salpeter	1367 National Press Bldg.
Hall Syndicate—NA 8-2091	Robert S. Allen	1292 National Press Bldg.
	Paul Scott	1292 National Press Bldg.
	Jack Neal	1292 National Press Bldg.
	Esther L. Coopersmith	1292 National Press Bldg.
DU 7-0165	Betty Beale	2324 Tracy Pl.
393-4488, ST 3-5445	Leslie E. Carpenter	784 National Press Bldg.
Harrisburg (Pa.) Patriot & Evening News (m., e., S.)—ST 3-1053.	Milton Jaques	711 14th St.
	Joseph M. Hochstein	711 14th St.
	Hoyt L. Gimlin	711 14th St.
Hartford (Conn.) Courant (m.) ST 3-7442.	Robert D. Byrnes	1037 National Press Bldg.
	Dorothy Seymour Byrnes	1037 National Press Bldg.
Hartford (Conn.) Times (e.) EX 3-3460	Paul L. Martin	795 National Press Bldg.
	William A. Garrett	795 National Press Bldg.
	Reginald F. Torrey	795 National Press Bldg.
	Eileen C. Timlin	795 National Press Bldg.
	James William Canan	795 National Press Bldg.

NEWSPAPERS REPRESENTED—Continued

Paper represented and telephone number	Name	Office
Hartford (Conn.) Times—Continued		
	Jack W. Germond	795 National Press Bldg.
	Edmund B. Lambeth	795 National Press Bldg.
	Richardson Gale	795 National Press Bldg.
Hearst Newspapers and Hearst Headline Service—EX 3-8322.	Milton L. Kaplan	301 Pennsylvania Bldg.
	Warren Rogers	301 Pennsylvania Bldg.
	Ruth S. Montgomery	301 Pennsylvania Bldg.
	David Sentner	301 Pennsylvania Bldg.
	Marianne Means	301 Pennsylvania Bldg.
	Leslie H. Whitten, Jr	301 Pennsylvania Bldg.
	Catherine Mackin	301 Pennsylvania Bldg.
Henderson (Ky.) Gleaner & Journal (m., S.)—393-0979.	Joseph A. Dear	1011 National Press Bldg.
	Cyrene Dear	1011 National Press Bldg.
	Gretchen R. Doss	1011 National Press Bldg.
	Robert E. Hennessee	1011 National Press Bldg.
Het Volk (Ghent, Belgium) 347-0733.	Maarten C. Bolle	1140 National Press Bldg.
Het Vrije Volk (Amsterdam) (e.) 347-0733.	Maarten C. Bolle	1140 National Press Bldg.
Hilo Tribune Herald (e., S.)—NA 8-7227	Kenneth M. Scheibel	1251 National Press Bldg.
	Dale Himes	1251 National Press Bldg.
Hindustan Times (New Delhi, India) 362-5865.	Ajit K. Bhattacharjea	6613 32d St.
Holland (Mich.) Sentinel (e.) NA 8-3335.	Esther van Wagoner Tufty	997 National Press Bldg.
	Lou G. van Wagoner	997 National Press Bldg.
Holyoke (Mass.) Transcript-Telegram (e.) NA 8-7350.	Bulkley Griffin	1237 National Press Bldg.
	Isabel Kinnear Griffin	1237 National Press Bldg.
	Donald R. Larrabee	1237 National Press Bldg.
Honolulu Advertiser (m., S.)—393-4488, ST 3-5445.	Leslie E. Carpenter	784 National Press Bldg.
	Ned Curran	784 National Press Bldg.
	Michael D. Mosettig	784 National Press Bldg.
	Barbara Kober	784 National Press Bldg.
	Theresa McMasters	784 National Press Bldg.
Honolulu Star-Bulletin (e.)—ST 3-4496	Frank Hewlett	720 National Press Bldg.
Houston (Tex.) Chronicle (e., S.) EX 3-0146.	Bascom N. Timmons	1253 National Press Bldg.
	Robert E. Hilburn	1253 National Press Bldg.
	William Ross MacKaye	1253 National Press Bldg.
	Jack Cleland	1253 National Press Bldg.
Houston (Tex.) Post (m., S.)—638-4332	Felton West, Jr	1276 National Press Bldg.
	Charles P. Culhane	1276 National Press Bldg.
	Grace Halsell	1276 National Press Bldg.
Hungarian News Agency—DU 3-6816	Csaba Kis	8510 16th St., Silver Spring, Md.
Huntsville (Ala.) Times (e., S.)—ST 3-1053	Edwin J. Safford	711 14th St.
	Joseph M. Hochstein	711 14th St.
	Hoyt L. Gimlin	711 14th St.
Il Resto del Carlino (Bologna, Italy) 347-0249.	Girolamo Modesti	790 National Press Bldg.
Il Tempo (Rome) NA 8-2451 (DU 3-3720).	Marino de Medici	2727 29th St.
India News & Feature Alliance 481-2533.	Mel Bergheim	5535 Dawes Ave., Alexandria, Va.
Indian Express Newspapers (India) 362-0475.	T. V. Parasuram	5442 Broad Branch Rd.
Indianapolis (Ind.) News (e., S.) NA 8-4140.	Louis C. Hiner	408 Albee Bldg.
Indianapolis (Ind.) Star (m., S.) NA 8-4140.	Benjamin R. Cole	408 Albee Bldg.
	Michael A. Padev	408 Albee Bldg.
Indianapolis (Ind.) Times (e., S.) DI 7-7750.	John V. Wilson	1013 13th St.
Ithaca (N.Y.) Journal (e.)—EX 3-3460	Paul L. Martin	795 National Press Bldg.
	Reginald F. Torrey	795 National Press Bldg.
	William A. Garrett	795 National Press Bldg.
	Eileen C. Timlin	795 National Press Bldg.
	James William Canan	795 National Press Bldg.
	Jack W. Germond	795 National Press Bldg.
	Edmund B. Lambeth	795 National Press Bldg.
	Richardson Gale	795 National Press Bldg.
"Izvestia" (Moscow, Russia) (e.) 589-9168.	Andrei Itskov	1401 Blair Mill Rd., Silver Spring, Md.
Jackson (Miss.) Clarion-Ledger (m., e., S.) EX 3-0146.	Bascom N. Timmons	1253 National Press Bldg.
	Sam Hanna	1253 National Press Bldg.
	Mary Ann Pardue	1253 National Press Bldg.
Jackson (Miss.) Daily News (e.) LI 7-8238.	Frank van der Linden	132 3d St. SE.
	John M. Steen, Jr	132 3d St. SE.
	Leland A. Bandy	132 3d St. SE.
Jackson (Miss.) State-Times (e., S.)	Craddock Goins	517 E. Capitol St.
Jackson (Mich.) Citizen Patriot (e., S.) 737-7770.	William F. Pyper	515 National Press Bldg.
	Paul A. Miltich	515 National Press Bldg.
Jacksonville (N.C.) Daily News (e.) LI 7-2616.	Wesley C. Hayden	130 3d St. SE.
	Lewis S. McCash	130 3d St. SE.
Japan Economic Journal (Tokyo & Osaka) 393-1388 or 737-8620.	Susumu Ohara	1325 E. St.

NEWSPAPERS REPRESENTED—Continued

Paper represented and telephone number	Name	Office
Jersey Journal (Jersey City, N.J.) (e.)____ ST 3-1053.	Aaron G. Benesch____	711 14th St.
	David C. Breasted____	711 14th St.
	Joseph M. Hochstein____	711 14th St.
	Hoyt L. Gimlin____	711 14th St.
Jewish Telegraphic Agency—RE 7-0935___	Milton Friedman____	834 National Press Bldg.
	Jessie Halpern____	834 National Press Bldg.
JiJi Press, Ltd. (m.)—ST 3-5086_____	Tatsuro Sato____	1230 National Press Bldg.
	Tetsuya Ozeki____	1230 National Press Bldg.
	Norio Iguchi____	1230 National Press Bldg.
Johnson City (Tenn.) Press-Chronicle____ 543-8889.	Lawrence Fernsworth____	1329 C St. SE.
Joliet (Ill.) Herald-News (e., S)_____ 296-8565.	Raymond J. McHugh____	1629 K St.
	Franklyn C. Nofziger____	1629 K St.
	Lucille Eddinger____	1629 K St.
	Edwin G. Martin____	1629 K St.
	John H. McLaren____	1629 K St.
	Lester M. Bell____	1629 K St.
	Paul L. Tsompanas____	1629 K St.
	Henry Goethals____	1629 K St.
	Larry C. Osius____	1629 K St.
Juneau (Alaska) Empire (e., S.)_____ NA 8-7227.	Kenneth M. Scheibel____	1251 National Press Bldg.
	Dale Himes____	1251 National Press Bldg.
Kalamazoo (Mich.) Gazette (e., S.)_____ 737-7770.	William F. Pyper____	515 National Press Bldg.
	Paul A. Miltich____	515 National Press Bldg.
Kansas City Star (e.) and Times (m.)____ ST 3-7474.	John R. Cauley____	610 Albee Bldg.
	Joseph Anthony Lastelic____	610 Albee Bldg.
Kennebec (Maine) Journal—RE 7-0004 ___	May Craig____	1228 National Press Bldg.
Kennett (Mo.) Democrat—HA 2-7041____	O. C. Miller____	P. O. Box 1759.
Kentucky Post and Times Star (e.)_____ DI 7-7750.	Robert W. Crater____	1013 13th St.
	Thomas M. Talburt____	1013 13th St.
King Features Syndicate—NA 8-8997____	George Dixon____	302 Pennsylvania Bldg.
HO 2-5630____	Mary Haworth____	2219 California St.
EX 3-2513____	Ralph de Toledano____	1061 National Press Bldg.
	Eugene D. Harris____	1061 National Press Bldg.
Knight Newspapers—ME 8-2844_____	Edwin A. Lahey____	1290 National Press Bldg.
	John E. McMullan____	1290 National Press Bldg.
	Robert S. Boyd____	1290 National Press Bldg.
	Philip E. Meyer____	1290 National Press Bldg.
	Jack E. Claiborne____	1290 National Press Bldg.
	Lee Winfrey____	1290 National Press Bldg.
	James L. Robinson____	1290 National Press Bldg.
Knoxville (Tenn.) News-Sentinel (e., S.)__ DI 7-7750.	Michael V. Miller____	1013 13th St.
Koelnische Rundschau (Germany) (m., e., S.)—ST 3-2265.	Hans B. Meyer____	1317 F St.
Korea Times____	Kuk-Whan Sul____	7115 Brookville Rd., Chevy Chase, Md.
Kyodo News Service—DI 7-5767, 5048____	Masakuni Hashimoto____	730 National Press Bldg.
	Takashige Otsuka____	730 National Press Bldg.
	Mitsuhiko Yamada____	730 National Press Bldg.
La Cross (Wis.) Tribune (e., S.)_____ NA 8-7227.	Kenneth M. Scheibel____	1251 National Press Bldg.
La Estrella (Panama City)—DU 3-6836___	Leopoldo Aragón____	2012 N. Daniel St. Arlington, Va.
La Hora (Guatemala)_____ 362-1303.	Oscar Padilla-Vidaurre____	5700 Connecticut Ave.
La Nazione (Florence, Italy)_____ 347-0245.	Girolamo Modesti____	790 National Press Bldg.
La Nueva Prensa (Bogotá)_____ EX 3-1076.	Edgar Arnold Triveri____	900 National Press Bldg.
La Republica (Bogota)_____ 265-9042.	Lilia Sanchez Albergo____	1750 16th St.
Las Vegas Review Journal (e., S.)_____ NA 8-7227.	Kenneth M. Scheibel____	1251 National Press Bldg.
	Dale Himes____	1251 National Press Bldg.
Lafayette (Ind.) Journal and Courier (e.)__ RE 7-2901.	Robert N. Branson____	1134 National Press Bldg.
	Cleve Corlett____	1134 National Press Bldg.
Lansing (Mich.) State Journal (e., S.)____ RE 7-2901.	Robert N. Branson____	1134 National Press Bldg.
	Cleve Corlett____	1134 National Press Bldg.
Lawton (Okla.) Constitution (m., e., S.)__ EX 3-0146.	John S. Sparks, Jr____	1253 National Press Bldg.
Leadville (Colo.) Herald-Democrat (e.)____ 462-1929.	Helene C. Monberg____	1618 17th St.
Leavenworth (Kans.) Times_____ OL 2-1803.	Steve Tillman____	3212 Cummings La., Chevy Chase, Md.
Le Monde (Paris) (e.)—338-2450_____	Alain Clément____	2327 49th St.
Levelland (Tex.) Sun-News (e., S.)_____ NA 8-7227.	Kenneth M. Scheibel____	1251 National Press Bldg.
	Dale Himes____	1251 National Press Bldg.
Lincoln (Nebr.) Journal—ST 3-6756-7____	Pat Munroe____	1249 National Press Bldg.
	Mary Munroe____	1249 National Press Bldg.
	Caryl Rivers____	1249 National Press Bldg.
	Timothy B. Clark____	1249 National Press Bldg.
Lithuanian Daily News of Chicago_____ OL 2-1142.	Will Allen____	5606 Madison St., Bethesda, Md.

NEWSPAPERS REPRESENTED—Continued

Paper represented and telephone number	Name	Office
London Daily Express (m.)—EX 3-0840	Ross Mark	1077 National Press Bldg.
	Kathleen M. Meyers	1077 National Press Bldg.
London Daily Mail (m.)—RE 7-2541	Boris Kidel	1202 National Press Bldg.
	Peggy Ward	1202 National Press Bldg.
London Jewish Chronicle—TU 2-3947	Murray Frank	7810 16th St.
London Observer (S.)—RE 7-1234	Godfrey M. T. Hodgson	3306 Porter St.
London Daily Telegraph (m.)—EX 3-5195	Vincent Ryder	1200 National Press Bldg.
	Jeremy J. Wolfenden	1200 National Press Bldg.
London Financial Times—737-8620	John David Watt	1325 E St.
London Sunday Telegraph EX 3-1335.	Stephen Guy Barber	1200 National Press Bldg.
London Sunday Times—EM 3-5950	Henry Brandon	3501 Rodman St.
London Times (m.)—DI 7-7659	Louis Heren	922 National Press Bldg.
	Dennis N. Herbert	922 National Press Bldg.
Long Beach (Calif.) Independent and Press-Telegram (m., e., S.)—737-8627.	Walter T. Ridder	1325 E St.
	William W. Broom	1325 E St.
	Marie Ridder	1325 E St.
	Baxter Omohundro	1325 E St.
	Ann Terry	1325 E St.
DI 7-5123	Fred W. Collins	1299 National Press Bldg.
EM 2-3965	Virginia W. Kelly	3930 Connecticut Ave.
Long Island Press (e., S.)—ST 3-1053	Andrew J. Viglietta	711 14th St.
	Aaron G. Benesch	711 14th St.
	David C. Breasted	711 14th St.
	Milton Jaques	711 14th St.
	Joseph M. Hochstein	711 14th St.
	Hoyt L. Gimlin	711 14th St.
Long Island Star Journal (e.)—ST 3-1053	Andrew J. Viglietta	711 14th St.
	Aaron G. Benesch	711 14th St.
	David C. Breasted	711 14th St.
	Milton Jaques	711 14th St.
	Joseph M. Hochstein	711 14th St.
	Hoyt L. Gimlin	711 14th St.
Los Angeles Herald-Examiner (m., e.) EX 3-8322.	Milton L. Kaplan	301 Pennsylvania Bldg.
	Warren Rogers	301 Pennsylvania Bldg.
	Catherine Mackin	301 Pennsylvania Bldg.
	Marianne Means	301 Pennsylvania Bldg.
	Ruth S. Montgomery	301 Pennsylvania Bldg.
	David Sentner	301 Pennsylvania Bldg.
	Leslie H. Whitten, Jr	301 Pennsylvania Bldg.
Los Angeles Times (m.)—298-7234	Robert J. Donovan	1701 Pennsylvania Ave.
	Laurence H. Burd	1701 Pennsylvania Ave.
	John H. Averill	1701 Pennsylvania Ave.
	Robert S. Barkdoll	1701 Pennsylvania Ave.
	Thomas J. Foley	1701 Pennsylvania Ave.
	Don Irwin	1701 Pennsylvania Ave.
	David J. Kraslow	1701 Pennsylvania Ave.
	Richard Reston	1701 Pennsylvania Ave.
	Ted Sell	1701 Pennsylvania Ave.
	Robert E. Thompson	1701 Pennsylvania Ave.
	Robert C. Toth	1701 Pennsylvania Ave.
	Joann L. Wilson	1701 Pennsylvania Ave.
Louisville (Ky.) Courier-Journal (m.) 628-7704.	Robert L. Riggs	1265 National Press Bldg.
	Richard Harwood	1265 National Press Bldg.
	Ivan Swift	1265 National Press Bldg.
Louisville (Ky.) Times (e.)—628-7704	Robert L. Riggs	1265 National Press Bldg.
	Richard Harwood	1265 National Press Bldg.
	Ivan Swift	1265 National Press Bldg.
Lowell (Mass.) Sun (e., S.)—NA 8-7350	Bulkley Griffin	1237 National Press Bldg.
	Isabel Kinnear Griffin	1237 National Press Bldg.
	Donald R. Larrabee	1237 National Press Bldg.
347-3549	Peter F. Barnes	917 Colorado Bldg.
Lubbock (Tex.) Avalanche-Journal (e., m., S.)—393-4488, ST 3-5445.	Leslie E. Carpenter	784 National Press Bldg.
	Ned Curran	784 National Press Bldg.
	Michael D. Mosettig	784 National Press Bldg.
	Barbara Kober	784 National Press Bldg.
	Theresa McMasters	784 National Press Bldg.
Lufkin (Tex.) Daily News (e., S.) 483-3791.	Sarah McClendon	2933 28th St.
Lynn (Mass.) Item (e.)—NA 8-7350	Bulkley Griffin	1237 National Press Bldg.
	Isabel Kinnear Griffin	1237 National Press Bldg.
	Donald R. Larrabee	1237 National Press Bldg.
McNaught Syndicate—NA 8-1511	Holmes Alexander	1391 National Press Bldg.
Madison (Wis.) State Journal (e., S.) NA 8-7227.	Kenneth M. Scheibel	1251 National Press Bldg.
Mainichi Newspapers—RE 7-2817	Kazuto Ishimaru	1024 National Press Bldg.
Malden (Mass.) Evening News (e.) ME 8-4523.	Edward J. Michelson	1014 National Press Bldg.

NEWSPAPERS REPRESENTED—Continued

Paper represented and telephone number	Name	Office
Malone (N.Y.) Telegram (e.)—EX 3-3460_	Paul L. Martin_____	795 National Press Bldg.
	Reginald F. Torrey_____	795 National Press Bldg.
	William A. Garrett_____	795 National Press Bldg.
	Eileen C. Timlin _____	795 National Press Bldg.
	James W. Canan_____	795 National Press Bldg.
	Jack W. Germond_____	795 National Press Bldg.
	Edmund B. Lambeth_____	795 National Press Bldg.
	Richardson Gale_____	795 National Press Bldg.
Mamaroneck (N.Y.) Daily Times (e.)____ 393-3460.	Paul L. Martin_____	795 National Press Bldg.
	Reginald F. Torrey_____	795 National Press Bldg.
	William A. Garrett_____	795 National Press Bldg.
	Eileen C. Timlin_____	795 National Press Bldg.
	James W. Canan_____	795 National Press Bldg.
	Jack W. Germond_____	795 National Press Bldg.
	Edmund B. Lambeth_____	795 National Press Bldg.
	Richardson Gale_____	795 National Press Bldg.
Manchester (England) Guardian (m.)_____ RE 7-1234.	Richard F. Scott_____	1515 L St.
Manila Chronicle (m., S.)—NA 8-5175___	A. L. Valencia_____	1277 National Press Bldg.
Marietta (Ga.) Journal (e., S.)—LI 7-2616_	Wesley F. Hayden_____	130 3d St. SE.
	Lewis S. McCash_____	130 3d St. SE.
Marion (Ind.) Chronicle & Leader Trib-une—RE 7-2901.	Robert C. Branson_____	1134 National Press Bldg.
	Cleve Corlett_____	1134 National Press Bldg.
Maryville-Alcoa (Tenn.) Daily Times_____ 543-8889.	Lawrence Fernsworth_____	329 C St. SE.
Mason City (Iowa) Globe-Gazette (e.)____ EX 3-4808.	Harry Lando_____	1126 National Press Bldg.
Medford (Oreg.) Mail Tribune (e., S.)_____ LI 4-5100.	A. Robert Smith_____	328 Pennsylvania Ave. SE.
	Yvonne Franklin Smith____	3439 Oliver St.
Medford (Mass.) Mercury (e.)_____ ME 8-4523.	Edward J. Michelson_____	1014 National Press Bldg.
Melbourne (Australia) Age_____ 363-9546.	Bruce A. Grant_____	6640 32d St.
Memphis Commercial Appeal (m., S.)____ DI 7-7750.	Morris Cunningham_____	1013 13th St.
Memphis Press-Scimitar (e.)—DI 7-7750_	Michael V. Miller_____	1013 13th St.
Miami (Fla.) Daily News (e.)_____ FE 7-2554 or NA 8-5962.	Florence S. Mahoney_____	614 Albee Bldg.
Miami (Fla.) Herald (m.)—ME 8-2844___	Lee Winfrey_____ (*See* Knight Newspapers.)	1290 National Press Bldg.
Michigan League of Home Dailies_____ NA 8-3335.	Esther Van Wagoner Tufty_	997 National Press Bldg.
	Lou G. Van Wagoner_____	997 National Press Bldg.
Midland (Mich.) Daily News (e.)_____ NA 8-3335.	Esther Van Wagoner Tufty_	997 National Press Bldg.
	Lou G. Van Wagoner_____	997 National Press Bldg.
Milwaukee Journal (e., S.)—RE 7-6453 &_ RE 7-2985.	Laurence C. Eklund_____	734 National Press Bldg.
	John W. Kole_____ __	734 National Press Bldg.
Milwaukee Sentinel—RE 7-6453 &_____ RE 7-2985.	Laurence C. Eklund_____	734 National Press Bldg.
	John W. Kole_____	734 National Press Bldg.
Minneapolis Star and Tribune (m., e., S.)_ DI 7-9111.	Richard L. Wilson_____	852 National Press Bldg.
	John B. Wilson_____	852 National Press Bldg.
	Clark R. Mollenhoff_____	852 National Press Bldg.
	Charles W. Bailey, 2d_____	852 National Press Bldg.
	Nathan K. Kotz_____	852 National Press Bldg.
Missoula (Mont.) Missoulian (m.)_____ NA 8-7227.	Kenneth M. Scheibel_____	1251 National Press Bldg.
Modesto (Calif.) Bee (e., S.)—NA 8-6590_	Gladstone Williams_____	1295 National Press Bldg.
JU 9-0459_____	Edward H. Dickson_____	7002 Sycamore Ave., Takoma Park, Md.
Monroe (La.) World & News Star (m., e., S.)—EX 3-0146.	Sam Hanna_____	1253 National Press Bldg.
Monrovia (Calif.) News-Post (e.)_____ 296-8565.	Raymond J McHugh_____	1629 K St.
	Franklyn C. Nofziger_____	1629 K St.
	Lucille Eddinger_____	1629 K St.
	Edwin G. Martin_____	1629 K St.
	John H. McLaren_____	1629 K St.
	Lester M. Bell_____	1629 K St.
	Paul L. Tsompanas_____	1629 K St.
	Henry Goethals_____	1629 K St.
	Larry C. Osius_____	1629 K St.
Monterey (Calif.) Peninsula-Herald (e.)___ NA 8-2091.	Robert S. Allen_____	1292 National Press Bldg.
	Paul Scott_____	1292 National Press Bldg.
Montreal Star (e.)—ST 3-5979_____	Raymond Heard_____	1096 National Press Bldg.
Motion Picture Daily—628-7955_____	Delores N. Poe_____	605 Albee Bldg.
Mt. Vernon (N.Y.) Daily Argus (e.)_____ 393-3460.	Paul L. Martin_____	795 National Press Bldg.
	Reginald F. Torrey_____	795 National Press Bldg.
	William A. Garrett_____	795 National Press Bldg.
	Eileen C. Timlin_____	795 National Press Bldg.
	James W. Canan_____	795 National Press Bldg.
	Jack W. Germond_____	795 National Press Bldg.
	Edmund B. Lambeth_____	795 National Press Bldg.
	Richardson Gale_____	795National Press Bldg.
Muncie (Ind.) Press (e.)—NA 8-4140_____	Louis C. Hiner_____	408 Albee Bldg.
Muncie (Ind.) Star (m., S.)—NA 8-4140__	Benjamin R. Cole_____	408 Albee Bldg.
	Michael A. Padev_____	408 Albee Bldg.

NEWSPAPERS REPRESENTED—Continued

Paper represented and telephone number	Name	Office
Muskegon Chronicle (e.)—737–7770	William F. Pyper	515 National Press Bldg.
	Paul A. Miltich	515 National Press Bldg.
National Negro Press Association 582–8565.	Daniel E. Day	P.O. Box 5105.
National Newspaper Syndicate RE 7–2511.	John Herling	1003 K St.
Nashville (Tenn.) Banner (e.) LI 4–8238.	Frank van der Linden	132 3d St. SE.
	John M. Steen, Jr	132 3d St. SE.
	Leland A. Bandy	132 3d St. SE.
Nashville (Tenn.) Tennessean (m., e.) EX 3–0146.	Bascom N. Timmons	1253 National Press Bldg.
	L. G. Laycook	1253 National Press Bldg.
296–5895	Martha Ann Clark	1200 LaSalle Bldg.
N. C. W. C. News Service—RE 7–3553	Floyd Anderson	1312 Massachusetts Ave.
	Frank A. Hall	1312 Massachusetts Ave.
	Burke Walsh	1312 Massachusetts Ave.
	William E. Ring	1312 Massachusetts Ave.
	John Joseph Daly, Jr	1312 Massachusetts Ave.
	John V. R. Lebkicher	1312 Massachusetts Ave.
	Elmer Von Feldt	1312 Massachusetts Ave.
	Paul W. McCloskey	1312 Massachusetts Ave.
	Russell B. Shaw	1312 Massachusetts Ave.
	Patrick G. D. Riley	1312 Massachusetts Ave.
	Thomas E. Kissling	1312 Massachusetts Ave.
	Donald F. Brophy	1312 Massachusetts Ave.
Nepszabadsag (Budapest, Hungary) 537–0670.	Istvan Arkus	4500 Connecticut Ave.
Neue Zuercher Zeitung (Switzerland) (m., e., S.)—EX 3–1162.	Werner Imhoof	1056 National Press Bldg.
New Bedford Standard-Times (e., S.) NA 8–7350.	Bulkley Griffin	1237 National Press Bldg.
	Isabel Kinnear Griffin	1237 National Press Bldg.
	Donald R. Larrabee	1237 National Press Bldg.
New Orleans (La.) States Item (e.) EX 3–0146.	Bascom N. Timmons	1253 National Press Bldg.
	Sam Hanna	1253 National Press Bldg.
New Orleans Times Picayune (m.) 737–2934.	Edgar Poe	1029 National Press Bldg.
	Alice B. Haggett	1029 National Press Bldg.
New Rochelle (N.Y.) Standard-Star (e.) 393–3460.	Paul L. Martin	795 National Press Bldg.
	Reginald F. Torrey	795 National Press Bldg.
	William A. Garrett	795 Natimal Press Bldg.
	Eileen C. Timlin	795 National Press Bldg.
	James W. Canan	795 National Press Bldg.
	Jack W. Germond	795 National Press Bldg.
	Edmund B. Lambeth	795 National Press Bldg.
	Richardson Gale	795 National Press Bldg.
New Ulm (Minn.) Daily Journal (e.) LI 3–2978.	Dodee Wick	135 D St. SE.
New York Daily News (m.) NA 8–5058.	Edward W. Lewis	1272 National Press Bldg.
	Paul F. Healy	1272 National Press Bldg.
	Charles J. Greene, Jr	1272 National Press Bldg.
	Gerry Van der Heuvel	1272 National Press Bldg.
	Michael J. O'Neill	1272 National Press Bldg.
	John H. Metcalfe	1272 National Press Bldg.
	Richard Joseph McGowan	1272 National Press Bldg.
	J. Stanley Carter	1272 National Press Bldg.
New York Film Daily (m.)—EX 3–4808	Harry Lando	1126 National Press Bldg.
New York Herald Tribune (m.) 298–9160	David Wise	1750 Pennsylvania Ave.
	Joseph R. Slevin	1750 Pennsylvania Ave.
	Victor Wilson	1750 Pennsylvania Ave.
	Frederick J. Farris	1750 Pennsylvania Ave.
	Andrew J. Glass	1750 Pennsylvania Ave.
	Tom Lambert	1750 Pennsylvania Ave.
	Laurence Barrett	1750 Pennsylvania Ave.
	Douglas Kiker	1750 Pennsylvania Ave.
	Dom Bonafede	1750 Pennsylvania Ave.
	Barnard L. Collier	1750 Pennsylvania Ave.
	Richard Dougherty	1750 Pennsylvania Ave.
	Geoffrey Drummond	1750 Pennsylvania Ave.
	David H. Hoffman	1750 Pennsylvania Ave.
New York Herald Tribune Syndicate 298–7990.	Art Buchwald	1750 Pennsylvania Ave.
298–9160	Roscoe Drummond	1750 Pennsylvania Ave.
DI 7–9307	Robert G. Spivack	1076 National Press Bldg.
298–7850	Rowland Evans, Jr	1750 Pennsylvania Ave.
298–7850	Robert D. Novak	1750 Pennsylvania Ave.
New York Journal American (e.) EX 3–8322.	Milton L. Kaplan	301 Pennsylvania Bldg.
	Warren Rogers	301 Pennsylvania Bldg.
	Catherine Mackin	301 Pennsylvania Bldg.
	Marianne Means	301 Pennsylvania Bldg.
	Ruth S. Montgomery	301 Pennsylvania Bldg.
	David Sentner	301 Pennsylvania Bldg.
	Leslie H. Whitten, Jr	301 Pennsylvania Bldg.

NEWSPAPERS REPRESENTED—Continued

Paper represented and telephone number	Name	Office
New York Journal of Commerce (m.) 737–8620.	Oscar E. Naumann	1325 E St.
	Robert F. Morison	1325 E St.
	Thomas J. Connors	1325 E St.
	Richard A. Lawrence	1325 E St.
	David P. Cazalas	1325 E St.
	Stanley E. Wilson	1325 E St.
737–8627	Walter T. Ridder	1325 E St.
	Marie W. Ridder	1325 E St.
	Ann Terry	1325 E St.
	Gus Constantine	1325 E St.
	Ronald G. Burns	1325 E St.
New York Post (e., S.)—ME 8–1466	Bruce A. Agnew	1369 National Press Bldg.
New York Times (m.)—NA 8–3016	Thomas G. Wicker	1701 K St.
	Russell Baker	1701 K St.
	Felix Belair	1701 K St.
	William M. Blair	1701 K St.
	Nona Baldwin Brown	1701 K St.
	Evert B. Clark	1701 K St.
	Edwin L. Dale, Jr	1701 K St.
	Barbara I. Dubivsky	1701 K St.
	John Warren Finney	1701 K St.
	Max Frankel	1701 K St.
	Benjamin A. Franklin	1701 K St.
	Fred P. Graham	1701 K St.
	John Herbers	1701 K St.
	Marjorie Hunter	1701 K St.
	E. W. Kenworthy	1701 K St.
	Arthur Krock	1701 K St.
	Joseph A. Loftus	1701 K St.
	Charles H. Mohr	1701 K St.
	John D. Morris	1701 K St.
	Cabell Phillips	1701 K St.
	John D. Pomfret	1701 K St.
	Jack Raymond	1701 K St.
	James B. Reston	1701 K St.
	Steven V. Roberts	1701 K St.
	Nan Robertson	1701 K St.
	Robert B. Semple, Jr	1701 K St.
	Eileen Shanahan	1701 K St.
	Alvin Shuster	1701 K St.
	Tad Szulc	1701 K St.
	Charles P. Trussell	1701 K St.
	Warren Weaver, Jr	1701 K St.
	Robert F. Whitney	1701 K St.
	Fendall W. Yerxa	1701 K St.
New York World-Telegram and Sun (e.) DI 7–7750.	Ted Knap	1013 13th St.
Newark (N.J.) News (e., S.) NA 8–4240.	George R. Kentera	901 Colorado Bldg.
	William May	901 Colorado Bldg.
Newark Star Ledger (m., S.) ST 3–1053.	Aaron G. Benesch	711 14th St.
	David C. Breasted	711 14th St.
	Joseph M. Hochstein	711 14th St.
	Hoyt L. Gimlin	711 14th St.
Newburgh-Beacon (N.Y.) News (e.) EX 3–3460.	Paul L. Martin	795 National Press Bldg.
	Reginald F. Torrey	795 National Press Bldg.
	William A. Garrett	795 National Press Bldg.
	Eileen C. Timlin	795 National Press Bldg.
	James William Canan	795 National Press Bldg.
	Jack W. Germond	795 National Press Bldg.
	Edmund B. Lambeth	795 National Press Bldg.
	Richardson Gale	795 National Press Bldg.
Newhouse National News Service ST 3–1053.	Philip Hochstein	711 14th St.
	Dean Reed	711 14th St.
	Joseph M. Hochstein	711 14th St.
	Bonnie Angelo	711 14th St.
	Don Bacon	711 14th St.
	Aaron G. Benesch	711 14th St.
	David C. Breasted	711 14th St.
	Gene Bylinsky	711 14th St.
	James Free	711 14th St.
	Hoyt L. Gimlin	711 14th St.
	William E. Howard	711 14th St.
	Milton G. Jaques	711 14th St.
	Erwin Knoll	711 14th St.
	Wil Lepkowski	711 14th St.
	Edward J. Mowery	711 14th St.
	Edward W. O'Brien	711 14th St.
	Edgar Poe	711 14th St.
	Morton A. Reichek	711 14th St.
	Edwin J. Safford	711 14th St.
	Charles Schaeffer	711 14th St.
	Thomas S. Stimmel	711 14th St.
	Andrew Viglietta	711 14th St.
	Jules Witcover	711 14th St.

NEWSPAPERS REPRESENTED—Continued

Paper represented and telephone number	Name	Office
Newport (R.I.) Daily News (e.)_____ NA 8-7350.	Bulkley Griffin_____	1237 National Press Bldg.
	Isabel Kinnear Griffin_____	1237 National Press Bldg.
	Donald R. Larrabee_____	1237 National Press Bldg.
Newport News (Va.) Daily Press (m., S.)_ OL 4-6585.	Clarence G. Marshall_____	5713 Overlea Road.
OL 2-1803_____	Steve Tillman_____	3212 Cummings La., Chevy Chase, Md.
Newport News (Va.) Times Herald (e.)___ OL 4-6585.	Clarence G. Marshall_____	5713 Overlea Road.
Newsday—EX 3-6686_____	Robert E. Rhodes_____	605 National Press Bldg.
	Thomas Collins_____	605 National Press Bldg.
	Marguerite Higgins_____	605 National Press Bldg.
	Donald L. Smith_____	605 National Press Bldg.
Newspaper Enterprise Association_____ DI 7-7777.	Bruce Biossat_____	1013 13th St.
	Ray Cromley_____	1013 13th St.
	Thomas B. Nolan, Jr_____	1013 13th St.
Niagara Falls Gazette (e., S.)_____ EX 3-3460.	Paul Martin_____	795 National Press Bldg.
	Reginald F. Torrey_____	795 National Press Bldg.
	William A. Garrett_____	795 National Press Bldg.
	Eileen C. Timlin_____	795 National Press Bldg.
	James William Canan_____	795 National Press Bldg.
	Richardson Gale_____	795 National Press Bldg.
	Jack W. Germond_____	795 National Press Bldg.
	Edmund B. Lambeth_____	795 National Press Bldg.
Norfolk (Neb.) Daily News (e.)_____ EM 3-5744.	Vera R. Glaser_____	5000 Cathedral Ave.
Norfolk Virginia-Pilot (m.)—WO 6-5560___	Luther J. Carter_____	4522 Lowell St.
North American Newspaper Alliance_____ ME 8-6860.	David L. Barnett_____	1096 National Press Bldg.
	Edmund E. Hadley_____	1096 National Press Bldg.
	Thomas Robert Henry_____	1096 National Press Bldg.
FE 3-3674_____	Ann Cottrell Free_____	4500 Q Lane.
NA 8-4566_____	Jay G. Hayden_____	904 Colorado Bldg.
EM 3-5744_____	Vera Glaser_____	5000 Cathedral Ave.
Northampton (Mass.) Gazette (e.)_____ NA 8-7350.	Bulkley Griffin_____	1237 National Press Bldg.
	Isabel Kinnear Griffin_____	1237 National Press Bldg.
	Donald R. Larrabee_____	1237 National Press Bldg.
Northern Virginia Sun (e.)—JA 4-3000_____	John P. Sawicki_____	3409 Wilson Blvd., Arlington, Va.
	Glen M. Hearin_____	3409 Wilson Blvd., Arlington, Va
NA 8-2091_____	Robert S. Allen_____	1292 National Press Bldg.
	Paul Scott_____	1292 National Press Bldg.
Ogdensburg (N.Y.) Journal (e.)_____ NA 8-3335.	Esther Van Wagoner Tufty_	997 National Press Bldg.
Oil Daily (m.)—ME 8-0812_____	Lou G. Van Wagoner_____	997 National Press Bldg.
	Milburn Petty_____	329 National Press Bldg.
	James M. Collins_____	329 National Press Bldg.
	Charles R. Ten Eyck_____	329 National Press Bldg.
Okinawa Star_____ OL 2-1803.	Steve Tillman_____	3212 Cummings La., Chevy Chase, Md.
Oklahoma City Times (e.)—628-0335_____	Allan W. Cromley_____	905 National Press Bldg.
	Madelaine Wilson_____	905 National Press Bldg.
Okmulgee (Okla.) Daily Times (m., S.)____ NA 8-7227.	Kenneth M. Scheibel_____	1251 National Press Bldg.
	Dale Himes_____	1251 National Press Bldg.
Omaha World-Herald (m., e., S.)_____ EX 3-0644.	John W. Jarrell_____	1217 National Press Bldg.
	Darwin R. Olofson_____	1217 National Press Bldg.
Oregon Journal (Portland) (e.)—ST 3-1053_	Thomas S. Stimmel_____	711 14th St.
	Joseph M. Hochstein_____	711 14th St.
	Hoyt L. Gimlin_____	711 14th St.
Oregon Statesman (m., S.)_____ LI 4-5100.	A. Robert Smith_____	328 Pennsylvania Ave. SE.
Orient Press Agency (Seoul)—363-7479_____	Yyonne Franklin Smith_____	3439 Oliver St.
	Seong Jin Kim_____	3917 Military Rd.
Ossining (N.Y.) Citizen Register (e.)_____ 393-3460.	Paul L. Martin_____	795 National Press Bldg.
	Reginald F. Torrey_____	795 National Press Bldg.
	William A. Garrett_____	795 National Press Bldg.
	Eileen C. Timlin_____	795 National Press Bldg.
	James W. Canan_____	795 National Press Bldg.
	Jack W. Germond_____	795 National Press Bldg.
	Edmund B. Lambeth_____	795 National Press Bldg.
	Richardson Gale_____	795 National Press Bldg.
Oswego (N.Y.) Palladium-Times (e.)_____ ME 8-4642.	Alan S. Emory_____	1273 National Press Bldg.
Owosso (Mich.) Argus Press (e.)_____ NA 8-3335.	Esther Van Wagoner Tufty__	997 National Press Bldg.
	Lou G. Van Wagoner_____	997 National Press Bldg.
Pasadena Independent & Star News (m., e., S.)—737-8627.	Walter T. Ridder_____	1325 E St.
	William W. Broom_____	1325 E St.
	Marie Ridder_____	1325 E St.
	Baxter Omohundro_____	1325 E St.
	Ann Terry_____	1325 E St.
DI 7-5123_____	Fred W. Collins_____	1299 National Press Bldg.
EM 2-3965_____	Virginia W. Kelly_____	3930 Connecticut Ave.
Passaic (N.J.) Herald News (e.)—FE 7-4230_	Edward J. Reardon_____	2500 Wisconsin Ave.

NEWSPAPERS REPRESENTED—Continued

Paper represented and telephone number	Name	Office
Pawtucket (R.I.) Times (e.)—NA 8-7350	Bulkley Griffin	1237 National Press Bldg.
	Isabel Kinnear Griffin	1237 National Press Bldg.
	Donald R. Larrabee	1237 National Press Bldg.
Peekskill (N.Y.) Evening Star (e.) 393-3460.	Paul L. Martin	795 National Press Bldg.
	Reginald F. Torrey	795 National Press Bldg.
	William A. Garrett	795 National Press Bldg.
	Eileen C. Timlin	795 National Press Bldg.
	James W. Canan	795 National Press Bldg.
	Jack W. Germond	795 National Press Bldg.
	Edmund B. Lambeth	795 National Press Bldg.
	Richardson Gale	795 National Press Bldg.
Pendleton (Oreg.) East Oregonian (e.) LI 4-5100.	A. Robert Smith	328 Pennsylvania Ave. SE.
	Yvonne Franklin Smith	3439 Oliver St.
Philadelphia Bulletin (e., S.) 737-0403 or 7320.	Robert Roth	1238 National Press Bldg.
	Anthony Day	1238 National Press Bldg.
	Lawrence M. O'Rourke	1238 National Press Bldg.
	Hugh Flaherty	1238 National Press Bldg.
Philadelphia Daily News (e.)—NA 8-2091	Robert S. Allen	1292 National Press Bldg.
	Paul Scott	1292 National Press Blgd.
Philadelphia Inquirer (m., S.)—RE 7-4100	John C. O'Brien	1296 National Press Bldg.
	Paul J. McGahan	1296 National Press Bldg.
	Jerome S. Cahill	1296 National Press Bldg.
Phoenix Gazette (e.)—NA 8-4140	Louis C. Hiner	408 Albee Bldg.
	Michael A. Padev	408 Albee Bldg.
Pittsburgh (Pa.) Post-Gazette (m.) EX 3-4580.	Ingrid Jewell	1280 National Press Bldg.
	George R. Zielke	1280 National Press Bldg.
	George F. Jenks	1280 National Press Bldg.
Pittsburgh (Pa.) Press (e., S.)—347-7750	Douglas Smith	1013 13th St.
Pittsfield (Mass.) Berkshire Evening Eagle. ME 8-4523.	Edward J. Michelson	1014 National Press Bldg.
Plainfield (N.J.) Courier-News (e.) EX 3-4523.	Paul L. Martin	795 National Press Bldg.
	Reginald F. Torrey	795 National Press Bldg.
	William A. Garrett	795 National Press Bldg.
	Eileen C. Timlin	795 National Press Bldg.
	James William Canan	795 National Press Bldg.
	Jack W. Germond	795 National Press Bldg.
	Edmund B. Lambeth	795 National Press Bldg.
	Richardson Gale	795 National Press Bldg.
Polish Press Agency (Warsaw)—DI 7-6996.	Henryk Zwiren	928 National Press Bldg.
Poplar Bluff (Mo.) American Republic HA 2-7041.	O. C. Miller	P.O. Box 1759.
Port Arthur (Tex.) News (e., S.) 483-3791.	Sarah McClendon	2933 28th St.
Port Chester (N.Y.) Daily Item (e.) 393-3460.	Paul L. Martin	795 National Press Bldg.
	Reginald F. Torrey	795 National Press Bldg.
	William A. Garrett	795 National Press Bldg.
	Eileen C. Timlin	795 National Press Bldg.
	James W. Canan	795 National Press Bldg.
	Edmund B. Lambeth	795 National Press Bldg.
	Jack W. Germond	795 National Press Bldg.
	Richardson Gale	795 National Press Bldg.
Port Huron (Mich.) Times Herald (e., S.) NA 8-3335.	Esther Van Wagoner Tufty	997 National Press Bldg.
	Lou G. Van Wagoner	997 National Press Bldg.
Portland (Oreg.) Oregonian (m., S.) LI 4-5100.	A. Robert Smith	328 Pennsylvania Ave. SE.
	Yvonne Franklin Smith	3439 Oliver St.
Portland (Maine) Evening Express RE 7-0004.	May Craig	1228 National Press Bldg.
Portland (Maine) Press Herald (m.) RE 7-0004.	May Craig	1228 National Press Bldg.
Portland (Maine) Sunday Telegram RE 7-0004.	May Craig	1228 National Press Bldg.
Potomac News Associates—DI 7-9307	Robert G. Spivack	1076 National Press Bldg.
Pravda (Moscow, U.S.S.R.)—234-1498	Serguei Vichnevski	3020 Dent Pl.
Press Associates, Inc.—LI 7-4337	Harry F. Conn	312 Pennsylvania Ave. SE.
	Alexander H. Uhl	312 Pennsylvania Ave. SE.
Progress Reports (Science Service of Advance)—ST 3-1053.	William Howard	711 14th St.
	Charles Schaeffer	711 14th St.
	Gene Bylinsky	711 14th St.
	Wil Lepkowski	711 14th St.
Providence (R.I.) Journal-Bulletin (m., NA 8-6214 or 6215.	Lewis W. Wolfson	1203 National Press Bldg.
	William H. Young	1203 National Press Bldg.
Public Business Associates—LI 7-4285	Dillard Stokes	207 N. Columbus St., Alexandria, Va.
Pueblo (Colo.) Chieftain and Star-Journal. FE 8-4660.	Helene C. Monberg	1618 17th St.
Quincy (Mass.) Patriot-Ledger (e) NA 8-7350.	Bulkley S. Griffin	1237 National Press Bldg.
	Isabel Kinnear Griffin	1237 National Press Bldg.
	Donald R. Larrabee	1237 National Press Bldg.
Radio Television Daily (N.Y.) (m.) EX 3-4808.	Harry Lando	1126 National Press Bldg.

NEWSPAPERS REPRESENTED—Continued

Paper represented and telephone number	Name	Office
Raleigh News and Observer (m., S.)_____ EX 3-0146.	Bascom N. Timmons_____	1253 National Press Bldg.
	Roy Parker, Jr_____	1253 National Press Bldg.
Redondo Beach (Calif.) Daily Breeze (e., S.)—296-8565.	Raymond J. McHugh_____	1629 K St.
	Franklyn C. Nofziger_____	1629 K St.
	Lucille Eddinger_____	1629 K St.
	Edwin G. Martin_____	1629 K St.
	John H. McLaren_____	1629 K St.
	Lester M. Bell_____	1629 K St.
	Paul L. Tsompanas_____	1629 K St.
	Henry Goethals_____	1629 K St.
	Larry C. Osius_____	1629 K St.
Religious News Service—273-7451_____	William F. Willoughby_____	1105 Ashby Rd., Fairfax, Va.
Reuters-Australian Associated Press_____ NA 8-9212.	John W. Heffernan_____	615 National Press Bldg.
	Ralph Harris_____	615 National Press Bldg.
	John J. McGrain_____	615 National Press Bldg.
	David J. Mathew_____	615 National Press Bldg.
	Quentin S. King_____	615 National Press Bldg.
	Daniel W. Gottlieb_____	615 National Press Bldg.
	Lorelies Oehlschlaeger_____	615 National Press Bldg.
Rhein Zeitung (Germany) (m., e., S.)_____ 462-1978.	Wilhelm M. Manthey_____	3019 Cambridge Pl.
Ridder Publications—737-8627_____	Walter T. Ridder_____	1325 E St.
	William W. Broom_____	1325 E St.
	Marie Ridder_____	1325 E St.
	Baxter Omohundro_____	1325 E St.
	Ann Terry_____	1325 E St.
DI 7-5123____	Fred W. Collins_____	1299 National Press Bldg.
Roanoke Rapids (N.C.) Daily Herald (e., S.)—LI 3-2978.	Dodee Wick_____	135 D St. SE.
Rochester Democrat and Chronicle (m.)___ EX 3-3460.	Paul L. Martin_____	795 National Press Bldg.
	Reginald F. Torrey_____	795 National Press Bldg.
	William A. Garrett_____	795 National Press Bldg.
	Eileen C. Timlin_____	795 National Press Bldg.
	James William Canan_____	795 National Press Bldg.
	Jack W. Germond_____	795 National Press Bldg.
	Edmund B. Lambeth_____	795 National Press Bldg.
	Richardson Gale_____	795 National Press Bldg.
Rochester Times-Union (e.)—EX 3-3460___	Paul L. Martin_____	795 National Press Bldg.
	Reginald F. Torrey_____	795 National Press Bldg.
	William A. Garrett_____	795 National Press Bldg.
	Eileen C. Timlin_____	795 National Press Bldg.
	James William Canan_____	795 National Press Bldg.
	Jack W. Germond_____	795 National Press Bldg.
	Edmund B. Lambeth_____	795 National Press Bldg.
	Richardson Gale_____	795 National Press Bldg.
Rock Island Argus (e.)—EX 3-0146_____	Sam Hanna_____	1253 National Press Bldg.
Rockford (Ill.) Morning Star—EX 3-0146__	Joseph A. Fisher_____	1253 National Press Bldg
Rockford (Ill.) Register-Republic_____ EX 3-0146.	Joseph A. Fisher_____	1253 National Press Bldg.
Rocky Mountain News (Colo.) (m., S.)____ DI 7-7750.	Dan K. Thomasson_____	1013 13th St.
Rogers (Ark.) Daily News (e., S.)_____ NA 8-7227.	Kenneth M. Scheibel_____	1251 National Press Bldg.
	Dale Himes_____	1251 National Press Bldg.
Rude Pravo (Prague)_____ NO 7-0274.	Jiri Hochman_____	1629 Columbia Rd.
Rutland (Vt.) Herald (m.)—LI 7-4404_____	Vonda Bergman_____	513 Constitution Ave. NE.
St. Joseph (Mo.) News Press and Gazette__ LI 7-3554.	Dorothy E. Williams_____	19 5th St. SE.
St. Louis Globe-Democrat (m., S.)_____ ST 3-1053.	Edward W. O'Brien_____	711 14th St.
	Aaron G. Benesch_____	711 14th St.
St. Louis (Mo.) Post-Dispatch (e., S.)_____ 296-5775.	Raymond P. Brandt_____	1028 Connecticut Ave.
	James Deakin_____	1028 Connecticut Ave.
	Marquis W. Childs_____	1028 Connecticut Ave.
	Richard Dudman_____	1028 Connecticut Ave.
	Thomas W. Ottenad_____	1028 Connecticut Ave.
	Helen-Marie Fruth_____	1028 Connecticut Ave.
	William K. Wyant, Jr_____	1028 Connecticut Ave.
	James C. Millstone_____	1028 Connecticut Ave.
St. Paul (Minn.) Pioneer Press & Dispatch (m., e., S.)—737-8627.	Walter T. Ridder_____	1325 E St.
	William W. Broom_____	1325 E St.
	Marie Ridder_____	1325 E St.
	Baxter Omohundro_____	1325 E St.
	Ann Terry_____	1325 E St.
DI 7-5123____	Fred W. Collins_____	1299 National Press Bldg.
EM 2-3965___	Virginia W. Kelly_____	3930 Connecticut Ave.
St. Petersburg Independent (e.)_____ 296-6800.	Jerald Blizin_____	1735 K St.
St. Petersburg Times (m., S.)—296-6800 ___	Nelson P. Poynter_____	1735 K St.
	Jerald Blizin_____	1735 K St.
St. Thomas (Virgin Islands) Daily News__ 387-3309.	George Spencer_____	1817 16th St.
	Annette L. Gray_____	1817 16th St.

NEWSPAPERS REPRESENTED—Continued

Paper represented and telephone number	Name	Office
Sacramento (Calif.) Bee (e.)—NA 8–6590___	Gladstone Williams_____	1295 National Press Bldg.
JU 9–0459____	Edward H. Dickson_____	7002 Sycamore Ave., Takoma Park, Md.
Saginaw (Mich.) News (e., S.)—737–7770____	William F. Pyper_____	515 National Press Bldg.
	Paul A. Miltich_____	515 National Press Bldg.
Salt Lake City Deseret News & Telegram (e.)—SO 5–5478.	Gordon E. White_____	516 N. Kings Hwy., Alexandria, Va.
	Mary J. White_____	516 N. King's Hwy. Alexandria, Va.
Salt Lake Tribune (m., S.)—ST 3–4496____	Frank Hewlett_____	720 National Press Bldg.
San Angelo (Tex.) Standard-Times (m., e., S.)—393–4488, ST 3–5445.	Leslie E. Carpenter_____	784 National Press Bldg.
	Ned Curran_____	784 National Press Bldg.
	Michael D. Mosettig_____	784 National Press Bldg.
	Barbara Kober_____	784 National Press Bldg.
	Theresa McMasters_____	784 National Press Bldg.
San Antonio Express & Evening News (m., e., S.)—393–4488, ST 3–5445.	Leslie E. Carpenter_____	784 National Press Bldg.
	Ned Curran_____	784 National Press Bldg.
	Michael D. Mosettig_____	784 National Press Bldg.
	Barbara Kober_____	784 National Press Bldg.
	Theresa McMasters_____	784 National Press Bldg.
OL 2–1803____	Steve Tillman_____	3212 Cummings La., Chevy Chase, Md.
San Antonio Light (e., S.)—EX 3–8322____	Milton L. Kaplan_____	301 Pennsylvania Bldg.
	Warren Rogers_____	301 Pennsylvania Bldg.
	Catherine Mackin_____	301 Pennsylvania Bldg.
	Marianne Means_____	301 Pennsylvania Bldg.
	Ruth S. Montgomery_____	301 Pennsylvania Bldg.
	David Sentner_____	301 Pennsylvania Bldg.
	Leslie H. Whitten, Jr_____	301 Pennsylvania Bldg.
483–3791_____	Sarah McClendon_____	2933 28th St.
San Diego (Calif.) Tribune (e.)_____ 296–8565.	Raymond J. McHugh_____	1629 K St.
	Franklyn C. Nofziger_____	1629 K St.
	Lucille Eddinger_____	1629 K St.
	Edwin G. Martin_____	1629 K St.
	John H. McLaren_____	1629 K St.
	Lester M. Bell_____	1629 K St.
	Paul L. Tsompanas_____	1629 K St.
	Henry Goethals_____	1629 K St.
	Larry C. Osius_____	1629 K St.
San Diego (Calif.) Union (m., e., S.)_____ 296–8565.	Raymond J. McHugh_____	1629 K St.
	Franklyn C. Nofziger_____	1629 K St.
	Lucille Eddinger_____	1629 K St.
	Edwin G. Martin_____	1629 K St.
	John H. McLaren_____	1629 K St.
	Lester M. Bell_____	1629 K St.
	Paul L. Tsompanas_____	1629 K St.
	Henry Goethals_____	1629 K St.
	Larry C. Osius_____	1629 K St.
San Francisco News-Call Bulletin (e.)_____ EX 3–8322.	Milton L. Kaplan_____	301 Pennsylvania Bldg.
	Warren Rogers_____	301 Pennsylvania Bldg.
	Catherine Mackin_____	301 Pennsylvania Bldg.
	Marianne Means_____	301 Pennsylvania Bldg.
	Ruth S. Montgomery_____	301 Pennsylvania Bldg.
	David Sentner_____	301 Pennsylvania Bldg.
	Leslie H. Whitten, Jr_____	301 Pennsulvania Bldg.
San Francisco Daily Pacific Builder (m.)__ 296–2160.	Ernest P. Mickel_____	1030 15th St.
San Francisco Examiner (m.)—EX 3–8322.	Milton L. Kaplan_____	301 Pennsylvania Bldg.
	Warren Rogers_____	301 Pennsylvania Bldg.
	Catherine Mackin_____	301 Pennsylvania Bldg.
	Marianne Means_____	301 Pennsylvania Bldg.
	Ruth S. Montgomery_____	301 Pennsylvania Bldg.
	David Sentner_____	301 Pennsylvania Bldg.
	Leslie H. Whitten, Jr_____	301 Pennsylvania Bldg.
San Jose (Calif.) Mercury-News (m.,e.,S.)_ 737–8627.	Walter T. Ridder_____	1325 E St.
	William W. Broom_____	1325 E St.
	Marie Ridder_____	1325 E St.
	Baxter Omohundro_____	1325 E St.
	Ann Terry_____	1325 E St.
DI 7–5123____	Fred W. Collins_____	1299 National Press Bldg.
San Juan Star (Puerto Rico) (m.)_____ DI 7–9111.	Walter S. Priest_____	852 National Press Bldg.
San Pedro (Calif.) News-Pilot (e.)_____ 296–8565.	Raymond J. McHugh_____	1629 K St.
	Franklyn C. Nofziger_____	1629 K St.
	Lucille Eddinger_____	1629 K St.
	Edwin G. Martin_____	1629 K St.
	John H. McLaren_____	1629 K St.
	Lester M. Bell_____	1629 K St.
	Paul L. Tsompanas_____	1629 K St.
	Henry Goethals_____	1629 K St.
	Larry C. Osius_____	1629 K St.

NEWSPAPERS REPRESENTED—Continued

Paper represented and telephone number	Name	Office
Sankei Shimbun (m., e.)—DI 7-9718_____	Shunpei Kato_____	846 National Press Bldg.
	Makoto Kawanago_____	846 National Press Bldg.
347-4501_____	Yoneo Sakai_____	832 National Press Bldg.
Santa Barbara (Calif.) News-Press (e.)____ NA 8-2091.	Robert S. Allen_____	1292 National Press Bldg.
	Paul Scott_____	1292 National Press Bldg.
Santa Fe New Mexican_____ 483-3791.	Sarah McClendon_____	2933 28th St.
Saratoga Springs Saratogian (e.)_____	Paul L. Martin_____	795 National Press Bldg.
EX 3-3460.	Reginald F. Torrey_____	795 National Press Bldg.
	William A. Garrett_____	795 National Press Bldg.
	Eileen C. Timlin_____	795 National Press Bldg.
	James William Canan_____	795 National Press Bldg.
	Jack W. Germond_____	795 National Press Bldg.
	Edmund B. Lambeth_____	795 National Press Bldg.
	Richardson Gale_____	795 National Press Bldg.
Schenectady (N.Y.) Gazette (m.)_____ ME 8-4642.	Alan S. Emory_____	1273 National Press Bldg.
Science Service—NO 7-2255_____	Watson Davis_____	1719 N St.
	Ann Ewing_____	1719 N St.
	Dorothy Schriver_____	1719 N St.
	Faye Marley_____	1719 N St.
	Judith Viorst_____	1719 N St.
	Barbara Jean Tufty_____	1719 N St.
	Charles A. Betts_____	1719 N St.
	Ruby M. Yoshioka_____	1719 N St.
	Jonothan Eberhart_____	1719 N St.
	Edith Lederer_____	1719 N St.
	William McCann_____	1719 N St.
Scripps-Howard Newspaper Alliance_____ DI 7-7750.	Walker Stone_____	1013 13th St.
	Frank R. Ford_____	1013 13th St.
	Earl H. Richert_____	1013 13th St.
	Charles Egger_____	1013 13th St.
	Oland D. Russell_____	1013 13th St.
	Jim G. Lucas_____	1013 13th St.
	Kermit McFarland_____	1013 13th St.
	Jack Steele_____	1013 13th St.
	R. H. Shackford_____	1013 13th St.
	Marshall McNeil_____	1013 13th St.
	Dickson J. Preston_____	1013 13th St.
	John Troan_____	1013 13th St.
	Walter Friedenberg_____	1013 13th St.
	Richard H. Boyce_____	1013 13th St.
	Robert W. Dietsch_____	1013 13th St.
	Ludwell Denny_____	1013 13th St.
	William Steif_____	1013 13th St.
	Seth Kantor_____	1013 13th St.
	Richard Starnes_____	1013 13th St.
	Gene Basset_____	1013 13th St.
	George Carmack_____	1013 13th St.
Seattle Post-Intelligencer (m., S.)_____	Milton L. Kaplan_____	301 Pennsylvania Bldg.
EX 3-8322.	Warren Rogers_____	301 Pennsylvania Bldg.
	Catherine Mackin_____	301 Pennsylvania Bldg.
	Marianne Means_____	301 Pennsylvania Bldg.
	Ruth S. Montgomery_____	301 Pennsylvania Bldg.
	David Sentner_____	301 Pennsylvania Bldg.
	Leslie H. Whitten, Jr_____	301 Pennsylvania Bldg.
Seattle Times (e., S.)—OL 6-1880_____	Alice Frein Johnson_____	5900 Bradley Blvd., Bethesda, Md.
347-4350_____	William W. Prochnau___	1244 National Press Bldg.
Sedalia (Mo.) Democrat (e.)_____	Joseph A. Dear_____	1011 National Press Bldg.
393-0979.	Gretchen R. Doss_____	1011 National Press Bldg.
	Cyrene Dear_____	1011 National Press Bldg.
	Robert E. Hennessee_____	1011 National Press Bldg.
Seoul (Korea) Orient Press—296-7418_____	Toh Sang Moon_____	3917 Military Rd.
Sherman (Tex.) Democrat (e., S.)_____	Sarah McClendon_____	2933 28th St.
483-3791.	Nancy M. Fagg_____	2933 28th St.
Shreveport (La.) Journal (e.)—LI 4-8238___	Frank van der Linden_____	132 3d St. SE.
	John M. Steen, Jr_____	132 3d St. SE.
	Leland A. Bandy_____	132 3d St. SE.
Shreveport (La.) Times (m., S.)_____	Bascom N. Timmons_____	1253 National Press Bldg.
EX 3-0146.	Sam Hanna_____	1253 National Press Bldg.
Sioux City (Iowa) Journal (e.)_____	Bulkley Griffin_____	1237 National Press Bldg.
NA 8-7350.	Isabel Kinnear Griffin_____	1237 National Press Bldg.
	Don Larrabee_____	1237 National Press Bldg.
Sioux Falls (S. Dak.) Argus-Leader (e., S.)_ 234-5175.	Dorothy H. Marks_____	2914 P St.
Southern Illinoisan—LI 7-3554_____	Dorothy Williams_____	19 5th St. SE.
Spokane Spokesman Review (m., S.)_____ ST 3-4496.	Frank Hewlett_____	720 National Press Bldg.
Springer Foreign News Service (Hamburg, Germany)—527-8244.	Kurt T. Leissler_____	1200 S. Courthouse Rd., Arlington, Va.

NEWSPAPERS REPRESENTED—Continued

Paper represented and telephone number	Name	Office
Springfield (Ill.) State Journal (m., S.) 296–8565.	Raymond J. McHugh	1629 K St.
	Franklyn C. Nofziger	1629 K St.
	Lucille Eddinger	1629 K St.
	Edwin G. Martin	1629 K St.
	John H. McLaren	1629 K St.
	Lester M. Bell	1629 K St.
	Paul L. Tsompanas	1629 K St.
	Henry Goethals	1629 K St.
	Larry C. Osius	1629 K St.
Springfield (Ill.) State Register (e.) 296–8565.	Raymond J. McHugh	1629 K St.
	Franklyn C. Nofziger	1629 K St.
	Lucille Eddinger	1629 K St.
	Edwin G. Martin	1629 K St.
	John H. McLaren	1629 K St.
	Lester M. Bell	1629 K St.
	Paul L. Tsompanas	1629 K St.
	Henry Goethals	1629 K St.
	Larry C. Osius	1629 K St.
Springfield (Mass.) Daily News (e.) 393–4488, ST 3–5445.	Leslie E. Carpenter	784 National Press Bldg.
	Ned Curran	784 National Press Bldg.
	Michael D. Mosettig	784 National Press Bldg.
	Barbara Kober	784 National Press Bldg.
	Theresa McMasters	784 National Press Bldg.
Springfield (Mass.) Union (m.) NA 8–7350.	Bulkley Griffin	1237 National Press Bldg.
	Isabel Kinnear Griffin	1237 National Press Bldg.
	Don Larrabee	1237 National Press Bldg.
Springfield (Mo.) Leader and Press (e.) 422–7041.	O. C. Miller	P.O. Box 1759.
Springfield (Mo.) Daily News (m., S.) 422–7041.	O. C. Miller	P. O. Box 1759.
Stamford (Conn.) Advocate (e.) ST 3–1070.	Carey Cronan	1205 National Press Bldg.
Staten Island Advance (e.)—ST 3–1053	Aaron G. Benesch	711 14th St.
	David C. Breasted	711 14th St.
	Joseph M. Hochstein	711 14th St.
	Hoyt L. Gimlin	711 14th St.
Stuttgarter Zeitung (m., e., S.) 298–6535.	Joachim H. Schwelien	2553 North Utah St., Arlington, Va.
Sydney (Australia) Morning Herald ME 8–5090.	Alan R. Dobbyn	1137 National Press Bldg.
	A. D. Rothman	1137 National Press Bldg.
Sydney (Australia) Sun and Sun-Herald ME 8–5090.	Maurice Adams	1137 National Press Bldg.
Syracuse Herald-American (S.) ST 3–1053.	Edwin J. Safford	711 14th St.
	Joseph M. Hochstein	711 14th St.
	Hoyt L. Gimlin	711 14th St.
	Julies Witcover	711 14th St.
Syracuse Herald-Journal (e.) ST 3–1053.	Edwin J. Safford	711 14th St.
	Joseph M. Hochstein	711 14th St.
	Hoyt L. Gimlin	711 14th St.
	Jules Witcover	711 14th St.
Syracuse Post-Standard (m., S.) ST 3–1053.	Edwin J. Safford	711 14th St.
	Joseph M. Hochstein	711 14th St.
	Hoyt L. Gimlin	711 14th St.
Tacoma (Wash.) News Tribune (e., S.) LI 4–5100.	A. Robert Smith	328 Pennsylvania Ave. SE.
	Yvonne Franklin Smith	3439 Oliver St.
WO 6–3913	Emily Walker	3863 Rodman St.
Tampa (Fla.) Times & Tribune LI 7–2616.	Wesley F. Hayden	130 3d St. SE.
	Lewis S. McCashy	130 3d St. SE.
Tanjug News Agency (Yugoslavia) ME 8–6884.	Davor Culic	950 National Press Bldg.
Tarrytown (N.Y.) Daily News (e.) 393–3460.	Paul L. Martin	795 National Press Bldg.
	Reginald F. Torrey	795 National Press Bldg.
	William A. Garrett	795 National Press Bldg.
	Eileen C. Timlin	795 National Press Bldg.
	James W. Canan	795 National Press Bldg.
	Jack W. Germond	795 National Press Bldg.
	Edmund B. Lambeth	795 National Press Bldg.
	Richardson Gale	795 National Press Bldg.
TASS Telegraph Agency of the U.S.S.R. NA 8–7858, 7863.	Vladimir V. Vashedchenko	307 National Press Bldg.
	Vitaly V. Petroussenko	307 National Press Bldg.
	Viktor V. Kopytin	307 National Press Bldg.
Texas City Sun (e., S.)—638–4332	Felton West, Jr	1276 National Press Bldg.
	Charles P. Culhane	1276 National Press Bldg.
	Grace Halsell	1276 National Press Bldg.
The Hindu (Madras, India)—347–9226	Easwar Sagar	619 National Press Bldg.
The Times of India—EM 3–8656	Hans Rai Vohra	2823 Cortland Pl.
Thomson Newspapers (England) EM 3–5950.	Henry Brandon	3501 Rodman St.
Three Rivers (Mich.) Commercial (e.) NA 8–3335.	Esther Van Wagoner Tufty	997 National Press Bldg.
	Lou G. Van Wagoner	997 National Press Bldg.
Tiffin (Ohio) Advertiser-Tribune (e.) DI 7–1856.	Glenn D. Everett	926 National Press Bldg.

NEWSPAPERS REPRESENTED—Continued

Paper represented and telephone number	Name	Office
Toledo (Ohio) Blade (e.)—EX 3-4580	George F. Jenks	1280 National Press Bldg.
	George R. Zielke	1280 National Press Bldg.
Topeka Capital Journal (m., e., S.) LI 6-1005.	Jessie Stearns	100 5th St., SE.
Toronto Daily Star (e.)—338-9180	Martin W. Goodman	3134 Q St.
Toronto Globe & Mail (m.) DI 7-1373.	Bruce MacDonald	1099 National Press Bldg.
Toronto Telegram (e.)—DI 7-2124	Gordon Donaldson	844 National Press Bldg.
Traffic World—ST 3-7325	Joseph C. Scheleen	815 Washington Bldg.
	Lewis W. Britton	815 Washington Bldg.
	J. Delton Pattie	815 Washington Bldg.
	David Highsmith, Jr	815 Washington Bldg.
	Stanley Hamilton	815 Washington Bldg.
	Robert M. Butler	815 Washington Bldg.
	R. Stanley Chapman	815 Washington Bldg.
	William O. Craig	815 Washington Bldg.
	Colin Barrett	815 Washington Bldg.
Trenton Times Newspapers—347-1819	George E. Amick, Jr	1235 National Press Bldg.
Trenton (N.J.) Trentonian (m.) JU 8-4904.	Cyril J. O'Brien	10004 Reddick Dr., Silver Spring, Md.
Trybuna Ludu (Warsaw)—DI 7-6996	Zygmunt Broniarek	999 National Press Bldg.
Tufty News Service—NA 8-3335	Esther Van Wagoner Tufty	997 National Press Bldg.
	Lou G. Van Wagoner	997 National Press Bldg.
Tulsa (Okla.) Tribune (e.)—547-4968	J. Bob Lucas	300 G St. SE.
Tulsa (Okla.) World (m.)—544-2998	Malvina Stephenson	330 A St. SE.
Twin City Sentinel (Winston-Salem, NC.) EX 3-0146.	Bascom N. Timmons	1253 National Press Bldg.
	Roy Parker, Jr	1253 National Press Bldg.
United Features Syndicate—EM 3-0096	William S. White	5223 Reno Rd.
	Milena Choumenkovitch	5223 Reno Rd.
HO 2-3244	Doris Fleeson	2120 S St.
LI 3-5000	Mary McGrory	2710 Macomb St.
DI 7-7770	Richard Starnes	1013 13th St.
United Press International—EX 3-3430	Julius Frandsen	714 National Press Bldg.
	Carroll H. Kenworthy	714 National Press Bldg.
	Merriman Smith	714 National Press Bldg.
	J. L. Myler	714 National Press Bldg.
	Charles W. Corddry, Jr	714 National Press Bldg.
	Raymond M. Lahr	714 National Press Bldg.
	Charlotte G. Moulton	714 National Press Bldg.
	Frank Eleazer	714 National Press Bldg.
	Grant Dillman	714 National Press Bldg.
	Elizabeth Wharton	714 National Press Bldg.
	M. Stewart Hensley	714 National Press Bldg.
	Louis Cassels	714 National Press Bldg.
	John A. Goldsmith	714 National Press Bldg.
	Warren S. Duffee	714 National Press Bldg.
	Gaylord P. Godwin	714 National Press Bldg.
	Harry W. Sharpe	714 National Press Bldg.
	Dick S. West	714 National Press Bldg.
	Arnold B. Sawislak	714 National Press Bldg.
	Helen Thomas	714 National Press Bldg.
	William J. Eaton	714 National Press Bldg.
	Sam R. Fogg	714 National Press Bldg.
	Darrell Garwood	714 National Press Bldg.
	Alvin A. Spivak	714 National Press Bldg.
	J. William Theis	714 National Press Bldg.
	William L. Umstead, Jr	714 National Press Bldg.
	Hale Montgomery	714 National Press Bldg.
	Marguerite Davis	714 National Press Bldg.
	Steven V. Gerstel	714 National Press Bldg.
	Joseph D. Hutnyan	714 National Press Bldg.
	Roy L. McGhee	714 National Press Bldg.
	Michael L. Posner	714 National Press Bldg.
	Daniel Rapoport	714 National Press Bldg.
	Donald H. May	714 National Press Bldg.
	Norman R. Runnion	714 National Press Bldg.
	George C. Weeks	714 National Press Bldg.
	Jack C. Vandenberg	714 National Press Bldg.
	Elmer W. Lammi	714 National Press Bldg.
	Daniel F. Kelly	714 National Press Bldg.
	Robert J. Serling	714 National Press Bldg.
	Douglas D. Richards	714 National Press Bldg.
	Frederick L. Ferris	714 National Press Bldg.
	Robert F. Buckhorn	714 National Press Bldg.
	Henry Keys	714 National Press Bldg.
	Harry Ferguson	714 National Press Bldg.
	Robert M. Andrews	714 National Press Bldg.
	Jerome F. Brazda	714 National Press Bldg.
	Margaret A. Kilgore	714 National Press Bldg.
	Neil Martin	714 National Press Bldg.
	Rolf Breitenstein	714 National Press Bldg.
	Patrick J. Sloyan	714 National Press Bldg.
	Francis Jackman	714 National Press Bldg.
	Carlos J. Villar-Borda	714 National Press Bldg.

NEWSPAPERS REPRESENTED—Continued

Paper represented and telephone number	Name	Office
United Press International—Continued	Lowry Bowman	714 National Press Bldg.
	John Pierson	714 National Press Bldg.
	Leon R. Burnett	714 National Press Bldg.
	Cliff Sessions	714 National Press Bldg.
	Marlyn E. Aycock	714 National Press Bldg.
Utica (N.Y.) Daily Press (m.). EX 3–3460.	Paul L. Martin	795 National Press Bldg.
	Reginald F. Torrey	795 National Press Bldg.
	William A. Garrett	795 National Press Bldg.
	Eileen C. Timlin	795 National Press Bldg.
	James William Canan	795 National Press Bldg.
	Jack W. Germond	795 National Press Bldg.
	Edmund B. Lambeth	795 National Press Bldg.
	Richardson Gale	795 National Press Bldg.
Utica (N.Y.) Observer-Dispatch (e., S.). EX 3–3460.	Paul L. Martin	795 National Press Bldg.
	Reginald F. Torrey	795 National Press Bldg.
	William A. Garrett	795 National Press Bldg.
	Eileen C. Timlin	795 National Press Bldg.
	James William Canan	795 National Press Bldg.
	Jack W. Germond	795 National Press Bldg.
	Edmund B. Lambeth	795 National Press Bldg.
	Richardson Gale	795 National Press Bldg.
Vancouver Sun (e.)—ME 8–0966	Jack Brooks	1096 National Press Bldg.
Variety Daily (Calif.)—393–4488, ST 3–5445.	Leslie E. Carpenter	784 National Press Bldg.
	Ned Curran	784 National Press Bldg.
	Michael D. Mosettig	784 National Press Bldg.
	Barbara Kober	784 National Press Bldg.
	Theresa McMasters	784 National Press Bldg.
Venice (Calif.) Vanguard (e.). 296–8565.	Raymond J. McHugh	1629 K St.
	Franklyn C. Nofziger	1629 K St.
	Lucille Eddinger	1629 K St.
	Edwin G. Martin	1629 K St.
	John H. McLaren	1629 K St.
	Lester M. Bell	1629 K St.
	Paul L. Tsompanas	1629 K St.
	Henry Goethals	1629 K St.
	Larry C. Osius	1629 K St.
Vineland (N.J.) Times-Journal (e.). JU 8–4904.	Cyril J. O'Brien	10004 Reddick Dr., Silver Spring, Md.
Waco News-Tribune (m.)—393–4488, ST 3–5445.	Leslie E. Carpenter	784 National Press Bldg.
	Ned Curran	784 National Press Bldg.
	Michael D. Mosettig	784 National Press Bldg.
	Barbara Kober	784 National Press Bldg.
	Theresa McMasters	784 National Press Bldg.
Waco Times-Herald (e., S.)—393–4488	Leslie E. Carpenter	784 National Press Bldg.
	Ned Curran	784 National Press Bldg.
	Michael D. Mosettig	784 National Press Bldg.
	Barbara Kober	784 National Press Bldg.
	Theresa McMasters	784 National Press Bldg.
Wall Street Journal (m.)—ST 3–0164	Henry Gemmill	1015 14th St.
	Alan L. Otten	1015 14th St.
	John A. Grimes	1015 14th St.
	Edward A. Behr	1015 14th St.
	Arlen J. Large	1015 14th St.
	Hugh Craig	1015 14th St.
	Robert W. Irelan	1015 14th St.
	William Beecher	1015 14th St.
	Jonathan M. Spivak	1015 14th St.
	Louis M. Kohlmeier	1015 14th St.
	Philip L. Geyelin	1015 14th St.
	Jerry G. Landauer	1015 14th St.
	James Harwood	1015 14th St.
	Monroe W. Karmin	1015 14th St.
	Joseph W. Sullivan III	1015 14th St.
	Richard F. Janssen	1015 14th St.
	Eric Wentworth	1015 14th St.
	Howard Dan Cordtz	1015 14th St.
	George F. Taylor	1015 14th St.
622–2900	Daniel Hinson	11501 Columbia Pike, Silver Spring, Md.
622–2900	Charles C. Lee	11501 Columbia Pike, Silver Spring, Md.
622–2900	Donald Halsband	11501 Columbia Pike, Silver Spring, Md.
622–2900	William P. Schlitz	11501 Columbia Pike, Silver Spring, Md.
622–2900	Leonard H. Hoyle, Jr.	11501 Columbia Pike, Silver Spring, Md.
Washington Capital News Service. NA 8–6621.	John Vogt	707 National Press Bldg.
	Robert J. Taylor	707 National Press Bldg.

NEWSPAPERS REPRESENTED—Continued

Paper represented and telephone number	Name	Office
Washington Daily News (e.) DI 7-7777.	John T. O'Rourke	1013 13th St.
	Richard Hollander	1013 13th St.
	John T. Burch	1013 13th St.
	Milton R. Berliner	1013 13th St.
	Nicholas Blatchford	1013 13th St.
	Cornelia M. Ball	1013 13th St.
	John F. Cramer	1013 13th St.
	Thomas V. Kelly	1013 13th St.
	Henry Altman	1013 13th St.
	Cordelia Ruffin	1013 13th St.
	Eugene C. Shumate	1013 13th St.
	Don Maclean	1013 13th St.
	Tom Donnelly	1013 13th St.
	Rice Odell	1013 13th St.
	John R. Hoover	1013 13th St.
	George Clifford	1013 13th St.
	Daniel B. Hoik	1013 13th St.
	Julian K. Morrison	1013 13th St.
	Gail Perrin	1013 13th St.
	Stanford Felder	1013 13th St.
	J. W. Maxwell	1013 13th St.
	Samuel A. Stafford	1013 13th St.
	Gloria A. Ohliger	1013 13th St.
	Claire W. Crawford	1013 13th St.
	Harry C. Kelly	1013 13th St.
	Wauhillau La Hay	1013 13th St.
	Shirley Elder	1013 13th St.
	Kenneth Schlossberg	1013 13th St.
Washington Evening Star—LI 3-5000	G. Gould Lincoln	225 Virginia Ave. SE.
	Benjamin M. McKelway	225 Virginia Ave. SE.
	John H. Cline	225 Virginia Ave. SE.
	William M. Hines, Jr	225 Virginia Ave. SE.
	Garnett D. Horner	225 Virginia Ave. SE.
	Joseph Young	225 Virginia Ave. SE.
	John C. Henry	225 Virginia Ave. SE.
	Miriam Ottenberg	225 Virginia Ave. SE.
	Robert K. Walsh	225 Virginia Ave. SE.
	William H. Harrison	225 Virginia Ave. SE.
	George D. Beveridge, Jr	225 Virginia Ave. SE.
	Newbold Noyes, Jr	225 Virginia Ave. SE.
	Cecil Holland	225 Virginia Ave. SE.
	Mary McGrory	225 Virginia Ave. SE.
	L. Edgar Prina	225 Virginia Ave. SE.
	Charles B. Seib, Jr	225 Virginia Ave. SE.
	Isabelle Shelton	225 Virginia Ave. SE.
	Edwin Tribble	225 Virginia Ave. SE.
	Leon M. Cohn	225 Virginia Ave. SE.
	Grace Bassett	225 Virginia Ave. SE.
	Richard Fryklund	225 Virginia Ave. SE.
	Charles D. Pierce	225 Virginia Ave. SE.
	John M. McKelway	225 Virginia Ave. SE.
	David S. Broder	225 Virginia Ave. SE.
	Haynes B. Johnson	225 Virginia Ave. SE.
	Sam Eastman	225 Virginia Ave. SE.
	Sidney Epstein	225 Virginia Ave. SE.
	Bernard M. Gwertzman	225 Virginia Ave. SE.
	Truman R. Temple	225 Virginia Ave. SE.
	David G. Braaten	225 Virginia Ave. SE.
	I. William Hill	225 Virginia Ave. SE.
	Clarence H. Hunter	225 Virginia Ave. SE.
	Betty Beale	225 Virginia Ave. SE.
	Paul B. Hope	225 Virginia Ave. SE.
	Alexander Preston	225 Virginia Ave. SE.
	Lyle W. Denniston	225 Virginia Ave. SE.
	Anne H. Christmas	225 Virginia Ave. SE.
	Walter L. Gold	225 Virginia Ave. SE.
	John Barron	225 Virginia Ave. SE.
	Casper Nannes	225 Virginia Ave. SE.
	Walter H. Pincus	225 Virginia Ave. SE.
	Burton Hoffman	225 Virginia Ave. SE.
	John H. Cassady	225 Virginia Ave. SE.
	Thomas E. Noyes	225 Virginia Ave. SE.
Washington Post (m., S.)—RE 7-1234	J. R. Wiggins	1515 L St.
	Edward T. Folliard	1515 L St.
	Merlo J. Pusey	1515 L St.
	Jerry Kluttz	1515 L St.
	Robert Albright	1515 L St.
	John J. W. Riseling	1515 L St.
	Ben. W. Gilbert	1515 L St.
	Katharine Graham	1515 L St.
	John G. Norris	1515 L St.
	Herbert L. Block	1515 L St.
	William E. Gold	1515 L St.

NEWSPAPERS REPRESENTED—Continued

Paper represented and telephone number	Name	Office
Washington Post (M., S.)—Continued	Chalmers M. Roberts	1515 L St.
	Alan Barth	1515 L St.
	Alfred Friendly	1515 L St.
	Carroll Kilpatrick	1515 L St.
	Aubrey A. Graves	1515 L St.
	Richard L. Lyons	1515 L St.
	Nathan S. Haseltine	1515 L St.
	Warren W. Unna	1515 L St.
	Lawrence B. Laurent	1515 L St.
	Richard A. Thornburgh	1515 L St.
	Elsie Carper	1515 L St.
	Eve Edstrom	1515 L St.
	Jean M. White	1515 L St.
	Julius Duscha	1515 L St.
	Karl E. Meyer	1515 L St.
	Laurence M. Stern	1515 L St.
	Murray Marder	1515 L St.
	J. W. Anderson	1515 L St.
	Robert E. L. Baker	1515 L St.
	Marie D. Smith	1515 L St.
	Morton Mintz	1515 L St.
	James E. Clayton	1515 L St.
	Edwin O. Gritz	1515 L St.
	Joseph Paull	1515 L St.
	Marie F. Sauer	1515 L St.
	Howard Simons	1515 L St.
	Dan Kurzman	1515 L St.
	Willard C. Clopton, Jr	1515 L St.
	Kenneth W. Harter	1515 L St.
	John P. MacKenzie	1515 L St.
	Richard J. Maloy	1515 L St.
	Paul A. Schuette	1515 L St.
	Frank C. Porter	1515 L St.
	Jack E. Eisen	1515 L St.
	Harvey H. Segal	1515 L St.
	Dorothy McCardle	1515 L St.
	Gerald P. Grant	1515 L St.
	George E. Lardner, Jr	1515 L St.
	Wolf Von Eckardt	1515 L St.
	Howard Margolis	1515 L St.
	John M. Goshko	1515 L St.
Washington Post & Syndicate. EM 2-3525.	Walter Lippmann	3525 Woodley Rd.
	Elizabeth F. Farmer	3525 Woodley Rd.
	Joanne Krause	3525 Woodley Rd.
965-1770	Joseph W. Alsop	2720 Dumbarton Ave.
Waterbury (Conn.) American (e.). ST 3-1070.	Carey Cronan	1205 National Press Bldg.
Waterbury (Conn.) Republican (m., S.). ST 3-1070.	Carey Cronan	1205 National Press Bldg.
Waterloo (Iowa) Courier (e., S.). NA 8-7350.	Bulkley Griffin	1237 National Press Bldg.
	Isabel Kinnear Griffin	1237 National Press Bldg.
	Donald R. Larrabee	1237 National Press Bldg.
Watertown (N.Y.) Daily Times (e.). ME 8-4642.	Alan S. Emory	1273 National Press Bldg.
Waterville (Maine) Sentinel (m.). RE 7-0004.	May Craig	1228 National Press Bldg.
Wheaton (Ill.) Journal (e.)—393-0979	Joseph A. Dear	1011 National Press Bldg.
	Cyrene Dear	1011 National Press Bldg.
	Gretchen R. Doss	1011 National Press Bldg.
	Robert E. Hennessee	1011 National Press Bldg.
White Plains (N.Y.) Reporter Dispatch (e.)—393-3460.	Paul L. Martin	795 National Press Bldg.
	Reginald F. Torrey	795 National Press Bldg.
	William A. Garrett	795 National Press Bldg.
	Eileen C. Timlin	795 National Press Bldg.
	James W. Canan	795 National Press Bldg.
	Jack W. Germond	795 National Press Bldg.
	Edmund B. Lambeth	795 National Press Bldg.
	Richardson Gale	795 National Press Bldg.
Wichita (Kans.) Beacon (e.). EX 3-0146.	Bascom N. Timmons	1253 National Press Bldg.
	John S. Sparks, Jr	1253 National Press Bldg.
Wichita (Kans.) Eagle (m., S.). EX 3-0146.	Bascom N. Timmons	1253 National Press Bldg.
	John S. Sparks, Jr	1253 National Press Bldg.
Wichita Falls (Tex.) Record-News & Times (m., e., S.)—393-4488, ST 3-5445.	Leslie E. Carpenter	784 National Press Bldg.
	Ned Curran	784 National Press Bldg.
	Michael D. Mosettig	784 National Press Bldg.
	Barbara Kober	784 National Press Bldg.
	Theresa McMasters	784 National Press Bldg.
Williston (N.D.) Daily Herald. LI 3-2978.	Dodee Wick	135 D St. SE.
Wilmington (Del.) Evening Journal. EX 3-0146.	Bascom N. Timmons	1253 National Press Bldg.
	Sam Hanna	1253 National Press Bldg.

NEWSPAPERS REPRESENTED—Continued

Paper represented and telephone number	Name	Office
Wilmington (Del.) Morning News_____ EX 3-0146.	Bascom N. Timmons_____ Sam Hanna.	1253 National Press Bldg.
Windsor Daily Star (e.)_____ EM 3-7521.	Alicia Banos_____	3752 Jocelyn St.
Winston-Salem (N.C.) Journal (m.)_____ EX 3-0146.	Bascom N. Timmons_____ Roy Parker, Jr_____	1253 National Press Bldg. 1253 National Press Bldg.
Women's News Service_____ EM 3-5744.	Vera Glaser_____	5000 Cathedral Ave.
Worcester (Mass.) Telegram-Gazette (m., e., S.).—NA 8-7350.	Bulkley Griffin_____ Isabel Kinnear Griffin_____ Donald R. Larrabee_____	1237 National Press Bldg. 1237 National Press Bldg. 1237 National Press Bldg.
World Market Publications—ME 8-5078__	Walter Gerson_____	1 Thomas Circle.
World Press—EX 3-1260_____	Carl D. Soresi_____	739 National Press Bldg.
"Ya" Daily, Madrid, Spain (m.)_____ EM 2-9667.	Don Luis Mendez_____	4545 Connecticut Ave.
Yomiuri Shimbun (m., e.)—ST 3-0363, 783-0186.	Yasaburo Saito_____ Takeshi Ogawa_____ Hiroshi Ishihara_____	742 National Press Bldg. 742 National Press Bldg. 742 National Press Bldg.
Yonkers (N.Y.) Hearld Statesman (e.)____ 393-3460.	Paul L. Martin_____ Reginald F. Torrey_____ William A. Garrett _____ Eileen C. Timlin_____ James W. Canan_____ Jack W. Germond _____ Edmund B. Lambeth _____ Richardson Gale _____	795 National Press Bldg. 795 National Press Bldg. 795 National Press Bldg. 795 National Press Bldg. 795 National Press Bldg. 795 National Press Bldg. 795 National Press Bldg. 795 National Press Bldg.
York (Pa.) Dispatch (e.)—ME 8-0823_____	McLellan Smith_____	1131 National Press Bldg.
Youngstown (Ohio) Vindicator (e.)_____ EX 3-0146.	Bascom N. Timmons_____ Sam Hanna_____	1253 National Press Bldg. 1253 National Press Bldg.
Ypsilanti (Mich.) Press (e.)_____ 737-7770.	William F. Pyper_____ Paul A. Miltich_____	515 National Press Bldg. 515 National Press Bldg.

PRESS PHOTOGRAPHERS GALLERY

Room S-317, U. S. Senate

Phone, 225-6548

Superintendent.—William J. Forsythe, 1212 Longfellow Street, 20011.

Assistant Superintendent.—Frances Fitzgerald, Room S-317, U.S. Senate.

STANDING COMMITTEE OF PRESS PHOTOGRAPHERS

Byron H. Rollins, Chairman
William C. Beall, Secretary-Treasurer
C. Ed Alley
Charles J. Mack
Thomas J. O'Halloran
Fred Ward

RULES GOVERNING PRESS PHOTOGRAPHERS GALLERY

1. Administration of the press photographers' gallery is vested in a Standing Committee of Press Photographers elected by accredited members of the gallery. The committee consists of six persons elected to serve for terms of two years. Three members shall be elected in odd-numbered years and three in even-numbered years. The committee shall be composed of one member each from the Associated Press, United Press International Newspictures, newsreel media, magazine media, newspapers, and an "at large" member. The "at large" member must be selected from a media not already represented on the committee. Elections will be held in January. Vacancies on the committee will be filled by special election to be called by the Standing Committee.

2. Persons desiring admission to the photographers' gallery of Congress should make application in accordance with Rule 35 of the House of Representatives, subject to the direction and control of the Speaker, and Rule 34 of the Senate, which rules will be interpreted and administered by the Standing Committee of Press Photographers subject to the review and approval of the Senate Committee on Rules and Administration.

3. The Standing Committee of Press Photographers shall limit membership in the photographers' gallery to bona fide news photographers of repute in their profession and to Heads of Photographic Bureaus under such rules as the Standing Committee of Press Photographers shall prescribe.

4. Provided, however, that the Standing Committee of Photographers shall admit to the gallery no person who does not establish to the satisfaction of the Committee all of the following:

(a) That any member is not engaged in paid publicity or promotion work or in prosecuting any claim before Congress or before any department of the Government, and will not become so engaged while a member of the gallery.

(b) That he or she is not engaged in any lobbying activity and will not become so engaged while a member of the gallery.

The above rules have been approved by the Committee on Rules and Administration.

B. EVERETT JORDAN,
Chairman, Senate Committee on Rules and Administration.

MEMBERS ENTITLED TO ADMISSION

The * designates those whose wives accompany them

Name	Representing—	Residence
*Abbott, Gene	Washington Star	2000 S. Eads St., Arlington, Va.
*Abercrombie, Thomas J	National Geographic	607 Niblick Dr., Vienna, Va.
*Alley, C. Ed	United Press International Newspictures	1 Stanton Dr., Fairfax, Va.
*Atherton, James K. W	United Press International Newspictures	3222 Edgewood Rd., Kensington, Md.
*Atkins, Ollie	Saturday Evening Post	Box 11, Fairfax, Va.
*Baker, Elwood A	Washington Star	2346 Lyons St. SE.
*Beall, William C	Washington Daily News	934 Sweetbriar Dr., Alexandria, Va.
Bennett, Walter E	Time, Inc	4570 MacArthur Blvd.
*Berg, Paul	St. Louis Post-Dispatch	425 East 86th St., New York.
Blair, James P	National Geographic	1750 M St.
Bledsoe, John T	U.S. News & World Report	2514 K St.
*Boyer, David S	National Geographic	9406 Locust Hill Rd., Bethesda, Md.
Burchette, Robert	Washington Post	806 Thurman Ave., Hyattsville, Md.
*Burroughs, Henry	Associated Press Photos	5013 Ft. Sumner Dr., Washington, D.C.
*Cabell, Clifton G., Jr	Washington Afro-American	3335 Blaine St., SE.
*Cancellare, Frank	United Press International Newspictures	109 S. Utah St., Arlington, Va.
*Capa, Cornell	Magnum	2719 Dumbarton Ave.
*Casamento, Victor	Washington Post	3411 5th St. SE.
*Castens, Edward H	U. S. News & World Report	2122 Massachusetts Ave.
*Chevalier, Douglas	Washington Post	7325 Blair Rd. NW.
*Chinn, Augustus C	Washington Star	3606 N. Third Street, Arlington, Va.
*Clarity, Ed	New York News	55–15th Road, Broad Channel, N.Y.
*Clark, Edward	Editorial Magazine Photographer	6671 MacArthur Blvd., Glen Echo Hts., Md.
*Clark, Noel P	Editorial Magazine Photographer	6416 Wiscasset Rd., Glen Echo Hts., Md.
*Colton, William J	Washington Star	4401 Emden St., Silver Spring, Md.
*Conger, Dean D	National Geographic	6604 Melody Lane, Bethesda, Md.
*Converse, Gordon N	Christian Science Monitor	67 Pine St., Needham, Mass.
*Dale, Bruce A	National Geographic	1639 Arlington Blvd., Fairfax, Va.
*Danor, George	Washington Star	8329 Navahoe Dr., Silver Spring, Md.
*Darcey, Richard	Washington Post	4310 Emden St., Silver Spring, Md.
*Davis, Ellsworth J	Washington Post	4831 Meade St. NE.
*De Lort, Jean Guy	Fairchild Publications	12900 Bently Lane, Bowie, Md.
*Del Vecchio, Charles	Washington Post	103 Marion Ave., McLean, Va.
*DiJoseph, Jr., John M	Reni News Photo Service	7916 Kipling Parkway, District Heights, Md.
*Driscoll, Norman	Washington Post	715 Chestnut Ave., Falls Church, Va.
*Duprey, John	New York News	113 Lynn St., Harrington Park, N.J.
*Duvall, Owen E., Jr	Washington Star	3103 Lancer Pl., West Hyattsville, Md.
*Ellis, Arthur J	Washington Post	8519 Carroll Ave., Silver Spring, Md.
*Erwitt, Elliott	Magnum	2719 Dumbarton Ave.
*Farrell, Daniel B	New York News	291 Merrifield Ave., Oceanside, N.Y.
*Farrington, Jr., C. Max	Reni News Photo Service	624 Monroe St., Rockville, Md.
*Finnigan, Vincent A	Keystone Press Agency, Ltd	425 Whittier St.
*Flecknoe, Harold J	Washington Star	10011 Tenbrook Dr., Silver Spring, Md.
*Fletcher, John E	National Geographic	5315 Ninth Road North, Arlington, Va.
Forte, Benjamin E	AFP-DPA	602 Kennebec Rd., Oxon Hill, Md.
*Freeman, Thomas J	Associated Press Photos	9 Lakeview Circle, Greenbelt, Md.
*Gaylin, George R	United Press International Newspictures	1436 Primrose Rd. NW.
*Georges, Harvey W	Associated Press Photos	1802 Tucker Ave., McLean, Va.

810

Name	Representing—	Residence
*Georgia, Lowell J	Denver Post	8665 W. 67th Pl. Arvada, Colo.
*Gilbert, Geoffrey D	Washington Daily News	2614 39th St.
*Gilka, Robert E	National Geographic	4664 25th Street North, Arlington, Va.
Glinn, Burton	Magnum	2719 Dumbarton Ave.
*Goodman, Harry	Washington Star	3217 Pauline Dr., Chevy Chase, Md.
*Greitzer, Philip	New York News	2160 Bolton, St., Bronx, N.Y.
*Gorry, Charles P	Associated Press Photos	601 S. Magnolia Dr., Falls Church, Va.
*Griffin, Henry L	Associated Press Photos	3214 Gumwood Dr., University Hills, Hyattsville, Md.
*Harbutt, Charles	Magnum	2719 Dumbarton Ave.
*Hartmann, Erich	Magnum	2719 Dumbarton Ave.
*Heiberger, Joseph	Washington Post	10016 Portland Rd., Silver Spring, Md.
*Hoff, Charles	New York News	136-75 72d St., Flushing, N.Y.
*Hollis, Louis J	Washington Daily News	1008 Carol Lane, Falls Church, Va.
*Hoy, Frank	Washington Post	4607 28th Road South, Arlington, Va.
*Hoy, Thomas L	Washington Star	3226 Ravensworth Pl., Alexandria, Va.
*Hurley, Frank C	New York News	239 Kearny Ave., Perth Amboy, N.J.
*Huttenloch, Robert M	CBS News	5375 Pumphrey Dr.
Johnson, Maurice	United Press International Newspictures	7 Perrott Court, Little River Hills, Fairfax, Va.
*Kelleher, Thomas Walter	New York News	361 95th St., Brooklyn N.Y.
*Kelley, Thomas	Washington Post	1711 Henry Rd., Rockville, Md.
*Kraft, Jr., Frederick, G	Baltimore News-American	325 Whitfield Rd., Baltimore, Md.
*Landi, Lando	EPOCA	67 Elmira St., SW.
*Leach, Glen C	Washington Star	5003 Orleans Ct., Kensington, Md.
*Leffler, Warren K	U. S. News & World Report	11412 Grayling Lane, Rockville. Md.
*Lewis, Larry J	Reni News Photo Service	4325 Halley Terrace SE.
*Little William T	Northern Virginia Sun	3717 S. 3d St., Arlington, Va.
*Littlehales, Bates	National Geographic	1650 32nd St.
*Lumsden, Marshall	Saturday Evening Post	10 Carrigan Ave., White Plains, N.Y.
*Mack, Charles J	CBS News	5904 Aberdeen Rd., Bethesda, Md.
*Maggi, Carlos	City News Bureau	5814 Bradley Blvd., Bethesda, Md.
*Mahan, James B	Intercam	7402 Conrad Rd., Alexandria, Va.
*Maroon, Fred J	Editorial Magazine Photographer	3029 M St.
Martufi, Rosemary	Washington Star	1075 Wahler Pl., S.E.
*Matheny, Norman	Christian Science Monitor	3214 S. Stafford St., Arlington, Va.
*Mathewson, Harold	New York News	27 Kensico Knolls Pl., White Plains, N.Y.
*McNally, Lawrence	Baltimore News-American	708 Cator Ave., Baltimore, Md.
*McNamara, James	Washington Post	10210 Pierce Dr., Silver Spring, Md.
*McNamee, Wallace	Washington Post	3390 Martha Custis Dr., Alexandria, Va.
*Miller, Francis R	Life	5606 Jordan Road, Bethesda, Md.
*Miller, Hugh	Washington Post	4409 Yuma St.
Mims, Roddey E	United Press International Newspictures	1111 Army Navy Dr., Arlington, Va.
*Mobley, George F	National Geographic	7875 Livingston Rd., SE.
*Moldvay, Albert	National Geographic	1530 Live Oak Drive, Silver Spring, Md.
*Morgan, Fred	New York News	94–40 216th St., Queens Village, L.I., N.Y.
*Morris, John G	Washington Post	209 G St. SW.
*Mueller, John V	Washington Star	9316 East Parkhill Dr., Bethesda, Md.
*Naltchayan, Harry N	Washington Post	1365 Nicholson St.
*Nebbia, Thomas	National Geographic	301 Meadowview Rd., Falls Church, Va.
*Neil, Joseph H	CBS News	9746 Hedin Dr., Silver Spring, Md.
*Oates, Walter	Washington Star	7911 Harwood Pl., Springfield, Va.
*O'Halloran, Thomas J	U. S. News & World Report	3531 Duke St., Col. Park, Md.

MEMBERS ENTITLED TO ADMISSION—Continued

Name	Representing—	Residence
*Parks, Winfield	National Geographic	5601 13th St.
*Perkins, Robert F	Washington Star	8152 Eastern Ave. NW.
*Phillips, Robert H	Editorial Magazine Photographer	1528 33d St.
*Ranzini, Walter	New York News	205 East 69th St., New York, N.Y.
*Roberts, Joseph B	National Geographic	1212 North Inglewood St., Arlington, Va.
*Rohland, Henry	Washington Post	508 Derrydown Lane, Silver Spring, Md.
*Rollins, Byron H	Associated Press Photos	4421 Butterworth Pl.
*Rous, John	Associated Press Photos	3201 Russell Rd., Alexandria, Va.
*Routt, Francis	Washington Star	2505 Parker Ave., Silver Spring, Md.
*Routt, Randolph	Washington Star	303 Lexington Dr., Silver Spring. Md.
*Sachs, Arnold	AFP-DPA	4809 Winslow Rd. SE.
*Sauro, William E	New York Herald Tribune	217 Kendall Rd., Franklin Park, N.J.
Scherschel, Joseph J	National Geographic	4570 MacArthur Blvd.
Schmick, Paul M	Washington Star	514 North Montana, Arlington, Va.
*Schulman, Samuel	AFP-DPA	660 First Ave., New York, N.Y.
*Schutz, Robert H	Associated Press Photos	9504 Fern Pl., Annandale, Va.
*Shields, Thomas E	United Press International Newspictures	7413 17th Ave., West Hyattsville, Md.
*Silverman, Joseph A	Washington Star	8606 Garland Ave., Silver Spring, Md.
*Sisson, Robert F	National Geographic	1215 30th St.
*Slantis, Paul	Pittsburgh Post Gazette	330 Streets Run Rd., Pittsburgh, Pa.
*Smith, William J	Associated Press Photos	4513 17th St. NE.
*Sorrell, Maurice	Johnson Publications	5700 New Hampshire Ave. NE.
*Stearns, Stanley, F	United Press International Newspictures	12805 Keswick Lane, Bowie, Md.
*Stevens, Larry	Metropolitan Sunday Newspapers	344 Pine Spring Rd., Falls Church, Va.
*Stewart, B. Anthony	National Geographic	3280 Arcadia Pl.
*Stolley, Richard B	Life	9210 Fernwood Rd., Bethesda, Md.
*Streets, Wellner C	Washington Daily News	1936 Merrimac Dr., Hyattsville, Md.
*Striar, Robert	City News Bureau	3311 Fessenden St.
*Stroup, Barry E	Associated Press Photos	2245 N. Harrison St., Arlington, Va.
*Tames, George	New York Times	5922 Broad Branch Rd.
*Tasnadi, Charles	Associated Press Photos	4420 Chesapeake St.
*Taylor, Arnold	Washington Star	507 Third St. SE.
Thayer, Mary V. R	Magnum	2719 Dumbarton Ave.
Thurman, Frank J	City News Bureau	4748 Homer Ave., Suitland, Md.
*Tretick, Stanley	Look	4101 Cathedral Ave.
Trikosko, Marion S	U. S. News & World Report	2147 O St.
*Volz, Willard G	Washington Star	1006 Helena Dr., Silver Spring, Md.
*Ward, Fred	Black Star Publishing Co	6419 Dahlonega Rd., Glen Echo Heights, Md.
*Wayman, Stanley E	Life	3212 44th St.
Wentzel, Volkmar	National Geographic	3137 N St.
*Wood, Walter	Baltimore News-American	7525 San Juan Dr., Clinton, Md.
Wray, Mack Keith	Keystone Press Agency	1417 Ivanhoe St., Alexandria, Va.

SERVICES REPRESENTED

Service and telephone number	Name	Office
PICTURE SERVICES		
AFP–DPA Photos—393-0929	Arnold Sachs	204 Indiana Ave.
	Benjamin E. Forte	204 Indiana Ave.
	Samuel Schulman	204 Indiana Ave.
Associated Press Photos—AD 4-5400	Barry E. Stroup	1300 Connecticut Ave.
	Henry Burroughs	1300 Connecticut Ave.
	Thomas J. Freeman	1300 Connecticut Ave.
	Harvey W. Georges	1300 Connecticut Ave.
	Charles P. Gorry	1300 Connecticut Ave.
	Henry L. Griffin	1300 Connecticut Ave.
	Byron H. Rollins	1300 Connecticut Ave.
	John Rous	1300 Connecticut Ave.
	Robert Schutz	1300 Connecticut Ave.
	William J. Smith	1300 Connecticut Ave.
	Charles Tasnadi	1300 Connecticut Ave.
Black Star—657-3322	Fred Ward	6419 Dahlonega Rd., Glen Echo Heights, Md.
City News Bureau—CO 5-2000	Robert Striar	Sheraton-Park Hotel.
	Carlos Maggi	2600 Woodley Rd.
	Frank J. Thurman	4748 Homer Ave., Suitland, Md.
Intercam—CL 6-5550	James B. Mahan	7402 Conrad Rd., Alexandria, Va.
Keystone Press Agency, Ltd.—544-2945	Vincent A. Finnigan	806 Maryland Ave., N.E.
	Mack Keith Wray	806 Maryland Ave., N.E.
Magnum—AD 4-0278	Mary V. R. Thayer	2719 Dumbarton Ave.
	Cornell Capa	2719 Dumbarton Ave.
	Elliott Erwitt	2719 Dumbarton Ave.
	Burton Glinn	2719 Dumbarton Ave.
	Charles Harbutt	2719 Dumbarton Ave.
	Erich Hartmann	2719 Dumbarton Ave.
Reni News Photo Service—ME 8-2200	John M. DiJoseph, Jr	1319 F St.
	C. Max Farrington, Jr	1319 F St.
	Larry J. Lewis	1319 F St.
United Press International Newspictures—347-1124.	George R. Gaylin	1013 13th St.
	C. Ed Alley	1013 13th St.
	James K. W. Atherton	1013 13th St.
	Frank Cancellare	1013 13th St.
	Maurice Johnson	1013 13th St.
	Roddey E. Mims	1013 13th St.
	Thomas E. Shields	1013 13th St.
	Stanley F. Stearns	1013 13th St.
NEWSREEL AND TELEVISION SERVICES		
CBS News—OL 4-6231	Charles J. Mack	5904 Aberdeen Rd., Bethesda, Md.
	Robert Huttenlock	5375 Pumphrey Dr., Washington, D.C.
	Joseph H. Neil	9746 Hedin Dr., Silver Spring, Md.
NEWSPAPERS		
Baltimore News-American—PL 2-1212	Walter H. Wood	Lombard & South Sts., Baltimore, Md.
	Frederick G. Kraft, Jr	Baltimore, Md.
	Lawrence McNally	Baltimore, Md.
Christian Science Monitor—EX 3-4578	Gordon N. Converse	1293 National Press Bldg.
	Norman Matheny	1293 National Press Bldg.
Metropolitan Sunday Newspapers 560-3511.	Larry Stevens	344 Pine Spring Rd., Falls Church, Va.
New York News—NA 8-5050	Walter Ranzini, Picture Assignment Editor.	National Press Bldg.
	Ed Clarity	National Press Bldg.
	John Duprey	National Press Bldg.
	Daniel B. Farrell	National Press Bldg.
	Philip Greitzer	National Press Bldg.
	Charles Hoff	National Press Bldg.
	Frank C. Hurley	National Press Bldg.
	Thomas Walter Kelleher	National Press Bldg.
	Harold Mathewson	National Press Bldg.
	Fred Morgan	National Press Bldg.
New York Herald Tribune—298-9160	William E. Sauro	1750 Pennsylvania Ave.
New York Times—NA 8-3016	George Tames	1701 K St.
Northern Virginia Sun—JA 4-3000	William T. Little, Chief Photographer.	3409 Wilson Bvd., Arlington, Va.
Pittsburgh Post-Gazette—EX 3-4580	Paul Slantis	1280 National Press Bldg.
St. Louis Post-Dispatch—296-5775	Paul Berg	1028 Conn. Ave.
Washington Afro-American—DE 2-0080	Clifton G. Cabell, Jr	1800 11th St.

813

SERVICES REPRESENTED—Continued

Service and telephone number	Name	Office
NEWSPAPERS—continued		
Washington Daily News—DI 7-7777	William C. Beall, Chief Photographer.	1013 13th St.
	Geoffrey D. Gilbert	1013 13th St.
	Louis J. Hollis	1013 13th St.
	Wellner C. Streets	1013 13th St.
Washington Star—LI 3-5000	Gene Abbott	225 Virginia Ave. SE.
	Elwood A. Baker	225 Virginia Ave. SE.
	Augustus C. Chinn	225 Virginia Ave. SE.
	George Danor	225 Virginia Ave. SE.
	Owen E. Duvall, Jr	225 Virginia Ave. SE.
	Harold J. Flecknoe	225 Virginia Ave. SE.
	Harry Goodman	225 Virginia Ave. SE.
	Thomas L. Hoy	225 Virginia Ave. SE.
	Glen C. Leach	225 Virginia Ave. SE.
	Rosemary Martufi	225 Virginia Ave. SE.
	John C. Mueller	225 Virginia Ave. SE.
	Walter Oates	225 Virginia Ave. SE.
	Robert F. Perkins	225 Virginia Ave. SE.
	Francis Routt	225 Virginia Ave. SE.
	Randolph Routt	225 Virginia Ave. SE.
	Paul M. Schmick	225 Virginia Ave. SE.
	Joseph A. Silverman	225 Virginia Ave. SE.
	Arnold Taylor	225 Virginia Ave. SE.
	Willard G. Volz	225 Virginia Ave. SE.
Washington Post—RE 7-1234	John G. Morris, Graphics Editor.	1515 L St.
	Hugh Miller	1515 L St.
	Robert Burchette	1515 L St.
	Victor Casamento	1515 L St.
	Douglas Chevalier	1515 L St.
	Richard Darcey	1515 L St.
	Ellsworth Davis	1515 L St.
	Charles Del Vecchio	1515 L St.
	Norman Driscoll	1515 L St.
	Arthur J. Ellis	1515 L St.
	Joseph Heiberger	1515 L St.
	Frank Hoy	1515 L St.
	Thomas Kelley	1515 L St.
	James McNamara	1515 L St.
	Wallace McNamee	1515 L St.
	Harry N. Naltchayan	1515 L St.
	Henry Rohland	1515 L St.
NATIONAL NEWS MAGAZINES		
Epoca—JO 3-6383	Lando Landi	67 Elmira St., SW.
Fairchild Publications—RE 7-7090	Jean Guy De Lort	National Press Bldg.
Johnson Publications—298-7836	Maurice Sorrell	1750 Pennsylvania Ave.
Life—FE 7-8000	Richard B. Stolley, Chief of Bureau.	1120 Connecticut Ave.
	Francis R. Miller	1120 Connecticut Ave.
	Stanley E. Wayman	1120 Connecticut Ave.
Look—DI 7-9111	Stanley Tretick	852 National Press Bldg.
National Geographic—296-7500	Robert E. Gilka, Director of Photography.	17th and M Sts.
	Thomas J. Abercrombie	17th and M Sts.
	James P. Blair	17th and M Sts.
	David S. Boyer	17th and M Sts.
	Dean D. Conger	17th and M Sts.
	Bruce A. Dale	17th and M Sts.
	John E. Fletcher	17th and M Sts.
	Bates Littlehales	17th and M Sts.
	George F. Mobley	17th and M Sts.
	Albert Moldvay	17th and M Sts.
	Thomas Nebbia	17th and M Sts.
	Winfield Parks	17th and M Sts.
	Joseph B. Roberts	17th and M Sts.
	Joseph J. Scherschel	17th and M Sts.
	Robert F. Sisson	17th and M Sts.
	B. Anthony Stewart	17th and M Sts.
	Volkmar Wentzel	17th and M Sts.
Saturday Evening Post—NA 8-2152	Marshall Lumsden, Photography Editor.	1000 16th St.
	Ollie Atkins	1000 16th St.
Time—FE 7-8000	Walter E. Bennett	1120 Connecticut Ave.
U.S. News & World Report—FE 3-7400	Edward H. Castens, Picture Editor.	2300 N St.
	John T. Bledsoe, Jr	2300 N St.
	Warren Leffler	2300 N St.
	Thomas J. O'Halloran	2300 N St.
	Marion S. Trikosko	2300 N St.

WHITE HOUSE NEWS PHOTOGRAPHERS' ASSOCIATION

(Press Room, White House)
Association Phone, 273-1604

OFFICERS

Ollie Atkins, President
Maurice Johnson, Vice President
C. Ed Alley, Secretary
Byron Rollins, Treasurer

EXECUTIVE BOARD

Ralph Santos
Thomas J. O'Halloran
Walter E. Bennett
Arthur V. Lodovichetti
Jack Schultz

MEMBERS REPRESENTED

The * designates those whose wives accompany them; the † designates those whose unmarried daughters in society accompany them; the ‖ designates those having other ladies with them]

Name	Representing—	Residence
*Abbott, Gene	Evening Star	Crystal House, 2000 So. Eads St., Arlington, Va.
*Abercrombie, Thomas J	National Geographic	607 Niblick Dr., Vienna, Va.
*Abernathy, Robert G	NBC-TV	3407 Lowell St.
*Allen, William C	Department of Agriculture	Apt. 901, Crystal House, 2000 So. Eads St., Arlington, Va.
*Alley, C. Ed	United Press International Newspictures	1 Stanton Dr., Little River Hills, Fairfax, Va.
*Alvey, Murray	ABC News Film Production	8815 Sundale Dr., Silver Spring, Md.
*Anderson, Leroy	NBC-TV	5132 37th St. North, Arlington, Va.
*Atherton, James	United Press International Newspictures	2913 Stanton Ave., Silver Spring, Md.
*Atkins, Ollie	Saturday Evening Post	Box 11, Fairfax, Va.
*Baer, Robert	Associated Press	RFD 2, Emmitsburg, Md.
*Baker, Elwood	Evening Star	2346 Lyons St. SE.
*Beall, William C	Washington Daily News	934 Sweetbriar Dr., Alexandria, Va.
Bennett, Walter E	Time, Inc	4570 MacArthur Blvd.
Bessor, John	CBS News	726 Prosperity Ave., Fairfax, Va.
*Bittenbender, Milton D	CBS News	12401 Ellen Ct., Silver Spring, Md.
Blair, James P	National Geographic	17th & M Sts.
*Bowman, Guy D	Associated Press	4842 First St. South, Arlington, Va.
Bozick, Peter A		5923 28th Ave., Marlow Heights, Md.
*Brockhurst, Robert H	Republican Congressional Committee	3418 Tulip Dr., Falls Church, Va.
Burchette, Robert	Washington Post	806 Thurman Ave., Hyattsville, Md.
*Burroughs, Henry	Associated Press	6508 Cardigan Rd., Bethesda, Md.
*Cabell, Clifton George, Jr	Washington Afro-American	3335 Blaine St. NE.
*Cancellare, Frank	United Press International Newspictures	109 South Utah St., Arlington, Va.

MEMBERS REPRESENTED—Continued

Name	Representing—	Residence
*Candido, Al	Department of Agriculture	4511 Carlby Lane, Alexandria, Va.
*Casamento, Victor	Washington Post	Rt. 1, Box 366, Ellsworth Ave., Great Falls, Va.
*Castens, Edward H	U.S. News & World Report	2122 Massachusetts Ave.
Cheely, George	WRC-NBC	220 9th St., NE.
*Chevalier, Douglas	Washington Post	7325 Blair Rd.
*Chinn, Augustus C	Evening Star	3606 3d St. North, Arlington, Va.
*Clark, Edward		6691 MacArthur Blvd., Glen Echo Heights, Md.
*Clark, Noel P		6416 Wiscasset Rd., Glen Echo Heights, Md.
*Clark, Robert	USIA	5028 Massachusetts Ave.
*Clover, Robert M	United Press International Newspictures	2331 40th St.
*Colton, William James		
*Conger, Dean	National Geographic	1910 Columbia Pike, Arlington, Va.
*Corrigan, William	NBC-TV News	6505 Greyswood Rd., Bethesda, Md.
*Craven, Thomas J., Sr	UPI News Film	12 Covington St., Fairfax, Va.
*Craven, Thomas, Jr	CBS News	1000 Kerns Rd., Falls Church, Va.
*Culver, Willard R	National Geographic	1611 Myrtle St.
*Dale, Bruce A	National Geographic	1639 Arlington Blvd., Fairfax, Va.
*Danor, George	Evening Star	8329 Navahoe Dr., Silver Spring, Md.
*Darcey, Richard G	Washington Post	4310 Emden St., Silver Spring, Md.
*Davis, Ellsworth J	Washington Post	4831 Meade St. NE.
*DeLort, Jean Guy	Fairchild Publications	12900 Bently Lane, Bowie, Md.
*DelVecchio, Charles	Washington Post	103 Marion Ave., McLean, Va.
*Denton, Robert H	Paramount Pictures	1332 Locust Road.
*DeTitta, Arthur A	Movietone News	8218 Hollywood Blvd., Los Angeles, Calif.
*DiJoseph, John M	Reni Newsphotos	1739 Allison St. NE.
Dominis, John	Life Magazine	Contentment Island, Darien, Conn.
Dorsey, George M		1359 Kalmia Rd.
Dorsey, George A		605 West 40th St., Baltimore, Md.
*Driscoll, Norman	Washington Post	715 Chestnut Ave., Falls Church, Va.
Duvall, Owen E. Jr	Evening Star	3103 Lancer Pl., West Hyattsville, Md.
Ellis, Arthur	Washington Post	8519 Carroll Ave., Silver Spring, Md.
Esper, Henry Max	U.S. Senate Recording Studios	1909 North Rhodes St., Arlington, Va.
*Ferneyhough, Byrd F	Cameramen, Inc	2103 North Taft St., Arlington, Va.
*Fine, Nate	C.I.O. News	9214 Kingsbury Dr., Silver Spring, Md.
*Finnigan, Vincent A	{ Washington Films / Keystone Press Agency, Ltd	} 806 Maryland Ave. NE.
*Flecknoe, Harold J	Evening Star	10011 Tenbrook Dr., Silver Spring, Md.
*Fletcher, John E	National Geographic	5315 9th Rd. North, Arlington, Va.
Forsythe, William J	Senate Press Photographer's Gallery	1212 Longfellow St.
Forte, Benjamin E	Agence France Presse	Apt. 01, 462 Kennebec St., Oxon Hill, Md.
*Forte, Russell T	Department of Agriculture	5914 Chillumgate Rd., Chillum, Md.
*Foster, Burt E	Associated Press	28 Henry St., Bergenfield, N.J.
*Franks, Charles V	CBS News	2361 N. Quebec St., Arlington, Va.
*Freeman, Thomas J	Associated Press	9 Lakeview Circle, Greenbelt, Md.
*Freier, Milton	E. Leitz	17 Argyle Terrace, Yonkers, N.Y.
*Funk, Robert F	CBS News	Box 456, Route 5, Alexandria, Va.
*Ganser, James E	ABC News Film Production	4328 Starr Jordan Dr., Annandale, Va.
*Gaylin, George R	United Press International Newspictures	1436 Primrose Rd.
*Gelenter, Robert H	NBC News	261 Congressional Lane, Rockville, Md.

MEMBERS REPRESENTED—Continued

Name	Representing—	Residence
*Georges, Harvey	Associated Press	1802 Tucker Ave., McLean, Va.
*Gerlach, George J	ABC News Film Production	8211 Grove St., Silver Spring, Md.
Gerlach, George R	Telenews	3110 Brewton St., District Hts., Md.
*Gilka, Robert E	National Geographic	4664 25th St. N., Arlington, Va.
*Gilman, Edward M	ABC News	1020 19th St., Apt. 228.
Godbold, James		12310 Cobblestone, Houston, Texas.
*Goodman, Harry	Evening Star	3217 Pauline Dr., Chevy Chase, Md.
*Gorry, Charles P	Associated Press	601 South Magnolia Drive, Falls Church, Va.
*Gorry, William J	Associated Press	6581 Little Falls Road, Arlington, Va.
Greenberg, Hyman		8023 Eastern Ave., Silver Spring, Md.
*Griffin, Henry L	Associated Press	3214 Gumwood Drive, University Hills, Md.
*Grosvenor, Gilbert	National Geographic	4226 50th St.
*Havens, George P	USIA	APO 143, U.S.I.A., San Francisco, Calif.
*Heiberger, Joseph	Washington Post	10016 Portland Rd., Silver Spring, Md.
*Hemmig, Robert H	ABC News Film Production	208 Woodley Dr., Alexandria, Va.
Hess, Robert	CBS News	4106 Lawton St., McLean, Va.
Hoagland, Charles A., Jr	NBC-TV	9606 Page Ave., Bethesda, Md.
Hoertel, Bruce G	CBS News	Rt. 2, Box 222, Vienna, Va.
Hofen, John	NBC-TV	5913 9th St. North, Arlington, Va.
Hollis, Louis J	Washington Daily News	1008 Carol Lane, Falls Church, Va.
*Hoy, Frank	Washington Post	4607 S. 28th Rd., Arlington, Va.
*Hoy, Thomas L	Evening Star	8929 Sleaford Pl., Willow Woods, Annandale, Va.
*Huttenloch, Robert M	CBS News	5375 Pumphrey Dr., Washington, D.C.
*Jamieson, Joseph D	Associated Press	8504 Garfield St., Bethesda, Md.
Janes, Aurthur W	Associated Press	2224 North Quincy Street, Arlington, Va.
*Jenkins, Henry	Associated Press	12043 Remington Dr., Silver Spring, Md.
*Johnson, Hugo C	USIA	1506 Live Oak Dr., Silver Spring, Md.
Johnson, Maurice	United Press International Newspictures	7 Perrott Ct., Little River Hills, Fairfax, Va.
Johrden, Louis G	Associated Press	4901 Avondale Rd.
*Jones, Charles O	NBC-TV	7207 Thornapple Rd.
*Jones, Vernon Kennedy	UPI Newsfilm, Inc	4241 16th St. South, Arlington, Va.
*Kalec, George		4300 Howard Ave., Beltsville, Md.
*Kelley, Thomas	Washington Post	1711 Henry Rd., Rockville, Md.
Kraft, Charles A	U.S. News & World Report	1200 South Courthouse Rd., Arlington, Va.
*Kramer, Carl	United Press International Newspictures	208 Park Hill Pl., Fairfax, Va.
*Krebs, Lawrence	WMAL-TV	2828 Connecticut Ave.
*Kress, G. Bradford	NBC-TV	401 Franklin St., Alexandria, Va.
Kristof, Emory K., Jr	National Geographic	1907 35th Pl.
*Lambert, Horace "Skip"	Phoenix Films, Inc	7313 Maple Ave., Chevy Chase, Md.
*Langenegger, John R	NBC-TV	4612 Clemson Rd., College Park, Md.
*Larsen, Carl, Jr	ABC News Film Production	606 Heritage Dr., Fairfax, Va.
*Lartz, Jack	USIA	103 Nelson St., Rockville, Md.
Lauck, Dale E		208 So. Chestnut St., Kent, Ohio.
Lawrence, Fred	UPI Newsfilm, Inc	Marlboro House, Apt. 103, 3001 Branch Ave. SE.
Leach, Glen	Evening Star	11201 Buckworth La., Rockville, Md.

MEMBERS REPRESENTED—Continued

Name	Representing—	Residence
*Lee, Dean	United Press International Newspictures	7777 Maple Ave., Takoma Park, Md.
*Leffler, Warren K	U.S. News & World Reports	11412 Grayling Lane, Rockville, Md.
*Levy, John R	NBC-TV	6515 100th Ave., Seabrook Md.
Lincer, Arthur	UPI Newsfilm	448 W. 56th St., New York, N.Y.
*Lion, Harold H	Hearst Metrotone News—Telenews	8122 Gosport Lane, Springfield, Va.
*Littlehales, Bates W	National Geographic	2205 California.
*Lodovichetti, Arthur V	ABC News Film Production	6306 Dallas Pl. SE.
*Lord, Chester J	UPI Newsfilm, Inc	Capitol Park Apts., 800 4th St. SW.
*Lyons, James E		3028 Wisconsin Ave.
*Lyons, Paul	Telenews	618 Gibson Dr. SW., Vienna, Va.
*Mack, Charles J	CBS News	5904 Aberdeen Rd., Bethesda, Md.
*Mahan, James	International Cameramen	7402 Conrad Rd., Alexandria, Va.
Maroon, Fred J		3029 M St.
*Martin, Bert R	WGN-TV	910 San Carlos Dr., Fairfax, Va.
Martin, Jackie		National Press Bldg.
Martufi, Rosemary	Evening Star	4413 Chase Ave., Bethesda, Md.
*May, Andrew J	Harris & Ewing	1920 35th St.
May, John O	Hearst Metrotone News—Telenews	215 Nottingham Hill, Sherwood Forest, Md.
*McAvoy, Thomas		3306 Cameron Mill Rd., Alexandria, Va.
*McCormac, Robert, Jr	United Press International Newspictures	407 Brewster Ave., Silver Spring, Md.
*McDonald, Leo	NBC-TV	3319 Estelle Terrace, Silver Spring, Md.
McDonnell, Ellen E	Fox Movietone News	5616 Namakagan Rd.
*McDonough, J. Loftus	NBC-TV	Rt. 1, Box 50BB, Fairfax Station, Va.
*McNamara, James	Washington Post	10210 Pierce Drive, Silver Spring, Md.
*McNamee, Wallace	Washington Post	8707 Victoria Rd., E., Springfield, Va.
*Miller, Francis R	Life Magazine	5606 Jordan Road, Bethesda, Md.
*Miller, Hugh	Washington Post	4409 Yuma St., NW.
Mims, Roddey E	United Press International Newspictures	C-1405 River House, 1111 Army-Navy Dr., Arlington, Va.
*Mobley, George Frederick	National Geographic	7875 Livingston Rd. SE.
*Moldvay, Albert	National Geographic	1011 Highland Dr., Silver Spring, Md.
*Mole, Robert	NBC-TV	12409 Sexton Lane, Bowie, Md.
*Montague, Fred	NBC-TV	5813 Marbury Rd., Bethesda, Md.
*Morris, John G	Washington Post	209 G St. SW.
*Mueller, John C	Evening Star	9316 East Parkhill Dr., Bethesda, Md.
*Muse, Seth	Religious News Service	2924 South Buchanan St., Arlington, Va.
*Muto, Alfonso A	Senate Democratic Campaign Committee	1005 Oak St., Falls Church, Va.
*Naltchayan, Harry N	Washington Post	4027 Honey Lane, Annandale, Va.
*Nebbia, Thomas	National Geographic	301 Meadow View Rd., Falls Church, Va.
Neil, Joseph H	CBS News	9740 Hedin Dr., Silver Spring, Md.
Noel, Arnold C	UPI Newsfilm	2419 Davis Ave., Alexandria, Va.
*Norling, Richard V		12119 Edgemont St., Silver Spring, Md.
*Oakes, Robert S	National Geographic	933 Shreve Rd., Falls Church, Va.
*Oates, Walter	Evening Star	7911 Harwood Place, Springfield, Va.
*O'eth, Alfred J		5400 Pooks Hill Rd., Bethesda, Md.
*O'Halloran, Thomas, Jr	U.S. News & World Report	3531 Duke St., College Park, Md.
*Otey, Robert	Associated Press	613 Fern Lane, Annandale, Va.

News Photographers Association

819

MEMBERS REPRESENTED—Continued

Name	Representing—	Residence
*Parks, Winfield	National Geographic	National Geographic, 17th & M St.
*Payne, William Berkley	Cameramen, Inc	3731 Donnell Dr., SE.
*Pergola, Nicholas J	United Press International Newspictures	18–V Ridge Rd., Greenbelt, Md.
Perkins, Robert F	Evening Star	8152 Eastern Ave.
*Phillips, Robert H		1528 33d St.
*Pitts, Leo A	WTOP–TV	2911 North Greenbrier St., Arlington, Va.
Raley, Charles J	Republican Congressional Committee	6611 5th St.
Rhodes, James W	CBS News	103 G St. SW
*Richards, William T	NBC–TV	8501 Burning Tree Rd., Bethesda, Md.
*Richardson, Donald W	CBS News	4609 20th St., North, Arlington, Va.
Rickerby, Arthur	Life Magazine	Codfish Hill Road, Bethel, Conn.
*Riordan, Daniel		1220 Radnor Pl., Falls Church, Va.
*Roberts, Joseph B	National Geographic	1212 North Inglewood St., Arlington, Va.
*Rohland, Henry W	Washington Post	508 Derydown La., Silver Spring, Md.
*Rollins, Byron H	Associated Press	4421 Butterworth Pl.
*Ross, Kip	National Geographic	3601 Connecticut Ave.
*Rous, John H	Associated Press	3201 Russell Rd., Alexandria, Va.
*Routt, Francis R	Evening Star	2505 Parker Ave., Wheaton Hills, Md.
*Routt, Randolph J	Evening Star	303 Lexington Dr., Silver Spring, Md.
*Roy, Richard F	ABC News Film Production	1124 Connecticut Ave.
*Sachs, Arnold	Agence France Presse	4809 Winslow Rd. SE., Kirby Hills, Md.
*Santos, Ralph A	CBS News	421 Wake Forest Dr., Alexandria, Va.
*Scherschel, Joseph J	National Geographic Magazine	4570 MacArthur Blvd.
*Schmick, Paul M	Evening Star	514 North Montana St., Arlington, Va.
Schultz, Jack	UPI News Film	1–C Southway, Greenbelt, Md.
*Schutz, Robert	Associated Press	9504 Fern Lane, Annandale, Va.
*Scott, Arthur E	Republican Senatorial Campaign Committee.	Box 64, Centerville, Va.
*Senko, Michael	Republican Congressional Committee	18 Hilltop Rd., Silver Spring, Md.
*Shere, Jack	American Red Cross	1618 Oakview Dr., Silver Spring, Md.
Shields, Thomas E	United Press International Newspictures	7413 17th Ave., West Hyattsville, Md.
*Shutt, Charles E	Telenews	500 Ednor Rd., Silver Spring, Md.
Silverman, Joseph A	Evening Star	8606 Garland Ave., Silver Spring, Md.
Simonson, Al		3125 Buena Vista Terr.
Sisson, Robert F	National Geographic	2203 Lee Highway, Falls Church, Va.
Skadding, George		5180 NE 18th Ter., Ft. Lauderdale, Fla.
*Smith, William J	Associated Press	4513 17th St. NE.
*Smythe, William K		4711 Tecumseh St., College Park, Md.
*Sorrell, Maurice B	Johnson Publications	5700 New Hampshire Ave. NE.
*Sozio, George	NBC–TV	14 Chickavane Ct., Alexandria, Va.
*Stearns, Stanley F	United Press International Newspictures	12805 Keswick Lane, Bowie, Md.
*Steiner, Earl Joseph	ABC News Film Production	9708 Marshall Ave., Silver Spring, Md.
Stevens, Larry	Metro Group	344 Pine Spring Rd., Falls Church, Va.
*Stewart, B. Anthony	National Geographic	3280 Arcadia Pl.
*Stewart, Richard H	National Geographic	614 Sligo Ave., Silver Spring, Md.
Stinchcomb, J. Waring		5925 Tucker Rd. SE.
Stolley, Richard B	Life Magazine	9210 Fernwood Rd., Bethesda, Md.
*Streets, Wellner C	Washington Daily News	1936 Merrimac St., Adelphi, Md.
*Stroup, Barry Edward	Associated Press	2245 N. Harrison St. Arlington, Va.

MEMBERS REPRESENTED—Continued

Name	Representing—	Residence
*Suydam, Henry, Jr	Life Magazine	Dupont Plaza, Miami, Fla.
*Tames, George	New York Times	5922 Broad Branch Rd.
*Tasnadi, Charles B	Associated Press	4420 Chesapeake St.
*Taylor, Arnold	Evening Star	507 3d St., SE.
*Thompson, F. Irving	USIA	6002 32d St.
*Tretick, Stanley	Look Magazine	4101 Cathedral Ave.
Trikosko, Marion	U.S. News & World Report	2147 O St.
Tromer, Michael V	UPI Newsfilm	6204 Breezewood Dr., Greenbelt, Md.
*Tugander, Harry		253 W. 73d St., Hotel Riverside Plaza, New York, N.Y.
Van Tine, Harry		3315 Wisconsin Ave.
Van Nostrand, Richard W	Hearst Metrotone News	41 Wellesley Circle, Glen Echo, Md.
*Vines, Daniel E., Jr	U.S.A.F	514 Timber Lane, Falls Church, Va.
*Volz, Willard G	Evening Star	1006 Helena Drive, Silver Spring, Md.
*Walker, C. A		11801 Grandview Ave., Wheaton, Md.
Walker, Hank		2 Walsh Ave., Greenwich, Conn.
*Wallis, Ralph E	Associated Press	736 26th Pl. South, Arlington, Va.
*Ward, Fred	Black Star	6419 Dahlonega Rd., Glen Echo Heights, Md.
*Ward, Murray E	Telenews	3805 Beatty Drive, Alexandria, Va.
*Wayman, Stanley Edmond	Life Magazine	3212 44th St.
Wentzel, Volkmar	National Geographic	3137 N St.
Werner, Frank		3525 Alton Pl.
*Weston, Ronald	Hearst Metrotone News—Telenews	14016 Willoughby Rd., Upper Marlboro, Md.
*Wiegman, David	NBC–TV	3202 Wake Dr., Kensington, Md.
*Wilkinson, F. Clyde	Republican Senatorial Campaign Committee	3030 North Quincy St., Arlington, Va.
*Williams, Malcolm		687 6th Ave., Troy, N.Y.
*Willoner, Andrew	CBS News	4106 70th Ave., Landover Hills, Md.
Wilson, Donald M	USIA	5105 Lowell Lane.
Wilson, James	CBS News	Glenn Dale Rd., Glenn Dale, Md.
Wilson, Woodrow R	GSA	7113 Elmhurst St., District Heights, Md.
*Wingfield, Don	Sporting News	5833 Dannys Lane, Alexandria, Va.
*Wisherd, Edwin L	National Geographic	4704 Warren St.
*Wood, Walter	Baltimore News-Post	7525 San Juan Dr., Clinton, Md.

SERVICES REPRESENTED

Agency and telephone number	Name	Office
ABC News Film Production—393-7700	Murray Alvey	1124 Connecticut Ave.
	James E. Ganser	1124 Connecticut Ave.
	George J. Gerlach	1124 Connecticut Ave.
	Edward M. Gilman	1124 Connecticut Ave.
	Robert H. Hemmig	1124 Connecticut Ave.
	Carl Larsen, Jr	1124 Connecticut Ave.
	Arthur V. Lodovichetti	1124 Connecticut Ave.
	Richard F. Roy	1124 Connecticut Ave.
	Earl J. Steiner	1124 Connecticut Ave.
AFP-DPA—393-0929	Arnold Sachs	204 Indiana Ave.
	Benjamin E. Forte	204 Indiana Ave.
Associated Press Photos—234-5400	Barry E. Stroup, Manager	1300 Connecticut Ave.
	Robert Baer	1300 Connecticut Ave.
	Guy D. Bowman	1300 Connecticut Ave.
	Henry Burroughs	1300 Connecticut Ave.
	Thomas Freeman	1300 Connecticut Ave.
	Harvey Georges	1300 Connecticut Ave.
	Charles Gorry	1300 Connecticut Ave.
	William Gorry	1300 Connecticut Ave.
	Henry L. Griffin	1300 Connecticut Ave.
	Joseph D. Jamieson	1300 Connecticut Ave.
	Arthur W. Janes	1300 Connecticut Ave.
	Henry Jenkins	1300 Connecticut Ave.
	Louis G. Johrden	1300 Connecticut Ave.
	Robert Otey	1300 Connecticut Ave.
	Byron H. Rollins	1300 Connecticut Ave.
	John H. Rous	1300 Connecticut Ave.
	Robert Schutz	1300 Connecticut Ave.
	William J. Smith	1300 Connecticut Ave.
	Charles Tasnadi	1300 Connecticut Ave.
	Ralph Wallis	1300 Connecticut Ave.
Black Star—657-3322	Fred Ward	6419 Dahlonega Rd., Glen Echo Heights, Md.
Cameramen, Inc.—638-3344	Byrd F. Ferneyhough	724 9th St.
	William B. Payne	724 9th St.
CBS News—296-1234	Donald W. Richardson, Manager	2020 M St.
	John Bessor	2020 M St.
	Milton D. Bittenbender	2020 M St.
	Thomas Craven, Jr	2020 M St.
	Charles Franks	2020 M St.
	Robert F. Funk	2020 M St.
	Robert Hess	2020 M St.
	Bruce Hoertel	2020 M St.
	Robert Huttenloch	2020 M St.
	Charles J. Mack	2020 M St.
	Joseph Neil	2020 M St.
	James W. Rhodes	2020 M St.
	Ralph A. Santos	2020 M St.
	Andy Willoner	2020 M St.
	James Wilson	2020 M St.
Fairchild Publications—737-7090	Jean Guy DeLort	711 14th St.
Fox Movietone News—United Press Movietone News—347-6448.	Ellen E. McDonnell, manager	413 3d St.
Harris and Ewing—628-8700	Andrew J. May, manager	1304 G St.
Hearst Metrotone News of the Day— Hearst Metrotone News—Telenews. 393-8311.	Charles E. Shutt, manager	470 E St. SW.
	George R. Gerlach	470 E St. SW.
	Harold Lion	470 E St. SW.
	Paul Lyons	470 E St. SW.
	John O. May	470 E St. SW.
	Richard W. Van Nostrand	470 E St. SW.
	Murray Ward	470 E St. SW.
	Ronald Weston	470 E St. SW.
International Cameramen—CL 6-5550	James B. Mahan	7402 Conrad Rd., Alexandria, Va.
Johnson Publications—298-7836	Maurice B. Sorrell	1750 Pennsylvania Ave.
Keystone Press Agency, Ltd.—544-2945.	Vincent A. Finnigan	806 Maryland Ave., NE.
Life Magazine—337-8000	Francis Miller, Manager	1120 Connecticut Ave.
	John Dominis	1120 Connecticut Ave.
	Arthur Rickerby	1120 Connecticut Ave.
	Richard B. Stolley	1120 Connecticut Ave.
	Henry Suydam, Jr	1120 Connecticut Ave.
	Stanley E. Wayman	1120 Connecticut Ave.

SERVICES REPRESENTED—Continued

Agency and telephone number	Name	Office
Look Magazine—347-9111	Stanley Tretick	National Press Bldg.
Metro Group Newspapers—524-3355	Larry Stevens	1101 Lee Hwy., Rosslyn, Va.
National Geographic—296-7500	T. J. Abercrombie	17th and M Sts.
	James P. Blair	17th and M Sts.
	Dean D. Conger	17th and M Sts.
	Willard Culver	17th and M Sts.
	Bruce A. Dale	17th and M Sts.
	John E. Fletcher	17th and M Sts.
	Robert Gilka	17th and M Sts.
	Gilbert Grosvenor	17th and M Sts.
	Emory K. Kristof, Jr	17th and M Sts.
	Bates W. Littlehales	17th and M Sts.
	George F. Mobley	17th and M Sts.
	Albert Moldvay	17th and M Sts.
	Thomas Nebbia	17th and M Sts.
	Robert S. Oakes	17th and M Sts.
	Winfield Parks	17th and M Sts.
	Joseph B. Roberts	17th and M Sts.
	Kip Ross	17th and M Sts.
	Joseph Scherschel	17th and M Sts.
	Robert F. Sisson	17th and M Sts.
	B. Anthony Stewart	17th and M Sts.
	Richard H. Stewart	17th and M Sts.
	Volkmar Wentzel	17th and M Sts.
	Edwin L. Wisherd	17th and M Sts.
NBC Television—362-4000	Robert Abernathy	4100 Nebraska Ave.
	Leroy Anderson	4100 Nebraska Ave.
	George Cheely	4100 Nebraska Ave.
	William Corrigan	4100 Nebraska Ave.
	Robert H. Gelenter	4100 Nebraska Ave.
	Charles A. Hoagland, Jr	4100 Nebraska Ave.
	John Hofen	4100 Nebraska Ave.
	Charles Jones	4100 Nebraska Ave.
	G. Bradford Kress	4100 Nebraska Ave.
	John Langenegger	4100 Nebraska Ave.
	John R. Levy	4100 Nebraska Ave.
	Leo McDonald	4100 Nebraska Ave.
	J. Loftus McDonough	4100 Nebraska Ave.
	Robert Mole	4100 Nebraska Ave.
	Fred Montague	4100 Nebraska Ave.
	William T. Richards	4100 Nebraska Ave.
	George Sozio	4100 Nebraska Ave.
	David Wiegman	4100 Nebraska Ave.
New York Times Magazine—628-3016	George Tames	1701 K St.
Phoenix Films, Inc.—OLiver 2-6076	H. M. Lambert	7313 Maple Ave , Chevy Chase, Md.
Reni Photographers—ME 8-2200	John M. DiJoseph	1319 F St.
Saturday Evening Post—628-2152	Ollie Atkins	1000 16th St.
Time Magazine—337-8000	Walter E. Bennett	1120 Conn. Ave.
United Press International News Film—543-3113.	Vernon K. Jones, manager	1017 New Jersey Ave. SE.
	Thomas Craven, Sr	1017 New Jersey Ave. SE.
	Fred Lawrence	1017 New Jersey Ave. SE.
	Chester J. Lord	1017 New Jersey Ave. SE.
	Arnold C. Noel	1017 New Jersey Ave. SE.
	Jack Schultz	1017 New Jersey Ave. SE.
	Michael V. Tromer	1017 New Jersey Ave. SE.
United Press International Newspictures—347-1124.	George R. Gaylin, manager	1013 13th St.
	C. Ed Alley	1013 13th St.
	James Atherton	1013 13th St.
	Frank Cancellare	1013 13th St.
	Robert M. Clover	1013 13th St.
	Maurice Johnson	1013 13th St.
	Carl Kramer	1013 13th St.
	Dean Lee	1013 13th St.
	Robert McCormac, Jr	1013 13th St.
	Roddey Mims	1013 13th St.
	Nicholas J. Pergola	1013 13th St.
	Thomas E. Shields	1013 13th St.
	Stanley G. Stearns	1013 13th St.
U.S. News & World Report—333-7400	Thomas J. O'Halloran	24th and N Sts.
	Edward H. Castens	24th and N Sts.
	Charles A. Kraft	24th and N Sts.
	Warren Leffler	24th and N Sts.
	Marion Trikosko	24th and N Sts.
Washington Afro-American—DE 2-0080	Clifton G. Cabell, Jr	1800 11th St.
Washington Daily News—347-7777	William C. Beall, Chief	1013 13th St.
	Louis J. Hollis	1013 13th St.
	Wellner Streets	1013 13th St.

SERVICES REPRESENTED—Continued

Agency and telephone number	Name	Office
Washington Evening Star—543–5000	Gene Abbott	225 Virginia Ave. SE.
	Elwood Baker	225 Virginia Ave. SE.
	Augustus Chinn	225 Virginia Ave. SE.
	George Danor	225 Virginia Ave. SE.
	Owen E. Duvall, Jr	225 Virginia Ave. SE.
	Harold J. Flecknoe	225 Virginia Ave. SE.
	Harry Goodman	225 Virginia Ave. SE.
	Thomas Hoy	225 Virginia Ave. SE.
	Glen C. Leach	225 Virginia Ave. SE.
	Rosemary Martufi	225 Virginia Ave. SE.
	John Mueller	225 Virginia Ave. SE.
	Walter Oates	225 Virginia Ave. SE.
	Robert F. Perkins	225 Virginia Ave. SE.
	Francis Routt	225 Virginia Ave. SE.
	Randolph Routt	225 Virginia Ave. SE.
	Paul Schmick	225 Virginia Ave. SE.
	Joseph Silverman	225 Virginia Ave. SE.
	Arnold Taylor	225 Virginia Ave. SE.
	Willard Volz	225 Virginia Ave. SE.
Washington Film—547–2255	Vincent A. Finnigan	806 Maryland Ave. NE.
Washington Post—737–1234	John G. Morris	1515 L St.
	Robert Burchette	1515 L St.
	Victor Casamento	1515 L St.
	Douglas Chevalier	1515 L St.
	Richard G. Darcey	1515 L St.
	Ellsworth J. Davis	1515 L St.
	Charles Del Vecchio	1515 L St.
	Norman Driscoll	1515 L St.
	Arthur Ellis	1515 L St.
	Joseph Heiberger	1515 L St.
	Frank Hoy	1515 L St.
	Thomas Kelley	1515 L St.
	James McNamara	1515 L St.
	Wallace W. McNamee	1515 L St.
	Hugh Miller	1515 L St.
	Harry N. Naltchayan	1515 L St.
	Henry Rohland	1515 L St.
WGN-TV—393–6077	Bert R. Martin	1737 DeSales Pl.
WMAL-TV—537–1100	Lawrence Krebs	4461 Conn. Ave.
WTOP-TV—244–5678	Leo A. Pitts	40th & Brandywine Sts.

RADIO AND TELEVISION CORRESPONDENTS' GALLERIES

SENATE RADIO AND TELEVISION GALLERY

Phone 225-6421

Superintendent.—Robert C. Hough, 316 Kimblewick Drive, Silver Spring, Md.
Assistant Superintendents:
Con. J. D'Andrea, 4900 55th Avenue, Roger Heights, Hyattsville, Md.
Philip A. Regan, 8300 Cool Spring Lane, Adelphia, Md.
Elaine Daniels, 3729 Jenifer Street.

HOUSE RADIO AND TELEVISION GALLERY

Phone 225-5215

Superintendent.—Robert M. Menaugh, 2311 Valley Drive, Alexandria, Va.
Assistant Superintendents:
Mike Michaelson, 5001 Seminary Road, Alexandria, Va.
Max M. Barber, 110 D Street SE., No. 508.

EXECUTIVE COMMITTEE OF THE RADIO AND TELEVISION CORRESPONDENTS' GALLERIES

Stephen J. McCormick, Chairman
J. W. (Bill) Roberts, Vice Chairman
John F. Lynch, Secretary
Robert McCormick, Treasurer
Joseph F. McCaffrey, Member at Large
Vernon K. Jones, Member at Large
Roger H. Mudd, Member at Large
Wells Church, Member Ex Officio

RULES GOVERNING RADIO AND TELEVISION CORRESPONDENTS' GALLERIES

1. Persons desiring admission to the Radio and Television Galleries of Congress shall make application to the Speaker, as required by rule XXXIV of the House of Representatives, as amended, and to the Committee on Rules and Administration of the Senate, as required by rule VI, as amended, for the regulation of the Senate wing of the Capitol. Applicants shall state in writing the names of all radio stations, television stations, systems, or news-gathering organizations by which they are employed and what other occupation or employment they may have, if any. Applicants shall further declare that they are not engaged in the prosecution of claims or the promotion of legislation pending before Congress, the Departments, or the independent agencies, and that they will not become so employed without resigning from the galleries. They shall further declare that they are not employed in any legislative or executive department or independent agency of the Government, or by any foreign government or representative thereof; that they are not engaged in any lobbying activities; that they do not and will not, directly or indirectly, furnish special information to any organization, individual, or group of individuals for the influencing of prices on any commodity or stock exchange; that they will not do so during the time they retain membership

in the galleries. Holders of visitors' cards who may be allowed temporary admission to the galleries must conform to all the restrictions of this paragraph.

2. It shall be prerequisite to membership that the radio station, television station, system, or news-gathering agency which the applicant represents shall certify in writing to the Radio and Television Correspondents' Galleries that the applicant conforms to the regulations of paragraph 1.

3. The applications required by paragraph 1 shall be authenticated in a manner that shall be satisfactory to the executive committee of the Radio and Television Correspondents' Galleries who shall see that the occupation of the galleries is confined to bona fide news gatherers and/or reporters of reputable standing in their business who represent radio stations, television stations, systems, or news-gathering agencies engaged primarily in serving radio stations, television stations, or systems. It shall be the duty of the executive committee of the Radio and Television Correspondents' Galleries to report, at their discretion, violation of the privileges of the galleries to the Speaker or to the Senate Committee on Rules and Administration, and, pending action thereon, the offending individual may be suspended.

4. Persons engaged in other occupations, whose chief attention is not given to the gathering or reporting of news for radio stations, television stations, systems, or news-gathering agencies primarily serving radio stations or systems, shall not be entitled to admission to the Radio and Television Galleries. The Radio and Television Correspondents' List in the Congressional Directory shall be a list only of persons whose chief attention is given to the gathering and reporting of news for radio stations, television stations, and systems engaged in the daily dissemination of news, and of representatives of news-gathering agencies engaged in the daily service of news to such radio stations, television stations, or systems.

5. Members of the families of correspondents are not entitled to the privileges of the galleries.

6. The Radio and Television Galleries shall be under the control of the executive committee of the Radio and Television Correspondents' Galleries, subject to the approval and supervision of the Speaker of the House of Representatives and the Senate Committee on Rules and Administration.

Approved.

JOHN W. McCORMACK,
Speaker, House of Representatives.

B. EVERETT JORDAN,
Chairman, Senate Committee on Rules and Administration.

MEMBERS ENTITLED TO ADMISSION

The * designates those whose wives or husbands accompany them; the † designates those whose unmarried daughters in society accompany them; the ‖ designates those having other ladies with them

Name	Representing—	Residence
*Abel, Elie	NBC News	40 Grafton St., Chevy Chase, Md.
*Abernethy, Robert G	NBC News	3407 Lowell St.
*Adler, Lee E	CBS News	11209 Lund Pl., Kensington, Md.
*Allen, Donald C	WTOP News	6319 Landover Rd., Cheverly, Md.
*Allen, George N	NBC News	3850 Tunlaw Rd.
*Allen, Leonard	NBC News	5729 Bradley Blvd., Bethesda, Md.
*Alvey, Murray	ABC News	8815 Sundale Drive, Silver Spring, Md.
*Anderson, LeRoy	NBC News	5132 North 37th St., Arlington, Va.
*Asman, Robert W	NBC News	5715 Moreland St.
*Barber, Julian	WTOP News	Route 1, Clifton, Va.
*Basham, Christie R	NBC News	2309 Valley Drive, Alexandria, Va.
*Batchelder, Charles F	Mutual Broadcasting System	2828 Connecticut Ave.
*Beach, Claire M	WTOP News	1948 Rosemary Hills Drive, Silver Spring, Md.
*Beall, Harold Eugene	WTOP News	10920 Bangor Pl., Kensington, Md.
Beckman, Robert Dean, Jr	UPI Radio	114 4th St. NE.
Beebe, Norman Robert	WTOP News	6030 Logan Way, Bladensburg, Md.
Bell, Dorese	Mutual Broadcasting System	4201 Cathedral Ave.
*Belote, Ernest C., Jr	WTOP News	7311 Exmore St., Springfield, Va.
Bernhart, Lewis H	NBC News	4001 Nebraska Ave.
Bessor, John	CBS News	726 Prosperity Ave., Fairfax, Va.
Bibb, Terry Gearity	Metromedia, Inc	2102 South Knoll St., Arlington, Va.
*Bittenbender, Milton D	CBS News	12401 Ellen Court, Silver Spring, Md.
Blair, Anne D	Triangle Publications, Inc	3315 Dent Place.
*Bowers, Donald E	CBS News	7505 Jervis St., Springfield, Va.
*Boyd, Forrest J	Mutual Broadcasting System	10007 Gardiner Ave., Silver Spring, Md.
*Brenner, Bernard	UPI Radio	2513 Executive Ave., Falls Church, Va.
*Brinkley, David	NBC News	18 West Kirke St., Chevy Chase, Md.
*Brock, R. Norris	Time-Life Broadcast, KERO-TV, Bakersfield, Calif., KLZ, KLZ-TV, Denver, Colo., KOGO, KOGO-TV, San Diego, Calif., WFBM, WFBM-TV, Indianapolis, Ind., WOOD, WOOD-TV, Grand Rapids, Mich.	670 Americana Drive, Annapolis, Md.
*Brooks, Ned	Three-Star Extra (NBC)	4103 Oliver St., Chevy Chase, Md.
*Brown, Clarence J	UPI Newsfilm, Inc	3425 83d Ave., North Forestville, Md.
*Brubaker, Herbert M	Radio Press International	9903 Woodburn Rd., Silver Spring, Md.
Bryson, Paul Thomas	Westinghouse Broadcasting Co., Inc., KDKA, KDKA-TV, Pittsburgh, Pa., KPIX-TV, San Francisco, Calif., KYW, KYW-TV, Cleveland, Ohio, WBZ, WBZ-TV, Boston, Mass., WIND, Chicago, Ill., WINS, New York, N.Y., WJZ-TV, Baltimore, Md., WOWO, Fort Wayne, Ind.	3511 Davenport St.
*Burke, Bryce W	UPI Newsfilm, Inc	201 Springbrook Dr., Silver Spring, Md.
*Camfiord, Robert B	CBS News	7000 Montrose St., Alexandria, Va.
*Campbell, Joseph P	Mutual Broadcasting System	Buckland—Gainesville, Va.

827

Name	Representing—	Residence
*Cardin, Carl W	Three-Star Extra (NBC)	5313 29th Place, Hillcrest Heights, Md.
*Casserly, John J	ABC News	3706 Shepard St., Chevy Chase, Md.
*Catella, Anthony	Associated Press Radio	6402 9th Ave., Chillum, Md.
*Chamberlayne, Edward Pye	UPI Audio	1621 T St.
*Chambers, John	UPI Audio	1838 Ingleside Terrace.
*Chancellor, John W	NBC News	3126 Woodley Rd.
Chapman, Irwin M	ABC News	301 G St. SW.
*Childs, Prentiss	CBS News	2606 36th Place.
*Church, Wells	CBS News	6600 River Rd., Bethesda, Md.
*Clapper, Peter R	Westinghouse Broadcasting Co., Inc.— KDKA, KDKA-TV, Pittsburgh, Pa., KPIX-TV, San Francisco, Calif., KYW, KYW-TV, Cleveland, O., WBZ, WBZ-WBZ-TV, Boston, Mass., WIND, Chicago, Ill., WINS, New York, N.Y., WJZ-TV, Baltimore, Md., WOWO, Fort Wayne, Ind.	6500 Michaels Drive, Bethesda, Md.
*Clark, Robert E	ABC News	1200 N. Nash St., Arlington, Va.
*Clark, Theodore H	UPI Newsfilm, Inc	Box 323, Rt. 1, Deale, Md.
Clark, Timothy Blair	UPI Radio	1753 Church St.
*Clarke, James D	Evening Star Broadcasting Co. (WMAL AM-FM-TV).	491 Arlington Village, Arlington, Va.
*Clephas, Vincent R	Evening Star Broadcasting Co. (WMAL AM-FM-TV).	610 Paulonia Rd., Arlington, Va.
*Coffin, Tristram	Tris Coffin Associates	5601 Warwick Pl., Chevy Chase, Md.
Cole, Betty A	Meet The Press (NBC)	3726 Connecticut Ave.
*Coleman, Carl, Jr	Time-Life Broadcast, KERO-TV, Bakersfield, Calif., KLZ, KLZ-TV, Denver, Colo., KOGO, KOGO-TV, San Diego, Calif., WFBM, WFBM-TV, Indianapolis. Ind., WOOD, WOOD-TV, Grand Rapids, Mich.	1412 Cottage St., Vienna, Va.
*Coney, Charles Lee, Jr	CBS News	8311 Still Spring Court, Bethesda, Md.
Corrick, Ann M	Westinghouse Broadcasting Co., Inc.— KDKA, KDKA-TV, Pittsburgh, Pa.— KPIX-TV, San Francisco, Calif.—KYW, KYW-TV, Cleveland, Ohio—WBZ, WBZ-TV, Boston, Mass.—WIND, Chicago, Ill.—WINS, New York, N.Y.— WJZ-TV, Baltimore, Md.—WOWO, Fort Wayne, Ind.	3900 16th St.
*Corrigan, William T	NBC News	6505 Greyswood Rd., Bethesda, Md.
*Costello, William A. (Bill)	Mutual Broadcasting System	7508 16th St.
*Craven, Thos. J., Jr	CBS News	1000 Kerns Rd., Falls Church, Va.
*Craven, Thomas J., Sr	UPI Newsfilm, Inc	12 Covington St., Fairfax, Va.
*Creamer, Raymond W	CBS News	705 Pinehurst Ave., Fairfax, Va.
*Curtis, Chester	WTOP News	5540 Sanger Ave., Alexandria, Va.
*Cutler, Jay B	Youth Wants To Know	10302 Royal Rd., Silver Spring, Md.
*Dake, Marietta	Marietta Dake Associates	3719 Underwood St., Chevy Chase, Md.
Dale, David A	ABC News	433 South Fairfax St., Alexandria, Va.
*Dary, David A	WRC (NBC)	4006 Holland St., McLean, Va.
*Davenport, John N	NBC News	1211 Rippon Rd., Alexandria, Va.
Davis, B. Constance	Mutual Broadcasting System	2829 Connecticut Ave.
*Davis, Sid	Westinghouse Broadcasting Co., Inc.— KDKA, KDKA-TV, Pittsburgh, Pa.— KPIX-TV, San Francisco, Calif.—KYW, KYW-TV, Cleveland, Ohio—WBZ, WBZ-TV, Boston, Mass.—WIND, Chicago, Ill.—WINS, New York, N.Y.— WJZ-TV, Baltimore, Md.—WOWO, Fort Wayne, Ind.	6824 Old Stage Rd., Rockville, Md.
*Deibert, Leonard R	Evening Star Broadcasting Co. (WMAL AM-FM-TV).	3000 South Columbus St., Arlington, Va.
*Dickerson, Nancy H	NBC News	2220 Wyoming Ave.
*Diehl, William A	WTOP News	1150 12th St.
*Dillman, Audrey	NBC News	5161 North 38th St., Arlington, Va.

MEMBERS ENTITLED TO ADMISSION—Continued

Name	Representing—	Residence
*Doak, D. Donnell	WRC (NBC)	6502 Wilmett Rd., Bethesda, Md.
*Donaldson, Sam A	WTOP News	4720 Chevy Chase Dr. Chevy Chase, Md.
*Dorsey, George M	Spot News	1359 Kalmia Road.
*Downs, William R., Jr	ABC News	5535 Warwick Place, Chevy Chase, Md.
Dranov, Paula	UPI Radio	1850 Mintwood Place.
*Duke, Paul W	NBC News	3370 Gunston Rd., Alexandria, Va.
*Dulmage, Marcus M	UPI Newsfilm Inc	1162 W. Wakefield Drive, Alexandria, Va.
*Eck, Peg	Daveck Associates	3910 Mackall Ave., McLean, Va.
Eckstein, K. M.	West German Television, Channel 2	1427 33d St.
Edwards, Martin Allen	Mutual Broadcasting System	3802 Elby Ct., Silver Spring, Md.
*Einarsen, Edwin R	NBC News	4804 Mori Drive, Rockville, Md.
*Evenson, William J	Mutual Broadcasting System	913 Parkside Terrace, Fairfax, Va.
*Fanning, Wallace R., Jr	WRC (NBC)	Box 130, Rt. 1, Harwood, Md.
*Farkas, B. Ray	WRC (NBC)	5475 Sanger Ave., Alexandria, Va.
*Farrell, Albert V	CBS News	635 Country Hill Drive, Fairfax, Va.
*Fekete, Charles	NBC News	2410 20th St.
*Fielman, Sheldon	NBC News	555 Thayer Ave., Silver Spring, Md.
*Fleming, Robert H	ABC News	5448 33d St.
*Flocks, Lorraine	Evening Star Broadcasting Co. (WMAL AM-FM-TV)	4848 Loughboro Rd.
*Fookes, Gary P	Hearst Metrotone News, Inc	1822 Metzerott Rd., Adelphia, Md.
*Ford, Jaffray Charles	Mutual Broadcasting System	4620 Bayard Blvd.
*Foster, Cedric W	Mutual Broadcasting System	3713 Ingomar St.
*Foster, Robert F	WGN, Inc., *Chicago, Ill*	4921 Seminary Rd., Alexandria, Va.
*Fowler, W. P	ABC News	3000 Spout Run Parkway Arlington, Va.
*Franks, Charles V	CBS News	2361 North Quebec St., Arlington, Va.
Freedman, Marion L	CBS News	3040 Q St.
*French, Kenneth H	Mutual Broadcasting System	7329 Radcliffe Drive, College Park, Md.
Friedrichs, Hanns J	West German Television, Channel 2	2613 P St.
*Fulsom, Donald R	Radio Press International	10821 Madison St., Kensington, Md.
*Funk, Robert F	CBS Television Stations—KMOX-TV, St. Louis, Mo., KNXT, Los Angeles, Calif., WBBM-TV, Chicago, Ill., WCAU-TV, Philadelphia, Pa., WCBS-TV, New York, N.Y.	Box 456, Rt. 5, Alexandria, Va.
*Gaffney, Laurence F., Jr	NBC News	2907 Barrister Lane, Bowie, Md.
*Galbraith, William, H. Jr	CBS News	13309 Magellan Ave., Rockville, Md.
*Gallagher, John P	ABC News	502 McIntyre Rd., Rockville, Va.
*Gallant, James H	Evening Star Broadcasting Co. (WMAL AM-FM-TV).	5641 Sanger Ave., Alexandria, Va.
*Ganser, James E	ABC News	4328 Starr Jordan Drive, Annandale, Va.
*Geer, Stephen D	WTOP News	10120 Counselman Rd., Potomac, Md.
*Geiger, Robert E	Associated Press Radio	8508 Loughborough Pl.
*Gelenter, Robert H	NBC News	261 Congressional Lane, Rockville, Md.
*Gerlach, George J	ABC News	8211 Grove St., Silver Spring, Md.
*Gerlach, George R	Hearst Metrotone News	3110 Brewton St., District Height, Md.
Giannopoulos, Cleo	Mutual Broadcasting System	5513 Sanger Ave., Alexandria, Va.
*Gilman, Edward M	ABC News	1020 19th St.
*Gneiser, Robert H	Evening Star Broadcasting Co. (WMAL AM-FM-TV).	5720 Bradley Blvd., Bethesda, Md.
Goldsmith, John	WWDC	7405 Wyndale Rd., Chevy Chase, Md.
*Goralski, Robert S	NBC News	929 Great Falls Rd., Falls Church, Va.
*Gough, Edward J	WRC (NBC)	4109 Legation St.

830 Congressional Directory

MEMBERS ENTITLED TO ADMISSION—Continued

Name	Representing—	Residence
*Grand-Landau, Jean	Canadian Broadcasting Corp	3740 North Nelson St., Arlington, Va.
*Grant, George	UPI Newsfilm, Inc	4410 Briarwood Ct., North Annandale, Va.
*Griggs, Henry L., Jr	NBC News	5110 Wilson Lane, Bethesda, Md.
Guinan, J. Gregory	WGN., Inc., *Chicago, Ill*	420 North Van Dorn St., Alexandria, Va.
*Hackes, Peter	NBC News	5045 Klingle St.
*Hall, James Thomas	Mutual Broadcasting System	4119 North 3d Rd., Arlington, Va.
*Hamilton, Roulhac, Jr	Hamilton-Means Associates, WDSU, WDSU-TV, New Orleans, La.	4113 Southern Ave. SE.
*Harkness, Richard	NBC News	3035 Dumbarton Ave.
*Harpprecht, Klaus	West German Television, Channel 2	3302 Prospect St.
*Hart, John	CBS Television Stations, KMOX-TV, St. Louis, Mo., KNXT, Los Angeles, Calif., WBBM-TV, Chicago, Ill., WCAU-TV, Philadelphia, Pa., WCBS-TV, New York, N.Y.	3803 Everett St., Kensington, Md.
*Harter, John R	WWDC	4432 Butterworth Place.
*Hazam, Louis J	NBC News	419 Hillmoor Drive, Silver Spring, Md.
*Hemmig, Robert H	ABC News	208 Woodley Drive, Alexandria, Va.
*Henle, Ray	Three-Star Extra (NBC)	2737 Devonshire Pl.
*Henry, William M. (Bill)	Bill Henry Associates	Dorchester House.
Herbert, Donald	WTOP News	12015 Viers Mill Rd., Wheaton, Md.
*Herman, George E	CBS News	3115 O St.
Herrera, Antonio Alfredo, Jr	ABC News	1805 Phelps Pl.
*Hess, Robert H	CBS News	4106 Lawton St., McLean, Va.
*Hicks, Joseph Norman	WTOP News	6021 McKinley St., Bethesda, Md.
*Hill, Russell	Radio Free Europe	4611 29th Place.
*Hoagland, Charles A., Jr	NBC News	9606 Page Ave., Bethesda, Md.
*Hoertel, Bruce G	CBS News	Rt. 2, Box 222, Vienna, Va.
*Hofen, John F	NBC News	5913 9th St. North, Arlington, Va.
Hoshino, Kyoichi	Japan Broadcasting Corp. (NHK)	2400 Pennsylvania Ave.
*James, Anthony	WTOP News	2338 Glenmont Circle, Silver Spring, Md.
*Johnson, Jerome K	Evening Star Broadcasting Co. (WMAL AM-FM-TV).	11508 Highview Ave., Wheaton, Md.
*Johnson, Robert M	All America Wants To Know, Youth Wants To Know.	301 G St. S.W.
*Jones, Charles O	NBC News	7207 Thornapple Place, Chevy Chase, Md.
*Jones, Vernon Kennedy	UPI Newsfilm, Inc	4241 S. 16th St., Arlington, Va.
*Jurey, Jack O	WTOP News	3632 Warren St.
*Kalb, Marvin	CBS News	3155 Upland Ter.
*Kaplow, Herbert	NBC News	211 Van Buren, Falls Church, Va.
*Karasik, Daniel D	NBC News	5102 River Hill Rd.
*Klebau, James D	Evening Star Broadcasting Co. (WMAL AM-FM-TV).	8808 Lanier Dr., Silver Spring, Md.
*Krebs, Lawrence	Evening Star Broadcasting Co. (WMAL AM-FM-TV).	2828 Connecticut Ave.
*Kress, Bradford	NBC News	401 Franklin.
*LaCovey, Augustine Joseph	Evening Star Broadcasting Co. (WMAL AM-FM-TV).	2242 N. Burlington St. Arlington, Va.
*Lambert, Horace Madison (Skip).	Phoenix Film, Inc	7313 Maple Ave., Chevy Chase, Md.
Landers, Michael G	Radio Press International	20 E. St.
*Langenegger, John R	NBC News	4612 Clemson Rd., College Park, Md.
*Langton, Baden W	ABC News	4810 Morgan Dr.
*Larson, Carl	ABC News	606 Heritage Lane, Fairfax, Va.
*LaVie, Alfred R., Jr	Mutual Broadcasting System	6503 Winnepeg Rd., Bethesda, Md.
Lawrence, Fred	UPI Newsfilm, Inc	3001 Branch Ave., Suitland, Md.
Lawrence, William H	ABC News	1414 17th St.
*Levey, Stanley	CBS News	3701 Massachusetts Ave.
*Levy, John R	NBC News	6515 100th Ave., Seabrook, Md.
*Lewis, Fulton, jr	Mutual Broadcasting System	2800 Upton St.
Lewis, James Howard	WAVA AM-FM	3410 39th St.

MEMBERS ENTITLED TO ADMISSION—Continued

Name	Representing—	Residence
*Liebler, Paul E	WTOP News	13405 Oriental St., Rockville. Md.
*Linden, William E., Jr	ABC News	4931 Old Dominion Drive, Arlington, Va.
•Lion, Harold H	Hearst Metrotone News Inc	8112 Gasport Lane, Springfield, Va.
*Lodovichetti, Arthur V	ABC News	6306 Dallas Place, SE.
Loewe, Lothar	German Radio and Television (NDR and WDR)	1201 South Courthouse Rd., Arlington, Va.
*Lord, William	ABC News	10303 45th Pl., Beltsville, Md.
Lowe, Florence S	Metromedia, Inc	2727 29th St.
*Lynch, John	ABC News	1642 30th St.
*Lyons, Paul M	Hearst Metrotone News, Inc	618 Gibson Drive SW., Vienna, Va.
*MacNeil, Robert	NBC News	1404 26th St.
*McBee, Keith W	ABC News	1207 Berwick Rd., Ruxton, Md.
*McCaffrey, Joseph F	McCaffrey Reports	1309 Sunnyside Lane, McLean, Va.
*McCarthy, James John Fredrick.	Mutual Broadcasting System	4808 69th Ave., Landover Hills, Md.
*McCormick, Robert K	NBC News	6106 Bradley Blvd., Bethesda, Md.
*McCormick, Stephen J	Mutual Broadcasting System	12120 Glen Mill Rd., Potomac, Md.
McDonnell Ellen E	20th Century Fox	5616 Namakagan Rd.
*McDowell, Theodore N	Evening Star Broadcasting Co. (WMAL AM–FM–TV).	4926 Hillbrook Lane.
*McKinlay, Charles Murray	WTOP News	4917 Flanders Ave., Kensington, Md.
Magee, John P	ABC News	2105 Holmes Run Dr., Falls Church, Va.
*Marder, George J	UPI Radio	4819 Creekshore Dr., Rockville, Md.
*Markel, Hazel	Three Star Extra (NBC)	2727 29th St.
*Martin, Bert R	WGN, Inc., *Chicago, Ill.*	910 San Carlos Dr., Fairfax, Va.
*May, John O	Hearst Metrotone News Inc	Nottingham Hill, Sherwood Forest, Md.
*Meyer, Edwin	Evening Star Broadcasting Co. (WMAL AM–FM–TV).	2800 Wisconsin Ave.
*Meyer, John Bernard	CBS News	6318 Hardwood Dr., Lanham, Md.
•Minifie, James M	Canadian Broadcasting Corp	1417 31st St.
*Monroe, William B., Jr	NBC News	5328 Westpath Way, Fort Sumner Hills, Md.
*Montague, Fred	NBC News	5813 Marbury Rd., Bethesda, Md.
*Morgan, Edward P	ABC News	4507 Crest Lane, McLean, Va.
*Morgan, Richard R	WTTG TV News	2608 Fordham Rd., Alexandria, Va.
*Morrison, Fred W	Three Star Extra (NBC)	2364 Glenmont Circle, Silver Spring, Md.
*Morton, Bruce A	CBS News	741 A Delaware Ave. SW.
*Mudd, Roger H	CBS News	4025 Glenridge St., Kensington, Md.
*Mulera, John	UPI Newsfilm, Inc	3340 Curtis Dr., Hillcrest Heights, Md.
*Murphy, Charles E	NBC News	5437 33d St.
*Nash, C. Knowlton	Canadian Broadcasting Corp	431 N St. SW.
Neel, William R. P	Drew Pearson Programs	1679 32d St.
*Nessen, Ronald H	NBC News	11211 Mitscher St., Kensington, Md.
Nevas, Stephen E	Radio Press International	3970 Pennsylvania Ave. SE.
Newman, David P	ABC News	4757 North Williamsburg Blvd. Arlington, Va.
*Newman, Yale	WTTG TV News	4536 28th St.
Niven, Paul	CBS News	3629 Prospect St.
*Norling, Richard V	Spot News	12119 Edgemont St., Silver Spring, Md.
*Novak, Thomas	CBS News	2020 M St.
*O'Eth, Alfred J	Spot News	5400 Pooks Hill Rd., Bethesda, Md.
Olney, Susan Jo	WTTG TV News	4428 Alton Place.
*Owen, William C	Associated Press Radio	203 Dennis Drive, Vienna, Va.
*Parkin, Leonard	British Broadcasting Corp	3266 Aberfoyle Place.
*Pechel, Peter E., Dr	Bavarian, Berlin, South–West German, Hesse, Bremen Radio and TV Networks.	8810 Brierly Rd., Chevy Chase, Md.
*Pellegrino, Joseph A	Evening Star Broadcasting Co. (WMAL AM–FM–TV).	9138 Piney Branch Rd., Silver Spring, Md.

MEMBERS ENTITLED TO ADMISSION—Continued

Name	Representing—	Residence
*Peterson, Ralph Howard	NBC News	214 Holmes Run Rd., Falls Church, Va.
*Pierpoint, Robert C	CBS News	5503 Pollard Rd.
*Pitts, Leo A	WTOP News	2911 North Greenbrier St. Arlington, Va.
*Povich, Maurice R	WWDC	10827 Georgia Ave., Wheaton, Md.
*Priestland, Gerlad F	British Broadcasting Corp	1745 N St.
*Randolph, F. M. (Jim)	Metromedia, Inc.	6114 N. Washington Blvd., Arlington, Va.
*Rash, Bryson B	NBC News	4340 Garfield St.
Reilly, Ann L	CBS News	4319 Van Ness St.
*Remmey, Louise Austin	CBS News	2339 40th Place.
*Rendell, Richard	Mutual Broadcasting System	5107 Worthington Dr. Westmoreland Hills, Md.
*Renz, Karl Guenther	West German Television, Channel 2	2603 O St.
Rhodes, James W	Spot News	103 G St. SW.
*Richards, William T	NBC News	8501 Burning Tree Rd., Bethesda, Md.
*Richardson, Donald W	CBS News	4609 North 20th St., Arlington, Va.
*Roberts, J. W. (Bill)	Time—Life, Broadcast, KERO-TV, Bakersfield, Calif., KLZ, KLZ-TV, Denver, Colo., KOGO, KOGO-TV, San Diego, Calif.—WFBM, WFBM-TV, Indianapolis, Ind., WOOD, WOOD-TV, Grand Rapids, Mich.	6517 Nevius St., Falls Church, Va.
*Robinson, Robert E	WWDC	4312 Joplin Drive, Rockville, Md.
*Rogers, Robert	NBC News	6009 Kingsford Rd., Bethesda, Md.
*Romilly, George P	WTTG TV News	3 Pooks Hili Rd., Bethesda, Md.
Roppolo, Charles J	ABC News	1581 Colonial Terrace, Arlington, Va.
*Ruby, Elvera	NBC News	4201 Massachusetts Ave.
*Ruge, Gerd	German Radio and Television (NDR and WDR).	4501 Wisconsin Ave.
*Rush, David L	WRC (NBC)	14309 Blackmon Drive Rockville, Md.
*Ryan, Edward F	WTOP News	6901 Oak Ridge Ave., Chevy Chase, Md.
*Salzano, Carlo J	UPI Radio	4305 North Henderson Rd., Arlington, Va.
*Santos, Ralph A	CBS News	421 Wake Forest Dr., Alexandria, Va.
Sargent, Anthony H	CBS News	3225 Martha Custis Drive, Alexandria, Va.
*Saylor, Harold E. (Hal)	WTOP News	6507 Brookhill Court.
*Scali, John A	ABC News	5604 Chesterbrook Rd.
*Scherer, Raymond L	NBC News	3550 Springland Lane.
*Schindler, Max Arthur	NBC News	904 South Belfrade Rd., Silver Spring, Md.
*Schoumacher, David E	CBS News	506 Dellwood Drive, Vienna, Va.
*Schultz, Jack	UPI Newsfilm, Inc	1-C Southway Greenbelt, Md.
Schulz, William Martin	Mutual Broadcasting System	209 C St. SE.
*Scott, Ivan	CBS Television Stations—KNXT, Los Angeles, Calif., WBBM-TV, Chicago, Ill, WCAU-TV, Philadelphia, Pa., WCBS-TV, New York, N.Y. KMOX-TV, St. Louis, Mo.	4442 Greenwich Parkway
*Sevareid, Eric	CBS News	4313 Bradley Blvd., Chevy Chase, Md.
Sharp, Stokes L	ABC News	3905 Reservoir Rd.
*Sharpe, Maureen	NBC News	4201 Massachusetts Ave.
*Shepp, C. Lea	CBS News	2227 Candlewood Dr., Alexdria, Va.
*Shinkman, Paul	WASH and WDON	3040 Dent Place.
*Shutt, Charles E	Hearst Metrotone News, Inc	500 Ednor Road, Silver Spring, Md.
Simmons, Huston	NBC News	1750 16th St.
*Slappey, Sidney W	WAVA	898 North Lexington, Arlington, Va.
*Slingland, Frank D	NBC News	4718 River Rd.
*Small, William J	CBS News	9802 Inglemere Dr., Bethesda, Md.
*Smith, Howard K	ABC News	6450 Brooks Lane.
Smith, Mignon C	WATV, Birmingham, Ala.,—WKUL, Cullman, Ala.	220 2d St. SE.
*Smythe, William K	Spot News	4711 Tecumseh St., College Park, Md.

MEMBERS ENTITLED TO ADMISSION—Continued

Name	Representing—	Residence
*Snyder, James L	Westinghouse Broadcasting Co., Inc.—KDKA, KDKA-TV, Pittsburgh, Pa.—KPIX-TV, San Francisco, Calif.—KYW, KYW-TV, Cleveland, Ohio—WBZ, WBZ-TV, Boston, Mass.—WIND, Chicago, Ill.—WINS, New York, N.Y.—WJZ-TV, Baltimore, Md.—WOWO, Fort Wayne, Ind.	6005 Beech Ave., Bethesda, Md.
*Sozio, George A	NBC News	14 Chickawane Ct., Alexandria, Va.
*Spivak, Lawrence E	Meet The Press (NBC)	Sheraton Park Hotel.
*Steiner, Earl J	ABC News	9708 Marshall Ave., Silver Spring, Md.
Stoneback, Rolanda M	West German Television, Channel 2	2500 O St.
*Strawser, Neil E	CBS News	7202 Broxburn Dr., Bethesda, Md.
*Sveilis, Emil	UP Radio	1200 S. Courthouse Rd., Arlington, Va.
*Sylvester, Tony	WTOP News	6435 Dahlonega Rd.
*Tomlinson, Duff Thomas	UPI Audio	677 Monticello Dr., Falls Church, Va.
*Travieso, John Joseph	NBC News	5204 Roosevelt St., Bethesda, Md.
*Tromer, Michael	UPI Newsfilm, Inc	7803 Atwood St., District Heights, Md.
*Tsuchiya, Kozo	Japan Broadcasting Corp	900 National Press Bldg.
*Turney, Edgar W	Evening Star Broadcasting Co. (WMAL AM–FM–TV).	9305 Worth Ave., Silver Spring, Md.
*Valeriani, Richard	NBC News	114 3d St. SE.
*Van Nostrand, Ronald W	Hearst Metrotone News, Inc	41 Wellesley Circle, Glen Echo, Md.
*Viera, Gabriel	WRC (NBC)	12419 Seabury Lane, Bowie, Md.
Vitarelli, Robert E	CBS News	4201 Cathedral Ave.
*von Fremd, Charles	CBS News	5715 Huntington Parkway, Bethesda, Md.
von Sothen, David	WRC (NBC)	Arlington Towers, Arlington, Va.
Wadley, Ellen	CBS News	2231 California St.
*Walker, Harold W	WTOP News	1843 Ingleside Terrace.
*Ward, Murray E	Hearst Metrotone News, Inc	3805 Beatty Dr., Alexandria, Va.
*Ward, Russell H	NBC News	5948 Searl Terrace, Bethesda, Md.
*Warren, Charles	Mutual Broadcasting System	11605 Bucknell Dr., Silver Spring, Md.
Warren, Mary Worth	CBS Television Stations—KMOX-TV, St. Louis, Mo., KNXT, Los Angeles, Calif., WBBM-TV, Chicago, Ill., WCAU-TV, Philadelphia, Pa., WCBS-TV, New York, N.Y.	6706 Hillandale Rd., Chevy Chase, Md.
*Waters, Gerald A	CBS News	2500 Q St.
Watson, George H., Jr	ABC News	1009 24th St.
*Wells, Fay Gillis	Storer Broadcasting Co., KGBS, Los Angel. es, Calif., WAGA-TV, Atlanta, Ga., WGBS, Miami, Fla., WHN, New York, N.Y., WIBG, Philadelphia, Pa., WITI-TV, Milwaukee, Wis., WJBK, WJBK-TV, Detroit, Mich., WJW, WJW-TV, Cleveland, Ohio, WSPD WSPD-TV, Toledo, Ohio.	1330 New Hampshire Ave.
*Wells, Linton	Storer Broadcasting Co., KGBS, Los Angeles, Calif., WAGA-TV, Atlanta, Ga., WGBS, Miami, Fla., WHN, New York, N.Y., WIBG, Philadelphia, Pa., WITI-TV, Milwaukee, Wis., WJBK, WJBK-TV, Detroit, Mich., WJW, WJW-TV, Cleveland, Ohio, WSPD, WSPD-TV, Toledo, Ohio.	1330 New Hampshire Ave.
Westerman, Sylvia	CBS News	3120 R St.
*Weston, Ronald T	Hearst Metrotone News, Inc	14016 Willoughby Rd., Marlboro, Md.
*Whedon, Margaret B	ABC News	5605 Sonoma Rd., Bethesda, Md.
*Wiegman, David	NBC News	3202 Wake Dr., Kensington, Md.
Williams, Judith Bird	NBC News	8514 Salem Way, Bethesda, Md.
*Willoner, Andrew	CBS News	4106 70th Ave., Landover Hills, Md.
*Wills, David H	Daveck Associates	3910 Mackall Ave., McLean, Va.

MEMBERS ENTITLED TO ADMISSION—Continued

Name	Representing—	Residence
*Wilson, Frank H	WTOP News	2108 16th St.
*Wilson, James S	CBS Television Stations,—KMOX-TV, St. Louis, Mo., KNXT, Los Angeles, Calif., WCAU-TV, Philadelphia, Pa., WCBS-TV, New York, N.Y.	Glen Dale Rd., Glen Dale, Md.
*Windsor, G. Robert	WTOP News	7403 Garland Ave., Takoma Park, Md.
*Winkler, Thomas Robert	Evening Star Broadcasting Co. (WMAL AM–FM–TV).	3730 N. Dittmar Rd., Arlington, Va.
Wolf, Warner William	WQMR	3333 University Blvd.
*Yates, Frederick L	NBC News	3200 Highland Pl.
*Yoshino, Shoji	Japan Broadcasting Corp. (NHK)	10807 Georgia Ave., Wheaton, Md.
Young, Henrietta L	NBC News	4106 Ingomar St.
*Young, Paul DeWitt	Evening Star Broadcasting Co.—(WMAL– AM–FM–TV).	1955 North Woodrow St., Arlington, Va.
*Zimmerman, William N	WTOP News	4540 MacArthur Blvd.

NETWORKS, STATIONS, AND SERVICES REPRESENTED

Network, station, or service, and telephone number	Name	Office
All America Wants To Know—628-4600---	Robert M. Johnson_____	1627 K St.
	Jay B. Cutler_____	1627 K St.
ABC News—393-7700---------------------	Murray Alvey--------------	1124 Connecticut Ave.
	Edward L. Burch_____	1124 Connecticut Ave.
	John J. Casserly_____	1124 Connecticut Ave.
	Irwin M. Chapman_____	1124 Connecticut Ave.
	Robert E. Clark_____	1124 Connecticut Ave.
	David A. Dale_____	1124 Connecticut Ave.
	William R. Downs, Jr_____	1124 Connecticut Ave.
	Robert H. Fleming_____	1124 Connecticut Ave.
	W. P. Fowler_____	1124 Connecticut Ave.
	John P. Gallagher_____	1124 Connecticut Ave.
	James E. Ganser_____	1124 Connecticut Ave.
	George Gerlach_____	1124 Connecticut Ave.
	Edward M. Gilman_____	1124 Connecticut Ave.
	Robert Hemmig_____	1124 Connecticut Ave.
	Antoinio Alfreda Herrera, Jr_	1124 Connecticut Ave.
	Baden W. Langton_____	1124 Connecticut Ave.
	Carl Larsen_____	1124 Connecticut Ave.
	William H. Lawrence_____	1124 Connecticut Ave.
	William E. Linden, Jr_____	1124 Connecticut Ave.
	Arthur Lodovichetti_____	1124 Connecticut Ave.
	William Lord_____	1124 Connecticut Ave.
	John F. Lynch_____	1124 Connecticut Ave.
	Keith W. McBee_____	1124 Connecticut Ave.
	John P. Magee_____	1124 Connecticut Ave.
	Edward P Morgan_____	1124 Connecticut Ave.
	David P. Newman_____	1124 Connecticut Ave.
	Charles J. Roppolo_____	1124 Connecticut Ave.
	John A. Scali_____	1124 Connecticut Ave.
	Stokes L. Sharp_____	1124 Connecticut Ave.
	Howard K. Smith_____	1124 Connecticut Ave.
	Joseph Steiner_____	1124 Connecticut Ave.
	George H. Watson, Jr_____	1124 Connecticut Ave.
	Peggy Whedon_____	1124 Connecticut Ave.
Associated Press Radio—234-5400_____	Anthony Catella_____	1300 Connecticut Ave.
	Robert E. Geiger_____	1300 Connecticut Ave.
	William C. Owen_____	1300 Connecticut Ave.
Bavarian, Berlin, South-West German, Hesse and Bremen Radio and TV Networks—656-6765.	Dr. Peter E. Pechel_____	8810 Brierly Rd., Chevy Chase, Md.
Bill Henry Associates—332-1422_____	William M. (Bill) Henry____	2480 16th St.
British Broadcasting Corp.—393-1465_____	Leonard Parkin_____	907 National Press Bldg.
	Gerald Francis Priestland__	907 National Press Bldg.
Canadian Broadcasting Corp.—638-3286____	Jean Grand-Landau_____	766 National Press Bldg.
	James M. Minifie_____	766 National Press Bldg.
	C. Knowlton Nash_____	766 National Press Bldg.
CBS News—296-1234---------------------	Lee Elliott Adler_____	2020 M St.
	John Bessor_____	2020 M St.
	Milton D. Bittenbender____	2020 M St.
	Donald E. Bowers_____	2020 M St.
	Robert B. Camnford_____	2020 M St.
	Prentiss Childs_____	2020 M St.
	Wells Church_____	2020 M St.
	Charles Lee Coney, Jr_____	2020 M St.
	Thomas J. Craven, Jr_____	2020 M St.
	William B. Crawford_____	2020 M St.
	Raymond W. Creamer_____	2020 M St.
	Albert Farrell_____	2020 M St.
	Charles V. Franks_____	2020 M St.
	Marion L. Freedman_____	2020 M St.
	William H. Galbraith, Jr ___	2020 M St.
	George E. Herman_____	2020 M St.
	Robert H. Hess_____	2020 M St.
	Bruce G. Hoertel_____	2020 M St.
	Marvin Kalb_____	2020 M St.
	Stanley Levey_____	2020 M St.
	John Bernard Meyer_____	2020 M St.
	Bruce A. Morton_____	2020 M St.
	Roger H. Mudd_____	2020 M St.
	Paul Niven_____	2020 M St.
	Thomas M. Novak_____	2020 M St.
	Robert C. Pierpoint_____	2020 M St.
	Ann L. Reilly_____	2020 M St.
	Louise Austin Remmey_____	2020 M St.
	Donald W. Richardson_____	2020 M St.
	Ralph A. Santos_____	2020 M St.

NETWORKS, STATIONS, AND SERVICES REPRESENTED—Continued

Network, station, or service, and telephone number	Name	Office
CBS News—Continued	Anthony H. Sargent	2020 M St.
	David E. Schoumacher	2020 M St.
	Eric Sevareid	2020 M St.
	C. Lea Shepp	2020 M St.
	William J. Small	2020 M St.
	Neil E. Strawser	2020 M St.
	Robert E. Vitarelli	2020 M St.
	Charles von Fremd	2020 M St.
	Ellen Wadley	2020 M St.
	Gerald A. Waters	2020 M St.
	Sylvia Westerman	2020 M St.
	Andrew Willoner	2020 M St.
CBS Television Stations—296-1234	Robert F. Funk	2020 M St.
	John Hart	2020 M St.
	Ivan Scott	2020 M St.
	Mary Worth Warren	2020 M St.
	James S. Wilson	2020 M St.
Daveck Associates—356-9656	Peg Eck	3910 Mackall Ave., McLean, Va.
	David Wills	3910 Mackall Ave., McLean, Va.
Drew Pearson Programs—232-4321	William R. P. Neel	1313 29th St.
Evening Star Broadcasting Co. (WMAL AM–FM–TV)—537-1100.	James D. Clarke	4461 Connecticut Ave.
	Vincent R. Clephas	4461 Connecticut Ave.
	Leonard R. Deibert	4461 Connecticut Ave.
	Lorraine Flocks	4461 Connecticut Ave.
	James H. Gallant	4461 Connecticut Ave.
	Robert H. Gneiser	4461 Connecticut Ave.
	Jerome K. Johnson	4461 Connecticut Ave.
	James D. Klebau	4461 Connecticut Ave.
	Lawrence Krebs	4461 Connecticut Ave.
	A. Joseph LaCovey	4461 Connecticut Ave.
	Theodore N. McDowell	4461 Connecticut Ave.
	Edwin Meyer	4461 Connecticut Ave.
	Joseph A. Pellegrino	4461 Connecticut Ave.
	Edgar W. Turney	4461 Connecticut Ave.
	Thomas R. Winkler	4461 Connecticut Ave.
	Paul DeWitt Young	4461 Connecticut Ave.
20th Century Fox.—347-6448	Ellen E. McDonnell	413 3d St.
French Broadcasting System—393-2537	Michel J. Texier	614 National Press Bldg.
German Radio and Television (NDR and WDR) 363-1424.	Lothar Loewe	4501 Wisconsin Ave.
	Gerd Ruge	4501 Wisconsin Ave.
Hamilton-Means Associates—347-4653	Roulhac Hamilton	103 G St. SW.
Hearst Metrotone News, Inc.—393-8311	Gary P. Fookes	470 E St. SW.
	George R. Gerlach	470 E St. SW.
	Harold H. Lion	470 E St. SW.
	Paul M. Lyons	470 E St. SW.
	John O. May	470 E St. SW.
	Charles E. Shutt	470 E St. SW.
	Ronald Van Nostrand	470 E St. SW.
	Murray E. Ward	470 E St. SW.
	Ronald T. Weston	470 E St. SW.
Japan Broadcasting Corp. (NHK)—393-1076.	Kyoichi Hoshino	900 National Press Bldg.
	Kozo Tsuchiya	900 National Press Bldg.
	Shoji Yoshino	900 National Press Bldg.
KDKA, KDKA-TV, Pittsburgh, Pa. 783-0907.	Paul Thomas Bryson	1625 K St.
	Peter R. Clapper	1625 K St.
	Ann M. Corrick	1625 K St.
	Sid Davis	1625 K St.
	James L. Snyder	1625 K St.
KERO-TV, Bakersfield, Calif	Norris Brock	1120 Connecticut Ave.
	Carl C. Coleman	1120 Connecticut Ave.
	J. W. (Bill) Roberts	1120 Connecticut Ave.
KGBS, Los Angeles, Calif.—338-8884	Fay Gillis Wells	1725 K St.
	Linton Wells	1725 K St.
KLZ, KLZ-TV, Denver, Colo.—337-8000	R. Norris Brock	1120 Connecticut Ave.
	Carl C. Coleman, Jr	1120 Connecticut Ave.
	J. W. (Bill) Roberts	1120 Connecticut Ave.
KMOX-TV, St. Louis, Mo.—296-1234	Robert F. Funk	2020 M St.
	John Hart	2020 M St.
	Ivan Scott	2020 M St.
	Mary Worth Warren	2020 M St.
	James S. Wilson	2020 M St.
KNXT, Los Angeles, Calif.—296-1234	Robert F. Funk	2020 M St.
	John Hart	2020 M St.
	Ivan Scott	2020 M St.
	Mary Worth Warren	2020 M St.
	James S. Wilson	2020 M St.
KOGO, KOGO-TV, San Diego, Calif. 337-8000.	R. Norris Brock	1120 Connecticut Ave.
	Carl C. Coleman Jr	1120 Connecticut Ave.
	J. W. (Bill) Roberts	1120 Connecticut Ave.

NETWORKS, STATIONS, AND SERVICES REPRESENTED—Continued

Network, station, or service, and telephone number	Name	Office
KPIX–TV, San Francisco, Calif.—783–0907.	Paul Thomas Bryson	1625 K St.
	Peter R. Clapper	1625 K St.
	Ann M. Corrick	1625 K St.
	Sid Davis	1625 K St.
	James L. Snyder	1625 K St.
KYW, KYW–TV, Cleveland, Ohio—783–0907.	Paul Thomas Bryson	1625 K St.
	Ann M. Corrick	1625 K St.
	Sid Davis	1625 K St.
	James L. Snyder	1625 K St.
Marietta Dake Associates—656–6819	Marietta Dake	3719 Underwood St., Chevy Chase, Md.
McCaffrey Reports—225–5215	Joseph F. McCaffrey	House Radio-Television Gallery.
Meet the Press (NBC)—265–2000	Betty A. Cole	Sheraton-Park Hotel.
	Lawrence E. Spivak	Sheraton-Park Hotel.
Metromedia, Inc.—244–5151	Terry Gearity Bibb	5151 Wisconsin Ave.
	Florence S. Lowe	5151 Wisconsin Ave.
	F. M. (Jim) Randolph	5151 Wisconsin Ave.
Mutual Broadcasting System—265–6363	Charles F. Batchelder	Sheraton-Park Hotel.
	Dorese Bell	Sheraton-Park Hotel.
	Forrest J. Boyd	Sheraton-Park Hotel.
	Joseph P. Campbell	Sheraton-Park Hotel.
	William A. (Bill) Costello	Sheraton-Park Hotel.
	B. Constance Davis	Sheraton-Park Hotel.
	Martin Allen Edwards	Sheraton-Park Hotel.
	William J. Evenson	Sheraton-Park Hotel.
	Jaffray Charles Ford	Sheraton-Park Hotel.
	Cedric W. Foster	Sheraton-Park Hotel.
	Kenneth H. French	Sheraton-Park Hotel.
	Cleo Giannopoulos	Sheraton-Park Hotel.
	James Thomas Hall	Sheraton-Park Hotel.
	Alfred R. LaVie, Jr	Sheraton-Park Hotel.
	Fulton Lewis, Jr	Sheraton-Park Hotel.
	James John Fredrick McCarthy.	Sheraton-Park Hotel.
	Stephen J. McCormick	Sheraton-Park Hotel.
	Richard Rendell	Sheraton-Park Hotel.
	William Martin Schulz	Sheraton-Park Hotel.
	Charles Warren	Sheraton-Park Hotel.
NBC News—362–4000	Elie Abel	4001 Nebraska Ave.
	Robert G. Abernethy	4001 Nebraska Ave.
	George N. Allen	4001 Nebraska Ave.
	Leonard Allen	4001 Nebraska Ave.
	LeRoy Anderson	4001 Nebraska Ave.
	Robert W. Asman	4001 Nebraska Ave.
	Christie R. Basham	4001 Nebraska Ave.
	Lewis H. Bernhart	4001 Nebraska Ave.
	David Brinkley	4001 Nebraska Ave.
	John W. Chancellor	4001 Nebraska Ave.
	William T. Corrigan	4001 Nebraska Ave.
	Nancy H. Dickerson	4001 Nebraska Ave.
	Audrey Dillman	4001 Nebraska Ave.
	Donnell Doak	4001 Nebraska Ave.
	Paul W. Duke	4001 Nebraska Ave.
	Edwin R. Einarsen	4001 Nebraska Ave.
	Charles Fekete	4001 Nebraska Ave.
	Sheldon Fielman	4001 Nebraska Ave.
	Robert H. Gelenter	4001 Nebraska Ave.
	Robert S. Goralski	4001 Nebraska Ave.
	Henry L. Griggs, Jr	4001 Nebraska Ave.
	Peter Hackes	4001 Nebraska Ave.
	Richard Harkness	4001 Nebraska Ave.
	Louis J. Hazam	4001 Nebraska Ave.
	Charles A. Hoagland, Jr	4001 Nebraska Ave.
	John F. Hofen	4001 Nebraska Ave.
	Charles O. Jones	4001 Nebraska Ave.
	Herbert E. Kaplow	4001 Nebraska Ave.
	Daniel D. Karasik	4001 Nebraska Ave.
	Bradford Kress	4001 Nebraska Ave.
	John R. Langenegger	4001 Nebraska Ave.
	John R. Levy	4001 Nebraska Ave.
	Robert MacNeil	4001 Nebraska Ave.
	Robert K. McCormick	4001 Nebraska Ave.
	William B. Monroe, Jr	4001 Nebraska Ave.
	Fred Montague	4001 Nebraska Ave.
	Ronald H. Nesson	4001 Nebraska Ave.
	Ralph Howard Peterson	4001 Nebraska Ave.
	Bryson B. Rash	4001 Nebraska Ave.
	William T. Richards	4001 Nebraska Ave.
	Robert Rogers	4001 Nebraska Ave.
	Elvera Ruby	4001 Nebraska Ave.
	Raymond L. Scherer	4001 Nebraska Ave.

NETWORKS, STATIONS, AND SERVICES REPRESENTED—Continued

Network, station, or service, and telephone numbers	Name	Office
NBC News—Continued	Max Arthur Schindler	4001 Nebraska Ave.
	Maureen Sharpe	4001 Nebraska Ave.
	Huston Simmons	4001 Nebraska Ave.
	Frank D. Slingland	4001 Nebraska Ave.
	George Anthony Sozio	4001 Nebraska Ave.
	John Joseph Travieso	4001 Nebraska Ave.
	Richard Valeriani	4001 Nebraska Ave.
	Russell H. Ward	4001 Nebraska Ave.
	Judith Bird Williams	4001 Nebraska Ave.
	David Wiegman	4001 Nebraska Ave.
	Frederick L. Yates	4001 Nebraska Ave.
	Henrietta L. Young	4001 Nebraska Ave.
Phoenix Films, Inc.	Horace M. Lambert	7313 Maple Ave., Chevy Chase, Md.
Radio Free Europe—638-6363	Russell Hill	877 National Press Bldg.
Radio Press International, Inc.—393-0464	Herbert M. Brubaker	20 E St.
	Donald R. Fulsom	20 E St.
	Michael George Landers	20 E St.
	Stephen E. Nevas	20 E St.
Spot News ____ 723-7409	George M. Dorsey	1359 Kalmia Rd.
657-8763	Alfred J. O'Eth	5400 Pooks Hill Rd., Bethesda, Md.
942-8781	Richard V. Norling	12119 Edgemont St., Silver Spring, Md.
628-1979	James W. Rhodes	103 G St. SW.
474-4995	William K. Smythe	4711 Tecumseh, College Park, Md.
Storer Broadcasting Co.—338-8884	Fay Gillis Wells	1725 K St.
	Linton Wells	1725 K St.
Three-Star Extra (NBC)—393-7340	Ned Brooks	1625 K St.
	Carl W. Cardin	1625 K St.
	Ray Henle	1625 K St.
	Hazel Markel	1625 K St.
	Fred Morrison	1625 K St.
Time-Life Broadcast, Inc.—337-8000	R. Norris Brock	1120 Connecticut Ave.
	Carl C. Coleman, Jr.	1120 Connecticut Ave.
	J. W. (Bill) Roberts	1120 Connecticut Ave.
Triangle Publications, Inc.—333-3315	Anne Denton Blair	3315 Dent Place.
Tris Coffin Associates—654-3556	Tristram Coffin	5601 Warwick Place, Chevy Chase, Md.
UPI Audio—546-1196	Edward Pye Chamberlayne, Jr.	1017 New Jersey Ave. SE.
	John Chambers	1017 New Jersey Ave. SE.
	Duff Thomas Tomlinson	1017 New Jersey Ave. SE.
UPI Newsfilm, Inc.—543-3113	Clarence J. Brown	1017 New Jersey Ave. SE.
	Bryce W. Burke	1017 New Jersey Ave. SE.
	Theodore H. Clark	1017 New Jersey Ave. SE.
	Tom Craven, Jr	1017 New Jersey Ave. SE.
	Marcus M. Dulmage	1017 New Jersey Ave. SE.
	George Grant	1017 New Jersey Ave. SE.
	Vernon Kennedy Jones	1017 New Jersey Ave. SE.
	Fred Lawrence	1017 New Jersey Ave. SE.
	John Mulera	1017 New Jersey Ave. SE.
	Jack Schultz	1017 New Jersey Ave. SE.
	Michael Tromer	1017 New Jersey Ave. SE.
UPI Radio—393-3430	Robert Dean Beckmann, Jr.	714 National Press Bldg.
	Bernard Brenner	714 National Press Bldg.
	Timothy Blair Clark	707 National Press Bldg.
	Paula Dranov	714 National Press Bldg.
	George J. Marder	714 National Press Bldg.
	Carlo J. Salzano	714 National Press Bldg.
	Emil Sveilis	714 National Press Bldg.
WAGA-TV, Atlanta, Ga.—338-8884	Fay Gillis Wells	1725 K St.
	Linton Wells	1725 K St.
WASH-FM—347-1356	Paul Shinkman	1319 F St.
WATV, Birmingham, Ala	Mignon C. Smith	220 2d St. SE.
WAVA—536-9000	James Howard Lewis	5232 Lee Highway, Arlington, Va.
	Sidney W. Slappey	5232 Lee Highway, Arlington, Va.
WBBM-TV, Chicago, Ill.—296-1234	Robert F. Funk	2020 M St.
	John Hart	2020 M St.
	Ivan Scott	2020 M St.
	Mary Worth Warren	2020 M St.
	James S. Wilson	2020 M St.
WBZ, WBZ-TV, Boston, Mass.—783-0907	Paul Thomas Bryson	1625 K St.
	Peter R. Clapper	1625 K St.
	Ann M. Corrick	1625 K St.
	Sid Davis	1625 K St.
	James L. Snyder	1625 K St.

NETWORKS, STATIONS, AND SERVICES REPRESENTED—Continued

Network, station, or service, and telephone number	Name	Office
WCAU-TV, Philadelphia, Pa.—296-1234_	Robert F. Funk_____	2020 M St.
	John Hart_____	2020 M St.
	Ivan Scott_____	2020 M St.
	Mary Worth Warren_____	2020 M St.
	James S. Wilson_____	2020 M St.
WCBS-TV, New York, N.Y.—296-1234__	Robert F. Funk_____	2020 M St.
	John Hart_____	2020 M St.
	Ivan Scott_____	2020 M St.
	Mary Worth Warren_____	2020 M St.
	James S. Wilson_____	2020 M St.
WDON—347-1356_____	Paul A. Shinkman_____	1319 F St.
WDSU, WDSU-TV, New Orleans, La. 347-4653.	Roulhac Hamilton_____	103 G St. SW.
West German Television, Channel 2_____	K. M. Eckstein_____	2914 M St.
	Hanns J. Friedrichs_____	2914 M St.
	Klaus Harpprecht_____	2914 M St.
	Karl Guenther Renz_____	2914 M St.
	Rolanda M. Stoneback_____	2914 M St.
Westinghouse Broadcasting Co., Inc_____ 783-0907.	Paul Thomas Bryson_____	1625 K St.
	Peter R. Clapper_____	1625 K St.
	Ann M. Corrick_____	1625 K St.
	Sid Davis_____	1625 K St.
	James L. Snyder_____	1625 K St.
WFBM, WFBM-TV, Indianapolis, Ind__ 337-8000.	R. Norris Brock_____	1120 Connecticut Ave.
	Carl C. Coleman, Jr_____	1120 Connecticut Ave.
	J. W. (Bill) Roberts_____	1120 Connecticut Ave.
WGBS, Miami, Fla.—338-8884_____	Fay Gillis Wells_____	1725 K St.
	Linton Wells_____	1725 K St.
WGN, Inc., Chicago, Ill_____	Robert F. Foster_____	1735 DeSales St.
	J. Gregory Guinan_____	1735 DeSales St.
	Bert R. Martin_____	1735 DeSales St.
WHN, New York, N.Y.—338-8884_____	Fay Gillis Wells_____	1725 K St.
	Linton Wells_____	1725 K St.
WIBG, Philadelphia, Pa.—338-8884_____	Fay Gillis Wells_____	1725 K St.
	Linton Wells_____	1725 K St.
WIND, Chicago, Ill.—783-0907_____	Paul Thomas Bryson_____	1625 K St.
	Peter R. Clapper_____	1625 K St.
	Ann M. Corrick_____	1625 K St.
	Sid Davis_____	1625 K St.
	James L. Snyder_____	1625 K St.
WINS, New York, N.Y.—783-0907_____	Paul Thomas Bryson_____	1625 K St.
	Peter R. Clapper_____	1625 K St.
	Ann M. Corrick_____	1625 K St.
	Sid Davis_____	1625 K St.
	James L. Snyder_____	1625 K St.
WITI-TV, Milwaukee, Wis.—338-8884____	Fay Gillis Wells_____	1725 K St.
	Linton Wells_____	1725 K St.
WJBK, WJBK-TV, Detroit, Mich_____ 338-8884.	Fay Gillis Wells_____	1725 K St.
	Linton Wells_____	1725 K St.
WJW, WJW-TV, Cleveland, Ohio_____ 338-8884.	Fay Gillis Wells_____	1725 K St.
	Linton Wells_____	1725 K St.
WJZ-TV, Baltimore, Md.—783-0907_____	Paul Thomas Bryson_____	1625 K St.
	Peter R. Clapper_____	1625 K St.
	Ann M. Corrick_____	1625 K St.
	Sid Davis_____	1625 K St.
	James L. Snyder_____	1625 K St.
WKUL, Cullman, Ala._____	Mignon C. Smith_____	229 2d St. SE.
WOOD, WOOD-TV, Grand Rapids, Mich.—337-8000.	R. Norris Brock_____	1120 Connecticut Ave.
	Carl C. Coleman, Jr_____	1120 Connecticut Ave.
	J. W. (Bill) Roberts_____	1120 Connecticut Ave.
WOWO, Fort Wayne, Ind.—783-0907_____	Paul Thomas Bryson_____	1625 K St.
	Ann M. Corrick_____	1625 K St.
	Sid Davis_____	1625 K St.
	James L. Snyder_____	1625 K St.
WQMR—946-1050_____	Warner W. Wolf_____	11306 Kemp Mill Rd., Silver Spring, Md.
WRC (NBC)—362-4000_____	David A. Dary_____	4001 Nebraska Ave.
	John N. Davenport_____	4001 Nebraska Ave.
	Wallace R. Fanning, Jr_____	4001 Nebraska Ave.
	B. Ray Farkas_____	4001 Nebraska Ave.
	Laurence F. Gaffney, Jr____	4001 Nebraska Ave.
	Edward J. Gough_____	4001 Nebraska Ave.
	Charles E. Murphy_____	4001 Nebraska Ave.
	David L. Rush_____	4001 Nebraska Ave.
	David von Sothen_____	4001 Nebraska Ave.
	Gabriel Viera_____	4001 Nebraska Ave.
WSPD, WSPD-TV, Toledo, Ohio_____ 338-8884.	Fay Gillis Wells_____	1725 K St.
	Linton Wells_____	1725 K St.

NETWORKS, STATIONS, AND SERVICES REPRESENTED—Continued

Network, station, or service, and telephone number	Name	Office
WTOP News—244-5678	Donald C. Allen	40th and Brandywine Sts.
	Julian Barber	40th and Brandywine Sts.
	Claire M. Beach	40th and Brandywine Sts.
	Harold E. Beall	40th and Brandywine Sts.
	Norman Beebe	40th and Brandywine Sts.
	Ernest C. Belote, Jr	40th and Brandywine Sts.
	Chester Curtis	40th and Brandywine Sts.
	William A. Diehl	40th and Brandywine Sts.
	Sam A. Donaldson	40th and Brandywine Sts.
	Stephen D. Geer	40th and Brandywine Sts.
	Donald Herbert	40th and Brandywine Sts.
	Joseph Hicks	40th and Brandywine Sts.
	Anthony James	40th and Brandywine Sts.
	Jack O. Jurey	40th and Brandywine Sts.
	Paul Edward Liebler	40th and Brandywine Sts.
	Charles M. McKinlay	40th and Brandywine Sts.
	Leo A. Pitts	40th and Brandywine Sts.
	Edward F. Ryan	40th and Brandywine Sts.
	Harold (Hal) Saylor	40th and Brandywine Sts.
	Tony Sylvester	40th and Brandywine Sts.
	Harold W. Walker	40th and Brandywine Sts.
	Frank H. Wilson	40th and Brandywine Sts.
	J. Robert Windsor	40th and Brandywine Sts.
	William D. Zimmerman	40th and Brandywine Sts.
WTTG–TV News—244-5151	Richard R. Morgan	5151 Wisconsin Ave.
	Yale Newman	5151 Wisconsin Ave.
	Susan Jo Olney	5151 Wisconsin Ave.
	George P. Romilly	5151 Wisconsin Ave.
WWDC—882-7600	John Goldsmith	1627 K St.
	John R. Harter	1627 K St.
	Maurice R. Povich	1627 K St.
	Robert E. Robinson	1627 K St.
Youth Wants To Know—628-4600	Robert M. Johnson	1627 K St.
	Jay B. Cutler	1627 K St.

PERIODICAL PRESS GALLERIES

Phones, 224-3121; Senate Gallery, extension 5461
House Gallery, extension 2941

SENATE PERIODICAL PRESS GALLERY

Superintendent.—William M. Perry, 5320 85th Avenue, Lanham, Md., Apt. C-9. Phone, 577-5385.
Assistant Superintendent.—Lisa H. Dalton, 3213 13th Street South, Arlington, Va. Phone, 671-5982.

HOUSE PERIODICAL PRESS GALLERY

Superintendent.—Clarence T. Day, 3801 South 16th Street, Arlington, Va. Phone, 671-7119.
Assistant Superintendent.—Jack D. Kearns, 2607 Naylor Road SE. Phone, 584-0337.

EXECUTIVE COMMITTEE

Neil MacNeil, Chairman
Samuel Shaffer, Vice Chairman
Earl B. Abrams, Secretary
W. B. Ragsdale
David W. Secrest
George Cullen

RULES GOVERNING PERIODICAL PRESS GALLERIES

1. Persons desiring admission to the Periodical Press Galleries of Congress shall make application to the Speaker, as required by rule XXXIV of the House of Representatives, and to the Committee on Rules and Administration of the Senate, as required by rule VI for the regulation of the Senate wing of the Capitol; and shall state in writing the names of all newspapers or publications or news associations by which they are employed, and what other occupation or employment they may have, if any; and they shall further declare that they are not engaged in the prosecution of claims pending before Congress or the departments, and will not become so engaged while allowed admission to the galleries; that they are not employed in any legislative or executive department of the Government, or by any foreign government or any representative thereof; and that they are not employed, directly or indirectly, by any stock exchange, board of trade, or other organization, or member thereof, or brokerage house or broker, engaged in the buying and selling of any security or commodity, or by any person or corporation having legislation before Congress, and will not become so engaged while retaining membership in the galleries. Holders of visitor's cards who may be allowed temporary admission to the galleries must conform to the restrictions of this rule.
2. The applications required by rule 1 shall be authenticated in a manner that shall be satisfactory to the executive committee of the Periodical Correspondents' Association who shall see that the occupation of the galleries is confined to bona fide and accredited resident correspondents, newsgatherers, or reporters of reputable standing who represent one or more periodicals which regularly publish a

substantial volume of news material of either general or of an economic, industrial,
technical or trade character, published for profit and supported chiefly by advertising, and owned and operated independently of any industry, business, association, or institution; and it shall be the duty of the executive committee at their
discretion to report violation of the privileges of the galleries to the Speaker, or to
the Senate Committee on Rules and Administration, and pending action thereon
the offending correspondent may be suspended.

3. Persons engaged in other occupations whose chief attention is not given to
the gathering or reporting of news for periodicals requiring such continuous
service shall not be entitled to admission to the Periodical Press Galleries.   The
Periodical Correspondents' list in the CONGRESSIONAL DIRECTORY shall be a list
only of persons whose chief attention is given to such service for news periodicals,
as described in rule 2, except that admission shall not be denied if his other work
is such as to make him eligible to the Press Galleries or Radio Correspondents'
Galleries.

4. Members of the families of correspondents are not entitled to the privileges
of the galleries.

5. The Periodical Press Galleries shall be under the control of an executive
committee elected by members of the Periodical Correspondents' Association,
subject to the approval and supervision of the Speaker of the House of Representatives and the Senate Committee on Rules and Administration.

JOHN W. McCORMACK,
Speaker, House of Representatives.

B. EVERETT JORDAN,
Chairman, Senate Committee on Rules and Administration.

MEMBERS ENTITLED TO ADMISSION

[The * designates those whose wives or husbands accompany them]

Name	Representing—	Residence
*Abrams, Earl B	Broadcasting Magazine, Television Magazine.	3518 N. Utah St., Arlington, Va.
*Adams, Alan E	McGraw-Hill Publications	7223 Chestnut St., Chevy Chase, Md.
*Adams, Alvadee	U. S. Lady	3303 Carolina Pl., Alexandria, Va.
*Adams, John H	U. S. News & World Report	3700 N. Edison, Arlington, Va.
Agniel, Lucien D	U.S. News & World Report	3820 Kanawha St.
*Alsop, Stewart	The Saturday Evening Post	3520 Springland Lane.
*Amberg, Mathew K	BNA Publications	6-E Hillside Rd., Greenbelt, Md.
*Anderson, Howard J	BNA Publications	4201 Cathedral Ave.
Andronicos, Basil E	Army Times Publishing Co	2110 R St.
*Arndt, Carol H	Army Times Publishing Co	318 Valley Brook Dr., Falls Church, Va.
*Arnold, Mark R	The National Observer	706 Ripley St., Alexandria, Va.
*Ashlock, James R	Aviation Week	1110 Darwin Dr., Falls Church, Va.
*Bagdikian, Ben H	The Saturday Evening Post	3303 Highland Pl.
Bagley, Edna	Look	4840 St. Barnabas Rd. SE.
Baker, George H	Chilton Publications	9037 Fort Foote Rd., Washington, D.C.
Barney, Don	McGraw-Hill Publications	1418 44th St.
*Barron, John D	Reader's Digest	2406 Surrey Lane, Falls Church, Va.
*Booda, Larry L	Compass Publications	3170 N. Pollard St., Arlington, Va.
*Baukhage, H. R	Army Times Publishing Co	3100 Connecticut Ave.
*Bayless, Glen	McGraw-Hill Publications	5042 S. Chesterfield Rd., Arlington, Va.
Beach, Clarke	U. S. News & World Report	9628 Culver St., Kensington, Md.
*Becker, Donald	U. S. News & World Report	5756 Kirby Rd., Falls Church, Va.
*Beller, William	American Aviation	106 Denver Rd., Silver Spring, Md.
*Beman, Lewis B	McGraw-Hill Publications	3324 Highland Pl.
Berens, Raymond Alan	U.S. Investor	1600 N. Quinn St., Arlington, Va.
Berliner, Donald L	Western Aerospace	1426 21st St.
Best, Frank M	U.S. Medicine	1601 18th St.
*Blamphin, John M	Medical World News	1420 Oak Ridge Rd., Falls Church, Va.
Blanding, Warren	Transportation & Distribution Management.	Glenn Dale Rd., Glenn Dale, Md.
*Blumenthal, Frederick G	Parade Magazine	911 25th St.
*Bolton, George W	U. S. News & World Report	3115 Quebec Pl.
*Booker, Simeon S	Jet, Ebony, Hue and Tan	4405 Campbell Dr. SE.
Booth, Sidney E	Broadcasting Magazine-Television Magazine.	2029 Q St.
*Booth, Windsor	National Geographic Magazine	15 W. Kirke, Chevy Chase, Md.
*Born, Roscoe C., Jr	The National Observer	10416 Leslie Ct., Silver Spring, Md.
*Botzum, John R., Jr	Steel	444 Kennebec St., Oxon Hill, Md.
Bouchard, Joseph	Army Times Publishing Co	8110 Inverchapel Rd., Springfield, Va.
*Bourjaily, Monte, Jr	Army Times Publishing Co	3714 Underwood St. Chevy Chase, Md.
*Bradlee, Benjamin C	Newsweek	3321 N St.
*Bramley, Eric	American Aviation Publications	100 Morningside Dr., Alexandria, Va.
*Bratter, Herbert M	Banking	3000 39th St.
*Brayman, Harold M	The National Observer	5209 Augusta St.
*Brenner, Madeline H	Agricultural Services	2513 Executive Ave., Falls Church, Va.
*Bridge, John F	The National Observer	34 Quincy St., Chevy Chase, Md.
*Brodey, Sherman	Broadcasting	1360 Peabody St.
*Brome, Richard K	U. S. News & World Report	6515 Callander Dr., Bethesda, Md.

843

MEMBERS ENTITLED TO ADMISSION—Continued

Name	Representing—	Residence
Brownlow, Cecil	Aviation Week	6504 Rockhurst Rd., Bethesda, Md.
Bruch, Charles M	Public Utilities Fortnightly	614 North Carolina Ave. SE.
*Bryant, William C	U. S. News & World Report	803 Hall Pl., Alexandria, Va.
*Brynes, Asher	New Republic	1503 30th St.
*Bucknell, Martha B	Time-Life	3601 Tilden St.
*Bundy, David Reed	American Aviation	534 6th St. SE.
*Burkhardt, Robert	The Skipper, Air Transport World, Travel Weekly, Business Travel, Flying.	112 Calvert Rd., Rockville, Md.
*Bussmann, Charles H	Compass Publications	1302 S. Thomas St., Arlington, Va.
*Byrne, Don	American Aviation	4410 Briarwood Ct., Annandale, Va.
*Callahan, Vincent F., Jr	Quick Frozen Foods	1700 Devine St., McLean, Va.
*Callander, Bruce D	Army Times Publishing Co	Box 123, R. F. D. #3, Vienna, Va.
*Cameron, Juan M	Time-Life	4521 Garfield St.
*Campbell, Alexander	The Economist (London)	2832 Northampton St.
*Carlson, Herbert P	Conover-Mast Publications	115 Hilltop Rd., Silver Spring, Md.
Carney, Lawrence R	Army Times Publishing Co	672 Ripley St., Alexandria, Va.
*Carter, Don	The National Observer	2601 Woodley Pl.
*Carter, Philip D	Newsweek	3217 Volta Pl.
*Carty, Winthrop P	Vision Magazine	3062 Q st.
*Castaneda, Carlos M	Bohemia Libre	2920 Hickory St., Alexandria, Va.
Chamberlin, Anne N	The Saturday Evening Post	2704 O St.
Chandler, Ruth B	Army Times Publishing Co	4817 36th St.
*Cherry, Ralph L	Oil, Paint, and Drug Reporter	428 Meadow Lane, Falls Church, Va.
*Chew, Peter T	The National Observer	4664 Garfield St.
*Cheshire, Herbert W	McGraw-Hill Publications	117 White Oaks Dr., Alexandria, Va.
*Chiang, Joseph, Sr	Reconstruction (Formosa)	100 Woodridge Ave., Silver Spring, Md.
*Clark, Albert	U. S. News & World Report	1 Copa Court, Falls Church, Va.
*Clark, Blake	Reader's Digest	2440 Kalorama Rd.
*Cohen, Stanley E	Advertising Age	1106 Edgevale Rd., Silver Spring, Md.
*Coman, Thomas F	BNA Publications	7613 Takoma Ave., Takoma Park, Md.
Cook, Jesse L., Jr	Time-Life	1115 16th St.
*Cook, Robert H	American Aviation Publications	5100 Kenwood Dr., Annandale, Va.
*Corr, John H	B.N.A. Publications	25 E. Wayne Ave., Silver Spring, Md.
*Corum, Richard L	U. S. News & World Report	3220 South 5th St., Arlington, Va.
*Coughlin, William J	American Aviation	1330 New Hampshire Ave.
*Covey, Charles W	Compass Publications	4232 Dalmatian Drive, McLean, Va.
*Crawford, Kenneth G	Newsweek	1412 30th St.
*Crosby, Ralph W	Iron Age	1208 Van Buren Dr., Annapolis, Md.
*Cruikshank, George E	U. S. News & World Report	Rt. 2, Springfield Dr., Germantown, Md.
*Cullen, George	BNA Publications	4545 Connecticut Ave.
*Curran, Lawrence J	American Aviation	4510 31st St. South, Arlington, Va.
*Damtoft, Walter A	The National Observer	11013 Montrose Ave., Garrett Park, Md.
Daniel, Urcel	BNA Publications	3025 Ontario Rd.
Darlington, George	Broadcasting Magazine, Television Magazine.	1622 Wisconsin Ave.
*David, Heather M	American Aviation Publications	2506 I St.
*Davis, Arthur L	Miller Publishing Co., Putnam Publishing Co.	4804 Alton Pl.
*Davis, LaMonte F	Army Times Publishing Co	4267 Vacation Lane, Arlington, Va.
*Dawson, Luther A	U. S. News & World Report	2226 King Pl.
*de Bausset, Philippe	Paris Match	5005 Fort Sumner Drive.
*deBrossard, Phoebe	Contractors & Engineers	942 24th St.
*Degler, Stanley E	BNA Publications	948 N. Livingston St., Arlington, Va.
*Demaree, Allan T	McGraw-Hill Publications	3325 Senator Ave., SE.
*Diggs, J. Frank	U. S. News & World Report	5090 37th St. North, Arlington, Va.
*Dinwoodey, Dean	BNA Publications	7200 Meadow Lane, Chevy Chase, Md.

MEMBERS ENTITLED TO ADMISSION—Continued

Name	Representing—	Residence
*Dirks, Lee E	The National Observer	10002 Montauk Ave., Bethesda, Md.
*Doane, Donald P	U. S. News & World Report	3000 Connecticut Ave.
Donnel, Edward H., Jr	BNA Publications	Cobb Island, Md.
*Downing, Donn F	Time-Life	9808 E. Bexhill Dr., Kensington, Md.
*Drach, J. William	Army Times Publishing Co	134 Spring Ct., Falls Church, Va.
Drew, Elizabeth	The Reporter	2727 29th St.
Drury, Allen	Reader's Digest	2121 Massachusetts Ave.
*Duncan, Marie N	U.S. Investor	8637 11th Ave., Silver Spring, Md.
*Elswit, Jerome H	BNA Publications	205 Centre St., Fairfax, Va.
Ellis, Robert	Time-Life	1120 Conn. Ave.
*Evans, Tracy Lewis	BNA Publications	6603 Hopewell Ave., Springfield, Va.
Exton, Elaine	American School Board Journal	4200 Cathedral Ave.
*Famiglietti, Eugene P	Army Times Publishing Co	9519 Old Georgetown Rd., Bethesda, Md.
Farley, Florence P	Insurance Advocate	No. 1 Scott Circle.
*Fentress, Simmons	Time-Life	3606 Warren St.
Fingal, Wallace R	American Brewer, Gussow Publications	2005 North Woodrow St., Arlington, Va.
*Fink, Donald E., Jr	Aviation Week	8605 Adams Dr.
Fischer, Dean E	Time-Life	2146 I St.
*Fitzgerald, Fred	Broadcasting Magazine, Television Magazine.	10206 Duvawn Pl., Silver Spring, Md.
*Fleming, John R	U. S. News & World Report	4200 Rosemary St., Chevy Chase, Md.
*Flieger, Howard W	U. S. News & World Report	6818 Selkirk Dr., Bethesda, Md.
*Foltz, Charles, Jr	U. S. News & World Report	RFD 1, Box 21C, Brookeville, Md.
Footlick, Jerrold K	The National Observer	6164 Springhill Dr., Greenbelt, Md.
*Fox, Derek	U. S. News & World Report	Rte. 1, Box 471, Great Falls, Va.
*Ford, John J	Army Times Publishing Co	1110 Westbriar Ct., Vienna, Va.
*France, Boyd	McGraw-Hill Publications	10304 Summit Ave., Kensington, Md.
*Francis, Lorania K	Western Oil and Refining	2808 McKinley Pl.
*Franklin Jean A	Time-Life	1414 17th St.
*Freeland, Stephen	U. S. News & World Report	3430 Quebec St.
Freeman, Neal B	National Review	1337 21st St.
Fuller, Helen	New Republic	812 17th St.
Fulton, Kenneth	Army Times Publishing Co	4921 Seminary Rd., Alexandria, Va.
*Furlow, Barbara Blair	U. S. News & World Report	6005 Wynnwood Rd.
*Galbraith, Fred E., Jr	U. S. News & World Report	3854 Columbia Pike, Arlington, Va.
*Gapp, F. W	U. S. News & World Report	15 Dogwood La., Rt. 3, Box 108, Vienna, Va.
*Gardner, Charles S., III	McGraw-Hill Publications	5431 32d St.
*Gates, Edmond N	Army Times Publishing Co	3008 North Edison St., Arlington, Va.
*Gecowets, George A	Transportation & Distribution Management.	5651-222 Sanger Ave., Alexandria, Va.
*George, Gerald W	The National Observer	2711 Newton, Wheaton, Md.
*Gerecht, Ash	Contract	1109 Ruppert Rd., Silver Spring, Md.
*Gerlach, Leroy C	U.S. News & World Report	11836 Charles Rd., Silver Spring, Md.
Gilmore, Kenneth O	Reader's Digest	633 South Carolina Ave. SE.
Ginn, Opal B	Parade Magazine	5420 Connecticut Ave.
*Goldsmith, Al	Insurance Advocate	5515 Cornish Rd., Bethedsa, Md.
*Goldsmith, Alyce Moran	Insurance Advocate	5515 Cornish Rd., Bethesda, Md.
*Goodpaster, Edwin W	Time-Life	6304 Owen Pl., Bethesda, Md.
*Goolrick, William K	The Saturday Evening Post	5316 Blackstone Rd.
Gorey, Hays	Time-Life	1120 Connecticut Ave.
*Grant, Ben J	U. S. News & World Report	6707 Broxburn Dr., Bethesda, Md.
Granton, E. Fannie	Jet Magazine	2251 Mount View Pl. SE.
*Gray, William S	Newsweek	700 3d St., SW.
Greenfield, Meg	The Reporter	1324 35th St.
*Gretschel, Walter O	U. S. News & World Report	9631 Carriage Rd., Kensington, Md.
*Guy, Virginia	Flare Publications	4319 18th St.

MEMBERS ENTITLED TO ADMISSION—Continued

Name	Representing—	Residence
*Hacker, David W	The National Observer	9302 Sutton Pl., Silver Spring, Md.
*Haller, Ellis M	U. S. News & World Report	5125 Westpath Way.
Hall, Mildred P	The Billboard Publishing Co	4519 32d St., Mount Rainier, Md.
Hall, William	American Aviation	215 Kent Rd., Alexandria, Va.
*Halmos, E. E., Jr	Contractors and Engineers; Progressive Architecture; Western Construction; H. L. Peace Publications.	10 West Argyle St., Rockville, Md.
*Hansen, J. Woods	Aviation Week	805 Albany Ave., Alexandria, Va.
*Harbour, Daniel L	BNA Publications	2917 Legation St.
*Hart, N. Key	U. S. News & World Report	3710 Williams La., Chevy Chase, Md.
*Hallam, H. C	The National Underwriter, National Underwriter Life Insurance Edition, The Black Diamond, and The Tobacco Leaf.	3000 Tilden St.
*Handleman, Howard	U. S. News & World Report	4910 Brawner St., McLean, Va.
*Hannifin, Jerry	Time-Life	1378 4th St. SW.
*Harmon, Frederick M	U. S. News & World Report	1913 35th Pl.
*Harrison, Gilbert A	New Republic	3556 Macomb St.
*Heck, Peter R	Transportation & Distribution Management.	6800 East Ave., Chevy Chase, Md.
*Heinly, David R	BNA Publications	9805 Taylor Ave., Forrest Knolls, Md.
*Henck, Fred W	Telephone Engineer	2407 North Quebec St., Arlington, Va.
*Henkin, Daniel Z	Journal of the Armed Forces	5601 13th St.
*Henzey, William V	American Aviation Publications	2020 Crossley Pl., Alexandria, Va.
*Hercher, Wilmot W	U. S. News & World Report	5906 Aberdeen Rd., Bethesda, Md.
*Hermann, Arthur F	McGraw-Hill Publications	203 East Indian Springs Dr., Silver Spring, Md.
Hermann, Robert L	The National Observer	2900 Adams Mill Rd.
*Herzberg, Robert A	Petersen Publishing Co	3635 6th St. SE.
*Hirsch, Phil	Mayor and Manager Magazine	5916 Conway Rd., Bethesda, Md.
*Hoehling, A. A	Army Times Publishing Co	3818 Harrison St.
Hoffman, Shirlee	Newsweek	2311 15th St.
*Holcomb, George B	BNA Publications	3617 S. 19th St., Arlington, Va.
*Hornberger, A. Michael	Journal of the Armed Forces	1713 I St.
*Horowitz, Robert S	Army Times Publishing Co	4616 Chevy Chase Blvd., Chevy Chase, Md.
*Hotz, Robert B	Aviation Week	9720 Holmhurst Ave., Bethesda, Md.
Howard, John B	U.S. News & World Report	7315 Broxburn Ct., Bethesda, Md.
*Hudoba, Michael	Sports Afield	Leeds Manor, Hume, Va.
*Hughes, Thomas H	U.S. News & World Report	1113 Westbriar Ct., Vienna, Va.
*Hull, E. W. Seabrook	Electronic Design	Rt. 1, Box 145, Springfield, Va.
*Husted, Walter	U.S. News & World Report	Rt. 6, Box 761, Alexandria, Va.
*Ingram, Daniel T., Jr	BNA Publications	5121 Newport Ave.
*James, Edwin H	Broadcasting Magazine, Television Magazine.	8508 Burning Tree Rd., Bethesda, Md.
Jencks, Christopher	New Republic	530 Greenwood Rd., Towson, Md.
Jennings, Pauline	U.S. News & World Report	4706 Hunt Ave., Chevy Chase, Md.
Jensen, Anni	The Skipper, Air Transport World, Travel Weekly, Business Travel, Flying.	2214 Massachusetts Ave.
Johnsen, Katherine	Aviation Week	936 24th St.
*Johnson, Clair	U. S. News & World Report	3521 N. Kensington St., Arlington, Va.
Johnson, Keith R	Time-Life	2734 Olive St.
*Johnson, Max S	U. S. News & World Report	2910 Garfield St.
*Jones, George E	U. S. News & World Report	5004 Klingle St.
Jones, Lucy Cobb	U.S. News & World Report	2500 Q St.
*Judge, John F	American Aviation Publications	620 Scout Dr., Fairfax, Va.
Just, Ward	Newsweek	1750 Pennsylvania Ave.
*Kahn, Ephraim	Financial World	3610 Macomb St.
*Kahn, H. R	Automotive News	3610 Macomb St.
Kelly, Frances P	Time-Life	7413 Foster St., District Heights, Md.
Kelso, Arthur D	BNA Publications	1825 Q St.
Kennedy, Charlotte	Newsweek	2420 16th St.
*King, Art	Broadcasting Magazine, Television Magazine.	9318 East Parkhill Dr., Bethesda, Md.

MEMBERS ENTITLED TO ADMISSION—Continued

Name	Representing—	Residence
*Kinney, Gene T	Oil and Gas Journal	2601 S. Glebe Rd., Arlington, Va.
Klass, Philip J	Aviation Week	4201 Massachusetts Ave.
*Klebanoff, H	U. S. News & World Report	12802 Teaberry Rd., Silver Spring, Md.
*Klein, Donald	American Aviation Publications	1017 Flagtree Lane, Baltimore, Md.
Kline, Charles H	U.S. News & World Report	2123 California St.
Kopkind, Andrew	New Republic	1241 19th St.
*Kolcum, Edward H	Aviation Week	3108 Circle Hill Rd., Alexandria, Va.
*Kornberg, Warren	McGraw Hill Publications	1205 Holly St.
*Kranish, Arthur	Western Aerospace	3611 Taylor St., Chevy Chase, Md.
*Krauss, Lawrence	BNA Publications	2939 Van Ness St.
*Kreh, William R	Army Times Publishing Co	4029 Byrd Rd., Kensington, Md.
*Kraft, Joseph	Harpers Magazine	3021 N St.
*Kuett, John A	Exchange & Commissary News & Catering Magazine	3705 Wagon Wheel Rd., Alexandria, Va.
*LaFond, Charles D	American Aviation Publications	8601 London Ct., Springfield, Va.
Lawton, Virginia	Reader's Digest	1021 Arlington Blvd., Arlington, Va.
Lamont, Lansing	Time-Life	5163 Tilden St.
*Lee, James F	U. S. News & World Report	4201 Cathedral Ave.
Leighton, Frances Spatz	This Week Magazine	3636 16th St.
*LeRoy, L. David	U. S. News & World Report	Rt. 4, Box 336-A, Vienna, Va.
Lewis, Jay S	Television Age	1515 28th St.
*Lindsay, John J	Newsweek	7322 14th St.
*Long, E. John	Geo-marine Technology	7601 Exeter Rd., Bethesda, Md.
*Loomis, Donald O	McGraw-Hill Publications	1601 N. Roosevelt St., Arlington, Va.
*Lucas, Hugh	Army Times Publishing Co	3314 Jones Bridge Rd., Chevy Chase, Md.
*Lyman, Carson F	U. S. News & World Report	6740 Selkirk Dr., Bethesda, Md.
Lynch, Kathleen A	BNA Publications	1500 Arlington Blvd., Arlington, Va.
MacDougall, William L	U.S. News & World Report	2155 N. Quebec St., Arlington, Va.
*MacNeil, Neil	Time-Life	713 Quaint Acres Rd., Silver Spring, Md.
*MacKaye, Dorothy Disney	The Ladies Home Journal	2817 Woodley Rd.
*MacKaye, Milton	Saturday Evening Post	2817 Woodley Rd.
*McMahon, Thelma	Newsweek	12410 Shadow Lane, Belair, Md.
McManus, Michael J	Time-Life	1630 33d St.
McNair, Donald W	Baking Industry	429 Valley Lane, Falls Church, Va.
*Mace, Donald	Army Times Publishing Co	430 Vista Dr., Falls Church, Va.
*Magidson, Adolph	BNA Publications	201 E. Indian Spring Dr., Silver Spring, Md.
*Malia, Thomas M	Telephone Engineer	905 NW. Drive, Silver Spring, Md.
Mansfield, Anne	Vision Magazine	1666 33d St.
*Marashian, Onnic	McGraw-Hill Publishing Co	9732 Glen Ave., Forest Glen, Md.
*March, Anthony	Army Times Publishing Co	9006 Burdette Rd., Bethesda, Md.
Margolin, Nathan J	U.S. News & World Report	1311 Delaware Ave. SW.
*Mattingly, LeRoy S	U. S. News & World Report	13106 Holdridge, Silver Spring, Md.
*Methvin, Eugene H	The Reader's Digest	3105 Edgehill Dr., Alexandria, Va.
*Meyers, Harold B	Time-Life	12308 Clement Lane, Silver Spring, Md.
*Michie, Laurence	Television Digest	1960 Biltmore St.
*Midgely, John	The Economist (London)	2607 O St.
*Miller, Helen Hill	New Republic	1235 31st St.
Miller, Hope Ridings	The Diplomat	1868 Columbia Road.
*Miller, Isidore	BNA Publications	4200 Cathedral Ave.
Milligan, Norma	Newsweek	1908 Florida Ave.
*Mills, Bert	Sales Management, Motor, Motor Boating	310 Beverly Dr., Alexandria, Va.
*Moore, Arthur	McGraw-Hill Publications	1207 Duke St., Alexandria, Va.
Morrissey, deRosset	Time-Life	1545 18th St.

MEMBERS ENTITLED TO ADMISSION—Continued

Name	Representing—	Residence
*Mulliken, John	Time-Life	5515 Cedar Parkway, Chevy Chase, Md.
*Murphy, Charles J. V	Time-Life	1698 32d St.
*Musselman, Norman Burkey	McGraw-Hill Publications	4 West Grove Dr., Alexandria, Va.
*Nail, Dawson B	Television Digest	709 Arlington Blvd., Falls Church, Va.
*Neary, John Anthony, Jr	Time-Life	Alban Towers Hotel.
Nelan, Bruce	Time-Life	1120 Connecticut Ave.
*Neuhalter, John W	Exchange & Commissary News & Catering Magazine.	8508 16th St., Silver Spring, Md.
*Newman, David R	American Aviation Publications	6600 Luzon Ave.
Nicholson, John B	McGraw-Hill Publications	2025 I St.
Nicoll, A. Olivia	American Milk Review	2011 Key Blvd., Arlington, Va.
*Norman, Lloyd H	Newsweek	5420 31st St.
*Normyle, William J	Aviation Week	3900 Childs Lane, Alexandria, Va.
North, Margot B	Time-Life	4600 Connecticut Ave.
*Norton, Howard M	U.S. News & World Report	4002 Laird Pl., Chevy Chase, Md.
Nugent, Janet	Medical Economics, Putman Publishing Co., Miller Publishing Co.	1321 M St.
*Oberdorfer, Don	The Saturday Evening Post	4630 30th St.
*Olcheski, William J	Army Times Publishing Co	6711 Moly Dr., Falls Church, Va.
*Oliver, Wayne	U. S. News & World Report	2750 South Ives St., Arlington, Va.
*O'Lone, Richard G	Aviation Week	1016 Stirling Rd., Silver Spring, Md.
*O'Neill, Mary Jane	Medical World News	7116 Armat Dr., Bethesda, Md.
Paisner, Bruce L	Time-Life	2027 O St.
*Parker, James E	Army Times Publishing Co	5046 Dunlap St.
Parker, John R	Army Times Publishing Co	142 12th St. SE.
*Parker, Robert L	American Aviation Publications	6852 Columbia Pike, Arlington, Va.
Parker, William	The Civil Service Reporter	Hotel Plaza.
*Payne, Seth T	McGraw-Hill Publications	7006 Oak Forest Lane, Bethesda, Md.
Peter, George E	Farm News Service	Tyler Bldg., Arlington Towers, Arlington, Va.
*Perry, James M	The National Observer	1213 K St.
*Platt, Charles M	U. S. News & World Report	5503 Mass. Ave., Falls Church, Va.
Pruden, Wesley, Jr	The National Observer	9205 New Hampshire Ave., Silver Spring, Md.
*Pursglove, S. David	Popular Mechanics	320 Independence Ave. SE.
Raedy, Michael L	Pacific Shipper	2480 16th St.
*Ragsdale, W. B	U. S. News & World Report	406 Dale Dr., Silver Spring, Md.
*Raleigh, William G	BNA Publications	1408 N. Buchanan St., Arlington, Va.
*Ramsey, Roy S., Jr	BNA Publications	1211 5th St. SE.
Randall, Richard R	Bankers Monthly	2141 I St.
*Rathbun, Benjamin, Jr	BNA Publications	3711 Upton St.
Redmond, Wilfrid	Bakers Weekly	4113 Glenridge St., Kensington, Md.
*Reece, Paul E	Army Times Publishing Co	4091 North 35th St., Arlington, Va.
*Reed, Macon, Jr	Army Times Publishing Co	1230 New Hampshire Ave.
Reed, Patricia Jean	Conover-Mast Publications	4305 Underwood St., Hyattsville, Md.
*Regeimbal, Neil R	Chilton Publications	13811 Marianna Dr., Rockville, Md.
*Reid, F. Margaret	McGraw-Hill Publications	1659 Webster St., NE.
*Rhea, John	American Aviation Publications	2037 Park Rd.
Richardson, David B	U.S. News & World Report	3305 Rolling Rd., Chevy Chase, Md.
Ridgeway, James F	New Republic	1634 16th St. NW.
*Riley, John H., Jr	Time-Life	3541 S St.
*Rippey, Stephens	Drug Topics and Drug Trade News	6408 31st Pl.
*Risley, Ralph E	Army Times Publishing Co	2446 Wagner St. SE.
*Ritter, Richard D	Army Times Publishing Co	2201 M St.
Riveire, George M., Jr	BNA Publications	6820 Oregon Ave.
*Roberts, Charles W	Newsweek	8400 Fenway Rd., Bethesda, Md.
*Robertson, Caroline	McGraw-Hill Publications	7603 Glenside Dr., Takoma Park, Md.
*Robinson, Archie W	U. S. News & World Report	7209 Oakridge Ave., Chevy Chase, Md.
*Robinson, L. Noble	U. S. News & World Report	3107 Macomb St.

MEMBERS ENTITLED TO ADMISSION—Continued

Name	Representing—	Residence
*Rose, Turner	U. S. News & World Report	6006 Rhode Island Ave., Falls Church, Va.
Ross, Richard S	U. S. News & World Report	412 Tulane Rd., Alexandria, Va.
*Rowen, Hobart	Newsweek	5701 Warwick Pl., Chevy Chase, Md.
*Ruth, Robert W	U. S. News & World Report	9422 Locust Hill Rd., Bethesda, Md.
*Sadler, Christine	McCall's	2713 Dumbarton Ave.
*Salisbury, Grant A	U. S. News & World Report	R.F.D. #1, Myersville, Md.
*Sandifer, T. N	Lockwood Publications	1524 44th St.
*Saunders, Richard E	The Practical Builder	4120 Woodbind, Chevy Chase, Md.
*Sbrilli, Beverly B	Time-Life	901 N. Wayne St., Arlington, Va.
*Scanlan, Thomas R	Army Times Publishing Co	6128 32d Pl.
*Schappi, John V	BNA Publications	5030 Sherrier Pl.
Schatz, Gerald S	The National Observer	1930 Columbia Rd.
*Schecter, Mal	Modern Medicine	10512 Weymouth St., Bethesda, Md.
*Scheibla, Shirley H	Barron's	12 Tansey Dr., Falls Church, Va.
*Schüler, Alfred	Der Spiegel	5009 Greenway Dr.
*Schwartz, Adele Chidakel	American Aviation Publications	525 Thayer Ave., Silver Spring, Md.
*Schweitz, Robert E	Army Times Publishing Co	413 Haynsworth Pl., Fairfax, Va.
*Sclanders, Ian	Maclean's Magazine	3110 34th St.
*Scott, Philip Allen	Army Times Publishing Co	9621 Brunette Ave., Silver Spring, Md.
*Scott, John C	BNA Publications	6411 Stoneham Rd., Bethesda, Md.
*Scott, Owen L	U. S. News & World Report	2001 Plymouth St.
*Secrest, David W	McGraw-Hill Publications	6508 E. Halbert Rd., Bethesda, Md.
*Sellon, Perry K	U. S. News & World Report	7600 Arnet Lane, Bethesda, Md.
*Sentner, Mary Steele	Good Housekeeping	2601 Woodley Pl.
Serfass, D. Gail	Time-Life	122 Hunting Towers East, Alexandria, Va.
*Shaffer, Samuel	Newsweek	3750 Kanawha St.
*Shalett, Sidney	U. S. News & World Report	2853 Ontario Rd.,
*Shoenfeld, Jerome S	BNA Publications	367 Southampton Dr., Silver Spring, Md.
*Shoenfeld, Rosemary	BNA Publications	939 26th St.
*Shoemaker, Randall	Army Times Publishing Co	2148 O St.
*Sidey, Hugh S	Time-Life	10825 Stanmore Dr., Bethesda, Md.
*Silva, Michel	Time-Life	13224 Locksley Lane, Silver Spring, Md.
*Simmons, Henry T	Newsweek	2225 Hall Pl.
Sinaga, Edward D	Pembangunan	2122 Massachusetts Ave.
Siverts, Grant H	BNA Publications	1823 Riggs Pl.
*Slinkman, John	Army Times Publishing Co	6803 East Ave., Chevy Chase, Md.
*Sloat, Barbara	Time-Life	3612 N St.
*Smith, Beverly, Jr	The Saturday Evening Post	4907 Potomac Ave.
*Smith, Donald	U. S. News & World Report	6630 31st St.
*Smith, Grace Cutler	The Saturday Evening Post	4907 Potomac Ave.
Smith, Jane Denis	Reader's Digest	1727 Massachusetts Ave.
*Smith, Richard	McGraw-Hill Publications	1728 Church St.
*Smith, Vincent B	McGraw-Hill Publications	705 Terrace Dr., Annandale, Va.
*Smith, William	McGraw-Hill Publications	RFD 2, McLean, Va.
*Snyder, J. D	Clissold Publications	2921 24th St. North, Arlington, Va.
*Solomon, Goody L	Modern Textiles	1530 16th St.
*Sprinkle, Karl	Army Times Publishing Co	3114 Grove St., Alexandria, Va.
*Stanfield, Robert I	American Aviation Publications	4805 Chilton Ct., McLean, Va.
*Steele, John L	Time-Life	3100 Newark St.
Stefan, Patricia	U.S. Medicine	1427 33d St.
*Stern, Philip M	New Republic	2301 S St.
Stevens, Francis B	U. S. News & World Report	2100 N St.
*Stevenson, Charles	Reader's Digest Association	6800 Selkirk Dr., Bethesda, Md.
*Stewart, John D	BNA Publications	2869 Beechwood Cir., Arlington, Va.
*Still, Lawrence A	Johnson Publications	2904 Newton Ave. NE.
*Stockstill, Louis	Journal of the Armed Forces	4545 Connecticut Ave.
*Stolley, Richard B	Time-Life	1601 18th St.
*Stone, Marvin L	U. S. News & World Report	415 Waterway Dr., Falls Church, Va.
Stout, Richard T	Newsweek	1750 Pennsylvania Ave.

MEMBERS ENTITLED TO ADMISSION—Continued

Name	Representing—	Residence
*Straight, Michael	New Republic	6300 Green Spring Road, Alexandria, Va.
St. Germain, Denise	The Saturday Evening Post	2400 Pennsylvania Ave.
*Sutherland, John	U. S. News & World Report	3720 Gunston Rd., Alexandria, Va.
Szameitat, Dorothea	The Economist (England)	2144 California St.
*Taft, Walter J	Simmons-Boardman Publications	4606 Merivale Rd., Chevy Chase, Md.
Taishoff, Lawrence B	Broadcasting Magazine, Television Magazine.	4201 Cathedral Ave.
*Taishoff, Sol	Broadcasting Magazine, Television Magazine.	4201 Cathedral Ave.
*Tall, Robert E	Telephone Engineer, Popular Electronics; Industrial Electronic Engineer and Maintenance.	9401 Sierra St., Silver Spring, Md.
*Tanzer, Lester	U.S. News & World Report	4839 N. 30th St., Arlington, Va.
Taylor, Hal	American Aviation	2420 16th St.
*Taylor, Ray J	Washington World	6207 Lee Hwy., Arlington, Va.
*Tennant, Harry L	Watson Publications & Interavia Publications (Swiss).	Burke, Va.
*Terry, Wallace	Time-Life	1443 Chapin St.
*Thayer, Charles W	The Saturday Evening Post	2428 Tracy Pl.
Theobald, Richard J	U. S. News & World Report	3606 Norton Pl. NW.
*Thomas, Essel P., Jr	America's Textile Reporter and U. S. Investor.	4102 Stoconga Dr., Beltsville, Md.
*Thomas, Marilyn A	America's Textile Reporter and U. S. Investor.	4102 Stoconga Dr., Beltsville, Md.
*Trainor, James L	American Aviation Publications	6421 Fairbanks, Hyattsville, Md.
*Trippel, Peg O'Curran	The Fish Boat	2152 S. Taylor St., Arlington, Va.
*Turner, Richard L	U. S. News & World Report	2116 S. Buchanan St., Arlington, Va.
*Van Dernoot, Harry	McGraw-Hill Publications	10809 East Nolcrest Dr., Silver Spring, Md.
*Van Osten, Richard	American Aviation Publications	900 Albion Ct., Fairfax, Va.
*Van Voorst, L. Bruce	Newsweek	309 Bright Ave., McLean, Va.
*Volkov, Leon	Newsweek	6301 Crathie La., Bethesda, Md.
Vondracek, M. Jon	Time-Life	1825 24th St.
*Warner, Albert L	U. S. News & World Report	4502 Long Meadow Rd., McLean, Va.
*Warren, Albert	Television Digest	6005 28th St.
Waugh, Mildred O	Haire Publications	5808 Hitt Ave., McLean, Va.
*Weaver, Peter	Forbes Magazine	1504 Balls Hill Rd., McLean, Va.
*Wecksler, A. N	Conover-Mast Publications	8313 Woodhaven Blvd., Bethesda, Md.
*Weigel, Edwin Price	U. S. News & World Report	415 MacArthur Ave. NE., Vienna, Va.
Weingarten, Catherine	Northwester Miller Food Processing	2908 Q St.
Weintal, Edward	Newsweek	3111 N St.
*Welch, Francis X	Public Utilities Fortnightly	Churchton, Md.
Westlein, Patricia R	BNA Publications	1413 37th St.
White, Arthur	Time-Life	4201 Cathedral Ave.
*White, Dale B	U. S. News & World Report	Route 1, Box 322-B, Oakton, Va.
*White, Thomas D	Newsweek	4527 Jamestown Rd.
*Whiting, Charles E	U. S. News & World Report	6125 Western Ave.
*Whitney, Alan J	Army Times Publishing Co	109 Leesburg Pike, Falls Church, Va.
*Williamson, George E	McGraw-Hill Publications	118 W. Braddock Rd., Fairfax, Va.
*Wilson, George C	Aviation Week	6232 32d Pl.
*Wilson, Robert O	U. S. News & World Report	3418 Prospect St.
*Wise, Bill M	Time-Life	4000 Massachusetts Ave.
*Wolf, Anne	MAC Publications	4423 Stanford St., Chevy Chase, Md.
*Yap, Diosdado M	Weekly Graphic	5306 Belt Rd.
*Yudain, Bernard L	Time-Life	3126 Ordway St.
*Zeidenberg, Leonard	Broadcasting Magazine, Television Magazine.	5617 Northfield Rd., Bethesda, Md.
*Zim, Marvin	Time-Life	406 21st St.
*Zylstra, Donald L	American Aviation	506 Sudbury Rd., Linthicum Heights, Md.

PERIODICALS REPRESENTED

Phones, 224-3121; Senate Gallery, extension 5461
House Gallery, extension 2941

Periodical and telephone number	Name	Office
Advertising Age—RE 7-7659	Stanley E. Cohen	995 National Press Bldg.
Agricultural Services—RE 7-0174	Madeline H. Brenner	1616 H St.
Air Transport World—347-6492	Robert Burkhardt	1329 E St.
	Anni Jensen	1329 E St.
American Aviation Publications, Inc. ST 3-5400.	William Beller	1001 Vermont Ave.
	Eric Bramley	1001 Vermont Ave.
	David Reed Bundy	1001 Vermont Ave.
	Don Byrne	1001 Vermont Ave.
	Robert H. Cook	1001 Vermont Ave.
	William Coughlin	1001 Vermont Ave.
	Lawrence Curran	1001 Vermont Ave.
	Heather M. David	1001 Vermont Ave.
	William Hall	1001 Vermont Ave
	William V. Henzey	1001 Vermont Ave.
	John F. Judge	1001 Vermont Ave.
	Donald Klein	1001 Vermont Ave.
	Charles D. LaFond	1001 Vermont Ave.
	David R. Newman	1001 Vermont Ave.
	Robert L. Parker	1001 Vermont Ave.
	John Rhea	1001 Vermont Ave.
	Adele Chidakel Schwartz	1001 Vermont Ave.
	Robert I. Stanfield	1001 Vermont Ave.
	Hal Taylor	1001 Vermont Ave.
	James L. Trainor	1001 Vermont Ave.
	Richard Van Osten	1001 Vermont Ave.
	Donald L. Zylstra	1001 Vermont Ave.
American Brewer—ST 3-2482	Wallace R. Fingal	1210 National Press Bldg.
American Milk Review	A. Olivia Nicoll	1111 Barr Bldg.
America's Textile Reporter and U.S. Investors—347-3070.	Essell P. Thomas, Jr	1060 National Press Bldg.
	Marilyn A. Thomas	1060 National Press Bldg.
American School Board Journal 363-6944.	Elaine Exton	4200 Cathedral Ave.
American Salesman	Irvin D. Foos	1664 34th St.
	Basil E. Andronicos	2201 M St.
Army Times Publishing Co 296-8900.	H. R. Baukhage	2201 M St.
	Carol Arndt	2201 M St.
	Joseph Bouchard	2201 M St
	Monte Bourjaily, Jr	2201 M St.
	Bruce D. Callander	2201 M St.
	Lawrence Carney	2201 M St.
	Ruth B. Chandler	2201 M St.
	LaMonte F. Davis	2201 M St.
	J. William Drach	2201 M St.
	Eugene P. Famiglietti	2201 M St.
	John J. Ford	2201 M St.
	Kenneth Fulton	2201 M St.
	Edmond N. Gates	2201 M St.
	A. A. Hoehling	2201 M St.
	Robert S. Horowitz	2201 M St.
	William R. Kreh	2201 M St.
	Hugh Lucas	2201 M St.
	Donald Mace	2201 M St.
	William J. Olcheski	2201 M St.
	Anthony March	2201 M St.
	James E. Parker	2201 M St.
	John R. Parker	2201 M St.
	Macon Reed, Jr	2201 M St.
	Paul E. Reece	2201 M St.
	Ralph E. Risley	2201 M St.
	Richard D. Ritter	2201 M St.
	Thomas R. Scanlan	2201 M St.
	Robert E. Schweitz	2201 M St.
	Philip Allen Scott	2201 M St.
	Randall Shoemaker	2201 M St.
	John Slinkman	2201 M St.
	Karl Sprinkle	2201 M St.
	Alan J. Whitney	2201 M St.
Automotive News—NA 8-4303	H. R. Kahn	912 Colorado Bldg.
Aviation Week—RE 7-6630	James Ashlock	1174 National Press Bldg.
	Cecil Brownlow	1174 National Press Bldg.
	Donald Fink	1174 National Press Bldg.
	Woods Hansen	1174 National Press Bldg.

PERIODICALS REPRESENTED—Continued

Periodical and telephone number	Name	Office
Aviation Week—Continued	Robert B. Hotz	1174 National Press Bldg.
	Katherine Johnsen	1174 National Press Bldg.
	Philip J. Klass	1174 National Press Bldg.
	Edward H. Kolcum	1174 National Press Bldg.
	William Normyle	1174 National Press Bldg.
	Richard G. O'Lone	1174 National Press Bldg.
	George C. Wilson	1174 National Press Bldg.
Bakers Weekly—RE 7-4888	Wilfrid Redmond	1033 National Press Bldg.
Baking Industry—638-6707	Donald W. McNair	1317 F St.
Bankers Monthly—628-2609	Richard R. Randall	1104 National Press Bldg.
Banking—WO 6-7211	Herbert M. Bratter	3000 39th St.
Barron's—534-4231	Shirley H. Scheibla	12 Tansey Dr., Falls Church, Va.
Billboard Publishing Co—638-3422	Mildred P. Hall	889 National Press Bldg.
Black Diamond, The—ME 8-2253	H. C. Hallam	1331 G St.
Broadcasting Magazine, Television Magazine—ME 8-1022.	Sol Taishoff	1735 DeSales St.
	Earl B. Abrams	1735 DeSales St.
	Sidney E. Booth	1735 DeSales St.
	Sherman Brodey	1735 DeSales St.
	George Darlington	1735 DeSales St.
	Fred Fitzgerald	1735 DeSales St.
	Edwin H. James	1735 DeSales St.
	Art King	1735 DeSales St.
	Lawrence B. Taishoff	1735 DeSales St.
	Leonard Zeidenberg	1735 DeSales St.
BNA Publications—FE 3-6800	Mathew K. Amberg	1231 24th St.
	Howard J. Anderson	1231 24th St.
	Thomas F. Coman	1231 24th St.
	John H. Corr	1231 24th St.
	George Cullen	1231 24th St.
	Urcel Daniel	1231 24th St.
	Stanley E. Degler	1231 24th St.
	Dean Dinwoodey	1231 24th St.
	Edward H. Donnel, Jr	1231 24th St.
	Tracy Lewis Evans	1231 24th St.
	Jerome H. Elswit	1231 24th St.
	Daniel L. Harbour	1231 24th St.
	David R. Heinly	1231 24th St.
	George B. Holcomb	1231 24th St.
	Daniel T. Ingram Jr	1231 24th St.
	Arthur D. Kelso, Jr	1231 24th St.
	Lawrence Krauss	1231 24th St.
	Kathleen A. Lynch	1231 24th St.
	Adolph Magidson	1231 24th St.
	Isidore Miller	1231 24th St.
	William G. Raleigh	1231 24th St.
	Roy S. Ramsey, Jr	1231 24th St.
	Benjamin Rathbun, Jr	1231 24th St.
	George M. Riveire, Jr	1231 34th St.
	John V. Schappi	1231 24th St.
	John C. Scott	1231 24th St.
	Jerome S. Shoenfeld	1231 24th St.
	Rosemary Shoenfeld	1231 24th St.
	Grant H. Siverts	1231 24th St.
	John D. Stewart	1231 24th St.
	Patricia R. Westlein	1231 24th St.
Bohemia Libre—TE 6-6505	Carlos Castaneda	2920 Hickory St., Alexandria, Va.
Business Travel—347-6492	Bobert Burkhardt	1329 E St.
	Anni Jensen	1329 E St.
Chilton Publications—EX 3-3474	George Baker	1093 National Press Bldg.
	Neil R. Regeimbal	1093 National Press Bldg.
Civil Service Reporter, The—DI 7-4655	William Parker	836 Warner Bldg.
Clissold Publications—522-5961	J. D. Snyder	2921 24th St., North Arlington, Va.
Compass Publications	Charles H. Bussman	617 Lynn Bldg., 1111 N. 19th St., Arlington, Va.
	Larry L. Booda	617 Lynn Bldg., 1111 N. 19th St., Arlington, Va.
	Charles W. Covey	617 Lynn Bldg., 1111 N. 19th St., Arlington, Va.
Conover-Mast Publications—NA 8-2773	A. N. Wecksler	869 National Press Bldg.
	Herbert P. Carlson	869 National Press Bldg.
	Patricia Jean Reed	869 National Press Bldg.
Contract—ME 8-6113	Ash Gerecht	1319 F St.
Contractors and Engineers—DI 7-5506	E. E. Halmos, Jr	601 13th St.
	de Brossard, Phoebe	601 13th St.
Der Spiegel—656-9269	Alfred Schüler	5009 Greenway Dr.
Diplomat, The—DI 7-8223	Hope Ridings Miller	1379 National Press Bldg.
Drug Topics and Drug Trade News—NA 8-0225.	Stephens Rippey	1232 National Press Bldg.
Ebony—DI 7-5938	Simeon S. Booker	1750 Pennsylvania Ave.
	Lawrence A. Still	1750 Pennsylvania Ave.

PERIODICALS REPRESENTED—Continued

Periodical and telephone number	Name	Office
Economist, The (England)—ST 3-5753	John Midgley	609 National Press Bldg.
	Dorothea A. Szameitat	609 National Press Bldg.
Electronic Design—DI 7-4220	E. W. Seabrook Hull	1319 F St.
Exchange & Commissary News & Catering Magazine—ME 8-4557.	John A. Kuett	810 18th St.
	John W. Neubauer	810 18th St.
Farm News Service—AX 9-9488	George E. Peter	Tyler Bldg., Arlington Towers, Arlington, Va.
Financial World—NA 8-4303	Ephraim Kahn	996 National Press Bldg.
Fish Boat	Peg O'Curran Trippel	208 Homer Bldg.
Flare Publications—783-3270	Virginia Guy	715 G St. NW.
Flying—347-6492	Robert Burkhardt	1329 E St.
	Anni Jensen	1329 E St.
Forbes Magazine	Peter Weaver	1147 National Press Bldg.
Geo-Marine Technology	E. John Long	739 National Press Bldg.
Good Housekeeping—DE 2-6140	Mary Steele Sentner	2601 Woodley Pl.
Gussow Publications—DI 7-2654	Wallace R. Fingal	1210 National Press Bldg.
Haire Publications	Mildred O. Waugh	5808 Hitt Ave., McLean, Va.
Harpers' Magazine—462-6176	Joseph Kraft	3021 N St.
Hue—DI 7-5938	Simeon S. Booker	1750 Pennsylvania Ave.
Industrial Electronic Engineering and Maintenance—ST 3-2482.	Robert E. Tall	1327 F St.
Insurance Advocate—ME 8-0001	Al Goldsmith	1365 National Press Bldg.
	Alyce Moran Goldsmith	1365 National Press Bldg.
	Florence P. Farley	1365 National Press Bldg.
Interavia Publications (Swiss) 737-0349	Harry L. Tennant	803 National Press Bldg.
Iron Age—EX 3-3474	Ralph W. Crosby	1093 National Press Bldg.
Jet Magazine—DI 7-5938	Simeon S. Booker	1750 Pennsylvania Ave.
	E. Fannie Granton	1750 Pennsylvania Ave.
	Lawrence A. Still	1750 Pennsylvania Ave.
Journal of the Armed Forces—HO 2-1220	Daniel Z. Henkin	1710 Connecticut Ave.
	A. Michael Hornberger	1710 Connecticut Ave.
	Louis Stockstill	1710 Connecticut Ave.
Ladies Home Journal, The—HO 2-4250	Dorothy Disney MacKaye	2817 Woodley Rd.
Lockwood Publications—NA 8-7549	T. N. Sandifer	956 National Press Bldg.
Look Magazine—DI 7-9111	Edna Bagley	852 National Press Bldg.
MAC Publications	Anne Wolf	4423 Stanford St., Chevy Chase, Md.
Maclean's Magazine—EM 2-3742	Ian Sclanders	3110 34th St.
Mayor and Manager	Phil Hirsch	5916 Conway Rd., Bethesda, Md.
Medical Economics	Janet Nugent	774 National Press Bldg.
Medical World News	John M. Blamphin	1420 Oak Ridge Rd., Falls Church, Va.
	Mary Jane O'Neill	7116 Armat Dr., Bethesda, Md.
McCall's—DE 2-1429	Christine Sadler	1300 Connecticut Ave.
McGraw-Hill Publications—RE 7-6630	Arthur Moore	1189 National Press Bldg.
	Glen Bayless	1189 National Press Bldg.
	Donald Barney	1189 National Press Bldg.
	Lewis B. Beman	1189 National Press Bldg.
	Alan E. Adams	1189 National Press Bldg.
	Herbert W. Cheshire	1189 National Press Bldg.
	Alan Demaree	1189 National Press Bldg.
	Boyd France	1189 National Press Bldg.
	Charles S. Gardner, III	1189 National Press Bldg.
	Arthur F. Hermann	1189 National Press Bldg.
	Warren Kornberg	1189 National Press Bldg.
	Donald O. Loomis	1189 National Press Bldg.
	Onnic Marashian	1189 National Press Bldg.
	Norman Burkey Musselman	1189 National Press Bldg.
	John Nicholson	1189 National Press Bldg.
	Seth T. Payne	1189 National Press Bldg.
	F. Margaret Reid	1189 National Press Bldg.
	Caroline Robertson	1189 National Press Bldg.
	David W. Secrest	1189 National Press Bldg.
	Richard Smith	1189 National Press Bldg.
	Vincent B. Smith	1189 National Press Bldg.
	William Smith	1189 National Press Bldg.
	George E. Williamson	1189 National Press Bldg.
	Harry Van Dernoot	1189 National Press Bldg.
Miller Publishing Co.—347-3811	Arthur L. Davis	774 National Press Bldg.
	Janet Nugent	774 National Press Bldg.
	Catherine C. Weigarten	774 National Press Bldg.
Modern Medicine—942-0078	Mal Schecter	10512 Weymouth St., Bethesda, Md.
Modern Textiles—234-4954	Goody L. Solomon	1530 16th St.
Motor—NA 8-9494	Bert Mills	1244 National Press Bldg.
Motor Boating—NA 8-9494	Bert Mills	1244 National Press Bldg.
National Geographic Magazine DI 7-3330.	Windsor Booth	16th and M Sts.

39–650°—65——56

PERIODICALS REPRESENTED—Continued

Periodical and telephone number	Name	Office
National Observer, The—622-2900	Mark R. Arnold	11501 Columbia Pike, Silver Spring, Md.
	Harold H. Brayman	11501 Columbia Pike, Silver Spring, Md.
	Don Carter	11501 Columbia Pike, Silver Spring, Md.
	Lee Edward Dirks	11501 Columbia Pike, Silver Spring, Md.
	Jerrold K. Footlick	11501 Columbia Pike, Silver Spring, Md.
	Gerald W. George	11501 Columbia Pike, Silver Spring, Md.
	David W. Hacker	11501 Columbia Pike, Silver Spring, Md.
	Robert L. Hermann	11501 Columbia Pike, Silver Spring, Md.
	Roscoe C. Born, Jr	11501 Columbia Pike, Silver Spring, Md.
	John F. Bridge	11501 Columbia Pike, Silver Spring, Md.
	Peter T. Chew	11501 Columbia Pike, Silver Spring, Md.
	Walter A. Damtoft	11501 Columbia Pike, Silver Spring Md.
	James M. Perry	11501 Columbia Pike, Silver Spring. Md.
	Wesley Pruden, Jr	11501 Columbia Pike, Silver Spring, Md.
	Gerald S. Schatz	11501 Columbia Pike, Silver Spring, Md.
National Review—347-1551	Neal B. Freeman	1120 National Press Bldg.
National Underwriter Life Insurance Edition—ME 8-2253.	H. C. Hallam	1331 G St.
National Underwriter, The—ME 8-2253.	H. C. Hallam	1331 G St.
New Republic—FE 8-2494	Asher Brynes	1244 19th St.
	Alexander Campbell	1244 19th St.
	Helen Fuller	1244 19th St.
	Gilbert A. Harrison	1244 19th St.
	Christopher Jencks	1244 19th St.
	Andrew Kopkind	1244 19th St.
	Helen Hill Miller	1299 National Press Bldg.
	James F. Ridgeway	1244 19th St.
	Michael Straight	1244 19th St.
	Philip M. Stern	1712 I St.
Newsweek—298-7880	Benjamin C. Bradlee	1750 Pennsylvania Ave.
	Philip Carter	1750 Pennsylvania Ave.
	Kenneth G. Crawford	1750 Pennsylvania Ave.
	William S. Gray	1750 Pennsylvania Ave.
	Shirlee Hoffman	1750 Pennsylvania Ave.
	Ward Just	1750 Pennsylvania Ave.
	Charlotte Kennedy	1750 Pennsylvania Ave.
	John Lindsay	1750 Pennsylvania Ave.
	Thelma McMahon	1750 Pennsylvania Ave.
	Norma Milligan	1750 Pennsylvania Ave.
	Lloyd Norman	1750 Pennsylvania Ave.
	Charles W. Roberts	1229 National Press Bldg.
	Hobart Rowen	1229 National Press Bldg.
	Samuel Shaffer	1229 National Press Bldg.
	Henry T. Simmons	1229 National Press Bldg.
	Richard T. Stout	1229 National Press Bldg.
	L. Bruce Van Voorst	1229 National Press Bldg.
	Leon Volkov	1229 National Press Bldg.
	Edward Weintal	1229 National Press Bldg.
	Thomas D. White	1229 National Press Bldg.
Northwestern Miller	Catherine Weingarten	774 National Press Bldg.
Oil and Gas Journal—347-1710	Gene T. Kinney	768 National Press Bldg.
Oil, Paint, and Drug Reporter—NA 8-7549.	Ralph L. Cherry	956 National Press Bldg.
Pacific Shipper—DI 7-2275	Michael L. Raedy	412 Mills Bldg.
Parade Magazine—FE 3-6584	Frederick G. Blumenthal	911 25th St.
	Opal B. Ginn	1612 K Street.
Paris-Match Magazine—654-6152	Philippe de Bausset	5005 Fort Sumner Dr.
Petersen Publishing Co	Robert Anterzberg	3635 6th St. SE.
Popular Electronics—ST 3-2482	Robert E. Tall	1327 F St.
Popular Mechanics—LI 7-5264	S. David Pursglove	320 Independence Ave. SE.
Practical Builder, The—DI7-0707	Richard E. Saunders	1275 National Press Bldg.
Public Utilities Fortnightly—NA 8-3080.	Francis X. Welch	Pennslyvania Bldg.
	Charles M. Bruch	Pennsylvania Bldg.
Pembangunan—667-9378	Edward D. Sinaga	2122 Massachusetts Ave.
Putman Publishing Co.-347-3811	Arthur L. Davis	774 National Press Bldg.
	Janet Nugent	774 National Press Bldg.
	Catherine C. Weingarten	774 National Press Bldg.

PERIODICALS REPRESENTED—Continued

Periodical and telephone number	Name	Office
Quick Frozen Foods—FE 8-0443	Vincent F. Callahan, Jr	1722 Wisconsin Ave.
Reader's Digest Association—HO 2-1071	Charles Stevenson	1300 Connecticut Ave.
	Kenneth O. Gilmore	1300 Connecticut Ave.
	John D. Barron	1300 Connecticut Ave.
	Allen Drury	1300 Connecticut Ave.
	Blake Clark	2440 Kalorama Rd.
	Virginia Lawton	1300 Connecticut Ave.
	Eugene H. Methvin	1300 Connecticut Ave.
	Jane Denis Smith	1300 Connecticut Ave.
Reconstruction (Formosa)	Joseph Chiang, Sr	100 Woodridge Ave., Silver Spring, Md.
Reporter, The—298-8186	Elizabeth Drew	1750 Pennsylvania Ave.
	Meg Greenfield	1750 Pennsylvania Ave.
Sales Management—NA 8-9494	Bert Mills	1244 National Press Bldg.
Saturday Evening Post, The—NA 8-2152.	Stewart Alsop	1000 16th St.
	Ben Bagdikian	1000 16th St.
	Ann Chamberlin	1000 16th St.
	William K. Goolrick	1000 16th St.
	Milton MacKaye	1000 16th St.
	Don Oberdorfer	1000 16th St.
	Beverly Smith, Jr.	1000 16th St.
	Grace Cutler Smith	1000 16th St.
	Denise St. Germain	1000 16th St.
	Charles W. Thayer	1000 16th St.
Simmons-Boardman Publications NA 8-7484.	Walter J. Taft	1081 National Press Bldg.
Skipper, The—347-6492	Robert Burkhardt	1329 E. St.
	Anni Jensen	1329 E St.
Sports Afield—ST 3-6655	Michael Hudoba	National Press Bldg.
Steel—EX 3-6849	John R. Botzum, Jr	1123 National Press Bldg.
Tan—DI 7-5938	Simeon Booker	Albee Bldg.
Telephone Engineer—ST 3-2482	Fred W. Henck	1208 National Press Bldg.
	Thomas M. Malia	1208 National Press Bldg.
	Robert E. Tall	1327 F St.
Television Age—Re 7-3230	Jay Lewis	1118 National Press Bldg.
Television Digest—965-1985	Albert Warren	2025 I St.
	Laurence Michie	2025 I St.
	Dawson B. Nail	2025 I St.
This Week Magazine	Frances Spatz Leighton	3636 16th St.
Time-Life—FE 7-8000	John L. Steele	1120 Connecticut Ave.
	Martha B. Bucknell	1120 Connecticut Ave.
	Juan M. Cameron	1120 Connecticut Ave.
	Jesse L. Cook, Jr	1120 Connecticut Ave.
	Donn Downing	1120 Connecticut Ave.
	Robert Ellis	1120 Connecticut Ave.
	Dean Fisher	1120 Connecticut Ave.
	Simmons Fentress	1120 Connecticut Ave.
	Jean A. Franklin	1120 Connecticut Ave.
	Edwin Goodpaster	1120 Connecticut Ave.
	Hays Gorey	1120 Connecticut Ave.
	Jerry Hannifin	1120 Connecticut Ave.
	Keith R. Johnson	1120 Connecticut Ave.
	Frances P. Kelly	1120 Connecticut Ave.
	Lansing Lamont	1120 Connecticut Ave.
	Neil MacNeil	1120 Connecticut Ave.
	Harold B. Meyers	1120 Connecticut Ave.
	Mike McManus	1120 Connecticut Ave.
	deRossett Morrissey	1120 Connecticut Ave.
	John Mulliken	1120 Connecticut Ave.
	Charles J. V. Murphy	1120 Connecticut Ave.
	John A. Neary, Jr	1120 Connecticut Ave.
	Bruce Nelan	1120 Connecticut Ave.
	Margo North	1120 Connecticut Ave.
	Bruce L. Paisner	1120 Connecticut Ave.
	John Riley, Jr	1120 Connecticut Ave.
	Beverly S. Sbrilli	1120 Connecticut Ave.
	Gail Serfass	1120 Connecticut Ave.
	Hugh S. Sidey	1120 Connecticut Ave.
	Barbara Sloat	1120 Connecticut Ave.
	Mike Silva	1120 Connecticut Ave.
	Richard Stolley	1120 Connecticut Ave.
	Wallace Terry	1120 Connecticut Ave.
	M. Jon Vondracek	1120 Connecticut Ave.
	Arthur White	1120 Connecticut Ave.
	Bill M. Wise	1120 Connecticut Ave.
	Bernard L. Yudain	1120 Connecticut Ave.
	Marvin Zim	1120 Connecticut Ave.
Tobacco Leaf, The—ME 8-2253	H. C. Hallam	1331 G. St.
Transportation & Distribution Management—ST 3-7325.	Warren Blanding	815 Washington Bldg.
	Peter Heck	815 Washington Bldg.
	George A. Gecowets	815 Washington Bldg.
Travel Weekly—347-6492	Robert Burkhardt	1329 E St.
	Anni Jensen	1329 E St.

PERIODICALS REPRESENTED—Continued

Periodical and telephone number	Name	Office
U.S. Investor—347–3070	Raymond Alan Berens	1060 National Press Bldg.
	Marie N. Duncan	1060 National Press Bldg.
U.S. Lady—ST 3–2822	Alvadee Adams	620 Warner Bldg.
U.S. Medicine—234–1150	Frank M. Best	1601 18th St.
	Patricia Stefan	1601 18th St.
U. S. News & World Report FE 3–7400.	John H. Adams	24th and N Sts.
	Lucien D. Agniel	24th and N Sts.
	Clarke Beach	24th and N Sts.
	Donald Becker	24th and N Sts.
	George W. Bolton	24th and N Sts.
	Richard K. Brome	24th and N Sts.
	William C. Bryant	24th and N Sts.
	Albert Clark	24th and N Sts.
	Richard L. Corum	24th and N Sts.
	George E. Cruikshank	24th and N Sts.
	Luther A. Dawson	24th and N Sts.
	J. Frank Diggs	24th and N Sts.
	Donald Doane	24th and N Sts.
	John R. Fleming	24th and N Sts.
	Howard W. Flieger	24th and N Sts.
	Charles Foltz, Jr	24th and N Sts.
	Derek Fox	24th and N Sts.
	Stephen Freeland	24th and N Sts.
	Barbara Blair Furlow	24th and N Sts.
	Fred E. Galbraith, Jr	24th and N Sts.
	F. W. Gapp	24th and N Sts.
	LeRoy C. Gerlach	24th and N Sts.
	Ben J. Grant	24th and N Sts.
	Walter O. Gretschel	24th and N Sts.
	Ellis M. Haller	24th and N Sts.
	Howard Handleman	24th and N Sts.
	Frederick M. Harmon	24th and N Sts.
	N. Key Hart	24th and N Sts.
	Wilmot W. Hercher	24th and N Sts.
	Thomas H. Hughes	24th and N Sts.
	John B. Howard	24th and N Sts.
	Walter Husted	24th and N Sts.
	Pauline Jennings	24th and N Sts.
	Clair Johnson	24th and N Sts.
	Max S. Johnson	24th and N Sts.
	George E. Jones	24th and N Sts.
	Lucy Cobb Jones	24th and N Sts.
	H. Klebanoff	24th and N Sts.
	Charles H. Kline	24th and N Sts.
	James F. Lee	24th and N Sts.
	L. David LeRoy	24th and N Sts.
	Carson F. Lyman	24th and N Sts.
	William L. MacDougall	24th and N Sts.
	Nathan J. Margolin	24th and N Sts.
	LeRoy S. Mattingly	24th and N Sts.
	Howard Norton	24th and N Sts.
	Wayne Oliver	24th and N Sts.
	Charles M. Platt	24th and N Sts.
	W. B. Ragsdale	24th and N Sts.
	David B. Richardson	24th and N Sts.
	Archie W. Robinson	24th and N Sts.
	L. Noble Robinson	24th and N Sts.
	Turner Rose	24th and N Sts.
	Richard S. Ross	24th and N Sts.
	Robert W. Ruth	24th and N Sts.
	Grant A. Salisbury	24th and N Sts.
	Perry K. Sellon	24th and N Sts.
	Owen L. Scott	24th and N Sts.
	Sidney Shallett	24th and N Sts.
	Donald Smith	24th and N Sts.
	Francis B. Stevens	24th and N Sts.
	Marvin L. Stone	24th and N Sts.
	John Sutherland	24th and N Sts.
	Lester Tanzer	24th and N Sts.
	Richard J. Theobald	24th and N Sts.
	Richard L. Turner	24th and N Sts.
	Albert L. Warner	24th and N Sts.
	Edwin Price Weigel	24th and N Sts.
	Dale B. White	24th and N Sts.
	Charles E. Whiting	24th and N Sts.
	Robert C. Wilson	24th and N Sts.
Vision Magazine—737–0349	Winthrop P. Carty	803 National Press Bldg.
	Anne Mansfield	803 National Press Bldg.
Washington World—547–8300	Hal J. Taylor	53 D St. SE.
Watson Publications—393–3571	Harry L. Tennant	803 National Press Bldg.
Weekly Graphic—EM 2–6212	Diosdado M. Yap	5306 Belt Rd.
Western Aerospace—EX 3–0031	Arthur Kranish	1120 National Press Bldg.
	Donald L. Berliner	1120 National Press Bldg.
Western Oil and Refining—WO 6–3576	Lorania K. Francis	2808 McKinley Pl.

MAPS OF CONGRESSIONAL DISTRICTS

MAPS OF CONGRESSIONAL DISTRICTS

ALABAMA

(8 districts)

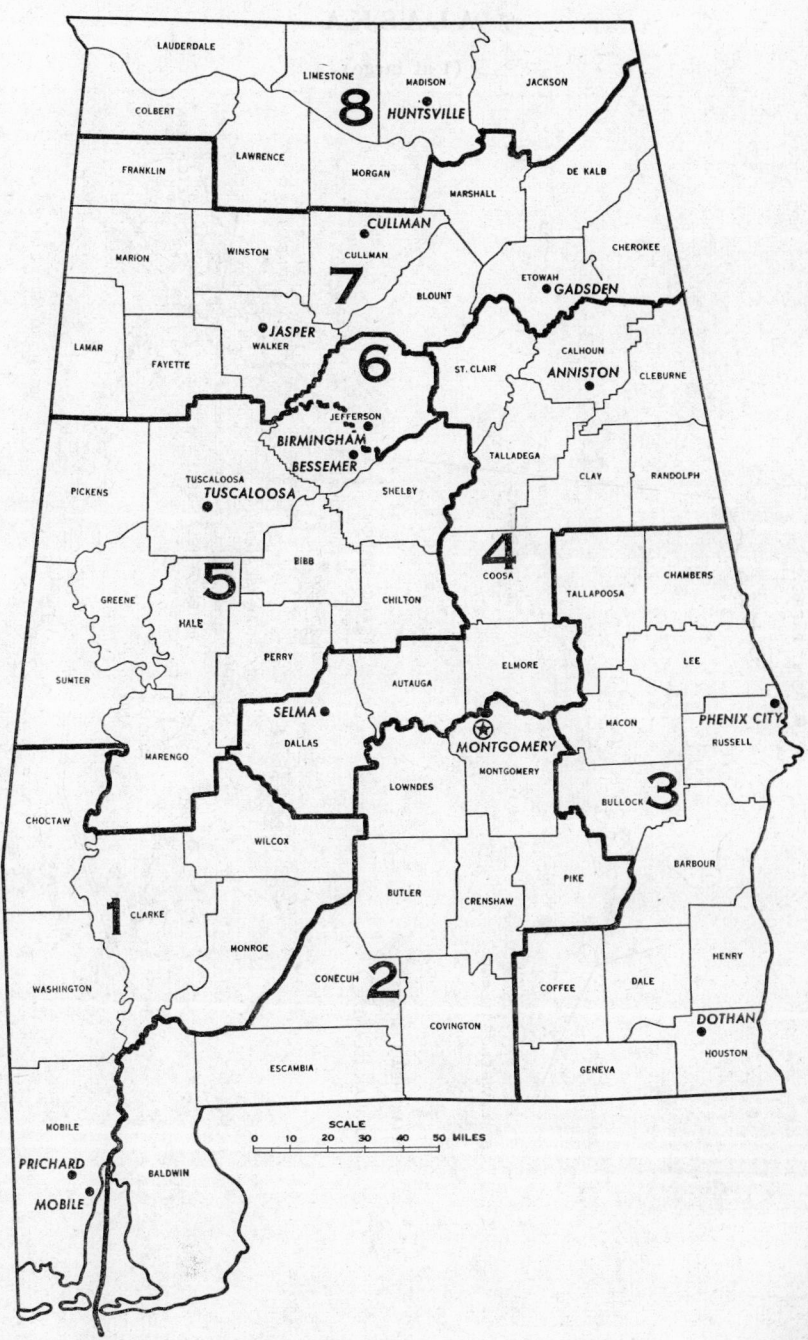

ALASKA

(1 at large)

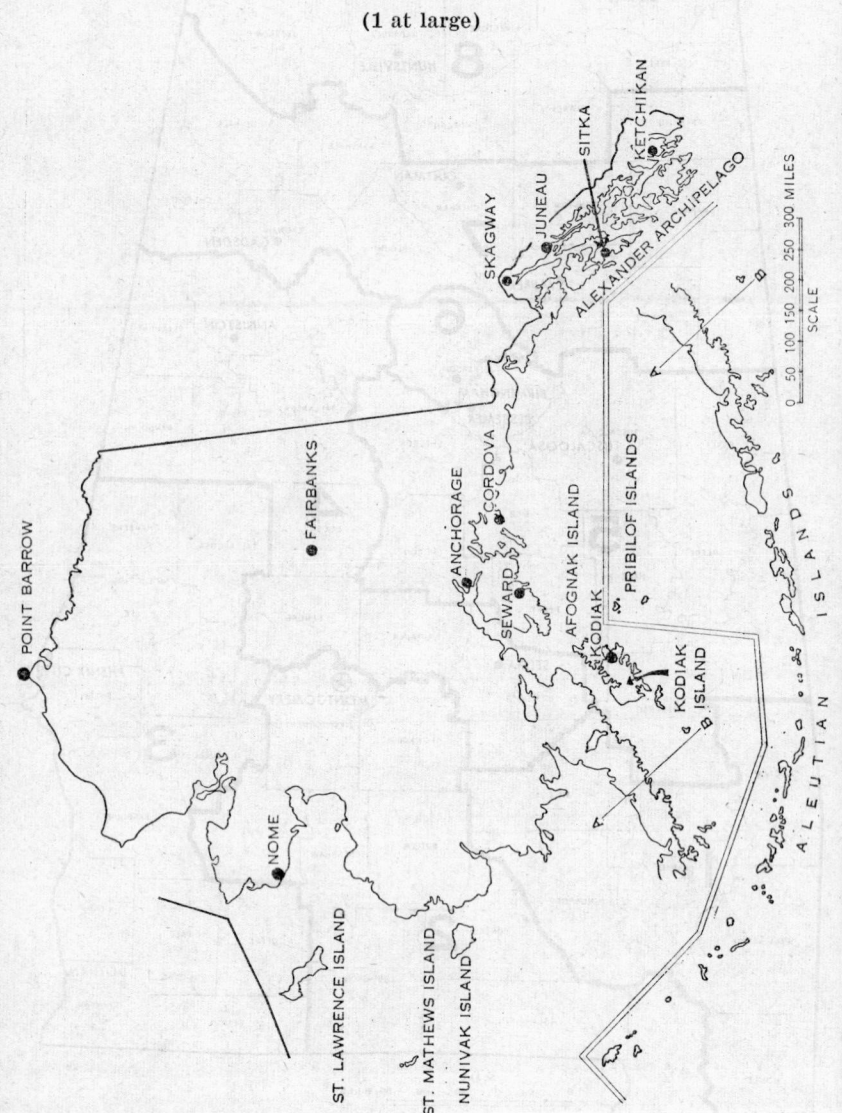

ARIZONA

(3 districts)

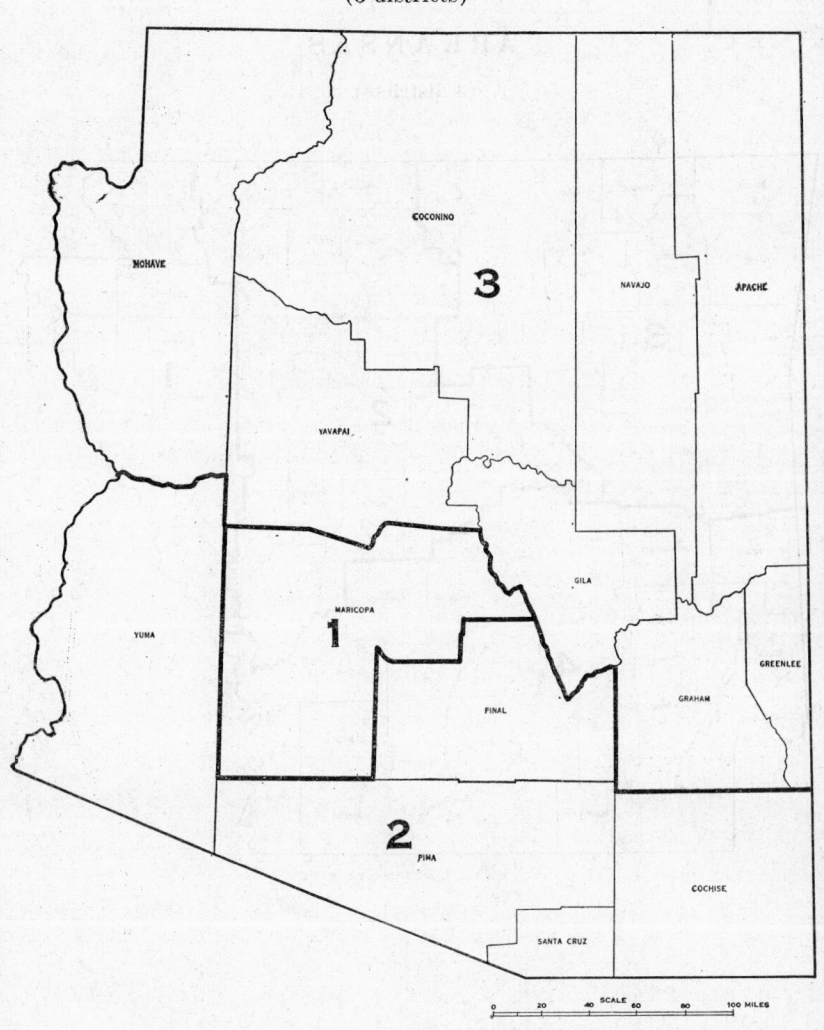

ARKANSAS

(4 districts)

CALIFORNIA

(38 districts)

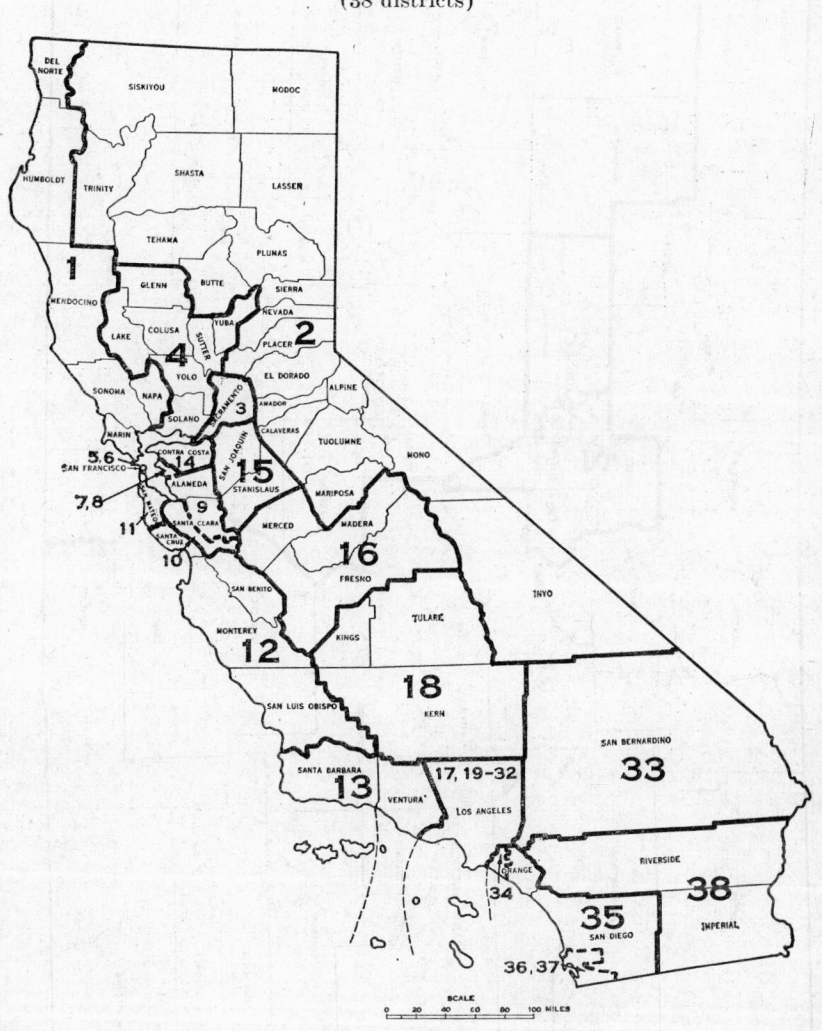

COLORADO

(4 districts)

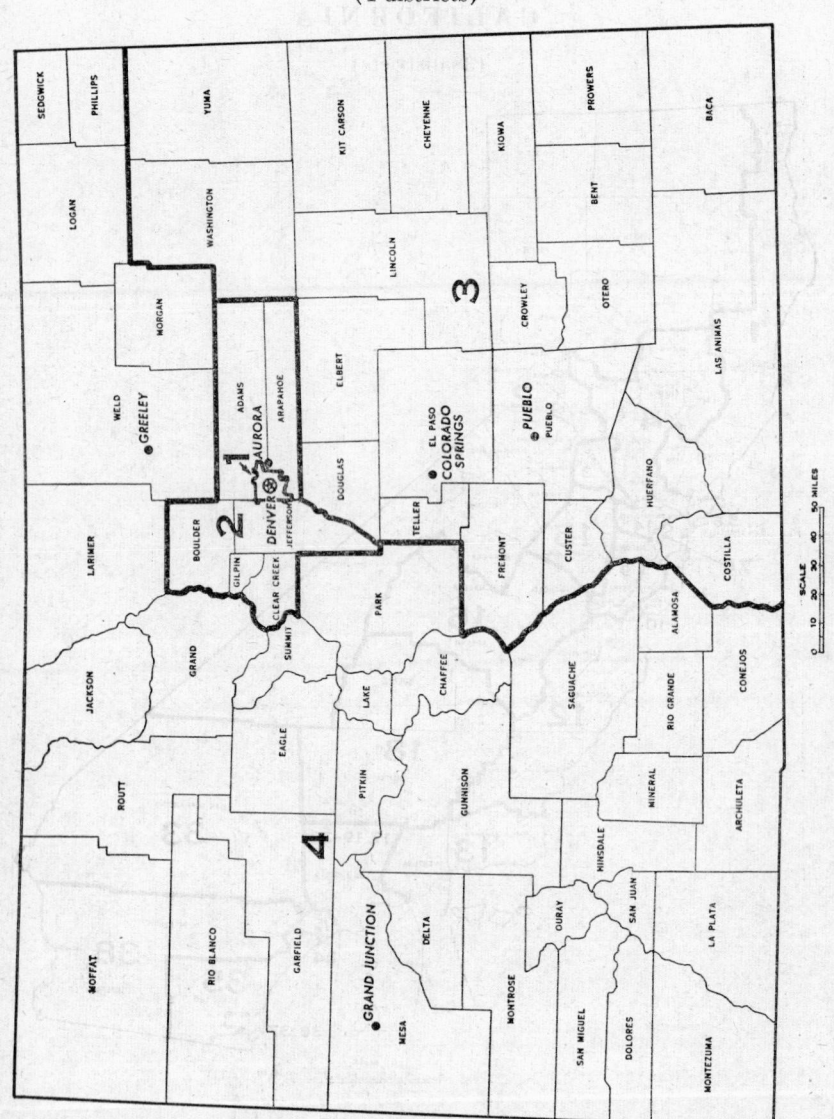

CONNECTICUT

(6 districts)

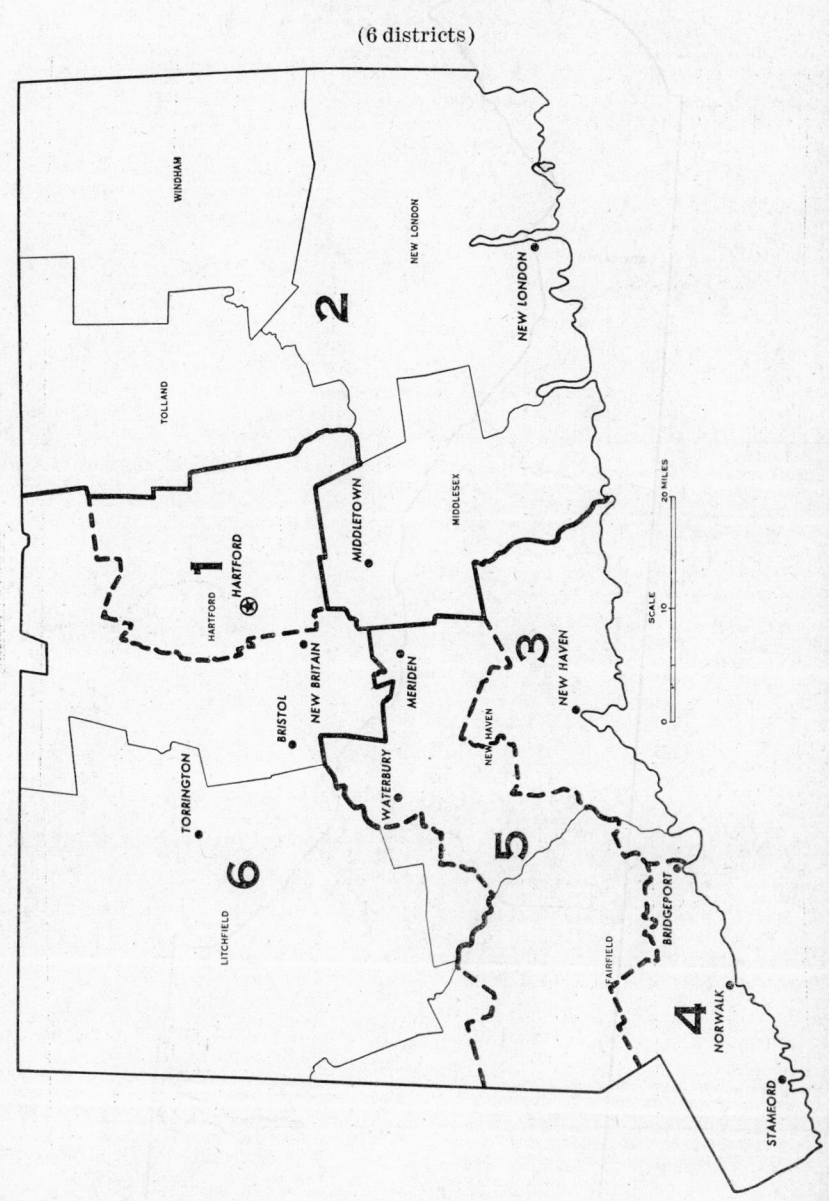

DELAWARE

(1 at large)

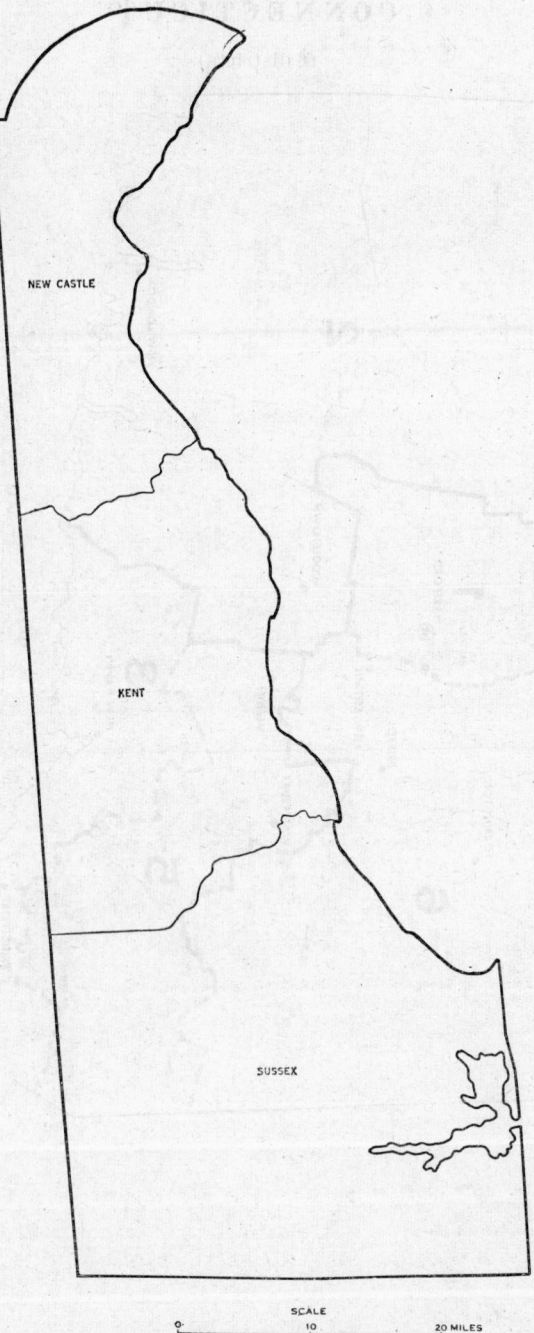

NEW CASTLE

KENT

SUSSEX

SCALE
0   10   20 MILES

FLORIDA

(12 districts)

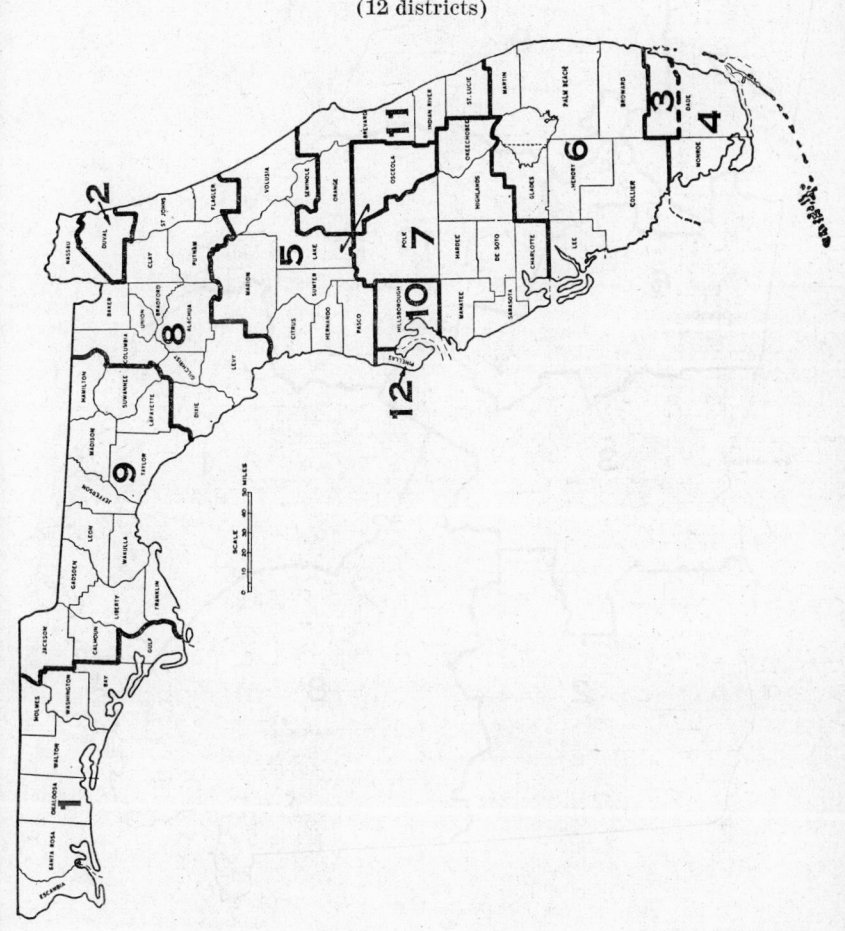

GEORGIA

(10 districts)

HAWAII

(2 at large)

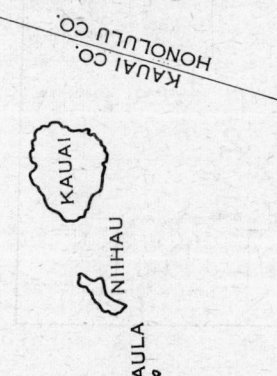

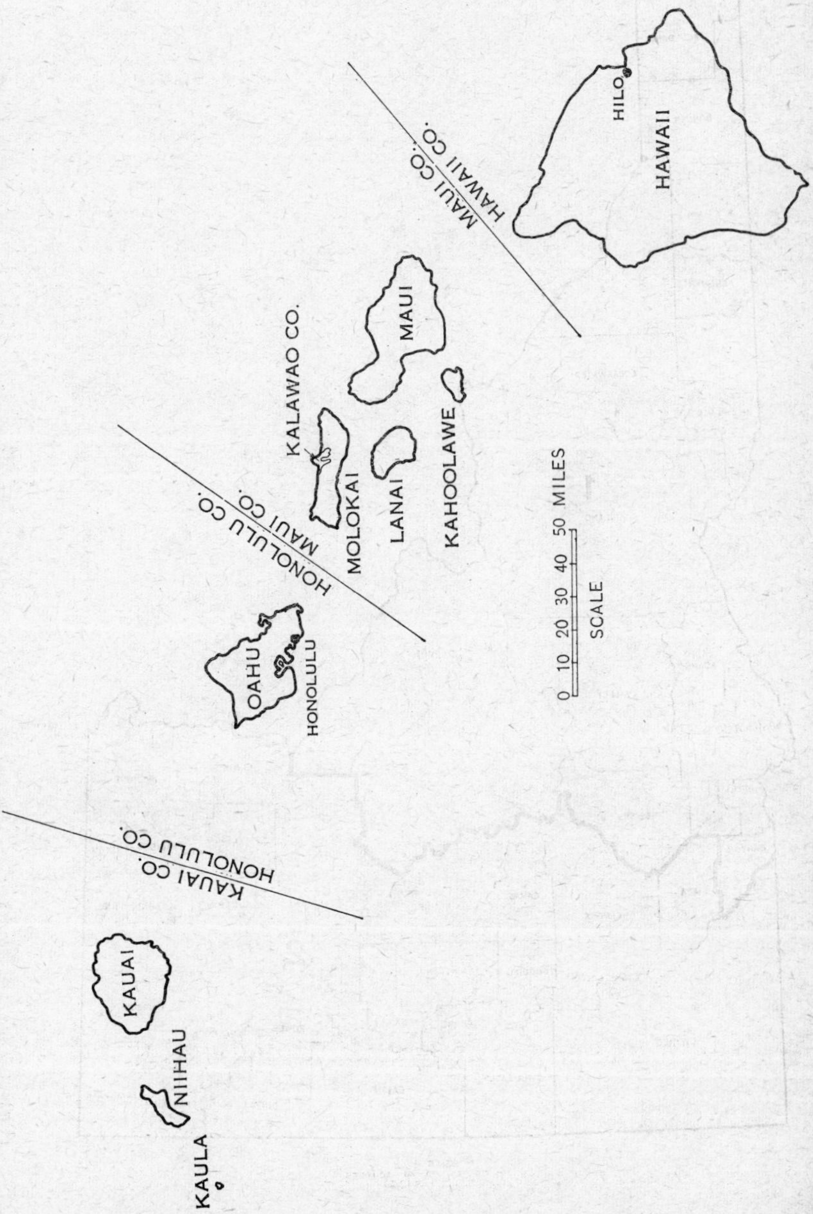
HILO
HAWAII
HAWAII CO.
MAUI CO.
MAUI
KALAWAO CO.
MOLOKAI
LANAI
KAHOOLAWE
MAUI CO.
HONOLULU CO.
OAHU
HONOLULU
HONOLULU CO.
KAUAI CO.
KAUAI
NIIHAU
KAULA
0 10 20 30 40 50 MILES
SCALE

39–650°—65——57

IDAHO

(2 districts)

ILLINOIS

(24 districts)

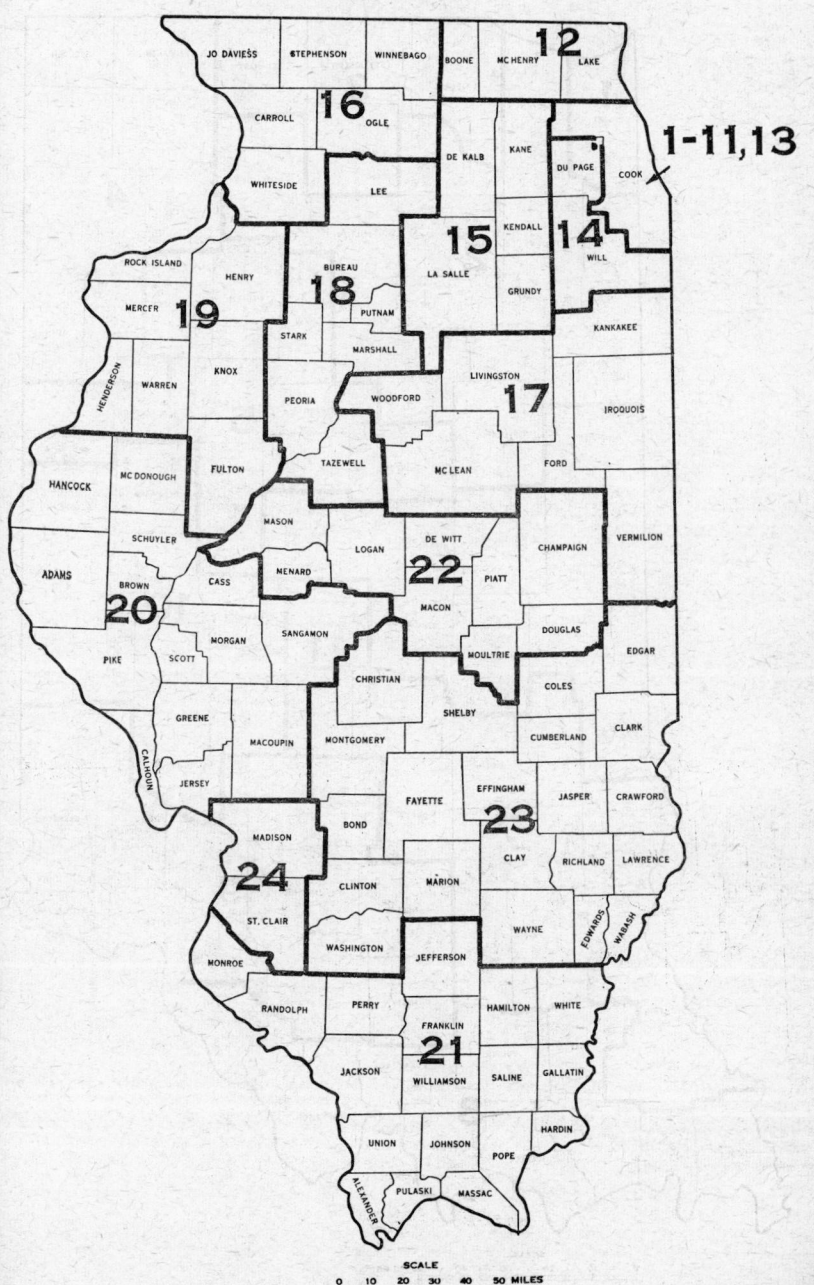

INDIANA

(11 districts)

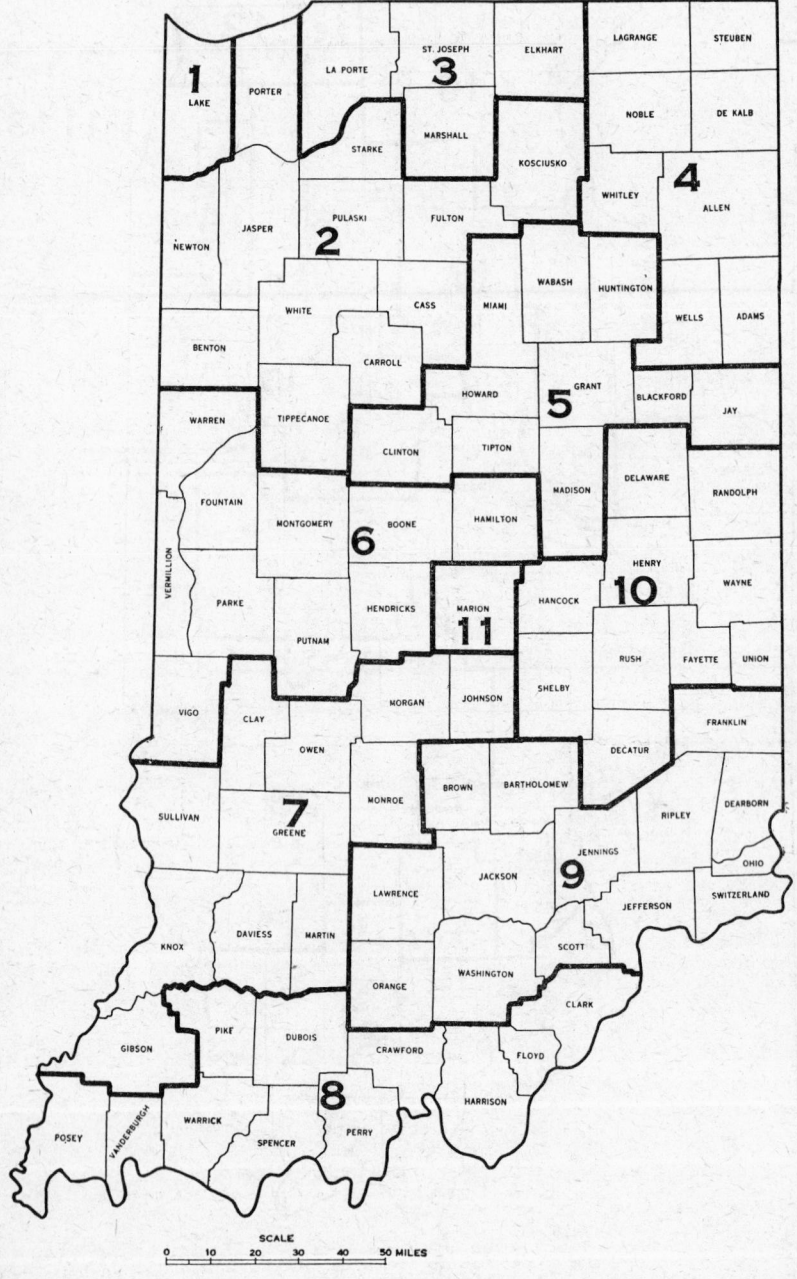

IOWA

(7 districts)

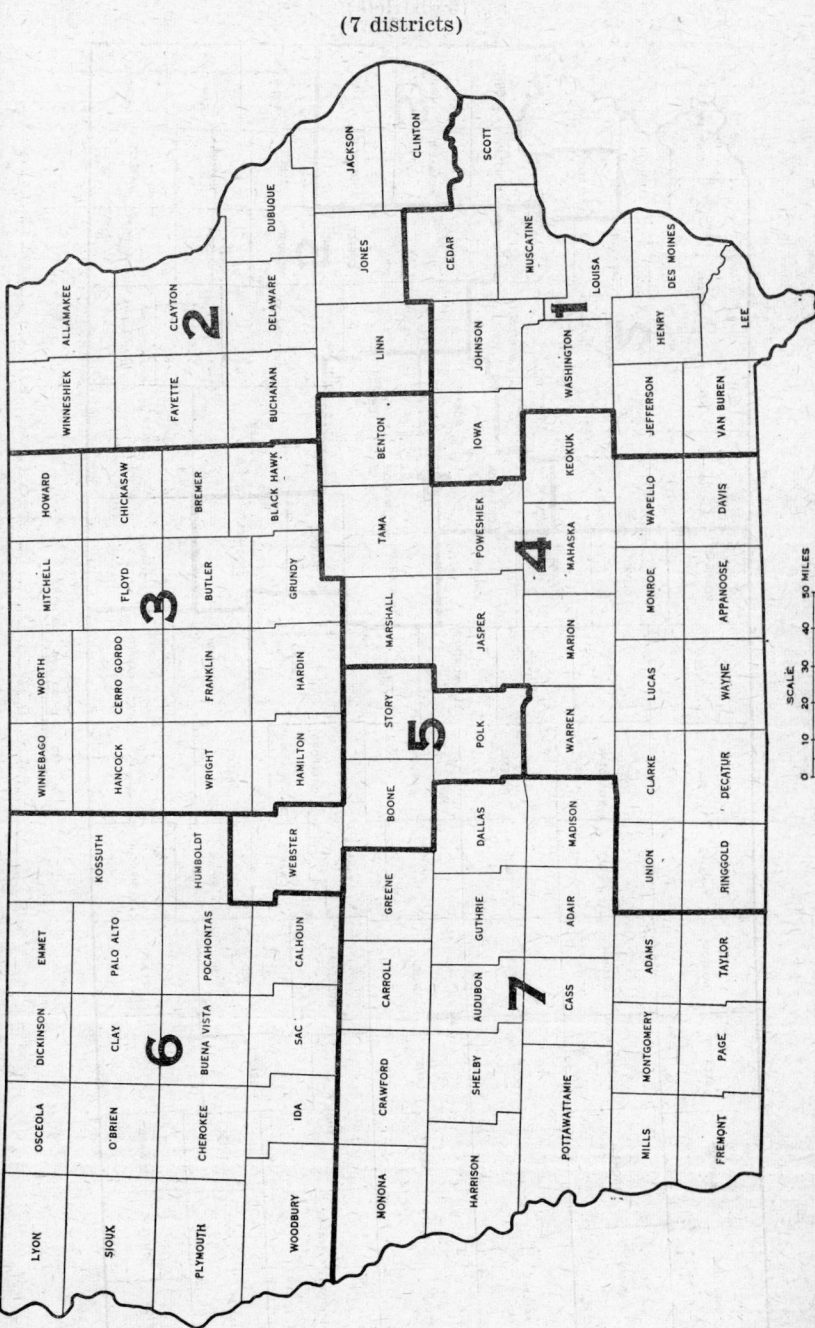

KANSAS

(5 districts)

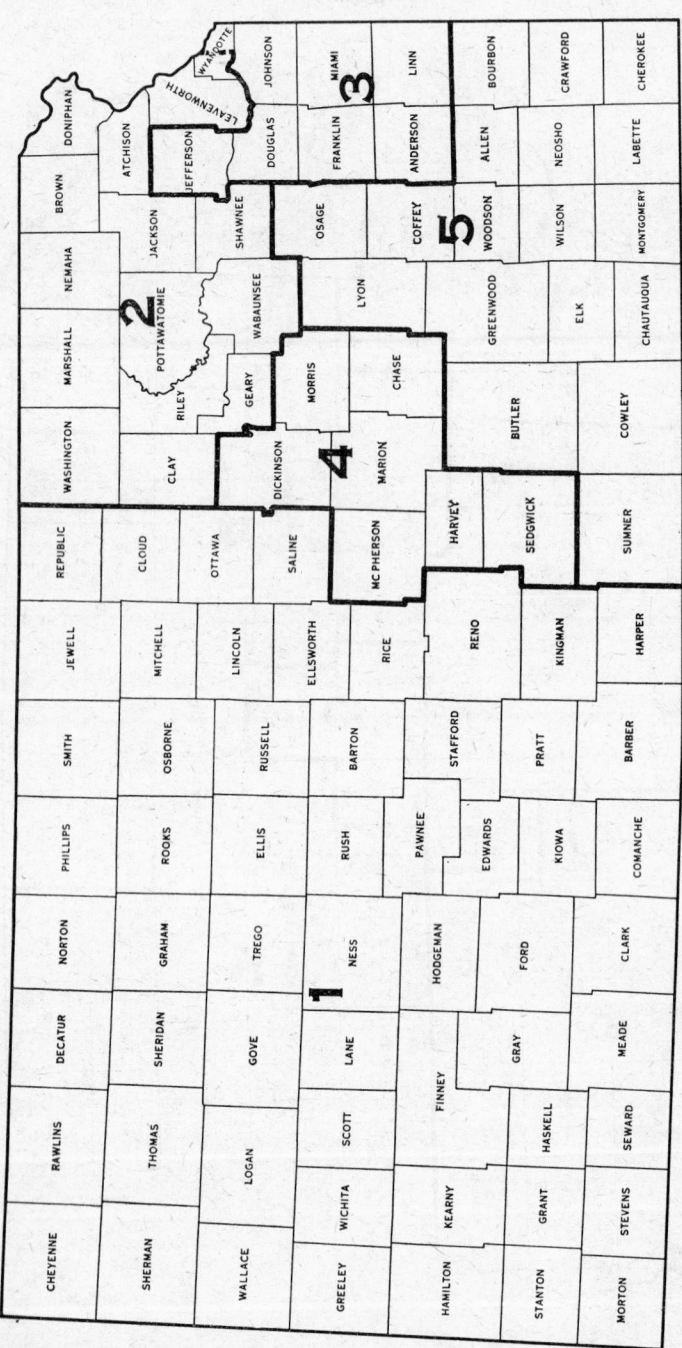

KENTUCKY

(7 districts)

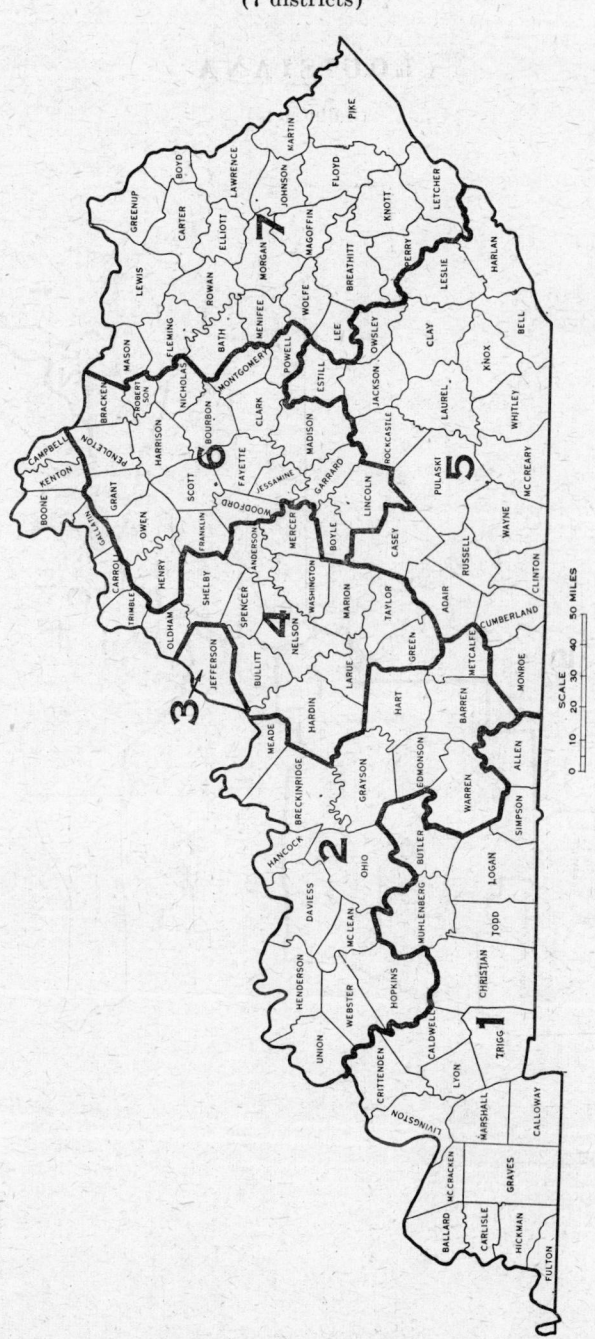

LOUISIANA

(8 districts)

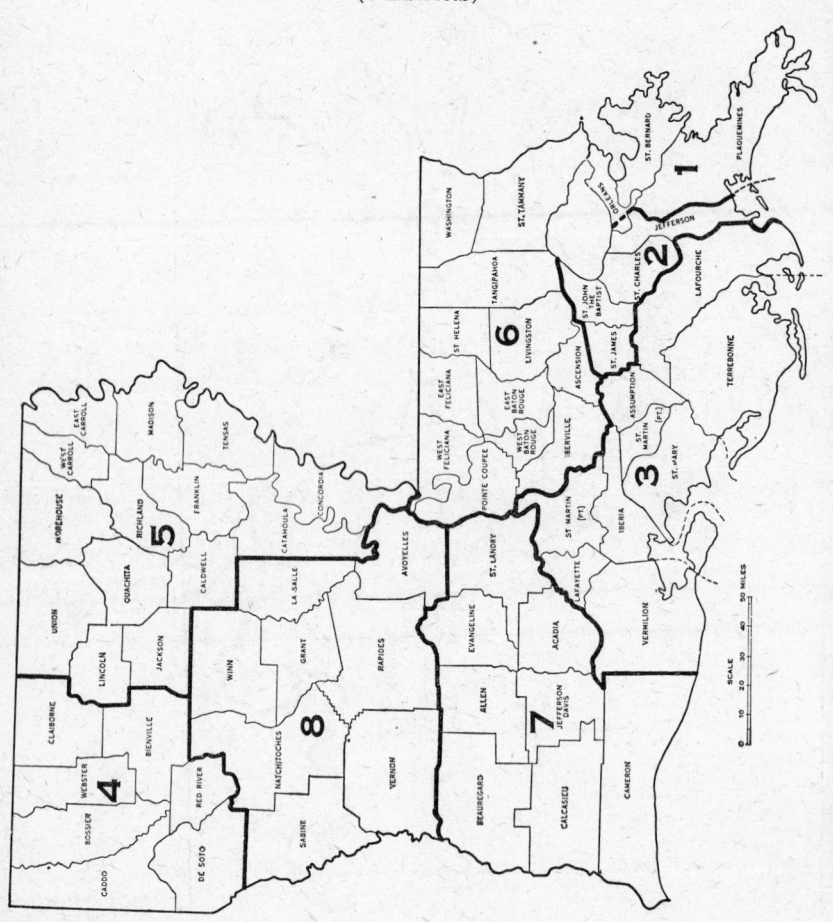

MAINE

(2 districts)

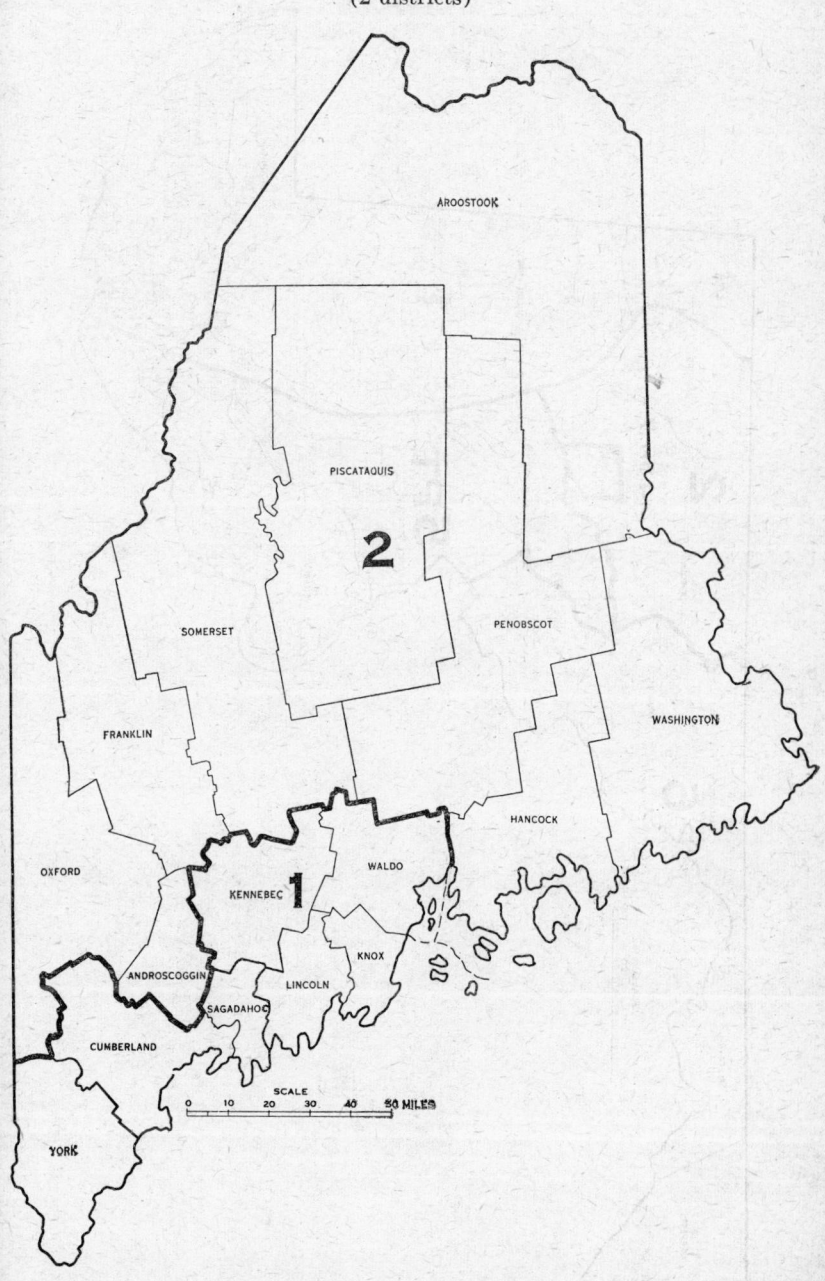

MARYLAND

(7 districts and 1 at large)

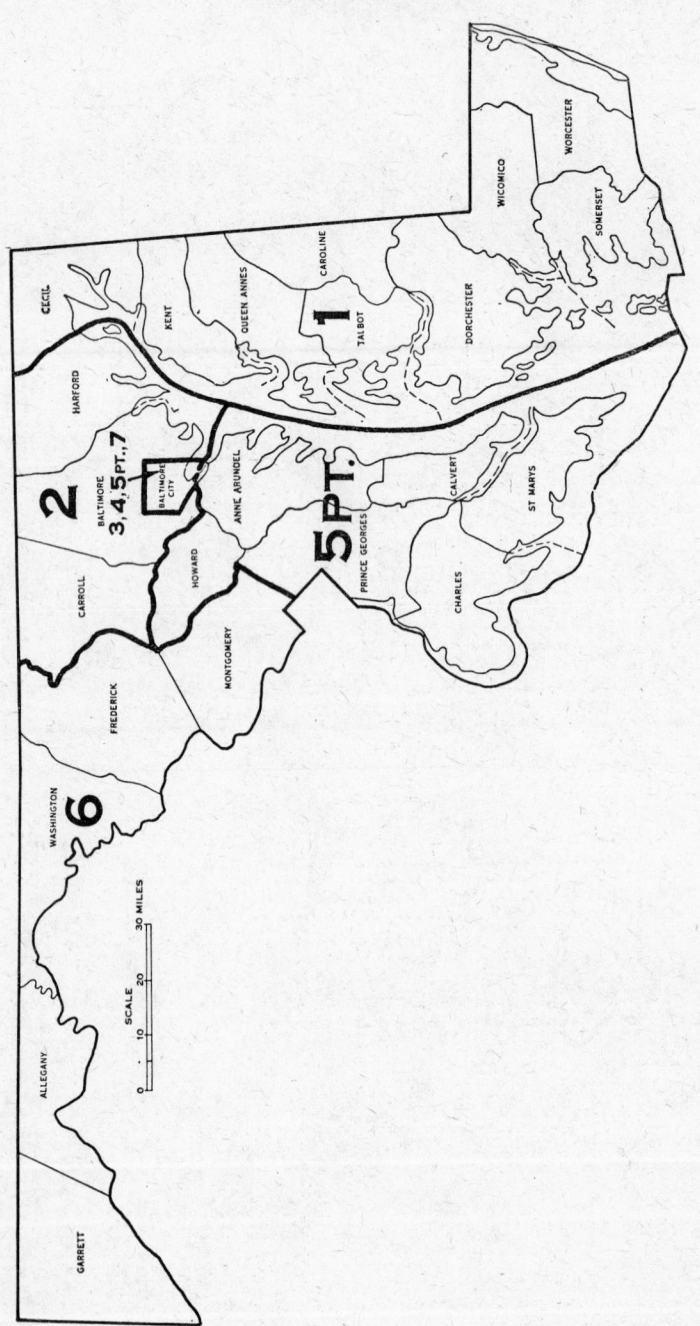

MASSACHUSETTS

(12 districts)

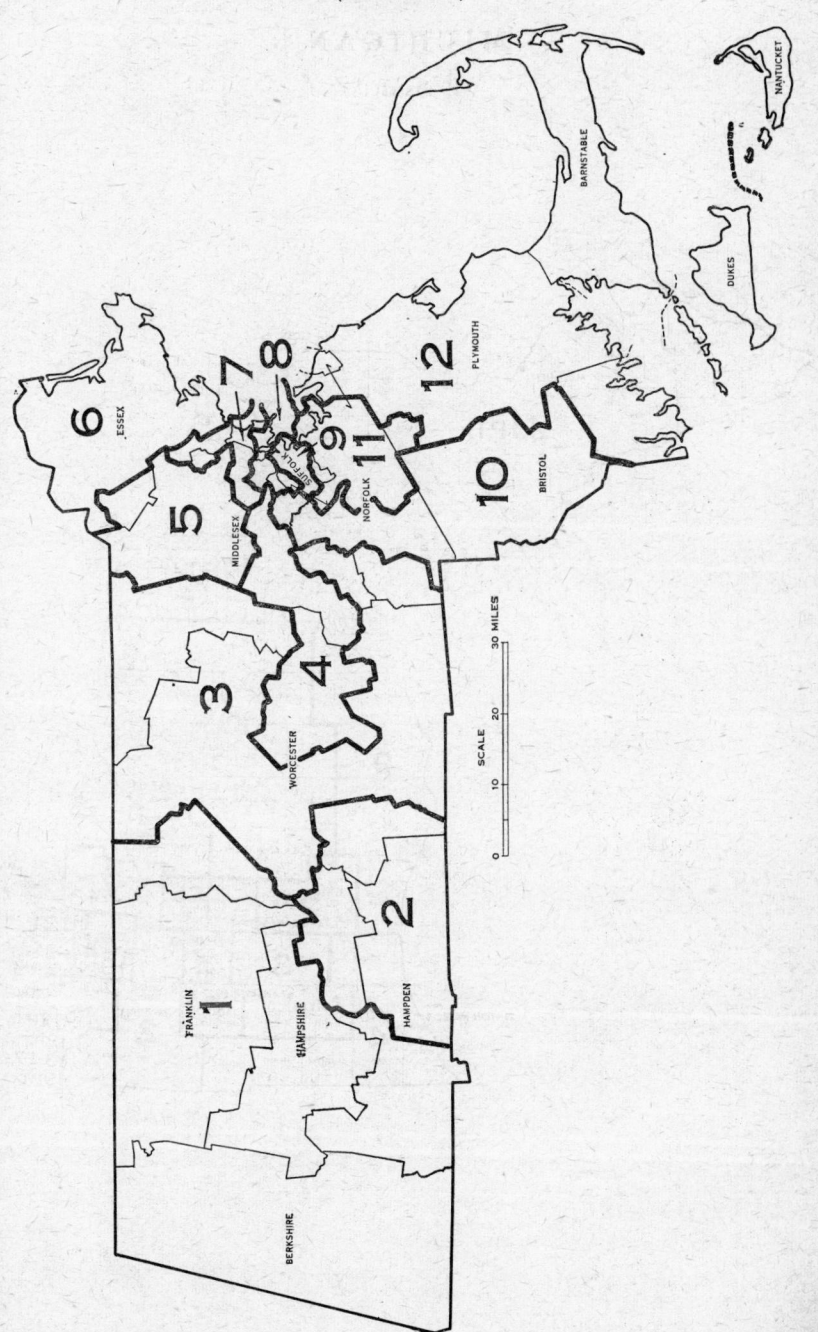

MICHIGAN

(19 districts)

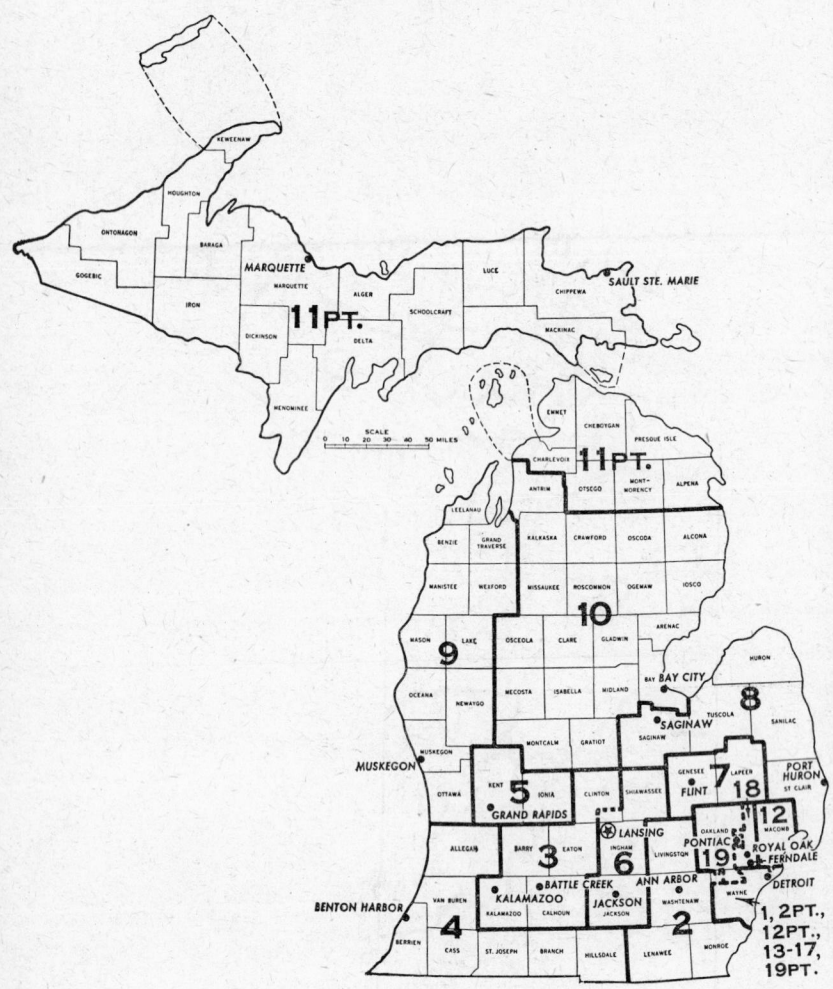

MINNESOTA

(8 districts)

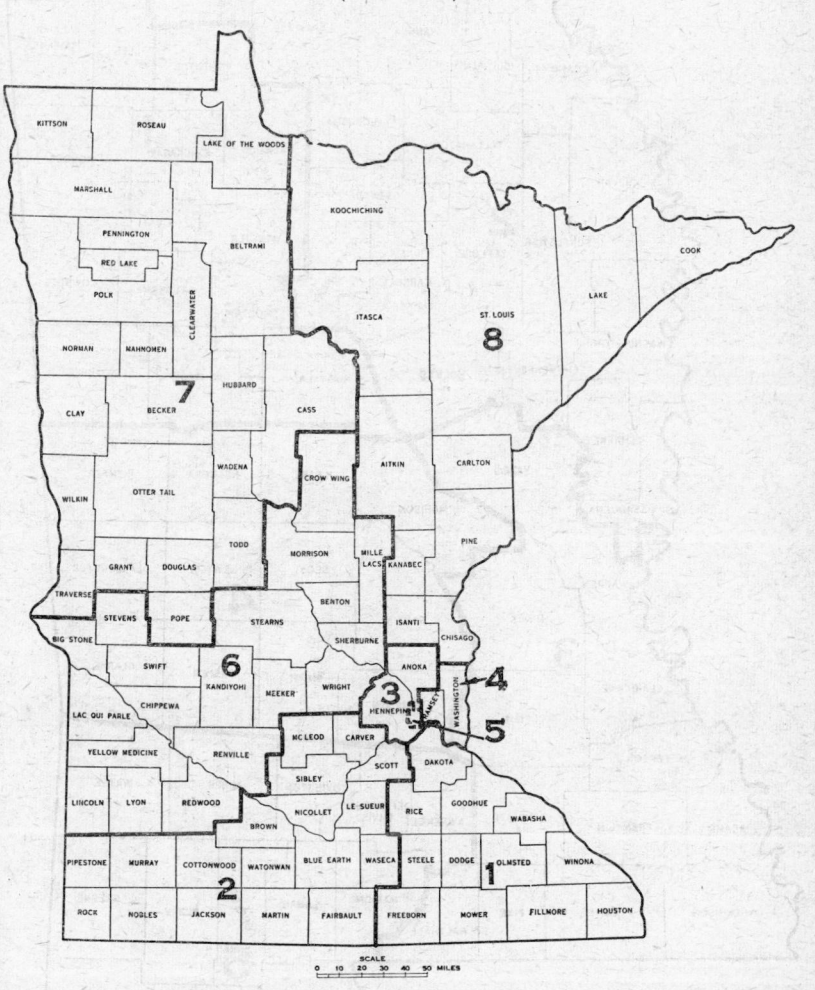

MISSISSIPPI

(5 districts)

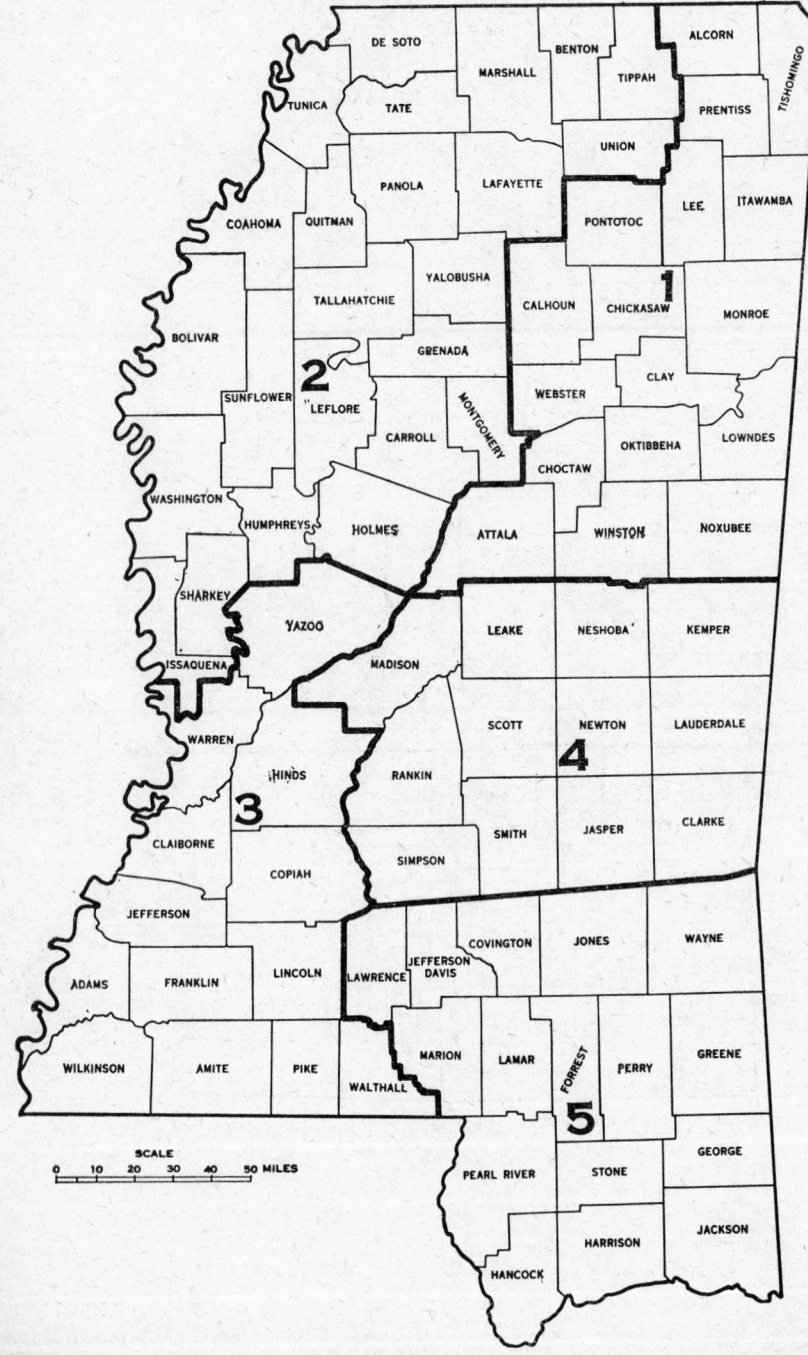

MISSOURI

(10 districts)

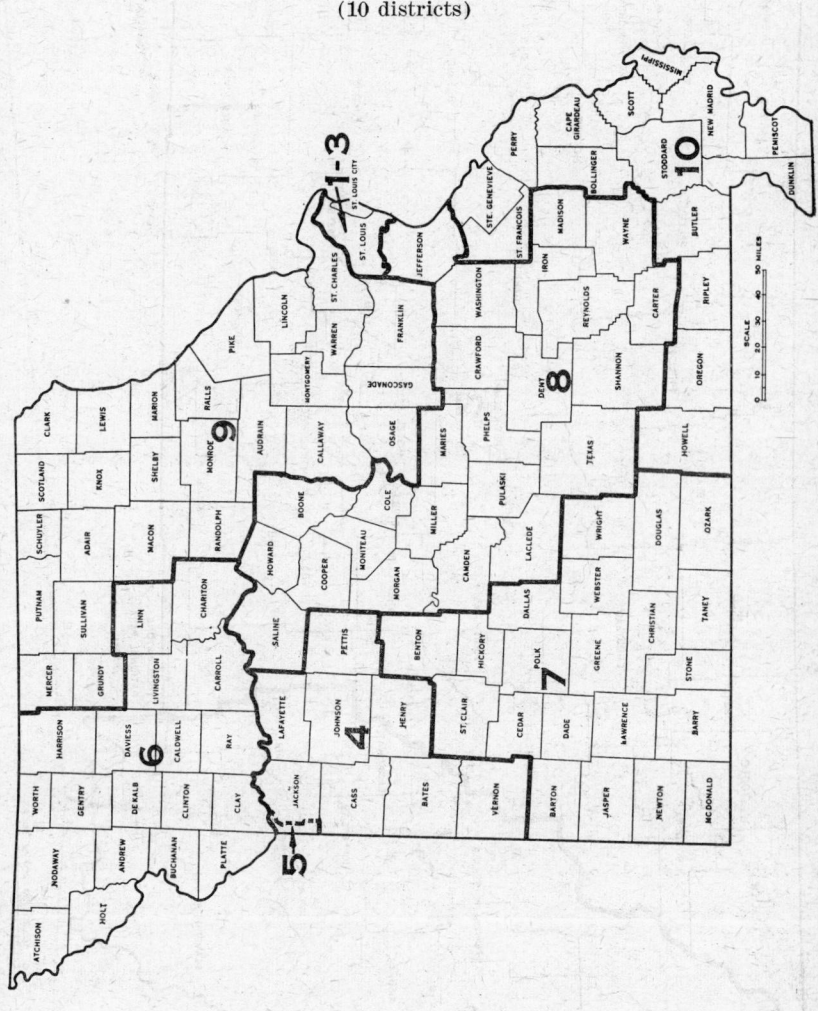

MONTANA

(2 districts)

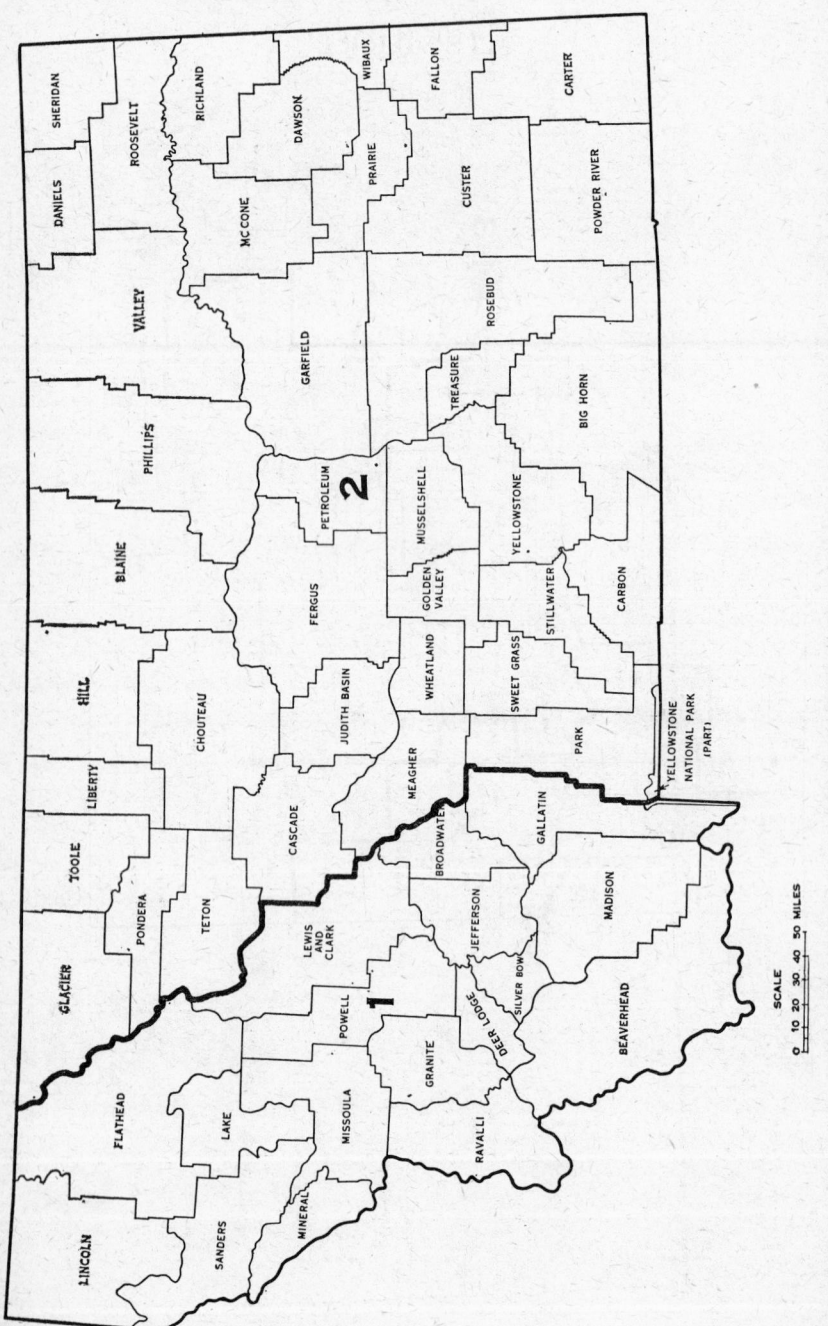

NEBRASKA

(3 districts)

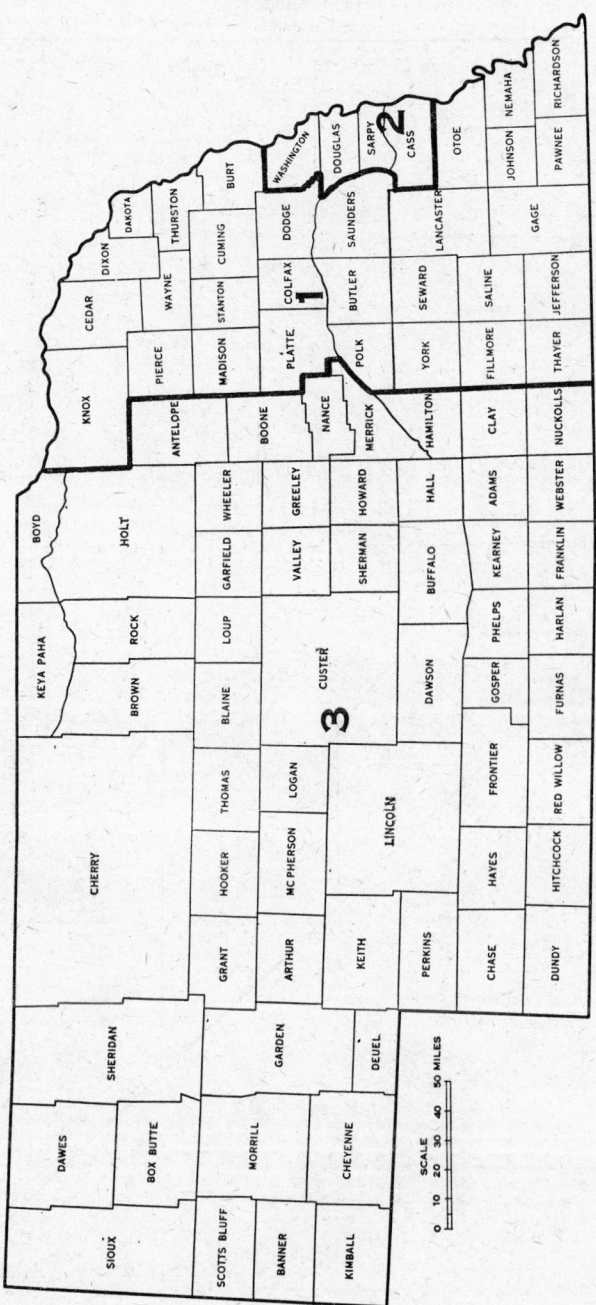

NEVADA

(1 at large)

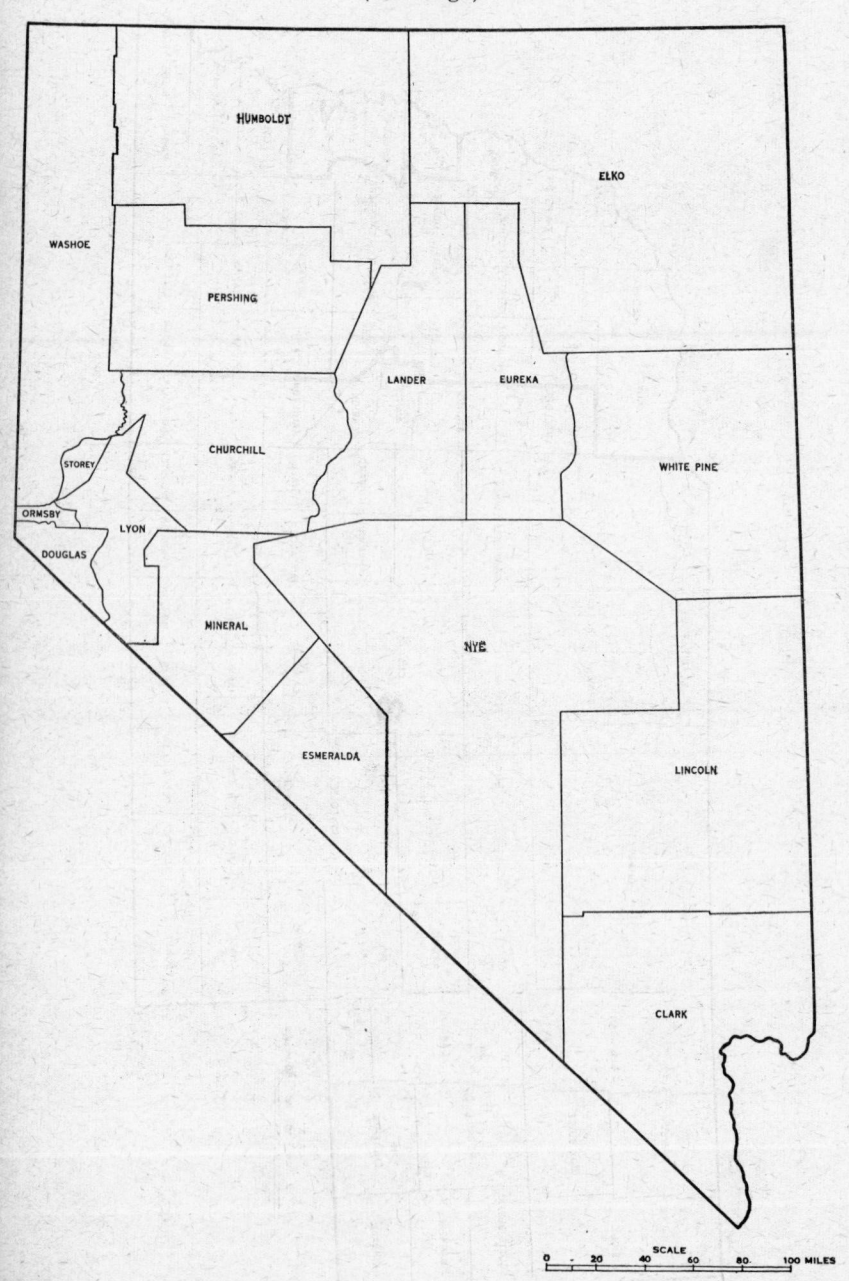

NEW HAMPSHIRE

(2 districts)

NEW JERSEY

(15 districts)

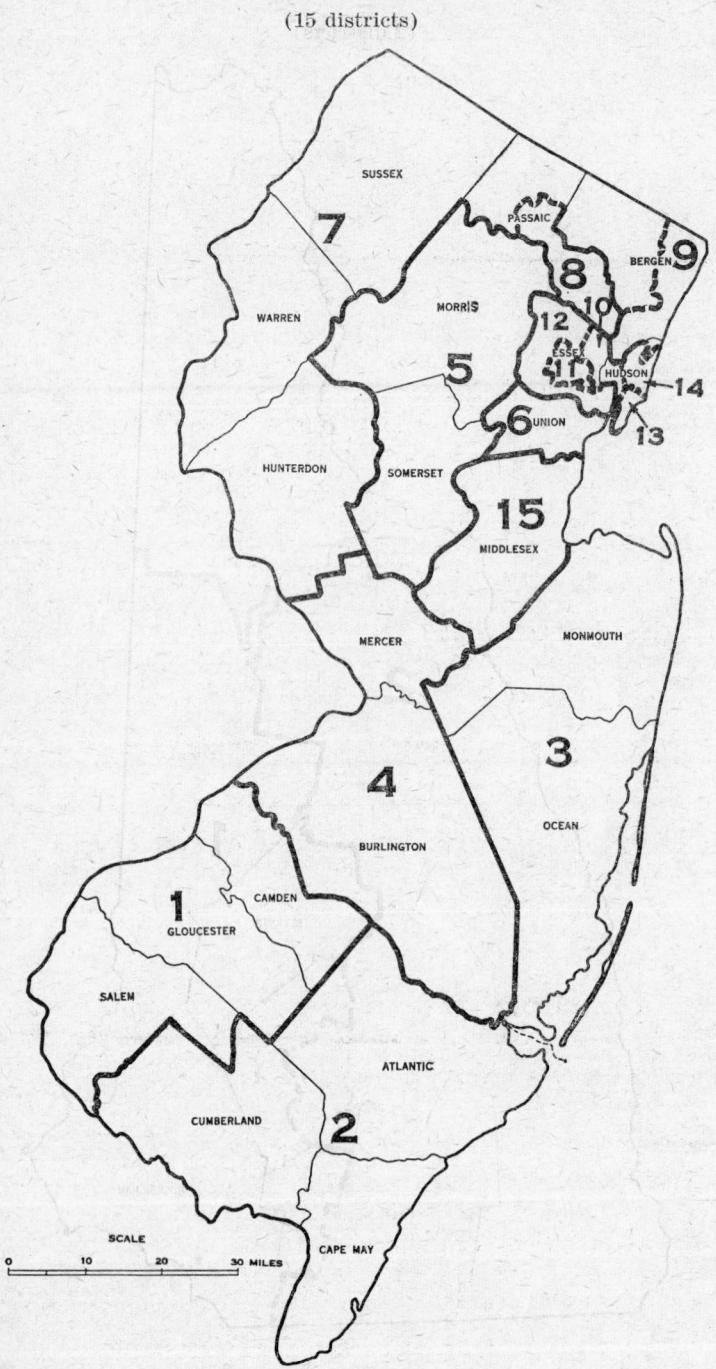

SUSSEX

PASSAIC

7

BERGEN   9

8

WARREN

MORRIS

10

12

5

ESSEX

HUDSON

11

14

6 UNION

13

HUNTERDON

SOMERSET

15

MIDDLESEX

MERCER

MONMOUTH

3

4

OCEAN

BURLINGTON

CAMDEN

1

GLOUCESTER

SALEM

ATLANTIC

2

CUMBERLAND

SCALE

0   10   20   30 MILES

CAPE MAY

NEW MEXICO

(2 at large)

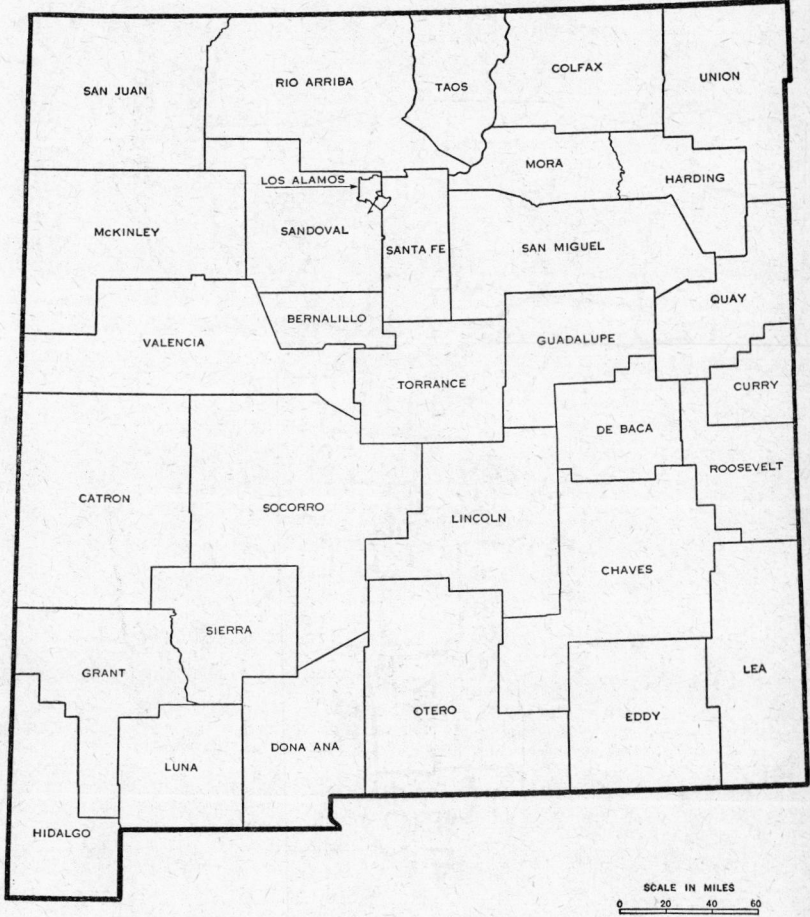

NEW YORK

(41 districts)

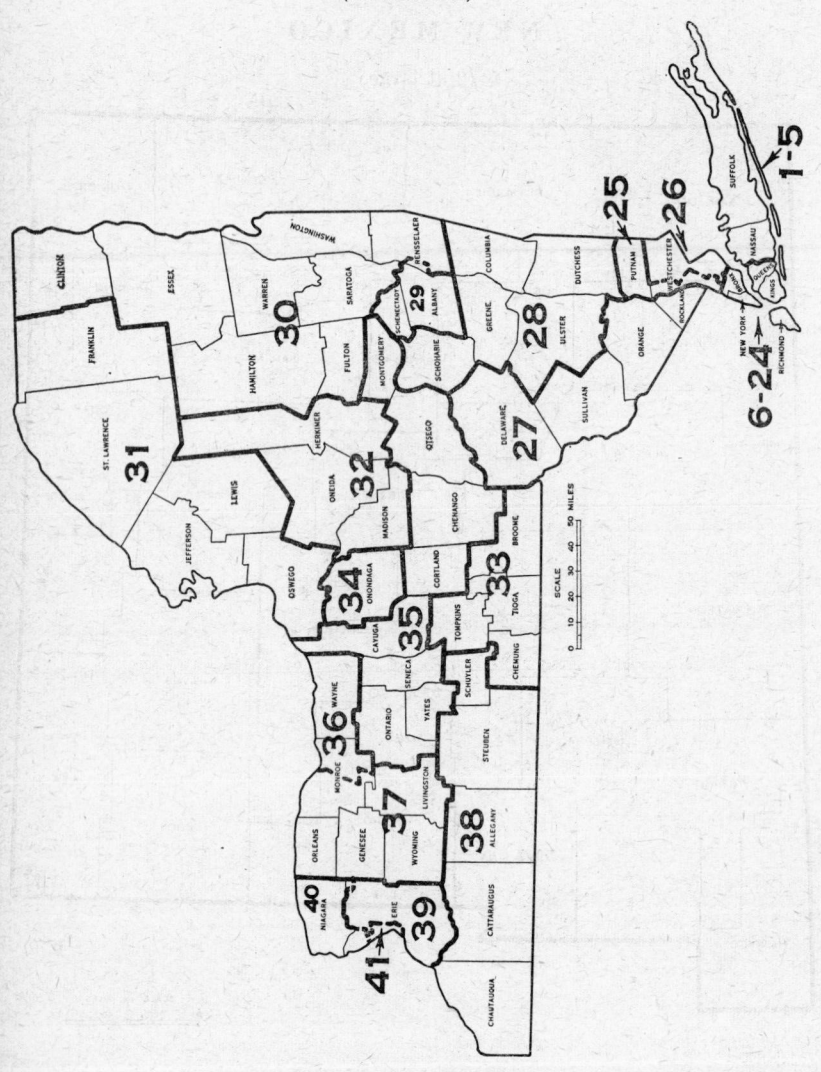

NORTH CAROLINA

(11 districts)

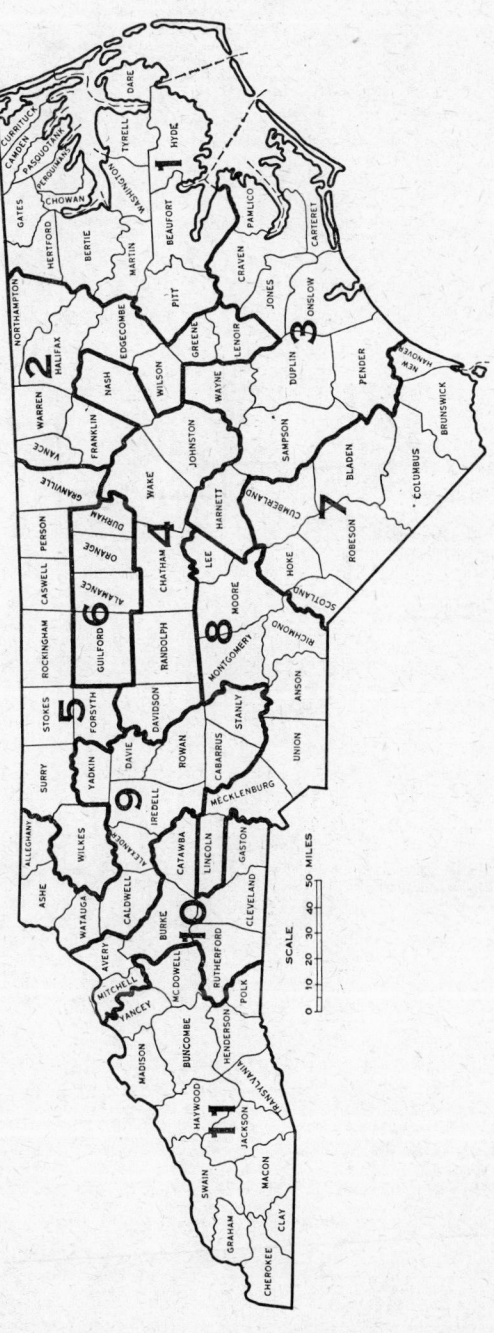

NORTH DAKOTA

(2 districts)

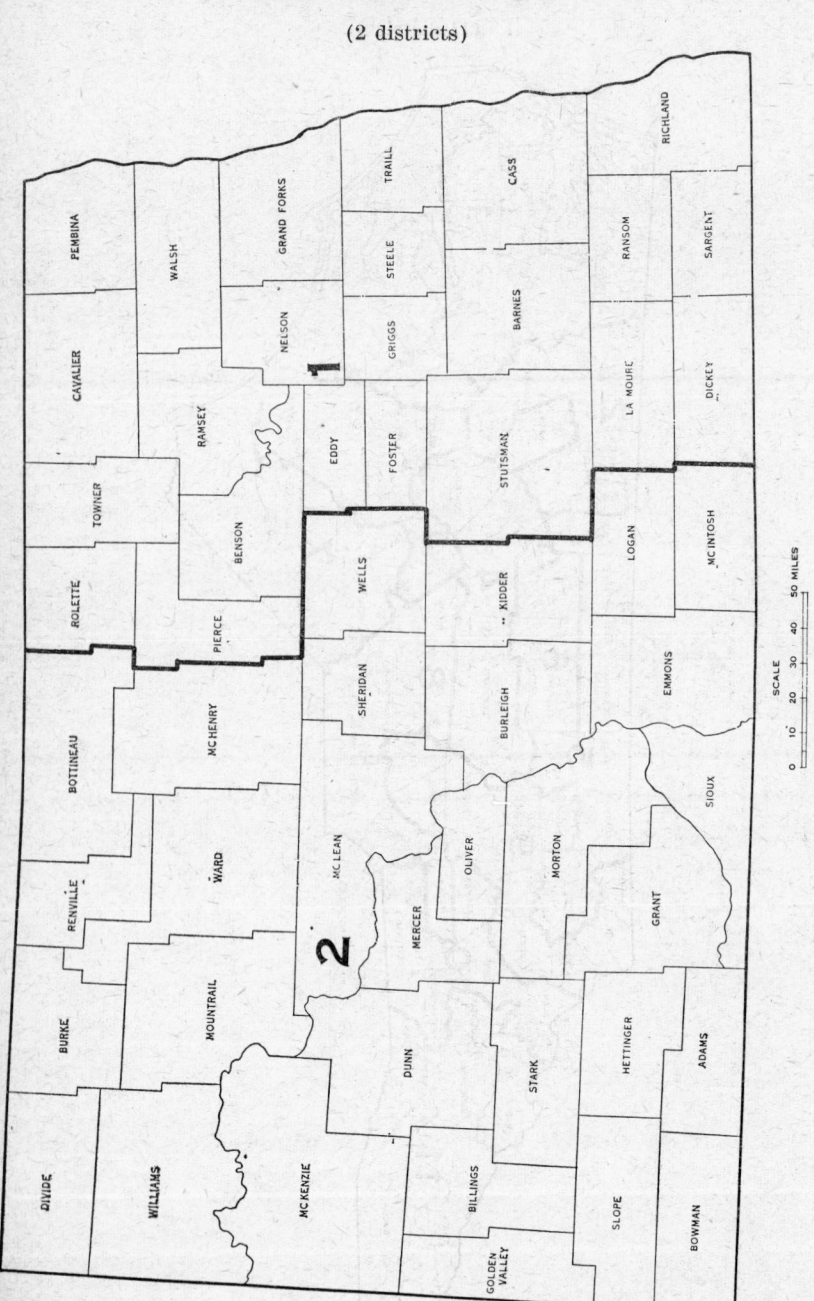

OHIO

(23 districts and 1 at large)

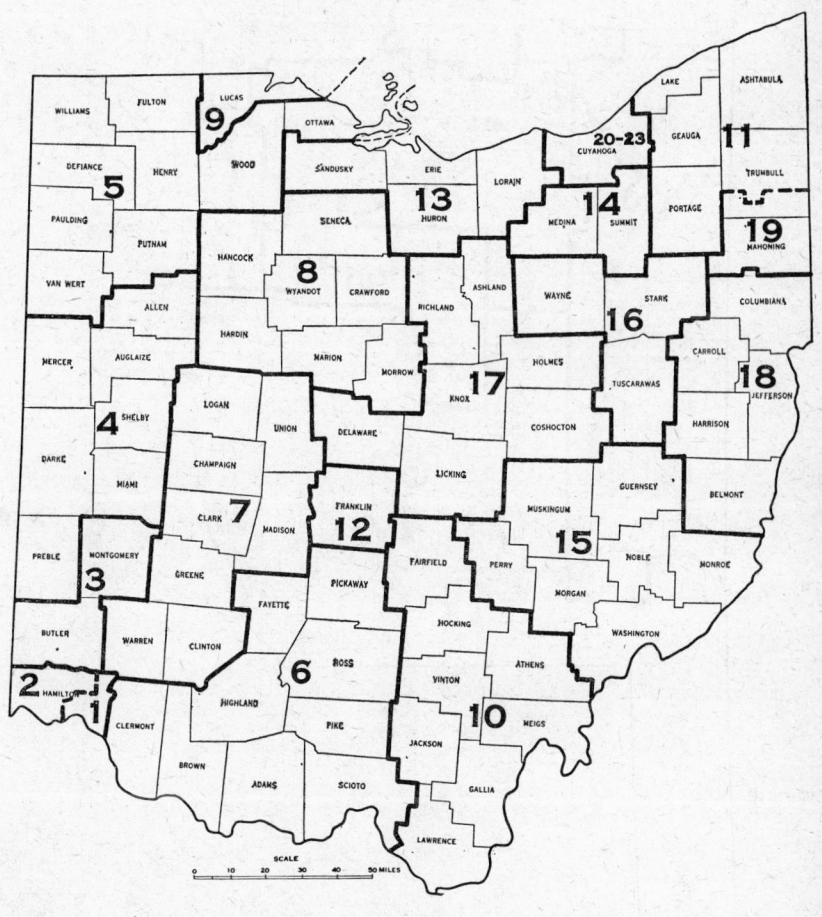

OKLAHOMA

(6 districts)

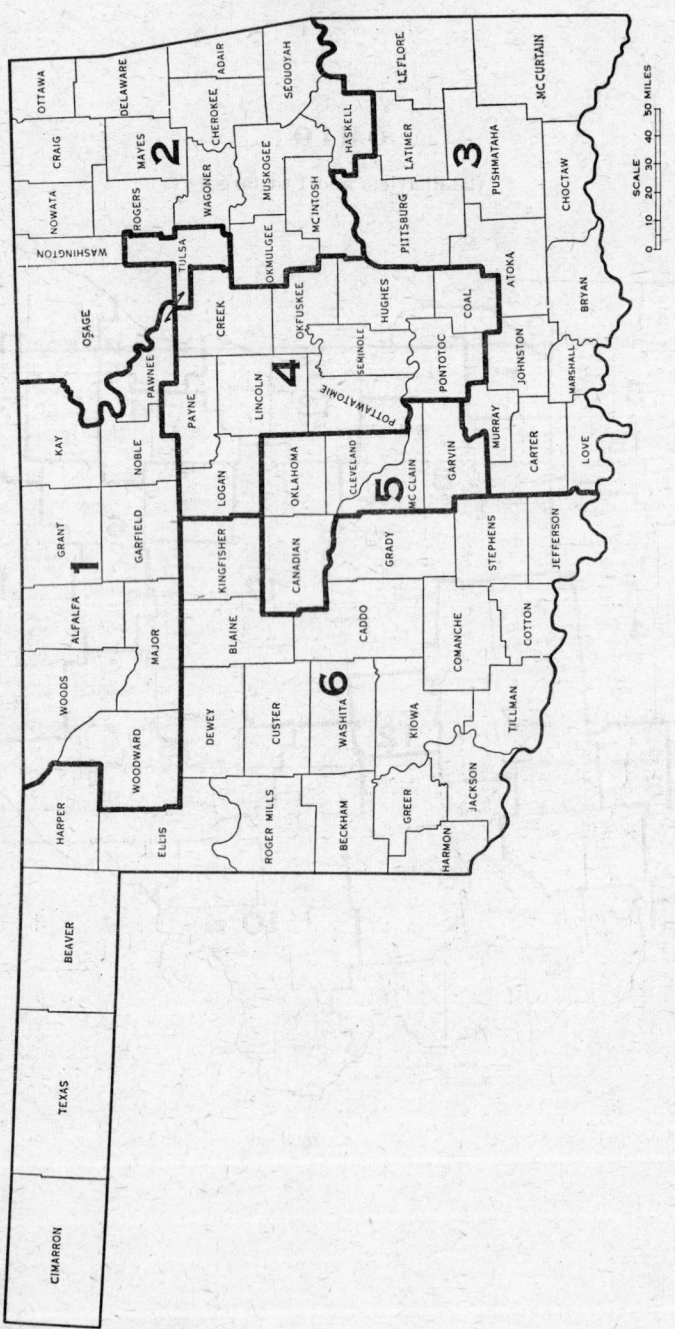

OREGON

(4 districts)

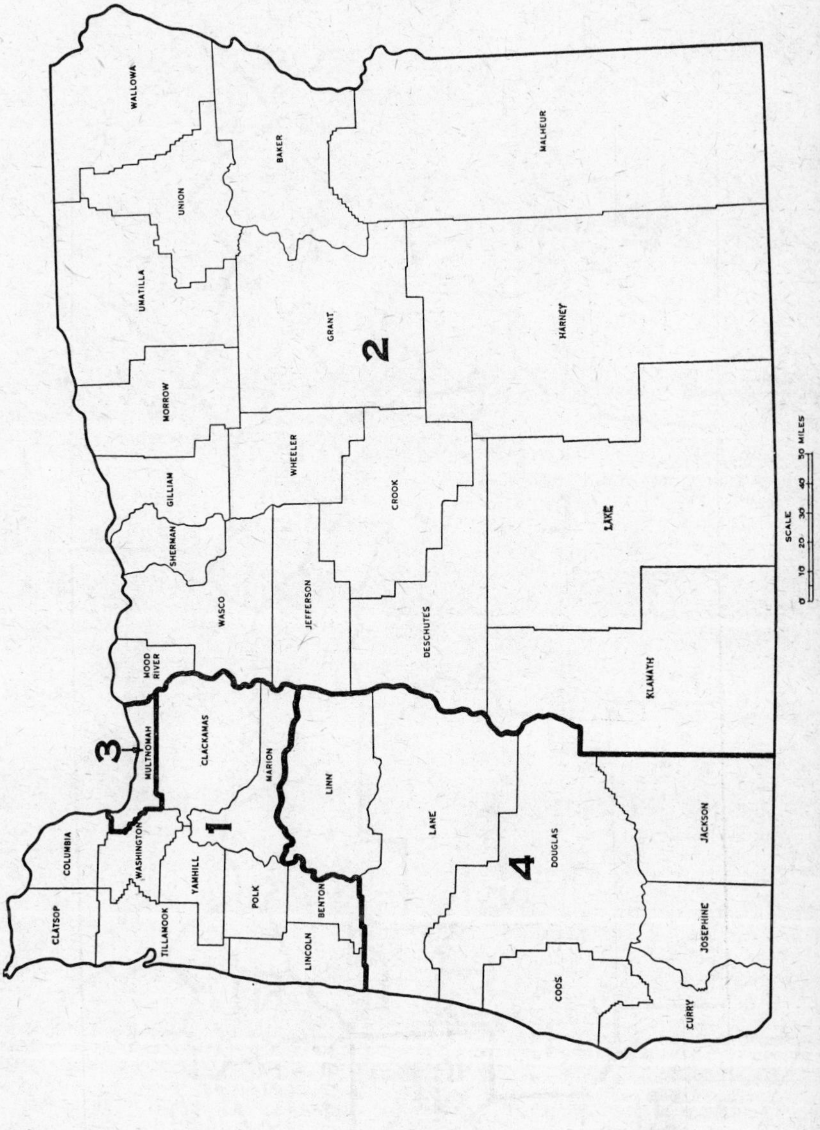

PENNSYLVANIA

(27 districts)

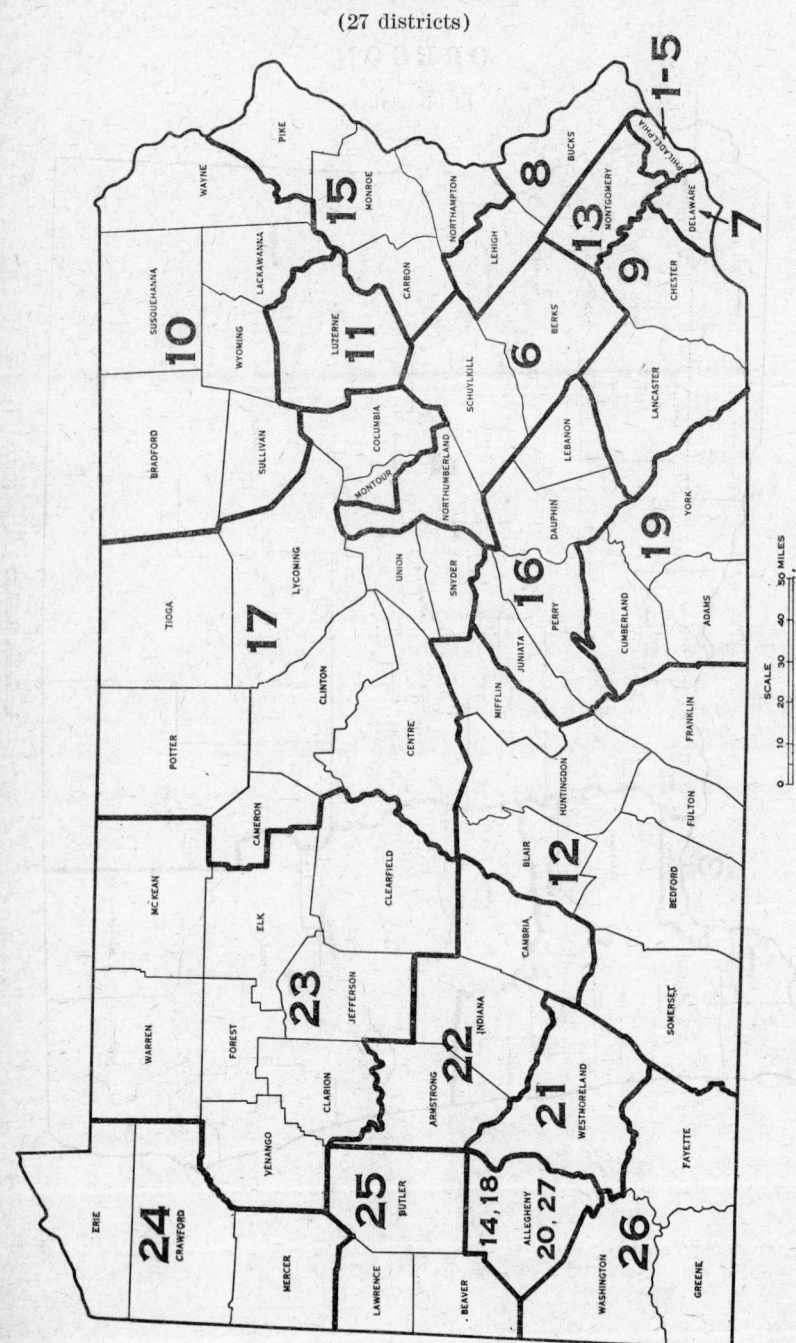

RHODE ISLAND

(2 districts)

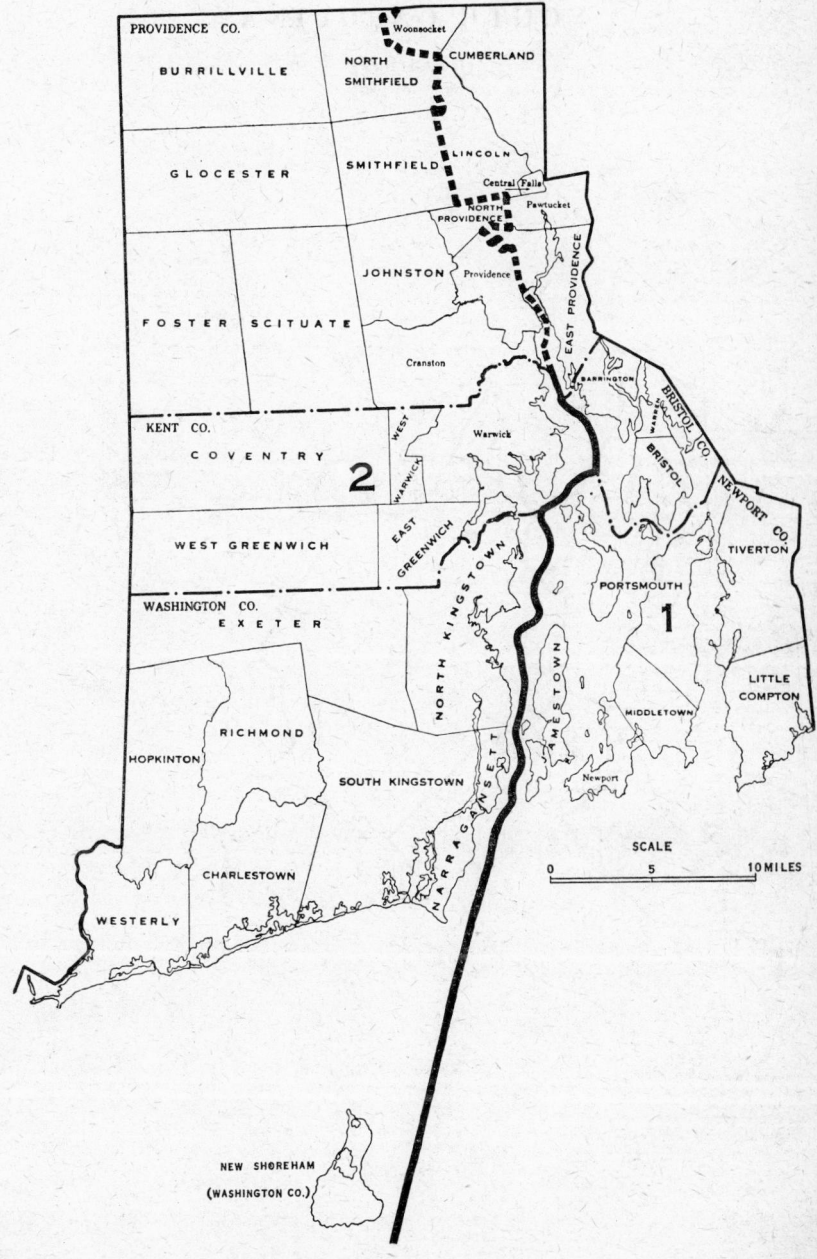

SOUTH CAROLINA

(6 districts)

SOUTH DAKOTA

(2 districts)

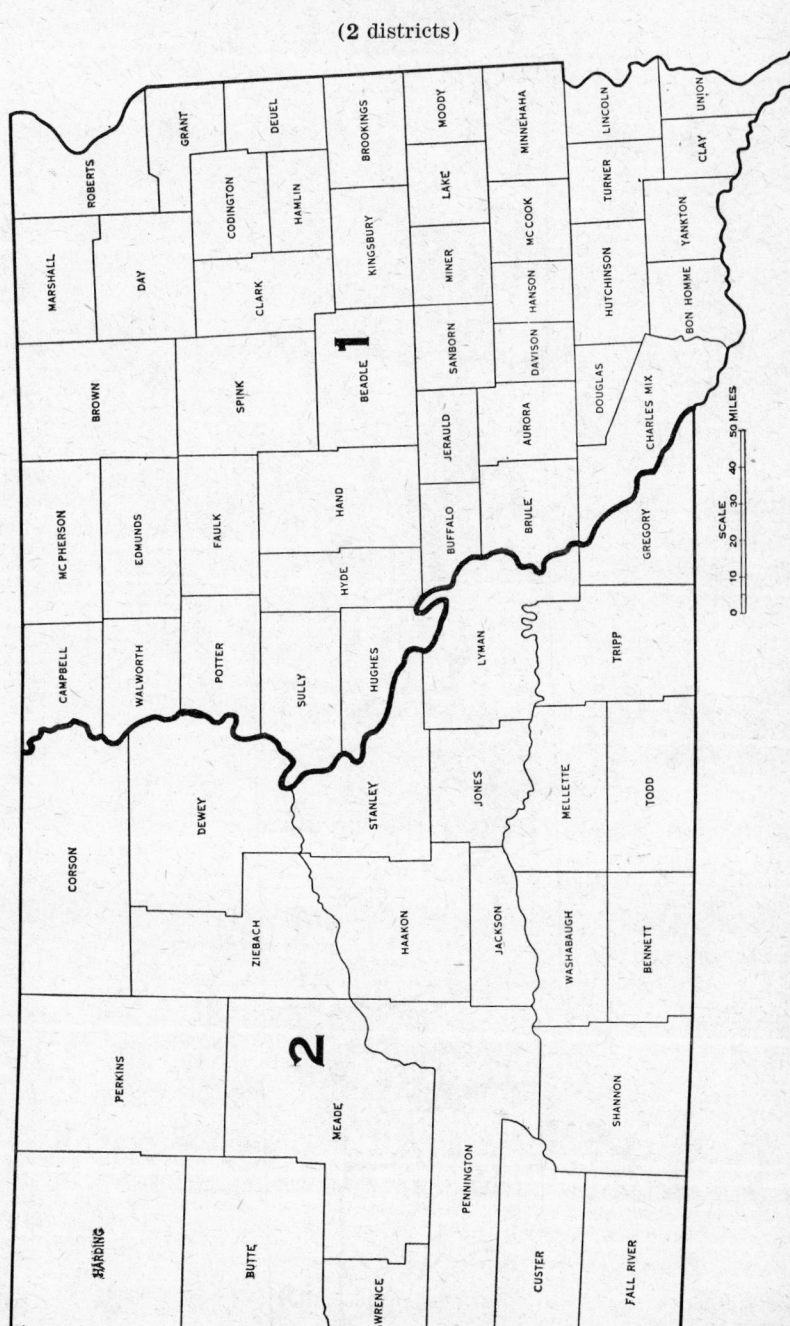

TENNESSEE

(9 districts)

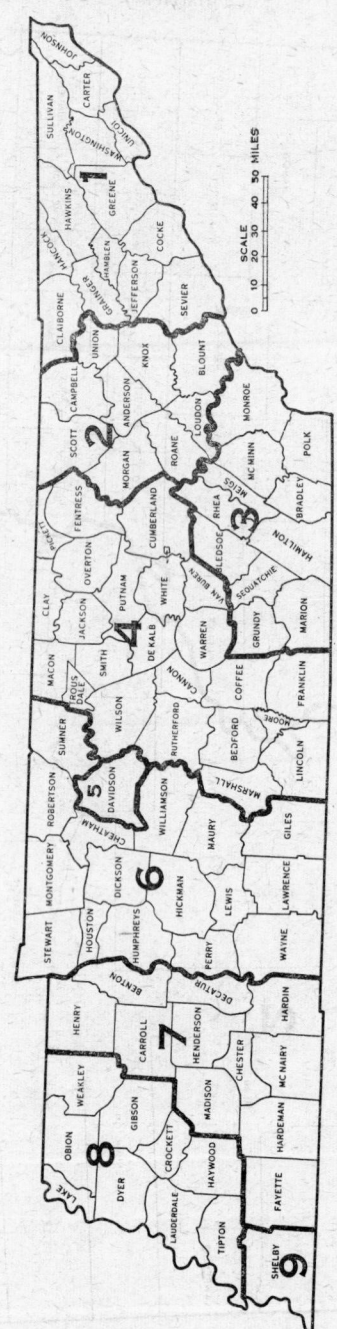

TEXAS

(22 districts and 1 at large)

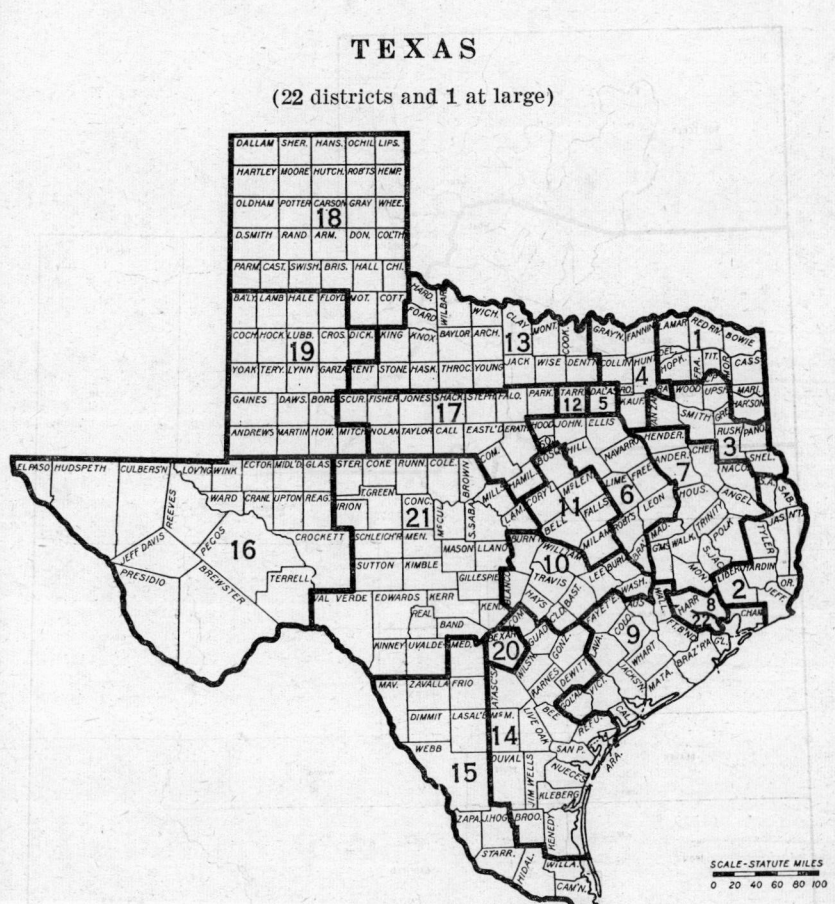

SCALE-STATUTE MILES
0 20 40 60 80 100

UTAH

(2 districts)

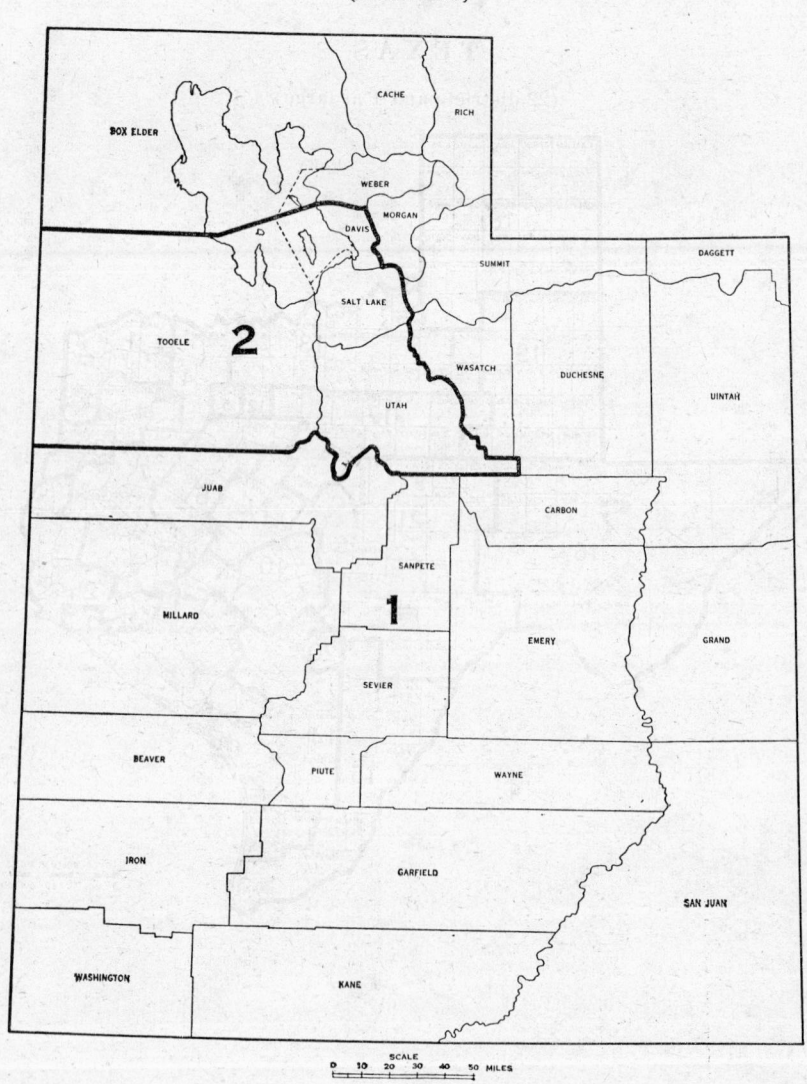

VERMONT

(1 at large)

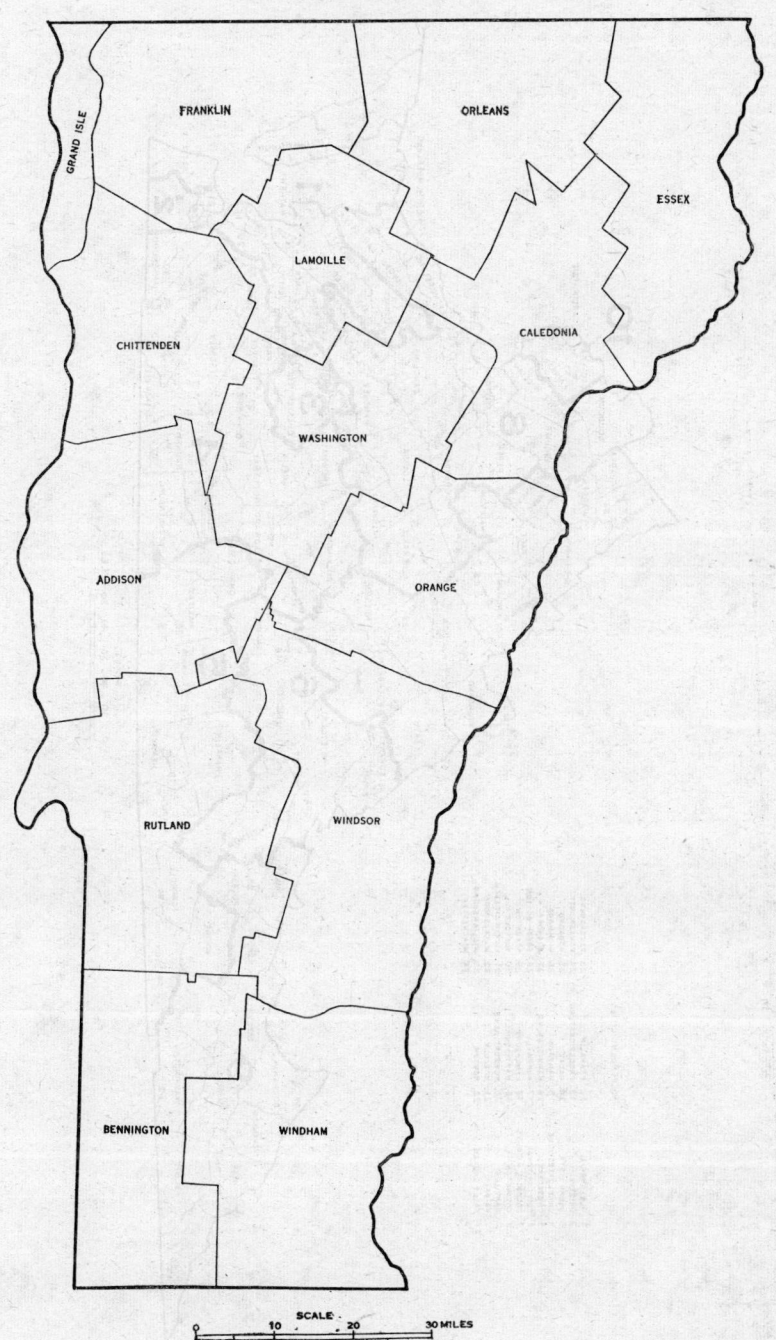

GRAND ISLE

FRANKLIN

ORLEANS

ESSEX

LAMOILLE

CHITTENDEN

CALEDONIA

WASHINGTON

ADDISON

ORANGE

RUTLAND

WINDSOR

BENNINGTON

WINDHAM

SCALE
0   10   20   30 MILES

VIRGINIA

(10 districts)

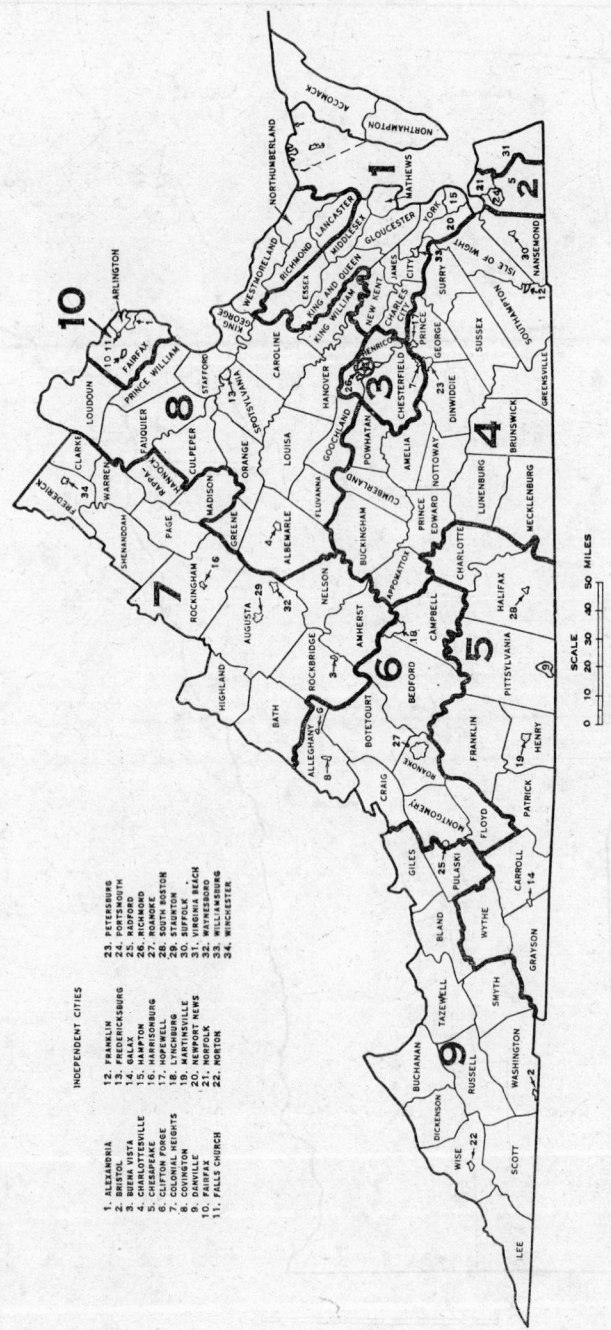

INDEPENDENT CITIES

1. ALEXANDRIA
2. BRISTOL
3. BUENA VISTA
4. CHARLOTTESVILLE
5. CHESAPEAKE
6. CLIFTON FORGE
7. COLONIAL HEIGHTS
8. COVINGTON
9. DANVILLE
10. FAIRFAX
11. FALLS CHURCH

12. FRANKLIN
13. FREDERICKSBURG
14. GALAX
15. HAMPTON
16. HARRISONBURG
17. HOPEWELL
18. LYNCHBURG
19. MARTINSVILLE
20. NEWPORT NEWS
21. NORFOLK
22. NORTON

23. PETERSBURG
24. PORTSMOUTH
25. RADFORD
26. RICHMOND
27. ROANOKE
28. SOUTH BOSTON
29. STAUNTON
30. SUFFOLK
31. VIRGINIA BEACH
32. WAYNESBORO
33. WILLIAMSBURG
34. WINCHESTER

SCALE

0 10 20 30 40 50 MILES

WASHINGTON

(7 districts)

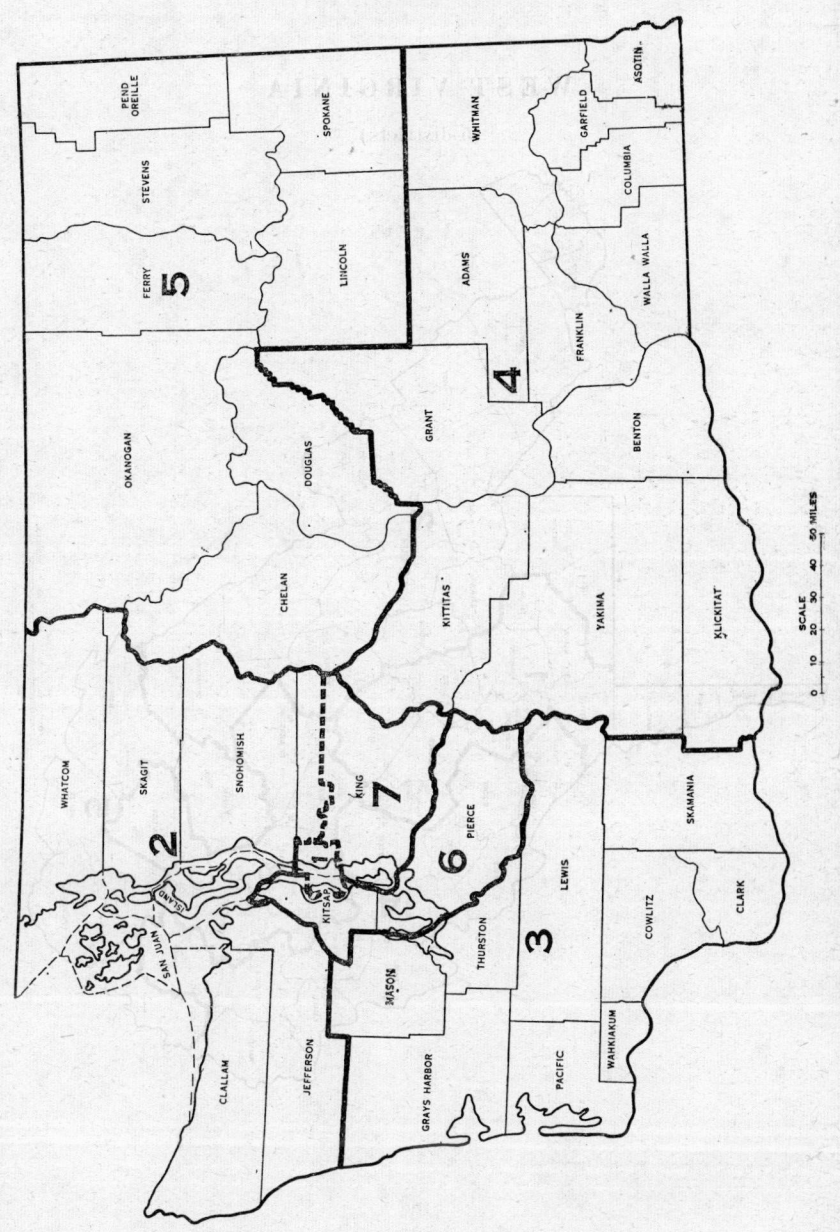

WEST VIRGINIA

(5 districts)

WISCONSIN

(10 districts)

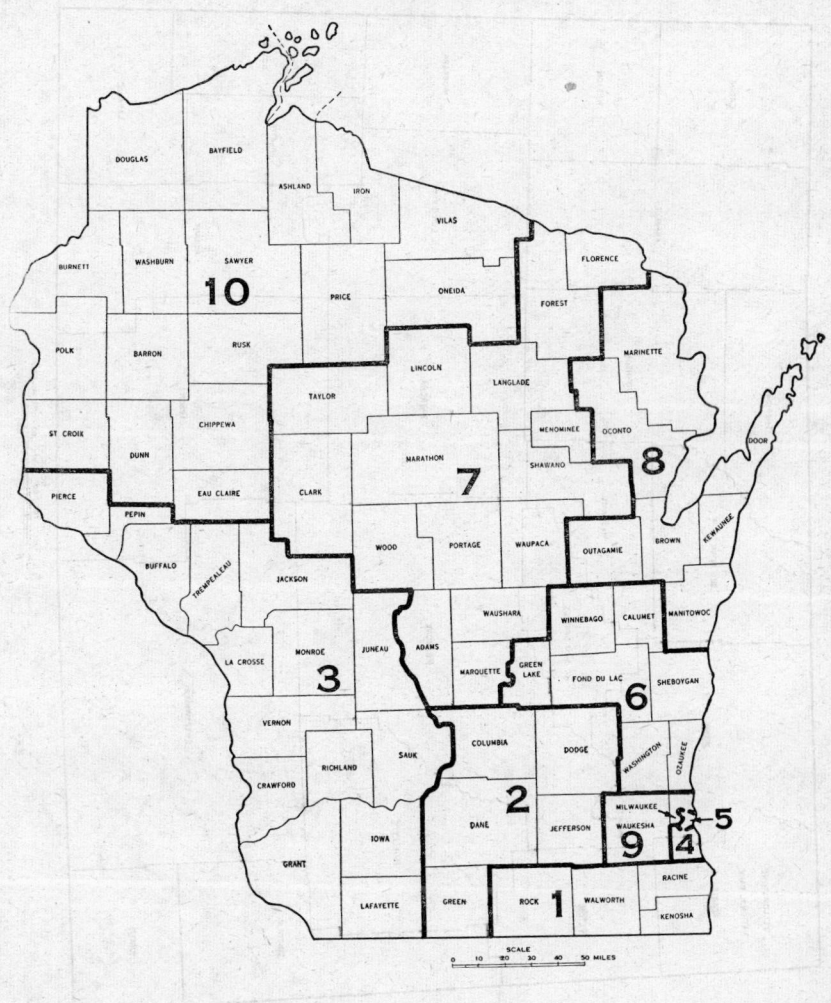

WYOMING

(1 at large)

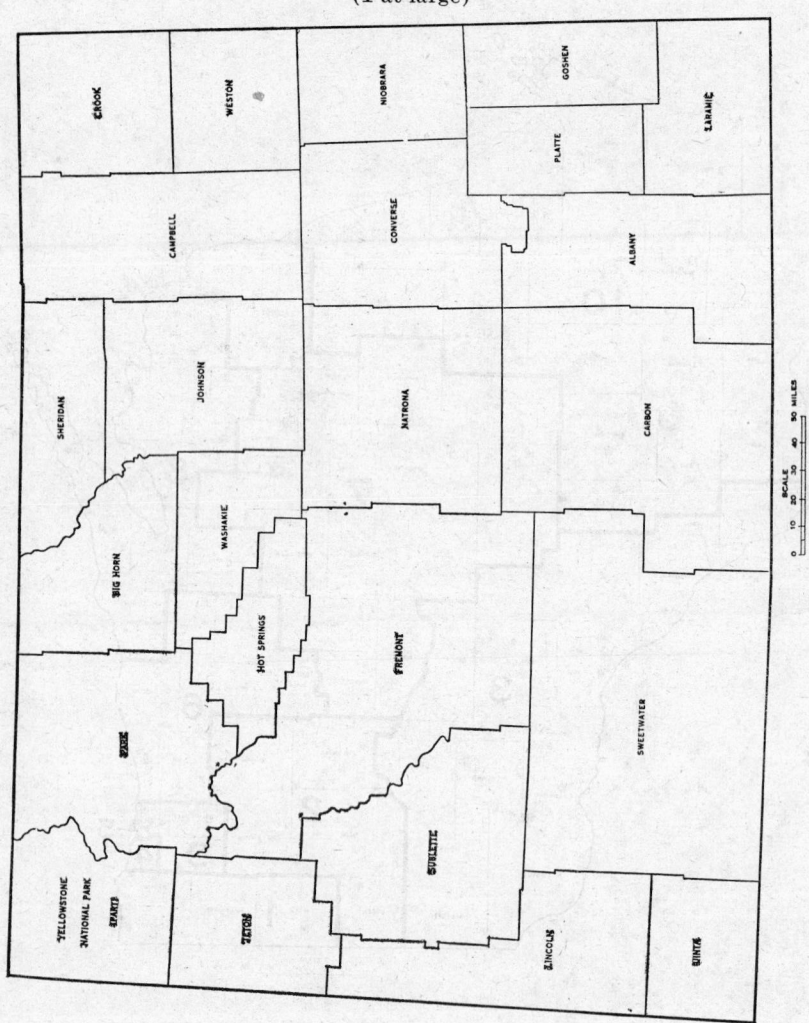

COMMONWEALTH OF PUERTO RICO

(1 Resident Commissioner)

INDIVIDUAL INDEX

INDIVIDUAL INDEX

(For list of Members of Congress with their addresses, see pp. 201–219)

913

Page

Page

Page

976   *Congressional Directory*

Individual Index

Page

Schafer, Raymond L., Senate Committee on Appropriations_____ 251
Schaffer, Orion F., Bureau of Finance, Post Office_____ 500
Schaffner, Philip P., Office of International Affairs, Treasury_____ 436
Schaller, Jerome D., administrative assistant to Senator Mondale_____ 319
Schalet, Jacob J., Office of the Solicitor, Labor__ 553
Schamp, Carl D., U.S. Capitol Police_____ 369
Schantz, Wilmer S., District of Columbia Court of General Sessions_____ 675
Scharer, Henry, Office of Secretary of Commerce_____ 535
Schartner, Arthur H., Rural Electrification Administration_____ 528
Scheer, Julian, National Aeronautics and Space Administration_____ 616
Scheibel, John A., National Capital Regional Planning Council_____ 619
Scheiderer, Capt. Edward D., Office of Chief of Staff, Coast Guard_____ 438
Schein, Ernest:
    Commission on International Rules of Judicial Procedure_____ 587
    District Board of Elections_____ 690
Schelin, Otto, International Monetary Fund_ 713
Schenkenberg, Philip, American National Red Cross_____ 575
Scherer, Robert H., Office of Defense Research and Engineering_____ 447
Scheuer, James H. (Representative from New York):
    Biography___ 113
    Education and Labor Committee_____ 257
Scheyven, Louis, Ambassador from Belgium___ 731
Schiferl, Max, Bureau of Labor Standards_____ 555
Schimmel, Jospeh, Patent Office_____ 548
Schisler, Gale (Representative from Illinois):
    Biography_____ 49
    Science and Astronautics Committee_____ 262
Schissell, Ethel, Senate Committee on Interior and Insular Affairs_____ 253
Schleef, Capt. W. H., Bureau of Naval Weapons_ 480
Schlei, Norbert A.:
    Commission on International Rules of Judicial Procedure_____ 586
    Office of Legal Counsel, Justice_____ 494
Schlesinger, Arthur, Jr., John F. Kennedy Center for the Performing Arts_____ 635
Schlesinger, Arthur M., National Historical Publications Commission_____ 606
Schlesinger, Eugene R., United States–Puerto Rico Commission on the Status of Puerto Rico_____ 285
Schlesinger, Prof. Rudolf B., Commission on International Rules of Judicial Procedure___ 587
Schloss, Clara F., Wage and Hour and Public Contracts Divisions, Labor Department_____ 555
Schmeltzer, Edward, Federal Maritime Commission_____ 595
Schmid, Bernard F.:
    Federal Records Council_____ 606
    Interstate Commerce Commission_____ 613
Schmid, Frank H., clerk, Ninth Judicial Circuit, U.S. Courts of Appeals_____ 648
Schmidhauser, John R. (Representative from Iowa):
    Biography_____ 55
    Public Works Committee_____ 262
Schmidt, Frederick H., Office of Secretary, Health, Education, and Welfare_____ 559
Schmidt, Orvis A., International Bank for Reconstruction and Development_____ 709
Schmidt, Reinhart C., Weather Bureau_____ 550
Schmidt, William A.:
    Federal Fire Council_____ 607
    National Capital Planning Commission_____ 618
    Public Buildings Service_____ 601
Schmitt, Richard G., Jr., Area Redevelopment Administration, Commerce_____ 538
Schmoll, Paul N., Veterans Administration_____ 639
Schneebeli, Herman T. (Representative from Pennsylvania):
    Biography_____ 145
    Ways and Means Committee_____ 263
Schneiber, Harvey P., Federal Maritime Commission_____ 595

Page

Schneider, Albert, Official Reporter, House_____ 366
Schneider, Charles W., National Labor Relations Board_____ 621
Schneider, William C., Office of Manned Space Flight, NASA_____ 616
Schnellbacher, E. E., Bureau of International Commerce_____ 539
Schnittker, John A:
    Commodity Credit Corporation_____ 517
    Director, Agricultural Economics_____ 515
Schnitz, Janet, secretary to Representative Yates_____ 331
Schoech, Vice Adm. William A., National Air Musuem_____ 633
Schoen, Luther F., National Science Foundation_____ 623
Schoenfelder, Otto W., Tax Court of the United States_____ 667
Schoenhaut, Arthur, General Accounting Office_ 374
Scholl, John C., Foreign Agricultural Service__ 522
Schomburg, Lt. Gen. August, Industrial College of the Armed Froces_____ 455
Schon, Donald A., National Bureau of Standards_____ 547
Schon, Hubert A., Office of Civil Defense_____ 461
Schooler, Lee W., Public Housing Administration_____ 611
Schoonover, Irl C., National Bureau of Standards_____ 546
Schoonover, Tedford E., National Mediation Board_____ 622
Schor, Sigmund, Office of Vocational Rehabilitation_____ 563
Schosberg, Paul, secretary to Representative Ottinger_____ 328
Schrader, Kenneth L., Department of Insurance, District_____ 691
Schram, Emil, Federal Prison Industries, Inc._ 496
Schreiber, Ann, secretary to Representative Baldwin_____ 322
Schreiber, David B., Railroad Retirement Board_____ 625
Schriever, Gen. Bernard A., Continental Commands, Air Force_____ 489
Schruben, Luke M., Federal Extension Service, Agriculture_____ 520
Schubmehl, Martha, secretary to Representative Widnall_____ 331
Schulkind, Gilbert A., Civil Service Commission_____ 583
Schulte, Cdr. J. H., Bureau of Medicine and Surgery, Navy_____ 476
Schulte, Philip W., Civil Service Commission__ 583
Schulte, William J., Federal Aviation Agency__ 591
Schultz, Edward W., Forest Service, Agriculture_____ 526
Schultz, Frederick C., District Board of Pharmacy_____ 694
Schultz, John D., District Department of Public Health_____ 695
Schultz, Col. Kenneth W., Research and Development, Air Force_____ 489
Schultz, Richard, Federal Trade Commission__ 600
Schupp, Franklin J., House Committee on Foreign Affairs_____ 268
Schurmann, Carl W. A., Ambassador from the Netherlands_____ 739
Schussheim, Morton J., Housing and Home Finance Agency_____ 607
Schwartz, Abba Pa.:
    American National Red Cross_____ 574
    Bureau of Security and Consular Affairs, State Department_____ 426
    Commission on International Rules of Judicial Procedure_____ 586
Schwartz, Carl H., Jr., Bureau of the Budget_ 421
Schwartz, David B., Department of Public Welfare, District_____ 697
Schwartz, Ferdinand, reporter, U.S. Customs Court_____ 661
Schwartz, Harry S., Federal Home Loan Bank Board_____ 594
Schwartz, Margaret W., Director, Foreign Assets Control, Treasury_____ 437
Schwartz, Maurice H., Board of Governors, Federal Reserve System_____ 581
Schwartz, Michael, House Committee on Education and Labor_____ 268

Page

○